William Bartram. From the portrait by Charles Willson Peale,
now in Old City Hall, Philadelphia

THE *TRAVELS* OF WILLIAM BARTRAM

Naturalist's Edition

THE

Travels OF WILLIAM BARTRAM

NATURALIST'S EDITION

Edited with commentary and an annotated index

by FRANCIS HARPER

Research Associate, the John Bartram Association, Philadelphia

New Haven: Yale University Press, 1958

PREFACE

I HOPE you will make Bartram live again." It was in essentially these words that the late William H. Mills, professor of rural economics at Clemson College, wrote me in 1939, a few weeks after he had pointed out an ancient stamping ground of William Bartram on the Seneca River in South Carolina. The present work, as well as two preceding ones on the Bartrams,[1] has been prepared from the outset, as best I could, in the spirit of Professor Mills' exhortation.

This edition may also be regarded as a rather belated answer to my friend Lane Cooper's "Bartram Redivivus?"—a query posed in *The Nation* (1905) shortly after those long-ago days when I had sat at his feet in freshman English: "Could not some patriotic Philadelphian be induced to revive the 'Travels' of the Quaker natural scientist, William Bartram?"

A long-standing need of students of American natural history has, in truth, been a fully annotated and indexed edition of Bartram's justly celebrated *Travels*—something, in fact, considerably more elaborate than the reprinting suggested by Professor Cooper. The inadequacy of the previous dozen or so editions has been felt less by literary scholars than by devotees of the natural sciences. The former may enjoy the author's descriptions of primitive nature without being unduly concerned with the detailed geography of the scenes portrayed or the correct nomenclature of the species mentioned; but the botanist and the zoologist must have the current names of the plants and animals recorded and precise information on their distribution (particularly the type localities of new species); the geographer and the historian need to be informed on routes pursued, on Indian traders and trading posts, on names and locations of streams and mountains, and on scores of incidental items in the colonial life of the Southeast; the ethnologist seeks authoritative knowledge of Indian village sites and tribal movements and characteristics. The aim of this naturalist's edition of the *Travels* is to supply all these needs—and others—in adequate measure, as far as time and resources have permitted.

1. See, under References, John Bartram (1942) and William Bartram (1943).

v

The Bartram Routes

Intrigued originally, many years ago, by Bartram's legendary account of my beloved Okefinokee Swamp (*Travels,* 24–26), I eventually found it more and more essential to consult and utilize the *Travels* in my own studies on the natural history of Georgia and neighboring states. As far back as 1917, while on a biological tour of Florida, I had followed (though perhaps not too consciously) the footsteps and paddle strokes of John and William Bartram along the St. John's from its mouth up to Lake Harney.

In later years the infectious enthusiasm of Arthur N. Leeds for unraveling the Bartrams' routes and collecting their plants in the original localities spurred us along the old colonial trails in eastern Georgia (1933, 1936) and led us to the rediscovery of the Buffalo Lick in Oglethorpe County (1934). Gradually we evolved plans for bringing out annotated editions of the works of both John and William Bartram. Unhappily, our collaboration in this enterprise had not progressed beyond the initial stages when my friend laid aside his earthly labors, but the continuation of the undertaking since that time can scarcely be termed single-handed, in view of the numerous valuable contributions of information and suggestions by fellow devotees of the Bartrams. The principal results to date have been the publication of John Bartram's diary of 1765–66 in 1942, and of William Bartram's report to Dr. Fothergill (1773–74) in 1943.

Two long trips through the Southeastern States in 1939 and 1940, devoted especially to Bartramian studies, resulted in the relocation of many choice spots that these pioneers had visited and described; also in the observation and collection of many plants and animals in the same localities where the Bartrams had reported them. In the former year (May to July) my route led across the Meherrin River in Virginia to the ancient Bartram plantation on the Cape Fear River and to Lake Waccamaw in North Carolina; thence along the coast to Charleston, South Carolina; across Georgia along the Fall-Line Sand Hills, with a digression to Wrightsborough, the Little River, and Athens; and across Alabama, along the Tallapoosa River, past Montgomery, and southwestward to the Mobile Delta (chiefly along the Old Federal Road). After a brief stop at Pensacola, Florida, the Bartram trail was picked up again on the Suwannee River and followed to the Alachua Savanna and the St. John's River as far up as Lake Harney; thence through eastern Georgia, northwestern South Carolina, and the valley of the Little Tennessee River in Georgia and North

Carolina. From Montgomery to Pensacola and Tallahassee I had been accompanied by Roland M. Harper.[2]

In 1940 (February to May) E. Perot Walker, of the Academy of Natural Sciences of Philadelphia, and I followed the general route of the previous year as far as Charleston, S.C.; then continued through eastern Georgia to the St. John's River in Florida, where we turned westward to the Ocklawaha River. Further investigations along the St. John's, to a point above Lake Harney, were interspersed with visits to Amelia Island, St. Augustine, Gainesville, and the Suwannee River. After Mr. Walker's return northward in April, I continued over more or less familiar routes in eastern Georgia through Brunswick, Savannah, and Augusta to Athens, then endeavored to trace Bartram's old trail along his "Great Ridge" and eastward to the point where the Tugaloo and the Seneca unite to form the Savannah River.

"Thus, through good fortune and the co-operation of many friends (whose names will appear in subsequent pages), the Bartram routes have been retraced in surprising detail. It is true that here and there the trail remains obscure, and yet over literally hundreds of miles the present-day follower of Bartram need not deviate more than a few feet (or rods at most) from his time-worn track."[3] These routes are shown on the map following the illustration section.

Editorial Note

Bartram's *Travels* is here republished in such form that it may be consulted, quoted, and cited with practically the same exactness as if it were the original edition of 1791. The pagination of that edition has been indicated by the insertion of italicized numbers in square brackets. The manner of dealing with problems of archaic, misspelled or misplaced words and incorrect or unorthodox punctuation and composition is explained in a special section below, pp. 695–701. The eight original plates (one of them here reduced in size, to avoid folding) are inserted in the positions they occupy in the Yale copy. In other copies of the 1791 edition these positions vary slightly. Other illustrations, prepared for this edition, are inserted at the end of the volume.

The present additions to the original work consist of this Preface; an Introduction, containing an account of Bartram's life and his *Travels*; a Commentary on geographical, historical, and various other matters that could not be so conveniently or so adequately discussed elsewhere;

2. For further details see John Bartram, 1942: 8; William Bartram, 1943: 126–127; Harper, 1939c.
3. Introduction to W. Bartram, 1943: 126.

an Annotated Index, providing, among other things, identifications of
Bartram's plants and animals, biographical notes on persons, definitions
of unusual or unfamiliar terms, information on Indian tribes, and the
location of geographical features; a Bibliography of publications,
manuscripts, maps, and atlases; a section on variant orthography, punctuation, and composition; a General Index to the Preface, Introduction, and Commentary and to certain words in the Annotated Index that do not constitute first-position entries; and various maps and
figures inserted at the end of the volume.

The Commentary provides the principal means for elucidating
Bartram's routes, step by step. The nature and scope of the Annotated
Index and the General Index are explained in detail at the commencement of those sections. All features are designed to provide
discriminating readers of the *Travels* with a maximum of aid and information in concise form and in the most convenient arrangement that
could be devised.

Acknowledgments

The preparation of this naturalist's edition of the *Travels* has been
supported primarily by the John Bartram Association, of Philadelphia.
A special committee, formed in 1939 and consisting of the late Charles
F. Jenkins (chairman), Mrs. Bayard Henry (then president of the association), Mrs. Edward M. Cheston, and the late Francis W. Pennell,
earned the gratitude of Bartram devotees by its long-continued interest
in, and encouragement of, the undertaking. The various members and
friends of the association, whose contributions at that period made it
possible to accomplish the major part of the work, will, it is hoped,
find here some slight reward for their generosity.

The years spent in preparation might still have gone for naught
had it not been for the faith of certain institutions and individuals
in the permanent inspiration of Bartram's masterpiece and in the need
for a detailed interpretation of his contributions as a naturalist. Those
who have more recently translated that faith into action by subscribing
to the cost of publication are the John Bartram Association, the
John Simon Guggenheim Memorial Foundation, the Longwood Foundation, Mrs. E. M. Calhoun, Mrs. C. Reed Cary, William Bacon Evans,
Felix Hargrett, Mrs. J. Norman Henry, Mrs. Roy Arthur Hunt, Mrs.
Charles F. Jenkins, Miss Esther Leeds, Mrs. Raymond Parrott, A.
Keith Smiley, Jr., and Mrs. A. C. Troutman. To Mrs. Edward M.
Cheston, Francis D. West, and John C. Wister (recent president of
the John Bartram Association), I would offer a special meed of praise

for their devoted efforts in furthering the aims of the association in general and the publication of the *Travels* in particular.

A grant from the Penrose Fund of the American Philosophical Society was an important aid to the investigation, particularly in providing for two long field trips in 1939 and 1940 along the Bartram routes in the Southeastern States. Moreover, the publication by this society of two previous Bartram papers [4] was an essential step in paving the way for the present volume.

The preparation of this edition and of a biography of Bartram as well was very materially advanced during the tenure of a John Simon Guggenheim Memorial Fellowship, 1950–1952.

The library resources and biological collections of the Academy of Natural Sciences of Philadelphia (of which Bartram was one of the earliest corresponding members) have been indispensable in the prolonged research involved. The library of this venerable institution, which has served as headquarters for the investigation, is particularly rich in the literature pertaining to the early phases of American natural history. Through the Academy's courtesy, a facsimile of the title page of Alexander Wilson's copy of Bartram's *Travels* appears in the present volume. The Historical Society of Pennsylvania, as the primary storehouse of Bartram letters and manuscripts, has provided material almost beyond reckoning and beyond price. Certain precious items in the library of the American Philosophical Society and in the William L. Clements Library have been utilized to great advantage, and the Free Library of Philadelphia and the Library of Congress have been drawn upon for various useful works. The Clements Library has very generously permitted the reproduction of certain parts of the immensely valuable Romans-Taitt map of 1772 and the use of several passages from the Shelburne Papers and Amherst Papers. Manuscript materials in the British Museum (Natural History), the Library Company of Philadelphia, the Library of Congress, the New-York Historical Society, and the Museum of Comparative Zoology at Harvard University have contributed much to an understanding of Bartram's life.

The late Mrs. Violetta W. Delafield, of New York, most kindly granted permission for the quotation of Bartram and Barton manuscripts in the Delafield Collection. The British Museum (Natural History) has generously allowed the reproduction of several Bartram drawings in that institution.

At the Academy of Natural Sciences I have derived great benefit from consulting Bayard Long, the late Francis W. Pennell, and Edgar T. Wherry on numerous botanical questions; Henry W. Fowler on

4. See above, p. v n.

ichthyological lore; H. A. Pilsbry, Richard A. McLean, and Horace G. Richards in regard to mollusks; and John W. Cadbury III, Philip P. Calvert, the late Ezra T. Cresson, Jr., James A. G. Rehn, H. Radclyffe Roberts, and Henry K. Townes on the determination of Bartram's insects. Dr. Pennell was also kind enough to examine critically certain portions of my manuscript. E. Perot Walker, formerly assistant curator of botany at the Academy, accompanied me during most of the field trip of 1940 through the Southeastern States, and gave valuable assistance with the botanical collections.

John R. Swanton, of the Bureau of American Ethnology, has rendered distinguished service to the cause of Bartramiana by very generously contributing, out of his special knowledge of the Southern Indians, critical notes on ethnological and archaeological subjects. These have been incorporated fully in the Commentary and the Annotated Index, and acknowledged by his initials, J.R.S.

Mrs. Margaret Davis Cate, of Sea Island, Ga., has kindly furnished, through her publications and by correspondence, much valuable information pertaining to Bartram's journeys in Georgia. To the late Charles C. Harrold, of Macon, I am indebted for many courtesies, and most particularly for making me acquainted with David Taitt's highly illuminating map of 1772. The rare enthusiasm of E. G. Swem, of Williamsburg, Va., for colonial history has been a distinct spur to my Bartram studies. Joseph Ewan, of Tulane University, in the course of his own studies on early American naturalists, has unearthed many choice Bartramian items, and with marked generosity has made them available to me. Wilbur H. Duncan, of the University of Georgia, has been most cooperative in discussing the distribution and identification of Bartramian plants in that state. Peter A. Brannon, of Montgomery, has very kindly pointed out Indian village sites and other important points on Bartram's route through Alabama. Roland M. Harper, of the Alabama Geological Survey, besides accompanying me for some days along the Bartram trail between Montgomery and Mobile, has offered many useful suggestions on botanical and geographical matters relating to Bartram's travels in general.

Among others who have been particularly helpful in the unraveling of Bartram's routes, mention must be made of the late Francis C. Pyle, of George School, Pa.; the late H. A. Rankin, of Fayetteville, N.C.; David Gillespie Robeson and the late John A. Robeson, of Bladen County, N.C.; Andrew L. Pickens, of Charlotte, N.C.; E. Milby Burton, of the Charleston Museum; Charles G. Cordle, Jouett Davenport, the late Eugene Edmund Murphey, and the late M. L. Reese, of Augusta, Ga.; the late T. G. Macfie, of Taliaferro County, Ga.; Clement E.

Sutton, of Washington, Ga.; R. B. Mallory, of Clyo, Ga.; Mrs. Louisa
Bryan Chaires Benham, of McMeekin, Fla.; E. W. Watkins and Randall
Wells, of Palatka, Fla.; A. J. Hanna, of Rollins College; Horton H.
Hobbs, Jr., Theodore H. Hubbell, and H. B. Sherman, of the University
of Florida; Z. C. Herlong, of Micanopy, Fla.; Mark F. Boyd, of Talla-
hassee; the late J. Clarence Simpson, of the Florida Geological Survey;
John Scipio, of King's Ferry, Fla.; R. P. Burke, of Montgomery, Ala.;
and Clair A. Brown, of Louisiana State University.

To John Mead Howells, former owner of the John Stuart House in
Charleston, I am indebted for a most interesting inspection of that
historic mansion.

Further particulars concerning the contributions of the above-
mentioned collaborators may be found in the introductory pages of
Bartram's report to Fothergill (1943) or here and there in the Commentary and the Annotated Index of the present volume. In the same
places appear the names of still other friends who have helped the
undertaking in various ways. It is no less a real pleasure than an urgent
duty to express my deep gratitude for all the generous cooperation
that has made this series of Bartram publications possible.

In Memoriam: Arthur Newlin Leeds

The present volume and two previous Bartram publications (1942,
1943) owe their inception in a very large measure to Arthur Newlin
Leeds [5] (1870–1939), late Research Fellow in the Department of
Botany of the Academy of Natural Sciences of Philadelphia. Long
accustomed to exploring the charming byways of the South, paddling
down its cypress-bordered streams, or climbing over its mountain
summits, he took particular delight in nature's offerings in that fair
region. It was thus quite natural and appropriate that he should have
become especially interested in the pioneer southern explorations of
his fellow Quakers John and William Bartram. It was my great privilege to be associated with him in several of the early efforts at re-
discovering the Bartram trail, as recounted above.

It was the cherished plan of Arthur Leeds and myself to work
jointly on the present undertaking, in which his botanical knowledge
would have been a contribution of the highest value. But destiny did
not permit him to go beyond the initial steps, and it has devolved upon
myself to carry the program forward, with a very great deal of generous assistance from others; yet the results are doubtless far short of

5. There are biographical sketches by Morris E. Leeds (1939), Pennell (1940),
and Harper (1939a).

what they might have been with his direct personal attention and devotion.

It is the special wish of the friends of Arthur Leeds who have contributed to, or have been engaged in, this undertaking that it should be a memorial to him—a reminder, to all lovers of the Bartrams, of a rare and noble spirit who helped to pave the way for a wider and better appreciation of these Quaker naturalists and their works.

CONTENTS

Preface   **v**

List of Illustrations and Facsimiles   xv

Introduction by Francis Harper   xvii

The TRAVELS   xxxvii

     Contents   xli

     Introduction   li

     Part One   1

     Part Two   37

     Part Three   195

     Part Four   306

Commentary   333

Annotated Index   425

References (literature)   668

Maps and Atlases Cited   690

Variant or Incorrect Orthography, Punctuation, and Composition   695

General Index   703

ILLUSTRATIONS AND FACSIMILES

	Page
William Bartram	*frontispiece*
I. Mico chlucco, the Long Warrior	*facing* xxxvii
II. Title page of the 1791 edition	xxxvii
III. Copyright page of the 1791 edition	xxxviii
IV. Dedication of the 1791 edition	xxxix
V. Map of the coast of East Florida	*facing* 1
VI. *Anona pygmea*	12
VII. *Anona grandiflora*	*facing* 14
VIII. *Ixea caelestina*	*facing* 98
IX. Head of great soft-shelled tortoise	113
X. Great soft-shelled tortoise	*facing* 114
XI. *Hydrangea quercifolia*	*facing* 242
XII. *Andromeda pulverulenta*	*facing* 302
XIII. Facsimile of the 1791 title page to Part Four	305

NOTE. A section of illustrations and maps follows page 727.

INTRODUCTION

$\mathbb{B}$ARTRAM'S long life-span (1739–1823) may be divided into a number of fairly distinct phases.

His early years (1739–1756) were passed at the famous Botanical Garden founded by his father, John Bartram, on the west bank of the Schuylkill River, near Philadelphia. More than any of his six brothers, he showed a strong inclination to follow in his father's footsteps as a naturalist. When no more than fourteen years of age, he began to draw birds, and within the next two or three years he turned out some highly creditable drawings of American maples and other plants. In September 1753 he accompanied his father on a memorable journey to the Catskills. In his teens he attended the Old College in Philadelphia, where he came under the tutelage of Charles Thomson, later secretary of the Continental Congress.

In the winter of 1756–1757 William began an apprenticeship with a merchant in Philadelphia. In this period of confinement he zealously devoted his few moments of leisure to the pursuit of natural history, and more especially to making illustrations of plants and animals. His father forwarded the drawings to his London friend, Peter Collinson, who passed on to George Edwards those of birds and turtles, and to J. F. Gronovius in Holland those of oaks. Edwards made use of the birds in his *Gleanings of Natural History* (3 vols. 1758–1764), and Collinson published on two of William's turtles in the *Gentleman's Magazine* for 1758.

In 1761 William cast off the bonds of mercantile life in Philadelphia and set out for fresh fields on the Cape Fear River in North Carolina, where his beloved uncle, Colonel William Bartram, gave him a warm welcome. There he set up a trading store as a means of livelihood; but the attractions of nature in that fascinating new environment claimed a considerable share of his attention, and his business did not prosper.

This first Carolina adventure came to an end in 1765, when John Bartram, just appointed botanist to His Majesty George III, visited his brother on his way to Florida. William thereupon became his father's assistant and companion for the remainder of the trip. This was the longest and apparently the last of John Bartram's expeditions (J. Bartram, 1942). Aside from making their first acquaintance with the floral and faunal riches of the St. John's and other parts of East Florida, father and son had the advantage of meeting and conferring with such men of affairs as John Stuart, Henry Laurens, Governor James Wright of Georgia, and Governor James Grant of Florida; also with Dr. Alexander Garden, of Charleston, the correspondent of Linnaeus, and with George Galphin, the influential trader of Silver Bluff, S.C. While the provincial administration was negotiating a treaty with the Seminoles at Picolata on the St. John's, William created something of a sensation by slaying a six-foot Rattlesnake and dragging it triumphantly into camp, where Governor Grant had it served up for dinner! (*Travels:* 271). We have comparatively little information on William's other activities at this period, except that he made some drawings. However, this pioneering Florida experience, under his father's guidance, undoubtedly furnished much of the basic training and qualification for his solitary travels and studies of nature in the Southeast in the next decade.

At the conclusion of the trip, in the spring of 1766, William chose to remain on the St. John's in an effort to raise indigo and rice. This, however, resulted in more disastrous failure than any of his other business ventures. His serious plight by the following summer is revealed in a letter written by Henry Laurens on August 9 to John Bartram (Darlington, 1849: 438–442). Soon thereafter William abandoned his plantation. Little is known as to the manner in which he spent the following winter, except that he evidently had some association with the colonial cartographer and historian John G. W. De Brahm, and was involved in a shipwreck on the Florida coast (cf. *Travels:* 144n., and Bartram Papers 4: 66).

From 1767 to 1770 William was once more in Philadelphia or vicinity, endeavoring to earn a livelihood first by agricultural, and then by mercantile, pursuits. Despite his humble situation, he was elected in February 1768 a corresponding member of the American Society Held in Philadelphia for Promoting Useful Knowledge; at the same meeting Benjamin Franklin and John Bartram were elected regular or resident members. In the following year this society was amalgamated with the American Philosophical Society; but it is not on record that William attended a single meeting of that august body during the remaining 54 years of his life! Evidently he preferred communion with nature to formal communion with fellow scientists and scholars. Meanwhile the benevolent Peter Collinson, just before his death in 1768, secured commissions for William to draw mollusks for the Duchess of Portland and mollusks and turtles for Dr. John Fothergill. His final good turn, in inducing Dr. Fothergill to take over the patronage of William, was far-reaching in its consequences, for without a Collinson and a Fothergill to point the way and provide the means, there could have been no Bartram's *Travels*.

During this Philadelphia interlude, however, William seems to have made little progress toward carrying out Dr. Fothergill's commission. His business duties and difficulties may have left him with very inadequate leisure or tranquillity for such pursuits. Finally, in 1770, with bankruptcy either impending or actually overtaking him, William disappeared from Philadelphia; and it was not until several months later that John Bartram heard from him in his old haunts on the Cape Fear River in North Carolina. There he remained until 1772, meanwhile having been deprived by death of his warm-hearted uncle, his aunt, and his cousin, William Bartram, Jr. He made some effort to collect local debts dating from the previous decade, and he supplied a certain number of drawings for Dr. Fothergill. In 1772 he received a letter from his brother Moses (Gratz Coll.), urging him to return home, and one from his father (Hist. Soc. Pennsylvania, Misc. Coll.), expressing surprise and indignation at his "wild notion" of proceeding once more to St. Augustine.

But the time had come for William to throw off, finally and irrevocably, the shackles of the mercantile world. He was about to cross his Rubicon. Most opportunely, Dr. Fothergill now came forward with a proposal to support a trip by William to Florida. "It is a pity that such a genius should sink under distress," he wrote to John Bartram (Bartram Papers 4: 18). A few weeks later, in October 1772, he sent William detailed instructions for collecting and shipping plants and for making drawings of plants and shells. This letter (Bartram Papers 4: 23) is notable as embodying one of the earliest sets of instructions ever issued for an American biological expedition.

In a letter of October 23, 1772 (Bartram Papers 4: 26), to Dr. Lionel Chalmers, of Charleston, who was to act as fiscal agent in the dealings with William, Dr. Fothergill proposed a remuneration of £50 per year, with additional allowances for expenses and for the drawings to be made. The confidence reposed in William by his distinguished London patron led John Bartram to acquiesce in the proposal (Bartram Papers 4: 23), and it doubtless mollified to some extent his recently expressed stern attitude toward his most gifted son.

Sometime between the fall of 1772 and the early part of 1773, our traveler returned to Philadelphia from his second Carolina adventure, presumably to make more complete preparations for his forthcoming long journey. He set sail again for Charleston on March 20, 1773. The ensuing period of nearly four years comprised the climactic experiences of his whole life. The record of those experiences, including the indelible impressions of his contacts with both wild and human nature, has carried his name and fame throughout the length and breadth of his native land and far overseas as well. With the passage of time that fame has increased rather than diminished, especially in the present century. Further discussion of the *Travels* itself is reserved for subsequent pages.

During his peregrinations of 1773–1777 Bartram undoubtedly kept field journals. This was in accordance with Dr. Fothergill's instructions of September 4, 1773 (Bartram Papers *4:* 27):

"It will be right to keep a little journal, marking the soil, situation, plants in general[,] remarkable animals, where found, and the several particulars relative to them as they cast up. . . . Mark the places, [the plants] grow in, under shade or in the open country." It is nothing short of a tragedy that all trace of these journals has been lost for more than a hundred years. However, two manuscript volumes of reports on the first two seasons of field work were dispatched to Dr. Fothergill, and these were eventually published in 1943. Numerous plant specimens that Bartram collected, as well as drawings of various plants and animals that he made during this trip, are preserved in the British Museum (Natural History).

The outbreak of the Revolution must have cut off the possibility of further communication with "the noble Fothergill" after a final shipment of specimens to him from Georgia in 1776. This last and greatest of Bartram's patrons died in 1780.

Preparation and Publication of the Travels

The events and influences that directed Bartram's tastes, inspired and trained him in literary composition, and eventually resulted in the production of his masterpiece, as the first publication under his separate authorship, at the age of 52, are not very difficult to trace. Of primary importance was the atmosphere of John Bartram's household and garden on the Schuylkill River, with the perennial activity of collecting, propagating, and shipping to distant patrons the seeds or roots of trees and shrubs from the glorious primeval forests of America. William was undoubtedly aware of the enthusiastic letters sent by his father to other naturalists, both American and European, and of the responses received from Franklin, Colden, Clayton, Mitchell, Garden, Collinson, Gronovius, Catesby, Fothergill, Linnaeus, and others of similar standing. Perhaps he was even allowed to peep at some of the letters himself.

There was no more likely source of William's inspiration than Catesby's *Natural History,* which had been presented to John Bartram by the author himself. As a boy he must have felt an urge to emulate Catesby in preparing colored plates; in later years he surpassed the latter's productions, both literary and artistic.

William was of course aware that his father was in the habit of sending his field journals to Collinson, and that several of these (New York, Georgia, and St. John's River journals) had been published in London between 1751 and 1769. It was very likely with the examples of Catesby, Edwards, and his father before him that he was inspired, in 1767 or thereabouts, to draw up an account (now lost) of the natural productions of Florida. An intermediate stage in his progress toward composing the *Travels* is represented by his report to Dr. Fothergill (1943). Consequently it required only a little elaboration of his previous custom to formulate plans for a whole volume devoted to his experiences and observations of 1773–1777 in the Southern Colonies.

Training in the classics at the Old College in Philadelphia and familiarity with the Bible (carried with him on his journey) clearly show their influence in the finished product: e.g. allusions to Elysium, the fields of Pharsalia, the Vale of Tempe, Ovid's *Metamorphoses,* and Nebuchadnezzar in the wilderness.

When the scientist and traveler Johann David Schoepf visited Philadelphia in 1783, he mentioned (1911, *1:* 91) Bartram's "unprinted manuscript on the nations and products" of Florida. It was apparently in 1786 that Enoch Story, Jr., a Philadelphia publisher, issued a broadside inviting subscriptions to a projected edition of the *Travels;* he also wrote to Benjamin Franklin (Franklin Papers *41:* 201), expressing Bartram's wish that the volume "might be dedicated to you." According to the broadside, it was to include "a catalogue of American trees and shrubs, . . . near one hundred" of which "have never yet been described." However, the book did not come to be published by Story, and we do not know what manner of reply Franklin may have made to him. (Harper, 1946*b*.)

Those who champion Bartram's botanical and zoological nomenclature may well regret that the volume did not see the light of day by 1787. If it had, he would have received more credit than has actually been accorded him in the naming of new species of plants and animals of his own discovery. The announced catalogue of trees and shrubs (never included in any edition of the *Travels*) would have been of much importance, especially if accompanied by validating descriptions. Between 1787 and 1791 there appeared Walter's *Flora Caroliniana* (1788), Aiton's *Hortus Kewensis* (1789), and parts of Lamarck's *Encyclopédie Méthodique* (1783–1797), L'Héritier's *Stirpes Novae* (1785–1791), and Gmelin's *Systema Naturae* (1788–1793)—all containing descriptions of certain new species that Bartram had found in the 1770's or earlier but did not name in print until 1791.

Meanwhile a new element enters the picture, in the shape of an enterprising young medical student of Philadelphia, Benjamin Smith Barton (1766–1815). In 1786 he went abroad to study medicine at the University of Edinburgh. During his three years' foreign residence, he wrote no less than five or six times to the sage of the Schuylkill. At least two of these letters (Bartram Papers *1:* 3 and 4) deal with a bold proposition to be allowed to publish Bartram's work, *with additions of his own.* Though we have no record of Bartram's response, he doubtless declined the proposition, but in such a kindly way as to bring about no impairment of his permanently friendly relations with Barton. The latter's subsequent career revealed numerous and frequently successful attempts to profit by Bartram's superior knowledge of natural history, without adequate acknowledgment of his indebtedness. In one of his letters from Edinburgh (August 26, 1787) he had castigated Story in a way that may have induced Bartram to break off relations with that publisher; in any event, several years were lost before other arrangements for publication were made.

It was apparently not until 1790 that another firm of Philadelphia printers and publishers, James and Johnson, issued new proposals for publishing the work. A copy has been preserved at the New York Public Library. The general announcement on the first page is followed by two pages containing an extract of Bartram's ecstatic description of the Alachua Savanna—a bit of the earth's surface that he evidently treasured in memory above nearly all others.

Robert Parrish, a Philadelphia friend of Bartram's and perhaps an employee of his publishing firm, wrote to him from New York on June 20, 1790 (Darlington Papers), reporting that he had secured subscriptions from President Washington and Vice President Adams, among others. Washington, in adherence to a consistent policy, had declined having the volume dedicated to himself; yet on the same day he wrote to Samuel Powel, mayor of Philadelphia: "I am happy in having [subscribed to the work]; and I sincerely wish it all the success, which its merits demand" (Fitzpatrick, 1939, *31:* 56–57). Three days later Thomas Jefferson (1944: 155), then in New York, "p^d subscription for Bartram's travels 16/."

The person finally selected for the dedication was Thomas Mifflin, a major general in the Revolution, president of Congress (1783–1784), president of the State of Pennsylvania (1788–1790), and governor of Pennsylvania (1790–1799). It is doubtless significant of Bartram's devotion to the Revolutionary cause that he should have considered for this indication of his esteem such men as Franklin, Washington, and Mifflin.

The price of the James and Johnson edition was advertised as "two Spanish milled dollars," whereas the price of the Story edition was to have been "one dollar in blue boards." It would be surprising if more than a thousand copies of the 1791 edition were ever printed or sold. A 10 per cent royalty on such a sale would have fetched the author a material reward of 200 "Spanish milled dollars." But who can measure the spiritual reward of having produced a classic of natural history and a literary gem of enduring fame?

A remark by the botanist William Baldwin, in a letter of July 3, 1817, to Dr. William Darlington (1843: 235), suggests that Bartram may not have even had the opportunity of reading the proof of his *Travels*. If such an opportunity had been properly utilized, many of the typographical errors and other inconsistencies in the published work might have been eliminated.

Although the title page bears the date 1791, no conclusive evidence seems to have been adduced to show that publication took place in that year. It was obviously published sometime after August 26, 1791— the date of the registration notice on the verso of the title page. The closest indication of the publication date so far discovered seems to be an entry for January 27, 1792, in Henry Muhlenberg's journal (MS, Am. Philos. Soc.), kindly brought to my attention by Willman Spawn: "I have perused William Bartram's Florida travel book, which displays an extraordinary amount of noteworthy material" (trans.). Publication was thus not later than January 1792, and it may have taken place toward the end of 1791. Unless or until more complete evidence may be forthcoming, it seems best to accept the date on the title page at its face value.

Reception of the Travels

Some further evidence as to the approximate date may be found in *The Universal Asylum and Columbian Magazine* (Philadelphia), Volume 1 for 1792. The January issue has an excerpt from the Introduction of the *Travels;* the February issue, an account of the various tribes of Southern Indians. In March there begins a review, noncritical as yet, and consisting of quotations and summaries. In April (p. 266) the review is concluded, in a severely critical vein:

> We cannot help thinking that he magnifies the virtues of the Indians, and views their vices through too friendly a medium. . . .
>
> The merits of the book, in general . . . entitle the author to a respectable place among those, who have devoted their time and talents to the improvement of natural science. . . . Many rhapsodical effusions might, we think, have been omitted, with advantage to the work. We are sorry to be under the necessity of finding fault with the style of the author, who has afforded us so much useful information and agreeable entertainment; but we cannot with any propriety countenance a style so very incorrect and disgustingly pompous, as that in which the greater part of these travels is written. These faults, however, with the judicious and inquisitive reader, will be but secondary considerations.

The general lack of appreciation—or rather of comprehension— shown by this anonymous critic may be the better understood if we compare the reception accorded Coleridge's "Christabel," "Kubla Khan," and "The Pains of Sleep" in the *Edinburgh Review* in 1816: "We look upon this publication as one of the most notable pieces of impertinence of which the press has lately been guilty . . . . The thing now before us is utterly destitute of value. It exhibits from beginning to end not a ray of genius."

The *Massachusetts Magazine,* in Volume 4 for 1792, under the enlightened editorship of Isaiah Thomas, deals much more fairly and judiciously with this new type of traveler's tale than had its Philadelphia contemporary. Its July, August, November, and December issues offer about ten extracts from some of the more novel and striking portions of the *Travels.* The November issue (pp. 686–687) includes a review, wherein the "trivial faults" are put in proper perspective:

> The amateur of natural science, cannot fail of being highly gratified by the perusal of this volume. Mr. Bartram, has accurately described a variety of birds, fish and reptiles, hitherto but little known: His American botanical researches are more copious than any other writers, with whom we are acquainted: Nor have the customs and manners of the Aboriginals, whom he visited, escaped the minutiae of attention: In description, he is rather too luxuriant and florid, to merit the palm of chastity and correctness: But a thousand of these trivial faults, the effect of a poetical imagination, are amply compensated for, by a rich vein of piety, blended with the purest morality.

The publication of the first London edition in 1792 brought forth a notice in *The Monthly Review; or Literary Journal, Enlarged* (*10* (January): 13–22; (February): 130–138, 1793). As a whole, the review is mildly critical, but by no means so severe as the one that appeared in Philadelphia. The January installment consists mostly of quotations on such subjects as Indians and Alligators. In the February issue the *Travels* is referred to as a "very entertaining publication." We read further (p. 131):

> The naturalist . . . will be gratified by lists of such peculiar plants and trees as Mr. Bartram observed, and with his remarks on the soil, or other local circumstances. The grandeur, indeed, of some of the scenes might well betray a warm imagination into rapturous effusions, which he occasionally indulges: but when he reviewed these in his cooler moments, he might have brought the language down nearer to the apprehension of readers who, not having viewed the scenes, may find some difficulty in exalting their fancies to the altitude of *his* admiration.

After reading about the Alligators, the reviewer confesses, "We prefer our old smoaky apartments in Grub-street." Perhaps we should not expect a Grub Street dweller of 1793 to have made any closer approach to a comprehension either of the charms of primeval Florida or of the exhilaration of their exponent. On the other hand, there is doubtless some justice in the reviewer's comment on Bartram's ultra-indulgent attitude toward the Indians (p. 137): "If we can safely infer any thing from the whole, it is that these Indians may be a good sort of people while their passions are dormant, and while they are without strong liquor."

Even years later the ultraprosaic type of reviewer could not refrain from caustic comment, as, for example, in the *American Quarterly Review* (2: 226, 1827): "The Travels of William Bartram . . . contain a great number of most interesting facts and observations. It is much to be regretted, however, that with his opportunities, this amiable author had not written with a greater degree of systematic precision, and with fewer pages of mere exclamatory admiration at the beauties and wonders of Nature."

By this time Bartram's "exclamatory admiration" had exerted ample influence on such poets as Wordsworth and Coleridge; but perhaps our reviewer disdained acquaintance with their productions. Doubtless he was also incapable of foreseeing the eagerness with which future generations of naturalists would scan even the "exclamatory" passages for precious information on the primeval flora and fauna of America.

Bartram was simply two or three generations ahead of his times in his appreciation of nature.

Few more shining examples of the adage, "A prophet is not without honor, save in his own country," could be found than in the total neglect of American publishers to bring out new editions of Bartram for fully 136 years after the original publication, whereas in Europe eight or nine editions in six different countries were called for within the first ten years.

The editor of the Berlin edition of 1793, E. A. W. Zimmermann, says in the Preface (pp. vii–ix, trans.):

> Anthropology and ethnology have been considerably enriched by our author. . . .
>
> But natural history proper receives the most important enrichment through this work. . . .
>
> He acquaints us with a considerable number of new plants. . . . The fauna also has gained much through him, both through the discovery of several hitherto unknown or doubtful species and through reports on the migratory birds and on the life histories of large, injurious animals, such as the Rattlesnake and the Alligator. . . . Especially he exhibits in the whole long journey fortitude, courage, and quiet endurance of all kinds of discomforts and dangers, whereby he is distinguished above many other travelers.

The following year the only American included in a list of "all living zoologists" by F. A. A. Meyer (1794: 73) was William Bartram! Even if the American list had been stretched to the utmost at that time, to include such figures as Abbot, Barton, the younger Brickell, Dunbar, Jefferson, F. V. Melsheimer, Muhlenberg, the elder Peale, and Wistar, Bartram's name and fame as a zoologist would still have stood above all the rest.

It would seem almost inconceivable that various friends or even strangers (in the role of "fans") should not have favored our author with appreciative notes on the appearance of the *Travels*. If they were written, perhaps he was too modest to preserve them, for scarcely one such letter survives. Surely the warm-hearted Muhlenberg must have spoken or written enthusiastically at some time prior to his letter of June 22, 1792 (Torrey-Redfield Coll.), wherein he merely refers to the book as follows: "I see you name many different Species of Quercus, Juglans cet. in your Travels." He wrote again on September 13, 1792 (Bartram Papers 4: 89): "Your fine Catalogue of American Animals in your Travels show that You are a close Observer." Where, meanwhile, were Barton, Jefferson, Thomas Mifflin, and Lachlan McIntosh?

For more than a century after the publication of the *Travels,* there was probably more general appreciation of it abroad than in America. Perhaps the best-known of the foreign comments is that of Carlyle in a letter of July 8, 1851, to Emerson (Carlyle-Emerson Correspondence 2: 198, 1883): "Do you know *Bartram's Travels?* This is of the Seventies (1770) or so; treats of *Florida* chiefly, has a wondrous kind of floundering eloquence in it; and has also grown immeasurably *old.* All American libraries ought to provide themselves with that kind of book; and keep them as a kind of *biblical* article."

Coleridge himself, who utilized the volume so profitably in various poems, including "The Ancient Mariner" and "Kubla Khan," testifies (*Table Talk:* 43): "The latest book of travels I know written in the spirit of the old travellers is Bartram's account of his tour in the Floridas. It is a work of high merit every way."

At least eight or nine editions of the *Travels* blossomed in Europe within ten years after its first publication in Philadelphia in 1791. There were two editions in London (1792, 1794), one in Dublin (1793), one in Berlin (1793,) one in Vienna (1793), one or two in Haarlem (1 vol. and 3 vols. 1794–1797), and two in Paris (2 vols. each, 1799, 1801). There are also rumors of an edition in Amsterdam (1797) and of "copies of the English edition on large paper" (Sabin, 1868, *1:* 513, 514). There is apparently not the least vestige of any correspondence between the various European publishers and the author or the publishers in Philadelphia; presumably all these editions were pirated. Actually the author may never have been aware of some of them.

Professor Cooper may be pleased to recall an estimate of the *Travels* that he offered more than half a century ago (1905: 152); for it seems to have been prophetic of the steadily growing esteem that the book has enjoyed during the intervening years:

> [His narrative] needs recalling to American botanists and ornithologists, or for that matter to European; as a scientific record, however florid in style, its value seems to have been understood from the first. . . .
>
> His book is . . . a typical specimen of romantic nature worship, deeply tinged with the doctrine of Rousseau, and all the more striking because from the hand of a recognized, though youthful, scientific observer. . . . Its place and possible influence in our own literature will, I hope, receive proper attention.

On the other hand, the record now available to us not only indicates a very general lack of proper appreciation of the *Travels* on the part of the American public during the remainder of Bartram's life, but—still worse—includes, as probably the most telling contemporary review, the scathing blast in *The Universal Asylum and Columbian Magazine* of 1792. As far as we know, the reaction of even his particular friends was not at first overly enthusiastic. The generally indifferent reception accorded his maximum effort must have been vastly discouraging. Doubtless Bartram himself was too modest to assess it at anything approximating its true worth, as well as unaware of having blazed an epochal new trail in nature appreciation. The trail simply led to a point beyond the proper comprehension of nearly all his contemporaries. Is it any wonder that the contributions from his pen during the next 31 years were so meager? Even these minor papers might not have come to pass if it had not been for the prodding of two or three scientific friends, of whom the most insistent was Benjamin Smith Barton. As a confirmed stay-at-home during this period, he had no more thrilling adventures in the wilderness to describe; yet there was ample opportunity within range of his own doorstep for recording worth-while observations and philosophical reflections on the plants and animals he loved so well. It is obvious that the world has been distinctly the loser by reason of the uncomprehending and unappreciative attitude of all but the merest handful of Bartram's own countrymen during his lifetime.

In retrospect of those days long past, we are tempted to say of Bartram as Wilson Flagg (1872: 396) said of Thoreau: "Those whose minds were too dull to perceive the hue of his genius did not respect him."

Later Years

After his return from the South in 1777, Bartram must have led a remarkably sedentary life. If, during his remaining 46 years, he ever ventured farther afield than a day's journey from Philadelphia, it does not seem to be on record. Yet his sedentary trait did not keep him from contact with a goodly number of American and foreign naturalists, who beat a path to his door. The visitors even included presidents, governors, and congressmen of the new republic. The course of his life during these years may perhaps be best brought out in a discussion of his relations with his principal friends and visitors.

Before the publication of the *Travels* in 1791, the chief attraction for visitors was probably the Botanical Garden itself; for Bartram was then unknown as an author (aside from his contribution of notes and drawings to Edwards' *Gleanings of Natural History*). Yet he had achieved a certain reputation as a traveler and a botanist that none of his brothers could equal. Thus it was William, if anyone, that the visiting scientists, authors, and statesmen sought out and mentioned in their records. John, Jr., remained distinctly in the background, although he had fallen heir to the proprietorship on his father's death in 1777. In view of William's unbroken series of failures in business and agriculture, it is understandable that the elder Bartram had decided that the Garden would be safer under John's management.

A foreign visitor arriving close upon the end of the Revolution was the erudite Johann David Schoepf (1752–1800), who left (1911, *1:* 90–92) an appreciative account of the Garden, Bartram, and his unprinted manuscript. At the time of the Constitutional Convention in Philadelphia in 1787, George Washington made two trips to the Garden, as briefly recorded in his diary (Fitzpatrick, 1925, *3:* 222, 234). On July 14 of that year a considerable party, consisting largely of delegates to the convention, rode out to the Garden; among them were "Mr. [Caleb] Strong, Governor [Alexander] Martin [of North Carolina], Mr. [George] Mason . . . Mr. [Hu] Williamson [of North Carolina], Mr. [James] Madison, Mr. [John] Rutledge [of South Carolina] . . . Mr. [Alexander] Hamilton . . . Mr. [John] Vaughan . . . Dr. [Gerardus] Clarkson," and Rev. Manasseh Cutler. An account of the visit by the last-mentioned person (in Cutler and Cutler, 1888, *1:* 272–274) is notable chiefly, perhaps, for its patronizing air.

The noted French botanist, André Michaux (1746–1802), began to visit Bartram at least by 1789, and probably earlier, with subsequent visits in 1792 and 1794 (A. Michaux, 1889: 57, 58, 68, 102, 103). During his explorations in the Southeast at this period Michaux covered so many parts of Bartram's old trail that we may readily imagine him having profited by suggestions of the elder naturalist as to choice collecting localities. Michaux's son, François André (1770–1855), also maintained cordial relations with the Bartrams in subsequent years (cf. F. A. Michaux, 1805: 22; Darlington, 1849: 477–478). For a time, in the 1790's, Thomas Jefferson lived on the opposite bank of the Schuylkill, and in the next decade, during his presidency, he and Bartram exchanged a number of very cordial letters, chiefly on natural history subjects. It was natural that William Hamilton (d. 1813), a near neighbor on the Schuylkill and proprietor of one of the most amply furnished private gardens in America, should have maintained a friendly intercourse with Bartram. Eleven of his letters are among the Bartram Papers.

The world owes to the renowned artist Charles Willson Peale (1741–1827) the only likeness made and preserved of William Bartram (frontisp.); it hangs in the Old City Hall on Independence Square. Although the two men must have known each other well, there are few tangible evidences of their relations, aside from the portrait and a copy of the catalogue of Peale's Museum presented to Bartram (now in the Historical Society of Pennsylvania).

There is a more voluminous record of Bartram's relations with Benjamin Smith Barton, the physician and naturalist, than with any other friend. Their acquaintance began by 1786, and their rather one-sided relationship continued as long as Barton lived (till 1815). While it was his policy to carefully guard his own unpublished knowledge and materials from others, it may be said that he was assiduously engaged, from the beginning to the end of his career, in absorbing whatever information he could from his associates, with the design of converting it to his own use. Bartram was probably his chief victim, but a willing or at least an uncomplaining one. The *Fragments of the Natural History of Pennsylvania*, published by Barton in 1799, was hailed by Elliott Coues (1878: 592) as "one of the most notable special treatises on North American ornithology of the [eighteenth] century." Actually, Barton had so little first-hand knowledge of birds that he did not venture to mention more than the merest handful of species in his various field journals. The *Fragments* is little more than a compilation by a closet naturalist, who managed over a period of years to wheedle out of Bartram, or to cull from his *Travels*, the essential part of the ornithological information it presents. The meteorological information was admittedly derived from David Rittenhouse.

On the other hand, we may be most grateful to Barton for having propounded to Bartram, apparently in 1789, a long series of questions on the Creek and Cherokee Indians; for the latter's answers provide more complete or comprehensive information on some of the topics than do pages 481–522 of the *Travels*. *One week* after these answers were transmitted, Barton issued a broadside (Barton Papers) announcing a proposed (but never published) ethnological work of his own, which doubtless would have made full use of his friend's contribution. Belated justice came to Bartram in 1853, when his manuscript was finally published under his own name.

William Dunlap (1766–1839), artist, author, and playright, furnishes (1832: 170) a homely but pleasant picture of our naturalist in 1797:

May 9. Rise about 5 o'clock, and join Charles Brockden Brown about 6, for the purpose of walking to Bartram's Botanic Garden.

. . . Arrived at the Botanist's Garden, we approached an old man who, with a rake in his hand, was breaking the clods of earth in a tulip bed. His hat was old and flapped over his face, his coarse shirt was seen near his neck, as he wore no cravat or kerchief; his waistcoat and breeches were both of leather, and his shoes were tied with leather strings. We approached and accosted him. He ceased his work, and entered into conversation with the ease and politeness of nature's noblemen. His countenance was expressive of benignity and happiness. This was the botanist, traveller, and philosopher we had come to see.

Henry Muhlenberg (1753–1815), a distinguished clergyman and botanist of Lancaster, Pa., was a prodigious epistolarian. A volume of his letters (Hist. Soc. Pennsylvania) consists largely of botanical correspondence. He probably contributed as much as any American of his time to keeping the spirit of botany alive among its devotees. His attitude was the antithesis of Barton's in being thoroughly altruistic. One of his particular aims, as brought out in the letters, was to elucidate certain puzzling or doubtful plants recorded in the *Travels*. Bartram's answers testify to his pleasure in communing with such a congenial spirit, and especially in receiving him as an occasional visitor at the Botanical Garden.

Alexander Wilson (1766–1813), a Scotch immigrant to America, weaver, peddler, and schoolmaster, would scarcely have developed into "the father of American ornithology" without the active encouragement and guidance of William Bartram. The location of his last school within a mile of the Botanical Garden led to an acquaintance that "grew into an uncommon friendship" (Ord, 1825, 9: xxvii). Although they lived in such proximity that visits might have been expected to largely take the place of correspondence, no less than several dozen of Wilson's letters to his mentor have been preserved. On the other hand, I have yet to lay eyes on a single original letter from Bartram to his devoted disciple. By 1804 Wilson had begun to send his friend colored drawings of the local birds, with an earnest request for criticism. At that time he did not even know the names of a considerable number of the species. The next year he had the "presumption," as he expressed it in a letter of July 2, to seriously begin a collection of drawings of Pennsylvania birds. He closed that letter with the following words: "To your advice and encouraging encomiums I am indebted for these few specimens, and for all that will follow. *They may yet tell posterity that I was honoured with your friendship, and that to your inspiration they owe their existence.*"

So earnestly and enthusiastically did Wilson apply himself to this task that by 1808 he had brought out the first volume of his epoch-making *American Ornithology*. Six other quarto volumes followed from 1810 to 1813. Each of the volumes contains nine colored plates by the author himself. Bartram contributed notes on a number of the species. Meanwhile Wilson resided at the Botanical Garden for the better part of the years 1811–1812. After his untimely death in 1813, his work was brought to completion by George Ord. The story of Wilson and Bartram has been so frequently told that it scarcely requires further discussion here.

Among other friends was William Baldwin (1779–1819), a Wilmington physician and botanist, who followed Bartram's footsteps in Georgia and Florida and visited him at his home. On one of these visits in 1817, "My being able to confirm several of his doubtful plants, was extremely gratifying to him . . . . Aware of the suspicions which some entertain of his veracity, it was truly a feast to me to observe how his time-worn countenance brightened up at the vindication of his character, which I informed him I was prepared to offer." (Darlington, 1843: 238.)

Zaccheus Collins (1764–1831) was a merchant of Philadelphia and a botanist by avocation. Though publishing nothing himself, he actively promoted science by his correspondence with some of the most eminent botanists of his day. About 60 of Muhlenberg's letters are preserved in the Collins Correspondence, and about 23 from Collins in the Muhlenberg Letters. From these we obtain some interesting glimpses of the venerable naturalist on the Schuylkill. Thus Collins on September 24, 1812: "Your friend W. Bartram whom I visited last week reciprocated in warm terms your expressions of esteem and remembrance." And Muhlenberg on August 27, 1813: "Bartram is to me a very valuable Traveller and I partake of all his Troubles and Pleasures"; and again on November 22, 1813: "Mr. William Bartram has a Library within himself. Some great and famous Botanists have robbed [him] of his Honey, without thanking him for his Trouble."

William Darlington (1782–1862), physician, botanist, and member of Congress, performed notable service to the history of science in publishing *Reliquiae Baldwinianae* (1843) and *Memorials of John Bartram and Humphry Marshall* (1849), both of which contain extremely valuable information on various phases of William Bartram's career. Through his efforts John Bartram's diary of his trip to Florida in 1765–1766 has been preserved at the Historical Society of Pennsylvania; and the four priceless volumes of Bartram Papers came to

that repository in perhaps the same manner. Thus all students of the
Bartrams are under deep and lasting obligation to Darlington for his
monumental labors. There is only a meager record of his personal relations with the author of the *Travels*. In his manuscript reminiscences
for 1804 (New-York Hist. Soc.), dealing with his student days at the
University of Pennsylvania, Darlington says that Professor B. S. Barton
"took his small class, occasionally . . . to the Bartram Botanic Garden
—where I recollect seeing the venerable *William Bartram*." It can
scarcely be doubted, however, that he enjoyed the allurements of the
Garden on later occasions, including some on which he had opportunities of conversing with the *genius loci* himself.

Frederick Pursh (1774–1820), a German immigrant, was employed
as a gardener on William Hamilton's estate in West Philadelphia, and
later at Dr. David Hosack's Elgin Botanical Garden in New York.
Meanwhile, under Benjamin Smith Barton's patronage, he made extensive collecting trips from Virginia to Vermont. Eventually he went
to England and there published his important *Flora Americae Septentrionalis* (2 vols. 1813). Here he makes frequent reference to
Bartram's *Travels* and to his drawings and specimens in England, besides paying him the following tribute: "In Mr. William Bartram . . .
I found a very intelligent, agreeable, and communicative gentleman;
and from him I received considerable information about the plants of
[the South] . . . . It is with the liveliest emotions of pleasure that I
call to mind the happy hours I spent in this worthy man's company."

George Ord (1781–1866), the devoted friend of Alexander Wilson,
completed the latter's *American Ornithology* after his death and published a sketch of his life. In this he included most of the Wilson-
Bartram correspondence. He was also, almost without question, the
author of the earliest biographical sketch of Bartram, published
anonymously in 1832. He was quite possibly the most erudite American naturalist of the first half of the nineteenth century.

Despite his great services to zoology, it is difficult not to charge him
with failure to make a determined effort to ensure the preservation of
some exceedingly precious manuscript materials that were in his hands
at one time or another, but are now completely lost: an autobiographi-
cal sketch by Wilson, some of the Wilson-Bartram letters, and apparently Bartram's original field journals. The close association of
Wilson and Ord must have led the latter with some frequency to the
pleasant confines of Bartram's Garden. At one time he received a
communication from the elder naturalist on the subject of the Coot. In
the biographical sketch of 1832 he remarks:

The rich fund of knowledge possessed by Mr. Bartram, after so many years of application and research, and the simple and unaffected manner in which he imparted instruction to those who sought it of him, made his society agreeable, and courted by the literary, scientific, and others on very many occasions . . . . There was scarcely an American or foreign writer who attempted the natural history of this country but applied to him for information on their relative treatises.

Thomas Nuttall (1786–1859), a distinguished English botanist and ornithologist, made lengthy sojourns in this country between 1808 and 1848. Soon after his arrival in Philadelphia he was referred by Professor Barton to "the celebrated Mr. William Bartram." No botanist up to his time had made such extensive travels in the United States as he eventually carried out. In 1834 he went overland to the Pacific, and two years later returned by sail around the Horn. His *Genera of North American Plants* (1818), his *Manual of the Ornithology of the United States and Canada* (1832, 1834), and his *North American Sylva* (1842–1846) are his best-known works. While engaged on the *Genera*, he "had a room expressly reserved for him at [Bartram's Garden], called *Nuttall's room*, which he occupied occasionally for a whole week" (Durand, 1860: 301). In the *Manual of Ornithology* there are a number of references to the *Travels*, besides a couple of passages contributed more directly by Bartram. In the *Sylva* also there is frequent reference to Bartram's *Travels* and Garden. Each of the two men was a genius in his own way, and each expressed a somewhat similar philosophy of life.

The Le Contes of Georgia constituted one of the most distinguished scientific families in all American history. During the first half of the nineteenth century Major John Eatton Le Conte (1784–1860) was probably the foremost authority on the natural history of that state, besides having a wide range of interests in the fauna and flora of other parts of the world. Although there is no record of correspondence between Bartram and Le Conte, the latter was a visitor at the Garden and his publications include comments on the author of the *Travels* and on species described in that work. His final and most significant judgment (1854: 13) was as follows:

> I remember when it was much the custom to ridicule Mr. Bartram, and to doubt the truth of many of his relations. For my own part I must say, that having travelled in his track I have tested his accuracy, and can bear testimony to the absolute correctness of all his statements. I travelled through Florida before it was overrun by

its present inhabitants, and found everything exactly as he reported it to be when he was there, even to the locality of small and insignificant plants. Mr. Bartram was a man of unimpeached integrity and veracity, of primeval simplicity of manner and honesty unsuited to these times, when such virtues are not appreciated.

William P. C. Barton (1786–1856), a nephew of Benjamin Smith Barton, was professor of botany at the University of Pennsylvania and author of several reputable botanical works, including *A Flora of North America* (3 vols. 1821–1823). His record is apparently wholly free from such questionable practices as detracted from his uncle's reputation. To him we owe one of the pleasantest pen pictures of Bartram by a contemporary (1818, 2: 107–108):

> Mr. Bartram is still living, though aged and infirm. He resides at Kingsess gardens, where he hallows by his venerable presence, and graces by his instructive converse and simple manners, the seat founded and supported by his family. He is one of the most unambitious lovers of nature I have ever seen. With a mind keen, penetrating, and vivacious, he applied himself early in life, to the study of botany, and indeed natural history generally; but more particularly devoted himself to the study of the manners and habits of our birds, and other interesting points of inquiry connected with their history and migrations. In his travels into Florida, he relates these in all the fervor of a real lover of nature's works, and with such innocent enthusiasm, that we cannot fail to love and venerate the author. He ranks as a botanist in a very high grade. All his observations have been communicated to others, for the good of science; and to him, the late Professor Barton, Dr. Muhlenberg, Wilson, the ornithologist, and many others, have been largely indebted for much useful information.

And finally the Elysian fields beckon a new and fitting dweller: "A few minutes before his death he wrote an article on the natural history of a plant, and, in rising from his desk to take a morning survey of the botanic grounds, he had proceeded only a few steps from his door when he burst a blood-vessel, which suddenly closed his useful life July 22d, 1823, in the 85th year of his age" (?Ord, 1832: vii).

THE *TRAVELS*

MICO CHLUCCO the LONG WARIOR
or KING of the SIMINOLES

TRAVELS

THROUGH

NORTH & SOUTH CAROLINA,

GEORGIA,

EAST & WEST FLORIDA,

THE CHEROKEE COUNTRY, THE EXTENSIVE
TERRITORIES OF THE MUSCOGULGES,
OR CREEK CONFEDERACY, AND THE
COUNTRY OF THE CHACTAWS;

CONTAINING

AN ACCOUNT OF THE SOIL AND NATURAL
PRODUCTIONS OF THOSE REGIONS, TOGE-
THER WITH OBSERVATIONS ON THE
MANNERS OF THE INDIANS.

EMBELLISHED WITH COPPER-PLATES.

By WILLIAM BARTRAM.

PHILADELPHIA:
PRINTED BY *JAMES & JOHNSON.*
M,DCC,XCI.

District of PENNSYLVANIA, to wit:

BE it remembered, that on the twenty-sixth day of August, in the sixteenth year of the Independence of the United States of America, WILLIAM BARTRAM, of the said District, hath deposited in this office the title of a book, the right whereof he claims as Author in the words following, to wit:

"Travels through North & South Carolina, Georgia, "East & West Florida, the Cherokee country, the exten- "sive territories of the Muscogulges, or Creek Confede- "racy, and the country of the Chactaws; containing an "account of the Soil and Natural Productions of those re- "gions, together with observations on the Manners of the "Indians.——Embellished with copper-plates.

"By WILLIAM BARTRAM."

In conformity to the Act of the Congress of the United States, entitled, "An Act for the encouragement of Learn-ing, by securing the Copies of Maps, Charts and Books, to the authors and proprietors of such Copies, during the times therein mentioned."

SAMUEL CALDWELL,
Clerk of the District of
PENNSYLVANIA.

TO

HIS EXCELLENCY

THOMAS MIFFLIN, Esq;

PRESIDENT OF THE STATE

OF

PENNSYLVANIA,

THIS VOLUME OF TRAVELS

IS GRATEFULLY INSCRIBED,

By his respectful friend and servant

WILLIAM BARTRAM.

CONTENTS.

[*iii*]   PART I.

                    INTRODUCTION.

                    CHAP. I.   [1]*

THE Author embarks at Philadelphia—arrives at Charleston.

                    CHAP. II. III.   [3, 11]

Embarks again for Georgia and arrives at Savanna—proceeds Southward and arrives at Sunbury—observations on the town, harbour, and
the island of St. Catharine, its soil and productions—account of the
establishment of St. John's district and Midway meeting-house—description of a beautiful fish—proceeds for the river Alatamaha, description of a tremendous thunder storm—crosses the river at fort Barrington and arrives at St. Ille—passes the frontier settlements and meets an
hostile Indian—crosses the river St. Mary and arrives at the trading-
house, account of the country thereabout, its natural productions, of
the lake Ouaquaphenogaw, said to be the source of the St. Mary—
returns to the Alatamaha and thence to Savanna.

                    CHAP. IV.   [19]

Sets off from Savanna to Augusta, one hundred sixty-five miles
North-West from the sea coast—describes the face of the country, the
river Savanna, the cataracts and village of Augusta—congress with
the Indians at St. Augusta—the village of Wrightsborough on Little
River—monuments of an ancient Indian town on Little River—Buffaloe
Lick—begins the survey of the New Purchase—high proof of Indian
sagacity—returns to Savanna.

[* Page numbers refer to the present volume. In the original the Contents
provided no references to the subsequent pages on which the successive chapters
began.—Ed.]

CHAP. V.   [31]

The Author leaves Broughton island and ascends the Alatamaha—
night scene—a tempest—description of the river—ruins of an ancient
fortification—Indian monuments at the Oakmulge fields—Creeks, account of their settlement in Georgia.

[iv]   PART II.

CHAP. I.   [37]

Sets off from Savanna to East Florida, proceeding by land to the
Alatamaha—descends that river to Frederica on the island of St. Simons
—describes the island and the city.

CHAP. II. III.   [41, 46]

Leaves Frederica for the lower trading-house on St. Juans—passes
through and describes the sound, &c.—leaves Amelia island and arrives
at the Cowford, on the river St. Juans—proceeds up the river alone
in a small canoe; suffers by a gale of wind in crossing the river; is
hospitably entertained at a gentleman's house, where he refits and sails
again—describes fort Picolata—various productions, i.e. Magnolia
grandiflora, Tillansia ulneadscites floating fields of the Pistia stratiotes,
the river and country, touches at Charlotteville—arrives at the lower
trading-house.

CHAP. IV.   [63]

Proceeds farther up the river—passes by Mount Hope, and came to
at Mount Royal—describes the mount, Indian highway, &c. beautiful
landscape of the country and prospect of the lake—enters Lake George
—description of the lake—forced by stress of weather to put into the
beautiful Isle Edelano, description of the island, ancient Indian town,
mount and highway—crossed over the lake and arrives at the upper
trading-house.

CHAP. V.   [73]

Provides for continuing his voyage higher up the river, engages an
Indian to assist in navigating his bark, and sets sail, the Indian becomes

tired and requests to be set on shore—encamps at a delightful Orange
grove—continues again alone up the river: description of the Palma
Elate: enters the Little Lake and comes to camp at an Orange grove—
fight of alligators; a battle with them; great embarrassments with
them; kills one: vast assemblage of fish: description of the alligator and
their nests, &c.—describes the Carica papaya—a very curious bird—
in danger of being taken napping by a huge crocodile—the banks of
the river admirably ornamented with festoons and tapestry, the work
of nature—sepulchres of the ancients—a hurricane—visits a plantation
on the banks of the Long Lake; description of the lake, a large sulphureous fountain—account of the found-[v]ing and present state of
New Smyrna, on the Musquitoe river—returns down the river—East
Lake—curious birds and a beautiful fish—leaves Cedar Point, touches
at the isle of Palms; robbed by a wolf—arrives at Six Mile Springs—
an account of that admirable fountain—describes the Gordonia, Zamia,
Cactus opuntia, Erythrina, Cacalia, &c.—touches at Rocky Point—
arrives again at the lower trading-house.

CHAP. VI.   [108]

Proceeds on a journey to Cuscowilla—describes the country and
waters—Annona incana, Annona pygmea, Kalmia ciliata, Empetrum
album, Andromeda ferruginia, Rhododendron spurium, Pica glandaria
non cristata, Lanius, Lacerta, Snakes, Chionanthus, Andromeda formosissima, Cyrilla—encamps at the Half-way Pond—describes the pond
and meadows, a beautiful landscape—pilgrimage of fish—describes
various kinds of fish—great soft shelled tortoise and great land tortoise
—moral reflections and meditations—leaves Half-way Pond and proceeds—situation, quality and furniture of the earth—arrives at Cuscowilla—reception from the Indian chief; his character—Siminoles predilection for Spanish customs and civilization—Indian slaves, their condition—departs for the Alachua savanna; description of the savanna—
Siminoles on horseback—returns to Cuscowilla—a council and Indian
feast—description of the town and Cuscowilla lake—returns to the
savanna—glass-snake—makes the tour of the savanna—vestiges of the
ancient Alachua—Orange groves, turkeys, deer, wolves, savanna crane
—arrives at the great bason or sink—description of the sink—account
of the alligators, incredible number of fish; their subterranean migrations—returns—old Spanish highway—Indian village—arrives again
at the trading-house on St. Juans—character and comparison of the
nations of the Lower and Upper Creeks or Siminoles.

CHAP. VII.   [136]

Sets out again on a journey to Tallahasochte—description of the
Siminole horse—encamps at an enchanting grotto on the banks of a
beautiful lake—rocky ridges and desert wilds—engagement between
a hawk and the coach-whip-snake—description of the snake—account
of the country, grand Pine forest—encamps on the borders of an extensive savanna—description of the savanna crane—came upon the verge
of extensive savannas, lying on a beautiful lake—the expansive fields
of Capola, decorated with delightful groves—squa-[vi]drons of Siminole horse—a troop under the conduct and care of an Indian dog—
the fields of Capola a delightful region—ferruginous rocks, rich iron
ore—arrives at Talahasochte on the river Little St. Juans—describes
the town and river—Indian canoes—their voyages and traffic—Indian
voyage to Cuba—a fishing party and naval race—an excursion to the
Manatee spring—description of that incomparable nympheum—an
account of the Manatee—crosses the river to explore the country—
Spanish remains—vast Cane wildernesses—ancient Spanish plantations
—Apalachean old fields—returns to town—White King's arrival—a
council and feast—character of the king—leaves the town on researches, and encamps in the forests—account of an extraordinary
eruption of waters—joins his companions at camp—entertainment by
the White King in Talahasochte—Contee its preparation and use—
returns to camp—great desert plains—entertainment with a party of
young Siminole warriors—various natural wells and sinks; conjectures
concerning them—account of the Long Pond, and delightful prospects
adjacent—returns for the trading-house on St. Juans—embarassments
occasioned by the wild horses—encamps at Bird Island pond—vast
number of wild fowl tending their nests—engagement with an alligator
who surprised the camp by night—observations on the great Alachua
savanna and its environs—arrival at the trading-house.

CHAP. VIII.   [159]

The Author makes an excursion again up St. Juans to Lake George—
revisits Six Mile Springs and Illisium groves, makes collections, and
recrosses the lake to the Eastern coast—that shore more bold and
rocky than the opposite—coasts round that shore, touching at old
deserted plantations—Perennial Cotton—Indigo—unpardonable devastation, and neglect of the white settlers, with respect to the native
Orange groves—returns to the trading-house.

CHAP. IX. X. [161, 167]

Indian warriors, their frolick—curious conference with the Long Warrior—ludicrous Indian farce relative to a rattle snake—war farce—farther account of the rattle snake—account and description of other snakes and animals—catalogue of birds of North America; observations concerning their migration, or annual passages from North to South, and back again.

[vii]   ### CHAP. XI. [192]

Visits an Indian village on the river—water melon feast—description of the banqueting-house—makes an excursion across the river; great dangers in crossing; lands on the opposite shore—discovers a bee tree, which yielded a great quantity of honey—returns to the shore—embarks for Frederica in Georgia, visits the plantations down the river, enters the sound and passes through; arrives at Frederica—embarks again—touches at Sunbury—arrives in Charleston, South Carolina—meditates a journey to the Cherokee country and Creek Nation, in West Florida.

PART III.

CHAP. I. [195]

The Author sets out for the Cherokee territories—passes through a fine cultivated country—crosses Savanna river and enters the state of Georgia—Dirca palustris—cowpens—civil entertainment at a plantation—pursues the road to Augusta, and recrosses the river at Silver Bluff—account of Mr. Golphin's villa and trading-stores, Silver Bluff, fort Moore, Augusta, Savanna river, mountains of large fossil oyster-shells.

CHAP. II. III. [203, 211]

Proceeds for fort James, Dartmouth—curious species of Azalea—crosses Broad River—establishment of Dartmouth—Indian mount, &c. —crosses Savanna river—violent gust of rain—curious species of Æsculus pavia—town of Senica—fort Prince George, Keowe—describes the country—Ocone vale—monuments of the ancient town—

crosses the mountains—their situation, views and productions—rests
on the top of Mount Magnolia—description of a new and beautiful
species of Magnolia—cascades of Falling Creek—thunder storm—
head of Tanasee—vale of Cowe—Indian graves—towns of Echoe,
Nucassee and Whatoga—nobly entertained by the prince of Whatoga
—arrives at the town of Cowe—makes an excursion with a young
trader on the hills of Cowe—incomparable prospects—horse-stamp—
discovers a company of Cherokee nymphs—a frolick with them—returns to town.

[*viii*]   CHAP. IV.   [227]

Set off from Whatoga to the Overhill towns—Jore village—Roaring
Creek—the Author and his guide part—surprised by an Indian—
salute and part friendly—mountainous vegetable productions—arrives
on the top of Jore mountain—sublime prospects—Atta-kul-kulla, grand
Cherokee chief—gracious reception—returns to Cowe—great council-
house—curious Indian dance—returns and stops at Senica—arrives
again at fort James, Dartmouth—list of Cherokee towns and villages.

CHAP. V. VI.   [237, 251]

Sets off from Dartmouth to the Upper Creeks and Chactaws country
—Flat Rock—a curious plant—Rocky Comfort—Ocone old town—
migration of the Ocones—crosses the river—fords the Oakmulge at
the Oakmulge fields—Stoney Creek—Great and Little Tabosachte—
new species of Hydrangia—crosses Flint River—describes the country
—persecuted by extraordinary heats and incredible numbers of biting
flies—Hippobosca and Asilus—extraordinary thunder gust—crosses
Chata Uche river—describes the town—very large and populous—
proceeds and arrives at the Apalachucla town—visits the old town—
extraordinary remains and monuments of the ancients—general face
of the country and vegetable productions—new species of Æsculus—
proceeds, and after three days journey arrives at Tallase, on the Tallapoose river—Coloome, a handsome town—great plains—further account of the country—Dog woods—crosses the river Schambe—comes
to Taensa on the East banks of the Mobile, thirty miles above the city
—French inhabitants—passes down the river, arrives at the city of
Mobile—short account of the city and fort Conde—returns to Taensa,
and proceeds up the river as far as the entrance of the Chicasaw branch
—floating forests of the Nyphæa Nilumbo—visits the adjacent lands
—returns to Mobile—goes to the river Perdido—continues on to Pensa-

cola—cordially received by governor Chester—some account of the town—discovers a new and beautiful species of Sarracenia—returns to Mobile.

CHAP. VII.   [265]

Leaves Mobile for Manchac on the Mississipi—proceeds by water to Pearl Island—kindly entertained by Mr. Rumsey—describes the island—large crimson Plum—a delicate species of Mimosa—passes Lake Pontchartrain—touches at the river Taensapaoa—passes over Lake Maurepas—proceeds [ix] up to Iberville—crosses by land to Manchac—goes up the Mississipi—settlements of New-Richmond— White Plains—curious muscle shells in the river—crosses over to Point Coupe—Spanish village and fortress—high cliffs opposite Point Coupe —returns to the Amete, thence down through the lakes and sounds— back again to Mobile.

CHAP. VIII.   [278]

Leaves Mobile on his return—proceeds with a company of traders for the Creek nation—his horse tires—is in great distress—meets a company of traders, of whom he purchases a fresh horse—Illisium groves—meets a company of emigrants from Georgia—great embarass- ment at a large creek swollen with late heavy rains—arrives at the banks of the Alabama—crosses it and arrives at Mucclasse—Indian marriage—serious reflections—perilous situation of the trader of Muc- classe—sets off for Ottasse—describes the country contiguous to the Tallapoose river—plantations and towns—Coolome—Tuckabatche— crosses the river and arrives at Ottasse—rotunda and square—black drink—spiral fire—Sabbath or holy day to the Great Spirit—sets off with a company of traders for Georgia—Chehaws and Ussetas, Creek towns on the Apalachucla river, almost join each other, yet the inhab- itants speak two languages radically different—arrives at the Oak- mulge—crosses the river in a portable leather boat—crosses the river Oconne—head branches of Great Ogeche—arrives at Augusta—takes leave of Augusta and his friends there, and proceeds for Savanna—list of Muscogulge towns and villages—conjectures concerning the rise of the Muscogulge confederacy.

CHAP. IX.   [295]

Short excursion in the South of Georgia—makes collections—gathers seed of two new and very curious shrubs.

CHAP. X.   [297]

Proceeds for Charleston—calls at a gentleman's plantation—Adoe, Tannier—wild pigeons—Aster fruticosus—leaves Charleston, proceeds on his return home to Pennsylvania—crosses Cooper river, nine miles above the city—Long Bay—reefs of rocks—meets a gang of Negroes— passes the boundary-house—large savanna—Dionæa muscipula—old towns—Brunswick—the Clarendon or Cape-Fear river—North West— Livingston's creek—Wackamaw lake—Carver's creek—Ashwood— various vegetable productions—cultivated vege-[x]tables—describes the face of the country on the North West and adjacent lands—strata of the earth or soil—rocks—petrifactions—ancient submarine produc- tions &c.—leaves Ashwood, continues up the river—vast trunks of trees with their roots, stumps of limbs, with the bark on, turned into very hard stone—Rock-Fish creek—Cross Creeks—the rise, progress and present state of Cambelton—curious species of scandent Fern— Deep River—crosses Haw River—Meherren river in Virginia—Cucur- bita lagenaria—curious species of Prinos—Alexandria—Georgetown— sudden deep fall of snow—extreme cold—crosses the river Susque- hanna upon the ice—river Schuylkill—arrives at his fathers house, within three miles of Philadelphia.

PART IV.

CHAP. I.   [306]

Persons, character and qualifications of the aborigines—most perfect human figure—Muscogulge women—women of the Cherokees—arro- gance of the Muscogulges, yet magnanimous and merciful to a van- quished enemy.

CHAP. II.   [313]

Government and civil society—constitution simply natural—the mico or king presides in the senate—elective—yet mysterious—the next man

in dignity and power is the great war chief—entirely independent of
the mico—his voice in council of the greatest weight concerning military affairs—the high priest a person of consequence, and maintains
great influence in their councils and constitution of state—these Indians not idolaters—they adore the Great Spirit, the giver and taker
away of the breath of life, with the most profound homage and purity
—anecdote.

CHAP. III.   [318]

Dress, feasts and divertisements—youth of both sexes are fond of
decorations with respect to dress—their ears lacerated—diadem plumes
&c.—painting their skin—dress of the females different from that of
the men—great horned owl-skin stuffed and born about by the priests
—insignia of wisdom and divination—fond of music, dancing and
routs—different classes of songs—variety of steps in their dances—sensible and powerful effects—ball play—festival of the Busk.

[xi]   CHAP. IV.   [325]

Concerning property, agriculture, arts and manufactures—private
property—produce of their agricultural labours—common plantation—
king's crib—public treasury—women the most ingenious and vigilant
in mechanic arts and manufactures.

CHAP. V.   [327]

Marriages and funeral rites—polygamy—take wives whilst they are
yet young children—adultery—Muscogulges bury their dead in a sitting posture—strange customs of the Chactaws relative to duties to
the deceased—bone-house—dirges—feast to the dead—methods which
the nurses pursue to flatten the infant's skull and retain its form.

CHAP. VI.   [330]

Language and monuments—Muscogulge language spoken throughout the confederacy—agreeable to the ear, Cherokee language loud—
pyramidal artificial hills or mounts, terraces, obelisks—high ways and
artificial lakes—chunk yards—slave posts.

INTRODUCTION.

THE attention of a traveller, should be particularly turned, in the first place, to the various works of Nature, to mark the distinctions of the climates he may explore, and to offer such useful observations on the different productions as may occur. Men and manners undoubtedly hold the first rank—whatever may contribute to our existence is also of equal importance, whether it be found in the animal or vegetable kingdoms; neither are the various articles, which tend to promote the happiness and convenience of mankind, to be disregarded. How far the writer of the following sheets has succeeded in furnishing information on these subjects, the reader will be capable of determining. From the advantages the journalist enjoyed under his father JOHN BARTRAM, botanist to the king of Great-Britain, and fellow of the Royal Society, it [xiv] is hoped that his labours will present new as well as useful information to the botanist and zoologist.

This world, as a glorious apartment of the boundless palace of the sovereign Creator, is furnished with an infinite variety of animated scenes, inexpressibly beautiful and pleasing, equally free to the inspection and enjoyment of all his creatures.

Perhaps there is not any part of creation, within the reach of our observations, which exhibits a more glorious display of the Almighty hand, than the vegetable world. Such a variety of pleasing scenes, ever changing, throughout the seasons, arising from various causes and assigned each to the purpose and use determined.

It is difficult to pronounce which division of the earth, within the polar circles, produces the greatest variety. The tropical division certainly affords those which principally contribute to the more luxurious scenes of splendor, as Myrtus communis, Myrt. caryophyllata, Myrt. pimenta, Caryophylus aromaticus, Laurus cinam. Laurus camphor. Laurus Persica, Nux mosch. Illicium, Camellia, Punica, Cactus melocactus; Cactus grandiflora, Gloriosa superba, Theobroma, Adansonia digitata, Nyctanthes, Psidium, Musa paradisica, Musa sa-[xv]pientum, Garcinia mangostana, Cocos nucifera, Citrus, Citrus aurantium, Cucurbita citrullus, Hyacinthus, Amaryllis, Narcissus, Poinciana pulcherima, Crinum, Cactus cochinellifer.

But the temperate zone (including by far the greater portion of the earth, and a climate the most favourable to the increase and support of animal life, as well as for the exercise and activity of the human faculties) exhibits scenes of infinitely greater variety, magnificence and consequence, with respect to human economy, in regard to the various uses of vegetables.

For instance, Triticum Cereale, which affords us bread, and is termed, by way of eminence, the staff of life, the most pleasant and nourishing food—to all terrestrial animals. Vitis vinifera, whose ex-hilarating juice is said to cheer the hearts of gods and men. Oryza, Zea, Pyrus, Pyrus malus, Prunus, Pr. cerasus, Ficus, Nectarin, Apricot, Cydonia. Next follow the illustrious families of forest-trees, as the Magnolia grandiflora and Quercus sempervirens, which form the venerated groves and solemn shades, on the Mississipi, Alatamaha and Florida, the magnificent Cupressus disticha of Carolina and Florida, the beautiful Water Oak *, whose vast hemispheric head, presents the likeness of a distant grove [xvi] in the fields and savannas of Carolina. The gigantic Black Oak †, Platanus occidentalis, Liquid-amber sty-raciflua, Liriodendron tulipifera, Fagus castania, Fagus sylvatica, Juglans nigra, Juglans cinerea, Jug. pecan, Ulmus, Acher sacharinum, of Virginia and Pennsylvania; Pinus phoenix, Pinus toeda, Magnolia acuminata, Nyssa aquatica, Populus heterophylla and the floriferous Gordonia lasianthus, of Carolina and Florida; the exalted Pinus strobus, Pin. balsamica, Pin. abies, Pin. Canadensis, Pin. larix, Fraxinus ex-celsior, Robinia pseudacacia, Guilandina dioica, Æsculus Virginica, Magnolia acuminata, of Virginia, Maryland, Pennsylvania, New-Jersey, New-York, New-England, Ohio and the regions of Erie and the Illinois; and the aromatic and floriferous shrubs, as Azalea coccinia, Azalea rosea, Rosa, Rhododendron, Kalmia, Syringa, Gardinia, Calycanthus, Daphne, Franklinia, Styrax and others equally celebrated.

In every order of nature, we perceive a variety of qualities distributed amongst individuals, designed for different purposes and uses, yet it appears evident, that the great Author has impartially distributed his favours to his creatures, so that the attributes of each one seem to be of sufficient importance to manifest the divine and inimitable workman-ship. The pompous Palms of Florida, and [xvii] glorious Magnolia, strike us with the sense of dignity and magnificence; the expansive umbrageous Live-Oak ‡ with awful veneration, the Carica papaya, supercilious with all the harmony of beauty and gracefulness; the

* Quercus Hemispherica.
† Quercus tinctoria.
‡ Quercus sempervirens.

Lillium superbum represents pride and vanity; Kalmia latifolia and Azalea coccinea, exhibit a perfect show of mirth and gaiety; the Illisium Floridanum, Crinum Floridanum, Convalaria majalis of the Cherokees, and Calycanthus floridus, charm with their beauty and fragrance. Yet they are not to be compared for usefulness with the nutritious Triticum, Zea, Oryza, Solanum tuberosa, Musa, Convolvulous, Batata, Rapa, Orchis, Vitis vinifera, Pyrus, Olea; for clothing, Linum, Canabis, Gossypium, Morus; for medical virtues, Hyssopus, Thymus, Anthemis nobilis, Papaver somniferum, Quinqina, Rheum rhabarbarum, Pisum, &c. though none of these most useful tribes are conspicuous for stateliness, figure or splendor, yet their valuable qualities and virtues, excite love, gratitude and adoration to the great Creator, who was pleased to endow them with such eminent qualities, and reveal them to us for our sustenance, amusement and delight.

But there remain of the vegetable world, several tribes that are distinguished by very [xviii] remarkable properties, which excite our admiration, some for the elegance, singularity and splendor of their vestment, as the Tulipa, Fritillaria, Colchicum, Primula, Lillium superbum, Kalmia, &c. Others astonish us by their figure and disposal of their vestiture, as if designed only to embellish and please the observer, as in the Nepenthes distillatoria, Ophrys insectoria, Cypripedium calceolus, Hydrangia quercifolia, Bartramia bracteata, Viburnum Canadense, Bartsea, &c.

Observe these green meadows how they are decorated; they seem enamelled with the beds of flowers. The blushing Chironia and Rhexia, the spiral Ophrys with immaculate white flowers, the Limodorum, Arethusa pulcherima, Sarracenia purpurea, Sarracenia galeata, Sarracenia lacunosa, Sarracenia flava. Shall we analyze these beautiful plants, since they seem cheerfully to invite us? How greatly the flowers of the yellow Sarracenia represent a silken canopy, the yellow pendant petals are the curtains, and the hollow leaves are not unlike the cornucopia or Amaltheas horn, what a quantity of water a leaf is capable of containing, about a pint! taste of it—how cool and animating—limpid as the morning dew: nature seems to have furnished them with this cordated appendage or lid, which turns over, to prevent a too sudden, and copious supply of water from heavy showers of rain, which would [xix] bend down the leaves, never to rise again; because their streight parallel nerves, which extend and support them, are so rigid and fragile, the leaf would inevitably break when bent down to a right angle; therefore I suppose these waters which contribute to their supplies, are the rebounding drops or horizontal streams wafted by the winds, which adventitiously find their way into them, when a blast of wind shifts the lid; see these short stiff hairs, they all point downwards, which direct the condensed vapours down into the funiculum; these stiff hairs also prevent the varieties of insects, which are caught, from returning, being invited down to sip the mellifluous exuvia, from the interior surface of the tube, where they inevitably perish; what quantities there are of them! These latent waters undoubtedly contribute to the support and refreshment of the plant; perhaps designed as a reservoir in case of long continued droughts, or other casualties, since these plants naturally dwell in low savannas liable to overflows, from rain water: for although I am not of the opinion that vegetables receive their nourishment, only through the ascending part of the plant, as the stem, branches, leaves, &c. and that their descending part, as the root and fibres, only serve to hold and retain them in their places, yet I believe they imbibe rain and dews through their leaves, stems and branches, by extreme-[xx]ly minute pores, which open on both surfaces of the leaves and on the branches, which may communicate to little auxiliary ducts or vessels; or, perhaps the cool dews and showers, by constricting these pores, and thereby preventing a too free perspiration, may recover and again invigorate the languid nerves, of those which seem to suffer for want of water, in great heats and droughts; but whether the insects caught in their leaves, and which dissolve and mix with the fluid, serve for aliment or support to these kind of plants, is doubtful. All the Sarracenia are insect catchers, and so is the Drossea rotundiflolia.

But admirable are the properties of the extraordinary Dionea muscipula! A great extent on each side of that serpentine rivulet, is occupied by those sportive vegetables—let us advance to the spot in which nature has seated them. Astonishing production! see the incarnate lobes expanding, how gay and ludicrous they appear! ready on the spring to intrap incautious deluded insects, what artifice! there behold one of the leaves just closed upon a struggling fly, another has got a worm, its hold is sure, its prey can never escape—carnivorous vegetable! Can we after viewing this object, hesitate a moment to confess, that vegetable beings are endued with some sensible faculties or attributes, similar to those that dignify animal nature; [xxi] they are organical, living and self-moving bodies, for we see here, in this plant, motion and volition.

What power or faculty is it, that directs the cirri of the Cucurbita, Momordica, Vitis and other climbers, towards the twigs of shrubs, trees and other friendly support? we see them invariably leaning, extending and like the fingers of the human hand, reaching to catch hold of what is nearest, just as if they had eyes to see with, and when their hold is fixed, to coil the tendril in a spiral form, by which artifice it becomes more elastic and effectual, than if it had remained in a direct line, for every revolution of the coil adds a portion of strength, and thus collected, they are enabled to dilate and contract as occasion or necessity require, and thus by yielding to, and humouring the motion of the limbs and twigs, or other support on which they depend, are not so liable to be torn off by sudden blasts of wind or other assaults; is it sense or instinct that influences their actions? it must be some impulse; or does the hand of the Almighty act and perform this work in our sight?

The vital principle or efficient cause of motion and action, in the animal and vegetable * system, perhaps, may be more familiar than we [xxii] generally apprehend. Where is the essential difference between the seed of peas, peaches and other tribes of plants and trees, and that of oviparous animals? as the eggs of birds, snakes or butterflies, spawn of fish, &c. Let us begin at the source of terrestrial existence. Are not the seed of vegetables, and the eggs of oviparous animals fecundated, or influenced with the vivific principle of life, through the approximation and intimacy of the sexes, and immediately after the eggs and seeds are hatched, the young larva and infant plant, by heat and moisture, rise into existence, increase, and in due time arrive to a state of perfect maturity. The physiologists agree in opinion, that the work of generation in viviparous animals, is exactly similar, only more secret and enveloped. The mode of operation that nature pursues in the production of vegetables, and oviparous animals is infinitely more uniform and manifest, than that which is or can be discovered to take place in viviparous animals.

The most apparent difference between animals and vegetables is, that animals have the powers of sound, and are locomotive, whereas vegetables are not able to shift themselves from the places where nature has planted them: yet vegetables have the power of moving and exercising their members, and have the means of transplanting or colonising their tribes almost over the surface of the [xxiii] whole earth, some seeds, for instance, grapes, nuts, smilax, peas, and others, whose pulp or kernel is food for animals, such seed will remain several days without injuring in stomachs of pigeons and other birds of passage; by this means such sorts are distributed from place to place, even across seas; indeed some seeds require this preparation, by the digestive heat of the stomach of animals, to dissolve and detach the oily, viscid pulp, and to soften the hard shells of others. Small seeds are sometimes furnished with rays of hair or down, and others with thin light membranes attached to them, which serve the purpose of wings,

* Vid. Sponsalia plantarum, Amoen. Acad l. n, 12. Linn.

on which they mount upward, leaving the earth, float in the air, and are carried away by the swift winds to very remote regions before they settle on the earth; some are furnished with hooks, which catch hold of the wool and hair of animals passing by them, are by that means spread abroad; other seeds ripen in pericarps, which open with elastic force, and shoot their seed to a very great distance round about; some other seeds, as of the Mosses and Fungi, are so very minute as to be invisible, light as atoms, and these mixing with the air, are wafted all over the world.

The animal creation also, excites our admiration, and equally manifests the almighty power, wisdom and beneficence of the Supreme Creator and Sovereign Lord of the u-[xxiv]niverse; some in their vast size and strength, as the mammoth, the elephant, the whale, the lion and alligator; others in agility; others in their beauty and elegance of colour, plumage and rapidity of flight, have the faculty of moving and living in the air; others for their immediate and indispensable use and convenience to man, in furnishing means for our clothing and sustenance, and administering to our help in the toils and labours through life; how wonderful is the mechanism of these finely formed, self-moving beings, how complicated their system, yet what unerring uniformity prevails through every tribe and particular species! the effect we see and contemplate, the cause is invisible, incomprehensible, how can it be otherwise? when we cannot see the end or origin of a nerve or vein, while the divisibility of mater or fluid, is infinite. We admire the mechanism of a watch, and the fabric of a piece of brocade, as being the production of art; these merit our admiration, and must excite our esteem for the ingenious artist or modifier, but nature is the work of God omnipotent: and an elephant, even this world is comparatively but a very minute part of his works. If then the visible, the mechanical part of the animal creation, the mere material part is so admirably beautiful, harmonious and incomprehensible, what must be the intellectual system? that inexpressibly [xxv] more essential principle, which secretly operates within? that which animates the inimitable machines, which gives them motion, impowers them to act, speak and perform, this must be divine and immortal?

I am sensible that the general opinion of philosophers, has distinguished the moral system of the brute creature from that of mankind, by an epithet wich implies a mere mechanical impulse, which leads and impels them to necessary actions, without any premeditated design or contrivance, this we term instinct, which faculty we suppose to be inferior to reason in man.

The parental, and filial affections seem to be as ardent, their sensibility and attachment, as active and faithful, as those observed to be in human nature.

When travelling on the East coast of the isthmus of Florida, ascending the South Musquitoe river, in a canoe, we observed numbers of deer and bears, near the banks, and on the islands of the river, the bear were feeding on the fruit of the dwarf creeping Chamerops, (this fruit is of the form and size of dates, and is delicious and nourishing food:) we saw eleven bears in the course of the day, they seemed no way surprized or affrighted at the sight of us; in the evening my hunter, who was an excel-[xxvi]lent marksman, said that he would shoot one of them, for the sake of the skin and oil, for we had plenty and variety of provisions in our bark. We accordingly, on sight of two of them, planned our approaches, as artfully as possible, by crossing over to the opposite shore, in order to get under cover of a small island, this we cautiously coasted round, to a point, which we apprehended would take us within shot of the bear, but here finding ourselves at too great a distance from them, and discovering that we must openly show ourselves, we had no other alternative to effect our purpose, but making oblique approaches; we gained gradually on our prey by this artifice, without their noticing us, finding ourselves near enough, the hunter fired, and laid the largest dead on the spot, where she stood, when presently the other, not seeming the least moved, at the report of our piece, approached the dead body, smelled, and pawed it, and appearing in agony, fell to weeping and looking upwards, then towards us, and cried out like a child. Whilst our boat approached very near, the hunter was loading his rifle in order to shoot the survivor, which was a young cub, and the slain supposed to be the dam; the continual cries of this afflicted child, bereft of its parent, affected me very sensibly, I was moved with compassion, and charging myself as if accessary to what now appeared to be a cruel murder, and endea-[xxvii]voured to prevail on the hunter to save its life, but to no effect! for by habit he had become insensible to compassion towards the brute creation, being now within a few yards of the harmless devoted victim, he fired, and laid it dead, upon the body of the dam.

If we bestow but a very little attention to the economy of the animal creation, we shall find manifest examples of premeditation, perseverance, resolution, and consummate artifice, in order to effect their purpose. The next morning, after the slaughter of the bears whilst my companions were striking our tent and preparing to re-embark, I resolved to make a little botanical excursion alone; crossing over a narrow isthmus of sand hills which separated the river from the ocean, I passed over a pretty high hill, its summit crested with a few Palm trees, surrounded with an Orange grove; this hill, whose base was washed on one side, by the floods of the Musquitoe river, and the other side by the billows of the ocean, was about one hundred yards diameter, and seemed to be an entire heap of sea hills. I continued along the beach, a quarter of a mile, and came up to a forest of the Agave vivipara (though composed of herbaceous plants, I term it a forest, because their scapes or flower-stems arose erect near 30 feet high) their tops regularly branching in the form of [*xxviii*] a pyramidal tree, and these plants growing near to each other, occupied a space of ground of several acres: when their seed is ripe they vegetate, and grow on the branches, until the scape dries when the young plants fall to the ground, take root, and fix themselves in the sand: the plant grows to a prodigious size before the scape shoots up from its centre. Having contemplated this admirable grove, I proceeded towards the shrubberies on the banks of the river, and though it was now late in December, the aromatic groves appeared in full bloom. The broad leaved sweet Myrtus, Erythrina corrallodendrum, Cactus cochenellifer, Cacalia suffruticosa, and particularly, Rhizophora conjugata, which stood close to, and in the salt water of the river, were in full bloom, with beautiful white sweet scented flowers, which attracted to them, two or three species of very beautiful butterflies, one of which was black, the upper pair of its wings very long and narrow, marked with transverse stripes of pale yellow, with some spots of a crimson colour near the body. Another species remarkable for splendor, was of a larger size, the wings were undulated and obtusely crenated round their ends, the nether pair terminating near the body, with a long narrow forked tail; the ground light yellow, striped oblique-transversely, with stripes of pale celestial blue, the ends of them adorned with [*xxix*] little eyes encircled with the finest blue and crimson, which represented a very brilliant rosary. But those which were the most numerous were as white as snow, their wings large, their ends lightly crenated and ciliated, forming a fringed border, faintly marked with little black crescents, their points downward, with a cluster of little brilliant orbs of blue and crimson, on the nether wings near the body; the numbers were incredible, and there seemed to be scarcely a flower for each fly, multitudinous as they were, besides clouds of them hovering over the mellifluous groves. Besides these papilios[?], a variety of other insects come in for share, particularly several species of bees.

As I was gathering specimens of flowers from the shrubs, I was greatly surprised at the sudden appearance of a remarkable large spider on a leaf, of the genus Araneus saliens, at sight of me he boldly faced about, and raised himself up as if ready to spring upon me; his body was about the size of a pigeons egg, of a buff colour, which with his legs were covered with short silky hair, on the top of the abdomen was a round red spot or ocellus encircled with black; after I had recovered from the surprise, and observing the wary hunter had retired under cover, I drew near again, and presently discovered that I had surprised him on predatory attempts against the insect tribes, I was there-[xxx]fore determined to watch his proceedings, I soon noticed that the object of his wishes was a large fat bomble bee (apis bombylicus) that was visiting the flowers, and piercing their nectariferous tubes; this cunning intrepid hunter (conducted his subtil approaches, with the circumspection and perseverance of a Siminole, when hunting a deer) advancing with slow steps obliquely, or under cover of dense foliage, and behind the limbs, and when the bee was engaged in probing a flower he would leap nearer, and then instantly retire out of sight, under a leaf or behind a branch, at the same time keeping a sharp eye upon me; when he had now got within two feet of his prey, and the bee was intent on sipping the delicious nectar from a flower, with his back next the spider, he instantly sprang upon him, and grasped him over the back and shoulder, when for some moments they both disappeared, I expected the bee had carried of his enemy, but to my surprise they both together rebounded back again, suspended at the extremity of a strong elastic thread or web, which the spider had artfully let fall, or fixed on the twig, the instant he leaped from it; the rapidity of the bee's wings, endeavouring to extricate himself, made them both together appear as a moving vapor, until the bee became fatigued by whirling round, first one way and then back again; at length, in about a quarter of [xxxi] an hour, the bee quite exhausted by his struggles, and the repeated wounds of the butcher, became motionless, and quickly expired in the arms of the devouring spider, who, ascending the rope with his game, retired to feast on it under cover of leaves; and perhaps before night became himself, the delicious evening repast of a bird or lizard.

Birds are in general social and benevolent creatures; intelligent, ingenious, volatile, active beings; and this order of animal creation consists of various nations, bands or tribes, as may be observed from their different structure, manners and languages or voice, as each nation, though subdivided into many different tribes, retain their general form or structure, a similarity of customs, and a sort of dialect or language, particular to that nation or genus from which they seem to have descended or separated: what I mean by a language in birds, is the common notes or speech, that they use when employed in feeding themselves and their young, calling on one another, as well as their menaces against their enemy; for their songs seem to be musical compositions, performed only by the males, about the time of incubation, in part to divert and amuse the female, entertaining her with melody, &c. this harmony, with the tender solicitude of the male, alleviates the toils, cares and distresses of the female, consoles her in solitary retire-[xxxii]ment whilst setting, and animates her with affection and attachment to himself in preference to any other. The volatility of their species, and operation of their passions and affections, are particularly conspicuous in the different tribes of the thrush, famous for song; on a sweet May morning we see the red thrushes (turdus rufus) perched on an elevated sprig of the snowy Hawthorn, sweet flowering Crab, or other hedge shrubs, exerting their accomplishments in song, striving by varying and elevating their voices to excel each other, we observe a very agreeable variation, not only in tone but in modulation; the voice of one is shrill, another lively and elevated, others sonorous and quivering. The mock-bird (turdus polyglottos) who excels, distinguishes himself in variety of action as well as air; from a turret he bounds aloft with the celerity of an arrow, as it were to recover or recall his very soul, expired in the last elevated strain. The high forests are filled with the symphony of the song or wood-thrush (turdus minor.)

Both sexes of some tribes of birds sing equally fine, and it is remarkable, that these reciprocally assist in their domestic cares, as building their nests and setting on their eggs, feeding and defending their young brood, &c. The oriolus (icterus, Cat.) is an instance in this case, and the female of the icterus minor is a bird of more splendid and gay dress [xxxiii] than the male bird. Some tribes of birds will relieve and rear up the young and helpless, of their own and other tribes, when abandoned. Animal substance seems to be the first food of all birds, even the granivorous tribes.

Having passed through some remarks, which appeared of sufficient consequence to be offered to the public, and which were most suitable to have a place in the introduction, I shall now offer such observations as must necessarily occur, from a careful attention to, and investigation of the manners of the Indian nations; being induced, while travelling among them, to associate with them, that I might judge for myself whether they were deserving of the severe censure, which prevailed against them among the white people, that they were incapable of civilization.

In the consideration of this important subject it will be necessary to enquire, whether they were inclined to adopt the European modes of civil society? whether such a reformation could be obtained, without using coercive or violent means? and lastly, whether such a revolution would be productive of real benefit to them, and consequently beneficial to the public? I was satisfied in discovering that they were desirous of becoming united with us, in civil and religious society. [*xxxiv*] It may, therefore, not be foreign to the subject, to point out the propriety of sending men of ability and virtue, under the authority of government, as friendly visitors, into their towns; let these men be instructed to learn perfectly their languages, and by a liberal and friendly intimacy, become acquainted with their customs and usages, religious and civil; their system of legislation and police, as well as their most ancient and present traditions and history. These men thus enlightened and instructed, would be qualified to judge equitably, and when returned to us, to make true and just reports, which might assist the legislature of the United States to form, and offer to them a judicious plan, for their civilization and union with us.

But I presume not to dictate in these high concerns of government, and I am fully convinced that such important matters are far above my ability; the duty and respect we owe to religion and rectitude, the most acceptable incense we can offer to the Almighty, as an atonement for our negligence, in the care of the present and future well being of our Indian brethren, induces me to mention this matter, though perhaps of greater concernment than we generally are aware of.

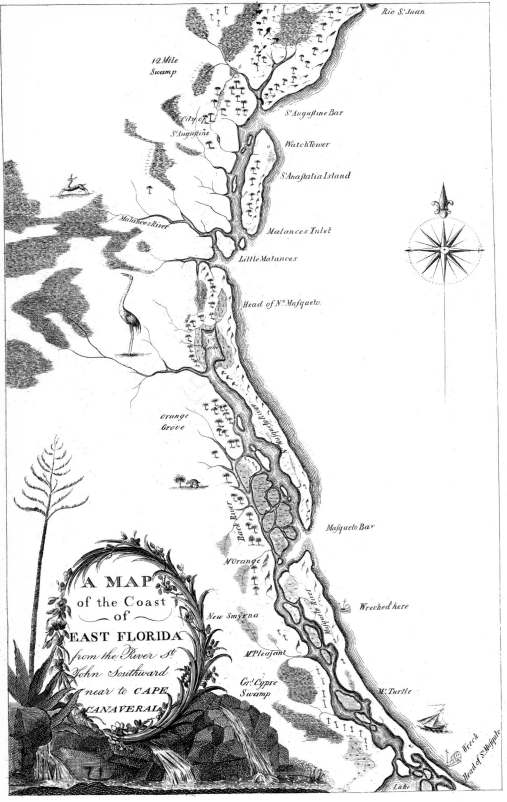

Rio S.ᵗ Juan

12 Mile
Swamp

City of
S.ᵗ Augustine

St Augustine Bar

WatchTower

S.ᵗ Anastalia Island

Malances River

Malances Inlet

Little Malances

Head of N.º Musqueto.

Orange
Grove

Back River

Masqueto Bar

M.ᵗ Orange

Wrecked here

A MAP
of the Coast
of
EAST FLORIDA
from the River St
John Southward
near to CAPE
CANAVERAL

New Smyrna

M.ᵗ Pleasant

Gr.ᵗ Cypre
Swamp

Musqueto River

M.ᵗ Turtle

Wreck
Head of S.ᵗ Musqueto

Lake

[V. Map of the coast of East Florida]

TRAVELS.

CHAP. I.

THE AUTHOR SETS SAIL FROM PHILADELPHIA, AND
ARRIVES AT CHARLESTON, FROM WHENCE HE BE-
GINS HIS TRAVELS.

AT the request of Dr. Fothergill, of London, to search the
Floridas, and the western parts of Carolina and Georgia, for the discovery of rare and useful productions of nature, chiefly in the vegetable kingdom; in April, 1773, I embarked for Charleston, South-
Carolina, on board the brigantine Charleston Packet, Captain Wright,
the brig - - - - - - - -, Captain Mason, being in company with us, and
bound to the same port. We had a pleasant run down the Delaware,
150 miles to Cape Henlopen, the two vessels entering the Atlantic together. For the first twenty-four hours, we had a prosperous gale, and
were cheerful and happy in [2] the prospect of a quick and pleasant
voyage; but, alas! how vain and uncertain are human expectations!
how quickly is the flattering scene changed! The powerful winds, now
rushing forth from their secret abodes, suddenly spread terror and
devastation; and the wide ocean, which, a few moments past, was
gentle and placid, is now thrown into disorder, and heaped into mountains, whose white curling crests seem to sweep the skies!

This furious gale continued near two days and nights, and not a little damaged our sails, cabin furniture, and state-rooms, besides re-
tarding our passage. The storm having abated, a lively gale from N. W.
continued four or five days, when shifting to N. and lastly to N. E. on
the tenth of our departure from Cape Henlopen, early in the morning,
we descried a sail astern, and in a short time discovered it to be Capt.
Mason, who soon came up with us. We hailed each other, being joyful to meet again, after so many dangers. He suffered greatly by the
gale, but providentially made a good harbour within Cape Hatteras.

1

As he ran by us, he threw on board ten or a dozen bass, a large and delicious fish, having caught a great number of them whilst he was detained in harbour. He got into Charleston that evening, and we the next morning, about eleven o'clock.

There are few objects out at sea to attract the notice of the traveller, but what are sublime, awful, and majestic: the seas themselves, in a tempest, exhibit a tremendous scene, where the winds assert their power, and, in furious conflict, seem to set the ocean on fire. On the other hand, nothing can be more sublime than the view of the encircling horizon, after the turbulent winds have taken [3] their flight, and the lately agitated bosom of the deep has again become calm and pacific; the gentle moon rising in dignity from the east, attended by millions of glittering orbs; the luminous appearance of the seas at night, when all the waters seem transmuted into liquid silver; the prodigious bands of porpoises foreboding tempest, that appear to cover the ocean; the mighty whale, sovereign of the watery realms, who cleaves the seas in his course; the sudden appearance of land from the sea, the strand stretching each way, beyond the utmost reach of sight; the alternate appearance and recess of the coast, whilst the far distant blue hills slowly retreat and disappear; or, as we approach the coast, the capes and promontories first strike our sight, emerging from the watery expanse, and, like mighty giants, elevating their crests towards the skies; the water suddenly alive with its scaly inhabitants; squadrons of sea-fowl sweeping through the air, impregnated with the breath of fragrant aromatic trees and flowers; the amplitude and magnificence of these scenes are great indeed, and may present to the imagination, an idea of the first appearance of the earth to man at the creation.

On my arrival at Charleston, I waited on Doctor Chalmer, a gentleman of eminence in his profession and public employments, to whom I was recommended by my worthy patron, and to whom I was to apply for counsel and assistance, for carrying into effect my intended travels: the Doctor received me with perfect politeness, and, on every occasion, treated me with friendship; and by means of the countenance which he gave me, and the marks of esteem with which he honoured me, I became acquainted with many of the worthy families, not only of Carolina and Georgia, but also in the distant countries of Florida.

ARRIVING in Carolina very early in the spring, vegetation was not sufficiently advanced to invite me into the western parts of this state; from which circumstance, I concluded to make an excursion into Georgia; accordingly, I embarked on board a coasting vessel, and in twenty-four hours arrived in Savanna, the capital, where, acquainting the Governor, Sir J. Wright, with my business, his Excellency received me with great politeness, shewed me every mark of esteem and regard, and furnished me with letters to the principal inhabitants of the state, which were of great service to me. Another circumstance very opportunely occurred on my arrival: the Assembly was then sitting in Savanna, and several members lodging in the same house where I took up my quarters, I became acquainted with several worthy characters, who invited me to call at their seats occasionally, as I passed through the country; particularly the Hon. B. Andrews, Esq; a distinguished, patriotic and liberal, character. This gentleman's seat, and well cultivated plantations, are situated near the south high road, which I often travelled; and I seldom passed his house without calling to see him, for it was the seat of virtue, where hospitality, piety, and philosophy, formed the happy family; where the weary traveller and stranger found a hearty welcome, and from whence it must be his own fault, if he departed without being greatly benefited.

[5]　After resting, and a little recreation for a few days in Savanna, and having in the mean time purchased a good horse, and equipped myself for a journey southward, I set off early in the morning for Sunbury, a sea-port town, beautifully situated on the main, between Medway and Newport rivers, about fifteen miles south of Great Ogeeche river. The town and harbour are defended from the fury of the seas by the north and south points of St. Helena and South Catharine's islands; between which is the bar and entrance into the sound: the harbour is capacious and safe, and has water enough for ships of great burthen. I arrived here in the evening, in company with a gentleman, one of the inhabitants, who politely introduced me to one of the principal families, where I supped and spent the evening in a circle of genteel and polite ladies and gentlemen. Next day, being

3

desirous of visiting the islands, I forded a narrow shoal, part of the sound, and landed on one of them, which employed me the whole day to explore. The surface and vegetable mould here is generally a loose sand, not very fertile, except some spots bordering on the sound and inlets, where are found heaps or mounds of sea-shell, either formerly brought there, by the Indians, who inhabited the island, or which were perhaps thrown up in ridges, by the beating surface of the sea: possibly both these circumstances may have contributed to their formation. These sea-shells, through length of time, and the subtle penetrating effects of the air, which dissolve them to earth, render these ridges very fertile, and which, when clear of their trees, and cultivated, become profusely productive of almost every kind of vegetable. Here are also large plantations of [6] indigo, corn, and potatoes,* with many other sorts of esculent plants. I observed, amongst the shells of the conical mounds, fragments of earthen vessels, and of other utensils, the manufacture of the ancients: about the centre of one of them, the rim of an earthen pot appeared amongst the shells and earth, which I carefully removed, and drew it out, almost whole: this pot was curiously wrought all over the outside, representing basket work, and was undoubtedly esteemed a very ingenious performance, by the people, at the age of its construction. The natural produce of these testaceous ridges, besides many of less note, are, the great Laurel Tree, (Magnolia grandiflora) Pinus taeda, Laurus Borbonia, Quercus sempervirens, or Live Oak, Prunus, Laura-cerasa, Ilex aquifolium, Corypha palma, Juniperus Americana. The general surface of the island being low, and generally level, produces a very great variety of trees, shrubs and herbaceous plants; particularly the great long-leaved Pitch-Pine, or Broom-Pine, Pinus Palustris, Pinus Squamosa, Pinus lutea, Gordonia Lasianthus, Liquid Amber (Styraciflua) Acer rubrum, Fraxinus excelcior, Fraxinus aquatica, Quercus aquatica, Quercus phillos, Quercus dentata, Quercus humila varietas, Vaccinium varietas, Andromeda varietas, Prinos varietas, Ilex varietas, Viburnum prunifolium, V. dentatum, Cornus Florida, C. alba, C. sanguinea, Carpinus betula, C. ostrya, Itea, Clethra alnifolia, Halesia taetraptera, H. diptera, Iva, Khamnus frangula, Callicarpa, Morus rubra Sapindus, Cassine, and of such as grow near water-courses, round about ponds and savannas, Fothergilla gardini, Myrica cerifera, Olea Americana, Cyrilla racemiflora, Magnolia glauca, Magnolia pyramidata, Cercis, [7] Kalmia angustifolia, Kalmia ciliata, Chionanthus, Cephalanthos, Aesculus parva, and the intermediate spaces, surrounding and lying between the ridges and savannas, are intersected with plains of the dwarf

* Convolvulus batata.

prickly fan-leaved Palmetto, and lawns of grass variegated with stately trees of the great Broom-Pine, and the spreading ever-green Water-Oak, either disposed in clumps, or scatteringly planted by nature. The upper surface, or vegetative soil of the island, lies on a foundation, or stratum, of tenacious cinereous coloured clay, which perhaps is the principal support of the vast growth of timber that arises from the surface, which is little more than a mixture of fine white sand and dissolved vegetables, serving as a nursery bed to hatch, or bring into existence, the infant plant, and to supply it with aliment and food, suitable to its delicacy and tender frame, until the roots, acquiring sufficient extent and solidity to lay hold of the clay, soon attain a magnitude and stability sufficient to maintain its station. Probably if this clay were dug out, and cast upon the surface, after being meliorated by the saline or nitrous qualities of the air, it would kindly incorporate with the loose sand, and become a productive and lasting manure.

The roebuck, or deer, are numerous on this island; the tyger, wolf, and bear, hold yet some possession; as also raccoons, foxes, hares, squirrels, rats and mice, but I think no moles; there is a large ground-rat, more than twice the size of the common Norway rat. In the night time, it throws out the earth, forming little mounds, or hillocks. Opposoms are here in abundance, as also pole-cats, wild-cats, rattle-snakes, glass-snake, coach-whip snake, and a variety of other serpents. [8]   Here are also a great variety of birds, throughout the seasons, inhabiting both sea and land. First I shall name the eagle, of which there are three species: the great grey eagle is the largest, of great strength and high flight; he chiefly preys on fawns and other young quadrupeds.

The bald eagle is likewise a large, strong, and very active bird, but an execrable tyrant: he supports his assumed dignity and grandeur by rapine and violence, extorting unreasonable tribute and subsidy from all the feathered nations.

The last of this race I shall mention is the falco piscatorius, or fishing-hawk: this is a large bird, of high and rapid flight; his wings are very long and pointed, and he spreads a vast sail, in proportion to the volume of his body. This princely bird subsists entirely on fish, which he takes himself, scorning to live and grow fat on the dear earned labours of another; he also contributes liberally to the support of the bald eagle.

Water-fowl, and the various species of land-birds, also abound, most of which are mentioned by Catesby, in his Hist. Carolina, particularly his painted finch (Emberiza Ceris Linn.) exceeded by none of the feathered tribes, either in variety and splendour of dress, or melody of song.

Catesby's ground doves are also here in abundance: they are remarkably beautiful, about the size of a sparrow, and their soft and
plaintive cooing perfectly enchanting.

How chaste the dove! "never known to violate the conjugal contract."
She flees the seats of envy and strife, and seeks the retired paths of
    peace.

[9] The sight of this delightful and productive island, placed in
front of the rising city of Sunbury, quickly induced me to explore it;
which I apprehended, from former visits to this coast, would exhibit
a comprehensive epitome of the history of all the sea-coast islands of
Carolina and Georgia, as likewise in general of the coast of the main;
and as I considered this excursion along the coast of Georgia and
northern border of Florida, a deviation from the high road of my intended travels, yet I performed it in order to employ to the most advantage the time on my hands, before the treaty of Augusta came on,
where I was to attend, about May or June, by desire of the Superintendent, J. Stewart, Esq; who, when I was in Charleston, proposed, in
order to facilitate my travels in the Indian territories, that, if I would
be present at the Congress, he would introduce my business to the
chiefs of the Cherokees, Creeks, and other nations, and recommend
me to their friendship and protection; which promise he fully performed, and it proved of great service to me.

Obedient to the admonitions of my attendant spirit, curiosity, as well
as to gratify the expectations of my worthy patron, I again set off
on my southern excursion, and left Sunbury, in company with several
of its polite inhabitants, who were going to Medway meeting, a very
large and well constructed place of worship, in St. John's parish, where
I associated with them in religious exercise, and heard a very excellent sermon, delivered by their pious and truly venerable pastor, the
Rev. - - - - - Osgood. This respectable congregation is [10] independent, and consists chiefly of families, and proselytes to a flock, which this
pious man led, about forty years ago, from South-Carolina, and settled
in this fruitful district. It is about nine miles from Sunbury to Medway
meeting-house, which stands on the high road, opposite the Sunbury
road. As soon as the congregation broke up, I re-assumed my travels,
proceeding down the high road towards Fort Barrington, on the
Alatamaha, passing through a level country, well watered by large
streams, branches of Medway and Newport rivers, coursing from
extensive swamps and marshes, their sources: these swamps are daily
clearing and improving into large fruitful rice plantations, aggrandizing
the well inhabited and rich district of St. John's parish. The road is

straight, spacious, and kept in excellent repair by the industrious inhabitants; and is generally bordered on each side with a light grove, consisting of the following trees and shrubs: Myrica Cerifera, Calycanthus, Halesia tetraptera, Itea, stewartia, Andromeda nitida, Cyrella racemiflora, entwined with bands and garlands of Bignonia sempervirens, B. crucigera, Lonicera sempervirens and Glycene frutescens; these were overshadowed by tall and spreading trees, as the Magnolia grandiflora, Liquid Amber, Liriodendron, Catalpa, Quercus sempervirens, Quercus dentata, Q. Phillos; and on the verges of the canals, where the road was causewayed, stood the Cupressus disticha, floriferous Gordonia Lacianthus, and Magnolia glauca, all planted by nature, and left standing, by the virtuous inhabitants, to shade the road and perfume the sultry air. The extensive plantations of rice and corn, now in early verdure, decorated here and there with groves of floriferous and fragrant trees and shrubs, under the [11] cover and protection of pyramidal laurels and plumed palms, which now and then break through upon the sight from both sides of the way as we pass along; the eye at intervals stealing a view at the humble, but elegant and neat habitation, of the happy proprietor, amidst arbours and groves, all day, and moon-light nights, filled with the melody of the chearful mockbird, warbling nonpareil, and plaintive turtle dove, altogether present a view of magnificence and joy, inexpressibly charming and animating.

In the evening, I arrived at the seat of the Hon. B. Andrews, Esq; who received and entertained me in every respect, as a worthy gentleman could a stranger, that is, with hearty welcome, plain but plentiful board, free conversation and liberality of sentiment. I spent the evening very agreeably, and the day following (for I was not permitted to depart sooner) I viewed with pleasure this gentleman's exemplary improvements in agriculture; particularly in the growth of rice, and in his machines for shelling that valuable grain, which stands in the water almost from the time it is sown, until within a few days before it is reaped, when they draw off the water by sluices, which ripens it all at once, and when the heads or panicles are dry ripe, it is reaped and left standing in the field, in small ricks, until the straw is quite dry, when it is hauled, and stacked in the barn yard. The machines for cleaning the rice are worked by the force of water. They stand on the great reservoir which contains the waters that flood the rice-fields below.

Towards the evening we made a little party at fishing. We chose a shaded retreat, in a beautiful grove of magnolias, myrtles, and sweet bay trees, [12] which were left standing on the bank of a fine creek,

that, from this place, took a slow serpentine course through the plantation. We presently took some fish, one kind of which is very beautiful;
they call it the red-belly. It is as large as a man's hand, nearly oval and
thin, being compressed on each side; the tail is beautifully formed; the
top of the head and back, of an olive green, besprinkled with russet
specks; the sides of a sea green, inclining to azure, insensibly blended
with the olive above, and beneath lightens to a silvery white, or pearl
colour, elegantly powdered with specks of the finest green, russet and
gold; the belly is of a bright scarlet red, or vermilion, darting up rays
or fiery streaks into the pearl on each side; the ultimate angle of the
branchiostege extends backwards with a long spatula, ending with
a round, or oval particoloured spot, representing the eye in the long
feathers of a peacock's train, verged round with a thin flame-coloured
membrane, and appears like a brilliant ruby fixed on the side of the
fish; the eyes are large, encircled with fiery iris; they are a voracious
fish, and are easily caught with a suitable bait.

The next morning I took leave of this worthy family, and set off for
the settlements on the Alatahama, still pursuing the high road for Fort
Barrington, till towards noon, when I turned off to the left, following
the road to Darian, a settlement on the river, twenty miles lower down,
and near the coast. The fore part of this day's journey was pleasant,
the plantations frequent, and the roads in tolerable good repair. But
the country being now less cultivated, the roads became bad, pursuing
my journey almost continually, through swamps and creeks, waters of
Newport and Sapello, till night, [13] when I lost my way; but coming
up to a fence, I saw a glimmering light, which conducted me to a house,
where I stayed all night, and met with very civil entertainment. Early
next morning, I set off again, in company with the overseer of the farm,
who piloted me through a large and difficult swamp, when we parted;
he in chase of deer, and I towards Darian. I rode several miles through
a high forest of pines, thinly growing on a level plain, which admitted
an ample view, and a free circulation of air, to another swamp; and
crossing a considerable branch of Sapello river, I then came to a
small plantation by the side of another swamp: the people were remarkably civil and hospitable. The man's name was M'Intosh, a family
of the first colony established in Georgia, under the conduct of General Oglethorpe. Was there ever such a scene of primitive simplicity, as
was here exhibited, since the days of the good King Tammany! The
venerable grey headed Caledonian smilingly meets me coming up to
his house. "Welcome, stranger, come in, and rest; the air is now very
sultry; it is a very hot day." I was there treated with some excellent
venison, and here found friendly and secure shelter from a tremendous

thunder storm, which came up from the N. W. and soon after my arrival, began to discharge its fury all around. Stepping to the door to observe the progress and direction of the tempest, the fulgour and rapidity of the streams of lightning, passing from cloud to cloud, and from the clouds to the earth, exhibited a very awful scene; when instantly the lightning, as it were, opening a fiery chasm in the black cloud, darted with inconceivable rapidity on the trunk of a large pine tree, that stood thirty or forty yards from me, and set it in a blaze. The flame instantly as-[14]cended upwards of ten or twelve feet, and continued flaming about fifteen minutes, when it was gradually extinguished, by the deluges of rain that fell upon it.

I saw here a remarkably large turkey of the native wild breed: his head was above three feet from the ground when he stood erect; he was a stately beautiful bird, of a very dark dusky brown colour, the tips of the feathers of his neck, breast, back, and shoulders, edged with a copper colour, which in a certain exposure looked like burnished gold, and he seemed not insensible of the splendid appearance he made. He was reared from an egg, found in the forest, and hatched by a hen of the common domestic fowl.

Our turkey of America is a very different species from the mileagris of Asia and Europe; they are nearly thrice their size and weight. I have seen several that have weighed between twenty and thirty pounds, and some have been killed that weighed near forty. They are taller, and have a much longer neck proportionally, and likewise longer legs, and stand more erect; they are also very different in colour. Our's are all, male and female, of a dark brown colour, not having a black feather on them; but the male exceedingly splendid, with changeable colours. In other particulars they differ not.

The tempest being over, I waited till the floods of rain had run off the ground, then took leave of my friends, and departed. The air was now cool and salubrious, and riding seven or eight miles, through a pine forest, I came to Sapello bridge, to which the salt tide flows. I here stopped, [15] at Mr. Bailey's, to deliver a letter from the Governor. This gentleman received me very civilly, inviting me to stay with him; but upon my urging the necessity of my accelerating my journey, he permitted me to proceed to Mr. L. M'Intosh's, near the river, to whose friendship I was recommended by Mr. B. Andrews.

Perhaps, to a grateful mind, there is no intellectual enjoyment, which regards human concerns, of a more excellent nature, than the remembrance of real acts of friendship. The heart expands at the pleasing recollection. When I came up to his door, the friendly man, smiling, and with a grace and dignity peculiar to himself, took me by the hand,

and accosted me thus: "Friend Bartram, come under my roof, and I desire you to make my house your home, as long as convenient to your
self; remember, from this moment, that you are a part of my family,
and, on my part, I shall endeavour to make it agreeable," which was
verified during my continuance in, and about, the southern territories
of Georgia and Florida; for I found here sincerity in union with all
the virtues, under the influence of religion. I shall yet mention a
remarkable instance of Mr. M'Intosh's friendship and respect for me;
which was, recommending his eldest son, Mr. John M'Intosh, as a companion in my travels. He was a sensible virtuous youth, and a very
agreeable companion through a long and toilsome journey of near a
thousand miles.

Having been greatly refreshed, by continuing a few days with this
kind and agreeable family, I prepared to prosecute my journey
southerly.

CHAP. III.

I SET off early in the morning for the Indian trading-house, in the river St. Mary, and took the road up the N. E. side of the Alatamaha to Fort-Barrington. I passed through a well-inhabited district, mostly rice plantations, on the waters of Cathead creek, a branch of the Alatamaha. On drawing near the fort, I was greatly delighted at the appearance of two new beautiful shrubs, in all their blooming graces. One of them appeared to be a species of Gordonia,* but the flowers are larger, and more fragrant than those of the Gordonia Lascanthus, and are sessile; the seed vessel is also very different. The other was equally distinguished for beauty and singularity; it grows twelve or fifteen feet high, the branches ascendant and opposite, and terminate with large panicles of pale blue tubular flowers, specked on the inside with crimson; but, what is singular, these panicles are ornamented with a number of ovate large bracteae, as white, and like fine paper, their tops and verges stained with a rose red, which, at a little distance, has the appearance of clusters of roses, at the extremities of the limbs; the flowers are of the Bl. Pentandria monogynia; the leaves are nearly ovate, pointed and petioled, standing opposite to one another on the branches.

After fifteen miles riding, I arrived at the ferry, which is near the site of the fort. Here is a considerable height and bluff on the river, and evident [17] vestiges of an ancient Indian town may be seen, such as old extensive fields, and conical mounds, or artificial heaps of earth. I here crossed the river, which is about five hundred yards over, in a good large boat, rowed by a Creek Indian, who was married to a white woman; he seemed an active, civil, and sensible man. I saw large, tall trees of the Nyssa coccinea, si. Ogeeche, growing on the banks of the river. They grow in the water, near the shore. There is no tree that exhibits a more desirable appearance than this, in the autumn, when their fruit is ripe, and the tree divested of its leaves; for then they look as red as scarlet, with their fruit, which is of that colour also. It is of the shape, but larger than the olive, containing an agreeable acid juice. The leaves are oblong lanceolate and entire, somewhat hoary un-

* Franklinia Alatahama.

[VI.] *Anona pygmea*

derneath; their upper surface of a full green, and shining; the petioles
short, pedunculis multifloris. The most northern settlement of this tree,
yet known, is on Great Ogeeche, where they are called Ogeeche limes,
from their acid fruit being about the size of limes, and their being
sometimes used in their stead.

Being safely landed on the opposite bank, I mounted my horse, and
followed the high road to the ferry on St. Ille, about sixty miles south
of the Alatamaha, passing through an uninhabited wilderness. The
sudden transition from rich cultivated settlements, to high pine forests,
dark and grassy savannas, forms in my opinion no disagreeable contrast; and the new objects of observation in the works of nature soon
reconcile the surprised imagination to the change. As soon as I had lost
sight [18] of the river, ascending some sand-hills, I observed a new and
most beautiful species of Annona, having clusters of large white
fragrant flowers, and a diminutive but elegant Kalmia. The stems are
very small, feeble, and for the most part undivided, furnished with little
ovate pointed leaves, and terminate with a simple raceme, or spike of
flowers, salver-formed, and of a deep rose red. The whole plant is
ciliated. It grows in abundance all over the moist savannas, but more
especially near ponds and bay-swamps. In similar situations, and commonly a near neighbour to this new Kalmia, is seen a very curious
species of Annona. It is a very dwarf, the stems seldom extending from
the earth more than a foot or eighteen inches, and are weak and almost decumbent. The leaves are long, extremely narrow, almost lineal.
However, small as they are, they retain the figure common to the
species, that is, lanceolate, broadest at the upper end, and attenuating
down to the petiole, which is very short; their leaves stand alternately,
nearly erect, forming two series, or wings, on the arcuated stems. The
flowers, both in size and colour, resemble those of the Antrilobe, and
are single from the axillae of the leaves on incurved pedunculi, nodding downwards. I never saw the fruit. The dens, or caverns, dug in
the sand hills, by the great land-tortoise, called here Gopher,* present
a very singular appearance; these vast caves are the castles and
diurnal retreats, from whence they issue forth in the night, in search of
prey. The little mounds, or hillocks of fresh earth, thrown up in great
numbers in the night, have also a curious appearance.

In the evening I arrived at a cow-pen, where [19] there was a habitation, and the people received me very civilly. I staid here all night, and
had for supper plenty of milk, butter, and very good cheese of their
own make, which is a novelty in the maritime parts of Carolina and
Georgia; the inhabitants being chiefly supplied with it from Europe

* Testudo Polyphaemus.

and the northern states. The next day's progress, in general, presented
scenes similar to the preceding, though the land is lower, more level
and humid, and the produce more varied: high open forests of stately
pines, flowery plains, and extensive green savannas, checquered with
the incarnate Chironia, Pillcherima, and Assclepias fragrans, perfumed
the air whilst they pleased the eye. I met with some troublesome cane
swamps, saw herds of horned cattle, horses and deer, and took notice of
a procumbent species of Hibiscus, the leaves palmated, the flowers
large and expanded, pale yellow and white, having a deep crimson eye;
the whole plant, except the corolla, armed with stiff hair. I also saw a
beautiful species of Lupin, having pale green villous lingulate * leaves;
the flowers are disposed in long erect spikes; some plants produce
flowers of the finest celestial blue, others incarnate, and some milk
white, and though they all three seem to be varieties of one species, yet
they associate in separate communities, sometimes approaching near
each other's border, or in sight at a distance. Their districts are situated on dry sandy heights, in open pine forests, which are naturally
thin of undergrowth, and appear to great advantage; generally, where
they are found, they occupy many acres of surface. The vegetative
mould is composed of fine white sand, mixed, and coloured, with
dissolved and calcined vegetable substances; [20] but this stratum is not
very deep, and covers one of a tenacious cinereous coloured clay, as we
may observe by the earth adhering to the roots of trees, torn up by
storms, &c. and by the little chimneys, or air holes of cray-fish, which
perforate the savannas. Turkeys, quails, and small birds, are here to
be seen; but birds are not numerous in desart forests; they draw near
to the habitations of men, as I have constantly observed in all my
travels.

I arrived at St. Ille's in the evening, where I lodged, and next morning having crossed over in a ferry boat, set forward for St. Mary's. The
situation of the territory, it's soil and productions between these two
last rivers, are nearly similar to those which I had passed over, except that the savannas are more frequent and extensive.

It may be proper to observe, that I had now passed the utmost
frontier of the white settlements on that border. It was drawing on
towards the close of day, the skies serene and calm, the air temperately
cool, and gentle zephyrs breathing through the fragrant pines; the
prospect around enchantingly varied and beautiful; endless green
savannas, checquered with coppices of fragrant shrubs, filled the air
with the richest perfume. The gaily attired plants which enamelled
the green had begun to imbibe the pearly dew of evening; nature

* Lupinus breunis, foliis integerimis oblongis villosis.

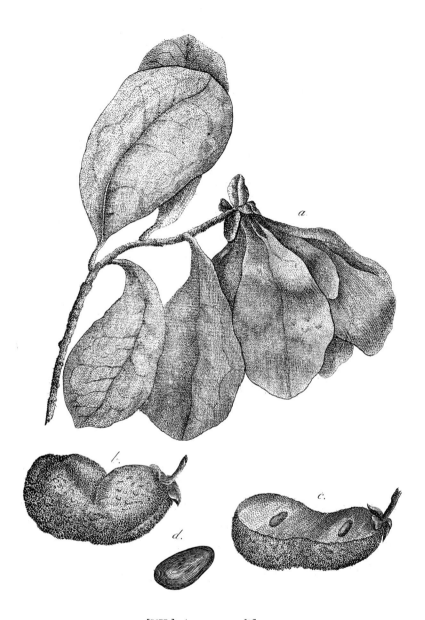

[VII.] *Anona grandiflora*

seemed silent, and nothing appeared to ruffle the happy moments of evening contemplation: when, on a sudden, an Indian appeared crossing the path, at a considerable distance before me. On perceiving that he was armed with a rifle, the first sight of him startled me, and I endeavoured to elude his sight, by stopping my pace, and keeping large trees between us; but he espied me, and turning short a-[21] bout, set spurs to his horse, and came up on full gallop. I never before this was afraid at the sight of an Indian, but at this time, I must own that my spirits were very much agitated: I saw at once, that being unarmed, I was in his power, and having now but a few moments to prepare, I resigned myself entirely to the will of the Almighty, trusting to his mercies for my preservation; my mind then became tranquil, and I resolved to meet the dreaded foe with resolution and chearful confidence. The intrepid Siminole stopped suddenly, three or four yards before me, and silently viewed me, his countenance angry and fierce, shifting his rifle from shoulder to shoulder, and looking about instantly on all sides. I advanced towards him, and with an air of confidence offered him my hand, hailing him, brother; at this he hastily jerked back his arm, with a look of malice, rage and disdain, seeming every way disconcerted; when again looking at me more attentively, he instantly spurred up to me, and, with dignity in his look and action, gave me his hand. Possibly the silent language of his soul, during the moment of suspense (for I believe his design was to kill me when he first came up) was after this manner: "White man, thou art my enemy, and thou and thy brethren may have killed mine; yet it may not be so, and even were that the case, thou art now alone, and in my power. Live; the Great Spirit forbids me to touch thy life; go to thy brethren, tell them thou sawest an Indian in the forests, who knew how to be humane and compassionate." In fine, we shook hands, and parted in a friendly manner, in the midst of a dreary wilderness; and he informed me of the course and distance to the trading-house, where I found he had been extremely ill treated the day before.

[22] I now set forward again, and after eight or ten miles riding, arrived at the banks of St. Mary's, opposite the stores, and got safe over before dark. The river is here about one hundred yards across, has ten feet water, and, following its course, about sixty miles to the sea, though but about twenty miles by land. The trading company here received and treated me with great civility. On relating my adventures on the road, particularly the last with the Indian, the chief replied, with a countenance that at once bespoke surprise and pleasure, "My friend, consider yourself a fortunate man: that fellow," said he, "is one of the greatest villains on earth, a noted murderer, and outlawed by his

countrymen. Last evening he was here, we took his gun from him, broke it in pieces, and gave him a severe drubbing: he, however, made his escape, carrying off a new rifle gun, with which, he said, going off, he would kill the first white man he met."

On seriously contemplating the behaviour of this Indian towards me, so soon after his ill treatment, the following train of sentiments insensibly crouded in upon my mind.

Can it be denied, but that the moral principle, which directs the savages to virtuous and praiseworthy actions, is natural or innate? It is certain they have not the assistance of letters, or those means of education in the schools of philosophy, where the virtuous sentiments and actions of the most illustrious characters are recorded, and carefully laid before the youth of civilized nations: therefore this moral principle must be innate, or they must be under the immediate influence and guidance of a more divine and powerful preceptor, [23] who, on these occasions, instantly inspires them, and as with a ray of divine light, points out to them at once the dignity, propriety, and beauty of virtue.

The land on, and adjacent to, this river, notwithstanding its arenaceous surface, appears naturally fertile. The Peach trees are large, healthy, and fruitful; and Indian Corn, Rice, Cotton, and Indigo, thrive exceedingly. This sandy surface, one would suppose, from it's loose texture, would possess a percolating quality, and suffer the rainwaters quickly to drain off; but it is quite the contrary, at least in these low maritime sandy countries of Carolina and Florida, beneath the mountains, for in the sands, even the heights, where the arenaceous stratum is perhaps five, eight, and ten feet above the clay, the earth, even in the longest droughts, is moist an inch or two under the surface; whereas, in the rich tenacious low lands, at such times, the ground is dry, and, as it were, baked many inches, and sometimes some feet deep, and the crops, as well as almost all vegetation, suffer in such soils and situations. The reason of this may be, that this kind of earth admits more freely of a transpiration of vapours, arising from intestine watery canals to the surface; and probably these vapours are impregnated with saline or nitrous principles, friendly and nutritive to vegetables; however, of these causes and secret operations of nature I am ignorant, and resume again my proper employment, that of discovering and collecting data for the exercise of more able physiologists.

The savannas about St. Mary's, at this season, display a very charming appearance of flowers and verdure; their more elevated borders are varied [24] with beds of Violets, Lupins, Amaryllis atamasco, and plats of a new and very beautiful species of Mimosa sensitiva, which I think as admirable, and more charming than the celebrated Humble plant, equally chaste and fearful of the hasty touch of the surprised admirer; the flower is larger, of a bright damask rose colour, and exceedingly fragrant: the whole plant is destitute of prickles, but hairy; it is procumbent, reclining itself upon the green turf, and from these trailing branches proceeds an upright peduncle, six or eight inches high, supporting an oblong head of flowerets, which altogether, at a small distance, have the appearance of an exuberant field of clover; and, what is singular, and richly varies the scene, there are interspersed patches of the same species of plants, having flowers of the finest golden yellow, and others snow white; but the incarnate is most prevalent. Magnolia glauca, Itea, Clethra, Chionanthus, Gordonia lasianthus, Ilex angustifolium, Olea Americana, Hopea tinctoria, &c. are seated in detached groves or clumps, round about the ponds or little lakes, at the lower end of the savannas. I observed, growing on the banks of this sequestered river, the following trees and shrubs: Quercus sempervirens, Q. aquatica, Q. Phillos, Q. dentata, Nyssa aquatica, N. sylvatica, N. Ogeeche, si. coccinea, Cupressus disticha, Fraxinus aquatica, Rhamnus frangula, Prunus laura cerapa, Cyrilla racemiflora, Myrica cerifera, Andromeda ferruginia, Andr. nitida, and the great evergreen Andromeda of Florida, called Pipe-stem Wood, to which I gave the name of Andromeda formosissima, as it far exceeds in beauty every one of this family.

The river St. Mary has its source from a vast lake, or marsh, called Ouaquaphenogaw, which lies [25] between Flint and Oakmulge rivers, and occupies a space of near three hundred miles in circuit. This vast accumulation of waters, in the wet season, appears as a lake, and contains some large islands or knolls, of rich high land; one of which the present generation of the Creeks represent to be a most blissful spot of the earth: they say it is inhabited by a peculiar race of Indians, whose women are incomparably beautiful; they also tell you, that this terrestrial paradise has been seen by some of their enterprising hunters, when in pursuit of game, who being lost in inextricable swamps and bogs, and on the point of perishing, were unexpectedly relieved by a company of beautiful women, whom they call daughters of the sun, who kindly gave them such provisions as they had with them, which were chiefly fruit, oranges, dates, &c. and some corn cakes, and then enjoined them to fly for safety to their own country; for that their husbands were fierce men, and cruel to strangers: they further say, that these hunters had a view of their settlements, situated on the elevated banks of an island, or promontory, in a beautiful lake; but that in their endeavours to approach it, they were involved in perpetual labyrinths, and, like inchanted land, still as they imagined they had

just gained it, it seemed to fly before them, alternately appearing
and disappearing. They resolved, at length, to leave the delusive pursuit, and to return; which, after a number of inexpressible difficulties,
they effected. When they reported their adventures to their countrymen, their young warriors were enflamed with an irresistable desire to
invade, and make a conquest of, so charming a country; but all their
attempts have hitherto proved abortive, [26] never having been able
again to find that enchanting spot, nor even any road or pathway to it;
yet they say that they frequently meet with certain signs of its being
inhabited, as the building of canoes, footsteps of men, &c. They tell
another story concerning the inhabitants of this sequestered country,
which seems probable enough, which is, that they are the posterity of
a fugitive remnant of the ancient Yamases, who escaped massacre after
a bloody and decisive conflict between them and the Creek nation
(who, it is certain, conquered, and nearly exterminated, that once
powerful people) and here found an asylum, remote and secure from
the fury of their proud conquerors. It is, however, certain that there is
a vast lake, or drowned swamp, well known, and often visited both
by white and Indian hunters, and on its environs the most valuable
hunting grounds in Florida, well worth contending for, by those powers
whose territories border upon it. From this great source of rivers,* St.
Mary arises, and meanders through a vast plain and pine forest, near an
hundred and fifty miles to the ocean, with which it communicates, between the points of Amelia and Talbert islands; the waters flow deep
and gently down from its source to the sea.

Having made my observations on the vegetable productions of this
part of the country, and obtained specimens and seeds of some curious
trees and shrubs (which were the principal objects of this excursion)
I returned by the same road to the Alatamaha, and arrived safe again
at the seat of my good friend, L. M'Intosh, Esq; where I tarried a few
days to rest and refresh myself, and to wait for [27] my young companion and fellow pilgrim, Mr. John M'Intosh, who, being fond of the
enterprize, had been so active during my absence, in the necessary
preparations, that we had nothing to wait for now but Mrs. M'Intosh's
final consent to give up her son to the perils and hardships of so long
a journey; which difficult point being settled, we set off with the prayers
and benevolent wishes of my companion's worthy parents.

* Source of rivers. It is said, that St. Ille, St. Mary, and the beautiful river Little
St. Juan, which discharges its waters into the bay of Apalachi, at St. Mark's,
take their rise from this swamp.

CHAP. IV.

E ARLY in the morning, we mounted our horses, and in two days arrived in Savanna; here we learned that the superintendent of Indian affairs had left the capital, and was on his way to Augusta. I remained but one day in Savanna, which was employed in making up and forwarding the collections for Charleston.

The day following we set off for Augusta, which is on Savanna river, at least an hundred and fifty miles by land from the capital, and about three hundred by water. We followed the course of the river, and arrived there after having had a prosperous journey, though a little incommoded by the heats of the season.

As nothing very material occurred on the road, I shall proceed to give a summary account of the observations I made concerning the soil, situation, and natural productions of the country.

In our progress from the sea coast, we rise gradually, by several steps or ascents, in the following manner: First, from the sea-coast, fifty miles back, is a level plain, generally of a loose sandy soil, producing spacious high forests, of Pinus taeda, P. lutea, P. squarosa, P. echinata, 1. Quercus sempervirens, 2. Quercus aquatica, 3. Q. phillos, 4. Q. tinctoria, 5. Q. dentata, 6. Q. prinos, 7. Q. alba, 8. Q. sinuata, 9. Q. rubra, Liriodendron tuli-[29]pifera, Liquid amber styraciflua, Morus rubra, Cercis, tilia, Populus heterophylla, Platanus occidentalis, Laurus sasafras, Laurus Borbonia, Hopea tinctoria, Fraxinus excelsior, Nyssa, Ulmus, Juglans exaltata, Halesa, Stewartia. Nearly one third of this vast plain is what the inhabitants call swamps, which are the sources of numerous small rivers and their branches: these they call salt rivers, because the tides flow near to their sources, and generally carry a good depth and breadth of water for small craft, twenty or thirty miles upwards from the sea, when they branch and spread abroad like an open hand, interlocking with each other, and forming a chain of swamps across the Carolinas and Georgia, several hundred miles parallel with the sea coast. These swamps are fed and replenished

1. Live Oak. 2. Della leaved Water Oak. 3. Willow-leaved Oak. 4. Great Black Oak. 5. Narrow-leaved Wintergreen Oak. 6. Swamp White Oak. 7. White Oak. 8. Spanish Oak. 9. Red Oak.

constantly by an infinite number of rivulets and rills, which spring out
of the first bank or ascent; their native trees and shrubs are, besides
most of those already enumerated above, as follow: Acer rubrum,
Nyssa aquatica, Chionanthus, Celtis, Fagus sylvatica, Sambricus; and
the higher knolls afford beautiful clumps of Azalea nuda and Azalea
viscosa, Corypha palma, Corypha pumila, and Magnolia grandiflora;
besides, the whole surface of the ground between the trees and shrubs
appears to be occupied with canes (Arundo gigantea) intangled with
festoons of the floriferous Glycine frutescens, Bignonia sempervirens,
Glycine apios, Smilax, various species, Bignonia crucigera, Bign. radicans, Lonicera sempervirens, and a multitude of other trees, shrubs,
and plants less conspicuous; and, in very wet places, Cupressus disticha.
The upper soil of these swamps is a perfectly black, soapy, rich earth,
or stiff mud, two or three feet deep, on a foundation or stratum of
calcareous fossil, [30] which the inhabitants call white marle; and this
is the heart or strength of these swamps; they never wear out or become poor, but, on the contrary, are more fertile by tillage; for when
they turn up this white marle, the air and winter frosts causing it to
fall like quicklime, it manures the surface: but it has one disadvantage,
that is, in great droughts, when they cannot have water sufficient in
their reservoirs to lay the surface of the ground under water, it binds,
and becomes so tough as to burn and kill the crops, especially the old
cleared lands; as, while it was fresh and new, the great quantity of
rotten wood, roots, leaves, &c. kept the surface loose and open. Severe
droughts seldom happen near the sea coast.

We now rise a bank of considerable height, which runs nearly
parallel to the coast, through Carolina and Georgia; the ascent is gradual by several flights or steps, for eight or ten miles, the perpendicular
height whereof, above the level of the ocean, may be two or three
hundred feet (and these are called the sand-hills) when we find ourselves on the entrance of a vast plain, generally level, which extends
west sixty or seventy miles, rising gently as the former, but more
perceptibly. This plain is mostly a forest of the great long-leaved pine
(P. palustris Linn.) the earth covered with grass, interspersed with an
infinite variety of herbaceous plants, and embellished with extensive
savannas, always green, sparkling with ponds of water, and ornamented
with clumps of evergreen, and other trees and shrubs, as Magnolia
grandiflora, Magnolia glauca, Gordonia, Ilex aquifolium, Quercus, various species, Laurus Borbonia, Chionanthus, Hopea tinctoria, Cyrilla,
Kalmia angustifolia, Andromeda, va-[31]rieties, Viburnum, Azalea,
Rhus vernix, Prinos, varieties, Fothergilla, and a new shrub of great
beauty and singularity; it grows erect, seven or eight feet high; a multi-

tude of erect stems arise from its root; these divide themselves into ascendant branches, which are garnished with abundance of narrow lanceolate obtuse pointed leaves, of a light green, smooth and shining. These branches, with their many subdivisions, terminate in simple racemes of pale incarnate flowers, which make a fine appearance among the leaves; the flowers are succeeded by desiccated triquetrous pericarps, each containing a single kernel.

The lowest sides of these savannas are generally joined by a great cane swamp, varied with coppices and hommocks of the various trees and shrubs already mentioned. In these swamps several rivulets take their rise, which drain them and the adjoining savannas, and thence meandering to the rivers through the forests, with their banks decorated with shrubs and trees. The earth under this level plain may be described after the following manner; the upper surface, or vegetative mould, is a light sandy loam, generally nine inches or a foot deep, on a stratum of cinereous coloured clay, except the sand-hills, where the loose sandy surface is much deeper upon the clay; stone of any sort, or gravel, is seldom seen.

The next ascent, or flight, is of much greater and more abrupt elevation, and continues rising by broken ridges and narrow levels, or vales, for ten or fifteen miles, when we rest again on another extensive nearly level plain of pine forests, mixed with various other forest trees, which continues west forty or fifty miles farther, and exhibits much [32] the same appearance with the great forest last mentioned; its vegetable productions nearly the same, excepting that the broken ridges by which we ascend to the plain are of a better soil; the vegetative mould is mixed with particles of clay and small gravel, and the soil of a dusky brown colour, lying on a stratum of reddish brown tough clay. The trees and shrubs are, Pinus taeda, great black Oak, Quercus tinctoria, Q. rubra, Laurus, Sasafras, Magnolia grandiflora, Cornus Florida, Cercis, Halesia, Juglans acuminata, Juglans-exaltata, Andromeda arborea; and, by the sides of rivulets (which wind about and between these hills and swamps, in the vales) Styrax latifolia, Ptelea trifoliata, Stewartia, Calycanthus, Chionanthus, Magnolia tripetala, Azalea, and others.

Thus have I endeavoured to give the reader a short and natural description of the vast plain lying between the region of Augusta and the sea coast; for from Augusta the mountainous country begins (when compared to the level sandy plain already passed) although it is at least an hundred and fifty miles west, thence to the Cherokee or Apalachean mountains; and this space may with propriety be called the hilly country, every where fertile and delightful, continually replenished by

innumerable rivulets, either coursing about the fragrant hills, or springing from the rocky precipices, and forming many cascades; the coolness
and purity of which waters invigorate the air of this otherwise hot and
sultry climate.

The village of Augusta is situated on a rich and fertile plain, on
the Savanna river; the buildings are near its banks, and extend nearly
two miles up to the cataracts, or falls, which are formed by the [33]
first chain of rocky hills, through which this famous river forces itself,
as if impatient to repose on the extensive plain before it invades the
ocean. When the river is low, which is during the summer months, the
cataracts are four or five feet in height across the river, and the waters
continue rapid and broken, rushing over rocks five miles higher up:
this river is near five hundred yards broad at Augusta.

A few days after our arrival at Augusta, the chiefs and warriors of
the Creeks and Cherokees being arrived, the Congress and the business
of the treaty came on, and the negociations continued undetermined
many days; the merchants of Georgia demanding at least two millions
of acres of land from the Indians, as a discharge of their debts, due, and
of long standing; the Creeks, on the other hand, being a powerful and
proud spirited people, their young warriors were unwilling to submit
to so large a demand, and their conduct evidently betrayed a disposition to dispute the ground by force of arms, and they could not at first
be brought to listen to reason and amicable terms; however, at length,
the cool and deliberate counsels of the ancient venerable chiefs, enforced by liberal presents of suitable goods, were too powerful induce-
ments for them any longer to resist, and finally prevailed. The treaty
concluded in unanimity, peace, and good order; and the honorable
Superintendent, not forgetting his promise to me, at the conclusion,
mentioned my business, and recommended me to the protection of the
Indian chiefs and warriors. The presents being distributed amongst
the Indians, they departed, returning home to their towns. A company
of sur-[34]veyors were appointed, by the Governor and Council, to
ascertain the boundaries of the new purchase; they were to be attended
by chiefs of the Indians, selected and delegated by their countrymen,
to assist, and be witnesses that the articles of the treaty were fulfilled,
as agreed to by both parties in Congress.

Col. Barnet, who was chosen to conduct this business on the part of
the Georgians, a gentleman every way qualified for that important
trust, in a very friendly and obliging manner, gave me an invitation to
accompany him on this tour.

It was now about the middle of the month of May; vegetation, in
perfection, appeared with all her attractive charms, breathing fra-

grance every where; the atmosphere was now animated with the
efficient principle of vegetative life; the arbustive hills, gay lawns, and
green meadows, which on every side invest the villa of Augusta, had
already received my frequent visits; and although here much delighted with the new beauties in the vegetable kindom, and many
eminent ones have their sequestered residence near this place, yet, as
I was never long satisfied with present possession, however endowed
with every possible charm to attract the sight, or intrinsic value to en-
gage and fix the esteem, I was restless to be searching for more, my
curiosity being insatiable.

Thus it is with regard to our affections and attachments, in the more
important and interesting concerns of human life.

Upon the rich rocky hills at the cataracts of Augusta, I first observed the perfumed Rhododendron [35] ferruginium, white robed
Philadelphus inodorus, and cerulean Malva; but nothing in vegetable
nature was more pleasing than the odoriferous Pancratium fluitans,
which almost alone possesses the little rocky islets which just appear
above the water.

The preparatory business of the surveyors being now accomplished,
Mr. J. M'Intosh, yet anxious for travelling, and desirous to accompany
me on this tour, we joined the caravan, consisting of surveyors, astronomers, artisans, chain-carriers, markers, guides and hunters, besides a
very respectable number of gentlemen, who joined us, in order to
speculate in the lands, together with ten or twelve Indians, altogether
to the number of eighty or ninety men, all or most of us well mounted
on horseback, besides twenty or thirty pack-horses, loaded with provisions, tents, and camp equipage.

The summer season now rapidly advancing, the air at mid-day, about
this region, is insufferably hot and sultry. We set off from Augusta,
early in the morning, for the Great Buffalo Lick, on the Great Ridge,
which separates the waters of the Savanna and Alatamaha, about
eighty miles distant from Augusta. At this Lick the surveyors were to
separate themselves, and form three companies, to proceed on different
routes. On the evening of the second day's journey, we arrived at a
small village on Little river, a branch of Savanna: this village, called
Wrightsborough, was founded by Jos. Mattock, Esq; of the sect called
Quakers; this public spirited man having obtained, for himself and his
followers, a district, comprehending upwards of forty thousand acres
of land, gave the new town this name, in honour of Sir James Wright,
then Governor of Georgia, who greatly promoted [36] the establishment of the settlement. Mr. Mattock, who is now about seventy years
of age, healthy and active, and presides as chief magistrate of the

settlement, received us with great hospitality. The distance from
Augusta to this place is about thirty miles; the face of the country is
chiefly a plain of high forests savannas, and cane swamps, until we
approach Little River, when the landscape varies, presenting to view
high hills and rich vales. The soil is a deep, rich, dark mould, on a
deep stratum of reddish brown tenacious clay, and that on a foundation
of rocks, which often break through both strata, lifting their backs
above the surface. The forest trees are chiefly of the deciduous order,
as, Quercus tinctoria, Q. lasciniata, Q. alba, Q. rubra, Q. prinus, with
many other species; Celtis, Fagus sylvatica, and, on the rocky hills,
Fagus castania, Fag. pumila, Quercus castania; in the rich vales,
Juglans nigra, Jug. cinerea, Gleditsia triacanthos, Magnolia acuminata,
Liriodendron, Platanus, Fraxinus excelsior, Cercea, Juglans exaltata,
Carpinus, Morus rubra, Calycanthus, Halesia, Aesculus pavia, Aesc.
arborea.

Leaving the pleasant town of Wrightsborough, we continued eight or
nine miles through a fertile plain and high forest, to the north branch
of Little River, being the largest of the two, crossing which, we entered
an extensive fertile plain, bordering on the river, and shaded by trees
of vast growth, which at once spoke its fertility. Continuing some time
through these shady groves, the scene opens, and discloses to view
the most magnificent forest I had ever seen. We rise gradually a sloping
bank of twenty or thirty feet elevation, and immediately entered this
sublime forest; the ground is perfectly [37] a level green plain, thinly
planted by nature with the most stately forest trees, such as the gigantic Black * Oak (Q. tinctoria) Liriodendron, Juglans nigra, Platanus,
Juglans exaltata, Fagus sylvatica, Ulmus sylvatica, Liquid-amber
styraciflua, whose mighty trunks, seemingly of an equal height, appeared like superb columns. To keep within the bounds of truth and
reality, in describing the magnitude and grandeur of these trees, would,
I fear, fail of credibility; yet, I think I can assert, that many of the
black oaks measured eight, nine, ten, and eleven feet diameter five
feet above the ground, as we measured several that were above thirty
feet girt, and from hence they ascend perfectly strait, with a gradual
taper, forty or fifty feet to the limbs; but, below five or six feet, these
trunks would measure a third more in circumference, on account of the
projecting jambs, or supports, which are more or less, according to the
number of horizontal roots that they arise from: the Tulip tree, Liquid-
amber, and Beech, were equally stately.

* Gigantic Black Oak. Querc. tinctoria; the bark of this species of oak is found
to afford a valuable yellow dye. This tree is known by the name of Black Oak in
Pennsylvania, New-Jersey, New-York, and New-England.

Not far distant from the terrace, or eminence, overlooking the low grounds of the river, many very magnificent monuments of the power and industry of the ancient inhabitants of these lands are visible. I observed a stupendous conical pyramid, or artificial mount of earth, vast tetragon terraces, and a large sunken area, of a cubical form, encompassed with banks of earth; and certain traces of a large Indian town, the work of a powerful nation, whose period of grandeur perhaps long preceded the discovery of this continent.

[38]   After about seven miles progress through this forest of gigantic Black Oaks, we enter on territories which exhibit more varied scenes: the land rises almost insensibly by gentle ascents, exhibiting desart plains, high forests, gravelly and stony ridges, ever in sight of rapid rivulets; the soil, as already described. We then passed over large rich savannas, or natural meadows, wide-spreading cane swamps, and frequently old Indian settlements, now deserted and overgrown with forests. These are always on or near the banks of rivers, or great swamps, the artificial mounts and terraces elevating them above the surrounding groves. I observed, in the antient cultivated fields, 1. Diospyros, 2. Gleditsia triacanthos, 3. Prunus Chicasaw,* 4. Callicarpa, 5. Morus rubra, 6. Juglans exaltata, 7. Juglans nigra, which inform us, that these trees were cultivated by the ancients, on account of their fruit, as being wholesome and nourishing food. Tho' these are natives of the forest, yet they thrive better, and are more fruitful, in cultivated plantations, and the fruit is in great estimation with the present generation of Indians, particularly Juglans exaltata* commonly called shell-barked hiccory; the Creeks store up the latter in their towns. I have seen above an hundred bushels of these nuts belonging to one family. They pound them to pieces, and then cast them into boiling water, which, after passing through fine strainers, preserves the most oily part of the liquid: this they call by a name which signifies Hiccory milk; it is as sweet and rich as fresh cream, and is an ingredient in most of their cookery, especially homony and corn cakes.

[39]   After four days moderate and pleasant travelling, we arrived in the evening at the Buffalo Lick. This extraordinary place occupies several acres of ground, at the foot of the S. E. promontory of the Great Ridge, which, as before observed, divides the rivers Savanna and Alatamaha. A large cane swamp and meadows, forming an immense plain, lies S. E. from it; in this swamp I believe the head

---

* The Chicasaw plumb I think must be excepted, for though certainly a native of America, yet I never saw it wild in the forests, but always in old deserted Indian plantations: I suppose it to have been brought from the S.W. beyond the Missisippi, by the Chicasaws.

branches of the great Ogeeche river take their rise. The place called the Lick contains three or four acres, is nearly level, and lies between the head of the cane swamp and the ascent of the Ridge. The earth, from the superficies to an unknown depth, is an almost white or cinereous coloured tenacious fattish clay, which all kinds of cattle lick into great caves, pursuing the delicious vein. It is the common opinion of the inhabitants, that this clay is impregnated with saline vapours, arising from fossil salts deep in the earth; but I could discover nothing saline in its taste, but I imagined an insipid sweetness. Horned cattle, horses, and deer, are immoderately fond of it, insomuch, that their excrement, which almost totally covers the earth to some distance round this place, appears to be perfect clay; which, when dried by the sun and air, is amost as hard as brick.

We were detained at this place one day, in adjusting and planning the several branches of the survey. A circumstance occurred during this time, which was a remarkable instance of Indian sagacity, and had nearly disconcerted all our plans, and put an end to the business. The surveyor having fixed his compass on the staff, and about to ascertain the course from our place of departure, which was to strike Savanna river at the confluence of a [40] certain river, about seventy miles distance from us; just as he had determined upon the point, the Indian Chief came up, and observing the course he had fixed upon, spoke, and said it was not right; but that the course to the place was so and so, holding up his hand, and pointing. The surveyor replied, that he himself was certainly right, adding, that that little instrument (pointing to the compass) told him so, which, he said, could not err. The Indian answered, he knew better, and that the little wicked instrument was a liar; and he would not acquiesce in its decisions, since it would wrong the Indians out of their land. This mistake (the surveyor proving to be in the wrong) displeased the Indians; the dispute arose to that height, that the Chief and his party had determined to break up the business, and return the shortest way home, and forbad the surveyors to proceed any farther: however, after some delay, the complaisance and prudent conduct of the Colonel made them change their resolution; the Chief became reconciled, upon condition that the compass should be discarded, and rendered incapable of serving on this business; that the Chief himself should lead the survey; and, moreover, receive an order for a very considerable quantity of goods.

Matters being now amicably settled, under this new regulation, the Colonel having detached two companies on separate routes, Mr. M'Intosh and myself attaching ourselves to the Colonel's party, whose excursion was likely to be the most extensive and varied, we set off

from the Buffalo Lick, and the Indian Chief, heading the party, conducted us on a straight line, as appeared by collateral observation, to
the desired place. We pursued nearly [41] a north course up the Great
Ridge, until we came near the branches of Broad River, when we
turned off to the right hand, and encamped on a considerable branch
of it. At this place we continued almost a whole day, constituting
surveyors and astronomers, who were to take the course, distance, and
observations on Broad River, and from thence down to its confluence
with the Savanna.

The Great Ridge consists of a continued high forest; the soil fertile,
and broken into moderately elevated hills, by the many rivulets which
have their sources in it. The heights and precipices abound in rock and
stone. The forest trees and other vegetable productions are the same
as already mentioned about Little River: I observed Halesia, Styrax,
Aesculus pavia, Aesc. sylvatica, Robinia hispida, Magnolia acuminata,
Mag. tripetala, and some very curious new shrubs and plants, particularly the Physic-nut, or Indian Olive. The stems arise many from a root,
two or three feet high; the leaves sit opposite, on every short petioles;
they are broad, lanceolate, entire, and undulated, having smooth surfaces of a deep green colour. From the bosom of each leaf is produced
a single oval drupe, standing erect, on long slender stems; it has a
large kernel, and thin pulp. The fruit is yellow when ripe, and about
the size of an olive. The Indians, when they go in pursuit of deer,
carry this fruit with them, supposing that it has the power of charming
or drawing that creature to them; from whence, with the traders, it
has obtained the name of the Physic-nut, which means, with them,
charming, conjuring, or fascinating. Malva scandens, Felix scandens,
perhaps species of Trichomanes; the leaves are palmated, or radi-
[42]ated; it climbs and roves about, on shrubs, in moist ground. A very
singular and elegant plant, of an unknown family, called Indian Lettuce, made its first appearance in these rich vales; it is a biennial; the
primary or radical leaves are somewhat spatuled, or broad, lanceolate,
and obtuse pointed, of a pale yellowish green, smooth surface, and
of a delicate frame, or texture; these leaves, spread equally on every
side, almost reclining on the ground; from their centre arises a strait
upright stem, five, six or seven feet high, smooth and polished; the
ground of a dark purple colour, which is elegantly powdered with
greenish yellow specks; this stem, three fourths of its length, is embellished with narrow leaves, nearly of the same form of the radical
ones, placed at regular distances, in verticillate order. The superior one
fourth division of this stem is formed into a pyramidal spike of flowers,
rather diffuse; these flowers are of the hexandria, large, and expanded;

of a dark purple colour, delicately powdered with green, yellow, and red, and divided into six parts, or petals; these are succeeded by triquetrous dry pericarps, when ripe.

This great ridge is a vast extended projection of the Cherokee or Alegany mountains, gradually encreasing in height and extent, from its extremity at the Lick, to its union with the high ridge of mountains anciently called the Apalachian mountains; it every where approaches much nearer the waters of the Alatamaha than those of the Savanna: at one particular place, where we encamped, on the Great Ridge, during our repose there, part of a day. Our hunters going out, and, understanding that their route was to the low lands on the Ocone, I accompanied them: we had not rode above [43] three miles before we came to the banks of that beautiful river. The cane swamps, of immense extent, and the oak forests, on the level lands, are incredibly fertile; which appears from the tall reeds of the one, and the heavy timber of the other.

Before we left the waters of Broad River, having encamped in the evening, on one of its considerable branches, and left my companions, to retire, as usual, on botanical researches, on ascending a steep rocky hill, I accidentally discovered a new species of Caryophyllata (Geum odoratissimum) on reaching to a shrub, my foot slipped, and, in recovering myself, I tore up some of the plants, whose roots filled the air with animating scents of cloves and spicy perfumes.

On my return towards camp, I met my philosophic companion, Mr. M'Intosh, who was seated on the bank of a rivulet, and whom I found highly entertained by a very novel and curious natural exhibition, in which I participated with high relish. The waters at this place were still and shoal, and flowed over a bed of gravel just beneath a rocky rapid: in this eddy shoal were a number of little gravelly pyramidal hills, whose summits rose almost to the surface of the water, very artfully constructed by a species of small cray-fish (Cancer macrourus) which inhabited them: here seemed to be their citadel, or place of retreat for their young, against the attacks and ravages of their enemy, the gold-fish: these, in numerous bands, continually infested them, except at short intervals, when small detachments of veteran cray-fish sallied out upon them, from their cells within the gravelly pyramids, at which time a brilliant sight presented: the little gold-fish instantly fled from every side, darting [44] through the transparent waters like streams of lightning; some even sprang above the surface, into the air, but all quickly returned to the charge, surrounding the pyramids as before, on the retreat of the cray-fish; in this manner the war seemed to be continual.

The gold-fish is about the size of the anchovy, nearly four inches long, of a neat slender form; the head is covered with a salade of an ultramarine blue, the back of a reddish brown, the sides and belly of a flame, or of the colour of a fine red lead; a narrow dusky line runs along each side, from the gills to the tail; the eyes are large, with the iris like burnished gold. This branch of Broad River is about twelve yards wide, and has two, three, and four feet depth of water, and winds through a fertile vale, almost overshadowed on one side by a ridge of high hills, well timbered with Oak, Hiccory, Liriodendron, Magnolia acuminata, Pavia sylvatica, and on their rocky summits, Fagus castania, Rhododendron ferruginium, Kalmia latifolia, Cornus Florida, &c.

One of our Indian young men, this evening, caught a very large salmon trout, weighing about fifteen pounds, which he presented to the Col. who ordered it to be served up for supper. The Indian struck this fish, with a reed harpoon, pointed very sharp, barbed, and hardened by the fire. The fish lay close under the steep bank, which the Indian discovered and struck with his reed; instantly the fish darted off with it, whilst the Indian pursued, without extracting the harpoon, and with repeated thrusts drowned it, and then dragged it to shore.

[45]   After leaving Broad River, the land rises very sensibly, and the country being mountainous, our progress became daily more difficult and slow; yet the varied scenes of pyramidal hills, high forests, rich vales, serpentine rivers, and cataracts, fully compensated for our difficulties and delays. I observed the great Aconitum napellus, Delphinium perigrinum, the carminative Angelica lucida,* and cerulean Malva.

We at length happily accomplished our line, arriving at the little river, where our hunters bringing in plenty of venison and turkeys, we had a plentiful feast at supper. Next morning we marked the corner tree, at the confluence of Little river and the Savanna; and, soon after, the Indians amicably took leave of us, returning home to their towns.

The rocks and fossils, which constitute the hills of this middle region, are of various species, as, Quartsum, Ferrum, Cos, Silex, Glarea, Arena, Ochra, Stalectites, Saxum, Mica, &c. I saw no signs of Marble, Plaster, or Lime-stone; yet there is, near Augusta, in the forests, great piles of a porous friable white rock, in large and nearly horizontal masses, which seems to be an heterogeneous concrete, consisting of pulverized sea shells, with a small proportion of sand; it is soft, and easily wrought into any form, yet of sufficient consistence for constructing any building.

As for the animal productions, they are the same which originally

* Called Nondo in Virginia: by the Creek and Cherokee traders, White Root.

inhabited this part of North America, except such as have been affrighted away since [46] the invasion of the Europeans. The buffalo (Urus) once so very numerous, is not at this day to be seen in this part of the country; a few elk, and those only in the Apalachian mountains. The dreaded and formidable rattle-snake is yet too common, and a variety of other serpents abound, particularly that admirable creature the glass-snake: I saw a very large and beautiful one, a little distance from our camp. The allegator, a species of crocodile, abounds in the rivers and swamps, near the sea coast, but is not to be seen above Augusta. Bears, tygers,° wolves, and wild cats (Felis cauda truncata) are numerous enough; and there is a very great variety of Papilio and Phalina, many of which are admirably beautiful, as well as other insects of infinite variety.

The surveyors having completed their observations, we set off next day on our return to Augusta, taking our route generally through the low lands on the banks of the Savanna. We crossed Broad River, at a newly settled plantation, near its confluence with the Savanna. On my arrival at Augusta, finding myself a little fatigued, I staid there a day or two, and then set off again for Savanna, the capital, where we arrived in good health.

Having, in this journey, met with extraordinary success, not only in the enjoyment of an uninterrupted state of good health, and escaping ill accidents, incident to such excursions, through uninhabited wildernesses, and an Indian frontier, but [47] also in making a very extensive collection of new discoveries of natural productions. On the recollection of so many and great favours and blessings, I now, with a high sense of gratitude, presume to offer up my sincere thanks to the Almighty, the Creator and Preserver.

° This creature is called, in Pennsylvania and the northern States, Panther; but in Carolina and the southern States, is called Tyger; they are very strong, much larger than any dog, of a yellowish brown, or clay colour, having a very long tail; they are a mischievous animal, and prey on calves, young colts, &c.

CHAP. V.

HAVING completed my Hortus Siccus, and made up my collections of seeds and growing roots, the fruits of my late western tour, and sent them to Charleston, to be forwarded to Europe, I spent the remaining part of this season in botanical excursions to the low countries, between Carolina and East Florida, and collected seeds, roots, and specimens, making drawings of such curious subjects as could not be preserved in their native state of excellence.

During this recess from the high road of my travels, having obtained the use of a neat light cypress canoe, at Broughton Island, a plantation, the property of the Hon. Henry Laurens, Esq. where I stored myself with necessaries, for the voyage, and resolved upon a trip up the Alatamaha.

I ascended this beautiful river, on whose fruitful banks the generous and true sons of liberty securely dwell, fifty miles above the white settlements.

How gently flow thy peaceful floods, O Alatamaha! How sublimely rise to view, on thy elevated shores, yon Magnolian groves, from whose tops the surrounding expanse is perfumed, by clouds of incense, blended with the exhaling balm of the Liquid-amber, and odours continually arising from circumambient aromatic groves of Illicium, Myrica, Laurus, and Bignonia.

When wearied, with working my canoe against the impetuous current (which becomes stronger by [49] reason of the mighty floods of the river, with collected force, pressing through the first hilly ascents, where the shores on each side the river present to view rocky cliffs rising above the surface of the water, in nearly flat horizontal masses, washed smooth by the descending floods, and which appear to be a composition, or concrete, of sandy lime-stone) I resigned my bark to the friendly current, reserving to myself the control of the helm. My progress was rendered delightful by the sylvan elegance of the groves, chearful meadows, and high distant forests, which in grand order presented themselves to view. The winding banks of the river, and the high projecting promontories, unfolded fresh scenes of grandeur and sublimity. The deep forests and distant hills re-echoed the chearing social lowings of domestic herds. The air was filled with the loud and shrill whooping of the wary sharp-sighted crane. Behold, on yon decayed, defoliated Cypress tree, the solitary wood-pelican, dejectedly perched upon its utmost elevated spire; he there, like an ancient venerable sage, sets himself up as a mark of derision, for the safety of his kindred tribes. The crying-bird, another faithful guardian, screaming in the gloomy thickets, warns the feathered tribes of approaching peril; and the plumage of the swift sailing squadrons of Spanish curlews (white as the immaculate robe of innocence) gleam in the cerulean skies.

Thus secure and tranquil, and meditating on the marvellous scenes of primitive nature, as yet unmodified by the hand of man, I gently descended the peaceful stream, on whose polished surface were depicted the mutable shadows from its pensile banks; whilst myriads of finny inhabitants sported in its pellucid floods.

[50]   The glorious sovereign of day, cloathed in light refulgent, rolling on his gilded chariot, speeds to revisit the western realms. Grey pensive eve now admonishes us of gloomy night's hasty approach: I am roused by care to seek a place of secure repose, ere darkness comes on.

Drawing near the high shores, I ascended the steep banks, where stood a venerable oak. An ancient Indian field, verdured o'er with succulent grass, and checquered with coppices of fragrant shrubs, offers to my view the Myrica cerifera, Magnolia glauca, Laurus benzoin, Laur. Borbonia, Rhamnus frangula, Prunus Chicasaw, Prun. Lauro cerasa, and others. It was nearly encircled with an open forest of stately pines (Pinus palustris) through which appears the extensive savanna, the secure range of the swift roebuck. In front of my landing, and due east, I had a fine prospect of the river and low lands on each side, which gradually widened to the sea coast, and gave me an unconfined prospect, whilst the far distant sea coast islands, like a coronet, limited the hoary horizon.

My barque being securely moored, and having reconnoitered the surrounding groves, and collected fire-wood, I spread my skins and blanket by my chearful fire, under the protecting shade of the hospitable Live-oak, and reclined my head on my hard but healthy couch. I listened, undisturbed, to the divine hymns of the feathered songsters of the groves, whilst the softly whispering breezes faintly died away.

The sun now below the western horizon, the moon majestically rising in the east; again the tuneful birds become inspired; how melodious is [51] the social mock-bird! the groves resound the unceasing cries of the whip-poor-will; the moon about an hour above the horizon; lo! a dark eclipse * of her glorious brightness comes slowly on; at length, a silver thread alone encircles her temples: at this boding change, an universal silence prevails.

Nature now weary, I resigned myself to rest; the night passed over; the cool dews of the morning awake me; my fire burnt low; the blue smoke scarce rises above the moistened embers; all is gloomy: the late starry skies, now overcast by thick clouds, I am warned to rise and be going. The livid purple clouds thicken on the frowning brows of the morning; the tumultuous winds from the east now exert their power. O peaceful Alatamaha! gentle by nature! how thou art ruffled! thy wavy surface disfigures every object, presenting them obscurely to the sight, and they at length totally disappear, whilst the furious winds and sweeping rains bend the lofty groves, and prostrate the quaking grass, driving the affrighted creatures to their dens and caverns.

The tempest now relaxes, its impetus is spent, and a calm serenity gradually takes place; by noon they break away, the blue sky appears, the fulgid sun-beams spread abroad their animating light, and the steady western wind resumes his peaceful reign. The waters are purified, the waves subside, and the beautiful river regains its native calmness: so it is with the varied and mutable scenes of human events on the stream of life. The higher powers and affections of the soul are so blended and connected with the inferior passions, that the most painful [52] feelings are excited in the mind when the latter are crossed: thus in the moral system, which we have planned for our conduct, as a ladder whereby to mount to the summit of terrestrial glory and happiness, and from whence we perhaps meditated our flight to heaven itself, at the very moment when we vainly imagine ourselves to have attained its point, some unforeseen accident intervenes, and surprises us; the chain is violently shaken, we quit our hold and fall: the well contrived system at once becomes a chaos; every idea of happiness recedes; the splendour of glory darkens, and at length totally disappears; every pleasing object is defaced, all is deranged, and the flattering scene passes quite away, a gloomy cloud pervades the understanding, and when we see our progress retarded, and our best intentions frustrated, we are apt to deviate from the admonitions and convictions of virtue, to shut our eyes upon our guide and protector, doubt of his power, and despair of his assistance. But let us wait and rely on our God, who in due time will shine forth in brightness, dissipate the envious cloud, and reveal to us how finite and circumscribed is human power, when assuming to itself independent wisdom.

* The air at this time being serene, and not a cloud to be seen, I saw this annual almost total autumnal eclipse, in its highest degree of perfection.

But, before I leave the river Alatamaha, we will proceed to give a
further and more particular account of it. It has its source in the
Cherokee mountains, near the head of Tugilo, the great west branch of
Savanna, and, before it leaves the mountains, is joined and augmented
by innumerable rivulets; thence it descends through the hilly country,
with all its collateral branches, and winds rapidly amongst the hills two
hundred and fifty miles, and then enters the flat plain country, by [53]
the name of the Oakmulge; thence meandering an hundred and fifty
miles, it is joined on the east side by the Ocone, which likewise heads
in the lower ridges of the mountains. After this confluence, having
now gained a vast acquisition of waters, it assumes the name of
Alatamaha, when it becomes a large majestic river, flowing with gentle
windings through a vast plain forest, near an hundred miles, and enters
the Atlantic by several mouths. The north channel, or entrance, glides
by the heights of Darien, on the east bank, about ten miles above the
bar, and, running from thence with several turnings, enters the ocean
between Sapello and Wolf islands. The south channel, which is
esteemed the largest and deepest, after its separation from the north,
descends gently, winding by M'Intosh's and Broughton islands; and
lastly, by the west coast of St. Simon's island, enters the ocean, through
St. Simon's Sound, between the south end of the island of that name
and the north end of Jekyl island. On the west banks of the south
channel, ten or twelve miles above its mouth, and nearly opposite
Darien, are to be seen, the remains of an ancient fort, or fortification;
it is now a regular tetragon terrace, about four feet high, with bastions
at each angle; the area may contain about an acre of ground, but the
fosse which surrounded it is nearly filled up. There are large Live
Oaks, Pines, and other trees, growing upon it, and in the old fields adjoining. It is supposed to have been the work of the French or Spaniards. A large swamp lies betwixt it and the river, and a considerable
creek runs close by the works, and enters the river through the swamp,
a small distance above Broughton Island. About seventy or eighty [54]
miles above the confluence of the Oakmulge and Ocone, the trading
path, from Augusta to the Creek nation, crosses these fine rivers, which
are there forty miles apart. On the east banks of the Oakmulge, this
trading road runs nearly two miles through ancient Indian fields, which
are called the Oakmulge fields: they are the rich low lands of the river.
On the heights of these low grounds are yet visible monuments, or
traces, of an ancient town, such as artificial mounts or terraces, squares
and banks, encircling considerable areas. Their old fields and planting
land extend up and down the river, fifteen or twenty miles from this
site.

And, if we are to give credit to the account the Creeks give of themselves, this place is remarkable for being the first town or settlement,
when they sat down (as they term it) or established themselves, after
their emigration from the west, beyond the Mississippi, their original
native country. On this long journey they suffered great and innumerable difficulties, encountering and vanquishing numerous and
valiant tribes of Indians, who opposed and retarded their march.
Having crossed the river, still pushing eastward, they were obliged to
make a stand, and fortify themselves in this place, as their only remaining hope, being to the last degree persecuted and weakened by
their surrounding foes. Having formed for themselves this retreat, and
driven off the inhabitants by degrees, they recovered their spirits, and
again faced their enemies, when they came off victorious in a memorable and decisive battle. They afterwards gradually subdued their
surrounding enemies, strengthening themselves by taking into confederacy the vanquished tribes.

[55]   And they say, also, that about this period the English were
establishing the colony of Carolina, and the Creeks, understanding that
they were a powerful, warlike people, sent deputies to Charleston, their
capital, offering them their friendship and alliance, which was accepted, and, in consequence thereof, a treaty took place between them,
which has remained inviolable to this day: they never ceased war
against the numerous and potent bands of Indians, who then surrounded and cramped the English plantations, as the Savannas,
Ogeeches, Wapoos, Santees, Yamasees, Utinas, Icosans, Paticas, and
others, until they had extirpated them. The Yamasees and their adherents sheltering themselves under the power and protection of the
Spaniards of East Florida, they pursued them to the very gates of St.
Augustine, and the Spaniards refusing to deliver them up, these faithful intrepid allies had the courage to declare war against them, and
incessantly persecuted them, until they entirely broke up and ruined
their settlements, driving them before them, till at length they were
obliged to retire within the walls of St. Augustine and a few inferior
fortified posts on the sea coast.

After a few days, I returned to Broughton Island. The Cherokees and
their confederates being yet discontented, and on bad terms with the
white people, it was unsafe to pursue my travels into the north western
regions of Carolina; and recollecting many subjects of natural history,
which I had observed in the south of the isthmus of Florida, when on
a journey some years ago with my father, John Bartram, that were
interesting, and not taken notice of by any traveller; and as it was then
[56] in the autumn and winter, I had reason to think that very many

curious subjects had escaped our researches: I now formed the resolution of travelling into East Florida; accordingly, I immediately wrote to Doctor Fothergill, in order that he might know where to direct to me.

CHAP. I.

W
E are, all of us, subject to crosses and disappointments, but more especially the traveller; and when they surprise us, we frequently become restless and impatient under them: but let us rely on Providence, and by studying and contemplating the works and power of the Creator, learn wisdom and understanding in the economy of nature, and be seriously attentive to the divine monitor within. Let us be obedient to the ruling powers in such things as regard human affairs, our duties to each other, and all creatures and concerns that are submitted to our care and control.

In the month of March, 1774, I set off from Savanna, for Florida, proceeding by land to the Alatamaha, where I diverted my time agreeably in short excursions, picking up curiosities, until the arrival of a small vessel at Frederica, from Savanna, which was destined to an Indian trading house high up St. John's, in East Florida. Upon information of this vessel's arrival, I immediately took boat and descended the Alatamaha, calling by the way of Broughton Island, where I was kindly received by Mr. James Bailey, Mr. Laurens's agent. Leaving Broughton Island in the evening, I continued descending the south channel nine or ten miles, when, after crossing the sound, I arrived at Frederica, on the island of St. Simon, where I was well received and entertained by James Spalding, Esq; This gen-[58]tleman carrying on a very considerable trade, and having extensive connections with the Indian tribes of East Florida, furnished me with letters to his agents residing at his trading houses, ordering them to furnish me with horses, guides, and every other convenient assistance.

Before the vessel was ready to sail again for St. John's, I had time to explore the island. In the cool of the morning early, I rode out of the town, directing my course to the south end of the island. After penetrating a thick grove of oaks, which almost surrounded the town on the land side, suddenly a very extensive and beautiful green savanna opened to view, in length nearly two miles, and in breadth near a mile,

well stocked with horned cattle, horses, sheep, and deer. Following an
old highway, now out of repair, across the Savanna, I ascended the
sloping green bank, and entered a noble forest of lofty pines, and then
a venerable grove of Live Oaks, under whose shady spreading boughs
opened a spacious avenue, leading to the former seat of General
Oglethorp, but now the property of Capt. Raimond Demere. After
leaving this town, I was led into a high pine forest; the trees were tall,
and generally of the species called Broom-pine (P. palustris Linn.) the
surface of the ground covered with grass, herbage, and some shrubbery: I continued through this forest nearly in a direct line towards the
sea coast, five or six miles, when the land became uneven, with ridges
of sand-hills, mixed with sea shells, and covered by almost impenetrable thickets, consisting of Live Oaks, Sweet-bay (L. Borbonia)
Myrica, Ilex aquifolium, Rhamnus frangula, Cassine, Sideroxylon,
Ptelea, Halesia, Callicarpa, Carpinus, entangled with Smilax, pseudo
China, and other [59] species, Bignonia sempervirens, B. crucigera,
Rhamnus volubllis, &c. This dark labyrinth is succeeded by a great extent of salt plains, beyond which the boundless ocean is seen. Betwixt
the dark forest and the salt plains, I crossed a rivulet of fresh water,
where I sat down a while to rest myself, under the shadow of sweet
Bays and Oaks; the lively breezes were perfumed by the fragrant
breath of the superb Crinum, called, by the inhabitants, White Lilly.
This admirable beauty of the sea-coast-islands dwells in the humid
shady groves, where the soil is made fertile and mellow by the admixture of sea shells. The delicate structure of its spadix, its green
broad leaves, and the texture and whiteness of its flowers, at once
charmed me. The Euphorbia picta, Salvia coccinea, and Ipomea
erecta, were also seated in front of my resting place, as well as the
Lycium salsum (perhaps L. Afrum Linn.) a very beautiful ever green
shrub, its cerulean flowers, and coral red berries, always on its branches,
forming not the least of its beauties.

Time now admonishing me to rise and be going, I, with reluctance,
broke away from this assembly of maritime beauties.

Continuing on, southward, the salt plains on my left hand insensibly
became narrower, and I at length reached the strand, which was level,
firm, and paved with shells, and afforded me a grand view of the
boundless ocean.

O thou Creator supreme, almighty! how infinite and incomprehensible thy works! most perfect, and every way astonishing!

I continued nearly a mile along this firm sandy beach, the waves of
the sea sometimes washing my [60] horse's feet. I observed a great
variety of shell-fish, as Echinitis, Corallinus, Patella, Medusa, Buccina,

Concha venerea, Auris marina, Cancer, Squilla, &c. some alive, and
others dead, having been cast upon the beach by the seas, in times of
tempest, where they became a prey to sea fowl, and other maritime
animals, or perished by the heat of the sun and burning sands. At
length I doubled the utmost south point of St. Simon's, which forms
the north cape of the south channel of the great river Alatamaha. The
sound, just within this cape, forms an excellent bay, or cove, on the
south end of the island, on the opposite side of which I beheld a house
and farm, where I soon arrived. This delightful habitation was situated
in the midst of a spacious grove of Live Oaks and Palms, near the
strand of the bay, commanding a view of the inlet. A cool area surrounded the low but convenient buildings, from whence, through
the groves, was a spacious avenue into the island, terminated by a large
savanna; each side of the avenue was lined with bee-hives, to the
number of fifty or sixty; they seemed to be well peopled, and exhibited
a lively image of a colony that has attained to a state of power and
affluence, by the practice of virtue and industry.

When I approached the house, the good man, who was reclining on
a bear-skin, spread under the shade of a Live Oak, smoking his pipe,
rose and saluted me: "Welcome, stranger, I am indulging the rational
dictates of nature, taking a little rest, having just come in from the
chace and fishing." After some conversation and rest, his servant
brought a bowl of honey and water, a very refreshing and agreeable
liquor, of which I drank. On rising to take my departure, he objected,
and [61] requested me to stay and dine with him; and on my pleading,
for excuse, the necessity of my being at Frederica, "Yet, I pray you, stay
a little, I will soon have some refreshment for you." Presently was laid
before us a plentiful repast of venison, &c. our drink being honey and
water, strengthened by the addition of brandy. Our rural table was
spread under the shadow of Oaks, Palms, and Sweet Bays, fanned by
the lively salubrious breezes wafted from the spicy groves. Our music
was the responsive love-lays of the painted nonpareil, and the alert
and gay mockbird; whilst the brilliant humming-bird darted through
the flowery groves, suspended in air, and drank nectar from the flowers
of the yellow Jasmine, Lonicera, Andromeda, and sweet Azalea.

But yet, how awfully great and sublime is the majestic scene eastward! the solemn sound of the beating surf strikes our ears; the
dashing of yon liquid mountains, like mighty giants, in vain assail the
skies; they are beaten back, and fall prostrate upon the shores of the
trembling island.

Taking leave of my sylvan friend, I set off on my return to the town,
where I arrived before night, having observed, on the way, many

curious vegetable productions, particularly Corypha Palma (or great Cabbage Palm) Corypha pumila, Corypha repens, frondibus expansis, flabelliformibus, plicatis, stipit. spinosis (Dwarf Saw Palmetto) Corypha) obliqua, caudex arboreus adscendens, frondibus expansis, flabelliformibus, plicatis, stipit. serratis, Cyrilla, Tillandsia monostachya, Till. lingulata, or Wild Pine; both these curious vegetables are parasites, living on the substance of others, particularly on the limbs of the Live Oak; the latter spe-[62]cies is a very large flourishing plant, greatly resembling, at some distance, a well grown plant of the Bromelia Ananas: the large deep green leaves are placed in an imbricated order, and ascendant; but their extremities are reflex, their bases gibbous and hollowed, like a ladle, and capable of containing near a pint of water: heavy tempests of wind and rain tear these plants from the trees; yet they live and flourish on the earth, under the shadow of these great Live Oaks. A very large part of this island had formerly been cleared and planted by the English, as appeared evidently to me, by vestiges of plantations, ruins of costly buildings, highways, &c. but it is now overgrown with forests. Frederica was the first town built by the English in Georgia, and was founded by General Oglethorp, who began and established the colony. The fortress was regular and beautiful, constructed chiefly with brick, and was the largest, most regular, and perhaps most costly, of any in North America, of British construction: it is now in ruins, yet occupied by a small garrison; the ruins also of the town only remain; peach trees, figs, pomegranates, and other shrubs, grow out of the ruinous walls of former spacious and expensive buildings, not only in the town, but at a distance in various parts of the island; yet there are a few neat houses in good repair, and inhabited: it seems now recovering again, owing to the public and liberal spirit and exertions of J. Spalding, Esq; who is president of the island, and engaged in very extensive mercantile concerns.

T HE vessel, in which I was to embark for East Florida, being now ready to pursue her voyage, we set sail with a fair wind and tide. Our course was south, through the sound, betwixt a chain of sea-coast-islands, and the main. In the evening we came to, at the south end of St. Simons, having been hindered by the flood tide making against us. The Captain and myself, with one of our crew, went on shore, with a view of getting some venison and sea fowl. We had not the good fortune to see any deer, yet we were not altogether unsuccessful, having taken three young racoons (Ursus cauda elongata) which are excellent meat: we had them for supper, served up in a pillo. Next morning early, we again got under way, running by Jekyl and Cumberland Islands, large, beautiful and fertile, yet thinly inhabited, and consequently excellent haunts for deer, bears and other game.

As we ran by Cumberland Isle, keeping the channel through the sound, we saw a sail a-head coming up towards us. Our Captain knew it to be the trading schooner from the stores on St. John's, and immediately predicted bad news, as she was not to sail, until our arrival there. As she approached us, his apprehensions were more and more confirmed, from the appearance of a number of passengers on deck. We laid to, until she came up, when we hailed her, "What news?" "Bad; the Indians have plundered the upper store, and the traders have escaped, only with their lives." Upon this both vessels came to anchor very near each other, when, [64] learning the particulars, it appeared, that a large party of Indians, had surprised and plundered two trading houses, in the isthmus, beyond the river St. Johns, and a third being timely apprised of their hostile intentions, by a faithful runner, had time to carry off part of the effects, which they secreted in a swamp at some distance from it, covering them with skins. The upper store had saved their goods in like manner, and the lower store, to which we were bound, had removed the chief of theirs, and deposited them on a small island, in the river, about five miles below the store. With these effects was my chest, which I had forwarded in this vessel, from Savanna, not being at that time determined, whether to make this journey by land, or water. The Captain of our vessel, re-

41

solved to put about and return to Frederica, for fresh instructions
how to proceed; but for my part, I was determined to proceed for the
island up St. John's, where my chest was lodged, there being some
valuable books and papers in it, which I could not do well without. I
accordingly desired our Captain to put me on shore, on Little St.
Simon's, which was not far distant, intending to walk a few miles to
a fort, at the south end of that island, where some fishermen resided,
who, as I expected, would set me over on Amelia Island, where was
a large plantation, the property of Lord Egmont, a British nobleman,
whose agent, while I was at Frederica, gave me an invitation to call on
him, as I passed toward East Florida; and here I had expectations of
getting a boat to carry me to St. John's. Agreeably to my desire, the
Captain put me on shore, with a young man, a passenger, for East Florida, who promised to continue with me, and share my adventures. We
landed safely, the Captain wishing us a prosperous journey, returned
on [65] board his vessel, and we proceeded for the fort, encountering
some harsh treatment from thorny thickets, and prickly vines. However we reached the fort in the evening. The commander was out in
the forest, hunting. My companion being tired, or indolent, betook
himself to rest, while I made a tour round the south point of the island,
walking the shelly paved sea beach, and picking up novelties. I had
not gone above a mile, before I came up to a roebuck, lying slain on
the sands, and hearing the report of a gun, not far off, and supposing
it to be from the Captain of the fort, whom I expected soon to return
to take up his game, I retired to a little distance, mounted the sand
hills, and sat down, enjoying a fine prospect of the rolling billows and
foaming breakers, beating on the bar, and north promontory of Amelia
Isle, opposite to me. The Captain of the fort soon came up, with a
slain buck on his shoulders. We hailed each other, and returned together to the fort, where we were well treated, and next morning, at
my request, the Captain obligingly set us over, landing us safely on
Amelia. After walking through a spacious forest of Live Oaks and
Palms, and crossing a creek, that ran through a narrow salt marsh, I
and my fellow traveller arrived safe at the plantation, where the
agent, Mr. Egan, received us very politely and hospitably. This gentleman is a very intelligent and able planter, having already greatly improved the estate, particularly in the cultivation of indigo. Great part
of this island consists of excellent hommocky land, which is the soil
this plant delights in, as well as cotton, corn, batatas, and almost every
other esculent vegetable. Mr. Egan politely rode with me, over great
part of the island. On [66] Egmont estate, are several very large In-

dian tumuli, which are called Ogeeche mounts, so named from that nation of Indians, who took shelter here, after being driven from their native settlements on the main near Ogeeche river. Here they were constantly harrassed by the Carolinians and Creeks, and at length slain by their conquerors, and their bones intombed in these heaps of earth and shells. I observed here the ravages of the common grey catterpillar, so destructive to forest and fruit trees, in Pennsylvania, and through the northern states, by stripping them of their leaves, in the spring, while young and tender (Phalena periodica.)

Mr. Egan having business of importance to transact in St. Augustine, pressed me to continue with him, a few days, when he would accompany me to that place, and if I chose, I should have a passage, as far as the Cow-ford, on St. Johns, where he would procure me a boat to prosecute my voyage.

It may be a subject worthy of some inquiry, why those fine islands, on the coast of Georgia, are so thinly inhabited; though perhaps Amelia may in some degree plead an exemption, as it is a very fertile island, on the north border of East Florida, and at the Capes of St. Mary, the finest harbour in this new colony. If I should give my opinion, the following seem to be the most probable reasons: the greatest part of these are as yet the property of a few wealthy planters, who having their residence on the continent, where lands on the large rivers, as Savanna, Ogeeche, Altamaha, St. Ille and others, are of a nature and quality adapted to the growth of rice, which the planters chiefly rely upon, for obtaining ready cash, and purchasing family articles; they settle a few poor families on their in-[67]sular estates, who rear stocks of horned cattle, horses, swine and poultry, and protect the game for their proprietors. The inhabitants of these islands also lay open to the invasion and ravages of pirates, and in case of a war, to incursions from their enemies armed vessels, in which case they must either remove with their families and effects to the main, or be stripped of all their movables, and their houses laid in ruins.

The soil of these islands appears to be particularly favourable to the culture of indigo and cotton, and there are on them some few large plantations for the cultivation and manufacture of those valuable articles. The cotton is planted only by the poorer class of people, just enough for their family consumption: they plant two species of it, the annual and West-Indian; the former is low, and planted every year; the balls of this are very large, and the phlox long, strong, and perfectly white; the West-Indian is a tall perennial plant, the stalk somewhat shrubby, several of which rise up from the root for several years successively, the stems of the former year being killed by the winter frosts. The balls of this latter species are not quite so large as those of the herbaceous cotton; but the phlox, or wool, is long, extremely fine, silky, and white. A plantation of this kind will last several years, with moderate labour and care, whereas the annual sort is planted every year.

The coasts, sounds, and inlets, environing these islands, abound with a variety of excellent fish, particularly Rock, Bass, Drum, Mullet, Sheepshead, Whiting, Grooper, Flounder, Sea-Trout, [this last seems to be a species of Cod] Skate, Skipjack, Stingray, the Shark, and great Black Sting-[68]ray, are insatiable cannibals, and very troublesome to the fishermen. The bays and lagoons are stored with oysters and varieties of other shell-fish, crabs, shrimp, &c. The clams, in particular, are large, their meat white, tender, and delicate.

There is a large space betwixt this chain of sea-coast-islands and the main land, perhaps generally near three leagues in breadth; but all this space is not covered with water: I estimate nearly two thirds of it to consist of low salt plains, which produce Barilla, Sedge, Rushes, &c. and which border on the main land, and the western coasts of the islands. The east side of these islands are, for the most part, clean, hard, sandy beaches, exposed to the wash of the ocean. Between these islands are the mouths or entrances of some rivers, which run down from the continent, winding about through these low salt marshes, and delivering their waters into the sounds, which are very extensive capacious harbours, from three to five and six to eight miles over, and communicate with each other by parallel salt rivers, or passes, that flow into the sound: they afford an extensive and secure inland navigation for most craft, such as large schooners, sloops, pettiaugers, boats, and canoes; and this inland communication of waters extends along the sea coast with but few and short interruptions, from the bay of Chesapeak, in Virginia, to the Missisippi, and how much farther I know not, perhaps as far as Vera Cruz. Whether this chain of sea-coast-islands is a step, or advance, which this part of our continent is now making on the Atlantic ocean, we must leave to future ages to determine. But it seems evident, even to demonstration, that those salt marshes adjoining the coast of the main, and the reedy and grassy islands and marshes in the rivers, which are now overflowed at [69] every tide, were formerly high swamps of firm land, affording forests of Cypress, Tupilo, Magnolia grandiflora, Oak, Ash, Sweet Bay, and other timber trees, the same as are now growing on the river swamps, whose surface is two feet or more above the spring tides that flow at this day; and it is plainly to be seen, by every planter along the coast of Carolina, Georgia, and Florida, to the Missisippi, when they bank in these grassy tide marshes for cultivation, that they cannot sink their drains above three or four feet below the surface, before they come to strata of Cypress stumps and other trees, as close together as they now grow in the swamps.

CHAP. III.

BEING now in readiness to prosecute our voyage to St. John's, we set sail in a handsome pleasure-boat, manned with four stout negro slaves, to row in case of necessity. After passing Amelia Narrows, we had a pleasant run, across Fort George's sound, where, observing the pelicans fishing, Mr. Egan shot one of them, which we took into the boat. I was greatly surprised on observing the pouch or sack, which hangs under the bill: it is capable of being expanded to a prodigious size. One of the people on board, said, that he had seen more than half a bushel of bran, crammed into one of their pouches. The body is larger than that of a tame goose, the legs extremely short, the feet webbed, the bill of a great length, bent inwards like a scythe, the wings extend near seven feet from tip to tip, the tail is very short, the head, neck and breast, nearly white, the body of a light bluish grey, except the quill feathers of the wings, which are black. They seem to be of the gull kind, both in form and structure, as well as manner of fishing. The evening following, we landed on the main. It was a promontory of high land, covered with orange-trees, and projecting into the sound, forming a convenient port. We pitched our tent under the shelter of a forest of Live Oaks, Palms and Sweet Bays; and having in the course of the day, procured plenty of sea fowl, such as curlews, willets, snipes, sand birds and others; we had them dressed for supper, and seasoned with excellent oysters, which lay in heaps in the water, close to our landing place. [71] The shrub Capsicum growing here in abundance, afforded us a very good pepper: we drank of a well of fresh water just at hand, amidst a grove of Myrtles (Myrica carefera.) Our repose however was incompleat, from the stings of musquetoes, the roaring of crocadiles, and the continual noise and restlessness of the sea fowl, thousands of them having their roosting-places very near us, particularly loons of various species, herons, pelicans, Spanish curlews, &c. all promiscuously lodging together, and in such incredible numbers, that the trees were entirely covered. They roost in inaccessible islets in the salt marshes, surrounded by lagoons, and shallow water. Just without the trees, betwixt them, the water and marshes, is a barricade of Palmetto royal (Yucca gloriosa) or Adam's needle, which grows so thick together, that a rat, or bird, can scarcely pass thro' them; and the stiff leaves of this Sword plant, standing nearly horizontally, are as impenetrable to man, or any other animal, as if they were a regiment of grenadiers with their bayonets pointed at you. The Palmetto royal is, however, a very singular and beautiful production. It may be termed a tree, from its durability and magnitude, as likewise from the ligneous quality of its stem, or trunk, when old; yet from its form and texture, I should be inclined to rank it amongst the herbaceous plants, for even the glorious Palm, although it rises to the altitude of a tree, and even transcends most of them, yet it bears the characters of the herbaceous ones: and this, like the Palm tree, rises with a strait, erect stem, about ten or twelve feet high, crowned with a beautiful chaplet of sword or dagger-like leaves, of a perfect green colour, each terminated with a stiff, sharp spur, and their edges finely crenated. This thorny crown is crested with a pyramid of sil-[72]ver white flowers, each resembling a tulip or lilly. These flowers are succeeded by a large fruit, nearly of the form and size of a slender cucumber, and when ripe, is of a deep purple colour, the skin smooth and shining, its pulp soft, very juicy, and of an agreeable aromatic flavour but rather bitter to the taste; it is, however, frequently eaten, but if eaten to excess, proves violently purgative. The seeds are numerous, flat and lunated.

The plant, or tree, when grown old, sometimes divides into two or three stems, which seem of equal height and thickness, and indeed nearly of the same thickness with the main stem; but generally, when they arrive to this age and magnitude, their own weight brings them to the ground, where they soon decay, the heart or pith first, leaving a hollow fibrous reticulated trunk or sleeve, which likewise soon after decays, and in fine, all is again reduced to its original earth, and replaces the vegetative mould. But the deceased are soon replaced by others, as there are younger ones of all ages and stature, ready to succeed their predecessors, and flourish for a time, with the same regal pomp and splendor. These plants are so multitudinous, where-ever they get a footing, that the earth is completely occupied with them, and scarcely any other vegetable is to be seen, where they are; yet they are sometimes scattered amongst other trees and vegetables.

In three days after leaving Amelia, we arrived at the Cow-ford, a public ferry, over St. Johns, about thirty miles above the bar or capes, the river here being above a mile wide.

Mr. Egan, after procuring a neat little sail-boat [73] for me, at a large Indigo plantation near the ferry, and for which I paid three guineas, departed for St. Augustine, which is on the sea-coast, about forty-five miles over land.

It was now about the middle of April, vegetation appearing every
where in high progress, I was anxious to be advancing southerly; and
having at this plantation, stored myself with necessaries for my voyage,
I sailed in the morning, with a fair wind. I was now again alone, for
the young man my fellow traveller, though stouter and heartier than
myself, having repented of his promise to accompany me, to the Indian
trading houses, I suppose not relishing the hardships and dangers,
which might perhaps befall us, chose rather to stay behind, amongst
the settlements. His leaving me, however, I did not greatly regret, as
I could not consider it a disappointment much to my disadvantage at
the moment. Our views were probably totally opposite; he, a young
mechanic on his adventures, seemed to be actuated by no other motives, than either to establish himself, in some well inhabited part of
the country, where, by following his occupation, he might be enabled
to procure without much toil and danger, the necessaries and conveniences of life; or by industry and frugality, perhaps establish his
fortune. Whilst I, continually impelled by a restless spirit of curiosity,
in pursuit of new productions of nature, my chief happiness consisted
in tracing and admiring the infinite power, majesty and perfection of
the great Almighty Creator, and in the contemplation, that through
divine aid and permission, I might be instrumental in discovering, and
introducing into my native country, some original [74] productions
of nature, which might become useful to society. Each of our pursuits,
were perhaps equally laudable; and upon this supposition, I was quite
willing to part with him upon amicable terms.

My little vessel being furnished with a good sail, and having fishing tackle, a neat light fusee, powder and ball, I found myself well
equipped, for my voyage, about one hundred miles to the trading
house.

I crossed the river to a high promontory of wood-land, on the west
shore, and being struck with the magnificence of a venerable grove of
Live Oak, Palms and Laurel (Magnolia grandiflora) I stepped on
shore to take a view of the place. Orange trees were in full bloom, and
filled the air with fragrance.

It was now past noon, and this place being about eight miles above
the Cow-ford, and the river near three miles in breadth, I wanted to
reach a plantation in sight, on the opposite shore, in order to get some
repairs, my vessel having sustained some damage from the violence of
the wind, in crossing over. I arrived late in the evening, and finding a
convenient landing place and harbour, I concluded to remain here till
morning, and then coast it, close along shore to the plantation.

It beginning to thunder, I was sufficiently warned to prepare against a wet night, and observing a very large Oak tree, which had been thrown down, by a hurricane and offered me a convenient shelter, as its enormous limbs bore up the trunk, a sufficient height from the earth, to admit me to sit or lie down under it, I spread my sail, slanting from the trunk of the tree, to the ground, on the [75] windward side; and having collected a quantity of wood, sufficient to keep up a fire, during the night, I struck one up in front, and spreading skins on the ground, and upon these placing a blanket, one half I laid down upon, turning the other over me for a covering.

The storm came up, with a furious wind and tremendous thunder and lightning, from the opposite N. W. coast, but luckily for me, little rain fell, and I rested very well. But as the wind next morning blew very fresh, right in upon the shore, there was no possibility of moving, with safety, from my present situation. I however arose to reconnoitre the ground, round about my habitation, being roused by the report of a musquet not far off. I had not left sight of my encampment, following a winding path through a grove of Live Oak, Laurel (Magn. grandiflora) and Sapindus, before an Indian stepped out of a thicket and crossed the path just before me, having a large turkey cock, flung across his shoulders, he saw me and stepping up and smiling, spoke to me in English, bidding me good-morning. I saluted him with "Its well brother," led him to my camp, and treated him with a dram. This friendly Indian informed me that he lived at the next plantation, employed as a hunter, I asked him how far it was to the house; he answered about half a mile by land, and invited me to go there, telling me that his master was a very good, kind man, and would be glad to see me. I replied, that I would, if my boat and effects in the mean time could be safe, he said that he would immediately return to the house, and acquaint his master of it, who would send trusty Negroes to bring my vessel [76] round the point, to the landing, I thanked him for his civility, and not willing to be troublesome, I told him I would leave my boat, and follow after him; so taking my fusee on my shoulder, and after dragging my bark as high up on shore as I could, I followed the Indian, and soon reached the house.

The gentleman received me, in the most polite manner, and after hearing my situation, he requested me to make my abode with him, a few days, to rest and refresh myself. I thanked him and told him I would stay a day. He immediately sent slaves who brought my boat round, and having carpenters at work, on a new building, he sat them about repairing my vessel, which by night was completely refitted.

I spent the day in the most agreeable manner, in the society of this man of singular worth, he led me over his extensive improvements, and we returned in company with several of his neighbours. In the afternoon the most sultry time of the day, we retired to the fragrant shades of an Orange grove. The house was situated on an eminence, about one hundred and fifty yards, from the river. On the right hand was the Orangery, consisting of many hundred trees, natives of the place, and left standing, when the ground about it was cleared. These trees were large, flourishing and in perfect bloom, and loaded with their ripe golden fruit. On the other side was a spacious garden, occupying a regular slope of ground, down to the water; and a pleasant lawn lay between. Here were large plantations of the Indigo plant, which appeared in a very thriving condition: it was then about five or six inches high, growing in streight parallel rows, about eighteen inches apart. The [77] Corn (Zea) and Potatoes (Convolv. Batata) were greatly advanced in growth, and promised a plentiful crop. The Indigo made in East Florida is esteemed almost equal to the best Spanish, especially that sort, which they call Flora. Mr. Marshall presented me, with a specimen of his own manufacture, at this plantation: it was very little, if any inferior; to the best Prussian blue.

In the morning following, intimating my intentions of proceeding on my voyage, Mr. Marshall, again importuned me to stay, but I obtained his consent to depart, on my promising to visit him, at my return to Georgia. After breakfast I therefore took my leave, attended to the shore, by several slaves, loaded with ammunition and provisions, which my friend had provided for me. On my expressing some difficulty in receiving so large a share of his bounty, he civilly replied, that it was too little to mention, and that, if I had continued with him a day or two longer, he should have had time to have served me in a much better manner.

Taking my leave of Mr. Marshall, I again embarked alone on board my little vessel, and blessed with a favourable steady gale, I set sail. The day was extremely pleasant, the late thunder storm had purified the air, by disuniting and dissipating the noxious vapours. The falling of heavy showers, with thunder and brisk winds, from the cool regions of the N. W. contributes greatly towards restoring the salubrity of the air, and purity of the waters, by precipitating the putrescent scum, that rises from the bottom, and floats upon the surface, near the shores of the rivers, in these southern climates, during the hot seasons. The [78] shores of this great river St. Juan, are very level and shoal, extending in some places, a mile or two, into the river, betwixt the high land, and the clear waters of the river, which is so level, as to be covered not above a foot or two deep, with water, and at a little distance appears as a green meadow having water-grass and other amphibious vegetables, growing in the oozy bottom, and floating upon the water.

Having a lively leading breeze, I kept as near the East shore, as possible, often surprised by the plunging of alligators, and greatly delighted with the pleasing prospect of cultivation, and the encrease of human industry, which frequently struck my view from the elevated, distant shores.

At night I ran in shore, at a convenient harbour, where I was received and welcomed by the gentleman, who was agent for the plantation, and at whose pleasant habitation, near the harbour, I took up my quarters for the night.

This very civil man, happened to be a person with whom I had formerly been acquainted in St. Augustine; and as he lived about twenty miles distant from it, I had good reason to expect that he would be a proper person, to obtain intelligence from, concerning the disturbances, which were thought still to subsist, between the Lower Creeks and the white inhabitants of East Florida. Upon enquiry, and conversation with him, I found my conjectures on that head, to have been well founded. My friend informed me, that there had, but a few days since, been a counsel held at St. Augustine, between the governor of East Florida, and the chiefs of the Lower Creeks. They had been delegated by their [79] towns, to make enquiry, concerning the late alarm and depredations, committed by the Indians upon the traders, which the nation being apprised of, recommended these deputies to be chosen and sent, as soon as possible, in order to make reasonable concessions, before the flame, already kindled, should spread into a general war. The parties accordingly met in St. Augustine, and the affair was amicably adjusted, to the satisfaction of both parties. The chiefs of the delinquent bands, whose young warriors had committed the mischief, promised to indemnify the traders for the loss of their goods, and requested that they might return to their store-houses, with goods as usual, and that they should be safe in their persons and property, The traders at this time, were actually preparing to return. It appeared upon a strict investigation of facts, that the affair had taken its rise from the licentious conduct of a few vagrant young hunters of the Siminole nation, who, imagining themselves to have been ill treated, in their dealings, with the traders (which by the bye was likely enough to be true) took this violent method of doing themselves justice. The culprits however endeavoured to exculpate themselves, by asserting, that they had no design or intention of robbing the traders of their effects, but meant it only as a threat, and that the traders, from a conciousness of their dishonesty, had been terrified and fled, leaving their stores, which they took possession of, to prevent their being totally lost.

This troublesome affair being adjusted, was very agreeable news to me, as I could now, without apprehensions, ascend this grand river, and visit its delightful shores, where, and when I pleased.

Bidding adieu to my obliging friend, I spread my sail to the favourable breeze, and by noon, came to [80] a-breast of fort Picolata, where, being desirous of gaining yet farther intelligence, I landed, but to my disappointment, found the fort dismantled and deserted. This fortress is very ancient, and was built by the Spaniards. It is a square tower, thirty feet high, invested with a high wall, without bastions, about breast high, pierced with loop holes and surrounded with a deep ditch. The upper story is open on each side, with battlements, supporting a cupola or roof: these battlements were formerly mounted with eight four pounders, two on each side.

The works are constructed with hewn stone, cemeted with lime. The stone was cut out of quarries, on St. Anastatius Island, opposite St. Augustine: it is of a pale reddish brick colour, and a testacious composition, consisting of small fragments of sea-shells and fine sand. It is well adapted to the constructing of fortifications. It lies in horizontal masses in the quarry, and constitutes the foundation of that island. The castle at St. Augustine, and most of the buildings of the town, are of this stone.

Leaving Picolata, I continued to ascend the river. I observed this day, during my progress up the river, incredible numbers of small flying insects, of the genus, termed by naturalists, Ephemera, continually emerging from the shallow water, near shore, some of them immediately taking their flight to the land, whilst myriads, crept up the grass and herbage, where remaining, for a short time, as they acquired sufficient strength, they took their flight also, following their kindred, to the main land. This resurrection from the deep, if I may so express it, commences early in the morning, and ceases after the sun is up. At evening they are seen in [81] clouds of innumerable millions, swarming and wantoning in the still air, gradually drawing near the river, descend upon its surface, and there quickly end their day, after committing their eggs to the deep; which being for a little while tossed about, enveloped in a viscid scum, are hatched, and the little Larvae descend into their secure and dark habitation, in the oozy bed beneath, where they remain, gradually increasing in size, until the returning spring; they then change to a Nymph, when the genial heat brings them, as it were, into existence, and they again arise into the world. This fly seems to be delicious food for birds, frogs and fish. In the morning, when they arise, and in the evening, when they return, the tumult is great indeed, and the surface of the water along shore broken into bubbles, or spirted into the air, by the contending aquatic tribes, and such is the avidity of the fish and frogs, that they spring into the air, after this delicious prey.

Early in the evening, after a pleasant days voyage, I made a convenient and safe harbour, in a little lagoon, under an elevated bank, on the West shore of the river, where I shall intreat the reader's patience, whilst we behold the closing scene of the short-lived Ephemera, and communicate to each other the reflections which so singular an exhibition might rationally suggest to an inquisitive mind. Our place of observation is happily situated, under the protecting shade of majestic Live Oaks, glorious Magnolias and the fragrant Orange, open to the view of the great river, and still waters of the lagoon just before us.

At the cool eves approach, the sweet enchanting [82] melody of the feathered songsters gradually ceases, and they betake themselves to their leafy coverts for security and repose.

Solemnly and slowly move onward, to the river's shore, the rustling clouds of the Ephemera. How awful the procession! innumerable millions of winged beings, voluntarily verging on to destruction, to the brink of the grave, where they behold bands of their enemies with wide open jaws, ready to receive them. But as if insensible of their danger, gay and tranquil each meets his beloved mate, in the still air, inimitably bedecked in their new nuptial robes. What eye can trace them, in their varied wanton amorous chaces, bounding and fluttering on the odoriferous air? with what peace, love and joy, do they end the last moments of their existence?

I think we may assert, without any fear of exaggeration, that there are annually of these beautiful winged beings, which rise into existence, and for a few moments take a transient view of the glory of the Creator's works, a number greater than the whole race of mankind that have ever existed since the creation; and that only, from the shores of this river. How many then must have been produced since the creation, when we consider the number of large rivers in America, in comparison with which, this river is but a brook or rivulet.

The importance of the existence of these beautiful and delicately formed little creatures, in the creation, whose frame and organization is equally wonderful, more delicate, and perhaps as complicated as that of the most perfect human being, is well worth a few moments contemplation; I mean par [83]ticularly when they appear in the fly state. And if we consider the very short period, of that stage of existence, which we may reasonably suppose, to be the only space of their life that admits of pleasure and enjoyment, what a lesson doth it not afford us of the vanity of our own pursuits.

Their whole existence in this world, is but one compleat year, and at least three hundred and sixty days of that time, they are in the form of an ugly grub, buried in mud, eighteen inches under water, and in this condition scarcely locomotive, as each Larva or grub, has but its own narrow solitary cell, from which it never travels, or moves, but in a perpendicular progression, of a few inches, up and down, from the bottom to the surface of the mud, in order to intercept the passing atoms for its food, and get a momentary respiration of fresh air; and even here it must be perpetually on its guard, in order to escape the troops of fish and shrimps, watching to catch it, and from whom it has no escape, but by instantly retreating back into its cell. One would be apt almost to imagine them created merely for the food of fish and other animals.

Having rested very well during the night, I was awakened in the morning early, by the cheering converse of the wild turkey-cock (Meleagris occidentalis) saluting each other, from the sun-brightened tops of the lofty Cupressus disticha and Magnolia grandiflora. They begin at early dawn, and continue till sun rise, from March to the last of April. The high forests ring with the noise, like the crowing of the domestic cock, of these social centinels, the watch-word being caught and repeated, from one to another, for hundreds of miles [84] around; insomuch that the whole country, is for an hour or more, in an universal shout. A little after sun-rise, their crowing gradually ceases, they quit their high lodging places, and alight on the earth, where, expanding their silver bordered train, they strut and dance round about the coy female, while the deep forests seem to tremble with their shrill noise.

This morning the winds on the great river, were high and against me, I was therefore obliged to keep in port, a great part of the day, which I employed in little excursions round about my encampment. The Live Oaks are of an astonishing magnitude, and one tree contains a prodigious quantity of timber, yet comparatively, they are not tall, even in these forests, where growing on strong land, in company with others of great altitude (such as Fagus sylvatica, Liquid-amber, Magnolia grandiflora, and the high Palm tree) they strive while young to be upon an equality with their neighbours, and to enjoy the influence of the sun-beams, and of the pure animating air; but the others at last prevail, and their proud heads are seen at a great distance, towering far above the rest of the forest, which consists chiefly of this species of oak, Fraxinus, Ulmus, Acer rubrum, Laurus Borbonia, Quercus dentata, Ilex aquifolium, Olea Americana, Morus, Gleditsia triacanthus, and I believe a species of Sapindus. But the latter spreads abroad his brawny arms, to a great distance. The trunk of the Live Oak is generally from twelve to eighteen feet in girt, and rises ten or twelve feet erect from the earth; some I have seen eighteen or twenty; then divides itself into three, four, or five great limbs, [85] which continue to grow in nearly an horizontal direction, each limb forming a gentle curve, or arch, from its base to its extremity. I have stepped above fifty paces, on a strait line, from the trunk of one of these trees, to the extremity of the limbs. They are ever green, and the wood almost incorruptible, even in the open air. It bears a prodigious quantity of fruit; the acorn is small, but sweet and agreeable to the taste when roasted, and is food for almost all animals. The Indians obtain from it a sweet oil, which they use in the cooking of hommony, rice, &c. and they also roast them in hot embers, eating them as we do chesnuts.

The wind being fair in the evening, I set sail again, and crossing the river, made a good harbour on the East shore, where I pitched my tent for the night. The bank of the river was about twelve or fifteen feet perpendicular, from its surface, but the ascent gentle. Although I arrived here early in the evening, I found sufficient attractions to choose it for my lodging-place, and an ample field for botanical employment. It was a high, airy situation, and commanded an extensive and varied prospect of the river and its shores, up and down.

Behold yon promontory, projecting far into the great river, beyond the still lagoon, half a mile distance from me, what a magnificent grove arises on its banks! how glorious the Palm! how majestically stands the Laurel, its head forming a perfect cone! its dark green foliage, seems silvered over with milk-white flowers. They are so large, as to be distinctly visible at the distance of a mile or more. The Laurel Magnolia, which grows on this river is the most beautiful and tall, that I have any where seen, unless we except those, which stand [86] on the banks of the Missisippi; yet even these must yield, to those of St. Juan, in neatness of form, beauty of foliage, and I think, in largeness and fragrance of flower. Their usual height is about one hundred feet, and some greatly exceed that. The trunk is perfectly erect, rising in the form of a beautiful column, and supporting a head like an obtuse cone. The flowers are on the extremities of the subdivisions of the branches, in the center of a coronet of dark green, shining, ovate pointed entire leaves: they are large, perfectly white, and expanded like a full blown Rose. They are polypetalous, consisting of fifteen, twenty, or twenty-five petals: these are of a thick coriaceous texture, and deeply concave, their edges being somewhat reflex, when mature. In the center stands the young cone, which is large, of a flesh colour, and elegantly studded with a gold coloured stigma; that by the end of summer, is greatly enlarged, and in the autumn ripens to a large crimson cone or strobile, disclosing multitudes of large coral red berries, which for a time hang down from them, suspended by a fine, white silky thread, four, six to nine inches in length. The flowers of this tree are the largest, and most compleat of any yet known: when fully expanded they are of six, eight and nine inches diameter. The pericarpium and berries, possess an agreeable spicy scent, and an aromatic bitter taste. The wood when seasoned is of a straw colour, compact, and harder and firmer than that of the Poplar.

It is really astonishing to behold the Grape-Vines in this place. From their bulk and strength, one would imagine, they were combined to pull down these mighty trees, to the earth, when in fact, a-[87]mongst other good purposes, they serve to uphold them: they are frequently nine, ten, and twelve inches in diameter, and twine round the trunks of the trees, climb to their very tops, and then spread along their limbs, from tree to tree, throughout the forest; the fruit is but small and ill tasted. The Grape vines with the Rhamnus volubilis, Bignonia radicans, Bignonia crucigera, and another rambling shrubby vine, which seems allied to the Rhamnus, perhaps Zizyphus scandens, seem to tie the trees together, with garlands and festoons, and form enchanting shades. The long moss, so called, (Tillandsea usneascites) is a singular and surprising vegetable production: it grows from the limbs and twigs of all trees in these southern regions, from N. lat. 35 down as far as 28, and I believe every where within the tropics. Wherever it fixes itself, on a limb, or branch, it spreads into short and intricate divarications; these in time collect dust, wafted by the wind, and which, probably by the moisture it absorbs, softens the bark and sappy part of the tree, about the roots of the plant, and renders it more fit for it to establish itself; and from this small beginning, it encreases, by sending downwards and obliquely, on all sides, long pendant branches, which divide and subdivide themselves ad infinitum. It is common to find the spaces, betwixt the limbs of large trees, almost occupied by this plant; it also hangs waving in the wind, like streamers, from the lower limbs, to the length of fifteen or twenty feet, and of bulk and weight, more than several men together could carry; and in some places, cart loads of it are lying on the ground, torn off, by the violence of the wind. Any part of the living plant, torn off and caught, in the limbs of a tree, will presently take root, [88] grow and encrease, in the same degree of perfection, as if it had sprung up from the seed.

When fresh, cattle and deer will eat it in the winter season. It seems particularly adapted to the purpose of stuffing mattresses, chairs, saddles, collars, &c. and for these purposes, nothing yet known equals it. The Spaniards in South America, and the West-Indies, work it into cables that are said to be very strong and durable; but, in order to render it useful, it ought to be thrown into shallow ponds of water, and exposed to the sun, where it soon rots, and the outside furry substance is dissolved. It is then taken out of the water, and spread to dry; when, after a little beating and shaking, it is sufficiently clean, nothing remaining but the interior, hard, black, elastic filament, entangled together, and greatly resembling horse-hair.

The Zanthoxilum clava Herculis also grows here. It is a beautiful spreading tree, and much like a well grown apple tree. Its aromatic berry is delicious food for the little turtle dove; and epicures say that it gives their flesh a fine flavor.

Having finished my observations, I betook myself to rest; and when the plunging and roaring of the crocodiles, and the croaking of the frogs, had ceased, I slept very well during the remainder of the night, as a breeze from the river had scattered the clouds of musquitoes that at first infested me.

It being a fine cool morning, and fair wind, I set sail early, and saw, this day, vast quantities of the Pistia stratiotes, a very singular aquatic plant. It associates in large communities, or floating islands, some of them a quarter of a mile in extent, and are impelled to and fro, as the wind and [89] current may direct. They are first produced on, or close to the shore, in eddy water, where they gradually spread themselves into the river, forming most delightful green plains, several miles in length, and in some places a quarter of a mile in breadth. These plants are nourished and kept in their proper horizontal situation, by means of long fibrous roots, which descend from the nether center, downwards, towards the muddy bottom. Each plant, when full grown, bears a general resemblance to a well grown plant of garden lettice, though the leaves are more nervous, of a firmer contexture, and of a full green colour, inclining to yellow. It vegetates on the surface of the still stagnant water, and in its natural situation, is propagated from seed only. In great storms of wind and rain, when the river is suddenly raised, large masses of these floating plains are broken loose, and driven from the shores, into the wide water, where they have the appearance of islets, and float about, until broken to pieces by the winds and waves; or driven again to shore, on some distant coast of the river, where they again find footing, and there, forming new colonies, spread and extend themselves again, until again broken up and dispersed as before. These

floating islands present a very entertaining prospect; for although we
behold an assemblage of the primary productions of nature only, yet
the imagination seems to remain in suspence and doubt; as in order
to enliven the delusion and form a most picturesque appearance, we
see not only flowery plants, clumps of shrubs, old weather-beaten trees,
hoary and barbed, with the long moss waving from their snags, but
we also see them compleatly inhabited, and alive, with crocodiles,
serpents, frogs, ot-[90]ters, crows, herons, curlews, jackdaws, &c. there
seems, in short, nothing wanted but the appearance of a wigwam and
a canoe to complete the scene.

Keeping along the West or Indian shore, I saw basking, on the
sedgy banks, numbers of alligators*, some of them of an enormous size.

The high forests on this coast, now wore a grand and sublime appearance, the earth rising gradually, from the river Westward, by easy
swelling ridges, behind one another, and lifted the distant groves up
into the skies. The trees are of the lofty kind, as the grand Laurel
Magnolia, Palm elata, Liquid-amber styraciflua, Fagus sylvatica,
Querci, Juglans hiccory, Fraxinus, and others.

On my doubling a long point of land, the river appeared surprisingly
widened, forming a large bay, of an oval form, and several miles in
extent. On the West side it was bordered round with low marshes, and
invested with a swamp of Cypress, the trees so lofty, as to preclude the
sight of the high-land forests, beyond them; and these trees, having
flat tops, and all of equal height, seemed to be a green plain, lifted up
and supported upon columns in the air, round the West side of the bay.

The Cupressus disticha stands in the first order of North American
trees. Its majestic stature is surprising, and on approaching them, we
are struck with a kind of awe, at beholding the stateliness of the trunk,
lifting its cumbrous top towards the skies, and casting a wide shade
upon the ground, as a dark intervening cloud, which, for a time, pre-
cludes [91] the rays of the sun. The delicacy of its colour, and texture
of its leaves, exceed every thing in vegetation. It generally grows in the
water, or in low flat lands, near the banks of great rivers and lakes,
that are covered, great part of the year, with two or three feet
depth of water, and that part of the trunk, which is subject to be
under water, and four or five feet higher up, is greatly enlarged,
by prodigious buttresses, or pilasters, which, in full grown trees, project
out on every side, to such a distance, that several men might easily
hide themselves in the hollows between. Each pilaster terminates under
ground, in a very large, strong, serpentine root, which strikes off, and

---

* I have made use of the terms alligator and crocodile indiscriminately for this
animal, alligator being the country name.

branches every way, just under the surface of the earth; and from these roots grow woody cones, called cypress knees, four, five, and six feet high, and from six to eighteen inches and two feet in diameter at their bases. The large ones are hollow, and serve very well for bee-hives; a small space of the tree itself is hollow, nearly as high as the buttresses already mentioned. From this place the tree, as it were, takes another beginning, forming a grand strait column eighty or ninety feet high, when it divides every way around into an extensive flat horizontal top, like an umbrella, where eagles have their secure nests, and cranes and storks their temporary resting places; and what adds to the magnificence of their appearance, is the streamers of long moss that hang from the lofty limbs and float in the winds. This is their majestic appearance, when standing alone, in large rice plantations, or thinly planted on the banks of great rivers.

Paroquets are commonly seen hovering and fluttering on their tops: they delight to shell the [92] balls, its seed being their favourite food. The trunks of these trees when hollowed out, make large and durable pettiaugers and canoes, and afford excellent shingles, boards, and other timber, adapted to every purpose in frame buildings. When the planters fell these mighty trees, they raise a stage round them, as high as to reach above the buttresses; on this stage, eight or ten negroes ascend with their axes, and fall to work round its trunk. I have seen trunks of these trees that would measure eight, ten, and twelve feet in diameter, for forty and fifty feet strait shaft.

As I continued coasting the Indian shore of this bay, on doubling a promontory, I suddenly saw before me an Indian settlement, or village. It was a fine situation, the bank rising gradually from the water. There were eight or ten habitations, in a row, or street, fronting the water, and about fifty yards distance from it. Some of the youth were naked, up to their hips in the water, fishing with rods and lines, whilst others, younger, were diverting themselves in shooting frogs with bows and arrows. On my near approach, the little children took to their heels, and ran to some women, who were hoeing corn; but the stouter youth stood their ground, and, smiling, called to me. As I passed along, I observed some elderly people reclined on skins spread on the ground, under the cool shade of spreading Oaks and Palms, that were ranged in front of their houses; they arose, and eyed me as I passed, but perceiving that I kept on, without stopping, they resumed their former position. They were civil, and appeared happy in their situation.

There was a large Orange grove at the upper [93] end of their village; the trees were large, carefully pruned, and the ground under them clean, open, and airy. There seemed to be several hundred acres of cleared land, about the village; a considerable portion of which was planted, chiefly with corn (Zea) Batatas, Beans, Pompions, Squashes, (Cucurbita verrucosa) Melons (Cucurbita citrullus) Tobacco (Nicotiana) &c. abundantly sufficient for the inhabitants of the village.

After leaving this village, and coasting a considerable cove of the lake, I perceived the river before me much contracted within its late bounds, but still retaining the appearance of a wide and deep river, both coasts bordered, for several miles, with rich deep swamps, well timbered with Cypress, Ash, Elm, Oak, Hiccory, Scarlet Maple, Nyssa aquatica, Nyssa tupilo, Gordonia lasianthus, Corypha palma, Corypha pumila, Laurus Borbonia, &c. The river gradually narrowing, I came in sight of Charlotia, where it is not above half a mile wide, but deep; and as there was a considerable current against me, I came here to an anchor. This town was founded by Den. Rolle, Esq; and is situated on a high bluff, on the east coast, fifteen or twenty feet perpendicular from the river, and is in length half a mile, or more, upon its banks. The upper stratum of the earth consists entirely of several species of fresh water Cochlae, as Cochelix, Coch. labyrinthus, and Coch. voluta; the second, of marine shells, as Concha mytulus, Concostrea, Conc. peeton, Haliotis auris marina, Hal. patella, &c. mixed with sea sand; and the third, or lower stratum, which was a little above the common level of the river, was horizontal masses of a pretty hard rock, composed almost entirely of the above shell, generally whole, and lying in every direction, pe-[94]trified or cemented together, with fine white sand; and these rocks were bedded in a stratum of clay. I saw many fragments of the earthen ware of the ancient inhabitants, and bones of animals, amongst the shells, and mixed with the earth, to a great depth. This high shelly bank continues, by gentle parallel ridges, near a quarter of a mile back from the river, gradually diminishing to the level of the sandy plains, which widen before and on each side eastward, to a seemingly unlimited distance, and appear green and delightful, being covered with grass and the Corypha repens, and thinly planted with trees of the long leaved, or Broom Pine, and decorated with clumps, or coppices of floriferous, evergreen, and aromatic shrubs, and enamelled with patches of the beautiful little Kalmea ciliata. These shelly ridges have a vegetable surface of loose black mould, very fertile, and naturally produce Orange groves, Live Oak, Laurus Borbonia, Palma elata, Carica papaya, Sapindus, Liquid-amber, Fraxinus exelsior, Morus rubra, Ulmns, Tilia, Sambucus, Ptelea, Tallow-nut, or Wild Lime, and many others.

Mr. Rolle obtained from the crown, a grant of forty thousand acres of land, in any part of East Florida, where the land was unlocated. It seems his views were to take up his grant near St. Marks, in the bay of Aplatchi; and set sail from England, with about one hundred families, for that place; but by contrary winds, and stress of weather, he missed his aim, and being obliged to put into St. Juan's, he, with some of the principal of his adherents, ascended the river in a boat, and being struck with its majesty, the grand situations of its banks, and fertility of its lands, and at the same time, considering the extensive navigation of the [95] river, and its near vicinity to St. Augustine, the capital and seat of government, he altered his views on St. Marks, and suddenly determined on this place, where he landed his first little colony. But it seems from an ill concerted plan, in its infant establishment, negligence, or extreme parsimony, in sending proper recruits, and other necessaries, together with a bad choice of citizens, the settlement by degrees grew weeker, and at length totally fell to the ground. Those of them who escaped the constant contagious fevers, fled the dreaded place, betaking themselves for subsistence, to the more fruitful and populous regions of Georgia and Carolina.

The remaining old habitations, are mouldering to earth, except the mansion house, which is a large frame building, of Cypress wood, yet in tolerable repair, and inhabited by an overseer and his family. There is also a black-smith with his shop and family, at a small distance from it. The most valuable district belonging to Mr. Rolle's grant, lies on Dunn's lake, and on a little river, which runs from it into St. Juan. This district consists of a vast body of rich swamp land, fit for the growth of Rice, and some very excellent high land surrounding it. Large swamps of excellent rice land are also situated on the West shore of the river, opposite to Charlotia.

The aborigines of America, had a very great town in this place, as appears from the great tumuli, and conical mounts of earth and shells, and other traces of a settlement which yet remain. There grew in the old fields on these heights great quantities of Callicarpa and of the beautiful shrub Annona: the flowers of the latter are large, white and sweet scented.

[96] Having obtained from the people here, directions for discovering the little remote island, where the traders and their goods were secreted, which was about seven miles higher up, I set sail again, with a fair wind, and in about one hour and an half, arrived at the desired place, having fortunately taken the right channel of the river, amongst a multitude of others, occasioned by a number of low swampy islands. But I should have ran by the landing, if the centinels had not, by chance seen me drawing near them; and who perceiving that I was a

whiteman, ventured to hail me; upon which I immediately struck sail, and came too. Upon my landing they conducted me to their encampment, forty or fifty yards from the river, in an almost impenetrable thicket. Upon my inquiry, they confirmed the accounts of the amicable treaty at St. Augustine, and in consequence thereof, they had already removed great part of the goods, to the trading-house, which was a few miles higher up, on the Indian shore. They shewed me my chest, which had been carefully preserved, and upon inspection I found every thing in good order. Having learned from them, that all the effects would, in a few days time, be removed to the store-house, I bid adieu to them, and in a little time, arrived at the trading-house, where I was received with great politeness, and treated during a residence of several months, with the utmost civility and friendship, by Mr. C. M'Latche, Messrs. Spalding and Kelsall's agent.

The river almost from Charlotia, and for near twelve mile higher up is divided into many channels by a great number of islands.

HAVING rested myself a few days, and by ranging about the neighbouring plains and groves, surrounding this pleasant place, pretty well recovered my strength and spirits, I began to think of planning my future excursions, at a distance round about this center. I found from frequent conferences with Mr. M'Latche, that I might with safety, extend my journeys every way, and with prudence, even into the towns and settlements of the Indians, as they were perfectly reconciled to us, and sincerely wished for the renewal of our trade.

There were three trading-houses to be established this summer, each of which had its supplies from the store on St. Juan, where I now had my residence, and in which the produce or returns were to center annually, in order to be shipped for Savanna or Sunbury, and from thence to Europe.

One of these trading-houses was to be fixed about sixty miles higher up the river, from this place, by the name of Spalding's upper store; a second at Alachua, about fifty miles West from the river St. Juan; and a third at Talahasochte, a considerable town of the Siminoles, on the river Little St. Juan, near the bay of Apalachi, about one hundred and twenty miles distance. Each of these places I designed to visit, before the return of the vessel to Frederica, in the autumn, that I might avail myself of an opportunity so favourable, for transporting my collections so far on their way towards Charleston.

[98]   The company for Alachua, were to set off in about a month. That to Little St. Juan, in July, which suited me exceedingly well, as I might make my tour to the upper store directly, that part of the country being at this season, enrobed in her richest and gayest apparel.

About the middle of May, every thing being in readiness, to proceed up the river, we set sail. The traders with their goods in a large boat, went ahead, and myself in my little vessel followed them; and as their boat was large, and deeply laden, I found that I could easily keep up with them, and if I chose, out-sail them; but I preferred keeping them company, as well for the sake of collecting what I could from conversation, as on account of my safety in crossing the great lake, expecting to return alone, and descend the river at my own leisure.

We had a pleasant day, the wind fair and moderate, and ran by
Mount Hope, so named by my father John Bartram, when he ascended
this river, about fifteen years ago. It is a very high shelly bluff, upon
the little lake. It was at that time a fine Orange grove, but now cleared
and converted into a large Indigo plantation, the property of an English gentleman, under the care of an agent. In the evening we arrived
at Mount Royal, where we came to, and stayed all night: we were
treated with great civility, by a gentleman whose name was - - - - - - - -
Kean, and had been an Indian trader.

From this place we enjoyed a most enchanting prospect of the great
Lake George, through a grand avenue, if I may so term this narrow
reach of the river, which widens gradually for about two miles, [99]
towards its entrance into the lake, so as to elude the exact rules of
perspective and appears of an equal width.

At about fifty yards distance from the landing place, stands a magnificent Indian mount. About fifteen years ago I visited this place, at
which time there were no settlements of white people, but all appeared
wild and savage; yet in that uncultivated state, it possessed an almost
inexpressible air of grandeur, which was now entirely changed. At that
time there was a very considerable extent of old fields, round about
the mount; there was also a large Orange grove, together with Palms
and Live Oaks, extending from near the mount, along the banks, downwards, all of which has since been cleared away to make room for
planting ground. But what greatly contributed towards compleating
the magnificence of the scene, was a noble Indian highway, which led
from the great mount, on a strait line, three quarters of a mile, first
through a point or wing of the Orange grove, and continuing thence
through an awful forest, of Live Oaks, it was terminated by Palms
and Laurel Magnolias, on the verge of an oblong artificial lake, which
was on the edge of an extensive green level savanna. This grand highway was about fifty yards wide, sunk a little below the common level,
and the earth thrown up on each side, making a bank of about two
feet high. Neither nature nor art, could any where present a more
striking contrast, as you approach this savanna. The glittering water
pond, plays on the sight, through the dark grove, like a brilliant
diamond, on the bosom of the illumined savanna, bordered with various
flowery shrubs and plants; and as we advance into the plain, the [100]
sight is agreeably relieved by a distant view of the forests, which
partly environ the green expanse, on the left hand, whilst the imagination is still flattered and entertained by the far distant misty points of
the surrounding forests, which project into the plain, alternately appearing and disappearing, making a grand sweep round on the right,

to the distant banks of the great lake. But that venerable grove is now
no more. All has been cleared away and planted with Indigo, Corn
and Cotton, but since deserted: there was now scarcely five acres of
ground under fence. It appeared like a desart, to a great extent, and
terminated, on the land side, by frightful thickets, and open Pine
forests.

It appears however, that the late proprietor had some taste, as he
has preserved the mount, and this little adjoining grove inviolate. The
prospect from this station is so happily situated by nature, as to com-
prise at one view, the whole of the sublime and pleasing.

At the reanimating appearance of the rising sun, nature again re-
vives; and I obey the chearful summons of the gentle monitors of the
meads and groves.

Ye vigilant and faithful servants of the Most High! ye who worship
the Creator, morning, noon and eve, in simplicity of heart; I haste to
join the universal anthem. My heart and voice unite with yours, in
sincere homage to the great Creator, the universal sovereign.

O may I be permitted to approach the throne of mercy! may these
my humble and penitent supplications, amidst the universal shouts of
homage, from thy creatures, meet with thy acceptance.

[101]   And although, I am sensible, that my service, cannot encrease,
or diminish thy glory, yet it is pleasing to thy servant, to be permitted
to sound thy praise; for O sovereign Lord! we know that thou alone
art perfect, and worthy to be worshiped. O universal Father! look
down upon us we beseech thee, with an eye of pity and compassion,
and grant that universal peace and love, may prevail in the earth, even
that divine harmony, which fills the heavens, thy glorious habitation.

And O sovereign Lord! since it has pleased thee to endue man with
power, and pre-eminence, here on earth, and establish his dominion
over all creatures, may we look up to thee, that our understanding may
be so illuminated with wisdom and our hearts warmed and animated,
with a due sense of charity, that we may be enabled to do thy will,
and perform our duty towards those submitted to our service, and
protection, and be merciful to them even as we hope for mercy.

Thus may we be worthy of the dignity, and superiority of the high,
and distinguished station, in which thou hast placed us here on earth.

The morning being fair, and having a gentle favourable gale, we
left our pleasant harbour, in pursuit of our desired port.

Now as we approach the capes, behold the little ocean of Lake
George, the distant circular coast gradually rising to view, from his
misty fringed horizon. I cannot entirely suppress my apprehensions of
danger. My vessel at once diminished to a nut-shell, on the swelling

seas, and at the distance of a few miles, must appear to the surprised [102] observer, as some aquatic animal, at intervals emerging from its surface. This lake is a large and beautiful piece of water; it is a dilatation of the river St. Juan, and is about fifteen miles wide, and generally about fifteen or twenty feet deep, excepting at the entrance of the river, where lies a bar, which carries eight or nine feet water. The lake is beautified with two or three fertile islands. The first lies in the bay, as we ascend into the lake, near the West coast, about S. W. from Mount Royal, from whence it appears to form part of the West shore of the bay. The second island seems to ride on the lake before us as we enter, about a mile within it. This island is about two miles in breadth, and three quarters of a mile where broadest, mostly high land, well timbered, and fertile. The third and last, lies at the South end of the lake, and near the entrance of the river; it is nearly circular, and contains but a few acres of land, the earth high and fertile, and almost an entire Orange grove, with grand Magnolias and Palms.

Soon after entering the lake, the wind blew so briskly from the West, and thunder-clouds gathering upon the horizon, we were obliged to seek a shelter, from the approaching tempest, on the large beautiful island, before mentioned. Where, having gained the South promontory, we met with an excellent harbour, in which we continued the remaining part of the day and the night. This circumstance gave me an opportunity to explore the greatest part of it.

This island appears, from obvious vestiges, to have been once the chosen residence of an Indian prince, there being to this day, evident remains of [103] a large town of the Aborigines. It was situated on an eminence, near the banks of the lake, and commanded a comprehensive and charming prospect of the waters, islands, East and West shores of the lake, the capes, the bay and Mount Royal, and to the South the view is in a manner infinite, where the skies and waters seem to unite. On the site of this ancient town, stands a very pompous Indian mount, or conical pyramid of earth, from which runs in a strait line, a grand avenue or Indian highway, through a magnificent grove of Magnolias, Live Oaks, Palms and Orange trees, terminating at the verge of a large green level savanna. This island appears to have been well inhabited, as is very evident, from the quantities of fragments of Indian earthenware, bones of animals and other remains, particularly in the shelly heights and ridges, all over the island. There are no habitations at present on the island, but a great number of deer, turkeys, bears, wolves, wild cats, squirrels, racoons, and opossoms. The bears are invited here to partake of the fruit of the Orange tree, which they are immoderately fond of, and both they and turkeys are made extremely fat and delicious, from their feeding on the sweet acorns of the Live Oak.

There grows on this island, many curious shrubs, particularly a beautiful species of Lantana (perhaps Lant. camerara. Lin. Syst. Veget. p. 473.) It grows in coppices in old fields, about five or six feet high, the branches adorned with rough serrated leaves, which sit opposite, and the twigs terminate with umbelliferous tufts of orange coloured blossoms, which are succeeded by a cluster of small blue berries: the flowers are of various colours, on the same plant, and even in the same cluster. As [104] crimson, scarlet, orange and golden yellow: the whole plant is of a most agreeable scent. The orange flowered shrub Hibiscus is also conspicuously beautiful (perhaps Hibisc. spinifex of Linn.) it grows five or six feet high, and subramous. The branches are divergent, and furnished with cordated leaves, which are crenated. The flowers are of a moderate size, and of a deep splendid yellow. The pericarps are spiny. I also saw a new and beautiful palmated leaved convolvulus *. This Vine rambles over the shrubs, and strolls about on the ground, its leaves are elegantly sinuated, of a deep grass green, and sit on long petioles. The flowers are very large, infundibuliform, of a pale incarnate colour, having a deep crimson eye.

There are some rich swamps on the shores of the island, and these are verged on the outside with large marshes, covered entirely with tall grass, rushes, and herbaceous plants: amongst these are several species of Hibiscus, particularly the Hibiscus coccineus. This most stately of all herbaceous plants, grows ten or twelve feet high, branching regularly, so as to form a sharp cone. These branches also divide again, and are embellished with large expanded crimson flowers: I have seen this plant of the size and figure of a beautiful little tree, having at once several hundred of these splendid flowers, and which may be then seen at a great distance. They continue to flower in succession all summer and autumn, when the stems wither and decay; but the perennial root sends forth new stems the next spring, and so on for many years. Its leaves are large, deeply and elegantly sinuated, having six or seven very narrow dentated seg-[105]ments; the surface of the leaves, and of the whole plant, is smooth and polished. Another species of Hibiscus, worthy of particular notice, is likewise a tall flourishing plant; several strong stems arise from a root, five, six, and seven feet high, embellished with ovate lanceolate leaves, covered with a fine down on their nether surfaces: the flowers are very large, and of a deep incarnate colour.

The last we shall now mention seems nearly allied to the Alcea; the

* Convol. dissectus.

flowers are a size less than the Hibiscus, and of a fine damask rose colour, and are produced in great profusion on the tall pyramidal stems.

The Lobelia cardinalis grows in great plenty here, and has a most splendid appearance amidst extensive meadows of the golden Corymbous Jacobea (Senecio Jacobea) and odorous Pancratium.

Having finished my tour, on this princely island, I prepared for repose. A calm evening had succeeded the stormy day. The late tumultuous winds had now ceased, the face of the lake had become placid, and the skies serene; the balmy winds breathed the animating odours of the groves around me; and as I reclined on the elevated banks of the lake, at the foot of a Live Oak, I enjoyed the prospect of its wide waters, its fringed coasts, and of the distant horizon.

The squadrons of aquatic fowls, emerging out of the water, and hastening to their leafy coverts on shore, closed the varied scenes of the past day. I was lulled asleep by the mixed sounds of the wearied [106] surf, lapsing on the hard beaten shore, and the tender warblings of the painted nonpareil and other winged inhabitants of the groves.

At the approach of day, the dreaded voice of the alligators shook the isle, and resounded along the neighbouring coasts, proclaiming the appearance of the glorious sun. I arose, and prepared to accomplish my daily task. A gentle favourable gale led us out of the harbour: we sailed across the lake, and, towards evening, entered the river, on the opposite South coast, where we made a pleasant and safe harbour, at a shelly promontory, the East cape of the river on that side of the lake. It is a most desirable situation, commanding a full view of the lake. The cape opposite to us was a vast cypress swamp, environed by a border of grassy marshes, which were projected farther into the lake, by floating fields of the bright green Pistia stratoites, which rose and fell alternately with the waters. Just to leeward of this point, and about half a mile in the lake, is the little round island already mentioned. But let us take notice of our harbour and its environs: it is a beautiful little cove, just within the sandy point, which defends it from the beating surf of the lake. From a shelly bank, ten or twelve feet perpendicular from the water, we entered a grove of Live Oaks, Palm, Magnolia, and Orange trees, which grow amongst shelly hills, and low ridges, occupying about three acres of ground, comprehending the isthmus, and a part of the peninsula, which joins it to the grassy plains. This enchanting little forest is partly encircled by a deep creek, a branch of the river, that has its source in the high forests of the main, South East from us, and winds through the extensive grassy plains which [107] surround this peninsula, to an almost infinite distance, and then unites its waters with those of the river, in this little bay which formed our harbour. This bay, about the mouth of the creek, is almost covered with the leaves of the Nymphaea nilumbo: its large sweet-scented yellow flowers are lifted up two or three feet above the surface of the water, each upon a green standard, representing the cap of Liberty.

The evening drawing on, and there being no convenient landing place, for several miles higher up the river, we concluded to remain here all night. Whilst my fellow travellers were employing themselves in collecting fire-wood, and fixing our camp, I improved the opportunity, in reconnoitering our ground; and taking my fusee with me, I penetrated the grove, and afterwards entered some almost unlimited savannas and plains, which were absolutely enchanting; they had been lately burnt by the Indian hunters, and had just now recovered their vernal verdure and gaiety.

How happily situated is this retired spot of earth! What an elisium it is! where the wandering Siminole, the naked red warrior, roams at large, and after the vigorous chase retires from the scorching heat of the meridian sun. Here he reclines, and reposes under the odoriferous shades of Zanthoxilon, his verdant couch guarded by the Deity; Liberty, and the Muses, inspiring him with wisdom and valour, whilst the balmy zephyrs fan him to sleep.

Seduced by these sublime enchanting scenes of primitive nature, and these visions of terrestrial happiness, I had roved far away from Cedar Point, [108] but awakening to my cares, I turned about, and in the evening regained our camp.

On my return, I found some of my companions fishing for trout, round about the edges of the floating nymphaea, and not unsuccessfully, having then caught more than sufficient for us all. As the method of taking these fish is curious and singular, I shall just mention it.

They are taken with a hook and line, but without any bait. Two people are in a little canoe, one sitting in the stern to steer, and the other near the bow, having a rod ten or twelve feet in length, to one end of which is tied a strong line, about twenty inches in length, to which is fastened three large hooks, back to back. These are fixed very securely, and covered with the white hair of a deer's tail, shreds of a red garter, and some particoloured feathers, all which form a tuft, or tassel, nearly as large as one's fist, and entirely cover and conceal the hooks: this is called a bob. The steersman paddles softly, and proceeds slowly along shore, keeping the boat parallel to it, at a distance just sufficient to admit the fisherman to reach the edge of the floating weeds along shore: he now ingeniously swings the bob backwards and forwards, just above the surface, and sometimes tips the

water with it; when the unfortunate cheated trout instantly springs
from under the weeds, and seizes the supposed prey. Thus he is caught
without a possibility of escape, unless he breaks the hooks, line, or rod,
which he, however, sometimes does by dint of strength; but, to prevent this, the fisherman used to the sport is careful not to raise the reed
suddenly up, but jerks it instantly backwards, then steadily drags the
sturdy reluctant fish to the side of the [109] canoe, and with a sudden
upright jerk brings him into it.

The head of this fish makes about one third of his length, and consequently the mouth is very large: birds, fish, frogs, and even serpents,
are frequently found in its stomach.

The trout is of lead colour, inclining to a deep blue, and marked
with transverse waved lists, of a deep slate colour, and when fully
grown, has a cast of red, or brick colour. The fins, with the tail, which
is large, and beautifully formed, are of a light reddish purple, or flesh
colour, the whole body is covered with large scales. But what is most
singular, this fish is remarkably ravenous; nothing living, that he can
seize upon, escapes his jaws, and the opening and extending of the
branchiosteges, at the moment he rises to the surface to seize his prey,
discovering his bright red gills, through the transparent waters, give
him a very terrible appearance. Indeed it may be observed, that all
fish of prey have this opening and covering of the gills very large, in
order to discharge the great quantity of water, which they take in at
their mouth, when they strike at their prey. This fish is nearly cuniform,
the body tapering gradually from the breast to the tail, and lightly compressed on each side. They frequently weigh fifteen, twenty and thirty
pounds, and are delicious food.

My companion, the trader, being desirous of crossing the river to the
opposite shore, in hopes of getting a turkey, I chose to accompany him,
as it offered a good opportunity to observe the natural productions of
those rich swamps and islands of the river. Having crossed the river,
which is here [110] five or six hundred yards wide, we entered a narrow channel, which after a serpentine course, for some miles, rejoins
the main river again, above; forming a large fertile island, of rich low
land. We landed on this island, and soon saw a fine roebuck *, at some
distance from us, who appeared leader of a company of deer, that were
feeding near him, on the verge of a green meadow. My companion
parting from me, in pursuit of the deer, one way, and I, observing a
flock of turkeys at some distance, on the other, directed my steps towards them, and with great caution, got near them; when singling
out a large cock, and being just on the point of firing, I observed that

* Cervus sylvaticus. The American deer.

several young cocks were affrighted, and in their language, warned the
rest to be on their guard, against an enemy, whom I plainly perceived
was industriously making his subtile approaches towards them, behind
the fallen trunk of a tree, about twenty yards from me. This cunning
fellow hunter, was a large fat wild cat (lynx) he saw me, and at times
seemed to watch my motions, as if determined to seize the delicious
prey before me. Upon which I changed my object, and levelled my
piece at him. At that instant, my companion, at a distance, also discharged his piece at the deer, the report of which alarmed the flock of
turkeys, and my fellow hunter, the cat, sprang over the log and trotted
off. The trader also missed his deer: thus we foiled each other. By this
time it being near night, we returned to camp, where having a delicious meal, ready prepared for our hungry stomachs, we sat down in
a circle round our wholesome repast.

How supremely blessed were our hours at this [111] time! plenty
of delicious and healthful food, our stomachs keen, with contented
minds; under no control, but what reason and ordinate passions dictated, far removed from the seats of strife.

Our situation was like that of the primitive state of man, peaceable,
contented, and sociable. The simple and necessary calls of nature, being
satisfied. We were altogether as brethren of one family, strangers to
envy, malice and rapine.

The night being over we arose, and pursued our course up the river,
and in the evening reached the trading-house, Spalding's upper store,
where I took up my quarters for several weeks.

On our arrival at the upper store, we found it occupied by a white
trader, who had for a companion, a very handsome Siminole young
woman. Her father, who was a prince, by the name of the White
Captain, was an old chief of the Siminoles, and with part of his family,
to the number of ten or twelve, were encamped in an Orange grove
near the stores, having lately come in from a hunt.

This white trader, soon after our arrival, delivered up the goods and
store-houses to my companion, and joined his father-in-law's camp, and
soon after went away into the forests on hunting and trading amongst
the flying camps of Siminoles.

He is at this time, unhappy in his connections with his beautiful
savage. It is but a few years since he came here, I think from North
Carolina, a stout genteel well-bred man, active, and of a heroic and
amiable disposition, and by his industry, honesty, and engaging manners, had gained the affections of the Indians, and soon made a little
for-[112]tune by traffic with the Siminoles: when, unfortunately, meeting with this little charmer, they were married in the Indian manner.

He loves her sincerely, as she possesses every perfection in her person
to render a man happy. Her features are beautiful, and manners engaging. Innocence, modesty, and love, appear to a stranger in every
action and movement; and these powerful graces she has so artfully
played upon her beguiled and vanquished lover, and unhappy slave,
as to have already drained him of all his possessions, which she dis-
honestly distributes amongst her savage relations. He is now poor,
emaciated, and half distracted, often threatening to shoot her, and
afterwards put an end to his own life; yet he has not resolution even
to leave her; but now endeavours to drown and forget his sorrows, in
deep draughts of brandy. Her father condemns her dishonest and cruel
conduct.

These particulars were related to me by my old friend the trader,
directly after a long conference which he had with the White Captain
on the subject, his son in law being present. The scene was affecting;
they both shed tears plentifully. My reasons for mentioning this affair,
so foreign to my business, was to exhibit an instance of the power of
beauty in a savage, and their art and finesse in improving it to their
private ends. It is, however, but doing justice to the virtue and moral
conduct of the Siminoles, and American Aborigines in general, to observe, that the character of this woman is condemned and detested by
her own people, of both sexes; and if her husband should turn her
away; according to the customs and usages of these people, she would
not get a husband again, as a divorce seldom takes place but in consequence of a [113] deliberate impartial trial, and public condemna-
tion, and then she would be looked upon as a harlot.

Such is the virtue of these untutored savages: but I am afraid this
is a common phrase epithet, having no meaning, or at least improperly
applied; for these people are both well tutored and civil; and it is
apparent to an impartial observer, who resides but a little time amongst
them, that it is from the most delicate sense of the honour and reputation of their tribes and families, that their laws and customs receive
their force and energy. This is the divine principle which influences
their moral conduct, and solely preserves their constitution and civil
government in that purity in which they are found to prevail amongst
them.

BEING desirous of continuing my travels and observations, higher up the river, and having an invitation from a gentleman who was agent for, and resident at a large plantation, the property of an English gentleman, about sixty miles higher up, I resolved to pursue my researches to that place; and having engaged in my service a young Indian, nephew to the White Captain, he agreed to assist me in working my vessel up as high as a certain bluff, where I was, by agreement, to land him, on the West or Indian shore, whence he designed to go in quest of the camp of the White Trader, his relation.

Provisions and all necessaries being procured, and the morning pleasant, we went on board and stood up the river. We passed for several miles on the left, by islands of high swamp land, exceedingly fertile, their banks for a good distance from the water, much higher than the interior part, and sufficiently so to build upon, and be out of the reach of inundations. They consist of a loose black mould, with a mixture of sand, shells and dissolved vegetables. The opposite Indian coast is a perpendicular bluff, ten or twelve feet high, consisting of a black sandy earth, mixed with a large proportion of shells, chiefly various species of fresh water Cochlea and Mytuli. Near the river, on this high shore, grew Corypha palma, Magnolia grandiflora, Live Oak, Callicarpa, Myrica cerifera, Hybiscus spinifex, and the beautiful evergreen shrub called Wild lime or Tallow nut. This last shrub grows six or eight feet high, many erect stems rising from a root; [115] the leaves are lanceolate and intire, two or three inches in length and one in breadth, of a deep green colour, and polished; at the foot of each leaf grows a stiff, sharp thorn; the flowers are small and in clusters, of a greenish yellow colour, and sweet scented; they are succeeded by a large oval fruit, of the shape and size of an ordinary plumb, of a fine yellow colour when ripe, a soft sweet pulp covers a nut which has a thin shell, enclosing a white kernel somewhat of the consistence and taste of the sweet Almond, but more oily and very much like hard tallow, which induced my father when he first observed it, to call it the Tallow nut.

At the upper end of this bluff is a fine Orange grove. Here my Indian companion requested me to set him on shore, being already tired of rowing under a fervid sun, and having for some time intimated a dislike to his situation, I readily complied with his desire, knowing the impossibility of compelling an Indian against his own inclinations, or even prevailing upon him by reasonable arguments, when labour is in the question; before my vessel reached the shore, he sprang out of her and landed, when uttering a shrill and terrible whoop, he bounded off like a roebuck, and I lost sight of him. I at first apprehended that as he took his gun with him, he intended to hunt for some game and return to me in the evening. The day being excessively hot and sultry, I concluded to take up my quarters here until next morning.

The Indian not returning this morning, I set sail alone. The coasts on each side had much the same appearance as already described. The Palm trees here seem to be of a different species from the Cabbage tree; their strait trunks are sixty, eighty or nine-[116]ty feet high, with a beautiful taper of a bright ash colour, until within six or seven feet of the top, where it is a fine green colour, crowned with an orb of rich green plumed leaves: I have measured the stem of these plumes fifteen feet in length, besides the plume, which is nearly of the same length.

The little lake, which is an expansion of the river, now appeared in view; on the East side are extensive marshes, and on the other high forests and Orange groves, and then a bay, lined with vast Cypress swamps, both coasts gradually approaching each other, to the opening of the river again, which is in this place about three hundred yards wide; evening now drawing on, I was anxious to reach some high bank of the river, where I intended to lodge, and agreeably to my wishes, I soon after discovered on the West shore, a little promontory, at the turning of the river, contracting it here to about one hundred and fifty yards in width. This promontory is a peninsula, containing about three acres of high ground, and is one entire Orange grove, with a few Live Oaks, Magnolias and Palms. Upon doubling the point, I arrived at the landing, which is a circular harbour, at the foot of the bluff, the top of which is about twelve feet high; and back of it is a large Cypress swamp, that spreads each way, the right wing forming the West coast of the little lake, and the left stretching up the river many miles, and encompassing a vast space of low grassy marshes. From this promontory, looking Eastward across the river, we behold a landscape of low country, unparalleled as I think; on the left is the East coast of the little lake, which I had just passed, and from the Orange bluff at the lower end, the high forests begin, and increase in breadth from the shore of the lake, mak-[117]ing a circular sweep to the right, and contain many hundred thousand acres of meadow, and this grand sweep of high forests encircles, as I apprehend, at least twenty miles of these green fields, interspersed with hommocks or islets of evergreen trees, where the sovereign Magnolia and lordly Palm stand conspicuous. The islets are high shelly knolls, on the sides of creeks or branches of the river, which wind about and drain off the super-abundant waters that cover these meadows, during the winter season.

The evening was temperately cool and calm. The crocodiles began to roar and appear in uncommon numbers along the shores and in the river. I fixed my camp in an open plain, near the utmost projection of the promontory, under the shelter of a large Live Oak, which stood on the highest part of the ground and but a few yards from my boat. From this open, high situation, I had a free prospect of the river, which was a matter of no trivial consideration to me, having good reason to dread the subtle attacks of the allegators, who were crouding about my harbour. Having collected a good quantity of wood for the purpose of keeping up a light and smoke during the night, I began to think of preparing my supper, when, upon examining my stores, I found but a scanty provision, I thereupon determined, as the most expeditious way of supplying my necessities, to take my bob and try for some trout. About one hundred yards above my harbour, began a cove or bay of the river, out of which opened a large lagoon. The mouth or entrance from the river to it was narrow, but the waters soon after spread and formed a little lake, extending into the marshes, its entrance and shores with-[118]in I observed to be verged with floating lawns of the Pistia and Nymphea and other aquatic plants; these I knew were excellent haunts for trout.

The verges and islets of the lagoon were elegantly embellished with flowering plants and shrubs; the laughing coots with wings half spread were tripping over the little coves and hiding themselves in the tufts of grass; young broods of the painted summer teal, skimming the still surface of the waters, and following the watchful parent unconscious of danger, were frequently surprised by the voracious trout, and he in turn, as often by the subtle, greedy alligator. Behold him rushing forth from the flags and reeds. His enormous body swells. His plaited tail brandished high, floats upon the lake. The waters like a cataract descend from his opening jaws. Clouds of smoke issue from his dilated nostrils. The earth trembles with his thunder. When immediately from the opposite coast of the lagoon, emerges from the deep his rival champion. They suddenly dart upon each other. The boiling surface of the lake marks their rapid course, and a terrific conflict commences. They now sink to the bottom folded together in horrid wreaths. The water becomes thick and discoloured. Again they rise, their jaws clap together, re-echoing through the deep surrounding forests. Again they sink, when the contest ends at the muddy bottom of the lake, and the vanquished makes a hazardous escape, hiding himself in the muddy turbulent waters and sedge on a distant shore. The proud victor exulting returns to the place of action. The shores and forests resound his dreadful roar, together with the triumphing shouts of the plaited tribes around, witnesses of the horrid combat.

[119]   My apprehensions were highly alarmed after being a spectator of so dreadful a battle; it was obvious that every delay would but tend to encrease my dangers and difficulties, as the sun was near setting, and the alligators gathered around my harbour from all quarters; from these considerations I concluded to be expeditious in my trip to the lagoon, in order to take some fish. Not thinking it prudent to take my fusee with me, lest I might lose it overboard in case of a battle, which I had every reason to dread before my return, I therefore furnished myself with a club for my defence, went on board, and penetrating the first line of those which surrounded my harbour, they gave way; but being pursued by several very large ones, I kept strictly on the watch, and paddled with all my might towards the entrance of the lagoon, hoping to be sheltered there from the multitude of my assailants; but ere I had half-way reached the place, I was attacked on all sides, several endeavouring to overset the canoe. My situation now became precarious to the last degree: two very large ones attacked me closely, at the same instant, rushing up with their heads and part of their bodies above the water, roaring terribly and belching floods of water over me. They struck their jaws together so close to my ears, as almost to stun me, and I expected every moment to be dragged out of the boat and instantly devoured, but I applied my weapons so effectually about me, though at random, that I was so successful as to beat them off a little; when, finding that they designed to renew the battle, I made for the shore, as the only means left me for my preservation, for, by keeping close to it, I should have my enemies on one side of me only, whereas I was before surrounded by them, and there was a probability, if pushed [120] to the last extremity, of saving myself, by jumping out of the canoe on shore, as it is easy to outwalk them on land, although comparatively as swift as lightning in the water. I found this last expedient alone could fully answer my expectations, for as soon as I gained the shore they drew off and kept aloof. This was a happy relief, as my confidence was, in some degree, recovered by it. On recollecting myself, I discovered that I had almost reached the entrance of the lagoon, and determined to venture in, if possible to take a few fish and

then return to my harbour, while day-light continued; for I could now, with caution and resolution, make my way with safety along shore, and indeed there was no other way to regain my camp, without leaving my boat and making my retreat through the marshes and reeds, which, if I could even effect, would have been in a manner throwing myself away, for then there would have been no hopes of ever recovering my bark, and returning in safety to any settlements of men. I accordingly proceeded and made good my entrance into the lagoon, though not without opposition from the alligators, who formed a line across the entrance, but did not pursue me into it, nor was I molested by any there, though there were some very large ones in a cove at the upper end. I soon caught more trout than I had present occasion for, and the air was too hot and sultry to admit of their being kept for many hours, even though salted or barbecued. I now prepared for my return to camp, which I succeeded in with but little trouble, by keeping close to the shore, yet I was opposed upon re-entering the river out of the lagoon, and pursued near to my landing (though not closely attacked) particularly by an old daring one, about twelve feet in length, [121] who kept close after me, and when I stepped on shore and turned about, in order to draw up my canoe, he rushed up near my feet and lay there for some time, looking me in the face, his head and shoulders out of water; I resolved he should pay for his temerity, and having a heavy load in my fusee, I ran to my camp, and returning with my piece, found him with his foot on the gunwale of the boat, in search of fish, on my coming up he withdrew sullenly and slowly into the water, but soon returned and placed himself in his former position, looking at me and seeming neither fearful or any way disturbed. I soon dispatched him by lodging the contents of my gun in his head, and then proceeded to cleanse and prepare my fish for supper, and accordingly took them out of the boat, laid them down on the sand close to the water, and began to scale them, when, raising my head, I saw before me, through the clear water, the head and shoulders of a very large alligator, moving slowly towards me; I instantly stepped back, when, with a sweep of his tail, he brushed off several of my fish. It was certainly most providential that I looked up at that instant, as the monster would probably, in less than a minute, have seized and dragged me into the river. This incredible boldness of the animal disturbed me greatly, supposing there could now be no reasonable safety for me during the night, but by keeping continually on the watch; I therefore, as soon as I had prepared the fish, proceeded to secure myself and effects in the best manner I could: in the first place, I hauled my bark upon the shore, almost clear out of the water, to prevent their oversetting or sinking her, after this every moveable was taken out and carried to my camp, [122] which was but a few yards off; then ranging some dry wood in such order as was the most convenient, cleared the ground round about it, that there might be no impediment in my way, in case of an attack in the night, either from the water or the land; for I discovered by this time, that this small isthmus, from its remote situation and fruitfulness, was resorted to by bears and wolves. Having prepared myself in the best manner I could, I charged my gun and proceeded to reconnoitre my camp and the adjacent grounds; when I discovered that the peninsula and grove, at the distance of about two hundred yards from my encampment, on the land side, were invested by a Cypress swamp, covered with water, which below was joined to the shore of the little lake, and above to the marshes surrounding the lagoon, so that I was confined to an islet exceedingly circumscribed, and I found there was no other retreat for me, in case of an attack, but by either ascending one of the large Oaks, or pushing off with my boat.

It was by this time dusk, and the alligators had nearly ceased their roar, when I was again alarmed by a tumultuous noise that seemed to be in my harbour, and therefore engaged my immediate attention. Returning to my camp I found it undisturbed, and then continued on to the extreme point of the promontory, where I saw a scene, new and surprising, which at first threw my senses into such a tumult, that it was some time before I could comprehend what was the matter; however, I soon accounted for the prodigious assemblage of crocodiles at this place, which exceeded every thing of the kind I had ever heard of.

How shall I express myself so as to convey an [123] adequate idea of it to the reader, and at the same time avoid raising suspicions of my want of veracity. Should I say, that the river (in this place) from shore to shore, and perhaps near half a mile above and below me, appeared to be one solid bank of fish, of various kinds, pushing through this narrow pass of St. Juans into the little lake, on their return down the river, and that the alligators were in such incredible numbers, and so close together from shore to shore, that it would have been easy to have walked across on their heads, had the animals been harmless. What expressions can sufficiently declare the shocking scene that for some minutes continued, whilst this mighty army of fish were forcing the pass? During this attempt, thousands, I may say hundreds of thousands of them were caught and swallowed by the devouring alligators. I have seen an alligator take up out of the water several great fish at a time, and just squeeze them betwixt his jaws, while the tails of the great trout flapped about his eyes and lips, ere he had swallowed them. The horrid noise of their closing jaws, their plunging amidst the broken banks of fish, and rising with their prey some feet upright above the water, the floods of water and blood rushing out of their mouths, and the clouds of vapour issuing from their wide nostrils, were truly frightful. This scene continued at intervals during the night, as the fish came to the pass. After this sight, shocking and tremendous as it was, I found myself somewhat easier and more reconciled to my situation, being convinced that their extraordinary assemblage here, was owing to this annual feast of fish, and that they were so well employed in their own element, that I had little occasion to fear their paying me a visit.

[124]   It being now almost night, I returned to my camp, where I had left my fish broiling, and my kettle of rice stewing, and having with me, oil, pepper and salt, and excellent oranges hanging in abundance over my head (a valuable substitute for vinegar) I sat down and regaled myself chearfully; having finished my repast, I re-kindled my fire for light, and whilst I was revising the notes of my past day's journey, I was suddenly roused with a noise behind me toward the main land; I sprang up on my feet, and listening, I distinctly heard some creature wading in the water of the isthmus; I seized my gun and went cautiously from my camp, directing my steps towards the noise; when I had advanced about thirty yards, I halted behind a coppice of Orange trees, and soon perceived two very large bears, which had made their way through the water, and had landed in the grove, about one hundred yards distance from me, and were advancing towards me. I waited until they were within thirty yards of me, they there began to snuff and look towards my camp, I snapped my piece, but it flashed, on which they both turned about and galloped off, plunging through the water and swamp, never halting as I suppose, until they reached fast land, as I could hear them leaping and plunging a long time; they did not presume to return again, nor was I molested by any other creature, except being occasionally awakened by the whooping of owls, screaming of bitterns, or the wood-rats running amongst the leaves.

The wood-rat is a very curious animal, they are not half the size of the domestic rat; of a dark brown or black colour; their tail slender and shorter in proportion, and covered thinly with short hair; they are [125] singular with respect to their ingenuity and great labour in the construction of their habitations, which are conical pyramids about three or four feet high, constructed with dry branches, which they collect with great labour and perseverance, and pile up without any apparent order, yet they are so interwoven with one another, that it it would take a bear or wild-cat some time to pull one of these castles to pieces, and allow the animals sufficient time to secure a retreat with their young.

The noise of the crocodiles kept me awake the greater part of the night, but when I arose in the morning, contrary to my expectations, there was perfect peace; very few of them to be seen, and those were asleep on the shore, yet I was not able to suppress my fears and apprehensions of being attacked by them in future; and indeed yesterday's combat with them, notwithstanding I came off in a manner victorious, or at least made a safe retreat, had left sufficient impression on my mind to damp my courage, and it seemed too much for one of my strength, being alone in a very small boat to encounter such collected danger. To pursue my voyage up the river, and be obliged every evening to pass such dangerous defiles, appeared to me as perilous as running the gauntlet betwixt two rows of Indians armed with knives and fire brands; I however resolved to continue my voyage one day longer, if I possibly could with safety, and then return down the river, should I find the like difficulties to oppose. Accordingly I got every thing on board, charged my gun, and set sail cautiously along shore; as I passed by Battle lagoon, I began to tremble and keep a good look out, when suddenly a huge alligator rushed out of the reeds, and [126] with a tremendous roar, came up, and darted as swift as an arrow under my boat, emerging upright on my lea quarter, with open jaws, and belching water and smoke that fell upon me like rain in a hurricane; I laid soundly about his head with my club and beat him off, and after plunging and darting about my boat, he went off on a strait line through the water, seemingly with the rapidity of lightning, and entered the cape of the lagoon; I now employed my time to the very best advantage in paddling close along shore, but could not forbear looking now and then behind me, and presently perceived one of them coming up again; the water of the river hereabouts, was shoal and very clear, the monster came up with the usual roar and menaces, and passed close by the side of my boat, when I could distinctly see a young brood of alligators to the number of one hundred or more, following after her in a long train, they kept close together in a column without straggling off to the one side or the other, the young appeared to be of an equal size, about fifteen inches in length, almost black, with pale yellow transverse waved clouds or blotches, much like rattle snakes in colour. I now lost sight of my enemy again.

Still keeping close along shore; on turning a point or projection of the river bank, at once I beheld a great number of hillocks or small pyramids, resembling hay cocks, ranged like an encampment along the banks, they stood fifteen or twenty yards distant from the water, on a high marsh, about four feet perpendicular above the water; I knew them to be the nests of the crocodile, having had a description of them before, and now expected a furious and general attack, as I saw several large cro-[127]codiles swimming abreast of these buildings. These nests being so great a curiosity to me, I was determined at all events immediately to land and examine them. Accordingly I ran my bark on shore at one of their landing places, which was a sort of nick or little dock, from which ascended a sloping path or road up to the edge of the meadow, where their nests were, most of them were deserted, and the great thick whitish egg-shells lay broken and scattered upon the ground round about them.

The nests or hillocks are of the form of an obtuse cone, four feet high and four or five feet in diameter at their bases; they are constructed with mud, grass and herbage: at first they lay a floor of this kind of tempered mortar on the ground, upon which they deposit a layer of eggs, and upon this a stratum of mortar seven or eight inches in thickness, and then another layer of eggs, and in this manner one stratum upon another, nearly to the top: I believe they commonly lay from one to two hundred eggs in a nest: these are hatched I suppose by the heat of the sun, and perhaps the vegetable substances mixed with the earth, being acted upon by the sun, may cause a small degree of fermentation, and so increase the heat in those hillocks. The ground for several acres about these nests shewed evident marks of a continual resort of alligators; the grass was every where beaten down, hardly a blade or straw was left standing; whereas, all about, at a distance, it was five or six feet high, and as thick as it could grow together. The female, as I imagine, carefully watches her own nest of eggs until they are all hatched, or perhaps while she is attending her own brood, she takes under her care and protection, as many as she can get at one time, ei-[128]ther from her own particular nest or others: but certain it is, that the young are not left to shift for themselves, having had frequent opportunities of seeing the female alligator, leading about the shores her train of young ones, just like a hen does her brood of chickens, and she is equally assiduous and courageous in defending the young, which are under their care, and providing for their subsistence; and when she is basking upon the warm banks, with her brood around her, you may hear the young ones continually whining and barking, like young puppies. I believe but few of a brood live to the years of full growth and magnitude, as the old feed on the young as long as they can make prey of them.

The alligator when full grown is a very large and terrible creature, and of prodigious strength, activity and swiftness in the water. I have seen them twenty feet in length, and some are supposed to be twenty-two or twenty-three feet; their body is as large as that of a horse; their shape exactly resembles that of a lizard, except their tail, which is flat or cuniform, being compressed on each side, and gradually diminishing from the abdomen to the extremity, which, with the whole body is covered with horny plates or squamae, impenetrable when on the body of the live animal, even to a rifle ball, except about their head and just behind their fore-legs or arms, where it is said they are only vulnerable. The head of a full grown one is about three feet, and the mouth opens nearly the same length, the eyes are small in proportion and seem sunk deep in the head, by means of the prominency of the brows; the nostrils are large, inflated and prominent on the top, so that the head in the water, resembles, at a distance, a great [129] chunk of wood floating about. Only the upper jaw moves, which they raise almost perpendicular, so as to form a right angle with the lower one. In the fore part of the upper jaw, on each side, just under the nostrils, are two very large, thick, strong teeth or tusks, not very sharp, but rather the shape of a cone, these are as white as the finest polished ivory, and are not covered by any skin or lips, and always in sight, which gives the creature a frightful appearance; in the lower jaw are holes opposite to these teeth, to receive them; when they clap their jaws together it causes a surprising noise, like that which is made by forcing a heavy plank with violence upon the ground, and may be heard at a great distance.

But what is yet more surprising to a stranger, is the incredible loud and terrifying roar, which they are capable of making, especially in the spring season, their breeding time; it most resembles very heavy distant thunder, not only shaking the air and waters, but causing the earth to tremble; and when hundreds and thousands are roaring at the same time, you can scarcely be persuaded, but that the whole globe is violently and dangerously agitated.

An old champion, who is perhaps absolute sovereign of a little lake or lagoon (when fifty less than himself are obliged to content themselves with swelling and roaring in little coves round about) darts forth from the reedy coverts all at once, on the surface of the waters, in a right line; at first seemingly as rapid as lightning, but gradually more slowly until he arrives at the center of the lake, when he stops; he now swells himself by drawing in wind and water through his mouth, which causes a loud [130] sonorous rattling in the throat for near a minute, but it is immediately forced out again through his mouth and nostrils, with a loud noise, brandishing his tail in the air, and the vapour ascending from his nostrils like smoke. At other times, when swollen to an extent ready to burst, his head and tail lifted up, he spins or twirls round on the surface of the water. He acts his part like an Indian chief when rehearsing his feats of war, and then retiring, the exhibition is continued by others who dare to step forth, and strive to excel each other, to gain the attention of the favourite female.

Having gratified my curiosity at this general breeding place and nursery of crocodiles, I continued my voyage up the river without being greatly disturbed by them: in my way I observed islets or floating fields of the bright green Pistia, decorated with other amphibious plants, as Senecio Jacobea, Persicaria amphibia, Coreopsis bidens, Hydrocotile fluitans, and many others of less note.

The swamps on the banks and islands of the river, are generally three or four feet above the surface of the water, and very level; the timber large and growing thinly, more so than what is observed to be in the swamps below Lake George; the black, rich earth is covered with moderately tall, and very succulent tender grass, which when chewed is sweet and agreeable to the taste, somewhat like young sugar-cane: it is a jointed decumbent grass, sending out radiculae at the joints into the earth, and so spreads itself, by creeping over its surface.

The large timber trees, which possess the low lands, are Acer rubrum, Ac. nigundo, Ac. glaucum, Ulmus sylvatica, Fraxinus excelsior, Frax. aquatica, Ulmus [131] suberifer, Gleditsia monosperma, Gledit. triacanthus, Diospyros Virginica, Nyssa aquatica, Nyssa sylvatica, Juglans cinerea, Quercus dentata, Quercus phillos, Hopea tinctoria, Corypha palma, Morus rubra, and many more. The Palm grows on the edges of the banks, where they are raised higher than the adjacent level ground, by the accumulation of sand, river-shells, &c. I passed along several miles by those rich swamps, the channels of the river which encircle the several fertile islands, I had passed, now uniting, formed one deep channel near three hundred yards over. The banks of the river on each side, began to rise and present shelly bluffs, adorned by beautiful Orange groves, Laurels and Live Oaks. And now appeared in sight, a tree that claimed my whole attention: it was the Carica papaya, both male and female, which were in flower; and the latter both in flower and fruit, some of which were ripe, as large, and of the form of a pear, and of a most charming appearance.

This admirable tree, is certainly the most beautiful of any vegetable production I know of; the towering Laurel Magnolia, and exalted Palm, indeed exceed it in grandeur and magnificence, but not in elegance, delicacy and gracefulness; it rises erect, with a perfectly strait tapering stem, to the height of fifteen or twenty feet, which is smooth and polished, of a bright ash colour, resembling leaf silver, curiously inscribed

with the footsteps of the fallen leaves, and these vestiges, are placed in
a very regular uniform imbricated order, which has a fine effect, as if
the little column were elegantly carved all over. Its perfectly spherical
top, is formed of very large lobe-sinuate leaves, supported on very long
footstalks; the lower leaves are the largest as well as their petioles the
longest, and make [132] a graceful sweep or flourish, like the long ∫
or the branches of a sconce candlestick. The ripe and green fruit are
placed round about the stem or trunk, from the lowermost leaves,
where the ripe fruit are, and upwards almost to the top; the heart or
inmost pithy part of the trunk is in a manner hollow, or at best consists
of very thin porous medullae or membranes; the tree very seldom
branches or divides into limbs, I believe never unless the top is by
accident broken off when very young: I saw one which had two tops or
heads, the stem of which divided near the earth. It is always green,
ornamented at the same time with flowers and fruit, which like figs
come out singly from the trunk or stem.

After resting and refreshing myself in these delightful shades, I left
them with reluctance, embarking again after the fervid heats of the
meridian sun were abated, for some time I passed by broken ridges of
shelly high land, covered with groves of Live Oak, Palm, Olea Americana, and Orange trees; frequently observing floating islets and green
fields of the Pistia near the shores of the river and lagoons.

Here is in this river and in the waters all over Florida, a very curious
and handsome bird, the people call them Snake Birds, I think I have
seen paintings of them on the Chinese screens and other India pictures: they seem to be a species of cormorant or loon (Colymbus cauda
elongata) but far more beautiful and delicately formed than any other
species that I have ever seen. The head and neck of this bird are extremely small and slender, the latter very long indeed, almost out of
all proportion, the bill long, strait and slender, ta-[133]pering from
its base to a sharp point, all the upper side, the abdomen and thighs,
are as black and glossy as a raven's, covered with feathers so firm and
elastic, that they in some degree resemble fish-scales, the breast and
upper part of the belly are covered with feathers of a cream colour, the
tail is very long, of a deep black, and tipped with a silvery white, and
when spread, represents an unfurled fan. They delight to sit in little
peaceable communities, on the dry limbs of trees, hanging over the still
waters, with their wings and tails expanded, I suppose to cool and air
themselves, when at the same time they behold their images in the
watery mirror: at such times, when we approach them, they drop
off the limbs into the water as if dead, and for a minute or two are not
to be seen; when on a sudden at a vast distance, their long slender

head and neck only appear, and have very much the appearance of a snake, and no other part of them is to be seen when swimming in the water, except sometimes the tip end of their tail. In the heat of the day they are seen in great numbers, sailing very high in the air, over lakes and rivers.

I doubt not but if this bird had been an inhabitant of the Tiber in Ovid's days, it would have furnished him with a subject, for some beautiful and entertaining metamorphoses. I believe they feed intirely on fish, for their flesh smells and tastes intolerably strong of it, it is scarcely to be eaten unless constrained by insufferable hunger.

I had now swamps and marshes on both sides of me, and evening coming on apace, I began to look out for high land to encamp on, but the extensive marshes seemed to have no bounds; and it was almost dark when I found a tolerable suitable place, [134] and at last was constrained to take up on a narrow strip of high shelly bank, on the West side. Great numbers of crocodiles were in sight on both shores; I ran my bark on shore at a perpendicular bank four or five feet above the water, just by the roots and under the spreading limbs of a great Live Oak: this appeared to have been an ancient camping place by Indians and strolling adventurers, from ash heaps and old rotten fire brands, and chunks, scattered about on the surface of the ground; but was now evidently the harbour and landing place of some sovereign alligator: there led up from it a deep beaten path or road, and was a convenient ascent.

I did not approve of my intended habitation from these circumstances; and no sooner had I landed and moored my canoe to the roots of the tree, than I saw a huge crocodile rising up from the bottom close by me, who, when he perceived that I saw him, plunged down again under my vessel; this determined me to be on my guard, and in time to provide against a troublesome night: I took out of my boat every moveable, which I carried upon the bank, then chose my lodging close to my canoe, under the spreading Oak; as hereabouts only, the ground was open and clear of high grass and bushes, and consequently I had some room to stir and look round about. I then proceeded to collect firewood which I found difficult to procure. Here were standing a few Orange trees. As for provisions, I had saved one or two barbecued trout; the remains of my last evenings collection in tolerable good order, though the sultry heats of the day had injured them; yet by stewing them up afresh with the lively juice of Oranges, they served well enough for my supper: having by this time but little relish or appe-[135]tite for my victuals; for constant watching at night against the attacks of alligators, stinging of musquitoes and sultry heats of the day; together, with the fatigues of working my bark, had almost deprived me of every desire but that of ending my troubles as speedy as possible. I had the good fortune to collect together a sufficiency of dry sticks, to keep up a light and smoke, which I laid by me, and then spread my skins and blankets upon the ground, kindled up a little fire and supped before it was quite dark. The evening was however, extremely pleasant, a brisk cool breeze sprang up, and the skies were perfectly serene, the stars twinkling with uncommon brilliancy. I stretched myself along before my fire; having the river, my little harbour and the stern of my vessel in view, and now through fatigue and weariness I fell asleep, but this happy temporary release from cares and troubles I enjoyed but a few moments, when I was awakened and greatly surprised, by the terrifying screams of Owls in the deep swamps around me, and what encreased my extreme misery was the difficulty of getting quite awake, and yet hearing at the same time such screaming and shouting, which increased and spread every way for miles around, in dreadful peals vibrating through the dark extensive forests, meadows and lakes, I could not after this surprise recover the former peaceable state and tranquility of mind and repose, during the long night, and I believe it was happy for me that I was awakened, for at that moment the crocodile was dashing my canoe against the roots of the tree, endeavouring to get into her for the fish, which I however prevented. Another time in the night I believe I narrowly escaped being dragged into the river by him, for when again through excessive fatigue I had fal-[136]len asleep, but was again awakened by the screaming owl, I found the monster on the top of the bank, his head towards me not above two yards distant, when starting up and seizing my fuzee well loaded, which I always kept under my head in the night time, he drew back and plunged into the water. After this I roused up my fire, and kept a light during the remaining part of the night, being determined not to be caught napping so again, indeed the musquitoes alone would have been abundantly sufficient to keep any creature awake that possessed their perfect senses, but I was overcome, and stupified with incessant watching and labour: as soon as I discovered the first signs of day-light, I arose, got all my effects and implements on board and set sail, proceeding upwards, hoping to give the musquitoes the slip, who were now, by the cool morning dews and breezes, driven to their shelter and hiding places; I was mistaken however in these conjectures, for great numbers of them, which had concealed themselves in my boat, as soon as the sun arose, began to revive, and sting me on my legs, which obliged me to land in order to get bushes to beat them out of their quarters.

It is very pleasing to observe the banks of the river ornamented with hanging garlands, composed of varieties of climbing vegetables, both shrubs and plants, forming perpendicular green walls, with projecting jambs, pilasters and deep apartments, twenty or thirty feet high and compleatly covered, with Glycine frutescens, Glyc. apios, Vitis labrusca, Vitis vulpina, Rajana, Hedera quinquifolia, Hedera arborea, Eupatorium scandens, Bignonia crucigera, and various species of Convolvulus, particularly an amazing tall climber of this [137] genus, or perhaps an Ipomea. This has a very large white flower, as big as a small funnel, its tube is five or six inches in length and not thicker than a pipe stem; the leaves are also very large, oblong and cordated, sometimes dentated or angled, near the insertion of the foot-stalk; they are of a thin texture, and of a deep green colour: it is exceedingly curious to behold the Wild Squash* climbing over the lofty limbs of the trees; their yellow fruit somewhat of the size and figure of a large orange, pendant from the extremities of the limbs over the water.

Towards noon, the sultry heats being intolerable, I put into shore, at a middling high bank, five or six feet above the surface of the river; this low sandy testaceous ridge along the river side was but narrow, the surface is light, black and exceedingly fertile, producing very large venerable Live Oaks, Palms and grand Magnolias, scatteringly planted by nature: there being no underwood to prevent the play of the breezes from the river, afforded a desirable retreat from the sun's heat: immediately back of this narrow ridge, were deep wet swamps, where stood some astonishingly tall and spreading Cypress trees: and now being weary and drowsy, I was induced to indulge and listen to the dictates of reason and invitations to repose, which consenting to, after securing my boat and reconnoitring the ground, I spread my blanket under the Oaks near my boat, on which I extended myself, where, falling to sleep, I instantaneously passed away the sultry hours of noon, what a blissful tranquil repose! undisturbed I awoke, refreshed and strengthened; I chearfully stepped on board again and continued to ascend the river. The [138] afternoon being cool and pleasant, and the trees very lofty on the higher Western banks of the river, by keeping near that shore I passed under agreeable shades the remaining part of the day. During almost all this day's voyage, the banks of the river on both shores were middling high, perpendicular, and washed by the brisk current; the shores were not lined with the green lawns of floating aquatics, and consequently not very commodious resorts or harbours for crocodiles, I therefore was not disturbed by them, and saw but few, but those were very large. I however did not like to lodge on

* Cucurbita peregrina.

those narrow ridges, invested by such dreary swamps, and evening approaching, I began to be anxious for high land for a camping place; it was quite dark before I came up to a bluff, which I had in view a long time, over a very extensive point of meadows. I landed however at last, in the best manner I could, at a magnificent forest of Orange groves, Oaks and Palms. I here, with little labour or difficulty, soon collected a sufficient quantity of dry wood: there was a pleasant vista of grass betwixt the grove and the edge of the river bank, which afforded a very convenient, open, airy camping place, under the protection of some spreading Oaks.

This was a high perpendicular bluff, fronting more than one hundred yards on the river, the earth black, loose and fertile, it is a composition of river-shells, sand, &c. back of it from the river, were open Pine forests and savannas. I met with a circumstance here, that, with some, may be reckoned worthy of mentioning, since it regards the monuments of the ancients; as I have already observed, when I landed it was quite dark, and in collecting [139] wood for my fire, strolling in the dark about the groves, I found the surface of the ground very uneven, by means of little mounts and ridges; in the morning I found I had taken up my lodging on the border of an ancient burying ground; sepulchres or tumuli of the Yamasees, who were here slain by the Creeks in the last decisive battle, the Creeks having driven them into this point, between the doubling of the river, where few of them escaped the fury of the conquerors. These graves occupied the whole grove, consisting of two or three acres of ground; there were near thirty of these cemeteries of the dead, nearly of an equal size and form, they were oblong, twenty feet in length, ten or twelve feet in width and three or four feet high, now overgrown with Orange trees, Live Oaks, Laurel Magnolias, Red bays and other trees and shrubs, composing dark and solemn shades.

I here, for the first time since I left the trading house, enjoyed a night of peaceful repose; I arose, greatly refreshed and in good spirits, stepped on board my bark and continued my voyage. After doubling the point I passed by swamps and meadows on each side of me, The river here is something more contracted within perpendicular banks, the land of an excellent quality, fertile, and producing prodigiously large timber and luxuriant herbage.

The air continued sultry and scarcely enough wind to flutter the leaves on the trees. The Eastern coast of the river now opens, and presents to view ample plains, consisting of grassy marshes and green meadows, and affords a prospect almost unlimited and extremely pleasing. The opposite shore presents to view a sublime contrast; a high bluff bearing magnificent forests of grand Magnolia, glori-[140] ous Palms, fruitful Orange groves, Live Oaks, Bays and others. This grand elevation continues four or five hundred yards, describing a gentle curve on the river, ornamented by a sublime grove of Palms, consisting of many hundreds of trees together; they intirely shade the ground under them. Above and below the bluff the grounds gradually descend to the common level swamps on the river: back of this eminence opens to view, expansive green meadows or savannas, in which are to be seen glittering ponds of water, surrounded at a great distance, by high open Pine forests and hommocks, and islets of Oaks and Bays projecting into the savannas. After ranging about these solitary groves and peaceful shades, I re-embarked and continued some miles up the river, between elevated banks of the swamps or low lands, when on the East shore in a capacious cove or winding of the river, were pleasing floating fields of Pistia, and in the bottom of this cove opened to view a large creek or branch of the river, which I knew to be the entrance to a beautiful lake, on the banks of which was the farm I was going to visit, and which I designed should be the last extent of my voyage up the river.

About noon the weather became extremely sultry, not a breath of wind stirring, hazy or cloudy, and very heavy distant thunder, which is answered by the crocodiles, sure presage of a storm!

Soon after ascending this branch of the river, on the right hand presents to view, a delightful little bluff, consisting chiefly of shells, and covered with a dark grove of Red Cedar, Zanthoxilon and Myrtle, I could not resist the temptation to stop here, although the tremendous thunder all around the [141] hemisphere alarmed me greatly, having a large lake to cross. From this grove presents to view, an expansive and pleasing prospect. The beauteous long lake in front, about North East from me, its most distant East shores adorned with dark, high forests of stately trees; North and South almost endless green plains and meadows, embellished with islets and projecting promontories of high, dark forests, where the pyramidal Magnolia grandiflora, Palma elata and shady Oak conspicuously tower.

Being heretofore so closely invested, by high forests and deep swamps of the great river, I was prevented from seeing the progress and increase of the approaching tempest, the terrific appearance of which now at once confounded me; how purple and fiery appeared the tumultuous clouds! swiftly ascending or darting from the horizon upwards; they seemed to oppose and dash against each other, the skies appeared streaked with blood or purple flame overhead, the flaming lightning streaming and darting about in every direction around, seems to fill the world with fire; whilst the heavy thunder keeps the earth in a constant tremor. I had yet some hopes of crossing the lake to the plantation in sight. On the opposite shore of the creek before me, and on the cape as we enter the lake, stood a large islet or grove of Oaks and Palms, here I intended to seek shelter and abide till the fury of the hurricane was overpast, if I found it too violent to permit me to cross the lake; in consequence of this precipitate determination I stepped into my boat and pushed off, what a dreadful rushing and roaring there is every where around me; and to my utter confusion and aston- ishment I could not find from what particular quarter its strongest current [142] or direction came, whereby I might have a proper chance of taking measures of securing a harbour or running from it. The high forests behind me bend to the blast, and the sturdy limbs of the trees crack; I had by this time got up a-breast of the grove or hommock, the hurricane close by, pursuing me, I found it dangerous and imprudent in the highest degree to put in here, as the groves were already torn up, and the spreading limbs of the ancient Live Oaks were flying over my head, and carried about in the air as leaves and stubble; I ran by and boldly entered the lake, (being hurried in by a strong current, which seemed a prodigy, the violent wind driving the stream of the creek back again into the lake) and as soon as possible took shelter under the high reedy bank of the lake, made fast my bark to the boughs of a low shrubby Hickory, that leaned over the water: such was the violence of the wind, that it raised the waters on the opposite shores of the lake several feet perpendicular, and there was a rapid flow of water from the creek into it, which was contrary to its natural course; such floods of rain fell during the space of half or three quarters of an hour that my boat was filled, and I expected every moment, when I should see her sink to the bottom of the lake; and the violence of the wind kept the cable so constantly extended, that it was beyond my ability to get to her; my box which contained my books of specimens and other collections, was floating about in her; and for a great part of the time the rain came down with such rapidity and fell in such quantities, that every object was totally obscured, excepting the continual streams or rivers of lightning, pouring from the clouds; all seemed a frightful chaos. When the wind and rain abated, I was overjoyed to see the face of nature again appear.

[143] It took me an hour or more to clear the water out of my bark. I then crossed the lake before a brisk and favourable breeze (it was about a mile over) and landed safely at the plantation.

When I arrived my friend was affrighted to see me, and imme- diately enquired of me in what manner I came there, supposing it impossible (until I had shewed him my boat) that I could have arrived by water, through so tremendous a hurricane.

Indeed I saw plainly that they were greatly terrified, having suffered almost irreparable damages from the violence of the storm; all the buildings on the plantation except his own dwelling-house, were laid almost flat to the ground, or the logs and roof rent asunder and twisted about; the mansion-house shook and reeled over their heads. He had nearly one hundred acres of the Indigo plant almost ripe for the first cutting, which was nearly ruined, and several acres of very promising Sugar-cane, totally spoiled for the season. The great Live Oaks which had been left standing about the fields, were torn to pieces, their limbs lying scattered over the ground: and one very large one which stood near his house torn down, which could not have been done by the united strength of a thousand men. But what is incredible, in the midst of this devastation and ruin, providentially no lives were lost, although there were about sixty Negro slaves on the plantation, and most of them in their huts when the storm came on, yet they escaped with their lives, though several were badly wounded.

I continued here three days, indeed it took most of the time of my abode with him, to dry my books and specimens of plants. But with attention and [144] care I saved the greatest number of them; though some were naturally so delicate and fragile, that it was impossible to recover them. Here is a vast body of land belonging to this estate; of high ridges fit for the culture of Corn, Indigo, Cotton, Batatas, &c. and of low swamps and marshes, which when properly drained and tilled, would be suitable for Rice, these rich low grounds when drained and ridged, are as productive as the natural high land, and vastly more durable, especially for Sugar-cane, Corn and even Indigo; but this branch of agriculture being more expensive, these rich lands are neglected, and the upland only is under culture. The farm is situated on the East shore of the beautiful Long Lake, which is above two miles long, and near a mile broad, which communicates with the St. Juan, by the little river which I ascended; it is about one and an half mile in length, and thirty or forty yards wide; this river, as well as the lake, abounds with fish, and wild fowl of various kinds, and incredible numbers especially during the winter season, when the geese and ducks arrive here from the North.

* New-Smyrna, a pretty thriving town, is a colony of Greeks and

---

* New-Smyrna is built on a high shelly bluff, on the West bank of the South branch of Musquito river, about ten miles above the capes of that river, which is about thirty miles North of Cape Canaveral, Lat. 28. I was there about ten years ago, when the surveyor run the lines or precincts of the colony, where there was neither habitation nor cleared field. It was then a famous Orange grove, the upper

Minorquies, established by Mr. Turnbull, on the Musquito river and very near its [145] mouth, is about thirty miles over land from this farm.

My friend rode with me, about four miles distance from the house, to shew me a vast fountain of warm or rather hot mineral water, which issued from a high ridge or bank on the river in a great cove or bay, a few miles above the mouth of the creek which I ascended to the lake; it boils up with great force, forming immediately a vast circular bason, capacious enough for several shallops to ride in, and runs with rapidity into the river three or four hundred yards distance. This creek, which is formed instantly by this admirable fountain, is wide and deep enough for a sloop to sail up into the bason. The water is perfectly diaphanous, and here are continually a prodigious number and variety of fish; they appear as plain as though lying on a table before your eyes, although many feet deep in the water. This tepid water has a most disagreeable taste, brassy and vitriolic, and very offensive to the smell, much like bilge water or the washings of a gun-barrel, and is smelt at a great distance. A pale bluish or pearl coloured coagulum covers every inanimate substance that lies in the water, as logs, limbs of trees, &c. Alligators and gar were numerous in the bason, even at the apertures where the ebullition emerges through the rocks, as also many other tribes of fish. In the winter season several kinds of fish and aquatic animals migrate to these warm fountains. The forbidding taste and smell of these waters seem to be owing to vitriolic and sulphurious fumes or vapours, and these being condensed, form this coagulum, which represents flakes of pearly clouds in the clear cerulean waters in the bason. A charm-[146]ing Orange grove, with Magnolias, Oaks and Palms, half surrounded this vast fountain. A delightful stream of cool salubrious water issues from the ridge, meandering along and enters the creek just below the bason. I returned in the evening, and next day set off again down the river.

My hospitable friend, after supplying me with necessaries, prevailed on me to accept of the company and assistance of his purveyor, one day's voyage down the river, whom I was to set on shore at a certain bluff, upwards of twenty miles below, but not above one third that

---

or South promontory of a ridge, nearly half a mile wide, and stretching North about forty miles, to the head of the North branch of the Musquito, to where the Tomoko river unites with it, nearly parallel to the sea coast, and not above two miles across to the sea beach. All this ridge was then one entire Orange grove, with Live Oaks, Magnolias, Palms, Red Bays and others: I observed then, near where New-Smyrna now stands, a spacious Indian mount and avenue, which stood near the banks of the river; the avenue ran on a strait line back, through the groves, across the ridge, and terminated at the verge of natural savannas and ponds.

distance by land; he was to be out in the forests one day, on a hunt for turkeys.

The current of the river being here confined within its perpendicular banks, ran briskly down; we chearfully descended the grand river St. Juan, enjoying enchanting prospects.

Before night we reached the destined port, at a spacious Orange grove. Next morning we separated, and I proceeded down the river. The prospects on either hand are now pleasing and I view them at leisure, and without toil or dread.

Induced by the beautiful appearance of the green meadows, which open to the Eastward, I determined not to pass this Elisium without a visit. Behold the loud, sonorous, watchful savanna crane (grus pratensis) with musical clangor, in detached squadrons. They spread their light elastic sail; at first they move from the earth heavy and slow, they labour and beat the dense air; they form the line with wide extended wings, tip to tip, they all rise and fall together as one bird; now they mount aloft, gradually wheeling about, each squadron performs its evolu-[147]tion, incircling the expansive plains, observing each one their own orbit; then lowering sail, descend on the verge of some glittering lake; whilst other squadrons, ascending aloft in spiral circles, bound on interesting discoveries, wheel round and double the promontory, in the silvery regions of the clouded skies, where, far from the scope of eye, they carefully observe the verdant meadows on the borders of the East Lake; then contract their plumes and descend to the earth, where, resting awhile on some verdant eminence, near the flowery border of the lake, with dignified, yet slow, respectful steps, approach the kindred band; they confer and treat for habitation; the bounds and precincts being settled, they confederate and take possession.

There is inhabiting the low shores and swamps of this river and the lakes of Florida, as well as Georgia, a very curious bird, called by an Indian name (Ephouskyca*) which signifies in our language the crying bird. I cannot determine what genus of European birds to join it with. It is about the size of a large domestic hen; all the body, above and beneath, is of a dark lead colour, every feather edged or tipped with white, which makes the bird appear speckled on a near view; the eye is large and placed high on the head, which is very prominent; the bill or beak is five or six inches in length, arched or bent gradually downwards, in that respect to be compared to one half of a bent bow, it is large or thick near the base, compressed on each side, and flatted at top and beneath, which makes it appear four square for more than

* Tantalus pictus.

inch, where the nostrils are placed, from whence to their tips, both mandibles are round, gradually lessening or tapering to [148] their extremities, which are thicker for about half an inch than immediately above, by which the mandibles never fit quite close their whole length; the upper mandible is a small matter longer than the under; the bill is of a dusky green colour, more bright and yellowish about the base and angles of the mouth; the tail is very short and the middle feather the longest, the others on each side shorten gradually, and are of the colour of the rest of the bird, only somewhat darker; the two shortest or outermost feathers are perfectly white, which the bird has a faculty of flirting out on either side, as quick as a flash of lightning, especially when he hears or sees any thing that disturbs him, uttering at the same instant an extreme harsh and loud shriek; his neck is long and slender, and his legs are also long and bare of feathers above the knee, like those of the bittern, and are black or of a dark lead colour.

There are two other species of this genus, which agree in almost every particular, with the above description, except in size and colour: the first * of these I shall mention is a perfect white, except the prime quill feathers, which are as black as those of a crow; the bill and legs of a beautiful clear red, as also a space clear of feathers about the eyes. The other species † is black on the upper side, the breast and belly white, and the legs and beak as white as snow; both these species are about half the size of the crying bird. They fly in large flocks or squadrons, evening and morning to and from their feeding places or roosts; both species are called Spanish curlews: these and the crying bird feed chiefly on cray fish, [149] whose cells they probe, and with their strong pinching bills drag them out: all the three species are esteemed excellent food.

It is a pleasing sight at times of high winds and heavy thunder storms, to observe the numerous squadrons of these Spanish curlews driving to and fro, turning and tacking about, high up in the air, when by their various evolutions in the different and opposite currents of the wind high in the clouds, their silvery white plumage gleams and sparkles like the brightest crystal, reflecting the sun-beams that dart upon them between the dark clouds.

Since I have turned my observation upon the birds of this country, I shall notice another very singular one, which though already most curiously and exactly figured by Catesby, yet it seems to be nearly allied to those before mentioned, I mean the bird which he calls the

* Tantalus albus. Numinus albus. Cat.
† Tantalus versicolor. Numinus fuscus. Cat.

wood pelican.* This is a large bird, perhaps near three feet high when standing erect. The bill is very long and strong, bending with a moderate curve, from the base to the tip, the upper mandible is the largest, and receives the edges of the nether one into it its whole length; the edges are very sharp and firm, the whole of a dark ash or horn colour; the forehead round the base of the beak, and sides of the head are bare of feathers, and of a dark greenish colour, in which space are placed the eyes, which are very large; the remainder of the head and neck is of a nut brown colour; the back of a light bluish grey; upper part of the wings, breast and belly almost white, with some slight dashes of grey; the quill-feathers and tail, which are very short, are of a dark slate colour, almost black; the legs which are ve-[150]ry long, and bare of feathers a great length above the knees, are of a dark dull greenish colour: they have a small bag or pouch under their throat: they feed on serpents, young alligators, frogs and other reptiles.

This solitary bird does not associate in flocks, but is generally seen alone; commonly near the banks of great rivers, in vast marshes or meadows; especially such as are caused by inundations, and also in the vast deserted Rice plantations; he stands alone on the topmost limb of tall dead Cypress trees, his neck contracted or drawn in upon his shoulders, and beak resting like a long scythe upon his breast: in this pensive posture and solitary situation, they look extremely grave, sorrowful and melancholy, as if in the deepest thought. They are never seen on the salt sea coast, and yet are never found at a great distance from it. I take this bird to be of a different genus from the tantalus, and perhaps approaches the nearest to the Egyptian ibis of any other bird yet known.

There are two species of vultures † in these regions I think not mentioned in history: the first we shall describe is a beautiful bird, near the size of a turkey buzzard ‡, but his wings are much shorter, and consequently, he falls greatly below that admirable bird in sail. I shall call this bird the painted vulture. The bill is long and strait almost to the point, when it is hooked or bent suddenly down and sharp; the head and neck bare of feathers nearly down to the stomach, when the feathers begin to cover the skin, and soon become long and of a soft texture, forming a ruff or tippet, in which the bird by contracting his neck can hide that as [151] well as his head; the bare skin on the neck appears loose and wrinkled, which is of a deep bright yellow colour,

* Tantalus loculator. Linn.
† Vultur sacra.
‡ Vultu aura.

intermixed with coral red; the hinder part of the neck is nearly covered with short, stiff hair; and the skin of this part of the neck is of a dun-purple colour, gradually becoming red as it approaches the yellow of the sides and forepart. The crown of the head is red; there are lobed lappets of a reddish orange colour, which lay on the base of the upper mandible. But what is singular, a large portion of the stomach hangs down on the breast of the bird, in the likeness of a sack or half wallet, and seems to be a duplicature of the craw, which is naked and of a reddish flesh colour, this is partly concealed by the feathers of the breast, unless when it is loaded with food, (which is commonly, I be-lieve, roasted reptiles) and then it appears prominent. The plumage of the bird is generally white or cream colour, except the quill-feathers of the wings and two or three rows of the coverts, which are of a beautiful dark brown; the tail which is large and white is tipped with this dark brown or black; the legs and feet of a clear white; the eye is encircled with a gold coloured iris; the pupil black.

The Creeks or Muscogulges construct their royal standard of the tail feather of this bird, which is called by a name signifying the eagle's tail; this they carry with them when they go to battle, but then it is painted with a zone of red within the brown tips; and in peaceable negociations it is displayed new, clean and white, this standard is held most sacred by them on all occasions; and is constructed and orna-mented with great ingenuity. These birds seldom appear but when the deserts are set on fire (which happens almost every day through-out the year, in [152] some part or other, by the Indians, for the pur-pose of rousing the game, as also by the lightning:) when they are seen at a distance soaring on the wing, gathering from every quarter, and gradually approaching the burnt plains, where they alight upon the ground yet smoking with hot embers; they gather up the roasted serpents, frogs and lizards; filling their sacks with them; at this time a person may shoot them at pleasure, they not being willing to quit the feast, and indeed seem to brave all danger.

The other species may very properly be called the coped vulture, and is by the inhabitants called the carrion crow; as to bulk or weight, he is nearly equal to either of the others before mentioned. His wings are not long and sharp pointed, but broad and round at their extrem-ities, having a clumsy appearance; the tail is remarkably short, which he spreads like a little fan, when on the wing; they have a heavy laborious flight, flapping their wings, then sail a little and then flap their wings again, and so on as if recovering themselves when falling; the beak is very long and strait, until it makes a sudden hook at the point, in the manner of the other vultures; the whole bird is of a sable

or mourning colour; the head and neck down to the breast is bare of
feathers, and the skin wrinkled, this unfeathered skin is of a deep livid
purple, appearing black and thinly set with short black hair; he has
a ruff or tippet of long soft feathers, like a collar bearing on his breast,
in which he can conceal his neck and head at pleasure.

Having agreeably diverted away the intolerable heats of sultry noon
in fruitful fragrant groves, with renewed vigour I again resume my
[153] sylvan pilgrimage. The afternoon and evening moderately warm,
and exceeding pleasant views from the river and its varied shores. I
passed by Battle lagoon and the bluff, without much opposition; but
the crocodiles were already assembling in the pass. Before night I
came to, at a charming Orange grove bluff, on the East side of the little
lake, and after fixing my camp on a high open situation, and collecting
a plenty of dry wood for fuel, I had time to get some fine trout for
supper and joyfully return to my camp.

What a most beautiful creature is this fish before me! gliding to and
fro, and figuring in the still clear waters, with his orient attendants
and associates: the yellow bream * or sun fish. It is about eight inches
in length, nearly of the shape of the trout, but rather larger in proportion over the shoulders and breast; the mouth large, and the branchiostege opens wide; the whole fish is of a pale gold (or burnished brass)
colour, darker on the back and upper sides; the scales are of a proportionable size, regularly placed, and every where variably powdered
with red, russet, silver, blue and green specks, so laid on the scales as
to appear like real dust or opaque bodies, each apparent particle being
so projected by light and shade, and the various attitudes of the fish,
as to deceive the sight; for in reality nothing can be of a more plain
and polished surface than the scales and whole body of the fish; the
fins are of an Orange colour; and like all the species of the bream, the
ultimate angle of the branchiostege terminates by a little spatula, the
extreme end of which represents a crescent of the finest ultramarine
blue, encircled with silver, [154] and velvet black, like the eye in the
feathers of a peacock's train; he is a fish of prodigious strength and
activity in the water; a warrior in a gilded coat of mail, and gives no
rest or quarters to small fish, which he preys upon; they are delicious
food and in great abundance.

The Orange grove, is but narrow, betwixt the the river banks and ancient Indian fields, where there are evident traces of the habitations of
the ancients, surrounded with groves of Live Oak, Laurel Magnolia,
Zanthoxilon, Liquid-amber, and others.

How harmonious and soothing is this native sylvan music now at

* Cyprinus coronarius.

still evening! inexpressibly tender are the responsive cooings of the
innocent dove, in the fragrant Zanthoxilon groves, and the variable
and tuneful warblings of the nonparel; with the more sprightly and
elevated strains of the blue linnet and golden icterus; this is indeed
harmony even amidst the incessant croaking of the frogs; the shades
of silent night are made more chearful, with the shrill voice of the
whip-poor-will * and active mock-bird.

My situation high and airy, a brisk and cool breeze steadily and
incessantly passing over the clear waters of the lake, and fluttering
over me through the surrounding groves, wings its way to the moon-
light savannas, while I repose on my sweet and healthy couch of the
soft Tillandsi ulnea-adscites, and the latter gloomy and still hours of
night passed rapidly away as it were in a moment; I arose, strengthen-
[155]ed and chearful, in the morning. Having some repairs to make
in the tackle of my vessel, I paid my first attention to them; which
being accomplished, my curiosity prompted me to penetrate the grove
and view the illumined plains.

What a beautiful display of vegetation is here before me! seemingly
unlimited in extent and variety; how the dew-drops twinkle and play
upon the sight, trembling on the tips of the lucid, green savanna,
sparkling as the gem that flames on the turban of the Eastern prince;
see the pearly tears rolling off the buds of the expanding Granadilla †;
behold the azure fields of cerulean Ixea! what can equal the rich golden
flowers of the Cana lutea, which ornament the banks of yon serpentine
rivulet, meandering over the meadows; the almost endless varieties of
the gay Phlox, that enamel the swelling green banks, associated with
the purple Verbena corymbosa, Viola, pearly Gnaphalium, and silvery
Perdicium; how fantastical looks the libertine Clitoria, mantling the
shrubs, on the vistas skirting the groves. My morning excursion finished,
I returned to the camp, breakfasted, then went on board my boat, and
gently descended the noble river and passed by several openings of
extensive plains and meadows, environing the East Lake, charming
beyond compare; at evening I came to at a good harbour, under the
high banks of the river, and rested during the night, amidst the
fragrant groves, exposed to the constant breezes from the river: here
I made ample collections of specimens and growing roots of curious
vegetables, which kept me fully employed the greatest part of the day,
and in the evening arrived at a charming spot on the East [156] bank,

* Caprimulgus rufus called chuck-will's-widow, from a fancied resemblance
of his notes to these words: they inhabit the maritime parts of Carolina and
Florida, and are more than twice the size of the night hawk or whip-poor-will.

† Passiflora incarnata, called May-Apple.

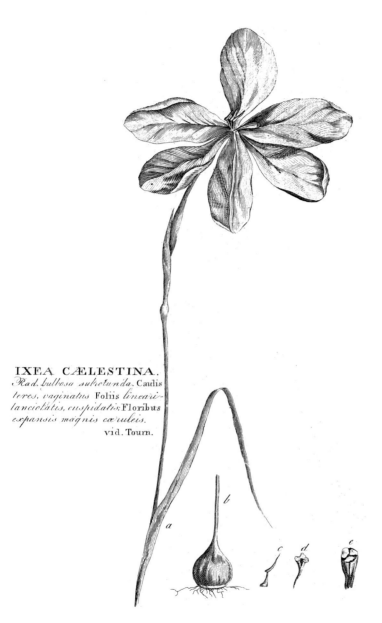

IXEA CÆLESTINA.
Rad. bulbosa subrotunda. Caulis
teres, vaginatus Foliis *lineari-*
lanciolatis, cuspidatis, Floribus
expansis magnis cœruleis.

vid. Tourn.

which I had marked on my ascent up the river, where I made some addition to my collections, and the next day I employed myself in the same manner, putting into shore frequently, at convenient places, which I had noticed; and in the evening arrived again at the upper store, where I had the pleasure of finding my old friend, the trader, in good health and chearful, and his affairs in a prosperous way. There were also a small party of Indians here, who had lately arrived with their hunts to purchase goods. I continued a few days at this post, searching its environs for curious vegetable productions, collecting seeds and planting growing roots in boxes, to be transported to the lower trading house.

Now, having procured necessaries to accommodate me on my voyage down to the lower store, I bid adieu to my old friend and benefactor, Mr. Job Wiggens, embarked alone on board my little fortunate vessel, and set sail; I chose to follow the Eastermost channel of the river to the Great Lake, because it ran by high banks and bluffs of the Eastern main the greatest part of the distance, which afforded me an opportunity of observing a far greater variety of natural subjects, than if I had taken the Western or middle channel, which flowed thro' swamps and marshes.

At evening I arrived at Cedar Point, my former safe and pleasant harbour, at the East cape of the Great Lake, where I had noticed some curious shrubs and plants; here I rested, and on the smooth and gentle current launch again into the little ocean of Lake George, meaning now, on my return, to coast his Western shores in search of new beauties in the bounteous kingdom of Flora.

[157] I was however induced to deviate a little from my intended course, and touch at the inchanting little Isle of Palms. This delightful spot, planted by nature, is almost an entire grove of Palms, with a few pyramidal Magnolias, Live Oaks, golden Orange, and the animating Zanthoxilon; what a beautiful retreat is here! blessed unviolated spot of earth! rising from the limpid waters of the lake; its fragrant groves and blooming lawns invested and protected by encircling ranks of the Yucca gloriosa; a fascinating atmosphere surrounds this blissful garden; the balmy Lantana, ambrosial Citra, perfumed Crinum, perspiring their mingled odours, wafted through Zanthoxilon groves. I at last broke away from the enchanting spot, and stepped on board my boat, hoisted sail and soon approached the coast of the main, at the cool eve of day; then traversing a capacious semicircular cove of the lake, verged by low, extensive grassy meadows, I at length by dusk made a safe harbour, in a little lagoon, on the sea shore or strand of a bold sandy point, which descended from the surf of the lake; this was

a clean sandy beach, hard and firm by the beating surf, when the wind
sets from the East coast; I drew up my light vessel on the sloping
shore, that she might be safe from the beating waves in case of a
sudden storm of wind in the night. A few yards back the land was a
little elevated, and overgrown with thickets of shrubs and low trees,
consisting chiefly of Zanthoxilon, Olea Americana, Rhamus frangula,
Sideroxilon, Morus, Ptelea, Halesia, Querci, Myrica cerifera and others;
these groves were but low, yet sufficiently high to shelter me from the
chilling dews; and being but a few yards distance from my vessel, here
I fixed my encampment. A brisk wind arising from the lake, [158]
drove away the clouds of musquitoes into the thickets. I now, with
difficulty and industry, collected a sufficiency of dry wood to keep up
a light during the night, and to roast some trout which I had caught
when descending the river; their heads I stewed in the juice of Oranges,
which, with boiled rice, afforded me a wholsome and delicious supper:
I hung the remainder of my broiled fish on the snags of some shrubs
over my head. I at last, after reconnoitring my habitation, returned,
spread abroad my skins and blanket upon the clean sands by my fire
side, and betook myself to repose.

How glorious the powerful sun, minister of the Most High, in the
rule and government of this earth, leaves our hemisphere, retiring from
our sight beyond the western forests! I behold with gratitude his de-
parting smiles, tinging the fleecy roseate clouds, now riding far away
on the Eastern horizon; behold they vanish from sight in the azure
skies!

All now silent and peaceable, I suddenly fell asleep. At midnight I
awake; when raising my head erect, I find myself alone in the wilderness of Florida, on the shores of Lake George. Alone indeed, but under
the care of the Almighty, and protected by the invisible hand of my
guardian angel.

When quite awake, I started at the heavy tread of some animal, the
dry limbs of trees upon the ground crack under his feet, the close
shrubby thickets part and bend under him as he rushes off.

I rekindled up my sleepy fire, lay in contact the exfoliated smoking
brands damp with the dew of heaven.

[159]   The bright flame ascends and illuminates the ground and groves
around me.

When looking up, I found my fish carried off, though I had thought
them safe on the shrubs, just over my head, but their scent, carried
to a great distance by the damp nocturnal breezes, I suppose were too
powerful attractions to resist.

Perhaps it may not be time lost, to rest awhile here, and reflect on the unexpected and unaccountable incident, which however pointed out to me an extraordinary deliverance, or protection of my life, from the rapacious wolf that stole my fish from over my head.

How much easier and more eligible might it have been for him to have leaped upon my breast in the dead of sleep, and torn my throat, which would have instantly deprived me of life, and then glutted his stomach for the present with my warm blood, and dragged off my body, which would have made a feast afterwards for him and his howling associates; I say would not this have been a wiser step, than to have made protracted and circular approaches, and then after, by chance, espying the fish over my head, with the greatest caution and silence rear up, and take them off the snags one by one, then make off with them, and that so cunningly as not to awaken me until he had fairly accomplished his purpose.

The morning being clear, I set sail with a favourable breeze, coasting along the shores; when on a sudden the waters became transparent, and discovered the sandy bottom, and the several nations of fish, passing and repassing each other. Fol-[160]lowing this course I was led to the cape of the little river, descending from Six mile Springs, and meandering six miles from its source, through green meadows. I entered this pellucid stream, sailing over the heads of innumerable squadrons of fish, which, although many feet deep in the water, were distinctly to be seen; I passed by charming islets of flourishing trees, as Palm, Red Bay, Ash, Maple, Nussa and others. As I approached the distant high forest on the main, the river widens, floating fields of the green Pistia surrounded me, the rapid stream winding through them. What an alluring scene was now before me! A vast bason or little lake of crystal waters, half encircled by swelling hills, clad with Orange and odoriferous Illisium groves. The towring Magnolia itself a grove, and the exalted Palm, as if conscious of their transcendent glories, tossed about their lofty heads, painting, with mutable shades, the green floating fields beneath. The social prattling coot enrobed in blue, and the squeeling water-hen, with wings half expanded, tripped after each other, over the watery mirror.

I put in at an ancient landing place, which is a sloping ascent to a level grassy plain, an old Indian field. As I intended to make my most considerable collections at this place, I proceeded immediately to fix my encampment but a few yards from my safe harbour, where I securely fastened my boat to a Live Oak which overshadowed my port.

After collecting a good quantity of fire-wood, as it was about the middle of the afternoon, I resolved to reconnoiter the ground about my encampment: having penetrated the groves next to me, I came to the open forests, consisting of exceed-[*161*]ingly tall strait Pines (Pinus Palustris) that stood at a considerable distance from each other, through which appeared at N. W. an almost unlimited plain of grassy savannas, embellished with a chain of shallow ponds, as far as the sight could reach. Here is a species of Magnolia that associates with the Gordonia lasianthus; it is a tall tree, sixty or eighty feet in height; the trunk strait; its head terminating in the form of a sharp cone; the leaves are oblong, lanceolate, of a fine deep green, and glaucous beneath; the flowers are large, perfectly white and extremely fragrant; with respect to its flowers and leaves, it differs very little from the Magnolia glauca. The silvery whiteness of the leaves of this tree, had a striking and pleasing effect on the sight, as it stood amidst the dark green of the Quercus dentata, Nyssa sylvatica, Nys. aquatica, Gordonia lasianthus and many others of the same hue. The tall aspiring Gordonia lasianthus, which now stood in my view in all its splendour, is every way deserving of our admiration. Its thick foliage, of a dark green colour, is flowered over with large milk-white fragrant blossoms, on long slender elastic peduncles, at the extremities of its numerous branches, from the bosom of the leaves, and renewed every morning; and that in such incredible profusion, that the tree appears silvered over with them, and the ground beneath covered with the fallen flowers. It at the same time continually pushes forth new twigs, with young buds on them; and in the winter and spring the third year's leaves, now partly concealed by the new and perfect ones, are gradually changing colour, from green to golden yellow, from that to a scarlet, from scarlet to crimson; and lastly to a brownish purple, and then fall [*162*] to the ground. So that the Gordonia lasianthus may be said to change and renew its garments every morning throughout the year; and every day appears with unfading lustre. And moreover, after the general flowering is past, there is a thin succession of scattering blossoms to be seen, on some parts of the tree, almost every day throughout the remaining months, until the floral season returns again. Its natural situation, when growing, is on the edges of shallow ponds, or low wet grounds on rivers, in a sandy soil, the nearest to the water of any other tree, so that in drouthy seasons its long serpentine roots which run near or upon the surface of the earth, may reach into the water. When the tree has arrived to the period of perfect magnitude, it is sixty, eighty or an hundred feet high, forming a pyramidal head. The wood of old trees when sawn into plank, is deservedly admired in cabinet-work or furniture; it has a cinnamon coloured ground, marbled and veined with many colours: the inner bark is used for dying a reddish or sorrel colour; it imparts this colour to wool, cotton, linnen and dressed deer skins, and is highly esteemed by tanners.

The Zamia pumila, the Erythryna corallodendrum and the Cactus opuntia grow here in great abundance and perfection. The first grows in the open pine forests, in tufts or clumps, a large conical strobile disclosing its large coral red fruit, which apears singularly beautiful amidst the deep green fern-like pinnated leaves.

The Erythryna corallodendrum is six or eight feet high; its prickly limbs stride and wreathe about with singular freedom, and its spikes of crimson flowers have a fine effect amidst the delicate foliage.

[163] The Cactus opuntia is very tall, erect and large, and strong enough to bear the weight of a man: some are seven or eight feet high: the whole plant or tree seems to be formed of great oval compressed leaves or articulations; those near the earth continually encrease, magnify and indurate as the tree advances in years, and at length lose the bright green colour and glossy surface of their youth, acquiring a ligneous quality, with a whitish scabrous cortex: every part of the plant is nearly destitute of aculei, or those fascicles of barbed bristles which are in such plenty on the common dwarf Indian Fig. The cochineal insects were feeding on the leaves: the female of this insect is very large and fleshy, covered with a fine white silk or cottony web, which feels always moist or dewy, and seems designed by nature to protect them from the violent heat of the sun. The male is very small in comparison to the female, and but very few in number, they each have two oblong pellucid wings. The large polypetalous flowers are produced on the edges of the last years leaves, are of a fine splendid yellow, and are succeeded by very large pear shaped fruit, of a dark livid purple when ripe: its pulp is charged with a juice of a fine transparent crimson colour, and has a cool pleasant taste, somewhat like that of a pomegranate; soon after eating this fruit the urine becomes of the same crimson colour, which very much surprises and affrights a stranger, but is attended with no other ill consequence, on the contrary, it is esteemed wholesome, though powerfully diuretic.

On the left hand of those open forests and savannas, as we turn our eyes Southward, South-west and West, we behold an endless wild desert, the upper stratum of the earth of which is a fine white sand, with small pebbles, and at some distance appears entirely covered with low trees and shrubs of [164] various kinds, and of equal height, as dwarf Sweet Bay (Laurus Borbonia) Olea Americana, Morus rubra, Myrica cerifera, Ptelea, Æsculus pavia, Quercus Ilex, Q. glandifer, Q. maritima, foliis obcuneiformibus obsolete trilobis minoribus, Q. pumila,

Rhamnus frangula, Halesia diptera, & Tetraptera, Cassine, Ilex aquifolium, Callicarpa Johnsonia, Erythryna corallodendrum, Hibiscus spinifex, Zanthoxilon, Hopea tinctoria, Sideroxilum, with a multitude of
other shrubs, many of which are new to me, and some of them admirably beautiful and singular. One of them particularly engaged my
notice, which, from its fructification I take to be a species of Cacalia.
It is an evergreen shrub, about six or eight feet high, the leaves are
generally somewhat cuniform, fleshy and of a pale whitish green, both
surfaces being covered with a hoary pubescence and vesiculae, that
when pressed feel clammy, and emit an agreeable scent; the ascendent branches terminate with large tufts or corymbs of rose coloured
flowers, of the same agreeable scent; these clusters of flowers, at a
distance, look like a large Carnation or fringed Poppy flower (Syngenesia Polyg. Oqul. Linn.) Cacalia heterophylla, foliis cuniformibus,
carnosis, papil. viscidis.

Here is also another species of the same genus, but it does not grow
quite so large; the leaves are smaller, of a yet duller green colour, and
the flowers are of a pale rose; they are both valuable evergreens.

The trees and shrubs which cover these extensive wilds, are about
five or six feet high, and seem to be kept down by the annual firing of
the desarts, rather than the barrenness of the soil, as I saw a few large
Live Oaks, Mulberry trees and Hicko-[165]ries, which evidently have
withstood the devouring flames. These adjoining wild plains, forests
and savannas, are situated lower than the hilly groves on the banks of
the lake and river, but what should be the natural cause of it I cannot
even pretend to conjecture, unless one may suppose that those high
hills, which we call bluffs, on the banks of this great river and its lakes,
and which support those magnificent groves and high forests, and are
generally composed of shells and sand, were thrown up to their present
height by the winds and waves, when the bed of the river was nearer
the level of the present surface of the earth; but then, to rest upon such
a supposition, would be admitting that the waters were heretofore in
greater quantities than at this time, or that their present channels and
receptacles are worn deeper into the earth.

I now directed my steps towards my encampment, in a different
direction. I seated myself upon a swelling green knoll, at the head of
the crystal bason. Near me, on the left, was a point or projection of an
entire grove of the aromatic Illisium Floridanum; on my right and
all around behind me, was a fruitful Orange grove, with Palms and
Magnolias interspersed; in front, just under my feet was the inchanting
and amazing crystal fountain, which incessantly threw up, from dark,
rocky caverns below, tons of water every minute, forming a bason,

capacious enough for large shallops to ride in, and a creek of four or five feet depth of water, and near twenty yards over, which meanders six miles through green meadows, pouring its limpid waters into the great Lake George, where they seem to remain pure and unmixed. About twenty yards from the upper edge of the bason, [166] and directly opposite to the mouth or outlet to the creek, is a continual and amazing ebullition, where the waters are thrown up in such abundance and amazing force, as to jet and swell up two or three feet above the common surface: white sand and small particles of shells are thrown up with the waters, near to the top, when they diverge from the center, subside with the expanding flood, and gently sink again, forming a large rim or funnel round about the aperture or mouth of the fountain, which is a vast perforation through a bed of rocks, the ragged points of which are projected out on every side. Thus far I know to be matter of real fact, and I have related it as near as I could conceive or express myself. But there are yet remaining scenes inexpressibly admirable and pleasing.

Behold, for instance, a vast circular expanse before you, the waters of which are so extremely clear as to be absolutely diaphanous or transparent as the ether; the margin of the bason ornamented with a great variety of fruitful and floriferous trees, shrubs and plants, the pendant golden Orange dancing on the surface of the pellucid waters, the balmy air vibrates the melody of the merry birds, tenants of the encircling aromatic grove.

At the same instant innumerable bands of fish are seen, some cloathed in the most brilliant colours; the voracious crocodile stretched along at full length, as the great trunk of a tree in size, the devouring garfish, inimical trout, and all the varieties of gilded painted bream, the barbed catfish, dreaded sting-ray, skate and flounder, spotted bass, sheeps head and ominous drum; all in their separate bands and communities, with free and unsus-[167]picious intercourse performing their evolutions: there are no signs of enmity, no attempt to devour each other; the different bands seem peaceably and complaisantly to move a little aside, as it were to make room for others to pass by.

But behold yet something far more admirable, see whole armies descending into an abyss, into the mouth of the bubbling fountain, they disappear! are they gone forever? is it real? I raise my eyes with terror and astonishment,- - -I look down again to the fountain with anxiety, when behold them as it were emerging from the blue ether of another world, apparently at a vast distance, at their first appearance, no bigger than flies or minnows, now gradually enlarging, their brilliant colours begin to paint the fluid.

Now they come forward rapidly, and instantly emerge, with the elastic expanding column of crystalline waters, into the circular bason or funnel, see now how gently they rise, some upright, others obliquely, or seem to lay as it were on their sides, suffering themselves to be gently lifted or born up, by the expanding fluid towards the surface, sailing or floating like butterflies in the cerulean ether: then again they as gently descend, diverge and move off; when they rally, form again and rejoin their kindred tribes.

This amazing and delightful scene, though real, appears at first but as a piece of excellent painting; there seems no medium, you imagine the picture to be within a few inches of your eyes, and that you may without the least difficulty touch any one of the fish, or put your finger upon the crocodile's eye, when it really is twenty or thirty feet under water.

[168]   And although this paradise of fish, may seem to exhibit a just representation of the peaceable and happy state of nature which existed before the fall, yet in reality it is a mere representation; for the nature of the fish is the same as if they were in lake George or the river; but here the water or element in which they live and move, is so perfectly clear and transparent, it places them all on an equality with regard to their ability to injure or escape from one another; (as all river fish of prey, or such as feed upon each other, as well as the unwieldy crocodile, take their prey by surprise; secreting themselves under covert or in ambush, until an opportunity offers, when they rush suddenly upon them:) but here is no covert, no ambush, here the trout freely passes by the very nose of the alligator and laughs in his face, and the bream by the trout.

But what is really surprising, that the consciousness of each others safety or some other latent cause, should so absolutely alter their conduct, for here is not the least attempt made to injure or disturb one another.

The sun passing below the horizon, and night approaching, I arose from my seat, and proceeding on arrived at my camp, kindled my fire, supped and reposed peaceably. And rising early, employed the fore part of the day in collecting specimens of growing roots and seeds. In the afternoon, left these Elisian springs and the aromatic groves, and briskly descend the pellucid little river, re-entering the great lake; the wind being gentle and fair for Mount Royal, I hoisted sail and successfully crossing the N. West bay, about nine miles, came to at Rocky Point, the West cape or promontory, as we enter the river descending towards Mount Royal: [169] these are horizontal slabs or flat masses of rocks, rising out of the lake two or three feet above its surface, and seem an aggregate composition or concrete of sand, shells and calcareous cement; of a dark grey or dusky colour; this stone is hard and firm enough for buildings, and serves very well for light hand millstones; and when calcined affords a coarse lime; they lay in vast horizontal masses upon one another, from one to two or three feet in thickness, and are easily separated and broke to any size or form, for the purpose of building. Rocky Point is an airy cool and delightful situation, commanding a most ample and pleasing prospect of the lake and its environs; but here being no wood, I re-embarked and sailed down a little farther to the island in the bay, where I went on shore at a magnificent grove of Magnolias and Oranges, desirous of augmenting my collections. Arose early next morning, and after ranging the groves and savannas, returned, embarked again, and descending, called at Mount Royal, where I enlarged my collections; and bidding adieu to the gentleman and lady, who resided here, and who treated me with great hospitality on my ascent up the river; arrived in the evening at the lower trading house.

CHAP. VI.

On my return from my voyage to the upper store, I understood the trading company designed for Cuscowilla, that they had been very active in their preparations, and would be ready to set off in a few days; I therefore availed myself of the little time allowed me to secure and preserve my collections, against the arrival of the trading schooner, which was hourly expected, that every thing might be in readiness to be shipped on board her, in case she should load again and return for Savanna during my absence.

Every necessary being now in readiness, early on a fine morning we proceeded, attended by four men under the conduct of an old trader, whom Mr. M'Latche had delegated to treat with the Cowkeeper and other chiefs of Cuscowilla, on the subject of re-establishing the trade, &c. agreeable to the late treaty of St. Augustine.

For the first four or five miles we travelled Westward, over a perfectly level plain, which appeared before and on each side of us, as a charming green meadow, thinly planted with low spreading Pine trees (P. palustri.) The upper stratum of the earth is a fine white crystalline sand, the very upper surface of which being mixed or incorporated with the ashes of burnt vegetables, renders it of sufficient strength or fertility to clothe itself perfectly, with a very great variety of grasses, herbage and remarkably low shrubs, together with a very dwarf species of Palmetto (Corypha pumila stipit. serratis.) [*171*] Of the low shrubs many were new to me and of a very pleasing appearance, particularly a species of Annona (Annona incarna, floribus grandioribus paniculatis;) this grows three, four or five feet high, the leaves somewhat cuniform or broad lanceolate, attenuating down to the petiole, of a pale or light green colour, covered with a pubescence or short fine down; the flowers very large, perfectly white and sweet scented, many connected together on large loose panicles or spikes; the fruit of the size and form of a small cucumber, the skin or exterior surface somewhat rimose or scabrous, containing a yellow pulp of the consistence of a hard custard, and very delicious, wholesome food. This seems a variety, if not the same that I first remarked, growing on the Alatamaha near Fort Barrington, Charlotia and many other places in

Georgia and East Florida; and I observed here in plenty, the very dwarf decumbent Annona, with narrow leaves, and various flowers already noticed at Alatamaha (Annona pigmea.) Here is also abundance of the beautiful little dwarf Kalmea ciliata, already described. The white berried Empetrum, a very pretty evergreen, grows here on somewhat higher and drier knolls, in large patches or clumps, associated with Olea Americana, several species of dwarf Querci (Oaks) Vaccinium, Gordonia lasianthus, Andromeda ferruginia and a very curious and beautiful shrub which seems allied to the Rhododendron, Cassine, Rhamnus frangula, Andromeda nitida, &c. which being of dark green foliage, diversifies and enlivens the landscape; but what appears very extraordinary, is to behold here, depressed and degraded, the glorious pyramidal Magnolia grandiflora, associated amongst these vile dwarfs, and even some of them rising above it though not five feet high; yet still [172] shewing large, beautiful and expansive white fragrant blossoms, and great heavy cones on slender procumbent branches, some even lying on the earth; the ravages of fire keep them down, as is evident from the vast excrescent tuberous roots, covering several feet of ground, from which these slender shoots spring.

In such clumps and coverts are to be seen several kinds of birds, particularly a species of jay; they are generally of an azure blue colour, have no crest or tuft of feathers on the head, nor are they so large as the great crested blue jay of Virginia, but are equally clamorous (pica glandaria cerulea noncrestata.) The towee bird (fringilla erythrophthalma) is very numerous, as is a species of bluish grey butcher bird (lanius.) Here were also lizards and snakes. The lizards were of that species called in Carolina, scorpions: they are from five to six inches in length, of a slender form; the tail in particular is very long and small; they are of a yellowish clay colour, varied with longitudinal lines or stripes of a dusky brown colour, from head to tail; they are wholly covered with very small squamae, vibrate their tail, and dart forth and brandish their forked tongue after the manner of serpents, when they are surprised or in pursuit of their prey, which are scarabei, locustae, musci, and other insects, but I do not learn that their bite is poisonous, yet I have observed cats to be sick soon after eating them. After passing over this extensive, level, hard, wet savanna, we crossed a fine brook or rivulet; the water cool and pleasant; its banks adorned with varieties of trees and shrubs, particularly the delicate Cyrilla racemiflora, Chionanthus, Clethra, Nyssa sylvatica, Andromeda nitida, Andromeda formosissima: and here were great quantities of a very [173] large and beautiful Filex osmunda, growing in great tufts or clumps. After leaving the rivulet we passed over a wet, hard, level glade or down, covered with a fine short grass, with abundance of low saw Palmetto, and a few shrubby Pine trees, Quercus nigra, Quercus sinuata or scarlet Oak: then the path descends to a wet bay-gale; the ground a hard, fine white sand, covered with black slush, which continued above two miles, when it gently rises the higher sand hills, and directly after passes through a fine grove of young long leaved Pines. The soil seemed here, loose, brown, coarse, sandy loam, though fertile. The ascent of the hill, ornamented with a variety and profusion of herbaceous plants and grasses, particularly Amaryllis atamasco, Clitoria, Phlox, Ipomea, Convolvulus, Verbena corymbosa, Ruellia, Viola, &c. A magnificent grove of stately Pines, succeeding to the expansive wild plains we had a long time traversed, had a pleasing effect, rousing the faculties of the mind, awakening the imagination by its sublimity, and arresting every active, inquisitive idea, by the variety of the scenery, and the solemn symphony of the steady Western breezes, playing incessantly, rising and falling through the thick and wavy foliage.

The Pine groves passed, we immediately find ourselves on the entrance of the expansive airy Pine forests, on parallel chains of low swelling mounds, called the Sand Hills, their ascent so easy, as to be almost imperceptible to the progressive traveller, yet at a distant view, before us in some degree exhibit the appearance of the mountainous swell of the ocean immediately after a tempest; but yet, as we approach them, they insensibly disappear, and seem to be lost, and we should be ready to conclude [174] all to be a visionary scene, were it not for the sparkling ponds and lakes, which at the same time gleam through the open forests, before us and on every side, retaining them on the eye, until we come up with them; and at last the imagination remains flattered and dubious, by their uniformity, being mostly circular or elliptical, and almost surrounded with expansive green meadows; and always a picturesque dark grove of Live Oak, Magnolia, Gordonia and the fragrant Orange, encircling a rocky shaded grotto, of transparent water, on some border of the pond or lake; which, without the aid of any poetic fable, one might naturally suppose to be the sacred abode or temporary residence of the guardian spirit, but is actually the possession and retreat of a thundering absolute crocodile.

Arrived early in the evening at the Halfway pond, where we encamped and stayed all night. This lake spreads itself in a spacious meadow, beneath a chain of elevated sand hills, the sheet of water at this time was about three miles in circumference; the upper end, and just under the hills, is surrounded by a crescent of dark groves, which shaded a rocky grotto. Near this place, was a sloping green bank, terminating by a point of flat rocks, which projected into the lake, and formed one point of the crescent that partly surrounded the vast grotto or bason of transparent waters, which is called by the traders a sink-hole, a singular kind of vortex or conduit, to the subteranean receptacles of the waters; but though the waters of these ponds in the summer and dry seasons, evidently tend towards these sinks, yet it is so slow and gradual, as to be almost imperceptible. There is always a [175] meandering channel winding through the savannas or meadows, which receives the waters spread over them, by several lateral smaller branches, slowly conveying them along into the lake, and finally into the bason, and with them nations of the finny tribes.

Just by the little cape of flat rocks, we fixed our encampment, where I enjoyed a comprehensive and varied scene, the verdant meadows spread abroad, charmingly decorated by green points of grassy lawns and dark promontories of wood-land, projecting into the green plains.

Behold now at still evening, the sun yet streaking the embroidered savannas, armies of fish pursuing their pilgrimage to the grand pellucid fountain, and when here arrived, all quiet and peaceable, encircle the little cerulean hemisphere, descend into the dark caverns of the earth; where probably they are separated from each other, by innumerable paths, or secret rocky avenues; and after encountering various obstacles, and beholding new and unthought of scenes of pleasure and disgust, after many days absence from the surface of the world, emerge again from the dreary vaults, and appear exulting in gladness, and sporting in the transparent waters of some far distant lake.

The various kinds of fish and amphibious animals, that inhabit these inland lakes and waters, may be mentioned here, as many of them here assembled, pass and repass in the lucid grotto: first the crocodile alligator; great brown spotted garr, accoutred in an impenetrable coat of mail; this admirable animal may be termed a cannibal amongst fish, as fish are his prey; when fully grown [176] he is from five to six feet in length, and of proportionable thickness, of a dusky brown colour, spotted with black. The Indians make use of their sharp teeth to scratch or bleed themselves with, and their pointed scales to arm their arrows. This fish is sometimes eaten, and to prepare them for food, they cover them whole in hot embers, where they bake them, the skin with the scales easily peels off, leaving the meat white and tender.

The mud fish is large, thick or round, and two feet in length; his meat white and tender, but soft and tastes of the mud, and is not much esteemed. The great devouring trout and catfish are in abundance; the golden bream or sunfish, the red bellied bream, the silver or white bream, the great yellow and great black or blue bream, also abound here. The last of these mentioned, is a large, beautiful and delicious fish; when full grown they are nine inches in length, and five to six inches in breadth; the whole body is of a dull blue or Indigo colour, marked with transverse lists or zones of a darker colour, scatteringly powdered with sky blue, gold and red specks; fins and tail of a dark purple or livid flesh colour; the ultimate angle of the branchiostege forming a spatula, the extreme end of which is broad and circular, terminating like the feather of the peacocks train, and having a brilliant spot or eye like it, being delicately painted with a fringed border of a fire colour.

The great yellow or particoloured bream is in form and proportion much like the forementioned, but larger, from a foot to fifteen inches in length; the upper part of his body (i. e.) his back from head to tail, is of a dark clay and dusky colour, with transverse dashes or blotches, of reddish [177] dull purple, or bluish, according to different exposures to light; the sides and belly of a bright pale yellow, the belly faintly stained with vermillion red, insensibly blended with the yellow on the sides, and all garnished with fiery, blue, green, gold and silver specks on the scales; the branchiostege is of a yellowish clay or straw colour, the lower edge or border next the opening of the gills, is near a quarter of an inch in breadth, of a sea green or marine blue, the ulterior angle protends backwards to a considerable length, in the form of a spatula or feather, the extreme end dilated and circular, of a deep black or crow colour, reflecting green and blue, and bordered round with fiery red, somewhat like red sealing wax, representing a brilliant ruby on the side of the fish; the fins reddish, edged with a dove colour: they are deservedly esteemed a most excellent fish.

Here are, as well as in all the rivers, lakes and ponds of East Florida, the great soft shelled tortoise *: they are very large when full grown, from twenty to thirty and forty pounds weight, extremely fat and delicious, but if eaten to excess, are apt to purge people not accustomed to eat their meat.

They are flat and very thin; two feet and a half in length, and eighteen inches in breadth across the back; in form, appearance and texture, very much resembling the sea turtle: the whole back shell, except the vertebrae or ridge, which is not at all prominent, and ribs on each side, is soft or cartilaginous, and easily reduced to a jelly when boiled; the anterior and posterior extremities of the back shell, appear to be embossed with round, [178] horny warts or tubercles, the belly or nether shell is but small and semicartilaginous, except a narrow cross bar connecting it at each end with the back shell, which is hard

* Testudo naso cylindracea elongato, truncato.

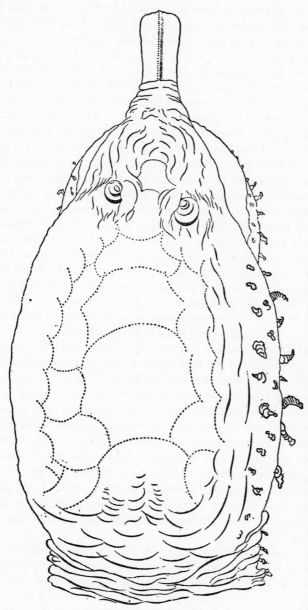

[IX. Head of great soft-shelled tortoise]

and osseous; the head is large and clubbed, of nearly an oval form, the upper mandible, however, is protended forward, and truncated, somewhat resembling a swine's snout, at the extreme end of which the nostrils are placed; on each side of the root or base of this proboscis are the eyes, which are large; the upper beak is hooked and sharp, like a hawk's bill; the lips and corners of the mouth large, tumid, wrinkled and barbed with long, pointed warts, which he can project and contract at pleasure, which gives the creature a frightful and disagreeable countenance. They bury themselves in the slushy bottoms of rivers and ponds, under the roots of flags and other aquatic herbage, leaving a hole or aperture just sufficient for their head to play through; in such places they withdraw themselves when hungry, and there seize their prey by surprise, darting out their heads as quick as lightning, upon the unwary animal that unfortunately strolls within their reach: they can extend their neck to a surprising length, which enables them to seize young fowl swimming on the surface of the water above them, which they instantly drag down. They are seen to raise their heads above the surface of the water, in the depths of the lakes and rivers, and blow, causing a faint puffing noise, somewhat like a porpoise; probably this is for pastime, or to charge themselves with a proper supply of fresh air. They are carnivorous, feeding on any animal they can seize, particularly young ducks, frogs and fish.

We had a large and fat one served up for our [179] supper, which I at first apprehended we had made a very extravagant waste of, not being able to consume one half of its flesh, though excellently well cooked; my companions however seemed regardless, being in the midst of plenty and variety, at any time within our reach, and to be obtained with little or no trouble or fatigue on our part; when herds of deer were feeding in the green meadows before us; flocks of turkeys, walking in the groves around us, and myriads of fish, of the greatest variety and delicacy, sporting in the crystalline floods before our eyes.

The vultures and ravens, crouched on the crooked limbs of the lofty Pines, at a little distance from us, sharpening their beaks, in low debate, waiting to regale themselves on the offals, after our departure from camp.

At the return of the morning, by the powerful influence of light; the pulse of nature becomes more active, and the universal vibration of life insensibly and irresistibly moves the wondrous machine: how chearful and gay all nature appears. Hark! the musical savanna cranes, ere the chirping sparrow flirts from his grassy couch, or the glorious sun gilds the tops of the Pines, spread their expansive wings, leave their lofty roosts, and repair to the ample plains.

[X. Great soft-shelled tortoise]

From Half-way pond, we proceed Westward, through the high forests of Cuscowilla.

The appearance of the earth for five or six miles, presented nearly the same scenes as heretofore.

Now the sand ridges become higher, and their bases proportionably more extensive; the savannas [180] and ponds more expansive; the summit of the ridges more gravelly; here and there, heaps or piles of rocks, emerging out of the sand and gravel: these rocks are the same sort of concrete of sand and shells as noticed on St. Juans and the great lake. The vegetable productions nearly the same as already mentioned.

We gently descend again over sand ridges, cross a rapid brook, ripling over the gravelly bed, hurrying the transparent waters into a vast and beautiful lake, through a fine fruitful Orange grove; which magnificently adorns the banks of the lake to a great distance on each side of the capes of the creek. This is a fine situation for a capital town. These waters are tributary to St. Juan's.

We alighted to refresh ourselves, and adjust our packs. Here are evident signs and traces of a powerful settlement of the ancients.

Set off again, and continued travelling over a magnificent Pine forest, the ridges low, but their bases extensive, with proportionable plains. The steady breezes gently and continually rising and falling, fill the high lonesome forests with an awful reverential harmony, inexpressibly sublime, and not to be enjoyed any where, but in these native wild Indian regions.

Crossing another large deep creek of St. Juan's, the country is a vast level plain, and the soil good for the distance of four or five miles, though light and sandy, producing a forest of stately Pines and laurels, with some others; and a vast profusion of herbage, such as Rudbeckia, Helianthus, Silphium, Polymnia, Ruellia, Verbena, Rhexea, Convol-[181]vulus, Sophora, Glycine, Vitia, Clitorea, Ipomea, Urtica, Salvia graviolens, Viola and many more. How chearful and social is the rural converse of the various tribes of tree frogs, whilst they look to heaven for prolific showers!

How harmonious the shrill tuneful songs of the wood thrush, and the soothing love lays of the amorous cuckoo *! seated in the cool leafy branches of the stately Magnolias and shadowy Elms, Maples and Liquid-amber, together with gigantic Fagus sylvatica, which shade and perfume these sequestered groves. How unexpected and enchanting the enjoyment, after traversing a burning sandy desert!

Now again we behold the open Pine forests, and rise the sandy hills,

* Cuculus Caroliniensis.

which continue for some miles, then gently descend again, when a level expansive savanna plain presents to view, which, after entering, and proceeding on, became wet, and covered by a fine short grass, with extensive parterres of the dwarf creeping Palmetto, their stipes sharply toothed or serrated together with clumps of low shrubs, as Kalmia, Andromeda, Annona pygmea, Myrica cerifera, Empetrum, Vaccinium and others.

We now rise a little again, and pass through a narrow Pine forest, when suddenly opens to view, a vastly extensive and sedgy marsh, expanding Southerly like an open fan, seemingly as boundless as the great ocean: our road crossed the head of it, about three hundred yards over; the bottom here, was hard sand, a foot or more under a soft muddy surface: the traders informed me that these vast marshes lay on the borders of a great lake, many [182] miles in length, in magnitude exceeding Lake George, and communicates with St. Juan's by a river *, its confluence above the lower store at the Little Lake.

Observed as we passed over the sand hills, the dens of the great land tortoise, called gopher: this strange creature remains yet undescribed by historians and travellers. The first signs of this animal's existence, as we travel Southerly, are immediately after we cross the Savanna River. They are to be seen only on the high dry sand hills. When arrived to their greatest magnitude, the upper shell is near eighteen inches in length, and ten or twelve inches in breadth; the back is very high, and the shell of a very hard bony substance, consisting of many regular compartments, united by sutures, in the manner of the other species of tortoise, and covered with thin horny plates. The nether or belly shell is large, and regularly divided transversely, into five parts: these compartments are not knit together like the sutures of the skull, or the back shell of the tortoise, but adhere, or are connected together by a very ridgy horny cartilage, which serves as hinges for him to shut up his body within his shell at pleasure. The fore part of the belly shell towards its extremity, is formed somewhat like a spade, extends forward near three inches, and is about an inch and an half in breadth; its extremity is a little bifid, the posterior division of the belly shell, is likewise protended backwards considerably, and is deeply bifurcated.

The legs and feet are covered with flat horny squamae; he seems to have no clefts in them or toes, but long flattish nails or talons, somewhat in [183] resemblance to the nails of the human fingers, five on the fore feet; the hind legs or feet appear as if truncated, or as stumps of feet, armed all round with sharp, flattish strong nails, the number undetermined or irregular; the head is of a moderate size, the upper

* Ockli-Waha Great.

mandible a little hooked, the edges hard and sharp; the eyes are large; the nose picked; the nostrils near together and very minute; the general colour of the animal is a light ash or clay, and at a distance, unless he is in motion, any one would disregard or overlook it as a stone or an old stump. It is astonishing what a weight one of these creatures will bear; it will easily carry any man standing on its back, on level ground. They form great and deep dens in the sand hills, casting out incredible quantities of earth. They are esteemed excellent food; the eggs are larger than a musket ball, perfectly round and the shell hard.

After crossing over this point or branch of the marshes, we entered a noble forest, the land level, and the soil fertile, being a loose, dark brown, coarse sandy loam, on a clay or marley foundation; the forests were Orange groves, overtopped by grand Magnolias, Palms, Live Oaks, Juglans cinerea, Morus rubra, Fagus sylvatica, Telia and Liquid-amber, with various kinds of shrubs and herbaceous plants, particularly Callicarpa, Halesia, Sambucus, Zanthoxilon, Ptelea, Rhamnus frangula, Rudbeckia, Silphium, Polymnia, Indigo fera, Sophora, Salvia graviolens, &c. We were chearfully received in this hospitable shade, by various tribes of birds, their sprightly songs seemed a prelude to the vicinity of human habitations. This magnificent grove was a wing of the vast forests lying upon the coast of the great and beautiful lake of Cus-cowilla, at no great distance [184] from us. Continuing eight or nine miles through the sublime forest, we entered on an open forest of lofty Pines and Oaks, on gently swelling sand hills, and presently saw the lake, its waters sparkling through the open groves. Near the path was a large artificial mound of earth, on a most charming, high situation, supposed to be the work of the ancient Floridans or Yamasees, with other traces of an Indian town; here were three or four Indian habita-tions, the women and children saluted us with chearfulness and com-plaisance. After riding near a mile farther we arrived at Cuscowilla, near the banks: a pretty brook of water ran through the town, and entered the lake just by.

We were welcomed to the town, and conducted by the young men and maidens to the chief's house, which stood on an eminence, and was distinguished from the rest by its superior magnitude, a large flag being hoisted on a high staff at one corner. We immediately alighted; the chief, who is called the Cowkeeper, attended by several ancient men, came to us, and in a very free and sociable manner, shook our hands (or rather arms) a form of salutation peculiar to the American Indians, saying at the same time, "You are come." We followed him to an apartment prepared for the reception of their guests.

The pipe being filled, it is handed around, after which a large bowl, with what they call "Thin drink," is brought in and set down on a small low table; in this bowl is a great wooden ladle; each person takes up in it as much as he pleases, and after drinking until satisfied, returns it again into the bowl, pushing the handle towards the person in the circle, and so it goes round.

[185]   After the usual compliments and enquiries relative to our adventures, &c. the chief trader informed the Cowkeeper, in the presence of his council or attendants, the purport of our business, with which he expressed his satisfaction. He was then informed what the nature of my errand was, and he received me with complaisance, giving me unlimited permission to travel over the country for the purpose of collecting flowers, medicinal plants, &c. saluting me by the name of Puc Puggy or the Flower hunter, recommending me to the friendship and protection of his people.

The next day being agreed on to hold a council and transact the business of our embassy, we acquainted the chief with our intention of making our encampment on the borders of the great ALACHUA SAVANNA, and to return at the time appointed to town, to attend the council according to agreement.

Soon after we had fixed on the time and manner of proceeding on the further settlement of the treaty, a considerable number of Indians assembled around their chief, when the conversation turned to common and familiar topics.

The chief is a tall well made man, very affable and cheerful, about sixty years of age, his eyes lively and full of fire, his countenance manly and placid, yet ferocious, or what we call savage; his nose aquiline, his dress extremely simple, but his head trimmed and ornamented in the true Creek mode. He has been a great warrior, having then attending him as slaves, many Yamasee captives, taken by himself when young. They were dressed better [186] than he, served and waited upon him with signs of the most abject fear. The manners and customs of the Alachuas, the most of the lower Creeks or Siminoles, appear evidently tinctured with Spanish civilization. Their religious and civil usages manifest a predilection for the Spanish customs. There are several Christians among them, many of whom wear little silver crucifixes, affixed to a wampum collar round their necks, or suspended by a small chain upon their breast. These are said to be baptized, and notwithstanding most of them speak and understand Spanish, yet they have been the most bitter and formidable Indian enemies the Spaniards ever had. The slaves, both male and female, are permitted to marry amongst them: their children are free, and considered in every respect equal to themselves, but the parents continue in a state of slavery as long as they live.

In observing these slaves, we behold at once, in their countenance and manners, the striking contrast betwixt a state of freedom and slavery. They are the tamest, the most abject creatures that we can possibly imagine: mild, peaceable and tractable, they seem to have no will or power to act but as directed by their masters; whilst the free Indians, on the contrary, are bold, active and clamorous. They differ as widely from each other as the bull from the ox.

The repast is now brought in, consisting of venison, stewed with bear's oil, fresh corn cakes, milk and homony, and our drink honey and water, very cool and agreeable. After partaking of this banquet, we took leave and departed for the great savanna.

[187] We soon entered a level, grassy plain, interspersed with low, spreading, three leaved Pine trees, large patches of low shrubs, consisting of Prinos glaber, low Myrica, Kalmia glauca, Andromedas of several species, and many other shrubs, with patches of Palmetto. We continued travelling through this savanna or bay-gale, near two miles, when the land ascends a little; we then entered a hommock or dark grove, consisting of various kinds of trees, as the Magnolia grandiflora, Corypha palma, Citrus Aurantium, Quercus sempervirens, Morus rubra, Ulmus sylvatica, Tilia, Juglans cinerea, Æsculus pavia, Liquidamber, Laurus Borbonia, Hopea tinctoria, Cercis, Cornus Florida, Halesia diptera, Halesia tetraptera, Olea Americana, Callicarpa, Andromeda arborea, Sideroxilon sericium, Sid. tenax, Vitis labrusca, Hedera arborea, Hedera quinquifolia, Rhamnus volubilis, Prunus Caroliniana (pr. flor. racemosis, foliis sempervirentibus, lato-lanceolatis, acuminatis, serratis) Fagus sylvatica, Zanthoxilon clava Herculis, Acer rubrum, Acer negundo, Fraxinus excelsior, with many others already mentioned. The land still gently rising, the soil fertile, loose, loamy and of a dark brown colour. This continues near a mile, when at once opens to view, the most sudden transition from darkness to light, that can possibly be exhibited in a natural landscape.

The extensive Alachua savanna is a level, green plain, above fifteen miles over, fifty miles in circumference, and scarcely a tree or bush of any kind to be seen on it. It is encircled with high, sloping hills, covered with waving forests and fragrant Orange groves, rising from an exuberantly fertile soil. The towering Magnolia grandiflora and transcen-[188]dent Palm, stand conspicuous amongst them. At the same time are seen innumerable droves of cattle; the lordly bull, lowing cow and sleek capricious heifer. The hills and groves re-echo their cheerful, social voices. Herds of sprightly deer, squadrons of the beautiful, fleet Siminole horse, flocks of turkeys, civilized communities of the sonorous, watchful crane, mix together, appearing happy and contented in the enjoyment of peace, 'till disturbed and affrighted by the warrior man. Behold yonder, coming upon them through the darkened groves, sneakingly and unawares, the naked red warrior, invading the Elysian fields and green plains of Alachua. At the terrible appearance of the painted, fearless, uncontrolled and free Siminole, the peaceful, innocent nations are at once thrown into disorder and dismay. See the different tribes and bands, how they draw towards each other! as it were deliberating upon the general good. Suddenly they speed off with their young in the centre; but the roebuck fears him not: here he lays himself down, bathes and flounces in the cool flood. The red warrior, whose plumed head flashes lightning, whoops in vain; his proud, ambitious horse strains and pants; the earth glides from under his feet, his flowing main whistles in the wind, as he comes up full of vain hopes. The bounding roe views his rapid approaches, rises up, lifts aloft his antlered head, erects the white flag *, and fetching a shrill whistle, says to his fleet and free associates, "follow;" he bounds off, and in a few minutes distances his foe a mile; suddenly he stops, turns about, and laughing says, "how vain, go chase meteors in the azure plains above, or hunt butterflies in the fields about your towns."

[189]   We approached the savanna at the South end, by a narrow isthmus of level ground, open to the light of day, and clear of trees or bushes, and not greatly elevated above the common level, having on our right a spacious meadow, embellished with a little lake, one verge of which was not very distant from us; its shore is a moderately high, circular bank, partly encircling a cove of the pond, in the form of a half moon; the water is clear and deep, and at the distance of some hundred yards, was a large floating field (if I may so express myself) of the Nymphea nilumbo, with their golden blossoms waving to and fro on their lofty stems. Beyond these fields of Nymphea were spacious plains, encompassed by dark groves, opening to extensive Pine forests, other plains still appearing beyond them.

This little lake and surrounding meadows, would have been alone sufficient to surprise and delight the traveller, but being placed so near the great savanna, the attention is quickly drawn off, and wholly engaged in the contemplation of the unlimited, varied, and truly astonishing native wild scenes of landscape and perspective, there exhibited: how is the mind agitated and bewildered, at being thus, as it were, placed on the borders of a new world! On the first view of such

* Alluding to his tail.

an amazing display of the wisdom and power of the supreme author of nature, the mind for a moment seems suspended, and impressed with awe.

This isthmus being the common avenue or road of Indian travellers, we pitched our camp at a small distance from it, on a rising knoll near the verge of the savanna, under some spreading Live Oaks: this situation was open and airy, and gave us an unbounded prospect over the adjacent plains. Dewy [190] evening now comes on, the animating breezes, which cooled and tempered the meridian hours of this sultry season, now gently cease; the glorious sovereign of day, calling in his bright beaming emanations, leaves us in his absence to the milder government and protection of the silver queen of night, attended by millions of brilliant luminaries. The thundering alligator has ended his horrifying roar; the silver plumed ganet and stork, the sage and solitary pelican of the wilderness, have already retired to their silent nocturnal habitations, in the neighbouring forests; the sonorous savanna crane, in well disciplined squadrons, now rising from the earth, mount aloft in spiral circles, far above the dense atmosphere of the humid plain; they again view the glorious sun, and the light of day still gleaming on their polished feathers, they sing their evening hymn, then in a strait line majestically descend, and alight on the towering Palms or lofty Pines, their secure and peaceful lodging places. All around being still and silent, we repair to rest.

Soon after sun-rise, a party of Indians on horseback, appeared upon the savanna, to collect together several herds of cattle which they drove along near our camp, towards the town. One of the party came up and informed us the cattle belonged to the chief of Cuscowilla, that he had ordered some of the best steers of his droves to be slaughtered for a general feast for the whole town, in compliment of our arrival, and pacific negotiations.

The cattle were as large and fat as those of the rich grazing pastures of Moyomensing in Pennsylvania. The Indians drove off the lowing herds, and we soon followed them to town, in order to be at council at the appointed hours, leaving two young men of our party to protect our camp.

[191] Upon our arrival we repaired to the public square or council-house, where the chiefs and senators were already convened, the warriors and young men assembled soon after, the business being transacted in public. As it was no more than a ratification of the late treaty of St. Augustine, with some particular commercial stipulations, with respect to the citizens of Alachua, the negociations soon terminated to the satisfaction of both parties.

The banquet succeeds; the ribs and choisest fat pieces of the bullocks, excellently well barbecued, are brought into the apartment of
the public square, constructed and appointed for feasting; bowls and
kettles of stewed flesh and broth are brought in for the next course, and
with it a very singular dish, the traders call it tripe soup; it is made
of the belly or paunch of the beef, not overcleansed of its contents, cut
and minced pretty fine, and then made into a thin soup, seasoned well
with salt and aromatic herbs; but the seasoning not quite strong enough
to extinguish its original savour and scent. This dish is greatly esteemed
by the Indians, but is, in my judgment, the least agreeable they have
amongst them.

The town of Cuscowilla, which is the capital of the Alachua tribe,
contains about thirty habitations, each of which consists of two houses
nearly the same size, about thirty feet in length, twelve feet wide, and
about the same in height; the door is placed midway on one side or
in the front; this house is divided equally, across, into two apartments,
one of which is the cook room and common hall, and the other their
lodging room. The other house is nearly of the same dimensions, standing about twenty yards from the dwelling house, its end fronting [192]
the door; this building is two stories high, and constructed in a different manner, it is divided transversely, as the other, but the end next
the dwelling house is open on three sides, supported by posts or pillars,
it has an open loft or platform, the ascent to which, is by a portable
stairs or ladder; this is a pleasant, cool, airy situation, and here the
master or chief of the family, retires to repose in the hot seasons, and
receives his guests or visitors: the other half of this building is closed
on all sides by notched logs; the lowest or ground part is a potatoe
house, and the upper story over it a granary for corn and other provisions. Their houses are constructed of a kind of frame; in the first place,
strong corner pillars are fixed in the ground, with others somewhat less,
ranging on a line between; these are strengthened by cross pieces of
timber, and the whole with the roof is covered close with the bark of
the Cypress tree. This dwelling stands near the middle of a square
yard, encompassed by a low bank, formed with the earth taken out of
the yard, which is always carefully swept. Their towns are clean, the
inhabitants being particular in laying their filth at a proper distance
from their dwellings, which undoubtedly contributes to the healthiness
of their habitations.

The town stands on the most pleasant situation, that could be well
imagined or desired, in an inland country; upon a high swelling ridge
of sand hills, within three or four hundred yards of a large and beautiful lake, the circular shore of which continually washes a sandy beach,

under a moderately high sloping bank, terminated on one side by extensive forests, consisting of Orange groves, overtopped with grand Magnolias, Palms, Poplar, Ti-[193]lia, Live Oaks and others already noticed; and the opposite point of the crescent, gradually retires with hommocky projecting points, indenting the grassy marshes, and lastly terminates in infinite green plains and meadows, united with the skies and waters of the lake; such a natural landscape, such a rural scene, is not to be imitated by the united ingenuity and labour of man. At present the ground betwixt the town and the lake is adorned by an open grove of very tall Pine trees, which standing at a considerable distance from each other, admit a delightful prospect of the sparkling waters. The lake abounds with various excellent fish and wild fowl; there are incredible numbers of the latter, especially in the winter season, when they arrive here from the North to winter.

The Indians abdicated the ancient Alachua town on the borders of the savanna, and built here, calling the new town Cuscowilla; their reasons for removing their habitation were on account of its unhealthiness, occasioned, as they say, by the stench of the putrid fish and reptiles in the summer and autumn, driven on shore by the alligators, and the exhalations from marshes of the savanna, together with the persecution of the musquitoes.

They plant but little here about the town, only a small garden spot at each habitation, consisting of a little Corn, Beans, Tobacco, Citruls, &c. their plantations which supply them with the chief of their vegetable provisions, such as Zea, Convolvulus batata, Cucurbita citrulus, Cuc. laginaria, Cuc. pepo, Cuc. melopepo, Cuc. verrucosa, Dolichos varieties, &c. lie on the rich prolific lands bordering on the great Alachua savanna, about two miles distance, which plantation is one common in-[194]closure, and is worked and tended by the whole community; yet every family has its particular part, according to its own appointment, marked off when planted, and this portion receives the common labour and assistance until ripe, when each family gathers and deposits in its granary its own proper share, setting apart a small gift or contribution for the public granary, which stands in the centre of the plantation.

The youth, under the supervisal of some of their ancient people, are daily stationed in their fields, who are continually whooping and hallooing, to chase away crows, jackdaws, black-birds and such predatory animals, and the lads are armed with bows and arrows, who, being trained up to it from their early youth, are sure at a mark, and in the course of the day load themselves with squirrels, birds, &c. The men in turn patrole the Corn fields at night, to protect their provisions from the depredations of night rovers, as bears, raccoons and deer; the two former being immoderately fond of young Corn, when the grain is filled with a rich milk, as sweet and nourishing as cream, and the deer are as fond of the Potatoe vines.

After the feast was over, we returned to our encampment on the great savanna, towards the evening. Our companions, whom we left at the camp, were impatient for our return, having been out horse hunting in the plains and groves during our absence. They soon left us, on a visit to the town, having there some female friends, with whom they were anxious to renew their acquaintance. The Siminole girls are by no means destitute of charms to please the rougher sex: the white traders, are fully sensible how greatly it is for their advantage [195] to gain their affections and friendship in matters of trade and commerce; and if their love and esteem for each other is sincere, and upon principles of reciprocity, there are but few instances of their neglecting or betraying the interests and views of their temporary husbands; they labour and watch constantly to promote their private interests, and detect and prevent any plots or evil designs which may threaten their persons, or operate against their trade or business.

In the cool of the evening I embraced the opportunity of making a solitary excursion round the adjacent lawns: taking my fuzee with me, I soon came up to a little clump of shrubs, upon a swelling green knoll, where I observed several large snakes entwined together; I stepped up near them, they appeared to be innocent and peaceable, having no inclination to strike at any thing, though I endeavoured to irritate them, in order to discover their disposition, nor were they anxious to escape from me. This snake is about four feet in length and as thick as a man's wrist; the upper side of a dirty, ash colour; the squamae large, ridged and pointed; the belly or under side of a reddish, dull flesh colour; the tail part not long but slender like most other innocent snakes. They prey on rats, land frogs, young rabbits, birds, &c. I left them, continuing my progress and researches, delighted with the ample prospects around and over the savanna.

Stopping again at a natural shrubbery, when turning my eyes to some flowering shrubs, I observed near my feet, the surprising glass snake (anguis fragilis;) they seem as innocent and harmless as worms. They are, when full grown, two feet and [196] an half in length, and three fourths of an inch in thickness; the abdomen or body part is remarkably short, and they seem to be all tail, which, though long, gradually attenuates to its extremity, yet not small and slender as in switch snakes; the colour and texture of the whole animal is so exactly like bluish green glass, which, together with its fragility, almost persuades a stranger that they are in reality of that brittle substance: but it is only the tail part that breaks off, which it does like glass, by a very gentle stroke from a slender switch. Tho' they are quick and nimble in twisting about, yet they cannot run fast from one, but quickly secrete themselves at the bottom of the grass or under leaves. It is a vulgar fable, that they are able to repair themselves after being broke into several pieces; which pieces, common report says, by a power or faculty in the animal, voluntarily approach each other, join and heal again. The sun now low, shoots the pointed shadows of the projecting promontories far on the skirts of the lucid green plain, flocks of turkeys calling upon their strolling associates, circumspectly march onward to the groves and high forests, their nocturnal retreats. Dewy eve now arrived; I turned about and regained our encampment in good time.

The morning cool and pleasant, and the skies serene, we decamped, pursuing our progress round the Alachua savanna. Three of our companions separating from us, went a-head and we soon lost sight of them: they again parting on different excursions, in quest of game and in search of their horses; some enter the surrounding groves and forests, others strike off into the green plains. My companion, the old trader and myself kept together, he [197] being the most intelligent and willing to oblige me; we coasted the green verge of the plain, under the surrounding hills, occasionally penetrating and crossing the projecting promontories, as the pathway or conveniency dictated, to avoid the waters and mud which still continued deep and boggy near the steep hills, in springy places; so that when we came to such places, we found it convenient to ascend and coast round the sides of the hills, or strike out a little into the savanna, to a moderately swelling ridge, where the ground being dry, and a delightful green turf, was pleasant travelling; but then we were under the necessity to ford creeks or rivulets, which are the conduits or drains of the shallow, boggy ponds or morasses just under the hills; this range or chain of morasses continues round the South and South-West border of the savanna, and appeared to me to be fed or occasioned by the great wet bay-gale or savanna Pine lands, which lay immediately back of the high, hilly forests on the great savanna, part of which we crossed in coming from Cuscowilla, which bottom is a flat, level, hard sand, lying between the sand ridge of Cuscowilla and these eminences of the great savanna, and is a vast receptacle or reservoir of the rain waters, which being defended from the active and powerful exhalations of the meridian sun, by the shadow of the Pine trees, low shrubs and grass, gradually filtering through the sand, drain through these hills and present themselves in innumerable little meandering rills, at the bases of the shady heights fronting the savanna.

Our progress this day was extremely pleasant, over the green turf, having in view numerous herds of cattle and deer, and squadrons of horse, peaceably browzing on the tender, sweet grass, or strolling [198] through the cool fragrant groves on the surrounding heights.

Besides the continued Orange groves, these heights abound with Palms, Magnolias, Red Bays, Liquid-amber, and Fagus sylvatica of incredible magnitude, their trunks imitating the shafts of vast columns: we observed Cassine, Prunus, Vitis labrusca, Rhamnus volubilis, and delightful groves of Æsculus pavia, Prunus Caroliniana, a most beautiful evergreen, decorated with its racemes of sweet, white blossoms.

Passing through a great extent of ancient Indian fields, now grown over with forests of stately trees, Orange groves and luxuriant herbage. The old trader, my associate, informed me it was the ancient Alachua, the capital of that famous and powerful tribe, who peopled the hills surrounding the savanna, when, in days of old, they could assemble by thousands at ball play and other juvenile diversions and athletic exercises, over those, then, happy fields and green plains; and there is no reason to doubt of his account being true, as almost every step we take over those fertile heights, discovers remains and traces of ancient human habitations and cultivation. It is the most elevated eminence upon the savanna, and here the hills descend gradually to the savanna, by a range of gentle, grassy banks. Arriving at a swelling green knoll, at some distance in the plains, near the banks of a pond, opposite the old Alachua town, the place appointed for our meeting again together; it being near night our associates soon after joined us, where we lodged. Early next morning we continued our tour; one division of our company directing their course across the plains to the North coast: my old companion, [199] with myself in company, continued our former rout, coasting the savanna W. and N. W. and by agreement we were all to meet again at night, at the E. end of the savanna.

We continued some miles crossing over, from promontory to promontory, the most enchanting green coves and vistas, scolloping and indenting the high coasts of the vast plain. Observing a company of wolves (lupus niger) under a few trees, about a quarter of a mile from shore, we rode up towards them, they observing our approach, sitting on their hinder parts until we came nearly within shot of them, when they trotted off towards the forests, but stopped again and looked at us, at about two hundred yards distance; we then whooped, and made a feint to pursue them, when they separated from each other, some stretching off into the plains and others seeking covert in the groves on shore; when we got to the trees we observed they had been feeding on the carcase of a horse. The wolves of Florida are larger than a dog, and are perfectly black, except the females, which have a white spot on the breast, but they are not so large as the wolves of Canada and Pennsylvania, which are of a yellowish brown colour. There were a number of vultures on the trees over the carcase, who, as soon as the wolves ran off, immediately settled down upon it; they were however held in restraint and subordination by the bald eagle (falco leucocephalus.)

On our route near a long projected point of the coast, we observed a large flock of turkeys; at our approach they hastened to the groves; we soon gained the promontory; on the ascending hills were vestiges of an ancient Indian town, now oversha-[200]dowed with groves of the Orange, loaded with both green and ripe fruit, and embellished with their fragrant bloom, gratifying the taste, the sight and the smell at the same instant. Leaving this delightful retreat, we soon came to the verge of the groves, when presented to view, a vast verdant bay of the savanna; we discovered a herd of deer feeding at a small distance, upon the sight of us they ran off, taking shelter in the groves on the opposite point or cape of this spacious meadow. My companions being old expert hunters, quickly concerted a plan for their destruction; one of our company immediately struck off, obliquely crossing the meadow for the opposite groves, in order to intercept them, if they should continue their course up the forest, to the main; and we crossed strait over to the point, if possible to keep them in sight, and watch their motions, knowing that they would make a stand thereabouts, before they would attempt their last escape: on drawing near the point, we slackened our gate, and cautiously entered the groves, when we beheld them thoughtless and secure, flouncing in a sparkling pond, in a green meadow or cove beyond the point; some were lying down on their sides in the cool waters, whilst others were prancing like young kids; the young bucks in playsome sport, with their sharp horns hooking and spurring the others, urging them to splash the water.

I endeavoured to plead for their lives, but my old friend though he was a sensible, rational and good sort of man, would not yield to my philosophy; he requested me to mind our horses, while he made his approaches, cautiously gaining ground on them, from tree to tree, when they all suddenly sprang up and herded together; a princely buck who headed the party, whistled and bounded off, [201] his retinue followed, but unfortunately for their chief, he led them with prodigious speed out towards the savanna very near us, and when passing by, the lucky old hunter fired and laid him prostrate upon the green turf, but a few yards from us; his affrighted followers at the instant, sprang off in every direction, streaming away like meteors or phantoms, and we quickly lost sight of them: he opened his body, took out the entrails and placed the carcase in the fork of a tree, casting his frock or hunting shirt over to protect it from the vultures and crows, who follow the hunter as regularly as his own shade.

Our companions soon arrived, we set forward again, enjoying the like scenes we had already past; observed parties of Siminole horses coursing over the plains, and frequently saw deer, turkeys and wolves, but they knew their safety here, keeping far enough out of our reach. The wary, sharp sighted crane, circumspectly observing our progress. We saw a female of them sitting on her nest, and the male, her mate, watchfully traversing backwards and forwards, at a small distance; they suffered us to approach near them before they arose, when they spread their wings, running and tipping the ground with their feet some time, and then mounted aloft, soaring round and round over the nest; they set upon only two eggs at a time, which are very large, long and pointed at one end, of a pale ash colour, powdered or speckled with brown. The manner of forming their nests and setting is very singular; choosing a tussock and there forming a rude heap of dry grass, or such like materials, near as high as their body is from the ground, when standing upon their feet; on the summit of this [202] they form the nest of fine soft dry grass, when she covers her eggs to hatch them, she stands over them, bearing her body and wings over the eggs.

We again came up to a long projecting point of the high forests, beyond which opened to view an extensive grassy cove of the savanna, several miles in circuit; we crossed strait over from this promontory to the opposite coast, and on the way were constrained to wade a mile or more through the water, though at a little distance from us it appeared as a delightful meadow, the grass growing through the water, the middle of which, however, when we came up, proved to be a large space of clear water almost deep enough to swim our horses; it being a large branch of the main creek which drains the savanna; after getting through this morass, we arrived on a delightful, level, green meadow as usual, which continued about a mile, when we reached the firm land; and then gradually ascending, we alighted on a hard sandy beach, which exhibited evident signs of being washed by the waves of the savanna, when in the winter season it is all under water, and then presents the appearance of a large lake. The coast here is much lower than the opposite side, which we had left behind us, and rises from the meadows with a gradual sloping ascent, covered scatteringly with low spreading Live Oaks, short Palms, Zanthoxilon, Laurus Borbonia, Cassine, Sideroxilon, Quercus nigra, Q. sinuata and others; all leaning from the bleak winds that oppress them. About one hundred yards back of this beach, the sand hills gradually rise, and the open Pine forests appear; we coasted a mile or two along the beach, then doubled a promontory of high forests, and soon after came to a swift running brook of [203] clear water, rolling over gravel and white sand, which being brought along with it, in its descent down the steeper sandy beach, formed an easy swelling bank or bar; the waters spread greatly at this place, exhibiting a shallow glittering sheet of clear water, but just sufficient continually to cover the clear gravelly bed, and seemed to be sunk a little below the common surface of the beach; this stream however is soon separated into a number of rivulets, by small sandy and gravelly ridges, and the waters are finally stole away from the sight, by a charming green meadow, which, again secretly uniting under the tall grass, forms a little creek, meandering through the turfy plain, marking its course by reeds and rushes, which spring up from its banks, joining the main creek that runs through the savanna, and at length delivers the water into the Great Sink. Proceeding about a mile farther we came up to, and crossed another brook larger than the former, which exhibited the like delightful appearance. We next passed over a level green lawn, a cove of the savanna, and arrived at a hilly grove. We alighted in a pleasant vista, turning our horses to graze while we amused ourselves with exploring the borders of the Great Sink. In this place a group of rocky hills almost surround a large bason, which is the general receptacle of the water, draining from every part of the vast savanna, by lateral conduits, winding about, and one after another joining the main creek or general conductor, which at length delivers them into this sink; where they descend by slow degrees, through rocky caverns, into the bowels of the earth, whence they are carried by secret subterraneous channels into other receptacles and basons.

[204] We ascended a collection of eminences, covered with dark groves, which is one point of the crescent that partly encircles the sink or bason, open only on the side next the savanna, where it is joined to the great channel or general conductor of the waters; from this point over to the opposite point of the crescent (which is a similar high rocky promontory) is about one hundred yards, forming a vast semicircular cove or bason, the hills encircling it rising very steep fifty or sixty feet, high, rocky, perpendicular and bare of earth next the waters of the bason. These hills, from the top of the perpendicular,

fluted, excavated, walls of rocks, slant off moderately up to their summits, and are covered with a very fertile, loose, black earth, which
nourishes and supports a dark grove of very large trees, varieties of
shrubs and herbaceous plants. These high forest trees surrounding the
bason, by their great height and spread, so effectually shade the waters,
that coming suddenly from the open plains, we seem at once shut up in
darkness, and the waters appear black, yet are clear; when we ascend
the top of the hills, we perceive the ground to be uneven, by round
swelling points and corresponding hollows, overspread with gloomy
shade, occasioned by the tall and spreading trees, such as Live Oak,
Morus rubra, Zanthoxilon, Sapindus, Liquid-amber, Tilia, Laurus Borbonia, Quercus dentata, Juglans cinerea, and others, together with
Orange trees of remarkable magnitude and very fruitful. But that
which is most singular and to me unaccountable, is the infundibuliform cavities, even on the top of these high hills, some twenty, thirty
and forty yards across, at their superficial rims exactly circular, as if
struck with a compass, sloping gradually inwards to a point at bottom,
forming an [205] inverted cone, or like the upper wide part of a funnel;
the perpendicular depth of them from the common surface is various,
some descending twenty feet deep, others almost to the bed of rocks,
which forms the foundation or nucleus of the hills, and indeed of the
whole country of East Florida; some of them seem to be nearly filled
up with earth, swept in from the common surface, but retain the same
uniformity; though sometimes so close together as to be broken one
into another. But as I shall have occasion to speak further of these
sinks in the earth hereafter, I turn my observation to other objects in
view round about me. In and about the Great Sink, are to be seen incredible numbers of crocodiles, some of which are of an enormous size,
and view the passenger with incredible impudence and avidity; and
at this time they are so abundant, that, if permitted by them, I could
walk over any part of the bason and the river upon their heads, which
slowly float and turn about like knotty chunks or logs of wood, except
when they plunge or shoot forward to beat off their associates, pressing
too close to each other, or taking up fish, which continually croud in
upon them from the river and creeks, draining from the savanna, especially the great trout, mudfish, catfish and the various species of bream;
the gar are rather too hard for their jaws and rough for their throats,
especially here where they have a superfluous plenty and variety of
those that are every way preferable; besides the gar being like themselves, a warlike voracious creature, they seem to be in league or confederacy together, to enslave and devour the numerous defenceless
tribes.

It is astonishing and incredible, perhaps, I may say, to relate what unspeakable numbers of fish repair to [206] this fatal fountain or receptacle, during the latter summer season and autumn, when the powerful sun-beams have evaporated the waters off the savanna, where those who are so fortunate as to effect a retreat into the conductor, and escape the devouring jaws of the fearful alligator and armed gar, descend into the earth, through the wells and cavities or vast perforations of the rocks, and from thence are conducted and carried away, by secret subterranean conduits and gloomy vaults, to other distant lakes and rivers; and it does not appear improbable, but that in some future day this vast savanna or lake of waters, in the winter season will be discovered to be in a great measure filled with its finny inhabitants, who are strangers or adventurers, from other lakes, ponds and rivers, by subterraneous rivulets and communications to this rocky, dark door or outlet, whence they ascend to its surface, spread over and people the winter lake, where they breed, increase and continue as long as it is under water, or during pleasure, for they are at all seasons to be seen ascending and descending through the rocks; but towards the autumn, when the waters have almost left the plains, they then croud to the sink in such multitudes, as at times to be seen pressing on in great banks into the bason, being urged by pursuing bands of alligators and gar, and when entering the great bason or sink, are suddenly fallen upon by another army of the same devouring enemy, lying in wait for them; thousands are driven on shore, where they perish and rot in banks, which was evident at the time I was there, the stench being intolerable, although then early in the summer. There are three great doors or vent holes through the rocks in the sink, two near the centre and the other one near the rim, much higher up than the [207] other two, which was conspicuous through the clear water. The beds of rocks lay in horizontal thick strata or laminae, one over the other, where the sink-holes or outlets are. These rocks are perforated by perpendicular wells or tubes, four, five and six feet in diameter, exactly circular as the tube of a cannon or walled well; many of these are broken into one another, forming a great ragged orifice, appearing fluted by alternate jambs and semicircular perpendicular niches or excavations.

Having satisfied my curiosity in viewing this extraordinary place and very wonderful work of nature, we repaired to our resting place, where we found our horses and mounted again. One of the company parting from us for the buck that we had shot and left in the fork of the tree. My friend, the old trader, led the shortest way across the plain, after repassing the wet morass which had almost swam our horses in the morning. At evening we arrived at the place of our destination, where our associates soon after rejoined us with some Indians, who were merry, agreeable guests as long as they staid; they were in full dress and painted, but before dark they mounted their horses, which were of the true Siminole breed, set spurs to them, uttering all at once a shrill whoop, and went off for Cuscowilla.

Though the horned cattle and horses bred in these meadows are large, sleek, sprightly and as fat as can be in general, yet they are subject to mortal diseases. I observed several of them dreadfully mortified, their thighs and haunches ulcerated, raw and bleeding, which, like a mortification or slow cancer, at length puts an end to their miserable existence. The traders and Indians call this dis-[208] ease the water-rot or scald, and say it is occasioned by the warm waters of the savanna, during the heats of summer and autumn, when these creatures wade deep to feed on the water-grass, which they are immoderately fond of; whereas the cattle which only feed and range in the high forests and Pine savannas are clear of this disorder. A sacrifice to intemperance and luxury.

We had heavy rains during the night, and though very warm yet no thunder and very little wind. It cleared away in the morning and the day very pleasant. Set off for the East end of the savanna, collecting by the way and driving before us, parties of horse, the property of the traders; and next morning set off on our return to the lower store on St. John's, coasting the savanna yet a few miles, in expectation of finding the remainder of their horses, though disappointed.

We at last bid adieu to the magnificent plains of Alachua, entered the Pine forests, and soon fell into the old Spanish highway, from St. Augustine across the isthmus of Florida, to St. Mark's in the bay of Apalache. Its course and distance from E. to W. is, from St. Augustine to Fort Picolata on the river St. Juan, twenty-seven miles; thence across the river to the Poopoa Fort, three miles; thence to the Alachua Savanna, forty-five miles; thence to Talahasochte on the river Little St. Juan, seventy-five miles; thence down this river to St. Mark's, thirty miles; the whole distance from St. Augustine to St. Mark's, one hundred and eighty miles. But that road having been unfrequented for many years past, since the Creeks subdued the remnant tribes of the ancient Floridans, and drove the Spaniards from their settlements in East [209] Florida into St. Augustine, which effectually cut off their communication between that garrison and St. Mark's; this ancient highway is grown up in many places with trees and shrubs, but yet has left so deep a track on the surface of the earth, that it may be traced for ages yet to come.

Leaving the highway on our left hand, we ascend a sandy ridge, thinly planted by nature with stately Pines and Oaks, of the latter genus, particularly Q. sinuata, S. flamule, Q. nigra, Q. rubra. Passed by an Indian village situated on this high, airy sand ridge, consisting of four or five habitations; none of the people were at home, they were out at their hunting camps; we observed plenty of corn in their cribs. Following a hunting path eight or nine miles, through a vast Pine forest and grassy savanna, well timbered, the ground covered with a charming carpet of various flowering plants, came to a large creek of excellent water, and here we found the encampment of the Indians, the inhabitants of the little town we had passed; we saw their women and children, the men being out hunting. The women presented themselves to our view as we came up, at the door of their tents, veiled in their mantle, modestly shewing their faces when we saluted them. Towards the evening we fell into the old trading path, and before night came to camp at the Half-way Pond. Next morning, after collecting together the horses, some of which had strolled away at a great distance, we pursued our journey and in the evening arrived at the trading house on St. Juan's, from a successful and pleasant tour.

On my return to the store on St. Juan's the trading schooner was there, but as she was not to re-[210]turn to Georgia until the autumn, I found I had time to pursue my travels in Florida, and might at leisure plan my excursions to collect seeds and roots in boxes, &c.

At this time the talks (or messages between the Indians and white people) were perfectly peaceable and friendly, both with the Lower Creeks and the Nation or Upper Creeks; parties of Indians were coming in every day with their hunts: indeed the Muscogulges or Upper Creeks very seldom disturb us. Bad talks from the Nation is always a very serious affair, and to the utmost degree alarming to the white inhabitants.

The Muscogulges are under a more strict government or regular civilization than the Indians in general. They lie near their potent and declared enemy, the Chactaws; their country having a vast frontier, naturally accessible and open to the incursions of their enemies on all sides, they find themselves under the necessity of associating in large, populous towns, and these towns as near together as convenient that they may be enabled to succour and defend one another in case of sudden invasion; this consequently occasions deer and bear to be scarce and difficult to procure, which obliges them to be vigilant and industrious; this naturally begets care and serious attention, which we may suppose in some degree forms their natural disposition and manners, and gives them that air of dignified gravity, so strikingly char-

acteristic in their aged people, and that steadiness, just and chearful
reverence in the middle aged and youth, which sits so easy upon them,
and appears so natural: for however strange it may appear to us, the
same moral duties which with us form the amiable, virtuous character,
and is so diffi-[211]cult to maintain, there, without compulsion or
visible restraint, operates like instinct, with a surprising harmony and
natural ease, insomuch that it seems impossible for them to act out of
the common highroad to virtue.

We will now take a view of the Lower Creeks or Siminoles, and
the natural disposition which characterises this people, when, from
the striking contrast, the philosopher may approve or disapprove, as
he may think proper, from the judgment and opinion given by different men.

The Siminoles, but a weak people, with respect to numbers, all of
them I suppose would not be sufficient to people one of the towns in
the Muscogulge (for instance, the Uches on the main branch of the
Apalachucla river, which alone contains near two thousand inhabitants.) Yet this handful of people possesses a vast territory, all East
Florida and the greatest part of West Florida, which being naturally
cut and divided into thousands of islets, knolls and eminences, by the
innumerable rivers, lakes, swamps, vast savannas and ponds, form so
many secure retreats and temporary dwelling places, that effectually
guard them from any sudden invasions or attacks from their enemies;
and being such a swampy, hommocky country, furnishes such a plenty
and variety of supplies for the nourishment of varieties of animals, that
I can venture to assert, that no part of the globe so abounds with wild
game or creatures fit for the food of man.

Thus they enjoy a superabundance of the necessaries and conveniencies of life, with the security of person and property, the two great
concerns of mankind. The hides of deer, bears, tigers and [212] wolves,
together with honey, wax and other productions of the country, purchase their cloathing, equipage and domestic utensils from the whites.
They seem to be free from want or desires. No cruel enemy to dread;
nothing to give them disquietude, but the gradual encroachments of
the white people. Thus contented and undisturbed, they appear as
blithe and free as the birds of the air, and like them as volatile and
active, tuneful and vociferous. The visage, action and deportment of
a Siminole, being the most striking picture of happiness in this life;
joy, contentment, love and friendship, without guile or affectation, seem
inherent in them, or predominant in their vital principle, for it leaves
them but with the last breath of life. It even seems imposing a constraint upon their ancient chiefs and senators, to maintain a necessary
decorum and solemnity, in their public councils; not even the debility

and decrepitude of extreme old age, is sufficient to erase from their visages, this youthful, joyous simplicity; but like the grey eve of a serene and calm day, a gladdening, cheering blush remains on the Western horizon after the sun is set.

I doubt not but some of my countrymen who may read these accounts of the Indians, which I have endeavoured to relate according to truth, at least as they appeared to me, will charge me with partiality or prejudice in their favour.

I will, however, now endeavour to exhibit their vices, immoralities and imperfections, from my own observations and knowledge, as well as accounts from the white traders, who reside amongst them.

[213] The Indians make war against, kill and destroy their own species, and their motives spring from the same erroneous source as it does in all other nations of mankind; that is, the ambition of exhibiting to their fellows, a superior character of personal and national valour, and thereby immortalize themselves, by transmitting their names with honour and lustre to posterity; or in revenge of their enemy, for public or personal insults; or lastly, to extend the borders and boundaries of their territories: but I cannot find upon the strictest enquiry, that their bloody contests, at this day are marked with deeper stains of inhumanity or savage cruelty, than what may be observed amongst the most civilized nations: they do indeed scalp their slain enemy, but they do not kill the females or children of either sex: the most ancient traders, both in the Lower and Upper Creeks, assured me they never saw an instance of either burning or tormenting their male captives; though it is said they used to do it formerly. I saw in every town in the Nation and Siminoles that I visited, more or less male captives, some extremely aged, who were free and in as good circumstances as their masters; and all slaves have their freedom when they may, which is permitted and encouraged; when they and their offspring, are every way upon an equality with their conquerors; they are given to adultery and fornication, but I suppose in no greater excess than other nations of men. They punish the delinquents, male and female, equally alike, by taking off their ears. This is the punishment for adultery. Infamy and disgrace is supposed to be a sufficient punishment for fornication, in either sex.

They are fond of games and gambling, and a-[214]muse themselves like children, in relating extravagant stories, to cause surprise and mirth.

They wage eternal war against deer and bear, to procure food and clothing, and other necessaries and conveniences; which is indeed carried to an unreasonable and perhaps criminal excess, since the white people have dazzled their senses with foreign superfluities.

CHAP. VII.

A JOURNEY FROM SPALDING'S LOWER TRADING HOUSE TO TALAHASOCHTE OR WHITE KING'S TOWN, ON THE RIVER LITTLE ST. JUAN, THIRTY MILES ABOVE FORT ST. MARKS IN THE BAY OF APALATCHE.

O N my return to the trading house, from my journey to the great savanna, I found the trading company for Little St. Juan's, were preparing for that post.

My mind yet elate with the various scenes of rural nature, which as a lively animated picture, had been presented to my view; the deeply engraven impression, a pleasing flattering contemplation, gave strength and agility to my steps, anxiously to press forward to the delightful fields and groves of Apalatche.

The trading company for Talahasochte being now in readiness to proceed for that quarter, under the direction of our chief trader, in the cool of the morning we set off, each of us having a good horse to ride, besides having in our caravan several pack horses laden with provisions, camp equipage and other necessaries; a young man from St. Augustine, in the service of the governor of East Florida accompanied us, commissioned to purchase of the Indians and traders, some Siminole horses. They are the most beautiful and sprightly species of that noble creature, perhaps any where to be seen; but are of a small breed, and as delicately formed as the American roe buck. A horse in the Creek or Mus-[216]cogulge tongue is echoclucco, that is the great deer, (echo is a deer and clucco is big:) the Siminole horses are said to descend originally from the Andalusian breed, brought here by the Spaniards when they first established the colony of East Florida. From the forehead to their nose is a little arched or aquiline, and so are the fine Chactaw horses among the Upper Creeks, which are said to have been brought thither from New-Mexico across Mississippi, by those nations of Indians who emigrated from the West, beyond the river. These horses are every way like the Siminole breed, only being larger, and perhaps not so lively and capricious. It is a matter of conjecture and enquiry, whether or not the different soil and situation of the country, may have contributed in some measure, in forming and establishing the difference in size and other qualities betwixt them. I have observed the horses and other animals in the high hilly country of Carolina, Georgia, Virginia and all along our shores, are of a much larger and stronger make, than those which are bred in the flat country next the sea coast; a buck-skin of the Upper Creeks and Cherokees will weigh twice as heavy as those of the Siminoles or Lower Creeks, and those bred in the low flat country of Carolina.

Our first days journey was along the Alachua roads, twenty-five miles to the Half-way Pond, where we encamped, the musquitoes were excessively troublesome the whole night.

Decamped early next morning, still pursuing the road to Alachua, until within a few miles of Cuscowilla, when the road dividing, one for the town and the other for the great savanna; here our company separated, one party chose to pass through the [217] town, having some concerns there; I kept with the party that went through the savanna, it being the best road, leading over a part of the savanna, when entering the groves on its borders, we travelled several miles over these fertile eminences and delightful, shady, fragrant forests, then again entered upon the savanna, and crossed a charming extensive green cove or bay of it, covered with a vivid green grassy turf, when we again ascended the woodland hills, through fruitful Orange groves and under shadowy Palms and Magnolias. Now the Pine forests opened to view, we left the magnificent savanna and its delightful groves, passing through a level, open, airy Pine forest, the stately trees scatteringly planted by nature, arising strait and erect from the green carpet, embellished with various grasses and flowering plants, and gradually ascending the sand hills soon came into the trading path to Talahasochte; which is generally, excepting a few deviations, the old Spanish highway to St. Mark's. At about five miles distance beyond the great savanna, we came to camp late in the evening, under a little grove of Live Oaks just by a group of shelly rocks, on the banks of a beautiful little lake, partly environed by meadows. The rocks as usual in these regions partly encircled a spacious sink or grotto, which communicates with the waters of the lake; the waters of the grotto are perfectly transparent, cool and pleasant, and well replenished with fish. Soon after our arrival here, our companions who passed through Cuscowilla joined us. A brisk cool wind during the night kept the persecuting musquitoes at a distance.

The morning pleasant, we decamped early, proceeding on, rising gently for several miles, over [218] sandy, gravelly ridges, we find ourselves in an elevated, high, open, airy region, somewhat rocky, on the backs of the ridges, and presents to view on every side, the most dreary, solitary, desart waste I had ever beheld; groups of bare rocks emerging out of the naked gravel and drifts of white sand; the grass thinly scattered and but few trees; the Pines, Oaks, Olives and Sideroxilons, poor, misshapen and tattered; scarce an animal to be seen or noise heard, save the symphony of the Western breeze, through the bristly Pine leaves, or solitary sand crickets screech, or at best the more social converse of the frogs, in solemn chorus with the swift breezes, brought from distant fens and forests. Next we joyfully enter the borders of the level Pine forest and savannas, which continued for many miles, never out of sight of little lakes or ponds, environed with illumined meadows, the clear waters sparkling through the tall Pines.

Having a good spirited horse under me, I generally kept a-head of my companions, which I often chose to do, as circumstances offered or invited, for the sake of retirement and observation.

The high road being here open and spacious, at a good distance before me, I observed a large hawk on the ground, in the middle of the road; he seemed to be in distress, endeavouring to rise; when, coming up near him, I found him closely bound up by a very long coach-whip snake, that had wreathed himself several times round the hawk's body, who had but one of his wings at liberty; beholding their struggles a while, I alighted off my horse with an intention of parting them; when, on coming up, they mutually agreed to separate themselves, each one seeking his own safety, probably [219] considering me as their common enemy. The bird rose aloft and fled away as soon as he recovered his liberty, and the snake as eagerly made off, I soon overtook him but could not perceive that he was wounded.

I suppose the hawk had been the aggressor, and fell upon the snake with an intention of making a prey of him, and that the snake dexterously and luckily threw himself in coils round his body, and girded him so close as to save himself from destruction.

The coach-whip snake is a beautiful creature; when full grown they are six and seven feet in length, and the largest part of their body not so thick as a cane or common walking stick; their head not larger than the end of a man's finger; their neck is very slender, and from the abdomen tapers away in the manner of a small switch or coach-whip; the top of the head and neck, for three or four inches, is as black and shining as a raven; the throat and belly as white as snow; and the upper side of their body of a chocolate colour, excepting the tail part, almost from the abdomen to the extremity, which is black: it may be proper to observe, however, that they vary in respect to the colour of the body; some I have seen almost white or cream colour, others of a pale chocolate or clay colour, but in all the head and neck is black, and the tail dark brown or black. They are extremely swift, seeming almost to fly over the surface of the ground, and that which is very singular, they can run swiftly on only their tail part, carrying their head and body upright: one very fine one accompanied me along the road side, at a little distance, raising himself erect, now and then looking [220] me in the face, although I proceeded on a good round trot on purpose to observe how fast they could proceed in that position. His object seemed mere curiosity or observation; with respect to venom they are as innocent as a worm, and seem to be familiar with man. They seem a particular inhabitant of East Florida, though I have seen some of them in the maritime parts of Carolina and Georgia, but in these regions they are neither so large or beautiful.

We rise again, passing over sand ridges of gentle elevation, savannas and open Pine forests. Masses or groups of rocks present to view on every side, as before mentioned, and with difficulty we escaped the circular infundibuliform cavities or sinks in the surface of the earth; generally a group of rocks, shaded by Palms, Live Oaks and Magnolias, is situated on their limb: some are partly filled up with earth, whilst others and the greater number of them are partly filled with transparent cool water, which discover the well or perforation through the rocks in the center. This day being remarkably sultry, we came to camp early, having chosen our situation under some stately Pines, near the verge of a spacious savanna.

After some refeshment, our hunters went out into the forest, and returned towards evening; amongst other game, they brought with them a savanna crane * which they shot in the adjoining meadows. This stately bird is above six feet in length from the toes to the extremity of the beak when extended, and the wings expand eight or nine feet; they are above five feet high when standing erect; the tail is remarkably short, but the flag or pendant [221] feathers which fall down off the rump on each side, are very long and sharp pointed, of a delicate texture, and silky softness; the beak is very long, strait and sharp pointed; the crown of the head bare of feathers, of a reddish rose colour, thinly barbed with short, stiff, black hair; the legs and thighs are very long, and bare of feathers a great space above the knees; the plumage of this bird is generally of a pale ash colour, with shades or clouds of pale brown and sky blue, the brown prevails on the shoulders and back; the barrels of the prime quill-feathers are long and of a large diameter, leaving a large cavity when extracted from the wing:

* Grus p.

all the bones of this bird have a thin shell, and consequently a large cavity or medullary receptacle. When these birds move their wings in flight, their strokes are slow, moderate and regular, and even when at a considerable distance or high above us, we plainly hear the quill-feathers, their shafts and webs upon one another, creak as the joints or working of a vessel in a tempestuous sea.

We had this fowl dressed for supper and it made excellent soup; nevertheless as long as I can get any other necessary food I shall prefer his seraphic music in the etherial skies, and my eyes and understanding gratified in observing their economy and social communities, in the expansive green savannas of Florida.

Next morning we arose early, and proceeding, gradually descended again, and continued many miles along a flat, level country, over delightful green savannas, decorated with hommocks or islets of dark groves, consisting of Magnolia grandiflora, Morus, tilia, Zanthoxilon, Laurus Borbonia, Sideroxilon, Quercus sempervirens, Halesia diptera, Cal-[222]licarpa, Corypha palma, &c. there are always groups of whitish testaceous rocks and sinks where these hommocks are. We next crossed a wet savanna, which is the beginning of a region still lower than we had traversed; here we crossed a rapid rivulet of exceeding cool, pleasant water, where we halted to refresh ourselves. But it must be remarked here, that this rivulet, though lively and rapid at this time, is not a permanent stream, but was formed by a heavy rain that fell the day before, as was apparent from its bed, besides it is at best but a jet or mere phantom of a brook, as the land around is rocky and hollow, abounding with wells and cavities. Soon after leaving the brook we passed off to the left hand, along the verge of an extensive savanna, and meadows many miles in circumference, edged on one border with detached groves and pompous Palms, and embellished with a beautiful sparkling lake; its verges decorated with tall, waving grass and floriferous plants; the pellucid waters gently rolling on to a dark shaded grotto, just under a semicircular, swelling, turfy ascent or bank, skirted by groves of Magnolias, Oaks, Laurels and Palms. In these expansive and delightful meadows, were feeding and roving troops of the fleet Siminole horse. We halted a while at this grotto, and after refreshing ourselves we mounted horse and proceeded across a charming lawn, part of the savanna, entering on it through a dark grove. In this extensive lawn were several troops of horse, and our company had the satisfaction of observing several belonging to themselves. One occurrence, remarkable here, was a troop of horse under the control and care of a single black dog, which seemed to differ in no respect from the wolf of Florida, except his being able to bark as the common dog. He was very careful and industrious in keeping them toge-[223]ther, and if any one strolled from the rest at too great a distance, the dog would spring up, head the horse and bring him back to the company. The proprietor of these horses is an Indian in Talahasochte, about ten miles distance from this place, who, out of humour and experiment, trained his dog up from a puppy to this business; he follows his master's horses only, keeping them in a separate company where they range, and when he is hungry or wants to see his master, in the evening he returns to town, but never stays at home a night.

The region we had journeyed through, since we decamped this morning, is of a far better soil and quality than we had yet seen since we left Alachua; generally a dark greyish, and sometimes brown and black loam, on a foundation of whitish marl, chalk and testaceous limestone rocks, and ridges of a loose, coarse, reddish sand, producing stately Pines in the plains, and Live Oak, Mulberry, Magnolia, Palm, Zanthoxilon, &c. in the hommocks, and also in great plenty the perennial Indigo; it grows here five, six and seven feet high, and as thick together as if it had been planted and cultivated. The higher ridges of hills afford great quantities of a species of iron ore, of that kind found in New-Jersey and Pennsylvania, and there called bog ore; it appears on the surface of the ground in large detached masses and smaller fragments; it is ponderous and seemed rich of that most useful metal; but one property remarkable in these terrigenous stones is, they appeared to be blistered, somewhat resembling cinders, or as if they had suffered a violent action of fire.

Leaving the charming savanna and fields of Capola, we passed several miles through delightful plains [224] and meadows, little differing from the environs of Capola, diversified with rocky islets or hommocks of dark woodland.

We next entered a vast forest of the most stately Pine trees that can be imagined, planted by nature at a moderate distance, on a level, grassy plain, enamelled with a variety of flowering shrubs, viz. Viola, Ruellia infundibuliformea, Amaryllis atamasco, Mimosa sensitiva, Mimosa intsia and many others new to me. This sublime forest continued five or six miles, when we came to dark groves of Oaks, Magnolias, Red bays, Mulberrys, &c. through which proceeding near a mile, we entered open fields and arrived at the town of Talahasochte, on the banks of Little St. Juan.

The river Little St. Juan may, with singular propriety, be termed the pellucid river. The waters are the clearest and purest of any river I ever saw, transmitting distinctly the natural form and appearance of the objects moving in the transparent floods, or reposing on the silvery bed, with the finny inhabitants sporting in its gently flowing stream.

The river at the town is about two hundred yards over, and fifteen or twenty feet in depth. The great swamp and lake Oaquaphenogaw is said to be its source, which is about one hundred miles by land North of this place, which would give the river a course of near two hundred miles from its source to the sea, to follow its meanders; as in general our rivers, that run any considerable distance through the country to the sea, by their windings and roving about to find a passage through the ridges and heights, at least double their distance.

The Indians and traders say that this river has no [225] branches or collateral brooks or rivers tributary to it, but that it is fed or augmented by great springs which break out through the banks. From the accounts given by them, and my own observations on the country round about, it seems a probable assertion, for there was not a creek or rivulet, to be seen, running on the surface of the ground, from the great Alachua Savanna to this river, a distance of about seventy miles; yet, perhaps, no part of the earth affords a greater plenty of pure, salubrious waters. The unparalleled transparency of these waters furnishes an argument for such a conjecture, that amounts at least to a probability, were it not confirmed by ocular demonstration; for in all the flat countries of Carolina and Florida, except this isthmus, the waters of the rivers are, in some degree, turgid, and have a dark hue, owing to the annual firing of the forests and plains, and afterwards the heavy rains washing the light surface of the burnt earth into rivulets, and these rivulets running rapidly over the surface of the earth, flow into the rivers, and tinge the waters the colour of lye or beer, almost down to the tide near the sea coast. But here behold how different the appearance, and how manifest the cause; for although the surface of the ground produces the same vegetable substances, the soil the same, and suffers in like manner a general conflagration, and the rains, in impetuous showers, as liberally descend upon the parched surface of the ground; but the earth being so hollow and porous, these superabundant waters cannot constitute a rivulet or brook, to continue any distance on its surface, before they are arrested in their course and swallowed up, thence descending, are filtered through the sands and o-[226]ther strata of earth, to the horizontal beds of porous rocks, which being composed of thin separable laminae, lying generally in obliquely horizontal directions over each other, admit these waters to pass on by gradual but constant percolation; which collecting and associating, augment and form little rills, brooks and even subterraneous rivers, which wander in darkness beneath the surface of the earth, by innumerable doublings, windings and secret labyrinths; no doubt in some places forming vast reservoirs and subterranean lakes, inhabited by multitudes of fish and aquatic animals: and possibly, when collected into large rapid brooks, meeting irresistible obstructions in their course, they suddenly break through these perforated fluted rocks, in high, perpendicular jets, nearly to their former level, flooding large districts of land: thus by means of those subterranean courses, the waters are purified and finally carried to the banks of great rivers, where they emerge and present themselves to open day-light, with their troops of finny inhabitants, in those surprising vast fountains near the banks of this river; and likewise on and near the shores of Great St. Juan, on the East coast of the isthmus, some of which I have already given an account of.

On our arrival at Talahasochte, in the evening we repaired to the trading house formerly belonging to our chief, where were a family of Indians, who immediately and complaisantly moved out to accommodate us. The White King with most of the male inhabitants were out hunting or tending their Corn plantations.

The town is delightfully situated on the elevated East banks of the river, the ground level to near the river, when it descends suddenly to the water; [227] I suppose the perpendicular elevation of the ground may be twenty or thirty feet. There are near thirty habitations constructed after the mode of Cuscowilla; but here is a more spacious and neat council-house.

These Indians have large handsome canoes, which they form out of the trunks of Cypress trees (Cupressus disticha) some of them commodious enough to accomodate twenty or thirty warriors. In these large canoes they descend the river on trading and hunting expeditions on the sea coast, neighbouring islands and keys, quite to the point of Florida, and sometimes cross the gulph, extending their navigations to the Bahama islands and even to Cuba: a crew of these adventurers had just arrived, having returned from Cuba but a few days before our arrival, with a cargo of spirituous liquors, Coffee, Sugar and Tobacco. One of them politely presented me with a choice ·piece of Tobacco, which he told me he had received from the governor of Cuba.

They deal in the way of barter, carrying with them deer skins, furs, dry fish, bees-wax, honey, bear's oil and some other articles. They say the Spaniards receive them very friendly, and treat them with the best spirituous liquors.

The Spaniards of Cuba likewise trade here or at St. Marks, and other sea ports on the West coast of the isthmus in small sloops; particularly at the bay of Calos, where are excellent fishing banks and grounds; not far from which is a considerable town of the Siminoles, where they take great quantities of fish, which they salt and cure on shore, and barter with the Indians and traders for skins, furs, &c. and return with their cargoes to Cuba.

[228] The trader of the town of Talahasochte informed me, that he had, when trading in that town, large supplies of goods, from these Spanish trading vessels, suitable for that trade; and some very essential articles, on more advantageous terms than he could purchase at Indian stores either in Georgia or St. Augustine.

Towards the evening after the sultry heats were past, a young man of our company, having previously procured the loan of a canoe from an Indian, proposed to me a fishing excursion for trout with the bob. We set off down the river, and before we had passed two miles caught enough for our household: he was an excellent hand at this kind of diversion; some of the fish were so large and strong in their element, as to shake his arms stoutly and dragged us with the canoe over the floods before we got them in. It is in the eddy coves, under the points and turnings of the river, where the surface of the waters for some acres is covered with the leaves of the Nymphea, Pistia and other amphibious herbs and grass, where the haunts and retreats of this famous fish are, as well as others of various tribes.

Observing a fishing canoe of Indians turning a point below and coming towards us, who hailing us, we waited their coming up; they were cheerful merry fellows, and insisted on our accepting of part of their fish, they having a greater quantity and variety, especially of the bream my favourite fish; we exchanged some of our trout with them.

Our chief being engaged with the chiefs of the town in commercial concerns, and others of our company, out in the forests with the Indians, hunt-[229]ing up horses belonging to the trading company; the young interpreter, my companion, who was obliging to me and whom our chief previously recommended to me as an associate; proposed to me another little voyage down the river; this was agreeable to me, being desirous of increasing my observations during our continuance at Talahasochte; as when the White King should return to town (which was expected every hour) we intended after audience and treaty to leave them and encamp in the forests, about fifteen miles distance and nearer the range of their horses.

Having supplied ourselves with ammunition and provision, we set off in the cool of the morning, and descended pleasantly, riding on the crystal flood, which flows down with an easy, gentle, yet active current, rolling over its silvery bed; how abundantly are the waters replenished with inhabitants! the stream almost as transparent as the air we breathe; there is nothing done in secret except on its green flowery verges, where nature at the command of the Supreme Creator, hath spread a mantle, as a covering and retreat at suitable and convenient times, but by no means a secure refuge from the voracious enemy and pursuer.

Behold the watery nations, in numerous bands roving to and fro, amidst each other, here they seem all at peace; though incredible to relate, but a few yards off, near the verge of the green mantled shore there is eternal war, or rather slaughter! Near the banks the waters become turgid, from substances gradually diverging from each side of the swift channel, and collections of opaque particles whirled to shore by the eddies, which afford a kind of nursery for [230] young fry, and its slimy bed a prolific nidus for generating and rearing of infinite tribes and swarms of amphibious insects, which are the food of young fish, who in their turn become a prey to the older. Yet when those different tribes of fish are in the transparent channel, their very nature seems absolutely changed, for here is neither desire to destroy or persecute, but all seems peace and friendship; do they agree on a truce, a suspension of hostilities? or by some secret divine influence, is desire taken away? or they are otherwise rendered incapable of pursuing each other to destruction?

About noon we approached the admirable Manate Spring, three or four miles down the river. This charming nympheum is the product of primitive nature, not to be imitated much less equalled by the united effort of human power and ingenuity! as we approach it by water, the mind of the enquiring traveller is previously entertained and gradually led on to greater discovery; first by a view of the sublime dark grove, lifted up on shore, by a range or curved chain of hills, at a small distance from the lively green verge of the river, on the East banks; as we gently descend floating fields of the Nymphea nilumbo, intersected with vistas of the yellow green Pistia stratiotes, which cover a bay or cove of the river opposite the circular woodland hills.

It is amazing and almost incredible, what troops and bands of fish, and other watery inhabitants are now in sight, all peaceable, and in what variety of gay colours and forms, continually ascending and descending, roving and figuring amongst one another, yet every tribe associating separately; we now ascended the crystal stream, the current swift, [231] we entered the grand fountain, the expansive circular bason, the source of which arises from under the bases of the high woodland hills, near half encircling it; the ebullition is astonishing, and continual, though its greatest force or fury intermits, regularly, for the space of thirty seconds of time; the waters appear of a lucid sea green colour, in some measure owing to the reflection of the leaves above; the ebullition is perpendicular upwards, from a vast ragged orifice through a bed of rocks, a great depth below the common surface of the bason, throwing up small particles or pieces of white shells, which subside with the waters, at the moment of intermission, gently settling down round about the orifice, form a vast funnel; at those moments, when the waters rush upwards, the surface of the bason immediately over the orifice is greatly swollen or raised a considerable height; and then it is impossible to keep the boat or any other floating vessel over the fountain; but the ebullition quickly subsides, yet, before the surface becomes quite even, the fountain vomits up the waters again, and so on perpetually; the bason is generally circular, about fifty yards over, and the perpetual stream from it into the river is twelve or fifteen yards wide, and ten or twelve feet in depth; the bason and stream continually peopled with prodigious numbers and variety of fish and other animals; as the alligator and the manate * or sea cow, in the winter season; part of a skeleton of one, which the Indians had killed last winter, lay upon the banks of the spring; the grinding teeth were about an inch in diameter; the ribs eighteen inches in length, and two inches and an half in thickness, bending with a gentle curve, this bone is esteemed equal to ivory; the flesh of this crea-[232]ture is counted wholesome and pleasant food; the Indians call them by a name which signifies the big beaver. My companion, who was a trader in Talahasochte last winter, saw three of them at one time in this spring: they feed chiefly on aquatic grass and weeds. The ground round about the head of the bason is generally level, for the distance of a few yards, then gradually ascends, forming moderately high hills; the soil at top is a light, greyish, sandy mould, which continues some feet in depth, lying on a stratum of yellowish clay, then clay and gravel, then sand, and so on, stratum upon stratum, down to the general foundation of testaceous rocks. In other places a deep stratum of whitish, chalky limestone. The vegetable productions which cover and ornament those eminences, are generally Live Oaks, Magnolia grandiflora, in the Creek tongue, Tolochlucco, which signifies the Big Bay, Laurus Borbonia or Red Bay, in the Creek tongue, Eto-mico, that is King's tree, Olea Americana and Liquid-amber, with other trees, shrubs and herbaceous plants common in East Florida.

The hills and groves environing this admirable fountain, affording amusing subjects of enquiry, occasioned my stay here a great part of the day, and towards evening we returned to the town.

* Trichechus manatus. Sea cow.

Next day, early in the morning, we crossed the river, landing on the other shore opposite the town, swimming our horses by the side of the canoe, each of us holding his horse by the bridle whilst an Indian paddled us over. After crossing, we struck off from the river into the forests, sometimes falling into, and keeping for a time, the ancient Spanish high road to Pensacola, now almost obliterated: passed four or five miles through old Spanish fields.

[233]   There are to be seen plain marks or vestiges of the old Spanish plantations and dwellings; as fence posts and wooden pillars of their houses, ditches and even Corn ridges and Batata hills. From the Indian accounts, the Spaniards had here a rich, well cultivated and populous settlement, and a strong fortified post, as they likewise had at the savanna and fields of Capola; but either of them far inferior to one they had some miles farther South-West towards the Apalachuchla River, now called the Apalachean Old Fields, where yet remain vast works and buildings as fortifications, temples, some brass cannon, mortars, heavy church bells, &c.

The same groups of whitish, testaceous rocks and circular sinks, with natural wells, make their appearance in these groves and fields, as observed on the side of the river opposite to Capola, and the same trees, shrubs and herbage without variation. Having passed five or six miles through these ancient fields and groves, the scene suddenly changes, after riding through a high forest of Oak, Magnolia, Fraxinus, Liquid-amber, Fagus sylvatica, &c,

Now at once opens to view, perhaps, the most extensive Cane-break * that is to be seen on the face of the whole earth; right forward, about South-West, there appears no bound but the skies, the level plain, like the ocean, uniting with the firmament; and on the right and left hand, dark shaded groves, old fields and high forests, such as we had lately passed through.

The alternate, bold promontories and misty points advancing and retiring, at length, as it were, insensi-[234]bly vanishing from sight, like the two points of a crescent, softly touching the horizon, represent the most magnificent amphitheatre or circus perhaps in the whole world. The ground descends gently from the groves to the edge of the Cane-break, forming a delightful, green, grassy lawn. The Canes are ten or twelve feet in height, and as thick as an ordinary walking staff; they grow so close together, there is no penetrating them without previously cutting a road. We came up to this vast plain where the ancient Spanish high way crosses it to Pensacola; there yet remain plain vestiges of the grand causeway, which is open like a magnificent avenue, and the

* Cane meadows, so called by the inhabitants of Carolina, &c.

Indians have a bad road or pathway on it. The ground or soil of the plain is a perfectly black, rich, soapy earth, like a stiff clay or marle, wet and boggy near shore, but, further in, firm and hard enough in the summer season, but wet and in some places under water during the winter.

This vast plain together with the forests contiguous to it, if permitted (by the Siminoles who are sovereigns of these realms) to be in possession and under the culture of industrious planters and mechanicks, would in a little time exhibit other scenes than it does at present, delightful as it is; for by the arts of agriculture and commerce, almost every desirable thing in life might be produced and made plentiful here, and thereby establish a rich, populous and delightful region; as this soil and climate appear to be of a nature favourable for the production of almost all the fruits of the earth, as Corn *, Rice, Indigo, Sugar-cane, Flax, Cotton, Silk, Cochineal and all the varieties of esculent vegetables; and I suppose no part of the earth affords such end-[235]less range and exuberant pasture for cattle, deer, sheep, &c. the waters every where, even in the holes in the earth abound with varieties of excellent fish; and the forests and native meadows with wild game, as bear, deer, turkeys, quail, and in the winter season geese, ducks and other fowl; and lying contiguous to one of the most beautiful navigable rivers in the world; and not more than thirty miles from St. Marks on the great bay of Mexico; is most conveniently situated for the West-India trade and the commerce of all the world.

After indulging my imagination in the contemplation of these grand diversified scenes, we turned to the right hand, riding over the charming green terrace dividing the forests from the plains, and then entering the groves again, continued eight or nine miles up the river, four or five miles distance from its banks; having continually in view on one side or other, expansive green fields, groves and high forests; the meadows glittering with distant lakes and ponds, alive with cattle, deer and turkeys, and frequently present to view remains of ancient Spanish plantations. At length, towards evening, we turned about and came within sight of the river, where falling on the Indian trading path, we continued along it to the landing-place opposite the town, when hallooing and discharging our pieces, an Indian with a canoe came presently over and conducted us to the town before dark.

On our arrival at the trading house, our chief was visited by the head men of the town, when instantly the White King's arrival in town was anounced; a messenger had before been sent in to prepare a feast, the king and his retinue having killed several bears. A fire is now kindled

* Zea.

in the [236] area of the public square; the royal standard is displayed, and the drum beats to give notice to the town of the royal feast.

The ribs and the choice pieces of the three great fat bears already well barbecued or broiled, are brought to the banqueting house in the square, with hot bread; and honeyed water for drink.

When the feast was over in the square, (where only the chiefs and warriors were admitted, with the white people) the chief priest, attended by slaves, came with baskets and carried off the remainder of the victuals &c. which was distributed amongst the families of the town; the king then withdrew, repairing to the council house in the square, whither the chiefs and warriors, old and young, and such of the whites as chose, repaired also; the king, war-chief and several ancient chiefs and warriors were seated on the royal cabins, the rest of the head men and warriors, old and young, sat on the cabins on the right hand of the king's, and the cabins of seats on the left, and on the same elevation are always assigned for the white people, Indians of other towns, and such of their own people as chose.

Our chief, with the rest of the white people in town, took their seats according to order; Tobacco and pipes are brought, the calumet is lighted and smoked, circulating according to the usual forms and ceremony, and afterwards black drink concluded the feast. The king conversed, drank Cassine and associated familiarly with his people and with us.

After the public entertainment was over, the young people began their music and dancing in the [237] square, whither the young of both sexes repaired, as well as the old and middle aged: this frolick continued all night.

The White King of Talahasochte is a middle aged man, of moderate stature, and though of a lofty and majestic countenance and deportment, yet I am convinced this dignity which really seems graceful, is not the effect of vain supercilious pride, for his smiling countenance and his cheerful familarity bespeak magnanimity and benignity.

Next a council and treaty was held, they requested to have a trading house again established in the town, assuring us that every possible means should constantly be pursued to prevent any disturbance in future on their part; they informed us that the murderers of M'Gee *

* M'Gee was the leader of a family of white people from Georgia, destined across the isthmus, to the Mobile river; they travelled on horse-back as far as this town, where they procured canoes of the Indians, continuing their travels, descending the river and coasting the main S. W. but at night, when on shore hunting provisions, their camp was surprised and attacked by a predatory band of Indians, who slew M'Gee and the rest of the men and carried off the plunder and a woman to their towns.

and his associates, were to be put to death, that two of them were already shot, and they were in pursuit of the other.

Our chief trader in answer, informed them that the re-establishment of friendship and trade was the chief object of his visit, and that he was happy to find his old friends of Talahasochte in the same good disposition, as they ever were towards him and the white people, that it was his wish to trade with them, and that he was now come to collect his pack-horses to bring them goods. The king and the chiefs having been already acquainted with my business and pursuits amongst them, received me very kindly; the king in particular complimented me, [238] saying that I was as one of his own children or people, and should be protected accordingly, while I remained with them, adding, "Our whole country is before you, where you may range about at pleasure, gather physic plants and flowers, and every other production;" thus the treaty terminated friendly and peaceably.

Next day early in the morning we left the town and the river, in order to fix our encampment in the forests about twelve miles from the river, our companions with the pack-horses went a head to the place of rendezvous, and our chief conducted me another way to shew me a very curious place, called the Alligator-Hole, which was lately formed by an extraordinary eruption or jet of water; it is one of those vast circular sinks, which we behold almost every where about us as we traversed these forests, after we left the Alachua savanna: this remarkable one is on the verge of a spacious meadow, the surface of the ground round about uneven by means of gentle rising knolls; some detached groups of rocks and large spreading Live-Oaks shade it on every side; it is about sixty yards over, and the surface of the water six or seven feet below the rim of the funnel or bason; the water is transparent, cool and pleasant to drink, and well stored with fish; a very large alligator at present is lord or chief; many have been killed here, but the throne is never long vacant, the vast neighbouring ponds so abound with them.

The account that this gentleman, who was an eye-witness of the last eruption, gave me of its first appearance; being very wonderful, I proceed to relate what he told me whilst we were in town, which was confirmed by the Indians, and one or more of [239] our companions, who also saw its progress, as well as my own observations after I came to the ground

This trader being near the place (before it had any visible existence in its present appearance) about three years ago (as he was looking for some horses which he expected to find in these parts) when, on a sudden, he was astonished by an inexpressible rushing noise, like a mighty hurricane or thunder storm, and looking around, he saw the earth overflowed by torrents of water, which came, wave after wave, rushing down a vale or plain very near him, which it filled with water, and soon began to overwhelm the higher grounds, attended with a terrific noise and tremor of the earth; recovering from his first surprise, he immediately resolved to proceed for the place from whence the noise seemed to come, and soon came in sight of the incomparable fountain, and saw, with amazement, the floods rushing upwards many feet high, and the expanding waters, which prevailed every way, spreading themselves far and near: he at length concluded (he said) that the fountains of the deep were again broken up, and that an universal deluge had commenced, and instantly turned about and fled to alarm the town, about nine miles distance, but before he could reach it he met several of the inhabitants, who, already alarmed by the unusual noise, were hurrying on towards the place, upon which he returned with the Indians, taking their stand on an eminence to watch its progress and the event: it continued to jet and flow in this manner for several days, forming a large, rapid creek or river, descending and following the various courses and windings of the valley, for the distance of seven or eight miles, emptying itself into a vast savan-[240]na, where was a lake and sink which received and gave vent to its waters.

The fountain, however, gradually ceased to overflow, and finally withdrew itself beneath the common surface of the earth, leaving this capacious bason of waters, which, though continually near full, hath never since overflowed. There yet remains, and will, I suppose, remain for ages, the dry bed of the river or canal, generally four, five and six feet below the natural surface of the land; the perpendicular, ragged banks of which, on each side, shew the different strata of the earth, and at places, where ridges or a swelling bank crossed and opposed its course and fury, are vast heaps of fragments of rocks, white chalk, stones and pebbles, which were collected and thrown into the lateral valleys, until the main stream prevailed over and forced them aside, overflowing the levels and meadows, for some miles distance from the principal stream, on either side. We continued down the great vale, along its banks, quite to the savanna and lake where it vented itself, while its ancient subterranean channel was gradually opening, which, I imagine, from some hidden event or cause had been choaked up, and which, we may suppose, was the immediate cause of the eruption.

In the evening having gained our encampment, on a grassy knoll or eminence, under the cover of spreading Oaks, just by the grotto or sink of the lake, which lay as a sparkling gem on the flowery bosom of the ample savanna; our roving associates soon came in from ranging the forests; we continued our encampment at this place for several days, ranging around the delightful country to a great [241] distance, every days excursion presenting new scenes of wonder and delight.

Early in the morning our chief invited me with him on a visit to the town, to take a final leave of the White King. We were graciously received, and treated with the utmost civility and hospitality; there was a noble entertainment and repast provided against our arrival, consisting of bears ribs, venison, varieties of fish, roasted turkeys (which they call the white man's dish) hot corn cakes, and a very agreeable, cooling sort of jelly, which they call conte; this is prepared from the root of the China brier (Smilax pseudo China; Smilax aspera, fructu nigro, radice nodosa, magna, laevi, farinacea. Sloan, tom 1. p. 31. t. 143. f. 1. habit. Jamaica, Virginia, Carolina and Florida;) they chop the roots in pieces, which are afterwards well pounded in a wooden mortar, then being mixed with clean water, in a tray or trough, they strain it through baskets, the sediment, which settles to the bottom of the second vessel, is afterwards dried in the open air, and is then a very fine, reddish flour or meal; a small quantity of this mixed with warm water and sweetened with honey, when cool, becomes a beautiful, delicious jelly, very nourishing and wholesome; they also mix it with fine Corn flour, which being fried in fresh bear's oil makes very good hot cakes or fritters.

On our taking leave of the king and head men, they intreated our chief to represent to the white people, their unfeigned desire to bury in oblivion the late breach of amity and intermission of commerce, which they trusted would never be reflected on the people of Tala-hasochte; and lastly, [242] that we would speedily return with mer-chandize as heretofore; all which was cheerfully consented to, assuring them their wishes and sentiments fully coincided with ours.

The chief trader, intending to shew me some remarkable barren plains, on our return to our encampment; about noon we set off; when we came within sight of them, I was struck with astonishment at their dreary appearance; the view Southerly seemed endless wastes, pre-senting rocky, gravelly and sandy barren plains, producing scarcely any vegetable substances, except a few shrubby, crooked Pine trees, grow-ing out of heaps of white rocks, which represented ruins of villages, planted over the plains; with clumps of mean shrubs, which served only to perpetuate the persecuting power and rage of fire, and to testify the aridity of the soil; the shrubs I observed were chiefly the follow-ing, Myrica cerifera, two or three varieties, one of which is very dwarfish; the leaves small, yet toothed or sinuated, of a yellowish green colour, owing to a farinaceous pubescence or vesicula which covers their surfaces; Prinos, varieties, Andromeda ferruginae, Andr. nitida, varieties, Rhamnus frangula, Sideroxilon sericium, Ilex aquifolium, Ilex myrtifolium, Empetrum, Kalmia ciliata, Cassine, and a great variety of shrub Oaks, evergreen and deciduous, some of them singularly beautiful; Corypha repens, with a great variety of herbage, particularly Cacalia, Prenanthus, Chrysocoma, Helianthus, Silphium, Lobelia, Globularia, Helenium, Polygala, varieties, Olinopodium, Cactus, various species, Euphorbia, various species, Asclepias carnosa, very beautiful and singular, Sophora, Dianthus, Cistus, Sisymbrium, Pedicularis, Gerardia, [243] Lechea, Gnaphalium, Smilax sarsaparilla, Smilax pumila, Solidago, Aster, Lupinus filifolius, Galega, Hedysarum, &c. with various species of grasses; but there appeared vast spaces of gravel and plains of flat rocks, just even with the surface of the earth, which seemed entirely destitute of any vegetation, unless we may except some different kinds of mosses of the crustaceous sorts, as lichen, alga, &c. and coralloides. After passing several miles on the borders of these deserts, frequently alighting on them for observation and making collections; they at length gradually united or joined with infinite savannas and ponds, stretching beyond the sight Southerly, parallel with the rocky barrens, being separated only by a narrow, low, rocky ridge of open groves, consisting of low, spreading Live Oaks, Zanthoxilon, Ilex, Sideroxilon, &c. and here and there, standing either in groups or alone, the pompous Palm tree, gloriously erect or gracefully bowing towards the earth; exhibiting a most pleasing contrast and wild Indian scene of primitive unmodified nature, ample and magnificent. We at length came a-breast of the expansive, glittering lake, which divided the ample meadows, one end of which stretching towards a verdant eminence, formed a little bay, which was partly encircled by groups of white, chalky rocks, shaded with Live Oaks, Bays, Zanthoxilon and Palm trees. We turned our horses to graze in the green lawns, whilst we traversed the groves and meadows. Here the palmated Convolvulus trailed over the rocks, with the Hedera carnosa (Fol. quinatis inciso-serratis, perennentibus) and the fantastic Clitoria, decorating the shrubs with garlands (Clit. caule volubili fol. ternatis pennetisque, flor. majore caeruleo, vexillo rotundiore, siliquis longissimis compressis.)

[244] Soon after entering the forests, we were met in the path by a small company of Indians, smiling and beckoning to us long before we joined them; this was a family of Talahasochte who had been out on a hunt, and were returning home loaded with barbecued meat, hides and honey; their company consisted of the man, his wife and children, well

mounted on fine horses, with a number of pack-horses; the man presently offered us a fawnskin of honey, which we gladly accepted, and at parting I presented him with some fish hooks, sewing needles, &c. For in my travels amongst the Indians, I always furnished myself with such useful and acceptable little articles of light carriage, for presents; we parted and before night rejoined our companions at the Long Pond.

On our return to camp in the evening, we were saluted by a party of young Indian warriors, who had pitched their camp on a green eminence near the lake, and at a small distance from our camp, under a little grove of Oaks and Palms. This company consisted of seven young Siminoles, under the conduct of a young prince or chief of Talahasochte, a town Southward in the isthmus, they were all dressed and painted with singular elegance, and richly ornamented with silver plates, chains, &c. after the Siminole mode, with waving plumes of feathers on their crests. On our coming up to them they arose and shook hands; we alighted and sat awhile with them by their cheerful fire.

The young prince informed our chief, that he was in pursuit of a young fellow, who had fled from the town, carrying off with him one of his favourite young wives or concubines; he said merrily he would have the ears of both of them before [245] he returned; he was rather above the middle stature, and the most perfect human figure I ever saw; of an amiable engaging countenance, air and deportment; free and familiar in conversation, yet retaining a becoming gracefulness and dignity. We arose, took leave of them, and crossed a little vale covered with a charming green turf, already illumined by the soft light of the full moon.

Soon after joining our companions at camp, our neighbours the prince and his associates paid us a visit; we treated them with the best fare we had, having till this time preserved some of our spirituous liquors; they left us with perfect cordiality and cheerfulness, wishing us a good repose, and retired to their own camp, having a band of music with them, consisting of a drum, flutes and a rattle gourd, they entertained us during the night with their music, vocal and instrumental.

There is a languishing softness and melancholy air in the Indian convivial songs, especially of the amorous class, irresistibly moving, attractive, and exquisitely pleasing, especially in these solitary recesses when all nature is silent.

Behold how gracious and beneficent smiles the roseate morn! now the sun arises and fills the plains with light, his glories appear on the

forests, encompassing the meadows, and gild the top of the tere-
binthine Pine and exalted Palms, now gently rustling by the pressure of
the waking breezes: the music of the seraphic crane resounds in the
skies, in separate squadrons they sail, encircling their precincts, slowly
descend beating the dense air, and alight on the green dewy verge
of the expansive lake; its surface yet smoking with the grey as-[246]
cending mists, which, condensed aloft in clouds of vapour, are born
away by the morning breezes and at last gradually vanish on the
distant horizon. All nature awakes to life and activity.

The ground during our progress this morning, every where about us
presenting to view, those funnels, sinks and wells in groups of rocks,
amidst the groves, as already recited.

Near our next encampment one more conspicuous than I had elsewhere observed presented, I took occasion from this favourable circumstance of observing them in all their variety of appearances: its
outer superficial margin being fifty or sixty yards over, which equally
and uniformly on every side sloped downwards towards the center; on
one side of it was a considerable path-way or road leading down to the
water, worn by the frequent resort of wild creatures for drink, when the
waters were risen even or above the rocky bed, but at this time they were
sunk many yards below the surface of the earth, we descended first
to the bed of rocks, which was perforated with perpendicular tubes,
exactly like a walled well, four, five or six feet in diameter, and may be
compared to cells in an honey-comb, through which appeared the
water at bottom, many of these were broken or worn one into another,
forming one vast well with uneven walls, consisting of projecting
jambs, pilasters or buttresses, and excavated semicircular niches, as if
a piece were taken out of an honey-comb; the bed of rocks is from
fifteen to twenty feet deep or in thickness, though not of one solid
mass, but of many generally horizontal laminae, or strata of various
thickness, from eighteen inches to two or three feet, and admit water
to weep through, trickling [247] down, drop after drop, or chasing
each other in winding little rills down to the bottom; one side of the
vast cool grotto was so shattered and broken in, I thought it possible
to descend down to the water at bottom, and my companion assuring
me that the Indians and traders frequently go down for drink, encouraged me to make the attempt as he agreed to accompany me.

Having provided ourselves with a long snagged sapling, called an
Indian ladder, and each of us a pole, by the assistance of these we both
descended safely to the bottom, which we found nearly level and not
quite covered over with water; on one side was a bed of gravel and

fragments of rocks or stones, and on the other a pool of water near two feet deep, which moved with a slow current under the walls on a bed of clay and gravel.

After our return to the surface of the earth, I again ranged about the groves and grottos, examining a multitude of them; being on the margin of one in the open forest, and observing some curious vegetable productions growing on the side of the sloping funnel toward its center, the surface of the ground covered with grass and herbage; unapprehensive of danger, I descended precipitately towards the group of shrubs, when I was surprised and providentially stopped in my career, at the ground sounding hollow under my feet, and observing chasms through the ground, I quickly drew back, and returning again with a pole with which I beat in the earth, when to my astonishment and dread appeared the mouth of a well through the rocks, and observed the water glimmering at the bottom. Being wearied with excursions, we returned to our pleasant situation on the verge of the lawn.

[248]   Next day we set off on our return to the lower trading-house, proposing to encamp at a savanna, about twelve miles distance from this, where we were to halt again and stay a day or two, in order to collect together another party of horses, which had been stationed about that range; the young wild horses often breaking from the company, rendered our progress slow and troublesome; we however arrived at the appointed place long before night.

I had an opportunity this day of collecting a variety of specimens and seeds of vegetables, some of which appeared new to me, particularly Sophora, Cistus, Tradescantia, Hypoxis, Tatropa, Gerardia, Pedicularis, Mimosa sensitiva, Helonias, Melanthium, Lillium, Aletris, Agave, Cactus, Zamia, Empetrum, Erythryna, Echium, &c.

Next day, the people being again engaged in their business of ranging the forests and plains, in search of their horses, I accompanied them, and in our rambles we again visited the great savanna and lake, called the Long Pond: the lake is nearly in the middle of the spacious lawn, of an oblong form; above two miles wide and seven in length; one end approaching the high, green banks adjoining the forests, where there is an enchanting grove and grotto of pellucid waters, inhabited with multitudes of fish, continually ascending and descending through the clean, white rocks, gradually sloping from the green verged shore, by gradual steps, from smooth, flat pavements washed by the swelling undulations of the waters.

Arrived in the evening at camp, where we found the rest of our companions busily employed in se-[249]curing the young freakish horses. The next day was employed in like manner, breaking and tutoring the young steeds to their duty. The day following we took a final leave of this land of meadows, lakes, groves and grottos, directing our course for the trading path, having traversed a country, in appearance, little differing from the region lying upon Little St. Juan; we gained about twelve miles on our way, and in the evening encamped on a narrow ridge, dividing two savannas from each other, near the edge of a deep pond; here our people made a large pen or pound to secure their wild horses during the night. There was a little hommock or islet containing a few acres of high ground, at some distance from the shore, in the drowned savanna, almost every tree of which was loaded with nests of various tribes of water fowl, as ardea alba, ar. violacea, ar. cerulea, ar. stellaris crestata, ar. stellaris maxima, ar. virescens, colymbus, tantalus, mergus and others; these nests were all alive with young, generally almost full grown, not yet fledged, but covered with whitish or cream coloured soft down. We visited this bird isle, and some of our people taking sticks or poles with them, soon beat down, loaded themselves with these squabs and returned to camp; they were almost a lump of fat, and made us a rich supper; some we roasted and made others into a pilloe with rice: most of them, except the bitterns and tantali, were so excessively fishy in taste and smell, I could not relish them. It is incredible what prodigious numbers there were, old and young, on this little islet, and the confused noise which they kept up continually, the young crying for food incessantly, even whilst in their throats, and the old alarmed and displeased at our near residence, and the depredations we [250] had made upon them; their various languages, cries and fluttering caused an inexpressible uproar, like a public fair or market in a populous trading city, when suddenly surprised by some unexpected, calamitous event.

About midnight, having fallen asleep, I was awakened and greatly surprised at finding most of my companions up in arms, and furiously engaged with a large alligator but a few yards from me. One of our company, it seems, awoke in the night, and perceived the monster within a few paces of the camp, who giving the alarm to the rest, they readily came to his assistance, for it was a rare piece of sport; some took fire-brands and cast them at his head, whilst others formed javelins of saplins, pointed and hardened with fire; these they thrust down his throat into his bowels, which caused the monster to roar and bellow hideously, but his strength and fury was so great that he easily wrenched or twisted them out of their hands, which he wielded and brandished about and kept his enemies at distance for a time; some were for putting an end to his life and sufferings with a rifle ball, but the majority thought this would too soon deprive them of the diversion and pleasure of exercising their various inventions of torture; they at length however grew tired, and agreed in one opinion, that he had suffered sufficiently, and put an end to his existence. This crocodile was about twelve feet in length: we supposed that he had been allured by the fishy scent of our birds, and encouraged to undertake and pursue this hazardous adventure which cost him his life: this, with other instances already recited, may be sufficient to prove the intrepidity and subtilty of those voracious, formidable animals.

[251]   We set off early next morning, and soon after falling into the trading path, accomplished about twenty miles of our journey, and in the evening encamped as usual, near the banks of savannas and ponds, for the benefit of water and accommodations of pasture for our creatures. Next day we passed over part of the great and beautiful Alachua Savanna, whose exuberant green meadows, with the fertile hills which immediately encircle it, would if peopled and cultivated after the manner of the civilized countries of Europe, without crouding or incommoding families, at a moderate estimation, accommodate in the happiest manner, above one hundred thousand human inhabitants, besides millions of domestic animals; and I make no doubt this place will at some future day be one of the most populous and delightful seats on earth.

We came to camp in the evening, on the banks of a creek but a few miles distance from Cuscowilla, and two days more moderate travelling brought us safe back again to the lower trading-house, on St. Juan, having been blessed with health and a prosperous journey.

On my arrival at the stores, I was happy to find all well as we had left them, and our bringing with us friendly talks from the Siminole towns, and the Nation likewise, compleated the hopes and wishes of the trading company, with respect to their commercial concerns with the Indians, which, as the chearing light of the sun-beams after a dark, tempestuous night, diffused joy and conviviality throughout the little community, where were a number of men with their families, who had been put out of employment and subsistence, anxiously waiting the happy event.

CHAP. VIII.

A S a loading could not be procured until late in the autumn, for the schooner that was to return to Georgia, this circumstance allowed me time and opportunity to continue my excursions in this land of flowers, as well as at the same time to augment my collections of seeds, growing roots, &c.

I resolved upon another little voyage up the river; and after resting a few days and refitting my bark, I got on board the necessary stores, and furnishing myself with boxes to plant roots in, with my fuzee, ammunition and fishing tackle, I set sail, and in the evening arrived at Mount Royal. Next morning being moderately calm and serene, I set sail with a gentle leading breeze, which delightfully wafted me across the lake to the West coast, landing on an airy, sandy beach, a pleasant, cool situation, where I passed the night, but not without frequent attacks from the musquitoes, and next day visited the Great Springs, where I remained until the succeeding day, encreasing my collections of specimens, seeds and roots, and then recrossed the lake to the Eastern coast. This shore is generally bolder and more rocky than the Western, it being exposed to the lash of the surf, occasioned by the W. and N. W. winds, which are brisk and constant from nine or ten o'clock in the morning till towards midnight, almost the year round; though the S. winds are considerable in the spring, and by short intervals during the summer and winter; and the N. E. though sometimes very violent in the spring [253] and autumn, does not continue long. The day was employed in coasting slowly, and making collections. In the evening I made a harbour under cover of a long point of flat rocks, which defended the mole from the surf; having safely moored my bark, and chosen my camping ground just by, during the fine evening I reconnoitred the adjacent groves and lawns; here is a deserted plantation, the property of Dr. Stork, where he once resided. I observed many lovely shrubs and plants in the old fields and Orange groves, particularly several species of Convolvulus and Ipomea, the former having very large, white, sweet scented flowers; they are great ramblers, climbing and strolling on the shrubs and hedges. Next morning I re-embarked and continued traversing the bold coast North-Eastward, and searching the shores at all convenient landings, where I was amply rewarded for my assiduity in the society of beauties in the blooming realms of Florida. Came to again, at an old deserted plantation, the property of a British gentleman, but some years since vacated. A very spacious frame building was settling to the ground and mouldering to earth; here are very extensive old fields, where were growing the West-Indian or perennial Cotton and Indigo, which had been cultivated here, and some scattered remains of the ancient Orange groves, which had been left standing at the clearing of the plantation.

I have often been affected with extreme regret, at beholding the destruction and devastation which has been committed, or indiscreetly exercised on those extensive, fruitful Orange groves, on the banks of St. Juan, by the new planters under the British government, some hundred acres of which, at a [254] single plantation, has been entirely destroyed to make room for the Indigo, Cotton, Corn, Batatas, &c. or as they say, to extirpate the musquitoes, alledging that groves near their dwellings are haunts and shelters for those persecuting insects; some plantations have not a single tree standing, and where any have been left, it is only a small coppice or clump, nakedly exposed and destitute; perhaps fifty or an hundred trees standing near the dwelling-house, having no lofty cool grove of expansive Live Oaks, Laurel Magnolias and Palms to shade and protect them, exhibiting a mournful, sallow countenance; their native perfectly formed and glossy green foliage as if violated, defaced and torn to pieces by the bleak winds, scorched by the burning sun-beams in summer, and chilled by the winter frosts.

In the evening I took up my quarters in the beautiful isle in sight of Mount Royal. Next day, after collecting what was new and worthy of particular notice, I set sail again and called by the way at Mount Royal, in the evening arrived safe at the stores, bringing along with me valuable collections.

CHAP. IX.

AT the trading-house I found a very large party of the Lower Creeks encamped in a grove, just without the pallisadoes; this was a predatory band of the Siminoles, consisting of about forty warriors destined against the Chactaws of West Florida. They had just arrived here from St. Augustine, where they had been with a large troop of horses for sale, and furnished themselves with a very liberal supply of spirituous liquors, about twenty kegs, each containing five gallons.

These sons of Mars had the continence and fortitude to withstand the temptation of even tasting a drop of it until their arrival here, where they purposed to supply themselves with necessary articles to equip them for the expedition, and proceed on directly; but here meeting with our young traders and pack-horse men, they were soon prevailed on to broach their beloved nectar; which in the end caused some disturbance, and the consumption of most of their liquor, for after they had once got a smack of it, they never were sober for ten days, and by that time there was but little left.

In a few days this festival exhibited one of the must ludicrous bacchanalian scenes that is possible to be conceived, white and red men and women without distinction, passed the day merrily with these jovial, amorous topers, and the nights in convivial songs, dances and sacrifices to Venus, as long as they could stand or move; for in these frolicks both sexes take those liberties with each other, and [256] act, without constraint or shame, such scenes as they would abhor when sober or in their senses; and would endanger their ears and even their lives; but at last their liquor running low, and being most of them sick through intoxication, they became more sober, and now the dejected lifeless sots would pawn everything they were in possession of, for a mouthful of spirits to settle their stomachs, as they termed it. This was the time for the wenches to make their market, as they had the fortitude and subtilty by dissimulation and artifice to save their share of the liquor during the frolick, and that by a very singular stratagem, for, at these riots, every fellow who joins in the club, has his own quart bottle of rum in his hand, holding it by the neck so sure that he never looses hold of it day or night, drunk or sober, as long as the frolick continues, and with this, his beloved friend, he roves about continually, singing, roaring and reeling to and fro, either alone or arm in arm with a brother toper, presenting his bottle to every one, offering a drink, and is sure to meet his beloved female if he can, whom he complaisantly begs to drink with him, but the modest fair, veiling her face in a mantle, refuses (at the beginning of the frolick) but he presses and at last insists; she being furnished with an empty bottle, concealed in her mantle, at last consents, and taking a good long draught, blushes, drops her pretty face on her bosom and artfully discharges the rum into her bottle, and by repeating this artifice soon fills it; this she privately conveys to her secret store, and then returns to the jovial game, and so on during the festival; and when the comic farce is over, the wench retails this precious cordial to them at her own price. [257] There were a few of the chiefs, particularly the Long Warrior their leader, who had the prudence and fortitude to resist the alluring temptation during the whole farce; but though he was a powerful chief, a king and a very cunning man, he was not able to control these madmen, although he was acknowledged by the Indians to have communion with powerful invisible beings or spirits, and on that account esteemed worthy of homage and great respect.

After the Indians became sober they began to prepare for their departure; in the morning early the Long Warrior and chiefs sent a messenger to Mr. M'Latche, desiring to have a talk with him upon matters of moment; accordingly about noon they arrived; the conference was held in the piazza of the council house; the Long Warrior and chiefs who attended him, took their seats upon a long bench adjoining the side or front of the house, reaching the whole length of it, on one hand; and the principal white traders on the other, all on the same seat; I was admitted at this conference, Mr. M'Latche and the Long Warrior sat next to each other, my late companion, the old trader and myself sat next to him.

The Long Warrior spake, saying, that he and his companions were going to fight their enemies the Chactaws, and that some of his associates being in want of blankets, shirts and some other articles, which they declined supplying themselves with at St. Augustine, because they had rather stick close to their old friend Mr. Spalding, and bring their buckskins, furs and other produce of their country to his trading house, (which they knew [258] were acceptable) to purchase what they wanted; But not having the skins, &c. with them to pay for such things as they had occasion for, yet doubted not, but that on their return, they should bring with them sufficient not only to pay their debts, about to be contracted, but be able to make other considerable purchases, as the principal object of this expedition was hunting on the plentiful borders of the Chactaws. Mr. M'Latche hesitating, and expressing some dissatisfaction at his request; particularly at the length of time and great uncertainty of obtaining pay for the goods, and moreover his being only an agent for Messrs. Spalding & Co. and the magnitude and unprecedented terms of the Long Warrior's demands, required the company's assent and directions before he could comply with their request.

This answer displeased the Indian chief, and I observed great agitation and tumult in his passions, from his actions, hurry and rapidity of speech and expression; the old interpreter who sat by asked me if I fully understood the debate, I answered that I apprehended the Long Warrior was displeased, he told me he was so, and then recapitulated what has been said respecting his questions and Mr. M'Latche's answer; adding that upon his hesitation he immediately replied, in seeming disgust and great expressions of anger, "Do you presume to refuse me credit; certainly you know who I am and what power I have; but perhaps you do not know that if the matter required it, and I pleased, that I could command and cause the terrible thunder * now rolling in the skies above, to descend [259] upon your head, in rapid fiery shafts, and lay you prostrate at my feet, and consume your stores, turning them instantly into dust and ashes." Mr. M'Latche calmly replied, that he was fully sensible that the Long Warrior was a great man, a powerful chief of the bands of the respectable Siminoles, that his name was terrible to his enemies, but still he doubted if any man upon earth had such power, but rather believed that thunder and lightning was under the direction of the Great Spirit, but however, since we are not disposed to deny your power, supernatural influence and intercourse with the elements and spiritual agents, or withhold the respect and homage due to so great a prince of the Siminoles, friends and allies to the white people; if you think fit now in the presence of us all here, command and cause yon terrible thunder with its rapid fiery shafts, to descend upon the top of that Live Oak † in front of us, rend it in pieces, scatter his brawny limbs on the earth and consume them to ashes before our eyes, we will then own your supernatural power and dread your displeasure.

After some silence the prince became more calm and easy, and returned for answer, that recollecting the former friendship and good understanding, which had ever subsisted betwixt the white people and red people of the Siminole bands, and in particular, the many acts of

---

* It thundered, lightened and rained in a violent manner during these debates.
† A large ancient Live Oak stood in the yard about fifty yards distance.

friendship and kindness received from Mr. M'Latche, he would look over this affront; he acknowledged his reasoning and expostulations to be just and manly, that he should suppress his resentment, and withhold his power and vengeance at present. Mr. M'Latche concluded, by saying that he was not [260] in the least intimidated by his threats of destroying him with thunder and lightning, neither was he disposed in any manner to displease the Siminoles, and should certainly comply with his requisitions, as far as he could proceed without the advice and directions of the company, and finally agreed to supply him and his followers with such things as they stood most in need of, such as shirts, blankets and some paints, one half to be paid for directly, and the remainder to stand on credit until their return from the expedition. This determination entirely satisfied the Indians. We broke up the conference in perfect amity and good humour, and they returned to their camp and in the evening, ratified it with feasting and dancing which continued all next day with tolerable decorum. An occurrence happened this day, by which I had an opportunity of observing their extraordinary veneration or dread of the rattle snake; I was in the forenoon busy in my apartment in the council-house, drawing some curious flowers; when, on a sudden, my attention was taken off by a tumult without, at the Indian camp; I stepped to the door opening to the piazza, where I met my friend the old interpreter, who informed me that there was a very large rattle snake in the Indian camp, which had taken possession of it, having driven the men, women and children out, and he heard them saying that they would send for Puc-Puggy (for that was the name which they had given me, signifying the Flower Hunter) to kill him or take him out of their camp; I answered that I desired to have nothing to do with him, apprehending some disagreeable consequences, and desired that the Indians might be acquainted that I was engaged in business that required application and quiet, and was determined to avoid it if [261] possible; my old friend turned about to carry my answer to the Indians, I presently heard them approaching and calling for Puc-Puggy; starting up to escape from their sight by a back door, a party consisting of three young fellows, richly dressed and ornamented, stepped in, and with a countenance and action of noble simplicity, amity and complaisance, requested me to accompany them to their encampment; I desired them to excuse me at this time; they plead and entreated me to go with them, in order to free them from a great rattle snake which had entered their camp, that none of them had freedom or courage to expel him, and understanding that it was my pleasure to collect all their animals and other natural productions of their land, desired that I would come with them and take him away,

that I was welcome to him. I at length consented and attended on
them to their encampment, where I beheld the Indians greatly disturbed indeed. The men with sticks and tomahawks, and the women
and children collected together at a distance in affright and trepidation,
whilst the dreaded and revered serpent leisurely traversed their camp,
visiting the fire places from one to another, picking up fragments of
their provisions and licking their platters. The men gathered around
me, exciting me to remove him: being armed with a lightwood knot,
I approached the reptile, who instantly collected himself in a vast coil
(their attitude of defence) I cast my missile weapon at him, which
luckily taking his head, dispatched him instantly, and laid him trembling at my feet; I took out my knife, severed his head from his body,
then turning about, the Indians complimented me with every demonstration of satisfaction and approbation for my heroism, and friendship
for them. I carried off [262] the head of the serpent bleeding in my
hand as a trophy of victory, and taking out the mortal fangs, deposited them carefully amongst my collections. I had not been long
retired to my apartment before I was again roused from it by a tumult
in the yard, and hearing Puc-Puggy called on, I started up, when instantly the old interpreter met me again, and told me the Indians
were approaching in order to scratch me; I asked him for what; he
answered for killing the rattle snake within their camp. Before I could
make any reply or effect my escape, three young fellows singing, arm
in arm, came up to me; I observed one of the three was a young prince
who had, on my first interview with him, declared himself my friend
and protector, when he told me that if ever occasion should offer in
his presence, he would risk his life to defend mine or my property.
This young champion stood by his two associates, one on each side
of him, the two affecting a countenance and air of displeasure and
importance, instantly presenting their scratching instruments, and
flourishing them, spoke boldly, and said that I was too heroic and
violent, that it would be good for me to loose some of my blood to
make me more mild and tame, and for that purpose they were come
to scratch me; they gave me no time to expostulate or reply, but attempted to lay hold on me, which I resisted, and my friend, the young
prince, interposed and pushed them off, saying that I was a brave
warrior and his friend, that they should not insult me, when instantly
they altered their countenance and behaviour; they all whooped in
chorus, took me friendly by the hand, clapped me on the shoulder and
laid their hands on their breasts in token of sincere friendship, and
laughing aloud, said I was a sincere friend to the Siminoles, [263] a
worthy and brave warrior, and that no one should hereafter attempt

to injure me: they then all three joined arm in arm again and went off, shouting and proclaiming Puc-Puggy was their friend, &c. Thus it seemed that the whole was a ludicrous farce to satisfy their people and appease the manes * of the slain rattle snake.

The next day was employed by the Indians in preparations for their departure, such as taking up their goods from the trading house, collecting together their horses, making up their packs, &c. and the evening joyfully spent in songs and dances. The succeeding morning after exhibiting the war farce they decamped, proceeding on their expedition against their enemy.

* These people never kill the rattle snake or any other serpent, saying if they do so, the spirit of the killed snake will excite or influence his living kindred or relatives to revenge the injury or violence done to him when alive.

CHAP. X.

BUT let us again resume the subject of the rattle snake; a wonderful creature, when we consider his form, nature and disposition,
it is certain that he is capable by a puncture or scratch of one of his
fangs, not only to kill the largest animal in America, and that in a few
minutes time, but to turn the whole body into corruption; but such is
the nature of this dreaded reptile, that he cannot run or creep faster
than a man or child can walk, and he is never known to strike until
he is first assaulted or fears himself in danger, and even then always
gives the earliest warning by the rattles at the extremity of his tail. I
have in the course of my travels in the Southern states (where they
are the largest, most numerous and supposed to be the most venemous
and vindictive) stept unknowingly so close as almost to touch one of
them with my feet, and when I perceived him he was already drawn
up in circular coils ready for a blow. But however incredible it may
appear, the generous, I may say magnanimous creature lay as still and
motionless as if inanimate, his head crouched in, his eyes almost shut,
I precipitately withdrew, unless when I have been so shocked with
surprise and horror as to be in a manner riveted to the spot, for a
short time not having strength to go away, when he often slowly extends himself and quietly moves off in a direct line, unless pursued
when he erects his tail as far as the rattles extend, and gives the warning alarm by intervals, but if you pursue and overtake him with a shew
of enmity, he instantly throws himself into [267 *] the spiral coil, his
tail by the rapidity of its motion appears like a vapour, making a
quick tremulous sound, his whole body swells through rage, continually rising and falling as a bellows; his beautiful particoloured skin
becomes speckled and rough by dilatation, his head and neck are
flattened, his cheeks swollen and his lips constricted, discovering his
mortal fangs; his eyes red as burning coals, and his brandishing forked
tongue of the colour of the hottest flame, continually menaces death
and destruction, yet never strikes unless sure of his mark.

The rattle snake is the largest serpent yet known to exist in North
America, I have heard of their having been seen formerly, at the first

[* Pp. 265 and 266 not included in the original pagination.—Ed.]

settling of of Georgia, seven, eight and even ten feet in length, and six or eight inches diameter, but there are none of that size now to be seen, yet I have seen them above six feet in length, and about six inches in thickness, or as large as a man's leg, but their general size is four, five and six feet in length. They are supposed to have the power of fascination in an eminent degree, so as to inthral their prey. It is generally believed that they charm birds, rabbits, squirrels and other animals, and by stedfastly looking at them possess them with infatuation; be the cause what it may, the miserable creatures undoubtedly strive by every possible means to escape, but alas! their endeavours are in vain, they at last loose the power of resistance, and flutter or move slowly, but reluctantly towards the yawning jaws of their devourers, and creep into their mouths or lay down and suffer themselves to be taken and swallowed.

[268]   Since, within the circle of my acquaintance, I am known to be an advocate or vindicator of the benevolent and peaceable disposition of animal creation in general, not only towards mankind, whom they seem to venerate, but also towards one another, except where hunger or the rational and necessary provocations of the sensual appetites interfere. I shall mention a few instances, amongst many, which I have had an opportunity of remarking during my travels, particularly with regard to the animal I have been treating of, I shall strictly confine myself to facts.

When on the sea coast of Georgia, I consented, with a few friends, to make a party of amusement at fishing and fowling on Sapello, one of the sea coast islands; we accordingly descended the Alatamaha, crossed the sound and landed on the North end of the island, near the inlet, fixing our encampment at a pleasant situation, under the shade of a grove of Live Oaks and Laurels *, on the high banks of a creek which we ascended, winding through a salt marsh, which had its source from a swamp and savanna in the island: our situation elevated and open, commanded a comprehensive landscape; the great ocean, the foaming surf breaking on the sandy beach, the snowy breakers on the bar, the endless chain of islands, checkered sound and high continent all appearing before us. The diverting toils of the day were not fruitless, affording us opportunities of furnishing ourselves plentifully with a variety of game, fish and oysters for our supper.

About two hundred yards from our camp was a cool spring, amidst a grove of the odoriferous My-[269]rica; the winding path to this salubrious fountain led through a grassy savanna; I visited the spring several times in the night, but little did I know, or any of my careless

* Magnolia grandiflora, called by the inhabitants the Laurel.

drowsy companions, that every time we visited the fountain we were in imminent danger, as I am going to relate; early in the morning, excited by unconquerable thirst, I arose and went to the spring, and having, thoughtless of harm or danger, nearly half past the dewy vale, along the serpentine foot path, my hasty steps were suddenly stopped by the sight of a hideous serpent, the formidable rattle snake, in a high spiral coil, forming a circular mound half the height of my knees, within six inches of the narrow path; as soon as I recovered my senses and strength from so sudden a surprise, I started back out of his reach, where I stood to view him: he lay quiet whilst I surveyed him, appearing no way surprised or disturbed, but kept his half-shut eyes fixed on me; my imagination and spirits were in a tumult, almost equally divided betwixt thanksgiving to the Supreme Creator and preserver, and the dignified nature of the generous though terrible creature, who had suffered us all to pass many times by him during the night, without injuring us in the least, although we must have touched him, or our steps guided therefrom by a supreme guardian spirit: I hastened back to acquaint my associates, but with a determination to protect the life of the generous serpent; I presently brought my companions to the place, who were, beyond expression, surprised and terrified at the sight of the animal, and in a moment acknowledged their escape from destruction to be miraculous; and I am proud to assert, that all of us, except one person, agreed to let him lay undisturbed, and [270] that person at length was prevailed upon to suffer him to escape.

Again, when in my youth, attending my father on a journey to the Catskill Mountains, in the government of New-York; having nearly ascended the peak of Giliad, being youthful and vigorous in the pursuit of botanical and novel objects, I had gained the summit of a steep rocky precipice, a-head of our guide, when, just entering a shady vale, I saw at the root of a small shrub, a singular and beautiful appearance, which I remember to have instantly apprehended to be a large kind of Fungus which we call Jews ears, and was just drawing back my foot to kick it over, when at the instant, my father being near, cried out, a rattle snake my son, and jerked me back, which probably saved my life; I had never before seen one, this was of the kind which our guide called a yellow one, it was very beautiful, speckled and clouded. My father plead for his life, but our guide was inexorable, saying he never spared the life of a rattle snake, and killed him; my father took his skin and fangs.

Some years after this, when again in company with my father on a journey into East Florida, on the banks of St. Juan, at Fort Picolata, attending the congress at a treaty between that government and the

Creek Nation, for obtaining a territory from that people to annex to the new government. After the Indians and a detachment from the garrison of St. Augustine had arrived and encamped separately, near the fort, some days elapsed before the business of the treaty came on, waiting the arrival of a vessel from St. Augustine, on board of which were the presents for the Indians. My father employed this time of leisure in little excur-[271]sions round about the fort; and one morning, being the day the treaty commenced, I attended him on a botanical excursion, some time after we had been rambling in a swamp about a quarter of a mile from the camp, I being a-head a few paces my father bid me observe the rattle snake before and just at my feet, I stopped and saw the monster formed in a high spiral coil, not half his length from my feet, another step forward would have put my life in his power, as I must have touched if not stumbled over him; the fright and perturbation of my spirits at once excited resentment, at that time I was entirely insensible to gratitude or mercy; I instantly cut off a little sapling and soon dispatched him: this serpent was about six feet in length, and as thick as an ordinary mans leg. The rencounter deterred us from proceeding on our researches for that day. So I cut off a long tough withe or vine, which fastening round the neck of the slain serpent I dragged him after me, his scaly body sounding over the ground, and entering the camp with him in triumph, was soon surrounded by the amazed multitude, both Indians and my countrymen. The adventure soon reached the ears of the commander, who sent an officer to request that, if the snake had not bit himself, he might have him served up for his dinner; I readily delivered up the body of the snake to the cooks, and being that day invited to dine at the governor's table, saw the snake served up in several dishes: governor Grant being fond of the flesh of the rattle snake; I tasted of it but could not swallow it. I however, was sorry after killing the serpent when cooly recollecting every circumstance, he certainly had it in his power to kill me almost instantly, and I make no doubt but that he was conscious of it. I promis-[272]ed myself that I would never again be accessary to the death of a rattle snake, which promise I have invariably kept to. This dreaded animal is easily killed, a stick no thicker than a man's thumb is sufficient to kill the largest at one stroke, if well directed either on the head or across the back, nor can they make their escape by running off, nor indeed do they attempt it when attacked.

The moccasin snake is a large and horrid serpent to all appearance, and there are very terrifying stories related of him by the inhabitants of the Southern states, where they greatly abound, particularly in East Florida: that their bite is always incurable, the flesh for a considerable

space about the wound rotting to the bone, which then becomes carious, and a general mortification ensues, which infallibly destroys the
patient; the members of the body rotting and dying by piecemeal, and
that there is no remedy to prevent a lingering miserable death but by
immediately cutting away the flesh to the bone, for some distance
round about the wound. In shape and proportion of parts they much
resemble the rattle snake, and are marked or clouded much after the
same manner, but their colours more dull and obscure; and in their
disposition seem to agree with that dreaded reptile, being slow of progression, and throw themselves in a spiral coil ready for a blow when
attacked. They have one peculiar quality, which is this, when discovered, and observing their enemy to take notice of them, after throwing themselves in a coil, they gradually raise their upper mandible or
jaw until it falls back nearly touching their neck, at the same time
slowly vibrating their long purple forked tongue, their crooked poisonous fangs directed right at you, gives the [273] creature a most terrifying appearance. They are from three to four and even five feet in
length, and as thick as a man's leg; they are not numerous, yet too
common, and a sufficient terror to the miserable naked slaves, who are
compelled to labour in the swamps and low lands where they only
abound.

I never could find any that knew an instance of any person's loosing
their life from the bite of them, only by hearsay. Yet I am convinced
it is highly prudent for every person to be on their guard against them.
They appear to be of the viper tribe, from their swelling of their body
and flattening their neck when provoked, and from their large poisonous fangs; their head, mouth and eyes are remarkably large.

There is another snake in Carolina and Florida called the moccasin,
very different from this, which is a very beautiful creature, and I believe not of a destructive or vindictive nature; these when grown to
their greatest size are about five feet in length, and near as thick as
a man's arm; their skin scaly but smooth and shining, of a pale grey
and sky colour ground, uniformly marked with transverse undulatory
ringlets or blotches of a deep nut brown, edged with red or bright
Spanish brown; they appear innocent, very active and swift, endeavouring to escape from one; they have no poisonous fangs. These are
seen in high forest lands, about rotten logs or decayed fallen limbs of
trees, and they harbour about old log buildings. They seem to be a
species, if not the very same snake which in Pennsylvania and Virginia,
is called the wampom snake, but here in warmer Southern climes they
grow to a much larger size, and from the same accident their colour
may be more variable and deeper. They are by [274] the inhabitants

asserted to be dangerously venemous, their bite incurable, &c. But as I could never learn an instance of their bite being mortal or attended with any dangerous consequence, and having had frequent opportunities of observing their nature and disposition, I am inclined to pronounce them an innocent creature, with respect to mankind.

The bastard rattle snake, by some called ground rattle snake, is a dangerous little creature, their bite is certainly mortal if present medical relief is not administered: they seem to be much of the nature of the asp or adder of the old world.

This little viper is in form and colour much like the rattle snake, but not so bright and uniformly marked; their head is broader and shorter in proportion with the other parts of their body; their nose prominent and turned upwards; their tail becomes suddenly small from the vent to the extremity, which terminates with three minute articulations, resembling rattles; when irritated they turn up their tail which vibrates so quick as to appear like a mist or vapour, but causes little or no sound or noise, yet it is the common report of the inhabitants, that they cause that remarkable vehement noise, so frequently observed in forests in the heat of summer and autumn, very terrifying to strangers, which is, probably, caused by a very sable, small insect of the genus cicadae, or which are called locusts in America, yet it is possible I may be mistaken in this conjecture. This dangerous viper is from eight to ten inches in length, and of proportionable thickness; they are a spiteful, snappish creature, throwing themselves into a little coil, swell and flatten themselves, continually darting out their head, and they seem capable of springing [275] beyond their length. They seem destitute of the pacific disposition and magnanimity of the rattle snake, and are unworthy of an alliance with him; no man ever saves their lives, yet they remain too numerous, even in the oldest settled parts of the country.

The green snake is a beautiful innocent creature; they are from two to three feet in length, but not so thick as a persons little finger, of the finest green colour. They are very abundant, commonly seen on the limbs of trees and shrubs: they prey upon insects and reptiles, particularly the little green chameleon; and the forked tailed hawk or kite feeds on both of them, snatching them off the boughs of the trees.

The ribband snake is another very beautiful innocent serpent; they are eighteen inches in length, and about the thickness of a man's little finger; the head is very small; the ground colour of a full, clear vermilion, variegated with transverse bars or zones of a dark brown, which people fancy represents a ribband wound round the creature's body:

they are altogether inoffensive to man, and are in a manner domestic, frequenting old wooden buildings, open grounds and plantations.

The chicken snake is a large, strong and swift serpent, six or seven feet in length, but scarcely so thick as a man's wrist; they are of a cinereous, earthy colour, and striped longitudinally with broad lines or lists, of a dusky or blackish colour. They are a domestic snake, haunting about houses and plantations, and would be useful to man if tamed and properly tutored, being great devourers of rats, [276] but they are apt to disturb hen roosts and prey upon chickens. They are as innocent as a worm with respect to venom, are easily tamed and soon become very familiar.

The pine or bull snake is very large and inoffensive with respect to mankind, but devours squirrels, birds, rabbits and every other creature they can take as food. They are the largest snake yet known in North America, except the rattle snake, and perhaps exceed him in length; they are pied black and white; they utter a terrible loud hissing noise, sounding very hollow and like distant thunder, when irritated, or at the time of incubation, when the males contend with each other for the desired female. These serpents are also called horn snakes, from their tail terminating with a hard, horny spur, which they vibrate very quick when disturbed, but they never attempt to strike with it; they have dens in the earth, whither they retreat precipitately when apprehensive of danger.

There are many other species of snakes in the regions of Florida and Carolina, as the water snake, black snake, garter snake, copper belly, ring neck and two or three varieties of vipers besides those already noticed in my journal. Since I have begun to mention the animals of these regions, this may be a proper place to enumerate the other tribes which I observed during my peregrinations. I shall begin with the frogs (RANAE.)

(1) The largest frog known in Florida and on the sea coast of Carolina, is about eight or nine inches in length from the nose to the extremity of the toes; they are of a dusky brown or black colour on the upper side, and their belly or under side [277] white, spotted and clouded with dusky spots of various size and figure; their legs and thighs also are variegated with transverse ringlets, of dark brown or black, and are yellow and green about their mouth and lips: they live in wet swamps and marshes, on the shores of large rivers and lakes; their voice is loud and hideous, greatly resembling the grunting of a swine, but not near as loud as the voice of the bull frog of Virginia and Pennsylvania, neither do they arrive to half their size, the bull frog

being frequently eighteen inches in length, and their roaring as loud as that of a bull.

(2) The bell frog, so called because their voice is fancied to be exactly like the sound of a loud cow bell. This tribe being very numerous, and uttering their voices in companies or by large districts, when one begins another answers, thus the sound is caught and repeated from one to another, to a great distance round about, causing a surprising noise for a few minutes, rising and sinking according as the wind sets, when it nearly dies away, or is softly kept up by distant districts or communities, thus the noise is repeated continually, and as one becomes familiarised to it is not unmusical, though at first, to strangers, it seems clamorous and disgusting.

(3) A beautiful green frog inhabits the grassy, marshy shores of these large rivers. They are very numerous, and their noise exactly resembles the barking of little dogs, or the yelping of puppies; these likewise make a great clamour, but as their notes are fine, and uttered in chorus, by separate bands or communities, far and near, rising and falling with the gentle breezes, affords a pleasing kind of music.

[278] (4) There is besides this a less green frog, which is very common about houses: their notes are remarkably like that of young chickens; these raise their chorus immediately preceding a shower of rain, with which they seem delighted.

(5) A little grey speckled frog is in prodigious numbers in and about the ponds and savannas on high land, particularly in Pine forests; their language or noise is also uttered in chorus, by large communities or separate bands; each particular note resembles the noise made by striking two pebbles together under the surface of the water, which when thousands near you utter their notes at the same time, and being wafted to your ears by a sudden flow of wind, is very surprising, and does not ill resemble the rushing noise made by a vast quantity of gravel and pebbles together, at once precipitated from a great height.

(6) There is yet an extreme diminutive species of frogs, which inhabits the grassy verges of ponds in savannas: these are called savanna crickets, are of a dark ash or dusky colour, and have a very picked nose. At the times of very great rains in the autumn, when the savannas are in a manner inundated, they are to be seen in incredible multitudes clambering up the tall grass, weeds, &c. round the verges of the savannas, bordering on the higher ground, and by an inattentive person might be taken for spiders or other insects. Their note is very feeble, not unlike the chattering of young birds or crickets.

(7) The shad frog, so called in Pennsylvania from their appearing and croaking in the spring season, at the time the people fish for shad:

these are a [279] beautiful spotted frog, of a slender form, five or six inches in length from the nose to the extremities; of a dark olive green, blotched with clouds and ringlets of a dusky colour: these are remarkable jumpers, and enterprising hunters, leaving their ponds to a great distance in search of prey. They abound in rivers, swamps and marshes, in the Southern regions; in the evening and sultry summer days, particularly in times of drought, are very noisy, and at some distance one would be almost persuaded that there were assemblies of men in serious debate. These have also a sucking or clucking noise, like that which is made by sucking in the tongue under the roof of the mouth. These are the kinds of water frogs that have come under my observation, yet I am persuaded that there are yet remaining several other species.

(8) The high land frogs, commonly called toads, are of two species, the red and black. The former, which is of a reddish brown or brick colour, is the largest, and may weigh upwards of one pound when full grown; they have a disagreeable look, and when irritated, they swell and raise themselves up on their four legs and croak, but are no ways venomous or hurtful to man. The other species is one third less, and of a black or dark dusky colour; the legs and thighs of both are marked with blotches and ringlets of a darker colour, which appear more conspicuous when provoked: the smaller black species is the most numerous. Early in the spring season, they assemble by numberless multitudes in the drains and ponds, when their universal croaking and shouts are great indeed, yet in some degree not unharmonious: after this breeding time they crawl out of the waters and spread themselves [280] all over the country. Their spawn being hatched in the warm water, the larva is there nourished, passing through the like metamorphoses as the water frogs, and as soon as they obtain four feet, whilst yet no larger than crickets, they leave the fluid nursery-bed and hop over the dry land after their parents.

The food of these amphibious creatures, when out of the water, is every kind of insect, reptile, &c. they can take, even ants and spiders, nature having furnished them with an extreme long tongue, which exudes a viscid or glutinous liquid, they being secreted under covert, spring suddenly upon their prey, or dart forth their tongues as quick as lightning, and instantly drag into their devouring jaws the unwary insect. But whether they prey upon one another as the water frogs do, I know not.

There are several species of the lizard kind besides the alligator, which is by naturalists allowed to be a species of that genus.

The green lizard or little green chameleon is a pretty innocent creature; the largest I have seen were not more than seven inches in length; they appear commonly of a fine green colour, having a large red gill under their throat; they have the faculty of changing colour, which, notwithstanding the specious reasoning of physiologists, is a very surprising phenomenon. The striped lizard, called scorpion, and the blue bellied squamous lizards I have already mentioned. There is a large copper coloured lizard, and a very slender one of a fine blue colour, and very swift; the tail of this last, which is very long and slender, is as subject to be broken off as that of the glass snake. These two [281] last are become very scarce, and when seen are discovered about old log buildings.

Here are several species of the tortoise, besides those already mentioned; as the small land tortoise, already described by every traveller. There is a good figure and description of him in G. Edwards's Gl. Nat Hist. vol. II. p. 205. There are two species of fresh-water tortoises inhabiting the tide water rivers, one of which is large, weighing ten or twelve pounds, the back shell of nearly an oval form, and raised very high, the belly shell flat and entire, but deeply scolloped opposite their legs. The other species are small comparatively, and the back shell lightly raised; both species are food for mankind and esteemed delicious.

Of beasts the otter (lutra) is common, but more so in West-Florida, towards the mountains. The several species of mustela are common, as the mink, weasel and polecat (putorius); racoons and opossums, are in great abundance, these animals are esteemed delicious and healthy food. There are two species of wild-rats, but neither of them near as large as the European house-rat, which is common enough in the settlements of the white people: here are very few mice, yet I have seen some, particularly in Charleston; I saw two in a little wire cage, at a gentleman's house, which were as white as snow, and their eyes red. There are yet a few beavers in East-Florida and Georgia, but they abound most in the north of Georgia, and in West-Florida, near the mountains. But the muskrats (castor cauda lanciolata) are never seen in Carolina, Georgia or Florida, within one hundred miles of the sea coast and very few in the most northern parts of these regions; which must be considered [282] as a most favourable circumstance, by the people in countries where there is so much banking and draining of the land, they being the most destructive creatures to dykes.

The roe-buck I have already mentioned. The bears are yet too numerous: they are a strong creature, and prey on the fruits of the country, and will likewise devour young calves, swine and sheep, but I never could learn a well attested instance of their attacking mankind;

they weigh from five hundred to six hundred weight when full grown and fat, their flesh is greatly esteemed as food by the natives.

The wild-cats, felis cauda truncata, (lynx) are common enough; they are a fierce and bold little animal, preying on young pigs, fawns, turkeys, &c. they are not half the size of a common cur dog, are generally of a greyish colour, and somewhat tabbied; their sides bordering on the belly are varied with yellowish brown spots, and almost black waved streaks, and brindled. I have been credibly informed that the wolves here are frequently seen pied, black and white, and of other mixed colours. They assemble in companies in the night time, howl and bark altogether, especially in cold winter nights, which is terrifying to the wandering bewildered traveller.

The foxes of Carolina and Florida are of the smaller red species; they bark in the night round about plantations, but do not bark twice in the same place; they move precipitately and in a few minutes are heard on the opposite side of the plantation, or at a great distance: it is said that dogs are terrified at the noise, and cannot be persuaded [283] or compelled to pursue them, they commit depredations on young pigs, lambs, poultry, &c.

The mole is not so common here as in the northern states.

The bats of Florida seem to be the same species of those in Pennsylvania and Virginia, and very little different from the European.

Here are several species of squirrels, (sciurus) peculiar to the lower countries, or maritime parts of Carolina and the Floridas, and some of them are very beautiful creatures.

The great black fox squirrel is above two feet in length from the nose to the end of the tail, which for about two inches is milk white, as are the ears and nose. The red fox squirrel is of the same size and form, of a light reddish brown upper side, and white under side, the ears and tip end of the tail white.

The grey fox squirrel is rather larger than either of the foregoing, their belly white, as are the ears, nose, and tip of the tail: these three seem to be varieties of the same species.

The common grey squirrel is about half the size of the preceding.

The black squirrel is about the same size, and all over of a shining jet black.

The little grey squirrel is much less than either of the preceding species, they are of a brownish grey upper side, and white belly.

[284] The ground squirrel, or little striped squirrel of Pennsylvania and the northern regions, is never seen here, and very rarely in the mountains northwest of these territories; but the flying squirrel, (sciurus volans) is very common.

The rabbit (lepus minor, cauda abrupta, pupillis atris) is pretty common, and no ways differing from those of Pennsylvania and the northern states.

Having mentioned most of the animals in these parts of America, which are most remarkable or useful, there remains however yet some observations on birds, which by some may be thought not impertinent.

There are but few that have fallen under my observation but have been mentioned by the zoologists, and most of them very well figured in Catesby's, or Edwards's works.

But these authors have done very little towards illucidating the subject on the migration of birds, or accounting for the annual appearance and disappearance, and vanishing of these beautiful and entertaining beings, who visit us at certain stated seasons; Catesby has said very little on this curious subject, but Edwards more, and perhaps all, or as much as could be said in truth, by the most able and ingenious, who had not the advantage and opportunity of ocular observation, which can only be acquired by travelling, and residing a whole year at least in the various climates from north to south to the full extent of their peregrinations, or minutely examining the tracts and observations of curious and industrious travellers who have published their memoirs on this subject. There may perhaps be some persons who consider this enquiry not to be [285] productive of any real benefit to mankind, and pronounce such attention to natural history merely speculative, and only fit to amuse and entertain the idle virtuoso; however, the ancients thought otherwise, for with them, the knowledge of the passage of birds was the study of their priests and philosophers, and was considered a matter of real and indispensable use to the state, next to astronomy, as we find their system and practice of agriculture was in a great degree regulated by the arrival and disappearance of birds of passage, and perhaps a calender under such a regulation at this time, might be useful to the husbandman and gardener.

But however attentive and observant the ancients were on this branch of science, they seem to have been very ignorant, or erroneous in their conjectures concerning what became of birds, after their disappearance, until their return again. In the southern and temperate climates some imagined they went to the moon: in the northern regions they supposed that they retired to caves and hollow trees, for shelter and security, where they remained in a dormant state during the cold seasons; and even at this day, very celebrated men have asserted that swallows (hirundo) at the approach of winter, voluntarily plunge into lakes and rivers, descend to the bottom, and there creep into the mud and slime, where they continue overwhelmed by ice in a torpid state, until the returning summer warms them again into life, when they rise, return to the surface of the water, immediately take wing, and again people the air. This notion, though the latest, seems the most difficult to reconcile to reason or common sense; that a bird so swift of flight that can with ease and pleasure move through the air [286] even swifter than the winds, and in a few hours time shift themselves twenty degrees from north to south, even from frozen regions to climes where frost is never seen, and where the air and plains are replenished with flying insects of infinite variety, their favourite and only food.

Pennsylvania and Virginia appear to me to be the climates in North-America, where the greatest variety and abundance of these winged emigrants choose to celebrate their nuptials, and rear their offspring, which they annually return with, to their winter habitations in the southern regions of N. America; and most of these beautiful creatures who annually people and harmonize our forests and groves in the spring and summer seasons, are birds of passage from the southward. The eagle, i. e. falco leucocephalus, or bald eagle, falco maximus, or great grey eagle, falco major cauda ferruginio, falco pullarius, falco columbarius, strix pythaulis, strix acclamatus, strix assio, tetrao tympanus, or pheasant of Pennsylvania, tetrao urogallus, or mountain cock or grous of Pennsylvania, tetrao minor sive coturnix, or partridge of Pennsylvania, picus, or woodpeckers of several species, corvus carnivorus, or raven, corvus frugivora, or crow, corvus glandarius s. corvus cristatus, or blue jay, aluda maxima, regulus atrofuscus minor, or marsh wren, sitta, or nuthatch, meleagris, are perhaps nearly all the land birds which continue the year round in Pennsylvania. I might add to these the blue bird, motacilla sialis, mock bird, turdus polyglottos, and sometimes the robin redbreast, turdus migratorius, in extraordinary warm winters, and although I do not pretend to assert as a known truth, yet it may be found on future observation [287] that most of these above mentioned are strangers, or not really bred where they wintered, but are more northern families, or sojourners, bound southerly to more temperate habitations; thus pushing each other southerly, and possessing their vacated places, and then back again at the return of spring.

Very few tribes of birds build, or rear their young, in the south or maritime parts of Virginia and Carolina, Georgia and Florida; yet all these numerous tribes, particularly of the soft billed kinds, which breed in Pennsylvania, pass in the spring season through these regions in a few weeks time, making but very short stages by the way; and again, but few of them winter there, on their return southerly; and as I have never travelled the continent south of New Orleans, or the

point of Florida, where few or none of them are to be seen in the
winter, I am entirely ignorant how far southward they continue their
route during their absence from Pennsylvania, but perhaps none of
them pass the tropic.

When in my residence in Carolina and Florida, I have seen vast
flights of the house swallow (hirundo pelasgia) and bank martin
(hirundo riparia) passing onward north toward Pennsylvania, where
they breed in the spring, about the middle of March, and likewise in
the autumn in September or October, and large flights on their return
southward; and it is observable that they always avail themselves of
the advantage of high and favourable winds which likewise do all
birds of passage. The pewit, or black cap flycatcher, of Catesby, is the
first bird of passage which appears in the spring in Pennsylvania, which
is generally about the first, or [288] middle of March, and then
wherever they appear, we may plant peas and beans in the open
grounds (vitia sativa), French beans (phaccolus), sow raddishes
(raphanus), lettuce (lactuca), onions (cepa), pastinaca, daucus, and
almost every kind of esculent garden seeds, without fear or danger
from frosts; for although we have sometimes frosts after their first
appearance for a night or two yet not so severe as to injure the young
plants.

In the spring of the year the small birds of passage appear very
suddenly in Pennsylvania, which is not a little surprising, and no less
pleasing: at once the woods, the groves, and meads, are filled with
their melody, as if they dropped down from the skies. The reason or
probable cause is their setting off with high and fair winds from the
southward; for a strong south and south-west wind about the beginning
of April never fails bringing millions of these welcome visitors.

Being willing to contribute my mite towards illustrating the subject
of the peregrination of the tribes of birds of N. America, I shall sub-
join a nomenclature of the birds of passage, agreeable to my observation, when on my travels from New-England to New-Orleans, on the
Missiippi, and point of Florida.

Land birds which are seen in Pennsylvania, Maryland, Virginia, N.
and S. Carolina, Georgia and Florida, from the sea coast Westward,
to the Apalachian mountains, viz.

* These arrive in Pennsylvania in the spring season from the South,
which after building nests, and rearing their young, return again
Southerly in the autumn.

[289] † These arrive in Pennsylvania in the autumn, from the North,
where they continue during the winter, and return again the spring
following, I suppose to breed and rear they young; and these kinds
continue their journeys as far South as Carolina and Florida.

‡ These arrive in the spring in Carolina and Florida from the South, breed and rear their young, and return South again at the approach of winter, but never reach Pennsylvania, or the Northern States.

|| These are natives of Carolina and Florida, where they breed and continue the year round.

¶ These breed and continue the year round in Pennsylvania.

Strix. The Owl.

† Strix arcticus, capite levi corpore toto niveo, the great white owl.

¶ Strix pythaules, capite aurito, corpore rufo, the great horned owl.

† Strix maximus, capite aurito, corpore niveo, the great horned white owl.

¶ Strix acclamator, capite levi, corpore grisco, the whooting owl.

† Strix peregrinator, capite aurito, corpore versicolore, the sharp winged owl.

¶ Strix assio, capite aurito, corpore ferruginio, the little screech owl.

Vultur. The Vulture.

|| Vultur aura, the turkey-buzzard.

|| Vultur sacra, the white tailed vulture.

|| Vultur atratus, black vulture, or carrion crow.

[290]   ## Falco. Eagle and Hawk.

¶ Falco regalis, the great grey eagle.

¶ F. leucocephalus, the bald eagle.

* F. piscatorius, the fishing eagle.

¶ F. Aquilinus, cauda ferrug. great eagle hawk.

¶ F. gallinarius, the hen hawk.

¶ F. pullarius, the chicken hawk.

* F. columbarius, the pidgeon hawk.

¶ F. niger, the black hawk.

* F. ranivorus, the marsh hawk.

* F. sparverius, the least hawk or sparrow hawk.

a Milvus. Kite Hawk.

|| Falco furcatus, the forked tail hawk, or kite.

|| F. glaucus, the sharp winged hawk, of a pale sky-blue colour, the tip of the wings black.

a Kite hawks. These are characterised by having long sharp pointed wings, being of swift flight, sailing without flapping their wings, lean light bodies, and feeding out of their claws on the wing, as they gently sail round and round.

|| F. subcerulius, the sharp winged hawk, of a dark or dusky blue colour.

|| Psitticus Caroliniensis, the parrot of Carolina, or parrakeet.

Corvus. The Crow kind.

* Corvus carnivorus, the raven.

|| C. maritimus, the great sea-side crow, or rook.

¶ C. frugivorus, the common crow.

¶ C. cristatus, s. pica glandaria, the blue jay.

¶ C. Floridanus, pica glandaria minor, the little jay of Florida.

Pica glandaria cerulea non cristata, the little jay of East Florida.

["289" = 289 bis]

¶ Gracula quiscula, the purple jackdaw of the sea coast.

* Gracula purpurea, the lesser purple jackdaw, or crow blackbird.

* Cuculus Caroliniensis, the cuckoo of Carolina.

Picus. Woodpeckers.

|| Picus principalis, the greatest crested woodpecker, having a white back.

* P. pileatus, the great red crested black woodpecker.

* P. erythrocephalus, red headed woodpecker.

* P. auratus, the gold winged woodpecker.

¶ P. Carolinus, the red bellied woodpecker.

¶ P. pubescens, the least spotted woodpecker.

¶ P. villosus, the hairy, speckled and crested woodpecker.

¶ P. varius, yellow bellied woodpecker.

¶ Sitta Europea, grey black capped nuthatch.

† S. varia, ventre rubro, the black capped, red bellied nuthatch.

† Certhia rufa, little brown variegated creeper.

* C. pinus, the pine creeper.

* C. picta, blue and white striped or pied creeper.

* Alcedo alcyon, the great crested king-fisher.

* Trochilus colubris, the humming bird.

* Lanius griscus, the little grey butcher-bird of Pennsylvania.

* L. garrulus, the little black capped butcher-bird of Florida.

* L. tyrannus, the king bird.

* Muscitapa nunciola, the pewit, or black cap flycatcher.

* M. cristata, the great crested yellow bellied flycatcher.

* M. rapax, the lesser pewit, or brown and greenish flycatcher.

* M. subviridis, the little olive cold. flycatcher.

["290" = 290 bis]

* Muscicapa cantatrix, the little domestic flycatcher or green wren.
* M. sylvicola, the little red eye'd flycatcher.
* Columba Caroliniensis, the turtle dove.
|| C. passerina, the ground dove.
† C. migratoria, the pigeon of passage or wild pigeon.
* Alauda magna, the great meadow lark.
† A. campestris, gutture flavo, the sky lark.
† A. migratoria, corpore toto ferrugineo, the little brown lark.
¶ Turdus migratorius, the fieldfare, or robin redbreast.
* T. rufus, the great, or fox coloured thrush.
* T. polyglottos, the mocking bird.
* T. melodes, the wood thrush.
* T. minimus, vertice aurio, the least golden crown thrush.
* Oriolus Baltimore, Baltimore bird or hang nest.
* O. spurius, the goldfinch or icterus minor.
* Merula flammula, sand-hill redbird of Carolina.
* M. Marilandica, the summer red bird.
* Garrulus australis, the yellow breasted chat.
* Lucar lividus, apice nigra, the cat bird, or chicken bird.
¶ Ampelis garrulus, crown bird, or cedar bird.

GRANIVOROUS TRIBES.

¶ Meleagris Americanus, the wild turkey.
¶ Tetrao lagopus, the mountain cock, or grous.
¶ T. tympanus, the pheasant of Pennsylvania.
¶ T. minor, s. coturnix, the quail or partridge.
¶ Loxia cardinalis, the red bird, or Virginia nightingale.
† L. rostro forficato, the cross beak.
* L. cerulea, the blue cross beak.
[291]
* Emberiza oryzivora, (1) the rice bird.*
‡ E. livida, the blue or slate coloured rice bird.
* E. varia, (2) the pied rice bird.
‡ Linaria ciris, the painted finch, or nonpareil.
* L. cyanea, the blue linnet.
¶ Carduelus Americanus, the goldfinch.
† C. pinus, the lesser goldfinch.
† C. pusilus, the least finch.
* Fringilla erythrophthalma, the towhe bird.

* (1 2) Are generally supposed to be male and female of the same species (2)
or the pied rice bird the male, and (1) or the yellow, the female.

† F. purpurea, the purple finch.
† F. canabina, the hemp bird.
† F. rufa, the red, or fox-coloured ground or hedge sparrow.
† F. fusca, the large brown white throat sparrow
* Passer domesticus, the little house sparrow or chipping bird.
* P. palustris, the reed sparrow.
* P. agrestis, the little field sparrow.
† P. nivalis, the snow bird.
* Calandra pratensis, the May bird.
* Sturuus predatorius, the red winged sterling, or corn thief.
* S. stercorarius, the cowpen bird.
* Motacilla sialis, the blue bird. (Rebicula Americana, Cat.)
* M. fluviatilis, the water wagtail.
* M. domestica (regulus rufus) the house wren.
¶ * M. palustris, (reg. minor) the marsh wren.
* M. Caroliniana, (reg. magnus) the great wren of Carolina, the
    body of a dark brown, the throat and breast of a pale clay colour.
* Regulus griceus, the little bluish grey wren.
† R. cristatus, the golden crown wren.
[292]
† R. cristatus alter vertice rubini coloris, the ruby crown wren.
    (G. Edwards.)
* R. peregrinus, gutture flavo, the olive coloured yellow throated
    wren.
* Ruticilla Americana, the redstart.
* Luscinia, s. philomela Americana, the yellow hooded titmouse.
* Parus cristatus, bluish grey crested titmouse.
¶ P. Europeus, the black cap titmouse.
* P. luteus, the summer yellow bird.
* P. cedrus, uropygio flavo, the yellow rump.
* P. varius, various coloured little finch creeper.
* P. peregrinus, little chocolate breast titmouse.
* P. aureus vertice rubro, the yellow red pole.
* P. aurio vertice, the golden crown flycatcher.
* P. viridis gutture nigro, the green black throated flycatcher.
* P. alis aureis, the golden winged flycatcher.
* P. aureus alis ceruleis. the blue winged yellow bird.
* P. griccus gutture luteo, the yellow throated creeper.
* Hirundo pelasgia, cauda aculeata, the house swallow.
* H. purpurea, the great purple martin.
* H. riparia vertice purpurea, the bank martin.
* H. cerdo, the chimney swallow.

‡ Caprimulgus lucifugus, the great bat, or chuck wills widow.
* C. Americanus, night hawk, or whip poor will.

AMPHIBIOUS, or AQUATIC BIRDS,

Or such as obtain their food, and reside in, and near the water.

GRUS. The Crane.

|| Grus clamator, vertice papilloso, corpore niveo [293] remigibus nigris, the great whooping crane.
‡ G. pratensis, corpore cinereo, vertice papilloso, the great savanna crane.

ARDEA. The Heron.

¶ Ardea Herodias, the great bluish grey crested heron.
* A. immaculata, the great white river heron.
* A. alba minor, the little white heron.
‡ A. purpurea cristata, the little crested purple or blue heron.
* A. varra cristata, the grey white crested heron.
‡ A. maculata cristata, the speckled crested heron, or crabcatcher.
* A. mugitans, the marsh bitern, or Indian hen.
* A. clamator, corpore subceruleo, the quaw bird, or frogcatcher.
‡ A. subfusca stillata, the little brownish spotted bitern.
‡ A. violacca, the crested blue bitern, (called poor Jobe.)
* A. viriscens, the green bitern or poke.
* A. viriscens minor, the lesser green bitern.
* A. parva, the least brown and striped bitern.
* Platalea ajaja, the spoonbill, seen as far North as Alatamaha river in Georgia.

TANTALUS. The Wood Pelicane.

‡ Tantalus loculator, the wood pelicane.
‡ T. alber, the white Spanish curlew.
‡ T. fuscus, the dusky and white Spanish curlew.
|| T. pictus, (Ephouskyka Indian) the crying bird, beautifully speckled.
|| T. Ichthyophagus, the gannet, perhaps little different from the Ibis.
|| Numenius, alba varia, the white godwit.
¶ N. pectore ruso, the great red breasted godwit
["492" = 294]

¶ N. Americana, the greater godwit.

¶ N. fluvialis, the red shank or pool snipe.

¶ N. magnus rufus, the great sea coast curlew.

° N. minor campestris, the lesser field curlew.

¶ N. cinereus, the sea side lesser curlew.

° Scolopax Americana rufa, great red woodcock.

° S. minor arvensis, the meadow snipe.

° Tringa rufa, the red cootfooted tring.

T. cinerea, gutture albo, the white throated cootfooted tringa.

° T. vertice nigro, black cap cootfooted tringa.

¶ T. maculata, the spotted tringa.

¶ T. griceus, the little pond snipe.

¶ T. fusca, the little brown or ash coloured pool snipe.

¶ T. parva, the little trings of the sea shore, called sand birds.

° Morinella Americana, the turnstone or dotrill.

† Cygnus ferus, the wild swan.

† Anser Canadensis, the Canadian goose.

† A. aliis ceruliis, the blue winged goose.

† A. fuscus maculatus, the laughing goose.

† A. branta, corpore albo, remigibus nigris, the white brant goose.

† A. branta grisca maculata, the great particoloured brant, or grey goose.

† Anas fera torquata major, caput et collum viridi splendentis, dorsum griseo-fuscum, pectore rufescente speculum violaceum, the great wild duck, called duck and mallard.

† A. nigra maxima, the great black duck.

† A. bucephala, the bull-neck and buffaloe head.

† A. subcerulea, the blue bill.

† A. leucocephala, the black white faced duck.

† A. caudacuta, the sprig tail duck.

† A. rustica, the little brown and white duck.

[295]

† A. principalis, maculata, the various coloured duck, his neck and breast as tho' ornamented with chains of beads.

† A. minor picta, the little black and white duck called butterback.

QUERQUIDULAE. Teal.

° Anas sponsa, the summer duck.

† A. discors, the blue winged teal.

† A. migratoria, the least green winged teal.

° A. fistulosa, whistling duck.

† Mergus major pectore rufo, great fishing duck
† M. cucullatus, the round crested duck.
* Colymbus migratorius, the eel crow.
|| C. Floridanus, the great black cormorant of Florida, having a red beak.
|| C. colubrinus, cauda elongata, the snake bird of Florida.
¶ C. musicus, the great black and white pied diver or loon.
† Colymbus arcticus, the great speckled diver.
¶ C. auritus et cornutus, the little eared brown dobekick.
¶ C. minor fuscus, little crested brown dobekick.
‡ Phaeaton aethereus, the tropic bird.
¶ Larus alber, the great white gull.
¶ L. griceus, the great grey gull.
¶ L. alba minor, the little white river gull.
|| Onocratalus Americanus, the American sea pelicane.
|| Petrella pintada, the pintado bird.
¶ Rynchops niger, the shearwater or razor bill.
‡ Pelicanus aquilus, the frigat or man of war bird.
‡ P. sula, the booby.
‡ Sterna stolida, the sea swallow, or noddy.

[296]   C H A R A D R U S .   The Plover Kind.

* Charadrus vociferus, the kildea or chattering plover.
* C. maculatus, the great field spotted plover.
* C. minor, the little sea side ring necked plover.
* Hematopus ostrealegus, the will willet or oister catcher.
|| Fulica Floridana, the great blue or slate coloured coot of Florida.
* Rallus Virginianus, the soree bird or little brown rail, also called widgeon in Pennsyl.
‡ R. aquaticus minor, the little dark blue water rail.
* R. rufus Americanus, the greater brown rail.
|| R. major subceruleus, the blue or slate coloured water rail of Florida.
* Phoenicopterus ruber, the flamingo, seen about the point of Florida, rarely as far N. as St. Augustine.

I am convinced there are yet several kinds of land birds, and a great number of aquatic fowl that have not come under my particular notice, therefore shall leave them to the investigation of future travelling naturalists of greater ability and industry.

There yet remain some observations on the passage, and breeding of birds, &c. which may be proper to notice in this place.

I shall first mention the rice bird, (emberiza oryza vora.) It is the common received opinion that they are male and female of the same species, i. e. the black pied rice bird the male, and a yellowish clay coloured one the female: the last mentioned appearing only in the autumn, when the o-[297]ryz zizania is about ripening, yet in my opinion there are some strong circumstances which seem to operate against such a conjecture, though generally believed.

In the spring about the middle of May, the black pied rice bird (which is called the male) appear in Pennsylvania; at that time the great yellow ephemera, called May fly, and a species of locusta appear in incredible multitudes, the favourite delicious food of these birds, when they are sprightly, vociferous, and pleasingly tuneful.

When I was at St. Augustine, in E. Florida, in the beginning of April, the same species of grasshoppers were in multitudes on the fields and commons about the town, when great flights of these male rice birds suddenly arrived from the South, who by feeding on these insects became extremely fat and delicious, they continued here two or three weeks, until their food became scarce, when they disappeared, I suppose pursuing their journey North after the locusta and ephemera; there were a few of the yellow kind, or true rice bird, to be seen amongst them. Now these pied rice birds seem to observe the same order and time in their migrations Northerly, with the other spring birds of passage, and are undoubtedly on their way to their breeding place; but then there are no females with them, at least not one to ten thousand of the male colour, which cannot be supposed are a sufficient number to pair and breed by. Being in Charleston in the month of June, I observed at a gentleman's door, a cage full of rice birds, that is of the yellow or female colour, who were very merry and vociferous, having the same variable music with the pied or male [298] kind, which I thought extraordinary, and observing it to the gentleman, he assured me that they were all of the male kind, taken the preceding spring, but had changed their colour, and would be next spring of the colour of the pied, thus changing colour with the seasons of the year. If this is really the case, it appears they are both of the same species intermixt, spring and fall. In the spring they are gay, vociferous and tuneful birds.

Ampelis garrulus, crown bird or cedar bird. These birds feed on various sorts of succulent fruit and berries, associating in little flocks or flights, and are to be seen in all the regions from Canada to New Orleans on the Mississippi, and how much farther South and South-West I know not. They observe no fixed time of appearance in Pennsylvania, but are to be seen a few days every month of the year, so that it is difficult to determine at what season they breed, or where. The longest period of their appearance in Pennsylvania is in the spring and first of June, at the time the early cherries are ripe, when they are numerous; and in the autumn when the Cedar berries are ripe (Juniperus Americana;) they arrive in large flights, who, with the robins (turdus migratorius) and yellow rump (parus cedrus) soon strip those trees of their berries, after which they disappear again; but in November and December they appear in smaller flights, feeding on the fruit of the Pesimmon (Dyospyros Virginiana;) and some are seen till March, subsisting upon Smilax berries, Privet (Ligustrum ruelgare) and other permanent fruits; after which they disappear until May and June. I have been informed by some people in Pennsylvania, that they have found their nests at these seasons in Pennsylvania.

[299]   Linaria ciris (emberiza ciris Linn.) or painted finch, or nonpareil of Catesby is not seen North of Cape Fear in North Carolina, and seldom ten miles from the sea coast, or perhaps twenty or thirty miles, near the banks of great rivers, in fragrant groves of the Orange (Citrus aurantium) Zanthoxilon, Laurus Borbonia, Cassine, Sideroxilon, &c.

Linaria cianea (tanagra Linn.) the blue linet, is supposed by some to be the nonpareil, in an early stage of life, not being yet arrived to his brilliancy and variety of colours; but this is certainly a mistake, for the blue linet is longer and of a slenderer configuration, and their notes more variable, vehement and sonorous; and they inhabit the continent and sea coast islands from Mexico to Nova-Scotia, from the sea coast West beyond the Apalachean and Cherokee mountains. The songs of the nonpareil are remarkably low, soft and warbling, exceedingly tender and soothing.

Catesby in his history of Carolina, speaking of the cat-bird (muscicapa vertice nigro) says, "They have but one note, which resembles the mewing of a cat;" a mistake very injurious to the fame of that bird. He, in reality, being one of our most eminent songsters, little inferior to the philomela or mock-bird; and in some remarkable instances, perhaps, exceeds them both, in particular as a buffoon or mimick; he endeavours to imitate every bird and animal, and in many attempts does not ill succeed, even in rehearsing the songs, which he attentively listens to, from the shepherdess and rural swain, and will endeavour and succeed to admiration, in repeating the melodious and variable airs from instrumental music, and this in his wild state of nature. They being a kind of domestic bird du-[300]ring their spring and summer residence in Pennsylvania, building their nests in gardens and sheltering themselves in groves near the houses; they cause great trouble and vexation to hens that have broods of chickens, by imitating their distressing cries, in which they seem to enjoy much delight, and cause some amusement to persons who are diverted at such incidents. They are the first bird heard singing in the morning, even before break of day.

They seem to be a tribe of birds separated by nature from the motacilla, with which the zoologists havs classed them, and appear allied to a tribe peculiar to America, to which Edwards has given the name of manakin: in their nature they seem to take place between the thrush (turdus) and motacilla, their beak being longer, stronger and straiter than the motacilla, and formed for eating fruit, which is their chief food, yet they will feed on reptile insects, but never attempt to take their prey on the wing.

Catesby is chargeable with the like mistake with respect to the little thrush (t. minor) and the fox coloured thrush (t. rufes) both eminent singers, and the latter little inferior to the mock-bird. The former for his shrill, sonorous and elevated strains in the high, shady forests; and the latter for variety, softness and constant responses in the hedges and groves near houses.

But yet Catesby has some right of claim to our excuse and justification, for his detraction of the fame due to these eminent musicians of the groves and forests, when we consider that he resided and made his collections and observations, in the regions which are the winter re-treats and residence of [301] these birds, where they rarely sing, as it is observable and most true, that it is only at the time of incubation, that birds sing in their wild state of nature. The cat-bird, great and less thrush and field fare seldom or never build in Carolina beneath the mountains, except the great or fox coloured thrush in a few instances, but all these breed in Pennsylvania.

The parakeet (psitlicus Carolinienses) never reach so far North as Pennsylvania, which to me is unaccountable, considering they are a bird of such singular rapid flight, they could easily perform the journey in ten or twelve hours from North Carolina, where they are very numerous, and we abound with all the fruits which they delight in.

I was assured in Carolina, that these birds, for a month or two in the coldest winter weather, house themselves in hollow Cypress trees, clinging fast to each other like bees in a hive, where they continue in a torpid state until the warmth of the returning spring reanimates them, when they issue forth from their late dark, cold winter cloisters. But I lived several years in North Carolina and never was witness to an instance of it, yet I do not at all doubt but there have been instances of belated flocks thus surprised by sudden severe cold, and forced into such shelter, and the extraordinary severity and perseverance of the season might have benumbered them into a torpid, sleepy state; but that they all willingly should yield to so disagreeable and hazardous a situation, does not seem reasonable or natural, when we consider that they are a bird of the swiftest flight and impatient of severe cold. They are easily tamed, when they become docile and familiar, but never learn to imitate the human language.

[302]   Both species of the Baltimore bird (oriolus, Linn. icterus, Cat.) are spring birds of passage, and breed in Pennsylvania; they have loud and musical notes.

The yellow breasted chat (oenanthe, Cat. motacilla trochilus, Linn.) is in many instances a very singular bird; the variableness and mimickry of his notes or speech, imitating various creatures; and a surprising faculty of uttering a coarse, hollow sounding noise in their throats or crops, which at times seems to be at a great distance, though uttered by a bird very near, and vice versa. They arrive in Pennsylvania from the South late in the month of May, breed and return again early in autumn.

It is a matter of enquiry, who should have induced the zoologists to class this bird with the motacilla, when they discover no one characteristic to induce such an alliance. This bird having a remarkable thick, strong bill, more like the frugivorous tribes; and in my opinion they are guilty of the like oversight in classing the summer red-bird with the musicapa, this bird having a thick, strong bill, approaching nearer the sterling (sturnus.)

These historical observations being noted, we will again resume the subject of our journal.

AFTER the predatory band of Siminoles, under the conduct of the Long Warrior, had decamped, Mr. M'Latche invited me with him on a visit to an Indian town, about twelve miles distance from the trading-house, to regale ourselves at a feast of Water mellons and Oranges, the Indians having brought a canoe load of them to the trading-house the day preceding, which they disposed of to the traders. This was a circumstance pretty extraordinary to me, it being late in September, a season of the year when the Citruels are ripe and gone in Georgia and Carolina, but here the weather yet continued hot and sultry, and consequently this cool, exhilarating fruit was still in high relish and estimation.

After breakfasting, having each of us a Siminole horse completely equipped, we set off: the ride was agreeable and variously entertaining; we kept no road or pathway constantly, but as Indian hunting tracks, by chance suited our course, riding through high, open Pine forests, green lawns and flowery savannas in youthful verdure and gaity, having been lately burnt, but now overrun with a green enamelled carpet, checquered with hommocks of trees of dark green foliage, intersected with serpentine rivulets, their banks adorned with shrubberies of various tribes, as Andromeda formosissima, And. nitida, And. virides, And. calyculata, And. axilaris, Halmea spuria, Annona alba, &c. About noon we arrived at the town, the same little village [*304*] I passed by on my ascent of the river, on the banks of the little lake below Charlotia.

We were received and entertained friendly by the Indians, the chief of the village conducting us to a grand, airy pavilion in the center of the village. It was four square; a range of pillars or posts on each side supporting a canopy composed of Palmetto leaves, woven or thatched together, which shaded a level platform in the center that was ascended to from each side, by two steps or flights, each about twelve inches high, and seven or eight feet in breadth, all covered with carpets or matts, curiously woven of split canes dyed of various colours; here being seated or reclining ourselves, after smoking tobacco, baskets of choicest fruits were brought and set before us.

The fields surrounding the town and groves were plentifully stored with Corn, Citruels, Pumpkins, Squashes, Beans, Peas, Potatoes, Peaches, Figs, Oranges, &c.

Towards evening we took our leave, and arrived at the stores before night, having in the course of the day collected a variety of curious specimens of vegetables, seeds and roots.

The company being busily employed in forming their packs of leather and loading the vessel, and I being eager to augment my collections during my stay here, I crossed the river with a party of our people, who were transporting a gang of horses to range in the meadows and plains on the side opposite to the trading-house; we carried them over in a large flat or scow. The river was here above a mile wide, but divided into a number of streams by [305] numerous islands, which occasioned the voyage to be very troublesome, as most of the horses were lately taken wild out of their ranges, and many of them young and untutored; being under the necessity of passing near the points of the islands, they grew restless and impatient to land, and it was with great difficulty we kept them on board, and at last when within a quarter of a mile of the opposite shore, passing between two islands, the horses became ungovernable, and most of them plunged into the river and forced over board one of our people; I being a pretty good swimmer, in the midst of the bustle, and to avoid being beat over and perhaps wounded, I leapt out and caught hold of the dock of one of the horses; we all landed safe on one of the islands, about one hundred and fifty yards distance, and the flat followed us: after a deal of trouble and loss of time we got the horses again into the scow, where securing them by withs and vines, we again set off, and soon landed safe on the main, at a high bluff or bank of the river, where, after turning the horses to pasture and resting ourselves, we set off on a visit to a plantation on the river, six or eight miles distance: on the way thither we discovered a bee tree, which we cut down and regaled ourselves on the delicious honey; leaving one of our companions to protect the remainder until our return with a tub, to collect it and carry it with us, and in the evening we all returned safe with our sweet booty to the trading-house.

The vessel being loaded and ready to depart, I got all my collections on board. My trusty and fortunate bark I presented to the old interpreter, Job Wiggens, often my travelling companion, friend and [306] benefactor, and taking an affectionate and final leave of the worthy C. M'Latche and the whole trading company, we set sail in a neat little schooner for Frederica in Georgia, about the last of September. We had a pleasant and prosperous voyage down the grand river St.

Juans, frequently visiting the plantations on the banks of the river, especially at such times as opposed by contrary winds, and according to promise did not neglect calling on the generous and friendly Mr. Marshall, who received me so politely, and treated me with such unparalleled friendship and hospitality, when ascending the river alone, last spring.

We never once went out to sea during the voyage, for when we had descended the river below the Cow-Ford, we entered the sound by a channel between Fort George Island and the main, through which we passed, and continued sailing between the sea coast islands and the main to Frederica on St. Simons.

On my arrival at Frederica, I was again, as usual, friendly received and accommodated by the excellent J. Spalding, Esq. and here learning that the honourable Henry Lawrens, Esq. had a large ship loading at Sunbury for Liverpool, I determined to embrace so favourable an offer for conveying my collections to Europe, and hearing at the same time that Mr. Lawrens was daily expected in a vessel of his own, at his plantations on Broton Island and New Hope, in order to take a loading of rice for the cargo of the ship at Sunbury; I transported my collections to Broton, where meeting with Mr. Lawrens, he generously permitted me to put my things on board his vessel, and gave me room with himself in the cabin, and the merchant in Liverpool, to whom [307] the ship was consigned, being his friend and correspondent, and a friend of Dr. Fothergill's, Mr. Lawrens proposed to recommend my collections and letters to his care.

These favourable circumstances thus co-operating, after bidding adieu to my friends and liberal patrons in these parts, I embarked on board this vessel, and after a short and pleasant passage through the sound, arrived at Sunbury, from whence, after shipping my collections, I set sail again for Charleston, South Carolina; where being arrived I spent the season in short excursions until next spring, and during this time of my recess I had leisure to plan my future travels, agreeable to Dr. Fothergill's instructions and the council and advice of Dr. Chalmers of Charleston, with other gentlemen of that city, eminent for the promotion of science and encouraging merit and industry.

It was agreed that my future route should be directed West and South-West, into the Cherokee country and the regions of the Muscogulges or Creeks.

JOURNAL

OF THE

TRAVELS

CONTINUED.

PART "II" [-III].

CHAP. I.

APRIL 22d, 1776, I set off from Charleston for the Cherokee nation, and after riding this day about twenty-five miles, arrived in the evening at Jacksonsburg, a village on Ponpon river. The next day's journey was about the same distance, to a public house or inn on the road.

The next day, early in the morning, I set off again, and about noon stopped at a public house to dine; after the meridian heats were abated, proceeding on till evening, obtained good quarters at a private house, having rode this day about thirty miles. At this plantation I observed a large orchard of the European Mulberry trees (Morus alba) some of which were grafted on stocks of the native Mulberry (Morus rubra;) these trees were cultivated for the purpose of feeding silk-worms (phalaena bombyca.) Having breakfasted I set forward again.

[309] I soon entered a high forest, continuing the space of fifteen miles to the Three Sisters, a public ferry on Savanna River: the country generally very level; the soil a dark, loose, fertile mould, on a stratum of cinereous coloured tenacious clay; the ground shaded with its native forests, consisting of the great Black Oak, Quercus tinctoria,

195

Q. rubra, Q. phellos, Q. prinos, Q. hemispherica, Juglans nigra, J. rustica, J. exaltata, Magnolia grandiflora, Fraxinus excelsior, Acer rubrum, Liriodendron tulipifera, Populus heterophylla, Morus rubra, Nyssa sylvatica, Platanus occidentales, Tilia, Ulmus campestris, U. subifer, Laurus sassafras, L. Borbonia, Ilex aquifolium, Fagus sylvatica, Cornus Florida, Halesia, Æsculus pavia, Sambucus, Callicarpa and Stewartia malachodendron, with a variety of other trees and shrubs. This ancient sublime forest is frequently intersected with extensive avenues, vistas and green lawns, opening to extensive savannas and far distant Rice plantations, agreeably employs the imagination and captivates the senses by their magnificence and grandeur.

The gay mock-bird, vocal and joyous, mounts aloft on silvered wings, rolls over and over, then gently descends and presides in the choir of the tuneful tribes.

Having dined at the ferry, I crossed the river into Georgia; on landing and ascending the bank, which has here a North prospect, I observed the Dirca palustris, growing six or seven feet high. I rode about twelve miles further through Pine forests and savannas; in the evening I took up my quarters at a delightful habitation, though not a common tavern; having ordered my horse a stable and provender, and refreshed my spirits with a [310] draught of cooling liquor, I betook myself to contemplation in the groves and lawns; directing my steps towards the river, I observed in a high Pine forest on the border of a savanna, a great number of cattle herded together, and on my nearer approach discovered it to be a cow pen; on my coming up I was kindly saluted by my host and his wife, who I found were superintending a number of slaves, women, boys and girls, that were milking the cows. Here were about forty milch cows and as many young calves, for in these Southern countries the calves run with the cows a whole year, the people milking them at the same time. The pen including two or three acres of ground, more or less, according to the stock, adjoining a rivulet or run of water, is inclosed by a fence; in this inclosure the calves are kept while the cows are out at range; a small part of this pen is partitioned off to receive the cows when they come up at evening; here are several stakes drove into the ground, and there is a gate in the partition fence for a communication between the two pens. When the milkmaid has taken her share of milk, she looses the calf, who strips the cow, which is next morning turned out again to range.

I found these people, contrary to what a traveller might, perhaps, reasonably expect, from their occupation and remote situation from

the capital or any commercial town, to be civil and courteous, and
though educated as it were in the woods, no strangers to sensibility
and those moral virtues which grace and ornament the most approved
and admired characters in civil society.

After the vessels were filled with milk, the daily and liberal aid of
the friendly kine, and the good [311] wife, with her maids and servants,
were returning with it to the dairy: the gentleman was at leisure to
attend to my enquiries and observations, which he did with complaisance, and apparent pleasure. On my observing to him that his
stock of horned cattle must be very considerable to afford so many
milch cows at one time, he answered, that he had about fifteen hundred head: "my stock is but young, having lately removed from some
distance to this place; I found it convenient to part with most of my
old stock and begin here anew; Heaven is pleased to bless my endeavours and industry with success even beyond my own expectations."
Yet continuing my interrogatories on this subject: your stock I apprehend must be very profitable, being so convenient to the capital and
sea port, in affording a vast quantity of beef, butter, and cheese, for
the market, and must thereby contribute greatly towards your emolu-
ment: "yes, I find my stock of cattle very profitable, and I constantly
contribute towards supplying the markets with beef, but as to the
articles of butter and cheese, I make no more than what is expended
in my own household, and I have a considerable family of black people
who though they are slaves must be fed, and cared for; those I have
were either chosen for their good qualities, or born in the family, and
finding from long experience and observation, that the better they
are fed, clothed and treated, the more service and profit we may expect to derive from their labour: in short, I find my stock produces no
more milk, or any article of food or nourishment, than what is expended to the best advantage amongst my family and slaves."

He added, come along with me towards the ri-["212" = 312]ver bank,
where I have some men at work squaring Pine and Cypress timber
for the West-India market; I will shew you their days work, when you
will readily grant that I have reason to acknowledge myself sufficiently gratified for the little attention bestowed towards them. At
yonder little new habitation near the bluff, on the banks of the river
I have settled my eldest son; it is but a few days since he was married
to a deserving young woman.

Having at length arrived near the high banks of the majestic savanna,
we stood at the timber landing: almost every object in our progress
having contributed to demonstrate this good man's system of economy

to be not only practicable but eligible, and the slaves appeared on all sides as a crowd of witnesses to justify his industry, humanity and liberal spirit.

The slaves comparatively of a gigantic stature, fat and muscular, mounted on the massive timber logs, the regular heavy strokes of their gleaming axes re-echo in the deep forests, at the same time contented and joyful the sooty sons of Afric forgetting their bondage, in chorus sing the virtues and beneficence of their master in songs of their own composition.

The log or timber landing is a capacious open area, the lofty pines * having been felled and cleared away for a considerable distance round about, near an almost perpendicular bluff or steep bank of the river, rising up immediately from the water to the height of sixty or seventy feet. The logs being dragged by timber wheels to this yard, and land-[313]ed as near the brink of this high bank as possible with safety, and laid by the side of each other, are rolled off and precipitated down the bank into the river, where being formed into rafts, they are conducted by slaves down to Savanna, about fifty miles below this place.

Having contemplated these scenes of art and industry, my venerable host in company with his son, conducted me to the neat habitation which is situated in a spacious airy forest, a little distance from the river bank, commanding a comprehensive and varied prospect; an extensive reach of the river in front, on the right hand a spacious lawn or Savanna, on the left the timber yard, the vast fertile low lands and forest on the river upwards, and the plantations adjoining; a cool evening arrived after a sultry day, as we approach the door conducted by the young man, his lovely bride arrayed in native innocence and becoming modesty, with an air and smile of grace and benignity, meets and salutes us: what a Venus! what an Adonis! said I in silent transport; every action and feature seemed to reveal the celestial endowments of the mind: though a native sprightliness and sensibility appeared, yet virtue and discretion direct and rule. The dress of this beauteous sylvan queen was plain but clean, neat and elegant, all of cotton and of her own spinning and weaving.

Next morning early I set forward prosecuting my tour. I pursued the high road leading from Savanna to Augusta for the distance of one hundred miles or more, and then recrossed the river at Silver Bluff, a pleasant villa, the property and seat of G. Golphin, Esquire, a gentleman of very distin-[314]guished talents and great liberality, who possessed the most extensive trade, connections and influence,

* Pinus palustris, Linn. the long leaved Pitch pine, or yellow Pine.

amongst the South and South-West Indian tribes, particularly with the Creeks and Chactaws, of whom I fortunately obtained letters of recommendation and credit to the principal traders residing in the Indian towns.

Silver-Bluff is a very celebrated place; it is a considerable height upon the Carolina shore of the Savanna river, perhaps thirty feet higher than the low lands on the opposite shore, which are subject to be over-flowed in the spring and fall: this steep bank rises perpendicular out of the river, discovering various strata of earth; the surface for a considerable depth is a loose sandy loam, with a mixture of sea shells, especially ostreae; the next stratum is clay, then sand, next marl, then clays again of various colours and qualities, which last insensibly mixes or unites with a deep stratum of blackish or dark slate coloured saline and sulphureous earth, which seems to be of an aluminous or vitriolic quality, and lies in nearly horizontal laminae or strata of various thickness, we discovered bellemnites, pyrites, markasites and sulphureous nodules, shining like brass, some single of various forms, and others conglomerated, lying in this black slaty-like micaceous earth; as also sticks, limbs and trunks of trees, leaves, acorns and their cups, all transmuted or changed black, hard and shining as charcoal; we also see animal substances, as if petrified, or what are called sharks' teeth, (dentes charchariae) but these heterogeneous substances or petrifactions are the most abundant and conspicuous where there is a looser kind of earth, either immediately upon this vast stratum of black earth, or in the divisions of [315] the laminae. The surface of the ground upon this bluff, which extends a mile and an half or two miles on the river, and is from an half mile to a mile in breadth, nearly level, and a good fertile soil, as is evident from the vast Oaks, Hickory, Mulberry, Black walnut and other trees and shrubs, which are left standing in the old fields which are spread abroad to a great distance, and discover various monuments and vestiges of the residence of the ancients, as Indian conical mounts, terraces, areas, &c. as well as remains or traces of fortresses of regular formation, as if constructed after the modes of European military architects, and are supposed to be ancient camps of the Spaniards who formerly fixed themselves at this place in hopes of finding silver.

But perhaps Mr. Golphin's buildings and improvements will prove to be the foundation of monuments of infinitely greater celebrity and permanency than either of the preceding establishments.

The place which at this day is called fort Moore, is a stupendous bluff, or high perpendicular bank of earth, rising out of the river on the

Carolina shore, perhaps ninety or one hundred feet above the common surface of the water, and exhibits a singular and pleasing spectacle to a stranger, especially from the opposite shore, or as we pass up or down the river, presenting a view of prodigious walls of party-coloured earths, chiefly clays and marl of various colours, as brown, red, yellow, blue, purple, white, &c. in horizontal strata, one over the other.

Waiting for the ferry boat to carry me over, I walked almost round the under side of the bluff, betwixt its steep wall and the water of the river, [316] which glided rapidly under my feet; I came to the carcase of a calf, which the people told me had fallen down from the edge of the precipice above, being invited too far by grass and sweet herbs, which they say frequently happens at this place. In early times, the Carolinians had a fort, and kept a good garrison here as a frontier and Indian trading post, but Augusta superceding it, this place was dismantled, and since that time, which probably cannot exceed thirty years, the river hath so much encroached upon the Carolina shore, that its bed now lies where the site of the fort then was; indeed some told me that the opposite Georgia shore, where there is now a fine house and corn field, occupies the place.

The site of Augusta is perhaps the most delightful and eligible of any in Georgia for a city, an extensive level plain on the banks of a fine navigable river, which has its numerous sources in the Cherokee mountains, a fruitful and temperate region; whence after roving and winding about those fertile heights, they meander through a fertile hilly country, and one after another combine in forming the Tugilo and Broad rivers, and then the famous Savanna river, thence continues near an hundred miles more, following its meanders and falls over the cataracts at Augusta, which crosses the river at the upper end of the town: these falls are four or five feet perpendicular height in the summer season when the river is low: from these cataracts upwards, this river with all its tributaries, as Broad river, Little river, Tugilo, &c. are one continued rapid, with some short intervals of still water, navigable for canoes. But from Augusta downwards to the ocean, a distance of near three hundred miles [317] by water. The Savanna uninterruptedly flows with a gentle meandering course, and is navigable for vessels of twenty or thirty tons burthen to Savanna, where ships of three hundred tons lie in a capacious and secure harbour.

Augusta thus seated at the head of navigation, and just below the conflux of several of its most considerable branches, without a competitor, commands the trade and commerce of vast fruitful regions above it, and from every side to a great distance; and I do not hesitate to pronounce as my opinion, will very soon become the metropolis of Georgia.*

I chose to take this route up Savanna river, in preference to the strait and shorter road from Charleston to the Cherokee country by fort Ninety Six, because by keeping near this great river, I had frequent opportunities of visiting its steep banks, vast swamps and low grounds, and had the advantage without great delay, or deviating from the main high road, of observing the various soils and situations of the countries through which this famous river pursues its course, and of examining the various productions, mineral, vegetable and animal; whereas had I pursued the great trading path by Ninety-Six, should have been led over a high, dry, sandy and gravelly ridge, and a great part of the distance an old settled or resorted part of the country, and consequently void of the varieties of original or novel productions of nature.

Before I leave Augusta, I shall recite a curious phenomenon, which may furnish ample matter for [318] philosophical discussion to the curious naturalists. On the Georgia side of the river, about fifteen miles below Silver Bluff, the high road crosses a ridge of high swelling hills of uncommon elevation, and perhaps seventy feet higher than the surface of the river; these hills are from three feet below the common vegetative surface, to the depth of twenty or thirty feet, composed entirely of fossil oyster shells, internally of the colour and consistency of clear white marble; they are of an incredible magnitude, generally fifteen or twenty inches in length, from six to eight wide and two to four in thickness, and their hollows sufficient to receive an ordinary man's foot; they appear all to have been opened before the period of petrifaction, a transmutation they seem evidently to have suffered; they are undoubtedly very ancient or perhaps antediluvian. The adjacent inhabitants burn them to lime for building, for which purpose they serve very well; and would undoubtedly afford an excellent manure when their lands require it, these hills being now remarkably fertile. The heaps of shells lie upon a stratum of yellowish sandy mould, of several feet in depth, upon a foundation of soft white rocks that has the outward appearance of free-stone, but on strict examination is really a testaceous concrete or composition of sand and pulverised sea shells; in short, this testaceous rock approaches near in quality and appearance to the Bahama or Bermudian white rock.

These hills are shaded with glorious Magnolia grandiflora, Morus

* A few years after the above remark, the seat of government was removed from Savanna to Augusta.

rubra, Tilia, Quercus, Ulmus, Juglans, &c. with aromatic groves of fragrant Callicanthus Floridus, Rhododendron ferruginium, Laurus Indica, &c. Æsculus pavia, Cornus Flori-[319]da, Azalea coccinea, Philadelphus inodorous and others; but who would have expected to see the Dirca palustris and Dodecathean meadea grow in abundance in this hot climate! it is true they are seen in the rich and deep shaded vales, between the hills and North exposure; but they attain to a degree of magnitude and splendor never seen in Pennsylvania.

AFTER conferring with gentlemen in Augusta, conversant in Indian affairs, concerning my future travels in those distant, unexplored regions, and obtaining letters to their agents in the Indian territories, I set off, proceeding for Fort James Dartmouth, at the confluence of Broad River with Savanna, the road leading me near the banks of the river for the distance of near thirty miles, crossing two or three of its considerable branches, besides rivulets and smaller brooks. The surface of the land uneven, by means of ridges or chains of swelling hills and corresponding vales, with level downs; the soil a loose, greyish brown loamy mould on the hills, but darker and more cohesive and humid in the vales and downs; this superficial, vegetative earth, covers a deep stratum of very tenacious yellowish clay: the downs afford grass and various herbage; the vales and hills forest trees and shrubs of various tribes, i. e. Quercus tinctoria, Q. alba, Q. rubra, Q. lobata, Acer rubrum, A. Saccharinum, A. glaucum, Morus rubra, Gleditsia triacanthus, Juglans hickory, various species, Quercus phillos, Quer. dentata, s. hemispherica, Quercus aquatica, or Maryland Water Oak, Ulmus sylvatica, Liriodendron, Liquid-amber, Diospyros, Cornus Florida, Prunus Indica, Prunus padus and Æsculus pavia: and near water courses in the vales, Stewartia malachodendron, Halesia, Æsculus sylvatica, Styrax, Carpinus, Magnolia acuminata, Mag. tripetala, Mag. auriculata, Azalea, &c. The rich humid lands in the vales bordering on creeks and bases of the hills, likewise produce various trees, shrubs and plants, as Cercis, Corylus, Ptelea, Evonimus, Philadelphus [321] inodorous, Staphylea trifoliata, Chionanthus, Hamamelis, Callicarpa, Sambucus, Cornus alba, Viburnum dentatum, Spirea opulifolia, Cornus sanguinea, Cephalanthus, &c. and of herbaccae a vast variety and abundance, as Verbesina, Rudbeckea, Phaciolus, Tripsacum, Aconitum napellus, Delphinium, Angelica luceda, Tradescantia, Trillium sessile, Trillium canuum, Actaea, Chelone, Glycine apios, Convalaria racemosa, Mediola, Carduus, Bidens frondosa, Arum triphyllum, Coreopsis alternifolia, Circea, Commelina, Aster, Solidago, Eupatorium, Helianthus and Silphium, together with a variety of other tribes and species new to me. In the evening I arrived at Little river, and took

203

up my quarters at a public house on its banks, near its confluence with the Savanna. This is a beautiful rapid water, about fifty yards over; on a branch of this river is situated the town of Wrightsborough.

Near the ford, on the banks of this river, I first observed a very curious shrub, a beautiful evergreen, which appears to be allied to the Rhododendron, though the seed vessels seem to bear more the characteristics of the Kalmia. This shrub grows in copses or little groves, in open, high situations, where trees of large growth are but scatteringly planted; many simple stems arise together from a root or source erect, four, five and six feet high; their limbs or branches, which are produced towards the top of the stems, also stand nearly erect, lightly diverging from the main stems, which are furnished with moderately large ovate pointed intire leaves, of a pale or yellowish green colour; these leaves are of a firm, compact texture, both surfaces smooth and shining, and stand nearly erect [322] upon short petioles; the branches terminate with long, loose panicles or spikes of white flowers, whose segments are five, long and narrow.

I arose early next morning and continued my journey for Fort James. This day's progress was agreeably entertaining, from the novelty and variety of objects and views; the wild country now almost depopulated, vast forests, expansive plains and detached groves; then chains of hills whose gravelly, dry, barren summits present detached piles of rocks, which delude and flatter the hopes and expectations of the solitary traveller, full sure of hospitable habitations; heaps of white, gnawed bones of the ancient buffaloe, elk and deer, indiscriminately mixed with those of men, half grown over with moss, altogether, exhibit scenes of uncultivated nature, on reflection, perhaps, rather disagreeable to a mind of delicate feelings and sensibility, since some of these objects recognize past transactions and events, perhaps not altogether reconcilable to justice and humanity.

How harmonious and sweetly murmur the purling rills and fleeting brooks, roving along the shadowy vales, passing through dark, subterranean caverns, or dashing over steep rocky precipices, their cold, humid banks condensing the volatile vapours, which fall and coalesce in crystalline drops, on the leaves and elastic twigs of the aromatic shrubs and incarnate flowers. In these cool, sequestered, rocky vales, we behold the following celebrated beauties of the hills, i. e. fragrant Calycanthus, blushing Rhododendron ferruginium, delicate Philadelphus inodorus, which displays the white wavy mantle, with the sky robed Delphinium, perfumed Convalaria and fiery Azalea, flaming on the ascending hills or wa-[323]vy surface of the gliding brooks. The epithet fiery, I annex to this most celebrated species of Azalea, as being expressive of the appearance of it in flower, which are in general of the colour of the finest red lead, orange and bright gold, as well as yellow and cream colour; these various splendid colours are not only in separate plants, but frequently all the varieties and shades are seen in separate branches on the same plant, and the clusters of the blossoms cover the shrubs in such incredible profusion on the hill sides, that suddenly opening to view from dark shades, we are alarmed with the apprehension of the hills being set on fire. This is certainly the most gay and brilliant flowering shrub yet known: they grow in little copses or clumps, in open forests as well as dark groves, with other shrubs, and about the bases of hills, especially where brooks and rivulets wind about them; the bushes seldom rise above six or seven feet in height, and generally but three, four and five, but branch and spread their tops greatly; the young leaves are but very small whilst the shrubs are in bloom, from which circumstance the plant exhibits a greater shew of splendour.

Towards evening I crossed Broad river at a good ford, just above its confluence with the Savanna, and arrived at Fort James, which is a four square stockade, with saliant bastions at each angle, mounted with a block-house, where are some swivel guns, one story higher than the curtains, which are pierced with loop-holes, breast high, and defended by small arms; the fortification encloses about an acre of ground, where is the governor's or commandant's house, a good building, which is flanked on each side by buildings for the officers and barracks [324] for the garrison, consisting of fifty rangers, including officers, each having a good horse well equipt, a rifle, two dragoon pistols and a hanger, besides a powder horn, shot pouch and tomahawk. The fort stands on an eminence in the forks between the Savanna and Broad rivers, about one mile above Fort Charlotta, which is situated near the banks of the Savanna, on the Carolina side; Fort James is situated nearly at an equal distance from the banks of the two rivers, and from the extreme point of the land that separates them. The point or peninsula between the two rivers, for the distance of two miles back from the fort, is laid out for a town, by the name of Dartmouth, in honour to the earl of Dartmouth, who, by his interest and influence in the British councils, obtained from the king a grant and powers in favour of the Indian trading company of Georgia, to treat with the Creeks for the cession of a quantity of land sufficient to discharge their debts to the traders, for the security and defence of which territory this fortress was established.

This territory, called the New Purchase, contains about two millions of acres, lying upon the head of Great Ogechee, between the banks of the Savanna and Alatamaha, touching on the Ocone and taking within its precincts all the waters of Broad and Little rivers, comprehends a body of excellent fertile land, well watered by innumerable rivers, creeks and brooks.

I made a little excursion up the Savanna river, four or five miles above the fort, with the surgeon of the garrison, who was so polite as to attend me to shew me some remarkable Indian monuments, which are worthy of every travellers notice. These wonderful labours of the ancients stand in a level [325] plain, very near the bank of the river, now twenty or thirty yards from it; they consist of conical mounts of earth and four square terraces, &c. The great mount is in the form of a cone, about forty or fifty feet high, and the circumference of its base two or three hundred yards, entirely composed of the loamy rich earth of the low grounds; the top or apex is flat; a spiral path or track leading from the ground up to the top is still visible, where now grows a large, beautiful spreading Red Cedar (Juniperus Americana;) there appear four niches, excavated out of the sides of this hill, at different heights from the base, fronting the four cardinal points; these niches or sentry boxes are entered into from the winding path, and seem to have been ment for resting places or look-outs. The circumjacent level grounds are cleared and planted with Indian Corn at present, and I think the proprietor of these lands, who accompanied us to this place, said that the mount itself yielded above one hundred bushels in one season: the land hereabouts is indeed exceeding fertile and productive.

It is altogether unknown to us, what could have induced the Indians to raise such a heap of earth in this place, the ground for a great space around being subject to inundations, at least once a year, from which circumstance we may conclude they had no town or settled habitations here: some imagine these tumuli were constructed for look-out towers. It is reasonable to suppose, however, that they were to serve some important purpose in those days, as they were public works, and would have required the united labour and attention of a whole nation, circumstanced as they were, to have constructed one of them almost in an age. There are [326] several less ones round about the great one, with some very large tetragon terraces on each side, near one hundred yards in length, and their surface four, six, eight and ten feet above the ground on which they stand.

We may however hazard a conjecture, that as there is generally a narrow space or ridge in these low lands, immediately bordering on the rivers bank, which is eight or ten feet higher than the adjoining low grounds, that lie betwixt the stream and the heights of the adjacent main land, which, when the river overflows its banks, are many feet under water, when, at the same time, this ridge on the river bank is above water and dry, and at such inundations appears as an island in the river. Now these people might have had a town on this ridge, and this mount raised for a retreat and refuge in case of inundations, which are unforeseen and surprise them very suddenly, spring and autumn.

Having finished my collections and observations, which were extended to a considerable distance in the environs of Dartmouth; May 10th set off again, proceeding for Keowe, rode six or eight miles up the river above the fort, crossed over into Carolina and soon got into the high road, but had not proceeded far when I was surprised by a sudden very heavy shower of rain, attended with terrific thunder, but luckily found present shelter at a farm house, where I continued above an hour before its fury abated, when I proceeded again, and notwithstanding this detention and obstacles in consequence of the heavy rains in raising the creeks, travelled thirty-five miles, and arrived in the evening at Mr. Cameron's, deputy commissary for Indian affairs for the Cherokee nation, to whom I was re-[327]commended by letters from the honourable John Stewart, superintendent, residing in Charleston, mentioning my business in the Cherokee country.

The road this day had led me over an uneven country, its surface undulated by ridges or chains of hills, sometimes rough with rocks and stones, yet generally productive of forests, with a variety of vegetables of inferior growth, i. e. Quercus, various species, Juglans hickory, varieties, Liriodendron, Fraxinus, Fagus sylvatica, Fagus castania, Fagus pumila, s. Chinkapin, Nyssa sylvatica, Acer rubrum, Æsculus sylvatica, Magnolia acuminata, Magnolia tripetala, Andromeda arborea, Hopea tinctoria, Æsculus pavia, Vibernum, Azalea flammea and other species; Hydrangea, Calycanthus, &c.

The season being uncommonly wet, almost daily showers of rain and frequently attended with tremenduous thunder, rendered travelling disagreeable, toilsome and hazardous, through an uninhabited wilderness, abounding with rivers and brooks; I was prevailed upon by Mr. Cameron to stay at his house a few days, until the rains ceased and the rivers could be more easily forded.

The Angelica lucido or Nondo grows here in abundance; its aromatic carminative root is in taste much like that of the Ginseng (Panax) though more of the taste and scent of Anise seed; it is in high estimation with the Indians as well as white inhabitants, and sells at a great price to the Southern Indians of Florida, who dwell near the sea coast where this never grows spontaneously. I observed a charming species of Malva, having panicles of large splendid purple or deep blue flowers, and another species of Malva, very singular indeed, for [328] it is a climber; the leaves are broad, which, with the whole plant, are hoary; the flowers are very small, of a greenish white: and here grows in abundance a beautiful species of Delphinium; the flowers differ in no respect from those of the common branching Larkspur of the gardens; they are of a fine deep blue colour, and disposed in long sparsed spikes; the leaves are compound, almost linear, but the segments not so fine cut as those of the garden Larkspur.

The weather now settled and fair, I prepared to proceed for Fort Prince George Keowe, having obtained of the agreeable and liberal Mr. Cameron, ample testimonials and letters of recommendation to the traders in the nation; this gentleman also very obligingly sent a young Negro slave along, to assist and pilot me as far as Senica.

May 15th I left Lough-abber, the seat of Mr. Cameron. In the course of this day's journey I crossed several rivers and brooks, all branches of Savanna, now called Keowe, above its confluence with the Tugilo, the West main branch. The face of the country uneven, by means of ridges of hills and water courses; the hills somewhat rocky near their summits and at the banks of rivers and creeks, but very fertile, as there is a good depth of a loose dark and moist vegetative mould, on a stratum of reddish brown tenacious clay, and sometimes a deep stratum of dusky brown marl. The vegetable productions observed during this day's progress, were generally the same as already recited since leaving Dartmouth. The flaming Azalea abounds and illuminates the hill sides, and a new and singularly beautiful species of Æsculus pavia, situated above them, towards the summits of these low hills; this [329] conspicuously beautiful flowering shrub, grows to the height of five or six feet, many divergent crooked stems arise together from a root or source, which dividing their branches, wreath about every way, after a very irregular and free order; the exterior subdivisions of these limbs terminate with a heavy cluster or thyrsus of rose or pink coloured flowers, speckled or variegated with crimson, larger, more expansive and regular in their formation than those of the Pavia; and these heavy spikes of flowers, charged with the morning dews, bend the slender flexile stems to the ground: the compound leaves are of the configuration of those of the Pavia, but broader and their veins more prominent. The shrubs growing about the tops of the more barren grassy hills, where large trees are few and scattered shew themselves to great advantage, and make a fine appearance.

There is abundance of Grape vines (Vitis vinifera) which ramble and spread themselves over the shrubs and low trees in these situations, and I was assured produce fruit affording an excellent juice; the grapes are of various colours when ripe, of the figure and about the size of the European wine grapes. Arrived at Sinica in the evening, after travelling forty five miles through an uninhabited wilderness.

The Cherokee town of Sinica is a very respectable settlement, situated on the East bank of the Keowe river, though the greatest number of Indian habitations are on the opposite shore, where likewise stands the council-house in a level plain betwixt the river and a range of beautiful lofty hills, which rise magnificently, and seem to bend over [330] the green plains and the river; but the chief's house, with those of the traders, and some Indian dwellings are seated on the ascent of the heights on the opposite shore; this situation in point of prospect far excels the other, as it overlooks the whole settlement, the extensive fruitful plains on the river above and below, and the plantations of the inhabitants, commanding a most comprehensive diversified view of the opposite elevations.

Sinica is a new town rebuilt since the late Indian war, when the Cherokees were vanquished and compelled to sue for peace, by general Middleton, commander of the Carolinian auxiliaries acting against them, when the lower and middle settlements were broken up: the number of inhabitants are now estimated at about five hundred, and they are able to muster about one hundred warriors.

Next day I left Sinica alone, and after riding about sixteen miles, chiefly through high forests of excellent land at a little distance from the river, arrived in the evening at fort Prince George Keowe.

Keowe is a most charming situation, and the adjacent heights are naturally so formed and disposed, as with little expence of military architecture to be rendered almost impregnable; in a fertile vale, at this season enamelled with the incarnate fragrant strawberries and blooming plants, through which the beautiful river meanders, sometimes gently flowing, but more frequently agitated, gliding swiftly between the fruitful strawberry banks, environed at various distances, by high hills and mountains, some rising boldly almost upright upon the verge of the expansive lawn, so as to overlook and shadow it, whilst others more lofty, superb, misty and blue, majestically mount far above.

[331] The evening still and calm, all silent and peaceable, a vivifying gentle breeze continually wafted from the fragrant strawberry fields, and aromatic Calycanthean groves on the surrounding heights, the wary moor fowl thundering in the distant echoing hills, how the groves and hills ring with the shrill perpetual voice of the whip-poor-will!

Abandoned as my situation now was, yet thank heaven many objects met together at this time, and conspired to conciliate, and in some degree compose my mind, heretofore somewhat dejected and unharmo-

nized: all alone in a wild Indian country, a thousand miles from my
native land, and a vast distance from any settlements of white people.
It is true, here were some of my own colour, yet they were strangers,
and though friendly and hospitable, their manners and customs of
living so different from what I had been accustomed to, administered
but little to my consolation: some hundred miles yet to travel, the
savage vindictive inhabitants lately ill-treated by the frontier Virginians, blood being spilt between them and the injury not yet wiped
away by formal treaty; the Cherokees extremely jealous of white people
travelling about their mountains, especially if they should be seen peeping in amongst the rocks or digging up their earth.

The vale of Keowe is seven or eight miles in extent, that is from
the little town of Kulsage * about a mile above, thence down the river
six or seven miles, where a high ridge of hills on each side of the river
almost terminates the vale, but opens again below the narrow ridge,
and continues ten or twelve [332] miles down to Sinica, and in width
one and two miles: this fertile vale within the remembrance of some
old traders with whom I conversed, was one continued settlement, the
swelling sides of the adjoining hills were then covered with habitations, and the rich level grounds beneath lying on the river, were cultivated and planted, which now exhibit a very different spectacle,
humiliating indeed to the present generation, the posterity and feeble
remains of the once potent and renowned Cherokees: the vestiges of
the ancient Indian dwellings are yet visible on the feet of the hills
bordering and fronting on the vale, such as posts or pillars of their
habitations, &c.

There are several Indian mounts or tumuli, and terraces, monuments of the ancients, at the old site of Keowe, near the fort Prince
George, but no Indian habitations at present; and here are several
dwellings inhabited by white people concerned in the Indian trade;
Mr. D. Homes is the principal trader here.

The old fort Prince George now bears no marks of a fortress, but
serves for a trading house.

* Sugar Town.

CHAP. III.

I waited two or three days at this post expecting the return of an Indian, who was out hunting; this man was recommended to me as a suitable person for a protector and guide to the Indian settlements over the hills, but upon information that he would not be in shortly, and there being no other person suitable for the purpose, rather than be detained, and perhaps thereby frustrated in my purposes, determined to set off alone and run all risks.

I crossed the river at a good ford just below the old fort. The river here is near one hundred yards over: after an agreeable progress for about two miles over delightful strawberry plains, and gently swelling green hills, began to ascend more steep and rocky ridges. Having gained a very considerable elevation, and looking around, I enjoyed a very comprehensive and delightful view: Keowe which I had but just lost sight of, appears again, and the serpentine river speeding through the lucid green plain apparently just under my feet. After observing this delightful landscape I continued on again three or four miles, keeping the trading path which led me over uneven rocky land, and crossing rivulets and brooks, rapidly descending over rocky precipices, when I came into a charming vale, embellished with a delightful glittering river, which meandered through it, and crossed my road: on my left hand upon the grassy bases of the rising hills, appears the remains of a town of the ancients, as [334] the tumuli, terraces, posts or pillars, old Peach and Plumb orchards, &c. sufficiently testify. These vales and swelling bases of the surrounding hills, afford vast crops of excellent grass and herbage fit for pasturage and hay; of the latter Plantago Virginica, Sanguisorba, Geum, Fragaria, &c. The Panax quinquifolium, or Ginseng, now appears plentifully on the North exposure of the hill, growing out of the rich mellow humid earth amongst the stones or fragments of rocks.

Having crossed the vales, began to ascend again the more lofty ridges of hills, then continued about eight miles over more gentle pyramidal hills, narrow vales and lawns, the soil exceedingly fertile, producing lofty forests and odoriferous groves of Calycanthus, near the banks of rivers, with Halesia, Philadelphus inodorus, Rhododendron ferruginium, Aazalea, Stewartia montana *, fol. ovatis acuminatis serratis, flor. nivea, staminum corona fulgida, pericarp. pomum exsuccum, apice acuminato dehiscens, Cornus Florida, Styrax, all in full bloom, and decorated with the following sweet roving climbers, i. e. Bignonia sempervirens, Big. crucigera, Lonicera sempervirens, Rosa paniculata, &c.

Now at once the mount divides, and discloses to view the ample Occonne vale, encircled by a wreath of uniform hills; their swelling bases clad in cheerful verdure, over which issuing from between the mountains, plays along a glittering river, meandering through the meadows, which crossing at the upper end of the vale, I began to ascend the Occonne mountain. On the foot of the hills are the [335] ruins of the antient Occonne town: the first step after leaving the verdant beds of the hills was a very high rocky chain of pointed hills, extremely well timbered with the following trees: Quercus tinctoria, Querc. alba, Querc. rubra, Fraxinus excelsior, Juglans hickory, various species, Ulmus, Tilia, Acer saccharinum, Morus, Juglans nigra, Juglans alba, Annona glabra, Robinia pseudacacia, Magnolia acuminata, Æsculus sylvatica with many more, particularly a species of Robinia new to me, though perhaps the same as figured and slightly described by Catesby in his Nat. Hist. Carol. This beautiful flowering tree grows twenty and thirty feet high, with a crooked leaning trunk, the branches spread greatly, and wreath about, some almost touching the ground; however there appears a singular pleasing wildness and freedom in its manner of growth, the slender subdivisions of the branches terminate with heavy compound panicles of rose or pink coloured flowers, amidst a wreath of beautiful pinnated leaves.

My next flight was up a very high peak, to the top of the Occonne mountain, where I rested; and turning about found that I was now in a very elevated situation, from whence I enjoyed a view inexpressibly magnificent and comprehensive. The mountainous wilderness through which I had lately traversed down to the region of Augusta, appearing regularly undulated as the great ocean after a tempest; the undulations gradually depressing, yet perfectly regular, as the squamae of fish or imbrications of tile on a roof: the nearest ground to me of a perfect full green, next more glaucous, and lastly almost blue as the ether with which the [336] the most distant curve of the horizon seems to be blended.

My imagination thus wholly engaged in the contemplation of this magnificent landscape, infinitely varied, and without bound, I was

---

* This is a new species of Stewartia, unknown to the European botanists, and not mentioned in any catalogues.

almost insensible or regardless of the charming objects more within my reach: a new species of Rhododendron foremost in the assembly of mountain beauties, next the flaming Azalea, Kalmia latifolia, incarnate Robinia, snowy mantled Philadelphus inodorus, perfumed Calycanthus, &c.

This species of Rhododendron grows six or seven feet high, many nearly erect stems arise together from the root forming a group or coppice. The leaves are three or four inches in length, of an oblong figure, broadest toward the extremity, and terminating with an obtuse point; their upper surface of a deep green and polished, but the nether surface of a rusty iron colour, which seems to be effected by innumerable minute reddish vesicles, beneath a fine short downy pubescence; the numerous flexile branches terminate with a loose spiked raceme, or cluster of large deep rose coloured flowers, each flower being affixed in the diffused cluster by a long peduncle, which with the whole plant possess an agreeable perfume.

After being recovered of the fatigue and labour in ascending the mountain, I began again to prosecute my task, proceeding through a shady forest, and soon after gained the most elevated crest of the Occonne mountain, and then began to descend the other side; the winding rough road carrying me over rocky hills and levels, shaded by incomparable forests, the soil exceedingly rich, and of an excel-[337]lent quality for the production of every vegetable suited to the climate, and seems peculiarly adapted for the cultivation of Vines (Vitis vinifera) Olives, (Olea Europea) the Almond tree (Amygdalus communis) Fig (Ficus carica) and perhaps the Pomgranate (Punica granatum) as well as Peaches, (Amyg. Persica) Prunus, Pyrus, of every variety: arising again steep rocky ascents, and then rich levels, where grew many trees and plants common in Pennsylvania, New-York and even Canada, as Pinus strobus, Pin. sylvestris, Pin. abies, Acer saccharinum, Acer striatum, s. Pennsylvanicum, Populus trimula, Betula nigra, Juglans alba, &c. but what seems remarkable, the yellow Jessamine, (Bignonia sempervirens) which is killed by a very slight frost in the open air in Pennsylvania, here on the summits of the Cherokee mountains associates with the Canadian vegetables, and appears roving with them in perfect bloom and gaiety; as likewise Halesia diptera, and Hal. tetraptera, mountain Stewartia, Styrax, Ptelea, and Æsculus pavia, but all these bear our hardest frosts in Pennsylvania. Now I enter a charming narrow vale, through which flows a rapid large creek, on whose banks are happily associated the shrubs already recited, together with the following; Staphylaea, Euonismus Americana, Hamamelis, Azalea, various species, Aristalochia frutescens, s. odoratissima, which rambles over the trees and shrubs on the prolific banks of these mountain brooks. Passed through magnificent high forests, and then came upon the borders of an ample meadow on the left, embroidered by the shade of a high circular amphitheatre of hills, the circular ridges rising magnificently one over the other: on the green turfy bases of these ascents appear the ruins [338] of a town of the ancients; the upper end of this spacious green plain is divided by a promontory or spur of the ridges before me, which projects into it; my road led me up into an opening of the ascents through which the glittering brook which watered the meadows ran rapidly down, dashing and roaring over high rocky steps. Continued yet ascending until I gained the top of an elevated rocky ridge, when appeared before me a gap or opening between other yet more lofty ascents, thro' which continuing as the rough rocky road led me, close by the winding banks of a large rapid brook, which at length turning to the left, pouring down rocky precipices, glided off through dark groves and high forests, conveying streams of fertility and pleasure to the fields below.

The surface of the land now for three or four miles is level, yet uneven, occasioned by natural mounds or rocky knobs, but covered with a good staple of rich earth, which affords forests of timber trees and shrubs. After this, gently descending again, I travelled some miles over a varied situation of ground, exhibiting views of grand forests, dark detached groves, vales and meadows, as heretofore, and producing the like vegetable and other works of nature; the meadows affording exuberant pasturage for cattle, and the bases of the encircling hills, flowering plants, and fruitful strawberry beds: observed frequently ruins of the habitations or villages of the ancients. Crossed a delightful river, the main branch of Tugilo, when I began to ascend again, first over swelling turfy ridges, varied with groves of stately forest trees, then ascending again more steep, grassy hill sides, rested on the top of mount Magnolia, which appeared to me to be the highest ridge of the Cherokee mountains, which separates [339] the waters of Savanna river from those of the Tanase or great main branch of the Cherokee river, which running rapidly a North-West course thro' the mountains, is joined from the North-East by the Holstein, thence taking a West course yet amongst the mountains receiving into it from either hand many large rivers, leaves the mountains immediately after being joined by a large river from the East, becomes a mighty river by the name of Hogehege, thence meanders many hundred miles through a vast country consisting of forests, meadows, groves, expansive savannas, fields and swelling hills, most fertile and delightful, flows into the beautiful Ohio, and in conjunction with its transparent waters, becomes tributary to the sovereign Missisippi.

This exalted peak I named mount Magnolia *, from a new and beautiful species of that celebrated family of flowering trees, which here, at the cascades of Falling Creek, grows in a high degree of perfection, for although I had noticed this curious tree several times before, particularly on the high ridges betwixt Sinica and Keowe, and on ascending the first mountain after leaving Keowe, when I observed it in flower, but here it flourishes and commands our attention.

This tree, or perhaps rather a shrub, rises eighteen to thirty feet in height, there are usually many stems from a root or source, which lean a little, or slightly diverge from each other, in this respect imitating the Magnolia tripetala; the crooked wreathing branches arising and subdividing from the main stem without order or uniformity, their [340] extremities turn upwards, producing a very large rosaceous, perfectly white, double or polypetalous flower, which is of a most fragrant scent; this fine flower sits in the center of a radius of very large leaves, which are of a singular figure, somewhat lanceolate, but broad towards their extremities, terminating with an acuminated point, and backwards they attenuate and become very narrow towards their bases, terminating that way with two long, narrow ears or lappets, one on each side of the insertion of the petiole; the leaves have only short footstalks, sitting very near each other, at the extremities of the floriferous branches, from whence they spread themselves after a regular order, like the spokes of a wheel, their margins touching or lightly lapping upon each other, form an expansive umbrella superbly crowned or crested with the fragrant flower, representing a white plume; the blossom is succeeded by a very large crimson cone or strobile, containing a great number of scarlet berries, which, when ripe, spring from their cells and are for a time suspended by a white silky web or thread. The leaves of these trees which grow in a rich, light, humid soil, when fully expanded and at maturity, are frequently above two feet in length and six or eight inches where broadest. I discovered in the maritime parts of Georgia, particularly on the banks of the Alatamaha, another new species of Magnolia, whose leaves were nearly of the figure of those of this tree, but they were much less in size, not more than six or seven inches in length, and the strobile very small, oblong, sharp pointed and of a fine deep crimson colour, but I never saw the flower. These trees grow strait and erect, thirty feet or more in height, and of a sharp conical form, much resembling the Cucumber tree (Mag. acuminata) in figure.

[341]   This day being remarkably warm and sultry, which, together with the labour and fatigue of ascending the mountains, made me very thirsty and in some degree sunk my spirits. Now past mid-day, I

* Magnolia auriculato.

sought a cool shaded retreat, where was water for refreshment and grazing for my horse, my faithful slave and only companion. After proceeding a little farther, descending the other side of the mountain, I perceived at some distance before me, on my right hand, a level plain supporting a grand high forest and groves; the nearer I approach my steps are the more accelerated from the flattering prospect opening to view; I now enter upon the verge of the dark forest, charming solitude! as I advanced through the animating shades, observed on the farther grassy verge a shady grove, thither I directed my steps; on approaching these shades, between the stately columns of the superb forest trees, presented to view, rushing from rocky precipices under the shade of the pensile hills, the unparalleled cascade of Falling Creek, rolling and leaping off the rocks, which uniting below, spread a broad, glittering sheet of crystal waters, over a vast convex elevation of plain, smooth rocks, and are immediately received by a spacious bason, where, trembling in the centre through hurry and agitation, they gently subside, encircling the painted still verge, from whence gliding swiftly, they soon form a delightful little river, which continuing to flow more moderately, is restrained for a moment, gently undulating in a little lake, they then pass on rapidly to a high perpendicular steep of rocks, from whence these delightful waters are hurried down with irresistible rapidity. I here seated myself on the moss clad rocks, under the shade of spreading trees and floriferous fragrant shrubs, in full view of the cascades.

[342]   At this rural retirement were assembled a charming circle of mountain vegetable beauties, Magnolia auriculata, Rhododendron ferruginium, Kalmia latifolia, Robinia montana, Azalea flammula, Rosa paniculata, Calycanthus Floridus, Philadelphus inodorus, perfumed Convalaria majalis, Anemone thalictroides, Anemone hepatica, Erythronium maculatum, Leontice thalictroides, Trillium sessile, Trillium cesnum, Cypripedium, Arethuza, Ophrys, Sanguinaria, Viola, uvularia, Epigea, Mitchella repens, Stewartia, Halesia, Styrax, Lonicera, &c. some of these roving beauties are strolling over the mossy, shelving, humid rocks, or from off the expansive wavy boughs of trees, bending over the floods, salute their delusive shades, playing on the surface, some plunge their perfumed heads and bathe their flexile limbs in the silver stream, whilst others by the mountain breezes are tossed about, their blooming tufts bespangled with pearly and crystalline dewdrops collected from the falling mists, glisten in the rain bow arch. Having collected some valuable specimens at this friendly retreat, I continued my lonesome pilgrimage. My road for a considerable time led me winding and turning about the steep rocky hills; the descent of

some of which was very rough and troublesome, by means of fragments of rocks, slippery clay and talc; but after this I entered a spacious
forest, the land having gradually acquired a more level surface; a
pretty grassy vale appears on my right, through which my wandering
path led me, close by the banks of a delightful creek, which sometimes
falling over steps of rocks, glides gently with serpentine meanders
through the meadows.

After crossing this delightful brook and mead, the land rises again
with sublime magnificence, and [343] I am led over hills and vales,
groves and high forests, vocal with the melody of the feathered songsters, the snow-white cascades glittering on the sides of the distant
hills.

It was now after noon; I approached a charming vale, amidst
sublimely high forests, awful shades! darkness gathers around, far
distant thunder rolls over the trembling hills; the black clouds with
august majesty and power, moves slowly forwards, shading regions of
towering hills, and threatening all the destructions of a thunder storm;
all around is now still as death, not a whisper is heard, but a total in-
activity and silence seems to pervade the earth; the birds afraid to
utter a chirrup, and in low tremulous voices take leave of each other,
seeking covert and safety; every insect is silenced, and nothing heard
but the roaring of the approaching hurricane; the mighty cloud now
expands its sable wings, extending from North to South, and is driven irresistibly on by the tumultuous winds, spreading his livid wings around
the gloomy concave, armed with terrors of thunder and fiery shafts of
lightning; now the lofty forests bend low beneath its fury, their limbs
and wavy boughs are tossed about and catch hold of each other; the
mountains tremble and seem to reel about, and the ancient hills to be
shaken to their foundations: the furious storm sweeps along, smoking
through the vale and over the resounding hills; the face of the earth is
obscured by the deluge descending from the firmament, and I am
deafened by the din of thunder; the tempestuous scene damps my
spirits, and my horse sinks under me at the tremendous peals, as I
hasten on for the plain.

The storm abating, I saw an Indian hunting ca-[344]bin on the side
of a hill, a very agreeable prospect, especially in my present condition;
I made up to it and took quiet possession, there being no one to dispute
it with me except a few bats and whip poor-wills, who had repaired
thither for shelter from the violence of the hurricane.

Having turned out my horse in the sweet meadows adjoining, and
finding some dry wood under shelter of the old cabin, I struck up a fire,
dried my clothes and comforted myself with a frugal repast of biscuit

and dried beef, which was all the food my viaticum afforded me by this time, excepting a small piece of cheese which I had furnished myself with at Charleston and kept till this time.

The night was clear, calm and cool, and I rested quietly. Next morning at day break I was awakened and summoned to resume my daily task, by the shrill cries of the social night hawk and active merry mockbird. By the time the rising sun had gilded the tops of the towering hills, the mountains and vales rang with the harmonious shouts of the pious and cheerful tenants of the groves and meads.

I observed growing in great abundance in these mountain meadows, Sanguisorba Canadensis and Heracleum maximum, the latter exhibiting a fine shew, being rendered conspicuous even at a great distance, by its great height and spread, vast pinnatifid leaves and expansive umbels of snow-white flowers; the swelling bases of the surrounding hills fronting the meadows, present, for my acceptance, the fragrant red strawberry, in painted beds of many acres surface, indeed I may safely say many hundreds.

[345]   After passing through this meadow, the road led me over the bases of a ridge of hills, which as a bold promontory dividing the fields I had just passed, form expansive green lawns. On these towering hills appeared the ruins of the ancient famous town of Sticoe. Here was a vast Indian mount or tumulus and great terrace, on which stood the council house, with banks encompassing their circus; here were also old Peach and Plumb orchards, some of the trees appeared yet thriving and fruitful; presently after leaving these ruins, the vale and fields are divided by means of a spur of the mountains pushing forward; here likewise the road forked, the left hand path continued up the mountains to the Overhill towns; I followed the vale to the right hand, and soon began again to ascend the hills, riding several miles over very rough, stony land, yielding the like vegetable productions as heretofore; and descending again gradually, by a dubious winding path, leading into a narrow vale and lawn, through which rolled on before me a delightful brook, water of the Tanase; I crossed it and continued a mile or two down the meadows, when the high mountains on each side suddenly receding, discover the opening of the extensive and fruitful vale of Cowe, through which meanders the head branch of the Tanase, almost from its source, sixty miles, following its course down to Cowe.

I left the stream for a little while, passing swiftly and foaming over its rocky bed, lashing the steep craggy banks, and then suddenly sunk from my sight, murmuring hollow and deep under the rocky surface of the ground: on my right hand the vale expands, receiving a pretty silvery brook of water, [346] which came hastily down from the adjacent hills, and entered the river a little distance before me; I now turn from the heights on my left, the road leading into the level lawns, to avoid the hollow rocky grounds, full of holes and cavities, arching over the river, through which the waters are seen gliding along, but the river is soon liberated from these solitary and gloomy recesses, and appears waving through the green plain before me. I continued several miles, pursuing my serpentine path, through and over the meadows and green fields, and crossing the river, which is here incredibly increased in size, by the continual accession of brooks flowing in from the hills on each side, dividing their green turfy beds, forming them into parterres, vistas and verdant swelling knolls, profusely productive of flowers and fragrant strawberries, their rich juice dying my horses feet and ancles.

These swelling hills, the prolific beds on which the towering mountains repose, seem to have been the common situations of the towns of the ancients, as appear from the remaining ruins of them yet to be seen; and the level rich vale and meadows in front, their planting grounds.

Continuing yet ten or twelve miles down the vale, my road leading at times close to the banks of the river, the Azalea, Kalmia, Rhododendron, Philadelphus, &c. beautifying his now elevated shores, and painting the coves with a rich and cheerful scenery, continually unfolding new prospects as I traverse the shores; the towering mountains seem continually in motion as I pass along, pompously rising their superb crests towards the lofty skies, traversing the far distant horizon.

[347] The Tanase is now greatly increased from the conflux of the multitude of rivulets and brooks, descending from the hills on either side, generously contributing to establish his future fame, already a spacious river.

The mountains recede, the vale expands, two beautiful rivulets stream down through lateral vales, gliding in serpentine mazes over the green turfy knolls, and enter the Tanase nearly opposite to each other. Strait forward the expansive green vale seems yet infinite: now on the right hand a lofty pyramidal hill terminates a spur of the adjacent mountain, and advances almost into the river; but immediately after doubling this promontory, an expanded wing of the vale spreads on my right, down which came precipitately, a very beautiful creek, which flowed into the river just before me; but now behold, high upon the side of a distant mountain overlooking the vale, the fountain of this brisk flowing creek; the unparalleled water fall appears as a vast edifice with crystal front, or a field of ice lying on the bosom of the hill.

I now approach the river at the fording place, which was greatly swollen by the floods of rain that fell the day before, and ran with foaming rapidity, but observing that it had fallen several feet perpendicular, and perceiving the bottom or bed of the river to be level, and covered evenly with pebbles, I ventured to cross over, however I was obliged to swim two or three yards at the deepest chanel of it, and landed safely on the banks of a fine meadow, which lay on the opposite shore, where I immediately alighted and spread abroad on the turf my linen, books and specimens of plants, &c. to dry, turned out my steed to graze and then avanced in-[348]to the strawberry plains to regale on the fragrant, delicious fruit, welcomed by communities of the splendid meleagris, the capricious roe-buck and all the free and happy tribes which possess and inhabit those prolific fields, who appeared to invite and joined with me in the participation of the bountiful repast presented to us from the lap of nature.

I mounted again and followed the trading path about a quarter of a mile through the fields, then gently ascended the green beds of the hills, and entered the forests, being a point of a chain of hills projecting into the green vale or low lands of the river; this forest continued about a mile, the surface of the land level but rough, being covered with stones or fragments of rocks, and very large, smooth pebbles of various shapes and sizes, some of ten or fifteen pounds weight: I observed on each side of the road many vast heaps of these stones, Indian graves undoubtedly *.

After I left the graves, the ample vale soon offered on my right hand, through the tall forest trees, charming views, and which exhibited a pleasing contrast, immediately out of the gloomy shades and scenes of death, into expansive, lucid, green, flowery fields, expanding between retiring hills and turfy eminences, the rapid Tanase gliding through as a vast serpent rushing after his prey.

My winding path now leads me again over the green fields into the meadows, sometimes visiting [349] the decorated banks of the river, as it meanders through the meadows, or boldly sweeps along the

* At this place was fought a bloody and decisive battle between these Indians and the Carolinians, under the conduct of general Middleton, when a great number of Cherokee warriors were slain, which shook their power, terrified and humbled them, insomuch that they deserted most of their settlements in the low countries, and betook themselves to the mountains as less accessible to the regular forces of the white people.

bases of the mountains, its surface receiving the images reflected from the flowery banks above.

Thus was my agreeable progress for about fifteen miles, since I came upon the sources of the Tanase, at the head of this charming vale: in the evening espying a human habitation at the foot of the sloping green hills, beneath lofty forests of the mountains on the left hand, and at the same time observed a man crossing the river from the opposite shore in a canoe and coming towards me, I waited his approach, who hailing me, I answered I was for Cowe; he intreated me very civilly to call at his house, adding that he would presently come to me.

I was received and entertained here until next day with the most perfect civility. After I had dined, towards evening, a company of Indian girls, inhabitants of a village in the hills at a small distance, called, having baskets of strawberries; and this man, who kept here a trading-house, and being married to a Cherokee woman of family, was indulged to keep a stock of cattle, and his helpmate being an excellent house-wife and a very agreeable good woman, treated us with cream and strawberries.

Next morning after breakfasting on excellent coffee, relished with bucanned venison, hot corn cakes, excellent butter and cheese, set forwards again for Cowe, which was about fifteen miles distance, keeping the trading path which coursed through the low lands between the hills and the river, now spacious and well beaten by travellers, [350] but somewhat intricate to a stranger, from the frequent collateral roads falling into it from villages or towns over the hills: after riding about four miles, mostly through fields and plantations, the soil incredibly fertile, arrived at the town of Echoe, consisting of many good houses, well inhabited; I passed through and continued three miles farther to Nucasse, and three miles more brought me to Whatoga: riding through this large town, the road carried me winding about through their little plantations of Corn, Beans, &c. up to the council-house, which was a very large dome or rotunda, situated on the top of an ancient artificial mount, and here my road terminated; all before me and on every side appeared little plantations of young Corn, Beans, &c. divided from each other by narrow strips or borders of grass, which marked the bounds of each one's property, their habitation standing in the midst: finding no common high road to lead me through the town, I was now at a stand how to proceed farther, when observing an Indian man at the door of his habitation, three or four hundred yards distance from me, beckoning to come to him, I ventured to ride through their lots, being careful to do no injury to the young plants, the rising hopes of their labour and industry, crossed a little grassy vale watered by a silver stream, which gently undulated through, then ascended a green hill to the house, where I was cheerfully welcomed at the door and led in by the chief, giving the care of my horse to two handsome youths, his sons. During my continuance here, about half an hour, I experienced the most perfect and agreeable hospitality conferred on me by these happy people; I mean happy in their dispositions, in their apprehensions of rectitude with regard to our social [351] or moral conduct: O divine simplicity and truth, friendship without fallacy or guile, hospitality disinterested, native, undefiled, unmodified by artificial refinements.

My venerable host gracefully and with an air of respect, led me into an airy, cool apartment, where being seated on cabins, his women brought in a refreshing repast, consisting of sodden venison, hot corn cakes, &c. with a pleasant cooling liquor made of hommony well boiled, mixed afterwards with milk; this is served up either before or after eating in a large bowl, with a very large spoon or ladle to sup it with.

After partaking of this simple but healthy and liberal collation and the dishes cleared off, Tobacco and pipes were brought, and the chief filling one of them, whose stem, about four feet long, was sheathed in a beautiful speckled snake skin, and adorned with feathers and strings of wampum, lights it and smoaks a few whiffs, puffing the smoak first towards the sun, then to the four cardinal points and lastly over my breast, hands it towards me, which I cheerfully receive from him and smoaked, when we fell into conversation; he first enquired if I came from Charleston? if I knew John Stewart, Esq.? how long since I left Charleston? &c. Having satisfied him in my answers in the best manner I could, he was greatly pleased, which I was convinced of by his attention to me, his cheerful manners and his ordering my horse a plentiful bait of corn, which last instance of respect is conferred on those only to whom they manifest the highest esteem, saying that corn was given by the Great Spirit only for food to man.

[352]   I acquainted this ancient prince and patriarch of the nature and design of my peregrinations, and that I was now for Cowe, but having lost my road in the town, requested that I might be informed. He cheerfully replied, that he was pleased I was come in their country, where I should meet with friendship and protection, and that he would himself lead me into the right path.

After ordering my horse to the door we went forth together, he on foot and I leading my horse by the bridle, thus walking together near two miles, we shook hands and parted, he returning home and I continuing my journey for Cowe.

This prince is the chief of Whatoga, a man universally beloved, and particularly esteemed by the whites for his pacific and equitable disposition, and revered by all for his exemplary virtues, just, moderate, magnanimous and intrepid.

He was tall and perfectly formed; his countenance cheerful and lofty and at the same time truly characteristic of the red men, that is, the brow ferocious and the eye active, piercing or fiery, as an eagle. He appeared to be about sixty years of age, yet upright and muscular, and his limbs active as youth.

After leaving my princely friend, I travelled about five miles through old plantations, now under grass, but appeared to have been planted the last season; the soil exceeding fertile, loose, black, deep and fat. I arrived at Cowe about noon; this settlement is esteemed the capital town; it is situated on the bases of the hills on both sides of the river, near to its bank, and here terminates the great vale [353] of Cowe, exhibiting one of the most charming natural mountainous landscapes perhaps any where to be seen; ridges of hills rising grand and sublimely one above and beyond another, some boldly and majestically advancing into the verdant plain, their feet bathed with the silver flood of the Tanase, whilst others far distant, veiled in blue mists, sublimely mount aloft, with yet greater majesty lift up their pompous crests and overlook vast regions.

The vale is closed at Cowe by a ridge of mighty hills, called the Jore mountain, said to be the highest land in the Cherokee country, which crosses the Tanase here.

On my arrival at this town I waited on the gentlemen to whom I was recommended by letter, and was received with respect and every demonstration of hospitality and friendship.

I took my residence with Mr. Galahan the chief trader here, an ancient respectable man who had been many years a trader in this country, and is esteemed and beloved by the Indians for his humanity, probity and equitable dealings with them, which to be just and candid I am obliged to observe (and blush for my countrymen at the recital) is somewhat of a prodigy, as it is a fact, I am afraid too true, that the white traders in their commerce with the Indians, give great and frequent occasions of complaint of their dishonesty and violence; but yet there are a few exceptions, as in the conduct of this gentleman, who furnishes a living instance of the truth of the old proverb, that "Honesty is the best policy," for this old honest Hibernian has often been protected by the Indians, when all others round [354] about him have been ruined, their property seized and themselves driven out of the country or slain by the injured, provoked natives.

Next day after my arrival I crossed the river in a canoe, on a visit to a trader who resided amongst the habitations on the other shore.

After dinner, on his mentioning some curious scenes amongst the hills, some miles distance from the river, we agreed to spend the afternoon in observations on the mountains.

After riding near two miles through Indian plantations of Corn, which was well cultivated, kept clean of weeds and was well advanced, being near eighteen inches in height, and the Beans planted at the Corn-hills were above ground; we leave the fields on our right, turning towards the mountains and ascending through a delightful green vale or lawn, which conducted us in amongst the pyramidal hills and crossing a brisk flowing creek, meandering through the meads which continued near two miles, dividing and branching in amongst the hills; we then mounted their steep ascents, rising gradually by ridges or steps one above another, frequently crossing narrow, fertile dales as we ascended; the air feels cool and animating, being charged with the fragrant breath of the mountain beauties, the blooming mountain cluster Rose, blushing Rhododendron and fair Lilly of the valley: having now attained the summit of this very elevated ridge, we enjoyed a fine prospect indeed; the enchanting Vale of Keowe, perhaps as celebrated for fertility, fruitfulness and beautiful prospects as the Fields of Pharsalia or the Vale of Tempe: the town, the elevated peeks of the Jore mountains, a very dis-[355]tant prospect of the Jore village in a beautiful lawn, lifted up many thousand feet higher than our present situation, besides a view of many other villages and settlements on the sides of the mountains, at various distances and elevations; the silver rivulets gliding by them and snow white cataracts glimmering on the sides of the lofty hills; the bold promontories of the Jore mountain stepping into the Tanase river, whilst his foaming waters rushed between them.

After viewing this very entertaining scene we began to descend the mountain on the other side, which exhibited the same order of gradations of ridges and vales as on our ascent, and at length rested on a very expansive, fertile plain, amidst the towering hills, over which we rode a long time, through magnificent high forests, extensive green fields, meadows and lawns. Here had formerly been a very flourishing settlement, but the Indians deserted it in search of fresh planting land, which they soon found in a rich vale but a few miles distance over a ridge of hills. Soon after entering on these charming, sequestered, prolific fields, we came to a fine little river, which crossing, and riding over fruitful strawberry beds and green lawns, on the sides of a circular ridge of hills in front of us, and going round the bases of this promontory, came to a fine meadow on an arm of the vale, through which meandered a brook, its humid vapours bedewing the fragrant strawberries which hung in heavy red clusters over the grassy verge; we crossed the rivulet, then rising a sloping, green, turfy ascent, alighted on the borders of a grand forest of stately trees, which we penetrated on foot a little distance to a horse-stamp, where was a large squadron of those [356] useful creatures, belonging to my friend and companion, the trader, on the sight of whom they assembled together from all quarters; some at a distance saluted him with shrill neighings of gratitude, or came prancing up to lick the salt out of his hand; whilst the younger and more timorous came galloping onward, but coyly wheeled off, and fetching a circuit stood aloof, but as soon as their lord and master strewed the crystalline salty bait on the hard beaten ground, they all, old and young, docile and timorous, soon formed themselves in ranks and fell to licking up the delicious morsel.

It was a fine sight; more beautiful creatures I never saw; there were of them of all colours, sizes and dispositions. Every year as they become of age he sends off a troop of them down to Charleston, where they are sold to the highest bidder.

Having paid our attention to this useful part of the creation, who, if they are under our dominion, have consequently a right to our protection and favour. We returned to our trusty servants that were regaling themselves in the exuberant sweet pastures and strawberry fields in sight, and mounted again; proceeding on our return to town, continued through part of this high forest skirting on the meadows; began to ascend the hills of a ridge which we were under the necessity of crossing, and having gained its summit, enjoyed a most enchanting view, a vast expanse of green meadows and strawberry fields; a meandering river gliding through, saluting in its various turnings the swelling, green, turfy knolls, embellished with parterres of flowers and fruitful strawberry beds; flocks of turkeys strolling about them; herds of deer prancing in the meads [357] or bounding over the hills; companies of young, innocent Cherokee virgins, some busily gathering the rich fragrant fruit, others having already filled their baskets, lay reclined under the shade of floriferous and fragrant native bowers of Magnolia, Azalea, Philadelphus, perfumed Calycanthus, sweet Yellow Jessamine and cerulian Glycine frutescens, disclosing their beauties to the fluttering breeze, and bathing their limbs in the cool fleeting streams; whilst other parties, more gay and libertine, were yet collecting strawberries or wantonly chasing their companions, tantalising them, staining their lips and cheeks with the rich fruit.

This sylvan scene of primitive innocence was enchanting, and perhaps too enticing for hearty young men long to continue idle spectators.

In fine, nature prevailing over reason, we wished at least to have a more active part in their delicious sports. Thus precipitately resolving, we cautiously made our approaches, yet undiscovered, almost to the joyous scene of action. Now, although we meant no other than an innocent frolic with this gay assembly of hamadryades, we shall leave it to the person of feeling and sensibility to form an idea to what lengths our passions might have hurried us, thus warmed and excited, had it not been for the vigilance and care of some envious matrons who lay in ambush, and espying us gave the alarm, time enough for the nymphs to rally and assemble together; we however pursued and gained ground on a group of them, who had incautiously strolled to a greater distance from their guardians, and finding their retreat now like to be cut off, took shelter under cover of a little grove, but on perceiving themselves to be discovered by us, kept their stati-[358]on, peeping through the bushes; when observing our approaches, they confidently discovered themselves and decently advanced to meet us, half unveiling their blooming faces, incarnated with the modest maiden blush, and with native innocence and cheerfulness, presented their little baskets, merrily telling us their fruit was ripe and sound.

We accepted a basket, sat down and regaled ourselves on the delicious fruit, encircled by the whole assembly of the innocently jocose sylvan nymphs; by this time the several parties under the conduct of the elder matrons, had disposed themselves in companies on the green, turfy banks.

My young companion, the trader, by concessions and suitable apologies for the bold intrusion, having compromised the matter with them, engaged them to bring their collections to his house at a stipulated price, we parted friendly.

And now taking leave of these Elysian fields, we again mounted the hills, which we crossed, and traversing obliquely their flowery beds, arrived in town in the cool of the evening.

CHAP. IV.

AFTER waiting two days at Cowe expecting a guide and protector to the Overhill towns, and at last being disappointed, I resolved to pursue the journey alone, though against the advice of the traders; the Overhill Indians being in an ill humour with the whites, in consequence of some late skirmishes between them and the frontier Virginians, most of the Overhill traders having left the nation.

Early in the morning I set off attended by my worthy old friend Mr. Gallahan, who obligingly accompanied me near fifteen miles, we passed through the Jore village, which is pleasingly situated in a little vale on the side of the mountain, a pretty rivulet or creek winds about through the vale, just under the village; here I observed a little grove of the Casine yapon, which was the only place I had seen it grow in the Cherokee country, the Indians call it the beloved tree, and are very careful to keep them pruned and cultivated, they drink a very strong infusion of the leaves, buds and tender branches of this plant, which is so celebrated, indeed venerated by the Creeks, and all the Southern maritime nations of Indians; then continued travelling down the vale about two miles, the road deviating, turning and winding about the hills, and through groves and lawns, watered by brooks and rivulets, rapidly rushing from the towering hill on [360] every side, and flowing into the Jore, which is a considerable branch of the Tanase.

Began now to ascend the mountain, following a small arm or branch of the vale, which led to a gap or narrow defile, compressed by the high pending hills on each side, down which came rapidly a considerable branch of the Jore, dashing and roaring over rocky precipices.

Now leaving Roaring creek on our right and accomplishing two or three ascents or ridges, another branch of the trading path from the Overhills to Cowe came in on our right, and here my transitory companion Mr. Gallahan parted from me, taking this road back to Cowe, when I was left again wandering alone in the dreary mountains, not indeed totally pathless, nor in my present situation entirely agreeable, although such scenes of primitive unmodified nature always pleased me.

May we suppose that mankind feel in their hearts, a predilection for the society of each other; or are we delighted with scenes of human

arts and cultivation, where the passions are flattered and entertained
with variety of objects for gratification?

I found myself unable notwithstanding the attentive admonitions
and pursuasive arguments of reason, entirely to erase from my mind,
those impressions which I had received from the society of the
amiable and polite inhabitants of Charleston; and I could not help comparing my present situation in some degree to Nebuchadnezzar's,
when expelled from the society of men, and constrained to roam in the
mountains and wilderness, there to herd and feed with the wild beasts
of the forest.

[361]   After parting with my late companion, I went forward with all
the alacrity that prudence would admit of, that I might as soon as possible see the end of my toil and hazard, being determined at all events
to cross the Jore mountain, said to be the highest land in the Cherokee
country.

After a gentle descent I entered on an extreme stony narrow vale,
through which coasted swiftly a large creek, twelve or fifteen yards
wide, roaring over a rocky bed, which I crossed with difficulty and
danger; the ford being incommoded by shelving rocks, full of holes and
cliffs; after leaving this rocky creek my path led me upon another
narrow vale or glade, down which came in great haste another noisy
brook, which I repeatedly crossed and recrossed, sometimes riding
on narrow level grassy verges close to its banks, still ascending, the
vale gradually terminated, being shut up by stupendous rocky hills
on each side, leaving a very narrow gap or defile, towards which my
road led me, ascending the steep sides of the mountains, when, after
rising several wearisome ascents, and finding myself over heated and
tired, I halted at a little grassy lawn through which meandered a
sweet rivulet; here I turned my horse to graze, and sat down to rest
on a green bank just beneath a high frowning promontory, or obtuse
point of a ridge of the mountain yet above me, the friendly rivulet
making a circuit by my feet, and now a little rested, I took out of my
wallet some biscuit and cheese, and a piece of neat's tongue, composing
myself to ease and refreshment; when suddenly appeared within a few
yards, advancing towards me from behind the point, a stout likely
young Indian fellow, armed with a rifle gun, and two dogs attending,
[362] upon sight of me he stood, and seemed a little surprised, as I was
very much; but instantly recollecting himself and assuming a countenance of benignity and cheerfulness, came briskly to me and shook
hands heartily; and smilingly enquired from whence I came, and
whither going, but speaking only in the Cherokee tongue, our con-

versation was not continued to a great length. I presented him with
some choice Tobacco, which was accepted with courtesy and evident
pleasure, and to my enquiries concerning the roads and distance to the
Overhill towns, he answered me with perfect cheerfulness and good
temper; we then again shook hands and parted in friendship, he descended the hills, singing as he went.

Of vegetable productions observed in this region, were the following
viz. Acer striatum, Ac. rubrum, Juglans nigra, Jug. alba, Jug. Hickory,
Magnolia acuminata, Quercus alba, Q. tinctoria, Q. rubra, Q. prinus,
with the other varieties common in Virginia: Panax ginseng, Angelica
lucida, Convalaria majalis, Halesia, Stewartia, Styrax, Staphylea,
Evonimus, Viburnum, Cornus Florida, Betula nigra, Morus, Telea,
Ulmus, Fraxinus, Hopea tinctorea, Annona, Bignonia sempervirens,
Aristalocha frutescens, Bignonia radicans, &c. Being now refreshed by
a simple but healthy meal, I began again to ascend the Jore mountains, which I at length accomplished, and rested on the most elevated
peak; from whence I beheld with rapture and astonishment, a sublimely awful scene of power and magnificence, a world of mountains
piled upon mountains. Having contemplated this amazing prospect of
grandeur, I descended the pinnacles, and again falling into the trading
path, continued gently descending through a grassy plain, scatteringly
planted [363] with large trees, and at a distance surrounded with high
forests, I was on this elevated region sensible of an alteration in the
air, from warm to cold, and found that vegetation was here greatly
behind, in plants of the same kind of the country below; for instance,
when I left Charleston, the yellow Jasmine was rather past the blooming days, and here the buds were just beginning to swell, though some
were in bloom: continued more than a mile through this elevated plain
to the pitch of the mountain, from whence presented to view an expansive prospect, exhibiting scenes of mountainous landscape, Westward vast and varied, perhaps not to be exceeded any where.

My first descent and progress down the West side of the mountain
was remarkably gradual, easy and pleasant, through grassy open
forests for the distance of two or three miles; when my changeable path
suddenly turned round an obtuse point of a ridge, and descended
precipitately down a steep rocky hill for a mile or more, which was
very troublesome, being incommoded with shattered fragments of the
mountains, and in other places with boggy sinks, occasioned by oozy
springs and rills stagnate sinking in micaceous earth; some of these
steep soft rocky banks or precipices seem to be continually crumbling
to earth; and in these mouldering cliffs I discovered veins or strata of

most pure and clear white earth *, having a faint bluish or pearl
colour gleam, somewhat exhibiting the appearance of the little cliffs or
wavy crests of new fallen snowdrifts; we likewise observe in these
dissolving rocky cliffs, veins of isinglass, (Mica. S. vitrum Muscoviticum) some [364] of the flakes or laminae incredibly large, entire
and transparent, and would serve the purpose of lights for windows
very well, or for lanthorns; and here appeared strata of black lead
(stibium.)

At length, after much toil and exercise, I was a little relieved by a
narrow grassy vale or lawn at the foot of this steep descent, through
which coursed along a considerable rapid brook, on whose banks grew
in great perfection the glorious Magnolia auriculata, together with
the other conspicuous flowering and aromatic shrubs already mentioned; and I observed here in the rich bottoms near the creek, a new
species of Hydrastis, having very large sinuated leaves and white
flowers: after this I continued several miles over ridges and grassy
vales, watered with delightful rivulets.

Next day proceeding on eight or ten miles, generally through
spacious high forests and flowery lawns; the soil prolific, being of an
excellent quality for agriculture; came near the banks of a large creek
or river, where this high forest ended on my left hand, the trees became more scattered and insensibly united with a grassy glade or
lawn bordering on the river; on the opposite bank of which appeared
a very extensive forest, consisting entirely of the Hemlock spruce
(P. abies) almost encircled by distant ridges of lofty hills.

Soon after crossing this large branch of the Tanase, I observed descending the heights at some distance, a company of Indians, all well
mounted on horse back; they came rapidly forward; on their nearer
approach I observed a chief at the head of the caravan, and apprehending him to be the Little Carpenter, emperor or grand chief of the [365]
Cherokees; as they came up I turned off from the path to make way,
in token of respect, which compliment was accepted and gratefully and
magnanimously returned, for his highness with a gracious and cheerful
smile came up to me, and clapping his hand on his breast, offered it to
me, saying, I am Ata-cul-culla, and heartily shook hands with me, and
asked me if I knew it; I answered that the Good Spirit who goes before me spoke to me, and said, that is the great Ata-cul-culla, and
added that I was of the tribe of white men, of Pennsylvania, who
esteem themselves brothers and friends to the red men, but particularly
so to the Cherokees, and that notwithstanding we dwelt at so great a

---

* Mica nitida, specimens of this earth have been exported to England, for the
purpose of making Porcelain or China ware.

distance we were united in love and friendship, and that the name of
Ata-cul-culla was dear to his white brothers of Pennsylvania.

After this compliment, which seemed to be acceptable, he enquired
if I came lately from Charleston, and if John Stewart was well, saying that he was going to see him; I replied that I came lately from
Charleston on a friendly visit to the Cherokees; that I had the honour
of a personal acquaintance with the superintendent, the beloved man,
who I saw well but the day before I set off, and who, by letters to the
principal white men in the nation, recommended me to the friendship and protection of the Cherokees: to which the great chief was
pleased to answer very respectfully, that I was welcome in their
country as a friend and brother; and then shaking hands heartily bid
me farewell, and his retinue confirmed it by an united voice of assent.
After giving my name to the chief, requesting my compliments to
the superintendent, the emperor moved, continuing his journey for
Charles-[366]ton, and I yet persisting in my intentions of visiting the
Overhill towns continued on; leaving the great forest I mounted the
high hills, descending them again on the other side and so on repeatedly for several miles, without observing any variation in the natural
productions since passing the Jore; and observing the slow progress
of vegetation in this mountainous, high country; and, upon serious
consideration, it appeared very plainly that I could not, with entire
safety, range the Overhill settlements until the treaty was over, which
would not come on till late in June, I suddenly came to a resolution to
defer these researches at this time, and leave them for the employment of another season and a more favourable opportunity, and return to Dartmouth in Georgia, to be ready to join a company of adventurers who were to set off in July for Mobile in West Florida. The
leader of this company had been recommended to me as a fit person
to assist me on so long and hazardous a journey, through the vast
territories of the Creeks.

Therefore next day I turned about on my return, proceeding
moderately, being engaged in noting such objects as appeared to be
of any moment, and collecting specimens, and in the evening of next
day arrived again at Cowe.

Next morning Mr. Galahan conducted me to the chief of Cowe,
who during my absence had returned from the chace. The remainder
of this day I spent in observations in and about the town, reviewing
my specimens, &c.

The town of Cowe consists of about one hundred dwellings, near
the banks of the Tanase, on both sides of the river.

[367] The Cherokees construct their habitations on a different plan

from the Creeks, that is but one oblong four square building, of one story high; the materials consisting of logs or trunks of trees, stripped of their bark, notched at their ends, fixed one upon another, and afterwards plaistered well, both inside and out, with clay well tempered with dry grass, and the whole covered or roofed with the bark of the Chesnut tree or long broad shingles. This building is however partitioned transversely, forming three apartments, which communicate with each other by inside doors; each house or habitation has besides a little conical house, covered with dirt, which is called the winter or hot-house; this stands a few yards distance from the mansion-house, opposite the front door.

The council or town-house is a large rotunda, capable of accommodating several hundred people; it stands on the top of an ancient artificial mount of earth, of about twenty feet perpendicular, and the rotunda on the top of it being above thirty feet more, gives the whole fabric an elevation of about sixty feet from the common surface of the ground. But it may be proper to observe, that this mount on which the rotunda stands, is of a much ancienter date than the building, and perhaps was raised for another purpose. The Cherokees themselves are as ignorant as we are, by what people or for what purpose these artificial hills were raised; they have various stories concerning them, the best of which amounts to no more than mere conjecture, and leave us entirely in the dark; but they have a tradition common with the other nations of Indians, that they found them in much the same condition as they now appear, when their forefathers arrived [368] from the West and possessed themselves of the country, after vanquishing the nations of red men who then inhabited it, who themselves found these mounts when they took possession of the country, the former possessors delivering the same story concerning them: perhaps they were designed and appropriated by the people who constructed them, to some religious purpose, as great altars and temples similar to the high places and sacred groves anciently amongst the Canaanites and other nations of Palestine and Judea.

The rotunda is constructed after the following manner, they first fix in the ground a circular range of posts or trunks of trees, about six feet high, at equal distances, which are notched at top, to receive into them, from one to another, a range of beams or wall plates; within this is another circular order of very large and strong pillars, above twelve feet high, notched in like manner at top, to receive another range of wall plates, and within this is yet another or third range of stronger and higher pillars, but fewer in number, and standing at a greater distance from each other; and lastly, in the centre stands a very

strong pillar, which forms the pinnacle of the building, and to which
the rafters centre at top; these rafters are strengthened and bound together by cross beams and laths, which sustain the roof or covering,
which is a layer of bark neatly placed, and tight enough to exclude the
rain, and sometimes they cast a thin superficies of earth over all. There
is but one large door, which serves at the same time to admit light from
without and the smoak to escape when a fire is kindled; but as there is
but a small fire kept, sufficient to give light at night, and that fed with
dry [369] small sound wood divested of its bark, there is but little
smoak; all around the inside of the building, betwixt the second range
of pillars and the wall, is a range of cabins or sophas, consisting of
two or three steps, one above or behind the other, in theatrical order,
where the assembly sit or lean down; these sophas are covered with
matts or carpets, very curiously made of thin splints of Ash or Oak,
woven or platted together; near the great pillar in the centre the fire
is kindled for light, near which the musicians seat themselves, and
round about this the performers exhibit their dances and other shews
at public festivals, which happen almost every night throughout the
year.

About the close of the evening I accompanied Mr. Galahan and
other white traders to the rotunda, where was a grand festival, music
and dancing. This assembly was held principally to rehearse the ball-
play dance, this town being challenged to play against another the
next day.

The people being assembled and seated in order, and the musicians
having taken their station, the ball opens, first with a long harangue or
oration, spoken by an aged chief, in commendation of the manly
exercise of the ball-play, recounting the many and brilliant victories
which the town of Cowe had gained over the other towns in the nation, not forgetting or neglecting to recite his own exploits, together
with those of other aged men now present, coadjutors in the performance of these athletic games in their youthful days.

This oration was delivered with great spirit and eloquence, and
was meant to influence the passions [370] of the young men present,
excite them to emulation and inspire them with ambition.

This prologue being at an end, the musicians began, both vocal and
instrumental, when presently a company of girls, hand in hand,
dressed in clean white robes and ornamented with beads, bracelets
and a profusion of gay ribbands, entering the door, immediately began
to sing their responses in a gentle, low and sweet voice, and formed
themselves in a semicircular file or line, in two ranks, back to back,
facing the spectators and musicians, moving slowly round and round;

this continued about a quarter of an hour, when we were surprised by a sudden very loud and shrill whoop, uttered at once by a company of young fellows, who came in briskly after one another, with rackets or hurls in one hand. These champions likewise were well dressed, painted and ornamented with silver bracelets, gorgets and wampum, neatly ornamented with moccasins and high waving plumes in their diadems, who immediately formed themselves in a semicircular rank also, in front of the girls, when these changed their order, and formed a single rank parallel to the men, raising their voices in responses to the tunes of the young champions, the semicircles continually moving round. There was something singular and diverting in their step and motions, and I imagine not to be learned to exactness but with great attention and perseverance; the step, if it can be so termed, was performed after the following manner, i. e. first, the motion began at one end of the semicircle, gently rising up and down upon their toes and heels alternately, when the first was up on tip-toe, the next began to raise the heel, and by the time the first rested again on the heel, the second was [371] on tip toe, thus from end of the rank to the other, so that some were always up and some down, alternately and regularly, without the least baulk or confusion; and they at the same time, and in the same motion, moved on obliquely or sideways, so that the circle performed a double or complex motion in its progression, and at stated times exhibited a grand or universal movement, instantly and unexpectedly to the spectators, by each rank turning to right and left, taking each others places; the movements were managed with inconceivable alertness and address, and accompanied with an instantaneous and universal elevation of the voice and shrill short whoop.

The Cherokees besides the ball play dance, have a variety of others equally entertaining; the men especially exercise themselves with a variety of gesticulations and capers, some of which are ludicrous and diverting enough; and they have others which are of the martial order, and others of the chace; these seem to be somewhat of a tragical nature, wherein they exhibit astonishing feats of military prowess, masculine strength and activity. Indeed all their dances and musical entertainments seem to be theatrical exhibitions or plays, varied with comic and sometimes lascivious interludes; the women however conduct themselves with a very becoming grace and decency, insomuch that in amorous interludes, when their responses and gestures seem consenting to natural liberties, they veil themselves, just discovering a glance of their sparking eyes and blushing faces, expressive of sensibility.

Next morning early I set off on my return, and meeting with no material occurrences on the road, in two days arrived safe at Keowe, where I tarried two or three days, employed in augmenting my [372] collections of specimens, and waiting for Mr. Galahan who was to call on me here, to accompany him to Sinica, where he and other traders were to meet Mr. Cameron, the deputy commissary, who were to hold a congress at that town, with the chiefs of the Lower Cherokees, to consult preliminaries introductory to a general congress and treaty with these Indians, which was to be convened next June, and held in the Overhill towns.

I observed in the environs of Keowe, on the bases of the rocky hills, immediately ascending from the low grounds near the river bank, a great number of very singular antiquities, the work of the ancients; they seem to me to have been altars for sacrifice or sepulchres; they were constructed of four flat stones, two set on an edge for the sides, one closed one end, a very large flat one lay horizontally at top, so that the other end was open; this fabric was four or five feet in length, two feet high and three in width. I enquired of the trader what they were, who could not tell me certainly, but supposed them to be ancient Indian ovens; the Indians can give no account of them: they are on the surface of the ground and are of different dimensions.

I accompanied the traders to Sinica, where we found the commissary and the Indian chiefs convened in counsel; continued at Sinica sometime, employing myself in observations and making collections of every thing worthy of notice; and finding the Indians to be yet unsettled in their determination and not in a good humour, I abandoned the project of visiting the regions beyond the Cherokee mountains for this season; set off for my return to fort James Dartmouth, lodged this night in the [373] forests near the banks of a delightful large creek, a branch of Keowe river, and next day arrived safe at Dartmouth.

List of the towns and villages in the Cherokee nation inhabited at this day, viz.

No.		
1	Echoe	
2	Nucasse	On the Tanase East of the Jore mountains.
3	Whatoga	4 towns.
4	Cowe	
5	Ticoloosa	
6	Jore	Inland on the branches of the Tanase.
7	Conisca	4 towns.
8	Nowe	

9 Tomothle ⎫
10 Noewe   ⎪
11 Tellico ⎪ On the Tanase over the Jore moun-
12 Clennuse ⎬ tains.
13 Ocunnolufte ⎪   8 towns.
14 Chewe   ⎪
15 Quanuse ⎪
16 Tellowe ⎭

17 Tellico ⎫
18 Chatuga ⎪ Inland towns on the branches of the
19 Hiwasse ⎬ Tanase and other waters over the
20 Chewase ⎪ Jore mountains.
21 Nuanha   ⎭   5 towns.

22 Tallase ⎫
23 Chelowe ⎪
24 Sette   ⎪ Overhill towns on the Tanase or
25 Chote great ⎬ Cherokee river.
26 Joco   ⎪   6 towns.
27 Tahasse ⎭

[374]
28 Tamahle ⎫
29 Tuskege ⎪ Overhill towns on the Tanase or
30 - - - - - - -. Big Island ⎬ Cherokee river.
31 Nilaque ⎪   5 towns.
32 Niowe   ⎭

Lower towns East of the mountains, viz.

No. 1 Sinica ⎫
    2 Keowe   ⎬ On the Savanna or Keowe river.
    3 Kulsage ⎭

    4 Tugilo ⎫ On Tugilo river.
    5 Estotowe ⎭

    6 Qualatche ⎫ On Flint river.
    7 Chote   ⎭

Towns on the waters of other rivers.

Estotowe great.   Allagae.   Jore.   Nae oche.

In all forty-three towns.

CHAP. V.

BEING returned from the Cherokee country to Dartmouth, I understood that the company of adventurers for West Florida were very forward in their preparations, and would be ready to set off in a few weeks, so that I had but a little time allowed me to make provision and equip myself for the prosecution of so long and hazardous a journey.

Our place of rendezvous was at fort Charlotte, on the opposite side of the river Savanna, and about a mile from fort James. Having a desire to make little botanical excursions towards the head of Broad river, in order to collect some curiosities which I had observed thereabouts, which being accomplished,

June 22d set out from fort Charlotte in company with Mr. Whitfield, who was chief of our caravan. We travelled about twenty miles and lodged at the farm of Mons. St. Pierre, a French gentleman, who received and entertained us with great politeness and hospitality. The mansion-house is situated on the top of a very high hill near the banks of the river Savanna, which overlooks his very extensive and well cultivated plantations of Indian Corn (Zea) Rice, Wheat, Oats, Indigo, Convolvulus Batata, &c. these are rich low lands, lying very level betwixt these natural heights and the river; his gardens occupy the gentle descent on one side of the mount, and a very thriving vineyard consisting of about five acres on the other side.

[376] Next morning after breakfast we set off again, continuing nine or ten miles farther down the river, when we stopped at a plantation, the property of one of our companions, where we were joined by the rest of the company. After dining here we prepared to depart, and the gentleman of the house taking an affectionate leave of his wife and children, we set off again, and proceeding six miles farther down the river, we crossed over into Georgia, taking a road which led us into the great trading path from Augusta to the Creek nation. As the soil, situation and productions of these parts, for several days journey, differ very little from the Northern districts of Georgia, already recited, when on the survey of the New Purchase, I appre-

hend it needless to enter again into a detail of particulars, since it
would produce but little more than a recapitulation of that journey.

Early in the evening of the 27th we arrived at the Flat-rock, where
we lodged. This is a common rendezvous or camping place for
traders and Indians. It is an expansive clean flat or horizontal rock,
but a little above the surface of the ground, and near the banks of a
delightful rivulet of excellent water which is one of the head branches
of Great Ogeche: in the loose, rich soil verging round this rock,
grew several very curious herbaceous plants, particularly one of
singular elegance and beauty, which I take to be a species of Ipomea
(Ipomea, caule erecto, ramoso, tripedali, fol. radicalibus, pinnatifidis,
liniaribus, humi-stratis, florib. incarnatis intus maculis coccinaeis
adsperso.) It grows erect, three feet high, with a strong stem, which
is decorated with plumed or pinnatifid linear leaves, somewhat resembling those of the Delphinium or [377] Ipomea quamoclet; from
about one half its length upwards, it sends out on all sides, ascendent
branches which divide again and again; these terminate with large
tubular or funnel formed flowers; their limbs equally divided into
five segments; these beautiful flowers are of a perfect rose colour,
elegantly besprinkled on the inside of their petals with crimson
specks; the flowers are in great abundance and together with the
branches and delicately fine cut leaves, compose a conical spike or
compound pannicle. I saw a species of this plant, if not the very
same, growing on the sea coast islands near St. Augustine. The blue
flowered Malva and Delphinium were its associates about the Flat-
rock.

There are extensive Cane brakes or Cane meadows spread abroad
round about, which afford the most acceptable and nourishing food
for cattle.

This evening two companies of Indian traders from Augusta arrived
and encamped near us; and as they were bound to the Nation, we
concluded to unite in company with them, they generously offering
us their assistance, having many spare horses and others lightly
loaded, several of ours by this time being jaded; this was a favourable
opportunity of relief in case of necessity.

Next morning, as soon as the horses were packed and in readiness,
we decamped and set forward together.

I thought it worthy of taking notice of a singular method the traders
make use of to reduce the wild young horses to their hard duty.
When any one persists in refusing to receive his load, if threats, [378]
the discipline of the whip and other common abuse prove insufficient,

after being haltered, a pack-horseman catches the tip end of one of his ears betwixt his teeth and pinches it, when instantly the furious strong creature, trembling, stands perfectly still until he is loaded.

Our caravan consisting of about twenty men and sixty horses, we made a formidable appearance, having now little to apprehend from predatory bands or out-laws.

This day's journey was for the most part over high gravelly ridges, and on the most elevated hills appeared emerging out of the earth, rocky cliffs of a dark reddish brown colour; their composition seemed to be a coarse, sandy, ferruginous concrete, but so firmly cemented as to constitute a perfect hard stone or rock, and appeared to be excavated or worn into cavities and furrows by the violence of the dashing billows and rapid currents of the ocean, which heretofore probably washed them; there were however strata or veins in these rocks, of a finer composition and compact consistence, and seemed ponderous, rich iron ore. A little depth below the sandy, gravelly surface lies a stratum of very compact reddish yellow clay and fragments of ochre. The trees and shrubs common on these gravelly ridges are as follows, Diospyros, Quercus rubra, Q. nigra, Q. tinctoria or great Black Oak, Q. alba, Q. lobata, post White Oak, Q. incana, foliis ovalibus integerrimis subtus incanis, Pinus lutea, Pinus taeda, foliis geminatis et trinis, strobilo ovato brevi, cortice rimoso, Pinus palustris, foliis trinis longissimis, strobilo elongato, Cornus Florida, Andromeda arborea, Nyssa sylvatica, Juglans hickory, Prunus padus, &c. Of herbacia, Solidago, Eupa-[379]torium, Sylphium, Rudbeckia, Gerardia, Asclepias, Agave Virginica, Eryngium, Thapsia, Euphorbia, Polymnia, &c.

In the course of this day's journey we crossed two considerable rivulets, running swiftly over rocky beds. There is some very good land on the gradual descents of the ridges and their bottoms bordering on creeks, and very extensive grassy savannas and Cane meadows always in view on one hand or the other. At evening we came to camp on the banks of a beautiful creek, a branch of Great Ogeche, called Rocky Comfort, where we found excellent accommodations, here being pleasant grassy open plains to spread our beds upon, environed with extensive Cane meadows, affording the best of food for our quadrupeds.

The next day's journey led us over a level district; the land generally very fertile and of a good quality for agriculture, the vegetable surface being of a dark, loose, rich mould, on a stratum of stiff reddish brown clay. Crossing several considerable creeks, branches of the Ocone, North branch of the Alatamaha, at evening, July 1st, en-

camped on the banks of the Ocone, in a delightful grove of forest
trees, consisting of Oak, Ash, Mulberry, Hickory, Black Walnut, Elm,
Sassafras, Gleditsia, &c. This flourishing grove was an appendage of
the high forests we had passed through, and projected into an extensive, green, open, level plain, consisting of old Indian fields and
plantations, being the rich low lands of the river, and stretching
along its banks upwards to a very great distance, charmingly diversified and decorated with detached groves and clumps of various
trees and shrubs, and indented on its verge by advancing and retreating promontories of the high land.

[380]   Our encampment was fixed on the site of the old Ocone town,
which, about sixty years ago, was evacuated by the Indians, who
finding their situation disagreeable from its vicinity to the white
people, left it, moving upwards into the Nation or Upper Creeks,
and there built a town, but that situation not suiting their roving
disposition, they grew sickly and tired of it, and resolved to seek a
habitation more agreeable to their minds; they all arose, directing
their migration South-Eastward towards the sea coast, and in the
course of their journey, observing the delightful appearance of the
extensive plains of Alachua and the fertile hills environing it, they sat
down and built a town on the banks of a spacious and beautiful lake,
at a small distance from the plains, naming this new town Cuscowilla:
this situation pleased them, the vast desarts, forests, lake and savannas
around, affording unbounded range of the best hunting ground for
bear and deer, their favourite game. But although this situation was
healthy and delightful to the utmost degree, affording them variety
and plenty of every desirable thing in their estimation, yet troubles
and afflictions found them out. This territory, to the promontory of
Florida, was then claimed by the Tomocos, Utinas, Calloosas, Yamases
and other remnant tribes of the ancient Floridans and the more
Northern refugees, driven away by the Carolinians, now in alliance
and under the protection of the Spaniards, who assisting them, attacked the new settlement and for many years were very troublesome,
but the Alachuas or Ocones being strengthened by other emigrants
and fugitive bands from the Upper Creeks, with whom they were
confederated, and who gradually established other towns in this low
country, stretching a line of settlements [381] across the isthmus,
extending from the Alatamaha to the bay of Apalache: these uniting
were at length able to face their enemies and even attack them in
their own settlements, and in the end, with the assistance of the
Upper Creeks, their uncles, vanquished their enemies and destroyed
them, and then fell upon the Spanish settlements, which they also

entirely broke up. But having treated of these matters in the journal of my travels into East Florida, I end this digression and proceed again on my journey.

After crossing the Ocone by fording it, which is about two hundred and fifty yards over, we travelled about twenty miles and came to camp in the evening; passed over a pleasant territory, presenting varying scenes of gentle swelling hills and levels, affording sublime forests, contrasted by expansive illumined green fields, native meadows and Cane brakes; the vegetables, trees, shrubs and plants the same as already noticed without any material variation. The next day's journey was about twenty miles, having crossed the Oakmulge by fording it three or four hundred yards over. This river is the main branch of the beautiful Alatamaha; on the East bank of the river lie the famous Oakmulge fields, where are yet conspicuous very wonderful remains of the power and grandeur of the ancients of this part of America, in the ruins of a capital town and settlement, as vast artificial hills, terraces, &c. already particularly mentioned in my tour through the lower districts of Georgia. The Oakmulge here is about forty miles distance from the Ocone, the other arm of the Alatamaha. In the evening we came to camp near the banks of Stony Creek, a large rapid water about six miles beyond the river.

[382]   Next day we travelled about twenty miles farther, crossing two considerable creeks named Great and Little Tobosochte, and at evening encamped close by a beautiful large brook called Sweet Water, the glittering wavy flood passing along actively over a bed of pebbles and gravel. The territory through which we passed from the banks of the Oakmulge to this place, exhibited a delightful diversified rural scene, and promises a happy, fruitful and salubrious region, when cultivated by industrious inhabitants, generally ridges of low swelling hills and plains supporting grand forests, vast Cane meadows, savannas and verdant lawns.

I observed here a very singular and beautiful shrub, which I suppose is a species of Hydrangia (H. quercifolia.) It grows in coppices or clumps near or on the banks of rivers and creeks; many stems usually arise from a root, spreading itself greatly on all sides by suckers or offsets; the stems grow five or six feet high, declining or diverging from each other, and are covered with several barks or rinds, the last of which being of a cinereous dirt colour and very thin, at a certain age of the stems or shoots, cracks through to the next bark, and is peeled off by the winds, discovering the under, smooth, dark reddish brown bark, which also cracks and peels off the next year, in like manner as the former; thus every year forming a new bark; the stems divide regularly or oppositely, though the branches are crooked or wreathe about horizontally, and these again divide, forming others which terminate with large heavy pannicles or thyrsi of flowers, but these flowers are of two kinds; the numerous partial spikes which compose the pannicles and consist of a multitude of very small fruitful flowers, ter-[383]minate with one or more very large expansive neutral or mock flowers, standing on a long, slender, stiff peduncle; these flowers are composed of four broad oval petals or segments, of a dark rose or crimson colour at first, but as they become older acquire a deeper red or purplish hue, and lastly are of a brown or ferruginous colour; these have no perfect parts of generation of either sex, but discover in their centre two, three or four papillae or rudiments; these neutral flowers, with the whole pannicle, are truly permanent, remaining on the plant for years, until they dry and decay; the leaves which clothe the plants are very large, pinnatifid or palmated and serrated, or toothed, very much resembling the leaves of some of our Oaks; they sit opposite, supported by slender petioles and are of a fine, full green colour.

Next day after noon we crossed Flint river by fording it, about two hundred and fifty yards over, and at evening came to camp near the banks of a large and deep creek, a branch of the Flint. The high land excellent, affording grand forests, and the low ground vast timber and Canes of great height and thickness, Arundo gigantea. I observed growing on the steep dry banks of this creek, a species of shrub Hypericum, of extraordinary shew and beauty (Hypericum aureum.) It grows erect, three or four feet high, forming a globular top, representing a perfect little tree; the leaves are large, oblong, firm of texture, smooth and shining; the flowers are very large, their petals broad and conspicuous, which, with their tufts of golden filaments, give the little bushes a very splendid appearance.

The adjacent low grounds and Cane swamp af-[384]forded excellent food and range for our horses, who, by this time, through fatigue of constant travelling, heat of the climate and season, were tired and dispirited, we came to camp sooner than usual and started later next day, that they might have time to rest and recruit themselves. The territory lying upon this creek and the space between it and the river, present every appearance of a delightful and fruitful region in some future day, it being a rich soil and exceedingly well situated for every branch of agriculture and grazing, diversified with hills and dales, savannas and vast Cane meadows, and watered by innumerable rivulets and brooks, all contiguous to the Flint river: an arm of the great Chata Uche or Apalachucla offers an uninterrupted

[XI.] *Hydrangea quercifolia*

navigation to the bay of Mexico and Atlantic ocean, and thence to the West India islands and over the whole world.

Our horses being hunted up and packed, set forward again, proceeding moderately, ascending a higher country and more uneven by means of ridges of gentle hills; the country however very pleasing, being diversified with expansive groves, savannas and Cane meadows, abounding with creeks and brooks gliding through the plains or roving about the hills, their banks bordered with forests and groves, consisting of varieties of trees, shrubs and plants; the summits of the hills frequently presenting to view piles and cliffs of the ferruginous rocks, the same species as observed on the ridges between the Flat-rock and Rocky Comfort.

Next day we travelled but a few miles; the heat and the burning flies tormenting our horses to such a degree, as to excite compassion even in the hearts of pack-horsemen. These biting flies are [385] of several species, and their numbers incredible; we travelled almost from sun-rise to his setting, amidst a flying host of these persecuting spirits, who formed a vast cloud around our caravan so thick as to obscure every distant object; but our van always bore the brunt of the conflict; the head, neck and shoulders of the leading horses were continually in a gore of blood: some of these flies were near as large as humble bees; this is the hippobosca. They are armed with a strong sharp beak or proboscis, shaped like a lancet, and sheathed in flexible thin valves; with this beak they instantly pierce the veins of the creatures, making a large orifice from whence the blood springs in large drops, rolling down as tears, causing a fierce pain or aching for a considerable time after the wound is made; there are three or four species of this genus of less size but equally vexatious, as they are vastly more numerous, active and sanguineous; particularly, one about half the size of the first mentioned, the next less of a dusky colour with a green head; another yet somewhat less, of a splendid green and the head of a gold colour; the sting of this last is intolerable, no less acute than a prick from a red-hot needle, or a spark of fire on the skin; these are called the burning flies. Besides the preceding tormentors, there are three or four species of the asilus or smaller biting flies; one of a greyish dusky colour, another much of the same colour, having spotted wings and a green head, and another very small and perfectly black: this last species lies in ambush in shrubby thickets and Cane brakes near water; whenever we approach the cool shades near creeks, impatient for repose and relief, almost sinking under the persecutions from the evil [386] spirits, who continually surround and follow us over the burning desert ridges and plains, and

here in some hopes of momentary peace and quietness, under cover
of the cool humid groves, we are surprised and quickly invested with
dark clouds of these persecuting demons, besides musquitoes and
gnats (culex et cynips.)

The next day being in like manner oppressed and harassed by
the stinging flies and heats; we halted at noon, being unable longer
to support ourselves under such grievances, even in our present situation charming to the senses; on the acclivity of a high swelling ridge
planted with open airy groves of the superb terebenthine Pines, glittering rills playing beneath, and pellucid brooks meandering through
an expansive green savanna, their banks ornamented with coppices
of blooming aromatic shrubs and plants perfuming the air. The
meridian heats just allayed, the sun is veiled in a dark cloud, rising
North-Westward; the air still, gloomy and sultry; the animal spirits
sink under the conflict, and we fall into a kind of mortal torpor
rather than refreshing repose; and startled or terrified at each others
plaintive murmurs and groans: now the earth trembles under the
peals of incessant distant thunder, the hurricane comes on roaring,
and I am shocked again to life: I raise my head and rub open my
eyes, pained with gleams and flashes of lightning; when just attempting to wake up my afflicted brethren and companions, almost overwhelmed with floods of rain, the dark cloud opens over my head,
developing a vast river of the etherial fire, I am instantly struck
dumb, inactive and benumbed; at length the pulse of life begins to
vibrate, the animal spirits begin to exert their powers, and I am by
degrees revived.

[387] In the evening this surprising heavy tempest passed off, we
had a serene sky and a pleasant cool night; having had time enough
to collect a great quantity of wood and Pine knots to feed our fires
and keep up a light in our camp, which was a lucky precaution, as
we found it absolutely necessary to dry our clothes and warm ourselves, for all our skins and bedding were cast over the packs of
merchandize to prevent them and our provision from being injured
by the deluge of rain; next day was cool and pleasant, the air having
recovered its elasticity and vivific spirit; I found myself cheerful and
invigorated; indeed all around us appeared reanimated, and nature
presents her cheerful countenance; the vegetables smile in their
blooming decorations and sparkling crystalline dew-drop.

The birds sing merrily in the groves, and the alert roe-buck whistles
and bounds over the ample meads and green turfy hills. After leaving
our encampment we travelled over a delightful territory, presenting
to view variable sylvan scenes, consisting of chains of low hills afford-

ing high forests, with expansive savannas, Cane meadows and lawns between, watered with rivulets and glittering brooks; towards evening we came to camp on the banks of Pintchlucco, a large branch of the Chata Uche river.

The next day's journey was over an uneven hilly country, but the soil generally fertile and of a quality and situation favourable to agriculture and grazing, the summits of the ridges rough with ferruginous rocks, in high cliffs and fragments, scattered over the surface of the ground; observed also high cliffs of stiff reddish brown clay, with veins or strata of ferruginous stones, either in detached masses or conglomerated nodules or hematites with veins or masses of ochre.

[388] Next day after traversing a very delightful territory, exhibiting a charming rural scenery of primitive nature, gently descending and passing alternately easy declivities or magnificent terraces supporting sublime forests, almost endless grassy fields, detached groves and green lawns for the distance of nine or ten miles, we arrived at the banks of the Chata Uche river opposite the Uche town, where after unloading our horses, the Indians came over to us in large canoes, by means of which, with the cheerful and liberal assistance of the Indians, ferried over their merchandize, and afterwards driving our horses altogether into the river swam them over: the river here is about three or four hundred yards wide, carries fifteen or twenty feet water and flows down with an active current; the water is clear, cool and salubrious.

The Uche town is situated in a vast plain, on the gradual ascent as we rise from a narrow strip of low ground immediately bordering on the river: it is the largest, most compact and best situated Indian town I ever saw; the habitations are large and neatly built; the walls of the houses are constructed of a wooden frame, then lathed and plaistered inside and out with a reddish well tempered clay or morter, which gives them the appearance of red brick walls, and these houses are neatly covered or roofed with Cypress bark or shingles of that tree. The town appeared to be populous and thriving, full of youth and young children: I suppose the number of inhabitants, men, women and children, might amount to one thousand or fifteen hundred, as it is said they are able to muster five hundred gun-men or warriors. Their own national language is altogether or radically different from [389] the Creek or Muscogulge tongue, and is called the Savanna or Savanuca tongue; I was told by the traders it was the same or a dialect of the Shawanese. They are in confederacy with the Creeks, but do not mix with them, and on account of their num-

bers and strength, are of importance enough to excite and draw upon
them the jealousy of the whole Muscogulge confederacy, and are
usually at variance, yet are wise enough to unite against a common
enemy, to support the interest and glory of the general Creek confederacy.

After a little refreshment at this beautiful town, we repacked and
set off again for the Apalachucla town, where we arrived after riding
over a level plain, consisting of ancient Indian plantations, a beautiful landscape diversified with groves and lawns.

This is esteemed the mother town or capital of the Creek or
Muscogulge confederacy: sacred to peace; no captives are put to
death or human blood spilt here. And when a general peace is proposed, deputies from all the towns in the confederacy assemble at
this capital, in order to deliberate upon a subject of so high importance for the prosperity of the commonwealth.

And on the contrary the great Coweta town, about twelve miles
higher up this river, is called the bloody town, where the Micos chiefs
and warriors assemble when a general war is proposed, and here
captives and state malefactors are put to death.

The time of my continuance here, which was about a week, was
employed in excursions round about this settlement. One day the chief
trader of Apalachucla obliged me with his company on a [390] walk
of about a mile and an half down the river, to view the ruins and
site of the ancient Apalachucla: it had been situated on a peninsula
formed by a doubling of the river, and indeed appears to have been
a very famous capital by the artificial mounds or terraces, and a very
populous settlement, from its extent and expansive old fields, stretching beyond the scope of the sight along the low grounds of the river.
We viewed the mounds or terraces, on which formerly stood their
town house or rotunda and square or areopagus, and a little back of
this, on a level height or natural step, above the low grounds is a vast
artificial terrace or four square mound, now seven or eight feet higher
than the common surface of the ground; in front of one square or side
of this mound adjoins a very extensive oblong square yard or
artificial level plain, sunk a little below the common surface, and
surrounded with a bank or narrow terrace, formed with the earth
thrown out of this yard at the time of its formation: the Creeks or
present inhabitants have a tradition that this was the work of the
ancients, many ages prior to their arrival and possessing this country.

This old town was evacuated about twenty years ago by the
general consent of the inhabitants, on account of its unhealthy situation, owing to the frequent inundations of the river over the low

grounds; and moreover they grew timorous and dejected, apprehending themselves to be haunted and possessed with vengeful spirits, on account of human blood that had been undeservedly * spilt in this old town, [391] having been repeatedly warned by apparitions and dreams to leave it.

At the time of their leaving this old town, like the ruin or dispersion of the ancient Babel, the inhabitants separated from each other, forming several bands under the conduct or auspices of the chief of each family or tribe. The greatest number, however, chose to sit down and build the present new Apalachucla town, upon a high bank of the river above the inundations. The other bands pursued different routes, as their inclinations led them, settling villages lower down the river; some continued their migration towards the sea coast, seeking their kindred and countrymen amongst the Lower Creeks in East Florida, where they settled themselves. My intelligent friend, the trader of Apalachucla, having from a long residence amongst these Indians acquired an extensive knowledge of their customs and affairs, I enquired of him what were his sentiments with respect to their wandering, unsettled disposition; their so frequently breaking up their old towns and settling new ones, &c. His answers and opinions were, the necessity they were under of having fresh or new strong land for their plantations; and new, convenient and extensive range or hunting ground, which unavoidably forces them into contentions and wars with their confederates and neighbouring tribes; to avoid which they had rather move and seek a plentiful and peaceable retreat, even at a distance, than to contend with friends and relatives or embroil themselves in [392] destructive wars with their neighbours, when either can be avoided with so little inconvenience. With regard to the Muscogulges, the first object in order to obtain these conveniencies was the destruction of the Yamases, who held the possession of Florida and were in close alliance with the Spaniards, their declared and most inveterate enemy, which they at length fully accomplished; and by this conquest they gained a vast and invaluable territory, comprehending a delightful region and a most

* About fifty or sixty years ago almost all the white traders then in the Nation were massacred in this town, whither they had repaired from the different towns, in hopes of an asylum or refuge, in consequence of the alarm, having been timely apprised of the hostile intentions of the Indians by their temporary wives, they all met together in one house, under the avowed protection of the chiefs of the town, waiting the event; but whilst the chiefs were assembled in council, deliberating on ways and means to protect them, the Indians in multitudes surrounded the house and set fire to it; they all, to the number of eighteen or twenty, perished with the house in the flames. The trader shewed me the ruins of the house where they were burnt.

plentiful country for their favourite game, bear and deer. But not yet satisfied, having already so far conquered the powerful Cherokees, as, in a manner, to force them in alliance, and compelled the warlike Chicasaws to sue for peace and alliance with them; they then grew arrogant and insatiable, and turned their covetous looks towards the potent and intrepid Chactaws, the only Indian enemy they had to fear, meaning to break them up and possess themselves of that extensive, fruitful and delightful country, and make it a part of their vast empire; but the Chactaws, a powerful, hardy, subtile and intrepid race, estimated at twenty thousand warriors, are likely to afford sufficient exercise for the proud and restless spirits of the Muscogulges, at least for some years to come, and they appear to be so equally matched with the Chactaws, it seems doubtful which of these powerful nations will rise victorious. The Creeks have sworn, it seems, that they never will make peace with this enemy as long as the rivers flow or the sun pursues his course through the skies.

Thus we see that war or the exercise of arms originates from the same motives, and operates in the spirits of the wild red men of America, as it formerly did with the renowned Greeks and Ro-[393] mans or modern civilized nations, and not from a ferocious, capricious desire of shedding human blood as carnivorous savages; neither does the eager avarice of plunder stimulate them to acts of madness and cruelty, that being a trifling object in their estimation, a duffield blanket, a polished rifle gun, or embroidered mantle; no, their martial prowess and objects of desire and ambition proceed from greater principles and more magnanimous intentions, even that of reuniting all nations and languages under one universal confederacy or commonwealth.

The vegetable productions in the rich low ground, near the banks of this great river, of trees and shrubs, are as follow, Platanus occidentalis, Liriodendron tulipifera, Populus heterophylla, Laurus sassafras, Laurus Borbonia, Laurus benzoin, Betula lenta, Salix fluvialis, Magnolia grandiflora, Annona glabra, Ulmus campestris, Ulmus suberifera, Carpinus, Quercus, various species, Juglans, various species, Æsculus pavia, Æsculus sylvatica, s. Virginiana, Morus, Hopea tinctoria, Fagus sylvatica, of surprising magnitude and comeliness, &c. The land rises from the river with sublime magnificence, gradually retreating by flights or steps one behind and above the other, in beautiful theatrical order, each step or terrace holding up a level plain; and as we travel back from the river the steps are higher, and the corresponding levels are more and more expansive; the ascents produce grand high forests, and the plains present to view a delightful varied landscape, consisting of extensive grassy fields, detached groves of high forest trees, and clumps of lower trees, evergreen shrubs and herbage; green knolls, with serpentine, wavy, glittering brooks [394] coursing through the green plains, and dark promontories, or obtuse projections of the side-long acclivities, alternately advancing or receding on the verge of the illumined native fields, to the utmost extent of sight; the summits of the acclivities afford, besides the forest trees already recited, Halesia, Ptelea, Circis, Cornus Florida and Amorpha. The upper mound or terrace holds up a·dilated level plain of excellent land, for the distance of five or six miles in width, which is a high forest of the majestic trees already mentioned, as Quercus tinctoria, Juglans nigra, Morus, Ulmus, Telea, Gleditsia, Juglans hickory, &c. The land after this distance, though almost flat and level, becomes leaner; the vegetative mould or surface is shallower, on a stratum of tenacious humid clay, for the distance of fifteen or twenty miles, more or less, according to the distance of the next great river; presenting to our view a fine expanse of level grassy plains, detached forests and groves of Quercus alba, Q. lobata, Q. phillos, Q. hemispherica, Q. aquatica, with entire groves of the splendid Nyssa sylvatica and perfumed Liquid-amber styraciflua, vast Cane meadows, and lastly a chain of grassy savannas: immediately from this we began to ascend gradually, the most elevated, gravelly and stony ridge, consisting of parallel chains of broken swelling hills, the very highest chain, frequently presenting to view cliffs of the ferrugineous rocks and red clay already noticed. This last mentioned high ridge divides the waters of the great rivers from each other, whence arise the sources of their numerous lateral branches, gradually increasing as they wind about the hills, fertilizing the vales, and level plains, by their inundations, as they pour forth from the vast humid forests and shaded prolific hills [395] and lastly, flow down, with an easy, meandering, steady course, into the rivers to which they are tributary.

Our horses by this time having recruited themselves, by ranging at liberty and feeding in the rich young cane swamps, in the vicinity of Apalachucla, we resumed our journey for Mobile, having here repaired our equipage and replenished ourselves with fresh supplies of provisions. Our caravan was now reduced to its original number; the companies of traders who joined us at the Flat-rock, on our arrival at this town separated from us, betaking themselves to the several towns in the Nation, where they were respectively bound. I shall just mention a very curious non-descript shrub, which I observed growing in the shady forests, beneath the ascents, next bordering on the rich low lands of the river.

This stoloniferous shrub grows five or six feet in height; many stems usually ascend from a root or the same source; these several stems diverge from each other, or incline a little towards the earth, covered with a smooth whitish bark, divided oppositely, and the branches wreath and twist about, being ornamented with compound leaves; there being five lanceolate serrated leaves, associated upon one general long slender petiole, which stand oppositely, on the branches, which terminate with a spike, or pannicle of white flowers, which have an agreeable scent; from the characters of the flowers, this shrub appears to be a species of Æsculus or Pavia, but as I could find none of the fruit and but a few flowers, quite out of season and imperfect, I am not certain.

CHAP. VI.

J ULY 13th we left the Apalachucla town, and three days journey
brought us to Talasse, a town on the Tallapoose river, North East
great branch of the Alabama or Mobile river, having passed over
a vast level plain country of expansive savannas, groves, Cane swamps
and open Pine forests, watered by innumerable rivulets and brooks,
tributary to Apalachucla and Mobile; we now alter our course, turning
to the left hand, Southerly, and descending near the river banks,
continually in sight of the Indian plantations and commons adjacent
to their towns. Passed by Otasse, an ancient famous Muscogulge
town. The next settlement we came to was Coolome, where we stayed
two days, and having letters for Mr. Germany, the principal trader of
Coolome, I meant to consult with him in matters relative to my affairs
and future proceedings.

Here are very extensive old fields, the abandoned plantations and
commons of the old town, on the East side of the river, but the
settlement is removed, and the new town now stands on the opposite
shore, in a charming fruitful plain, under an elevated ridge of hills,
the swelling beds or bases of which are covered with a pleasing
verdure of grass, but the last ascent is steeper, and towards the summit discovers shelving rocky cliffs, which appear to be continually
splitting and bursting to pieces, scattering their thin exfoliations over
the tops of the grassy knolls beneath. The plain is narrow where the
[397] town is built: their houses are neat, commodious buildings, a
wooden frame with plaistered walls, and roofed with Cypress bark
or shingles; every habitation consists of four oblong square houses,
of one story, of the same form and dimensions, and so situated as to
form an exact square, encompassing an area or court yard of about
a quarter of an acre of ground, leaving an entrance into it at each
corner. Here is a beautiful new square or areopagus, in the centre of
the new town; but the stores of the principal trader and two or three
Indian habitations, stand near the banks of the opposite shore on
the site of the old Coolome town. The Tallapoose river is here three
hundred yards over, and about fifteen or twenty feet water, which is

very clear, agreeable to the taste, esteemed salubrious, and runs with a steady, active current.

Being now recruited and refitted, having obtained a guide to set us in the great trading path for West Florida, early in the morning we set off for Mobile: our progress for about eighteen miles was through a magnificent forest, just without or skirting on the Indian plantations, frequently having a view of their distant towns, over plains or old fields, and at evening came to camp under shelter of a grove of venerable spreading Oaks, on the verge of the great plains; their enormous limbs loaded with Tillandsia ulneadscites, waving in the winds; these Oaks were some shelter to us from the violence of an extraordinary shower of rain, which suddenly came down in such floods as to inundate the earth, and kept us standing on our feet the whole night, for the surface of the ground was under water almost till morning. Early next morning, our guide having performed his duty, took [398] leave, returning home, and we continued on our journey, entering on the great plains; we had not proceeded far before our people roused a litter of young wolves, to which giving chase we soon caught one of them, it being entangled in high grass, one of our people caught it by the hind legs and another beat out its brains with the but of his gun,—barbarous sport!—This creature was about half the size of a small cur-dog, and quite black.

We continued over these expansive illumined grassy plains, or native fields, above twenty miles in length, and in width eight or nine, lying parallel to the river, which was about ten miles distance; they are invested by high forests, extensive points or promontories, which project into the plains on each side, dividing them into many vast fields opening on either hand as we passed along, which present a magnificent and pleasing sylvan landscape of primitive, uncultivated nature. Crossed several very considerable creeks, their serpentine courses being directed across the plain by gently swelling knolls, perceptible at a distance, but seem to vanish or disappear as we come upon them; the creeks were waters of the Alabama, the name of the East arm of the Mobile below the confluence of the Tallapoose. These rivulets were ornamented by groves of various trees and shrubs, which do not spread far from their banks; I observed amongst them the wild Crab (Pyrus coronaria) and Prunus Indica or wild Plumb, Cornus Florida, and on the grassy turf adjoining grew abundance of Strawberry vines; the surface of the plains or fields is clad with tall grass, intermixed with a variety of herbage; the most conspicuous, both for beauty and novelty, is a tall species of Silphium; the radical [399] leaves are large, long and lightly sinuated, but those which garnish the stem are few and less sinuated; these leaves with the whole plant, except the flowers, appear of a whitish green colour, which is owing to a fine soft silky down or pubescence; the flower stem, which is eight or ten feet in length when standing erect, terminates upwards with a long heavy spike of large golden yellow radiated flowers; the stem is usually seen bowing on one side or other, occasioned by the weight of the flowers, and many of them are broke, just under the pannicle or spike, by their own weight, after storms and heavy rains, which often cracks or splits the stem, from whence exudes a gummy or resinous substance, which the sun and air harden into semi-pellucid drops or tears of a pale amber colour; this resin possesses a very agreeable fragrance and bitterish taste, somewhat like frankincense or turpentine, which is chewed by the Indians and traders, to cleanse their teeth and mouth, and sweeten their breath.

The upper stratum or vegetative mould of these plains is perfectly black, soapy and rich, especially after rains, and renders the road very slippery; it lies on a deep bed of white, testaceous, limestone rock, which in some places resembles chalk, and in other places are strata or subterrene banks of various kinds of sea shells, as ostrea, &c. these dissolving near the surface of the earth, and mixing with the superficial mould, render it extremely productive.

Immediately after leaving the plains we enter the grand high forests. There were stately trees of the Robinea pseudacacia, Telea, Morus, Ulmus, Juglans exaltata, Juglans nigra, Pyrus coronaria, Cornus Florida, Cercis, &c. Our road now for [400] several miles led us near the Alabama, within two or three miles of its bank; the surface of the land is considerably broken into hills and vales, some of them of considerable elevation, but covered with forests of stately trees, such as already mentioned, but they are of a much larger growth than those of the same kind which grow in the Southern or inhabited parts of Georgia and Carolina. We now leave the river at a good distance, the Alabama bearing away Southerly, and enter a vast open forest which continued above seventy miles, East and West, without any considerable variation, generally a level plain, except near the banks of creeks that course through; the soil on the surface is a dusky brownish mould or sandy loam, on a foundation of stiff clay, and the surface pebbles or gravel mixed with clay on the summits of the ridges; the forests consist chiefly of Oak, Hickory, Ash, Sour Gum (Nyssa sylvatica) Sweet Gum (Liquid-amber styraciflua) Beech, Mulberry, Scarlet maple, Black walnut, Dog-wood, Cornus Florida, Æsculus pavia, Prunus Indica, Ptelea and an abundance of Chesnut (Fag. castania) on the hills, with Pinus taeda and Pinus lutea. During our progress over this vast high forest, we crossed extensive open plains, the soil gravelly, producing a few trees and shrubs or undergrowth, which were entangled with Grape vines (Vitis campestris) of a peculiar species; the bunches (racemes) of fruit were very large, as were the grapes that composed them, though yet green and not fully grown, but when ripe are of various colours, and their juice sweet and rich. The Indians gather great quantities of them, which they prepare for keeping, by first sweating them on hurdles over a gentle fire, and afterwards dry them on their bunches in the sun and air, and store them [401] up for provisions: these Grape vines do not climb into high trees, but creep along from one low shrub to another, extending their branches to a great distance horizontally round about, and it is very pleasing to behold the clusters pendant from the vines, almost touching the earth, indeed some of them lie upon the ground.

We now enter a very remarkable grove of Dog wood trees (Cornus Florida) which continued nine or ten miles unalterable, except here and there a towering Magnolia grandiflora; the land on which they stand is an exact level; the surface a shallow, loose, black mould, on a stratum of stiff, yellowish clay; these trees were about twelve feet high, spreading horizontally; their limbs meeting and interlocking with each other, formed one vast, shady, cool grove, so dense and humid as to exclude the sun-beams and prevent the intrusion of almost every other vegetable, affording us a most desirable shelter from the fervid sun-beams at noon-day. This admirable grove by way of eminence has acquired the name of the Dog woods.

During a progress of near seventy miles, through this high forest, there constantly presented to view on one hand or the other, spacious groves of this fine flowering tree, which must, in the spring season, when covered with blossoms present a most pleasing scene; when at the same time a variety of other sweet shrubs display their beauty, adorned in their gay apparel, as the Halesia, Stewartia, Æsculus pavia, Æsc. alba, Æsc. Florid. ramis divaricatis, thyrsis grandis, flosculis expansis incarnatis, Azalea, &c. intangled with garlands of Bignonea crucigera, [402] Big. radicans, Big. sempervirens, Glycine frutescens, Lonicera sempervirens, &c. and at the same time the superb Magnolia grandiflora, standing in front of the dark groves, towering far above the common level.

The evening cool, we encamped on the banks of a glittering rivulet amidst a spicy grove of the Illisium Floridanum.

Early next morning we arose, hunted up our horses and proceeded on, continuing about twenty miles, over a district which presented to view another landscape, expansive plains of Cane meadows, and detached groves, contrasted by swelling ridges, and vales supporting grand forests of the trees already noted, embellished with delightful creeks and brooks, their low grounds producing very tall canes, and their higher banks groves of the Illisium, Callicanthus, Stewartia, Halesia, Styrax and others, particularly Magnolia auriculata. In the evening we forded the river Schambe about fifty yards over, the stream active but shallow, which carries its waters into the bay of Pensacola. Came to camp, on the banks of a beautiful creek, by a charming grove of the Illisium Floridanum; from this we travelled over a level country about fifty miles, very gently but perceptibly descending South-Eastward before us; this district exhibited a landscape very different from what had presented to view since we left the nation, and not much unlike the low countries of Carolina; it is in fact one vast flat grassy savanna and Cane meadows, intersected or variously scrolled over with narrow forests and groves, on the banks of creeks and rivulets, or hommocks and swamps at their sources; with long leaved Pines, scatteringly planted, amongst the grass, [403] and on the high sandy knolls and swelling ridges, Quercus nigra, Quercus flammula, Quercus incana, with various other trees and shrubs as already noted, inhabiting such situations; the rivulets however exhibited a different appearance, they are shallower, course more swift over gravelly beds, and their banks adorned with Illisium groves, Magnolias, Azaleas, Halesia, Andromedas, &c. The highest hills near large creeks afford high forests with abundance of Chesnut trees.

We now approach the bay of Mobile, gently ascending a hilly district, being the highest forest adjoining the extensive rich low lands of the river; these heights are somewhat encumbered with pebbles, fragments and cliffs of rusty ferrugineous rocks, the stones were ponderous and indicated very rich iron ore; here was a small district of good land, on the acclivities and bases of these ridges, and a level forest below, watered by a fine creek, running into the Mobile. From hence we proceeded, again descending, and travelled about nine miles generally over a level country consisting of savannas, Cane swamps, and gentle rising knolls, producing Pinus taeda, Nyssa sylvatica, Quercus rubra, Fagus castania, Fraxinus, with other trees. Arrived at Taensa, a pretty high bluff, on the Eastern channel of the great Mobile river, about thirty miles above fort Conde, or city of Mobile, at the head of the bay.

Next day early in the morning I embarked in a boat, proceeded for Mobile; along the banks of islands (near twenty miles) which lay in the middle of the river, between the Eastern and Western shores of the main: the banks of these low flat rich islands are well cultivated, having on them extensive farms [404] and some good habitations, chiefly the property of French gentlemen, who reside in the city, as being more pleasant and healthy. Leaving these islands, we continued ten or twelve miles between the Eastern main and a chain of low grassy islands, too low and wet for cultivation; then crossed over the head of the bay and arrived in town in the evening.

The city of Mobile is situated on the easy ascent of a rising bank, extending near half a mile back on the level plain above; it has been near a mile in length, though now chiefly in ruins, many houses vacant and mouldering to earth; yet there are a few good buildings inhabited by French gentlemen, English, Scotch and Irish, and emigrants from the Northern British colonies. Messrs. Swanson and M'Gillivary who have the management of the Indian trade, carried on to the Chicasaws, Chactaws, Upper and Lower Creeks, &c. have made here very extraordinary improvements in buildings.

The fort Conde, which stands very near the bay, towards the lower end of the town is a large regular fortress of brick.

The principal French buildings are constructed of brick, and are of one story, but on an extensive scale, four square, encompassing on three sides a large area or court yard, the principal apartment is on the side fronting the street; they seem in some degree to have copied after the Creek habitation in the general plan; those of the poorer class are constructed of a strong frame of Cypress, filled in with brick, plaistered and white-washed inside and out.

July 31st, 1778, the air being very hot and sultry, thermometer up at 87. excessive thunder, and re-[405]peated heavy showers of rain, from morning until evening.

Not having an immediate opportunity from hence to Manchac, a British settlement on the Mississipi, I endeavoured to procure a light canoe, with which I designed to pursue my travels along shore to the settlements about Pearl river.

August 5th, set off from Mobile up the river in a trading boat, and was landed at Taensa bluff, the seat of Major Farmer, to make good my engagements, in consequence of an invitation from that worthy gentleman, to spend some days in his family; here I obtained the use of a light canoe, to continue my voyage up the river. The settlement of Taensa is on the site of an ancient town of a tribe of Indians of that name, which is apparent from many artificial mounds of earth and other ruins. Besides Mr. Farmer's dwellings, there are many others inhabited by French families; who are chiefly his tenants. It is a most delightful situation, commanding a spacious prospect up and down the river, and the low lands of his extensive plantations on the opposite shore. In my excursions about this place, I observed many curious vegetable productions, particularly a species of Myrica (Myrica inodora) this very beautiful evergreen shrub, which the French inhabitants call the Wax tree, grows in wet sandy ground about the edges of swamps, it rises erect nine or ten feet, dividing itself into a multitude of nearly erect branches, which are garnished with many shining deep green entire leaves of a lanceolate figure; the branches produce abundance of large round berries, nearly the size of bird cherries, which are covered with a scale or coat of white wax; no part of this plant [406] possesses any degree of fragrance. It is in high estimation with the inhabitants for the production of wax for candles, for which purpose it answers equally well with bees-wax, or preferable, as it is harder and more lasting in burning.

Early on a fine morning I set sail up the river, took the East channel, and passed along by well cultivated plantations, on the fertile islands, in the river on my left hand; these islands exhibit every shew of fertility, the native productions exceed any thing I had ever seen, particularly the Reeds or Canes (Arundo gigantea) grow to a great height and thickness.

Early one morning, passing along by some old uncultivated fields, a few miles above Taensa, I was struck with surprise at the appearance of a blooming plant, gilded with the richest golden yellow, stepping on shore, I discovered it to be a new species of the Oenothera (Oenothera grandiflora) Caule erecto, ramoso, piloso, 7, 8 pedali, foliis semi-amplexi-caulibus, lanceolatis, serrato-dentatis, floribus magnis, fulgidis, sessilibus, capsulis cylindricis, 4 angulis, perhaps the most pompous and brilliant herbaceous plant yet known to exist. It is an annual or biennial, rising erect seven or eight feet, branching on all sides from near the earth upwards, the lower branches extensive, and the succeeding gradually shorter to the top of the plant, forming a pyramid in figure; the leaves are of a broad lanceolate shape, dentated or deeply serrated, terminating with a slender point, and of a deep full green colour; the large expanded flowers, that so ornament this plant, are of a splendid perfect yellow colour; but when they contract again, before they drop off, the underside of the petals next the [407] calyx becomes of a reddish flesh colour, inclining to vermilion, the flowers begin to open in the evening, are fully expanded during the night, and are in their beauty next morning, but close and wither before noon. There is a daily profuse succession for many weeks, and one single plant at the same instant presents to view many hundred flowers. I have measured these flowers above five inches in diameter, they have an agreeable scent.

After leaving these splendid fields of the golden Oenothera, I passed by old deserted plantations and high forests, and now having advanced above ten miles, landed at a bluff, where mooring my bark in a safe harbour, I ascended the bank of the river, and penetrating the groves, came presently to old fields, where I observed ruins of ancient habitations, there being abundance of Peach and Fig trees, loaded with fruit, which affording a very acceptable desert after the heats and toil of the day, and evening drawing on apace, I concluded to take up my quarters here for the night. The Fig trees were large as well as their fruit, which was when ripe, of the shape of pears and as large, and of a dark bluish purple colour.

Next morning I arose early, continuing my voyage, passed by, on each hand, high forests and rich swamps, and frequently ruins of ancient French plantations; the Canes, and Cypress trees of an astonishing magnitude, as were the trees of other tribes, indicating an excellent soil. Came too at noon, and advancing forward from the river, and penetrating the awful shades, passed between the stately columns of the Magnolia grandiflora, and came to the ascents supporting the high forests and expansive plains above ----- What a sylvan scene is [408] here! the pompous Magnolia, reigns sovereign of the forests; how sweet the aromatic Illisium groves! how gaily flutters the radiated wings of the Magnolia auriculata! each branch supporting an expanded umbrella, superbly crested with a silver plume, fragrant blossom, or crimson studded strobile and fruits! I recline on the verdant bank, and view the beauties of the groves. Æsculus pavia, Prunus nemoralis, floribus racemosis, foliis sempervirentibus, nitidis. Æsculus alba, Hydrangia quercifolia, Cassine, Magnolia pyramidata, foliis ovatis, oblongis, acuminatis, basi auriculatis, strobilo oblongo ovato, Myrica, Rhamnus frangula, Halesea, Bignonia, Azalea, Lonicera, Sideroxilon, with many more.

Returned to the river, re-imbarked, and at evening came too, in sight of the confluence or junction of the two large arms of the great Mobile river i. e. the Tombigbe or Chicasaw with the Alabama or Coosau. About one hundred and fifty miles above this conflux at Ft. Thoulouse, the Alabama receives into it from the East the great Talapoose river, when the former takes the name of Coosau, which it bears to its source, which is in the So. West promontories of the Cherokee or Apalachean Mountains in the Chickasaw territories.

Observed very large alligators, basking on the shores, as well as swimming in the river and lagoons.

Next morning entered the Tombigbe, and ascended that fine river; just within its capes, on the left hand is a large lagoon, or capacious bay of still water, containing many acres in surface, which at a distant view presents a very singular and diverting scene, a delusive green wavy plain of the [409] Nymphaea Nilumbo, the surface of the water is overspread with its round floating leaves, whilst these are shadowed by a forest of umbrageous leaves with gay flowers, waving to and fro on flexible stems, three or four feet high: these fine flowers are double as a rose, and when expanded are seven or eight inches in diameter, of a lively lemon yellow colour. The seed vessel when ripe, is a large truncated, dry, porous capsule, its plane or disk regularly perforated, each cell containing an oval osseous gland or nut, of the size of a filbert; when these are fully grown, before they become quite hard, they are sweet and pleasant eating, and taste like chesnuts: I fed freely on them without any injury, but found them laxative. I have observed this aquatic plant, in my travels along the Eastern shores of this continent, in the large rivers and lakes, from New-Jersey to this place, particularly in a large pond or lake near Cape Fear river in North Carolina; this pond is about two miles over and twelve feet water, notwithstanding which its surface is almost covered with the leaves of this plant; they also abound in Wakamaw lake near the same river, and in Savanna river at Augusta, and all over East Florida.

Proceeding up the river, came to at a very high steep bluff of red and particoloured tenacious clay, under a deep stratum of loose sandy mould; after ascending this steep bank of the river, I found myself in an old field, and penetrating the forests surrounding, observed them to be young growth, covering very extensive old plantations, which was evident from the ridges and hillocks which once raised their Corn (Zea) Batatas, &c. I suppose this to be the site of an ancient fortified post of the [410] French, as there appear vestiges of a rampart and other traces of a fortress; perhaps fort Louis de la Mobile, but in all probability it will not remain long visible, the stream of the river making daily encroachments on it, by carrying away the land on which it stood.

Observed here amongst other vegetable productions, a new species, or at least a variety of Halesia diptera; these trees are of the size and figure of ordinary Mulberry trees, their stems short and tops regular and spreading, and the leaves large and broad, in size and figure resembling those of our common wild Mulberry.

Opposite this bluff, on the other side of the river, is a district of
swamp or low land, the richest I ever saw, or perhaps any where to
be seen; as for the trees I shall forbear to describe them, because it
would appear incredible, let it suffice to mention, that the Cypress,
Ash, Platanus, Populus, Liquid-amber, and others, are by far the
tallest, straitest and every way the most enormous that I have seen or
heard of. And as a proof of the extraordinary fertility of the soil, the
reeds or canes (Arundo gigantea) grow here thirty or forty feet high,
and as thick as a man's arm, or three or four inches in diameter; I
suppose one joint of some of them would contain above a quart of
water, and these reeds serve very well for setting poles, or masts for
barks and canoes. Continued yet ascending this fine river, passing by
the most delightful and fertile situations, observed frequently, on
bluffs of high land, deserted plantations (the houses always burnt
down to the ground) and ancient Indian villages. But observing little
variation in the natural vegetable productions, the current of the river
pressing down [411] with increased force and velocity, I turned about
descending the river, and next evening came to at a large well cultivated plantation, where I lodged all night, and the evening following
returned to Taensa.

Next day I felt symptoms of a fever, which in a few days laid me
up and became dangerous. But a dose of Tart. Emet. broke its violence, and care and good attendance after a few days, in some degree
restored my health, at least, so far as to enable me to rove about the
neighbouring forests; and here being informed of a certain plant of
extraordinary medical virtues, and in high estimation with the inhabitants, which grew in the hilly land about thirty miles higher up
the river, I resolved to set out in search of it, the Major being so
polite and obliging as to furnish me with horses to ride, and a Negro
to pilot and take care of me.

Set off in the morning, and in the course of the days journey crossed
several creeks and brooks, one of which swam our horses. On passing
by a swamp at the head of a bay or lagoon of the river, I observed a
species of Cypress; it differs a little from the white Cedar of New-
Jersey and Pennsylvania (Cypressus thyoides) the trunk is short and
the limbs spreading horizontally, the branches fuller of leaves and
the cones larger and of a crimson or reddish purple colour when ripe.

After leaving the low grounds and ascending the hills, discovered
the plant I went in search of, which I had before frequently observed
in my descent from the Creek nation down towards Taensa. This
plant appears to be a species of Collinsonia; [412] it is diuretic and
carminative, and esteemed a powerful febrifuge, an infusion of its tops

is ordinarily drunk at breakfast, and is of an exceeding pleasant taste and flavor; when in flower; which is the time the inhabitants gather it for preservation and use; it possesses a lively aromatic scent, partaking of lemon and aniseed. Lodged this night at a plantation near the river, and met with civility and good entertainment. The man and his three sons are famous hunters. I was assured from good authority that the old gentleman, for his own part, kills three hundred deer annually, besides bears, tygers and wolves.

Next morning early, set off again, on my return, and taking a different path back, for the sake of variety, though somewhat farther about and at a greater distance from the banks of the river, observed abundance of the tall blue Sage; it grows six or seven feet high; many stems arise from one root or source; these stems are thick, woody and quadrangular, the angles obtuse; the narrow lanceolate and serrated leaves are placed opposite, and are sessile, lightly embracing the branches, which terminate with spikes of large flowers of a celestial blue colour.

These stony, gravelly heights produce a variety of herbaceous plants, but one in particular I shall mention on account of its singular beauty; I believe it is a species Gerardea (Gerardea flammea) it grows erect, a single stem from a root, three or four feet in height, branching very regularly from about one half its length upwards, forming a cone or pyramid, profusely garnished with large tubular labiated scarlet or flame coloured flowers, which give the plant a very splendid appearance, even at [413] a great distance. Returned home in the evening fully satisfied with the day's excursion, from the discovery of many curious and beautiful vegetables.

Having advice from Mobile of an opportunity to Manchac, although my health was not established, feverish symptoms continuing to lurk about me, I resolved, notwithstanding, immediately to embrace this offer, and embarked again, descending the river to the city in company with Dr. Grant, a physician of the garrison, and late in the evening arrived in town, having suffered a smart fit of the fever by the way.

In the course of conversation with the doctor, I remarked that during my travels since leaving the Creek nation, and when there, I had not seen any honey bees; he replied that there were few or none West of the isthmus of Florida, and but one hive in Mobile, which was lately brought there from Europe; the English supposing that there were none in the country, not finding any when they took possession of it after the Spanish and French: I had been assured by the traders that there were none in West Florida, which to me seemed extraordinary and almost incredible, since they are so numerous all along the Eastern continent from Nova-Scotia to East Florida, even in the wild forests, as to be thought, by the generality of the inhabitants, aborigines of this continent.

The boat in which I had taken a passage to Pearl river, not being in readiness to depart for several days to come, I sought opportunities to fill up this time to the best advantage possible, and hearing of a boat going to the river Perdedo, for the purpose of securing the remains of a wreck, I appre-[414]hended this a favourable time to go and search that coast, the captain civilly offering me a passage and birth with him in a handsome light sailing-boat. Set sail early on a fine morning and having a brisk leading breeze, came to in the evening just within Mobile point, collected a quantity of drift wood to keep up a light and smoke away the musquetoes, and rested well on the clean sandy beach until the cool morning awoke us. We hoisted sail again and soon doubled the point or East promontory of the cape of the bay, stretching out many miles and pointing towards Dauphin island, between which and this cape is the ship channel.

Coasting along the sea-shore Eastward, we soon came up to the wreck, which being already stripped of her sails, &c. our captain kept on for Pensacola, where we arrived late in the evening.

My arrival at this capital, at present the seat of government, was merely accidental and undesigned; and having left at Mobile all my papers and testimonials, I designed to conceal my avocations, but my name being made known to Dr. Lorimer, one of the honourable council, he sent me a very polite invitation, and requested that he might acquaint governor Chester of my arrival, who he knew would expect that I should wait on him, and would be pleased to see me; I begged to be excused, at this time, as the boat would sail back for Mobile in a few hours, in which I was under the necessity of returning or loose my passage to the Missisipi; but during this expostulation I received a letter from Mr. Livingston the secretary, whom I waited upon, and was received very respectfully and treated with the utmost politeness and affability; soon after the governor's chariot passed by, his excellency returning [415] from a morning visit to his farm a few miles from Pensacola. Mr. Livingston went with me and introduced me to the governor, who commended my pursuits, and invited me to continue in West Florida in researches after subjects of natural history, &c. nobly offering to bear my expences, and a residence in his own family as long as I chose to continue in the colony; very judiciously observing that a complete investigation of its natural history could not be accomplished in a short space of time, since it would require the revolution of the seasons to discover and view vegetable nature in all her various perfections.

The captain of our fortunate bark by this time being ready to sail, I took leave of his excellency the governor, and bid adieu to my friends Dr. Lorimer, Mr. Livingston and others: set sail about noon on our return, and came to again within the capes of Mobile river.

Since I have hitherto given a superficial account of the towns, ports, improvements and other remarkable productions of nature, and human arts and industry, during the course of my peregrination, I shall not pass by Pensacola and its environs. This city is delightfully situated (and commands some natural advantages, superior to any other port in this province, in point of naval commerce, and such as human art and strength can never supply) upon gentle rising ascents environing a spacious harbour, safe and capacious enough to shelter all the navies of Europe, and excellent ground for anchorage; the West end of St. Rose island stretches across the great bay St. Maria Galves, and its South-West projecting point forms the harbour of Pensacola, which with the road or entrance is defended by a [416] block-house built on the extremity of that point, which at the same time serves the purpose of a fortress and look-out tower. There are several rivers which run into this great bay from the continent, but none of them navigable, for large craft, to any considerable distance into the country, the Shambe is the largest, which admits shallops some miles up, and Perreaugues upwards of fifty miles. There are some spots of good high land, and rich swamps, favourable for the production of rice on the banks of this river, which have given rise to some plantations producing Indigo, Rice, Corn, Batatas, &c. these rivers dividing and spreading abroad their numerous branches, over the expansive flat low country (between the two great rivers Apalachucla and Mobile) which consists of savannas and Cane meadows, fill them with brooks and water courses, and render them exuberant pasture for cattle.

There are several hundred habitations in Pensacola: the governor's palace is a large stone building ornamented with a tower, built by the Spaniards. The town is defended by a large stockado fortress, the plan a tetragon with salient angles at each corner, where is a block-house or round tower, one story higher than the curtains, where are light cannon mounted, it is constructed of wood. Within this fortress is the council chamber, here the records are kept, houses for the officers and barracks for the accommodation of the garrison, arsenal, magazine, &c. The secretary resides in a spacious, neat building: there are several merchants and gentlemen of other professions, who have respectable and convenient buildings in the town.

[*417*]   There were growing on the sand hills, environing Pensacola, several curious non-described plants; particularly one of the verticillate order, about eighteen inches in height, the flowers which formed loose spikes, were large and of a fine scarlet colour, but not having time, to examine the fructification, or collect good specimens, am ignorant of what order, or genus, it belongs to. And in the level wet savannas grew plentifully a new and very elegant species of Saracinia (Saracinia lacunosa) the leaves of this plant, which are twelve or fourteen inches in length, stand nearly erect, are round, tubular and ventricose; but not ridged with longitudinal angles or prominent nerves, as the leaves of the Saracinia flava are; the aperture at top may be shut up by a cap or lid, of a helmet form, which is an appendage of the leaf, turning over the orifice in that singular manner, the ventricose, or inflated part of the leaf, which is of a pale, but vivid green colour, is beautifully ornamented with rose coloured studs or blisters, and the inner surface curiously inscribed, or variegated with crimson veins or fibres. It was past the time for flowering, but the plant in any situation is a very great curiosity.

Next morning early we arose from our hard sandy sea-beaten couch, being disturbed the whole night by the troublesome musquitoes; set sail, and before night returned safe to the city of Mobile.

CHAP. VII.

THE next day after my return to Mobile, I found myself very ill, and not a little alarmed by an excessive pain in my head, attended with a high fever, this disorder soon settled in my eyes, nature pursuing that way to expel the malady, causing a most painful defluxion of pellucid, corrosive water; notwithstanding I next day set off on board a large trading boat, the property of a French gentleman, and commanded by him (he being general interpreter for the Chactaw nation) on his return to his plantations, on the banks of Pearl river; our bark was large, well equipped for sailing, and manned with three stout Negroes, to row in case of necessity. We embarked in the evening, and came to about six miles below the town, at a pleasant farm, the master of which (who was a Frenchman) entertained us in a very polite and friendly manner. The wind favourable, next morning early we set sail again, and having made extraordinary way, about noon came up abreast of a high steep bluff, or perpendicular cliffs of high land, touching on the bay of the West coast, where we went on shore, to give liberty to the slaves to rest and refresh themselves. In the mean time I accompanied the captain on an excursion into the spacious level forests, which spread abroad from the shore to a great distance back, observed vestiges of an ancient fortress and settlement, and there yet remain a few pieces of iron cannon; but what principally attracted my notice, was three vast iron pots or kettles, each of many hundred gallons contents, upon [419] enquiry, my associate informed me they were for the purpose of boiling tar to pitch, there being vast forests of Pine trees in the vicinity of this place. In Carolina the inhabitants pursue a different method; when they design to make pitch, they dig large holes in the ground, near the tar kiln, which they line with a thick coat of good clay, into which they conduct a sufficient quantity of tar, and set it on fire, suffering it to flame and evaporate a length of time sufficient to convert it into pitch, and when cool, lade it into barrels, and so on until they have consumed all the tar, or made a sufficient quantity of pitch for their purpose.

After re-imbarking, and leaving this bluff a few miles, we put into shore again, and came to a farm house, a little distance from the water, where we supplied ourselves with Corn meal, Batatas, bacon, &c. The French gentleman (proprietor of the plantation) was near eighty years old, his hair almost white with age, yet he appeared active, strong and muscular, and his mother who was present, was one hundred and five years old, active and cheerful, her eyes seemed as brisk and sparkling as youth, but of a diminutive size, not half the stature and weight of her son; it was now above fifty years since she came into America from old France.

I embarked again, proceeding down the bay, and in the evening doubled the west point or cape of the bay, being a promontory of the main, between which and Dauphin island, we entered the channel Oleron; from this time, until we arrived at this gentleman's habitation on Pearl river, I was incapable of making any observations, for my eyes could not bear the light, as the least ray admitted seemed [420] as the piercing of a sword, and by the time I had arrived at Pearl river, the excruciating pain had rendered me almost frantic and stupified for want of sleep, of which I was totally deprived, and the corroding water, every few minutes, streaming from my eyes, had stripped the skin off my face, in the same manner as scalding water would have done, I continued three days with this friendly Frenchman, who tried every remedy, that he or his family could recollect, to administer relief, but to no purpose, my situation was now become dangerous, and I expected to sink under the malady, as I believe my friends here did. At last the man informed me, on Pearl island, about twelve miles distance, resided an English gentleman, who had a variety of medicines, and if I chose to go to him he would take me there; I accordingly bid adieu to this hospitable family, and set off with him in a convenient boat, before night arrived at Mr. Rumsey's, who received me kindly, and treated me with the utmost humanity, during a stay of four or five weeks: the night however after my arrival here I sincerely thought would be my last, and my torments were so extreme as to desire it; having survived this tedious night, I in some degree recovered my senses and asked Mr. Rumsey if he had any Cantharides, who soon prepared a blister plaister for me, which I directed to be placed betwixt my shoulders, this produced the desired relief and more than answered my expectation, for it had not been there a quarter of an hour before I fell asleep, and remained so a whole day, when I awoke intirely relieved from pain, my senses in perfect harmony and mind composed; I do not know how to express myself on this occasion; all was peace and tranquility; although I had my sight perfectly, yet my [421] body seemed but as a light shadow, and my existence as a pleasing delirium, for I sometimes doubted of its reality. I however from that moment began to mend, until my health was perfectly restored, but it was several weeks before I could expose my eyes to open day light, and at last I found my left eye considerably injured, which suffered the greatest pain and weight of the disease.

As soon as I acquired strength to walk about, and bear the least impression of open day light on my eyes, I made frequent, indeed I may say daily excursions in and about this island, strolling through its awful shades, venerable groves and sublime forests, consisting of the Live Oaks and Magnolia grandiflora, Laurus Borbonia, Olea Americana, Fagus sylvatica, Laur. Sassafras, Quercus hemispherica, Telea, Liquid-amber styraciflua, Morus, Gleditsia, Callicarpa, Halesia, &c.

The island is six or seven miles in length, and four or five in width, including the salt marshes and plains, which invest it on every side, I believe we may only except a narrow strand at the South end of it, washed by Lake Borgone at the Regullets, which is a promontory composed of banks, of sea-shells and sand, cast up by the force of winds, and the surf of the lake; these shells are chiefly a small species of white clam shells, called les coquelles. Here are a few shrubs growing on these shelly heights, viz. Rhamnus frangula, Sideroxilon, Myrica, Zanthoxilon clava Herculis, Juniperus Americana, Lysium salsum; together with several new genera and species of the herbaceous and suffruticose tribes, Croton, Stillingia, &c. but particularly a species of Mimosa (Mimosa virgatia) which in respect of the elegancy of its pinnated [422] leaves, cannot be exceeded by any of that celebrated family. It is a perennial plant, sending up many nearly erect stems, from the root or source, these divide themselves into many ascendant slender rods like branches, which are ornamented with double pinnated leaves, of a most delicate formation. The compound flowers, are of a pale, greenish yellow, collected together in a small oblong head, upon a long slender peduncle, the legumes are large, lunated and flat, placed in a spiral or contorted manner, each containing several hard compressed seed, or little beans.

The interior and by far the greater part of the island consists of high land; the soil to appearance a heap of sea sand in some places, with an admixture of sea shells, this soil, notwithstanding its sandy and sterile appearance, when divested of its natural vegetative attire, has, from what cause I know not, a continual resource of fertility within itself, the surface of the earth, after being cleared of its original vegetable productions, exposed a few seasons to the sun, winds and triturations of agriculture, appears scarcely any thing but heaps of white sand, yet it produces Corn (Zea) Indigo, Batatas, Beans Peas, Cotton, Tobacco, and almost every sort of esculent vegetable, in a degree of luxuriancy very surprising and unexpected, year after year, incessantly, without any addition of artificial manure or compost; there is indeed a foundation of strong adhesive clay, consisting of strata of various colours, which I discovered by examining a well, lately dug in Mr. Rumsey's yard; but its lying at a great depth under the surface, the roots of small shrubs and herbage, cannot reach near to it, or receive any benefit, unless we may suppose, that ascending [423] fumes or exhalations, from this bed of clay, may have a vivific nutritive quality, and be received by the fibres of the roots, or being condensed in the atmosphere by nocturnal chills, fall with dews upon the leaves and twigs of these plants, and there absorbed, become nutritive or exhilarating to them.

Besides the native forest trees and shrubs already noted, manured fruit trees arrive in this island to the utmost degree of perfection, as Pears, Peaches, Figs, Grape Vines, Plumbs &c. of the last mentioned genus, there is a native species grows in this island, which produces its large oblong crimson fruit in prodigious abundance; the fruit though of a most inticing appearance, are rather too tart, yet are agreeable eating, at sultry noon, in this burning climate, they afford a most delicious and reviving marmalade, when preserved in sugar, and make excellent tarts: the tree grows about twelve feet high, the top spreading, the branches spiny and the leaves broad, nervous, serrated, and terminate with a subulated point.

My eyes having acquired sufficient strength to endure the open daylight, I set off from Pearl island, for Manchac on the Mississipi, in a handsome large boat with three Negroes to navigate her; leaving the friendly Mr. Rumsey's seat on Pearl Island, we descend a creek from the landing near his house; this creek led us about a mile, winding through salt sedgy marshes, into Lake Pontchartrain, along whose North shores, we coasted about twenty miles, having low, reedy marshes, on our starboard: these marshes were very extensive between us and the far distant high forests on the main, when at evening the shore becomes bolder, with sandy elevations, affording a few dwarf Oaks, Zanthoxilon, Myrica [424] and Rham. frangula. We came to in a little bay, kindled a fire, and after supper betook ourselves to repose; our situation open, airy and cool, on clean sand banks; we rested quietly, though sometimes roused by alarms from the crocodiles, which are here in great numbers, and of an enormous bulk and strength.

Next day early we got under way, pursuing our former course, nearly West ward, keeping the North shore several leagues; immediately back of this high sandy strand; (which is cast up by the beating surf and winds, setting from sea ward, across the widest part of the lake) the ground suddenly falls, and becomes extensive flat Cypress swamps, the sources of creeks and rivers, which run into the lake, or Pearl River, or at other places, the high forests of the main now gradually approaching the lake, advance up to the very shore, where we find houses, plantations and new settlements: we came to at one of them charmingly situated, set sail again, and came up to the mouth of the beautiful Taensapaoa, which takes that name from a nation of Indians, who formerly possessed the territories lying on its banks, which are fertile and delightful regions. This river is narrow at its entrance, but deep, and said to be navigable for large barks and perreauguas, upwards of fifty miles, just within its capes, on the leeward shore, are heights, or a group of low hills (composed of the small clam shells, called les coquelles) which gradually depress as we retreat back from the river, and the surface of the land is more level; these shells dissolving and mixing with the surface, render the vegetative mould black, rich, and productive. Here are a few habitations, and some fields cleared and cultivated; but [425] the inhabitants neglect agriculture; and generally employ themselves in hunting, and fishing: we however furnished ourselves here with a sufficiency of excellent Batatas. I observed no new vegetable productions, except a species of Cleome, (Cleome lupinifolia) this plant possesses a very strong scent, somewhat like Gum Assafetida, notwithstanding which the inhabitants give it a place in soups and sauces.

From Taensapaoa, we still coasted Westward, three or four miles, to the straits that communicate to the lake Mauripas; entering which and continuing six or eight miles, having low swampy land on each side, the channel divides, forming an island in the middle of the pass, we took the right hand channel, which continuing three or four miles, when the channels reunite in full view of the charming lake. We came to at an elevated point, or promontory on the starboard main shore, it being the North cape, from whence I enjoyed a very pleasing and complete view of the beautiful lake Mauripas, entering which next morning with a steady favourable gale, soon wafted us nine or ten miles over to the mouth of the river Amete; ascended between its low banks; the land on each side a level swamp, about two feet above the surface of the water, supporting a thick forest of trees, consisting chiefly of Fraxinus, Nyssa aquatica, Nyssa multiflora, Cupressus disticha, Quercus phillos, Acer rubrum, Ac. negundo, Acer glaucum, Sambuces, Laurus Borbonia, Carpinus, Ulmus and others. The soil or earth humid, black and rich. There is scarcely a perceptible current; the water dark, deep, turgid and stagnate, being from shore to shore covered with a scum or pellicle of a green [426] and purplish cast, and is perpetually throwing up from the muddy bottom to its surface minute air bladders or bubbles; in short, these dark loathsome waters, from every appearance seem to be a strong extract, or tincture of the leaves of the trees, herbs and reeds, arising from the shores, and which almost overspread them, and float on the surface, insomuch that a great part of these stagnate rivers, during the summer and autumnal seasons, are constrained to pass under a load of grass and weeds; which are continually vegetating and spreading over the surface from the banks, until the rising floods of winter and spring, rushing down from the main, sweep them way, and purify the waters. Late in the evening we discovered a narrow ridge of land close to the river bank, high and dry enough to suffer us to kindle up a fire, and space sufficient to spread our bedding on. But here, fire and smoke were insufficient to expel the hosts of musquitoes that invested our camp, and kept us awake during the long and tedious night, so that the alligators had no chance of taking us napping. We were glad to rise early in the morning, proceeding up the Amete. The land now gradually rises, the banks become higher, the soil drier and firmer four or five feet above the surface of the river; the trees are of an incredible magnitude, particularly Platanus occidentalis, Fraxinus, Ulmus, Quercus hemispherica, &c. The Cana Indica grows here in surprising luxuriance, presenting a glorious shew; the stem rises six, seven and nine feet high, terminating upwards with spikes of scarlet flowers.

Now having advanced near thirty miles up the Amete, we arrived at a very large plantation the property of a Scotch gentleman, who received me [427] with civility, intreating me to reside with him, but being impatient to get to the river, and pleading the necessity of prosecuting my travels with alacrity, on account of the season being so far advanced, I was permitted to proceed, and set off next morning; still ascending the Amete about twenty miles farther, and arrived at the forks; where the Iberville comes in on the left hand, ascending which a little way, we soon came to the landing, where are warehouses for disposing merchandize; this being the extremity of navigation up this canal, and here small vessels load and unload. From this place to Manchac, on the banks of the Mississipi, just above the mouth of the canal, is nine miles by land; the road strait, spacious, and perfectly level, under the shadow of a grand forest; the trees of the first order in magnitude and beauty, as Magnolia grandiflora, Liriodendron tulipifera, Platanus, Juglans nigra, Fraxinus excelsior, Morus rubra, Laurus sasafras, Laurus Borbonia, Telea, Liquid-amber styraciflua, &c.

At evening arrived at Manchac, where I directed my steps to the banks of the Mississipi, where I stood for a time as it were fascinated by the magnificence of the great sire * of rivers.

The depth of the river here, even in this season, at its lowest ebb is astonishing, not less than forty fathoms, and the width about a mile or somewhat less; but it is not expansion of surface alone that strikes us with ideas of magnificence, the altitude, and theatrical ascents of its pensile banks, the steady course of the mighty flood, the trees, high forests, even every particular object, as well as socie-[428]ties, bear the stamp of superiority and excellence; all unite or combine in exhibiting a prospect of the grand sublime. The banks of the river at Manchac, though frequently overflowed by the vernal inundations, are about fifty feet perpendicular height above the surface of the water (by which the channel at these times must be about two hundred and ninety feet deep) and these precipices being an accumulation of the sediment of muddy waters, annually brought down with the floods, of a light loamy consistence, are continually cracking and parting, present to view deep yawning chasms, in time split off, as the active perpetual current undermines, and the mighty masses of earth tumble headlong into the river, whose impetuous current sweeps away and lodges them elsewhere. There is yet visible some remains of a high artificial bank, in front of the buildings of the town, formerly cast up by the French, to resist the inundations, but found to be ineffectual, and now in part tumbled down the precipice, as the river daily incroaches on the bluff; some of the habitations are in danger, and must be very soon removed or swallowed up in the deep gulph of waters. A few of the buildings that have been established by the English, since taking possession of the colony, are large and commodious, particularly the ware-houses of Messrs. Swanson & Co. Indian traders and merchants.

The Spaniards have a small fortress and garrison on the point of land below the Iberville, close by the banks of the river, which has a communication with Manchac, by a slender narrow wooden bridge across the channel of Iberville, supported on wooden pillars, and not a bow shot from the habitations of Manchac. The Iberville in the summer [429] season is dry, and its bed twelve or fifteen feet above the surface of the Mississipi; but in the winter and spring has a great depth of water, and a very rapid stream which flows into the Amete, thence down through the lakes into the bay of Pearls to the ocean.

Having recommendations to the inhabitants of Batonrouge, now called New-Richmond, more than forty miles higher up the river; and

* Which is the meaning of the word Mississipi.

one of these gentlemen being present at Manchac, gave me a friendly and polite invitation to accompany him on his return home. A pleasant morning, we set off after breakfast, well accommodated in a handsome convenient boat, rowed by three blacks. Two miles above Manchac we put into shore at Alabama, this Indian village is delightfully situated on several swelling green hills, gradually ascending from the verge of the river: they are a remnant of the ancient Alabama nation, who inhabited the East arm of the great Mobile river, which bears their name to this day, now possessed by the Creeks or Muscogulges, who conquered the former.

My friend having purchased some baskets and earthen-ware, the manufactures of these people, we left the village, and proceeded twelve miles higher up the river, landed again at a very large and well cultivated plantation, where we lodged all night. Observed growing in a spacious garden adjacent to the house, many useful as well as curious exoticks, particularly the delicate and sweet Tube-rose (Polyanthus tuberosa) it grows here in the open garden, the flowers were very large and abundant on the stems, which were five, six or seven feet high, but I saw none here having double flowers. In one corner of the garden was a pond or marsh, round about [430] which grew luxuriantly the Scotch grass (Panicum hirtellum, gramen panicum maximum, spica devisa, aristis armatum, Sloan, Jam. Cat. p. 30.) the people introduced this valuable grass from the West-India islands: they mow or reap it at any time, and feed it green to cows or horses; it is nourishing food for all cattle. The Humble plant (Mimosa pudica) grows here five or six feet high, rambling like Brier vines over the fences and shrubs, all about the garden. The people here say it is an indigenous plant, but this I doubt, as it is not seen growing wild in the forests and fields, and it differs in no respect from that which we protect in green houses and stoves, except in the extent and luxuriancy of its branches, which may be owing to the productive virgin mould and temperature of the climate; the people however pay no attention to its culture, but rather condemn it as a noxious, troublesome weed, for wherever it gets footing, it spreads itself by its seed in so great abundance as to oppress and even extirpate more useful vegetables.

Next day we likewise visited several delightful and spacious plantations on the banks of the river, during our progress upwards; in the evening arrived at my friend's habitation, a very delightful villa, with extensive plantations of Corn (Zea) Indigo, Cotton and some Rice.

A day or two after our arrival we agreed upon a visit to Point Coupe, a flourishing French settlement on the Spanish shore of the Mississipi.

Early next morning we set off in a neat Cypress boat with three oars, proceeding up the river, and by night got to a large plantation near the White [431] cliffs, now called Brown's cliffs, in honour of the late governor of West Florida, now of the Bahama Islands, who is proprietor of a large district of country, lying on and adjacent to the Cliffs. At the time of my residence with Mr. Rumsey at Pearl island, governor Brown, then on his passage to his government of the Bahamas, paid Mr. Rumsey a visit, who politely introduced me to his excellency, acquainting him with my character and pursuits; he desired me to explore his territory, and give him my opinion of the quality of the White plains.

August 27th, 1787, having in readiness horses well equipped, early in the morning we set off for the plains. About a mile from the river we crossed a deep gully and small rivulet, then immediately entered the Cane forests, following a strait avenue cut through them, off from the river, which continued about eight miles, the ground gradually but imperceptibly rising before us; when at once opens to view expansive plains, which are a range of native grassy fields of many miles extent, lying parallel with the river, surrounded and intersected with Cane brakes and high forests of stately trees; the soil black, extremely rich and productive, but the virgin mould becomes thinner and less fertile as it verges on to the plains, which are so barren as scarcely to produce a bush or even grass, in the middle or highest parts; the upper stratum or surface of the earth is a whitish clay or chalk, with veins of sea shells, chiefly of those little clams called les coqueles, or interspersed with the white earth or clay, so tenacious and hard as to render it quite sterile, scarcely any vegetable growth to be seen, except short grass, crustaceous mosses, and some places [432] quite bare, where it is on the surface, but where it lies from eighteen inches to two or three feet below, it has the virtue of fertilizing the virgin mould above, rendering it black, humid, soapy, and incredibly productive.

I observed two or three scrubby Pine trees or rather dwarf bushes, upon the highest ridge of these plains, which are viewed here as a curiosity, there being no Pine forests within several leagues distance from the banks of this great river, but, on the contrary, seemingly an endless wilderness of Canes and the most magnificent forests of the trees already noted, but particularly Platanus occidentalis, Liriodendron, Magnolia grandiflora, Liquid-amber styraciflua, Juglans nigra, Juglans exaltata, Telea, Morus rubra, Gleditsia triacanthus, Laurus Borbonia and Laurus sassafras; this last grows here to a vast tree, forty or fifty feet strait trunk; its timber is found to be very useful, sawn into boards and scantling, or hewn into posts for building and fencing.

On the more fertile borders of the plains, adjoining the surrounding forests, are Sideroxilon, Pyrus coronaria and Strawberry vines (Fragaria) but no fruit on them; the inhabitants assured me they were fruitful in their season, very large, of a fine red colour, delicious and fragrant.

Having made our tour and observations on the White plains, we returned to the river at the close of the day, and next morning set off for Point Coupe; passed under the high painted cliffs, and then set our course across the Mississipi, which is here near two miles over: touched at a large island near the middle of the river, being led there, a little out [433] of our way, in pursuit of a bear crossing from the main, but he out-swam us, reached the island and made a safe retreat in the forests entangled with vines; we however pursued him on shore, but to no purpose. After resting a while we re-embarked and continued our voyage, coasting the East shore of the island to the upper end, here we landed again, on an extended projecting point of clean sand and pebbles, where were to be seen pieces of coal sticking in the gravel and sand, together with other fragments of the fossil kingdom, brought down by inundations and lodged there. We observed a large kind of muscle in the sand; the shell of an oval form, having horns or protuberances near half an inch in length and as thick as a crow-quill, which I suppose serve the purpose of grapnels to hold their ground against the violence of the current. Here were great numbers of wild fowl, wading in the shoal water that covers the sandy points, to a vast distance from the shores: they were geese, brant, gannet, and the great and beautiful whooping crane (grus alber.) Embarked again, doubled the point of the island and arrived at Point Coupe in the evening.

We made our visit to a French gentleman, an ancient man and wealthy planter, who, according to the history he favoured us with of his own life and adventures, must have been very aged; his hair was of a silky white, yet his complexion was florid and constitution athletic. He said that soon after he came to America, with many families of his countrymen, they ascended the river to the Cliffs of the Natches, where they sat down, being entertained by the natives; and under cover of a strong fortress and garrison, established a settlement, and by [434] cultivating the land and forming plantations, in league and friendship with the Indians, in a few years they became a populous, rich and growing colony; when, through the imprudent and tyrannical conduct of the commandant towards the Natches, the ancients of the country, a very powerful and civilized nation of red men, who were sovereigns of the soil, and possessed the country round about them, they became tired of these comers, and exasperated at their cruelty and licentiousness, at length determined to revenge themselves of such inhumanity

and ingratitude, secretly conspired their destruction, and their measures were so well concerted with other Indian tribes, that if it had not
been for the treachery of one of their princesses, with whom the
commander was in favour (for by her influence her nation attempted
the destruction of the settlement, before their auxilaries joined them,
which afforded an opportunity for some few of the settlers to escape)
they would have fully accomplished their purpose, however the settlement was entirely broken up, most of the inhabitants being slaughtered in one night, and the few who escaped betook themselves to
their canoes, descending the river until they arrived at this place,
where they established themselves again; and this gentleman had
only time and opportunity to take into his boat one heifer calf, which
he assured us was the mother of the numerous herds he now possesses,
consisting of many hundred head. Here is now a very respectable village, defended by a strong fortress and garrison of Spaniards, the
commander being governor of the district.

The French here are able, ingenious and industrious planters; they
live easy and plentifully, and are [435] far more regular and commendable in the enjoyment of their earnings than their neighbours
the English; their dress of their own manufactures, well wrought and
neatly made up, yet not extravagant or foppish; manners and conversation easy, moral and entertaining.

Next morning we set off again on our return home, and called by
the way of the Cliffs, which is a perpendicular bank or bluff, rising
up out of the river near one hundred feet above the present surface of
the water, whose active current sweeps along by it. From eight or
nine feet below the loamy vegetative mould at top, to within four or
five feet of the water, these cliffs present to view strata of clay, marle
and chalk, of all colours, as brown, red, yellow, white, blue and purple; there are separate strata of these various colours, as well as mixed
or particoloured: the lowest stratum next the water is exactly of the
same black mud or rich soil of the adjacent low Cypress swamps,
above and below the bluff; and here in the cliffs we see vast stumps
of Cypress and other trees, which at this day grow in these low, wet
swamps, and which range on a level with them. These stumps are
sound, stand upright, and seem to be rotted off about two or three
feet above the spread of their roots; their trunks, limbs, &c. lie in all
directions about them. But when these swampy forests were growing, and by what cause they were cut off and overwhelmed by the
various strata of earth, which now rise near one hundred feet above,
at the brink of the cliffs, and two or three times that height but a few
hundred yards back, is a phenomenon perhaps not easily developed;
the swelling heights rising gradually over and beyond this precipice

are now adorned [436] with high forests of stately Magnolia, Liquid-
amber, Fagus, Quercus, Laurus, Morus, Juglans, Telea, Halesia, Æsculus, Callicarpa, Liriodendron, &c. Arrived in the evening at the plantation below the Cliffs, and next day got safe back to my friend's
habitation.

Observed few vegetable productions different from what grow in
Carolina and Georgia; perhaps in the spring and early summer season, here may be some new plants, particularly in the high forests
and ridges, at some distance from the river: there is however growing in the rich high lands, near on the banks of the river, which I
observed in the settlement of Baton Rouge, an arborescent aromatic
vine, which mounts to the tops of the highest trees, by twisting or
writhing spirally round them; some of these vines are as thick as a
man's leg, of a soft spungy texture, and flexible, covered with a Cinnamon coloured bark, which is highly aromatic or spicy. The large
oblong leaves sit opposite on the branches, and are of a full deep
green colour, but its season of flowering being past, and the seed was
scattered, I am entirely ignorant to what genus it belongs; perhaps it
is a non-descript or new genus: here is likewise a new and beautiful species of Verbena, with decumbent branches and lacerated deep
green leaves; the branches terminate with corymbi of Violet blue
flowers, this pretty plant grows in old fields where there is a good soil.

The severe disorder in my eyes subverted the plan of my peregrinations, and contracted the span of my pilgrimage South-Westward.
This disappointment affected me very sensibly, but resignation and
reason resuming their empire over my mind, I submitted and determined to return to Carolina.

[437]   Receiving information that the company's schooner was ready
to sail for Mobile, I embarked on board a trading boat for Manchac,
where arriving in the evening, I took leave next morning of Messrs.
Swanson & Co. and set off for the forks of the Amite, and next day
set sail, descending the tardy current of the Amite. Observing two
bears crossing the river a-head, though our pieces were ready
charged, and the yawl along side to receive us, we pursued them in
vain, they swam swiftly across and escaped in the forests on the island
of Orleans. The breeze dying away at evening, we came to anchor,
and had variety of amusements at fishing and fowling.

Next day, November 13th 1777, with a steady leading breeze,
entered and sailed over the lake Maurepas, and through the streights
into the Pontchartrain, and continued under sail, but at midnight by
keeping too near the West shore we ran aground on a sand-bar, where
we lay beating the hard sandy bottom until morning, and our yawl

parting from us in the night, which we never recovered, we were left to the mercy of the winds and floods, but before noon the wind coming briskly from North-East, drove the sea into the lake, we got off, made sail again, and before night passed through the Regullets, entering the ocean through the bay of Pearls, sailing through the sound betwixt Cat island and the strand of the continent; passing by the beautiful bay St. Louis, into which descend many delightful rivers, which flow from the lower or maritime settlements of the Chactaws or Flatheads. Continuing through the sound between the oyster banks and shoals of Ship and Horn islands, and the high and bold coast of Biloxi on the main, [438] got through the narrow pass Aux Christian and soon came up abreast of Isle Dauphin, betwixt whose shoals and the West Cape of Mobile Bay we got aground on some sunken oyster banks, but next day a brisk Southerly wind raised the sea on the coast, which lifted us off again, and setting sail, shot through the Pass au Oleron, and entering the bay, by night came to anchor safe again at the city of Mobile.

After having made up my collections of growing roots, seeds and curious specimens, left them to the care of Messrs. Swanson and M'Gillavry, to be forwarded to Dr. Fothergill of London. I prepared to set off again to Augusta in Georgia, through the Creek Nation, the only practicable way of returning by land, being frustrated of pursuing my intended route which I had meditated, through the territories of the Siminoles or Lower Creeks, they being a treacherous people, lying so far from the eye and control of the nation with whom they are confederate: there having lately been depredations and murders committed by them at the bay of Apalache, on some families of white people who were migrating from Georgia, with an intention of setling on the Mobile. Having to pass the distance of near two hundred miles to the first town of the nation, through a solitary, uninhabited wilderness, the bloody field of Schambe, where those contending bands of American bravos, Creeks and Chactaws, often meet in dire conflict: for the better convenience and security, I joined company with a caravan of traders, now about setting off for the nation.

Observed growing in a garden in Mobile, two large trees of the Juglans pecan, and the Discorea [439] bulbifera, this last curious plant bears a large kidney shaped root, one, two or three at the bosom of the leaves, several feet from the ground, as they climb up poles or supports set by their roots; these roots when boiled or roasted, are esteemed a pleasant wholesome food, and taste like the ordinary Yam.

NOVEMBER 27th, 1777, set off from Mobile, in a large boat with the principal trader of the company, and at evening arrived at Taensa, where were the pack-horsemen with the merchandize, and next morning as soon as we had our horses in readiness, I took my last leave of Major Farmer, and left Taensa. Our caravan consisting of between twenty and thirty horses, sixteen of which were loaded, two pack-horsemen, and myself, under the direction of Mr. Tap ---- y the chief trader. One of our young men was a Mustee Creek, his mother being a Chactaw slave, and his father a half breed, betwixt a Creek and a white man. I loaded one horse with my effects, some presents to the Indians, to enable me to purchase a fresh horse, in case of necessity, for my old trusty slave which had served me faithfully almost three years, having carried me on his back at least six thousand miles, was by this time almost worn out, and I expected every hour he would give up, especially after I found the manner of these traders' travelling; who seldom decamp until the sun is high and hot; each one having a whip made of the toughest cowskin, they start all at once, the horses having ranged themselves in regular Indian file, the veteran in the van, and the younger in the rear; then the chief drives with the crack of his whip, and a whoop or shriek, which rings through the forests and plains, speaks in Indian, commanding them to proceed, which is repeated by all the company, when we start at once, keeping up a brisk and constant trot, [*441*] which is incessantly urged and continued as long as the miserable creatures are able to move forward, and then come to camp, though frequently in the middle of the afternoon, which is the pleasantest time of the day for travelling: and every horse has a bell on, which being stopped when we start in the morning with a twist of grass or leaves, soon shakes out, and they are never stopped again during the day; the constant ringing and clattering of the bells, smacking of the whips, whooping and too frequent cursing these miserable quadrupeds, cause an incessant uproar and confusion, inexpressibly disagreeable.

After three days travelling in this mad manner, my old servant was

on the point of giving out, and several of the company's horses were
tired, but were relieved of their burthens by the led horses which
attended for that purpose. I was now driven to disagreeable extremities, and had no other alternative, but either to leave my horse
in the woods, pay a very extravagant hire for a doubtful passage to
the Nation, or separate myself from my companions, and wait the
recovery of my horse alone: the traders gave me no other comfortable
advice in this dilemma, than that, there was a company of traders
on the road a-head of us from the nation, to Mobile, who had a large
gang of led horses with them for sale, when they should arrive; and
expected from the advice which he had received at Mobile before
we set off from thence, that this company must be very near to us, and
probably would be up tomorrow, or at least in two or three days: and
this man condescended so far as to moderate a little his mode of
travelling, that I might have a chance of keeping up with them until
the evening of next [442] day; besides I had the comfort of observing
that the traders and pack-horsemen carried themselves towards me,
with evident signs of humanity and friendship, often expressing sentiments of sympathy, and saying I must not be left alone to perish in
the wilderness.

Although my apprehensions on this occasion, were somewhat
tumultuous, since there was little hope, on the principle of reason,
should I be left alone, of escaping cruel captivity, and perhaps being
murdered by the Chactaws; for the company of traders was my
only security, as the Indians never attack the traders on the road,
though they be trading with nations at enmity with them. Yet I had
secret hopes of relief and deliverance, that cheered me, and inspired
confidence and peace of mind.

Now I am come within the atmosphere of the Illisium groves, how
reanimating is the fragrance! every part of this plant above ground
possesses an aromatic scent, but the large stellated pericarp is the
most fragrant part of it, which continually perspires an oleaginous
sweat, as warm and vivific as Cloves or Mace, I never saw it grow
naturally further North than Lat. 33°, on the Mobile river and its
branches, and but one place in East Florida near Lake George, Lat.
28°.

About the middle of the afternoon, we were joyfully surprised
at the distant prospect of the trading company coming up, and we
soon met, saluting each other several times with a general Indian
whoop, or shouts of friendship; then each company came to camp
within a few paces of each other; and before night I struck up a
bargain with them for a handsome strong young horse, which cost

[*443*] me about ten pounds sterling. I was now constrained to leave
my old slave behind, to feed in rich Cane pastures, where he was
to remain and recruit until the return of his new master from Mobile;
from whom I extorted a promise to use him gently, and if possibly, not
to make a pack-horse of him.

Next morning we decamped, proceeding again on my travels, now
alert and cheerful. Crossed a brisk rivulet ripling over a gravelly bed,
and winding through aromatic groves of the Illisium Floridanum,
then gently descended to the high forests, leaving Deadman's creek,
for at this creek a white man was found dead, supposed to have been
murdered, from which circumstance it has its name.

A few days before we arrived at the Nation we met a company
of emigrants from Georgia; a man, his wife, a young woman, several
young children and three stout young men, with about a dozen horses
loaded with their property. They informed us their design was to settle
on the Alabama, a few miles above the confluence of the Tombigbe.

Being now near the Nation, the chief trader with another of our
company sat off a-head for his town, to give notice to the Nation,
as he said, of his approach with the merchandize, each of them
taking the best horse they could pick out of the gang, leaving the
goods to the conduct and care of the young Mustee and myself. Early
in the evening we came to the banks of a large deep creek, a considerable branch of the Alabama: the waters ran furiously, being
overcharged with the floods of rain which had fallen the day before.
We discovered immediately that there was no possibility of crossing
it by ford-[*444*]ing; its depth and rapidity would have swept our
horses, loads and all, instantly from our sight; my companion, after
consideration, said we must make a raft to ferry over our goods, which
we immediately set about, after unloading our horses and turning
them out to range. I undertook to collect dry Canes, and my companion dry timber or logs and vines to bind them together: having
gathered the necessary materials, and laid them in order on the brink
of the river, ready to work upon, we betook ourselves to repose, and
early next morning set about building our raft. This was a novel scene
to me, and I could not, until finished and put to practice, well comprehend how it could possibly answer the effect desired. In the
first place we laid, parallel to each other, dry, sound trunks of trees,
about nine feet in length, and eight or nine inches diameter, which
binding fast together with Grape vines and withs, until we had
formed this first floor, about twelve or fourteen feet in length, then
binding the dry Canes in bundles, each near as thick as a man's
body, with which we formed the upper stratum, laying them close

by the side of each other and binding them fast; after this manner our raft was constructed: then having two strong Grape vines, each long enough to cross the river, we fastened one to each end of the raft, which now being completed, and loading on as much as it would safely carry, the Indian took the end of one of the vines in his mouth, plunged into the river and swam over with it, and the vine fixed to the other end was committed to my charge, to steady the raft and haul it back again after being unloaded; as soon as he had safe landed and hauled taught his vine, I pushed off the raft, which he drew over as quick as possible, I steadying it with [445] my vine: in this manner, though with inexpressible danger of loosing our effects, we ferried all safe over: the last load, with other articles, contained my property, with all my clothes, which I stripped off, except my breeches, for they contained matters of more value and consequence than all the rest of my property put together; besides I did not choose to expose myself entirely naked to the alligators and serpents in crossing the flood. Now seeing all the goods safe over, and the horses at a landing place on the banks of the river about fifty yards above, I drove them all in together, when, seeing them safe landed, I plunged in after them, and being a tolerable swimmer, soon reached the opposite shore; but my difficulties at this place were not yet at an end, for our horses all landing just below the mouth of a considerable branch of this river, of fifteen or twenty feet width, and its perpendicular banks almost as many feet in height above its swift waters, over which we were obliged to carry every article of our effects, and this by no other bridge than a sapling felled across it, which is called a raccoon bridge, and over this my Indian friend would trip as quick and light as that quadruped, with one hundred weight of leather on his back, when I was scarcely able to shuffle myself along over it astride. At last having re-packed and set off again, without any material occurrence intervening; in the evening we arrived at the banks of the great Tallapoose river, and came to camp under shelter of some Indian cabins, in expansive fields, close to the river bank, opposite the town of Savannuca. Late in the evening a young white man, in great haste and seeming confusion, joined our camp, who immediately related, that being on his journey from Pensacola, it happened that the [446] very night after we had passed the company of emigrants, he met them and joined their camp in the evening, when, just at dark, the Chactaws surrounded them, plundered their camp and carried all the people off captive, except himself, he having the good fortune to escape with his horse, though closely pursued.

Next morning very early, though very cold and the surface of the earth as hoary as if covered with a fall of snow, the trader standing on the opposite shore entirely naked except a breech-clout, and encircled by a company of red men in the like habit, hailed us, and presently, with canoes, brought us all over with the merchandize, and conducted us safe to the town of Mucclasse, a mile or two distant.

The next day was a day of rest and audience: the following was devoted to feasting, and the evening concluded in celebrating the nuptials of the young Mustee with a Creek girl of Mucclasse, daughter of the chief and sister to our trader's wife. The trader's house and stores formed a compleat square, after the mode of the habitations of the Muscogulges, that is, four oblong buildings of equal dimensions, two opposite to each other, encompassing an area of about a quarter of an acre; on one side of this a fence enclosed a yard of near an acre of ground, and at one of the farther corners of which a booth or pavilion was formed of green boughs, having two Laurel trees planted in front (Magnolia grandiflora.) This was the secret nuptial chamber. Dancing, music and feasting continued the forepart of the night, and towards morning the happy couple privately withdrew, and continued alone all the next day, no one presuming to approach the sacred, mysterious thalamus.

[447] The trader obliged me with his company on a visit to the Alabama, an Indian town at the confluence of the two fine rivers, the Tallapoose and Coosau, which here resign their names to the great Alabama, where are to be seen traces of the ancient French fortress, Thoulouse; here are yet lying, half buried in the earth, a few pieces of ordnance, four and six pounders. I observed, in a very thriving condition, two or three very large Apple trees, planted here by the French. This is, perhaps, one of the most elegible situations for a city in the world, a level plain between the conflux of two majestic rivers, which are exactly of equal magnitude in appearance, each navigable for vessels and perreauguas at least five hundred miles above it, and spreading their numerous branches over the most fertile and delightful regions, many hundred miles before we reach their sources in the Apalachean mountains.

Stayed all night at Alabama, where we had a grand entertainment at the public square, with music and dancing, and returned next day to Mucclasse, where being informed of a company of traders about setting off from Tuckabatche for Augusta, I made a visit to that town to know the truth of it, but on my arrival there they were gone, but being informed of another caravan who were to start from the Ottasse town in two or three weeks time, I returned to Mucclasse in order to prepare for my departure.

On my arrival, I was not a little surprised at a tragical revolution in the family of my friend the trader, his stores shut up, and guarded by a party of Indians: in a few minutes however, the whole affair was related to me. It appeared that this son of Adonis, had been detected in an amorous in-[448]trigue, with the wife of a young chief, the day after his arrival: the chief being out on a hunt, but arrived next day, who upon information of the affair, and the fact being confirmed, he with his friends and kindred resolved to exact legal satisfaction, which in this case is cutting off both ears of the delinquent, close to the head, which is called cropping. This being determined upon, he took the most secret and effectual methods to effect his purpose. About a dozen young Indian fellows, conducted by their chief (the injured husband) having provided and armed themselves with knotty cudgels of green Hickory, which they concealed under their mantles, in the dusk of the evening paid a pretended friendly visit to the trader at his own house; when the chief feigning a private matter of business, took him aside in the yard; then whistling through his fingers (the signal preconcerted) he was instantly surrounded, knocked down, and then stripped to his skin, and beaten with their knotty bludgeons; however he had the subtilty to feign himself speechless before they really killed him, which he supposed was their intention; when he had now lain for dead, the executioner drew out his knife with an intention of taking off his ears; this small respite gave him time to reflect a little; when he instantly sprang up, ran off, leaped the fence and had the good fortune to get into a dark swamp, overgrown with vines and thickets, where he miraculously eluded the earnest researches of his enemies, and finally made a safe retreat to the house of his father-in-law, the chief of the town; throwing himself under his protection, who gave his word that he would do him all the favour that lay in his power. This account I had from his own mouth, who hearing of my return, the next morn-[449]ing after my arrival, sent a trusty messenger, by whom I found means of access to him. He farther informed me that there had been a council of the chiefs of the town convened, to deliberate on the affair, and their final determination was that he must loose his ears, or forfeit all his goods, which amounted to upwards of one thousand pounds sterling, and even that forfeiture would not save his ears, unless Mr. Golphin interposed in his behalf; and after all the injured Indian declares that he will have his life. He entreated me with tears to make what speed I could to Silver Bluff, represent his dangerous situation to Mr. Golphin, and solicit that gentleman's most speedy and effectual interference; which I assured him I would undertake.

Now having all things prepared for my departure, early in the morning, after taking leave of my distressed friend the trader of Mucclasse, I set off; passed through continued plantations and Indian towns on my way up the Tallapoose river, being every where treated by the inhabitants with marks of friendship, even as though I had been their countryman and relation. Called by the way at the beautiful town of Coolome, where I tarried some time with Mr. Germany the chief trader of the town, an elderly gentleman, but active, cheerful and very agreeable; who received and treated me with the utmost civility and friendship: his wife is a Creek woman, of a very amiable and worthy character and disposition, industrious, prudent and affectionate; and by whom he had several children, whom he is desirous to send to Savanna or Charleston, for their education, but cannot prevail on his wife to consent to it: this affair affects him very sensibly, for he has accumulated a pretty fortune by his industry and commendable conduct.

[450] Leaving Coolome, I re-crossed the river at Tuccabache, an ancient and large town, thence continuing up the river, and at evening arrived at Attasse, where I continued near a week, waiting the preparations of the traders, with whom I was to join in company to Augusta.

The next day after my arrival, I was introduced to the ancient chiefs, at the public square or areopagus, and in the evening in company with the traders, who are numerous in this town, repaired to the great rotunda, where were assembled the greatest number of ancient venerable chiefs and warriors that I had ever beheld; we spent the evening and greater part of the night together, in drinking Cassine and smoking Tobacco. The great counsel-house or rotunda is appropriated to much the same purpose as the public square, but more private, and seems particularly dedicated to political affairs; women and youth are never admitted; and I suppose it is death for a female to presume to enter the door, or approach within its pale. It is a vast conical building or circular dome, capable of accomodating many hundred people; constructed and furnished within, exactly in the same manner as those of the Cherokees already described, but much larger than any I had seen there; there are people appointed to take care of it, to have it daily swept clean, to provide canes for fuel or to give light.

As their vigils and manner of conducting their vespers and mystical fire in this rotunda, is extremely singular, and altogether different from the customs and usages of any other people, I shall proceed to describe it. In the first place, the governor or officer who has the management of this business, with his servants attending, orders the black drink [451] to be brewed, which is a decoction or infusion of the leaves and tender shoots of the Cassine: this is done under an open shed or pavilion, at twenty or thirty yards distance, directly opposite the door of the council-house. Next he orders bundles of dry Canes to be brought in; these are previously split and broke in pieces to about the length of two feet, and then placed obliquely crossways upon one another on the floor, forming a spiral circle round about the great centre pillar, rising to a foot or eighteen inches in height from the ground; and this circle spreading as it proceeds round and round, often repeated from right to left, every revolution encreases its diameter, and at length extends to the distance of ten or twelve feet from the centre, more or less, according to the length of time the assembly or meeting is to continue. By the time these preparations are accomplished it is night, and the assembly have taken their seats in order. The exterior extremity or outer end of the spiral circle takes fire and immediately rises into a bright flame (but how this is effected I did not plainly apprehend; I saw no person set fire to it; there might have been fire left on the hearth, however I neither saw nor smelt fire or smoke until the blaze instantly ascended upwards) which gradually and slowly creeps round the centre pillar, with the course of the sun, feeding on the dry Canes, and affords a cheerful, gentle and sufficient light until the circle is consumed, when the council breaks up. Soon after this illumination takes place, the aged chiefs and warriors being seated on their cabbins or sophas, on the side of the house opposite the door, in three classes or ranks, rising a little, one above or behind the other; and the white people and red people of confederate towns in the like order on the left hand: a trans-[452] verse range of pillars, supporting a thin clay wall about breast high, separates them: the king's cabbin or seat is in front, the next back of it the head warriors, and the third or last accommodates the young warriors, &c. the great war chief's seat or place is on the same cabbin with, and immediately to the left hand of the king and next to the white people, and to the right hand of the mico or king the most venerable head men and warriors are seated. The assembly being now seated in order, and the house illuminated, two middle aged men, who perform the office of slaves or servants, pro tempore, come in together at the door, each having very large conch shells full of black drink, advancing with slow, uniform and steady steps, their eyes or countenances lifted up, singing very low but sweetly, advance within six on eight paces of the king's and white people's cabbins, when they stop together, and each rests his shell on a tripos or little table, but presently takes it up again, and, bowing very low, advances obsequiously, crossing or intersecting each other about midway: he who rested his shell before the white people now stands before the king, and the other who stopped before the king stands before the white people, when each presents his shell, one to the king and the other to the chief of the white people, and as soon as he raises it to his mouth the slave utters or sings two notes, each of which continues as long as he has breath, and as long as these notes continue, so long must the person drink, or at least keep the shell to his mouth. These two long notes are very solemn, and at once strike the imagination with a religious awe or homage to the Supreme, sounding somewhat like a-hoo---ojah and a-lu---yah. After this manner the whole assembly are treated, as long as the drink and light continue to hold out, [453] and as soon as the drinking begins, Tobacco and pipes are brought. The skin of a wild cat or young tyger stuffed with Tobacco is brought, and laid at the king's feet, with the great or royal pipe beautifully adorned; the skin is usually of the animals of the king's family or tribe, as the wild-cat, otter, bear, rattle-snake, &c. A skin of Tobacco is likewise brought and cast at the feet of the white chief of the town, and from him it passes on from one to another to fill their pipes from, though each person has besides his own peculiar skin of Tobacco. The king or chief smokes first in the great pipe a few whiffs, blowing it off ceremoniously, first towards the sun, or as it is generally supposed to the Great Spirit, for it is puffed upwards, next towards the four cardinal points, then towards the white people in the house, then the great pipe is taken from the hand of the mico by a slave, and presented to the chief white man, and then to the great war chief, whence it circulates through the rank of head men and warriors, then returns to the king. After this each one fills his pipe from his own or his neighbours skin.

The great or public square generally stands alone, in the centre and highest part of the town, it consists of foursquare or cubical buildings, or houses of one story, uniform, and of the same dimensions, so situated as to form an exact tetragon, encompassing an area of half an acre of ground, more or less, according to the strength or largeness of the town, or will of the inhabitants; there is a passage or avenue at each corner of equal width; each building is constructed of a wooden frame fixed strong in the earth, the walls filled in, and neatly plaistered with clay mortar; close [454] on three sides, that is the back and two ends, except within about two feet of the wall plate or eaves, which is left open for the purpose of a window and to admit a free passage of the air; the front or side next to the area is quite open like a piazza. One of these buildings which is properly the counsel-house, where the mico chiefs and warriors, with the citizens who have business, or choose to repair thither, assemble every day in counsel; to hear, decide and rectify all grievances, complaints and contentions, arising betwixt the citizens; give audience to ambassadors, and strangers, hear news and talks from confederate towns, allies or distant nations; to consult about the particular affairs of the town, as erecting habitations for new citizens, or establishing young families, concerning agriculture &c. &c. and this building is somewhat different from the other three; it is closely shut up on three sides, that is, the back and two ends, and besides a partition wall longitudinally from end to end divides it into two apartments, the back part totally dark, only three small arched apertures or holes opening into it from the front apartment or piazza, and are little larger than just to admit a man to crawl in upon his hands and knees. This secluded place appears to me to be designed as a sanctuary * dedicated to religion or rather priest craft; for here are deposited all the sacred things, as the physic pot, rattles, chaplets of deer's hoofs and other apparatus of conjuration; and likewise the calumet or great pipe of peace, the imperial standard, or eagle's tail, which is made of the feathers of the white eagles tail † curiously formed and displayed like an [455] open fan on a sceptre or staff, as white and clean as possible when displayed for peace; but when for war, the feathers are painted or tinged with vermilion. The piazza or front of this building, is equally divided into three apartments, by two transverse walls or partitions, about breast high, each having three orders or ranges of seats or cabins stepping one above and behind the other, which accommodate the senate and audience, in the like order as observed in the rotunda. The other three buildings which compose the square, are alike furnished with three ranges of cabins or sophas, and serve for a banqueting-house, to shelter and accommodate the audience and spectators at all times, particularly at feasts or public entertainments, where all classes of citizens resort day and night in the summer or moderate season; the children and females however are seldom or never seen in the public square.

* Sanctorium or sacred temple, and it is said to be death for any person but the mico, war-chief and high priest to enter in, and none are admitted but by permission of the priests, who guard it day and night.
† Vultura sacra.

The pillars and walls of the houses of the square were decorated with various paintings and sculptures; which I suppose to be hieroglyphic, and as an historic legendary of political and sacerdotal affairs: but they are extremely picturesque or caricature, as men in variety of attitudes, some ludicrous enough, others having the head of some kind of animal as those of a duck, turkey, bear, fox, wolf, buck, &c. and again those kind of creatures are represented having the human head. These designs were not ill executed, the outlines bold, free and well proportioned. The pillars supporting the front or piazza of the council-house of the square, were ingeniously formed in the likeness of vast speckled serpents, ascending upward; the Otasses being of the snake family or tribe. At this time the town was fasting, taking medicine, and I think [456] I may say praying, to avert a grevious calamity of sickness, which had lately afflicted them, and laid in the grave abundance of their citizens; they fast seven or eight days, during which time they eat or drink nothing but a meagre gruel, made of a little corn-flour and water; taking at the same time by way of medicine or physic, a strong decoction of the roots of the Iris versicolor, which is a powerful cathartic; they hold this root in high estimation, every town cultivates a little plantation of it, having a large artificial pond, just without the town, planted and almost overgrown with it, where they usually dig clay for pottery, and mortar and plaster for their buildings, and I observed where they had lately been digging up this root.

In the midst of a large oblong square adjoining this town (which was surrounded with a low bank or terrace) is standing a high pillar, round like a pin or needle, it is about forty feet in height, and between two and three feet in diameter at the earth, gradually tapering upwards to a point; it is one piece of Pine wood, and arises from the centre of a low circular, artificial hill, but it leans a little to one side. I enquired of the Indians and traders what it was designed for, who answered they knew not: the Indians said that their ancestors found it in the same situation, when they first arrived and possessed the country, adding, that the red men or Indians, then the possessors, whom they vanquished, were as ignorant as themselves concerning it, saying that their ancestors likewise found it standing so. This monument, simple as it is, may be worthy the observations of a traveller, since it naturally excites at least the following queries: for what purpose was it designed? its great antiquity and incorruptibility —[457] what method or machines they employed to bring it to the spot, and how they raised it erect? There is no tree or species of the Pine, whose wood, i. e. so large a portion of the trunk, is supposed to be incorruptible, exposed in the open air to all weathers, but the long-leaved Pine (Pin. palustris) and there is none growing within twelve or fifteen miles of this place, that tree being naturally produced only on the high, dry, barren ridges, where there is a sandy soil and grassy wet savannas. A great number of men uniting their strength, probably carried it to the place on handspikes, or some such contrivance.

On the Sabbath day before I set off from this place, I could not help observing the solemnity of the town, the silence and the retiredness of the red inhabitants, but a very few of them were to be seen, the doors of their dwellings shut, and if a child chanced to stray out, it was quickly drawn in doors again: I asked the meaning of this, and was immediately answered, that it being the white people's beloved day or Sabbath, the Indians kept it religiously sacred to the Great Spirit.

Last night was clear and cold, wind North West, and this morning January 2d, 1788, the face of the earth was perfectly white with a beautiful sparkling frost. Set off for Augusta with a company of traders, four men with about thirty horses, twenty of which were loaded with leather and furs, each pack or load supposed to weigh one hundred and fifty pounds upon an average; in three days we arrived at the Apalachucla or Chata Uche river, crossed at the point towns Chehaw and Usseta; these towns almost join each other, yet speak two languages, [458] as radically different perhaps as the Muscogulge's and Chinese. After leaving the river we met with nothing material, or worth particular observation, until our arrival at Oakmulge, towards evening, where we encamped in expansive ancient Indian fields, in view of the foaming flood of the river, now raging over its banks. Here were two companies of traders from Augusta, bound to the Nation, consisting of fifteen or twenty men, with seventy or eighty horses, most of which had their loads of merchandize; they crossed the river this morning and lost six horses in the attempt; they were drowned, being entangled in the vines under water at landing. But the river now falling again, we were in hopes that by next morning the waters would be again confined within the banks. We immediately set about rigging our portable leather boat, about eight feet long, which was of thick soal leather, folded up and carried on the top of a pack of deer skins; the people soon got her rigged, which was effected after the following manner. We in the first place cut down a White-Oak sapling, and by notching this at each end, bent it up, which formed the keel, stem and stern post of one piece, this being placed in the bottom of the boat, and pretty strong hoop-poles being fixed in the bottom across the keel, and, turning up their ends, expanded the hull of the boat, which being fastened by thongs to two other poles bent round, the outside of the rim forms the gunwales, thus in an hour's time our bark was rigged, to which afterwards we added two little oars or sculls. Our boat being now in readiness, and our horses turned out to pasture, each one retired to repose, or to such exercise as most effectually contributed to divert the mind. I was at this time rather dejected, and [459] sought comfort in retirement. Turning my course to the expansive fields, fragrant groves and sublime forests. Returned to camp by dusk, where I found my companions cheerful and thoughtless rather to an extreme. It was a calm still evening and warm, the wood-cock (scolopax) chirruping high up in the air, gently descends by spiral circular tract, and alights on the humid plain: this bird appears in Pennsylvania early in the spring, when the Elm and Maple begin to flower, and here the scarlet Maple, Elm and Alder began to shew their flowers, the yellow Jasmin just ready to open its fragrant golden blossoms, and the gay Azalea also preparing to expand its beauties.

The morning cool and pleasant, after reconnoitering the shores of the rivers, and consulting with our brethren in distress, who had not yet decamped, resolving to stay and lend their assistance in passing over this rapid gulph, we were encouraged to proceed, and launching our bark into the raging flood, after many successful trips ferried over all the goods, then drove in our horses altogether, and had the pleasure of seeing them all safely landed on the opposite shore; and lastly I embarked with three of our people, and several packs of leather, we then put off from shore, bidding adieu to our generous friends left behind, who re-echoed our shouts upon our safe landing. We proceeded again, crossed the Oconne in the same manner, and with the like success, and came to camp in the fertile fields, on the banks of that beautiful river, and proceeding thence next day, in the evening came to camp on the waters of great Ogeche, and the following day, after crossing several of its considerable branches, came to camp, and next day [460] crossed the main branch of that famous river, which being wide and very rapid proved difficult and dangerous fording, yet we crossed without any loss, but some of our pack-horses were badly bruised, being swept off their feet and dashed against the rocks, my horse too being carried away with the current, and plunging off sunken shelving rocks into deep holes, I got very wet, but I kept my seat and landed safe: however I suffered much, it being a cold freezing day. We came to camp early, and raising great fires with Pine knots and other wood, we dried ourselves and kept warm

during the long night, and after two days more hard travelling we
arrived at Augusta.

Being under a necessity of making two or three days stay here, in
order to refit myself, for by this time my stock of cloths were entirely
worn out. I took this opportunity of visiting my friend doctor Wells
at his plantations near the city. And now being again new clothed
and furnished with a tolerable Indian poney, I took leave of my host
and prepared to depart for Savanna.

Soon after I left Augusta, proceeding for Savanna, the capital, a
gentleman overtook me on the road, who was a native of Ireland, and
had lately arrived in this part of America with a view of settling a
plantation in Georgia, particularly for the culture of those very useful
fruits and vegetables that are cultivated up the Mediterranean, and
which so largely contribute towards supporting that lucrative branch
of commerce, i. e. the Levant trade, viz. Vitis vinifera, for wine, Vitis
Corinthiaca, for Currants, Vitis Allobrogica, for Raisins, Olives, Figs,
Morus, for feeding silk-worms, Amygdalus communis, Pistachia, Capparis, Citrus aurantium, Ci-[461]trus limon, Citrus verrucosa, the great
sweet scented Citron, &c. He was very ingenious, desirous of information and as liberal and free of communicating his own acquisitions and
discoveries in useful science, and consequently a very agreeable companion. On our journey down we stopped awhile to rest and refresh
ourselves at the Great Springs, near the road, on our left hand, about
midway between Augusta and Savanna. This amazing fountain of
transparent, cool water, breaks suddenly out of the earth, at the
basis of a moderately elevated hill or bank, forming at once a bason
near twenty yards over, ascending through a horizontal bed of soft
rocks, of a heterogeneous composition, chiefly a testaceous concretion
of broken, entire and pulverised sea shells, sand, &c. constituting a
coarse kind of lime-stone. The ebullition is copious, active and continual, over the ragged apertures in the rocks, which lie seven or eight
feet below, swelling the surface considerably immediately above it;
the waters descend swiftly from the fountain, forming at once a large
brook, six or eight yards over, and five or six feet deep. There are
multitudes of fish in the fountain of various tribes, chiefly the several
species of bream, trout, cat-fish and garr: it was amusing to behold
the fish continually ascending and descending through the rocky
apertures. Observed that we crossed no stream or brook of water
within twelve or fifteen miles of this fountain, but had in view vast
savannas, swamps and Cane meadows, at no great distance from our
road, on our right hand, which we may presume were the resources
or reservoirs which contributed to the supplies of this delightful

grotto. Here were growing on the ascents from the fountain, Magnolia grandiflora, Laurus Borbonia, Quercus sempervirens, Cal-[462]licarpa; at a little distance a grove of the Cassine, and in an old field, just by, are to be seen some small Indian mounts. We travelled several miles over ridges of low swelling hills, whose surfaces were covered with particoloured pebbles, streaked and clouded with red, white, brown and yellow: they were mostly broken or shivered to pieces, I believe by the ancients in forming arrow-heads, darts, knives &c. for I observed frequently some of these misshapen implements amongst them, some broken and others spoiled in the making. These stones seemed to be a species of jasper or agate.

On my way down I also called at Silver Bluff, and waited on the honourable G. Golphin, Esq. to acknowledge my obligations to him, and likewise to fulfil my engagements on the part of Mr. T----y, trader of Mucclasse. Mr. Golphin assured me that he was in a disagreeable predicament, and that he feared the worst, but said he would do all in his power to save him.

After five days pleasant travelling we arrived at Savanna in good health.

List of the towns and tribes in league, and which constitute the powerful confederacy or empire of the Creeks or Muscogulges, viz.

Towns on the Tallapoose or Oakfuske river, viz.

Oakfuske, upper.	
Oakfuske, lower.	
Ufale, upper.	These speak the Muscogulge
Ufale, lower.	or Creek tongue, called the
Sokaspoge.	Mother tongue.
Tallase, great.	
Coolome.	

[463]   Towns on the Tallapoose or Oakfuske river, viz.

Chuaclahatche.	
Otasse.	
Cluale.	These speak the Muscogulge
Fusahatche.	or Creek tongue, called the
Tuccabatche.	Mother tongue.
Cunhutke.	
Mucclasse.	Speak the Stincard tongue.
Alabama.	
Savannuca.	Speak the Uche tongue.
Whittumke.	Speak the Stincard tongue.
Coosauda.	

Towns on the Coosau river, viz.

Abacooche.	Speak a dialect of Chicasaw.
Pocontallahasse.	
Hickory ground, traders name.	Speak the Muscogulge tongue
Natche.	Speak Muscog. and Chicasaw.

Towns on the branches of the Coosau river, viz.

Wiccakaw.	
Fish pond, traders name.	
Hillaba.	Speak the Muscogulge
Kiolege	tongue.

Towns on the Apalachucla or Chata Uche river, viz.

Apalachucla.	
Tucpauska.	
Chockeclucca.	
Chata Uche.	Speak the Muscogulge
Checlucca-ninne.	tongue
Hothletega.	
Coweta.	
Usseta.	

[464] Towns on the Apalachucla or Chata Uche river, continued, viz.

Uche.	Speak the Savannuca tongue.
Hooseche.	Speak the Muscog. tongue.
Chehaw.	
Echeta.	
Occone.	Speak the Stincard.
Swaglaw, great.	
Swaglaw, little.	

Towns on Flint river, comprehending the Siminoles or Lower Creeks.

Suola-nocha.	
Cuscowilla or Allachua.	
Talahasochte.	
Caloosahatche.	
——Great island.	Traders name.
——Great hammock.	Traders name.
——Capon.	Traders name.
——St. Mark's.	Traders name.
——Forks.	Traders name.

With many others of less note.

The Siminoles speak both the Muscogulge and Stincard tongue.

In all fifty-five towns, besides many villages not enumerated, and reckoning two hundred inhabitants to each town on an average, which is a moderate computation, would give eleven thousand inhabitants.

It appears to me pretty clearly, from divers circumstances, that this powerful empire or confederacy of the Creeks or Muscogulges, arose from, and established itself upon the ruins of that of the Natch-[465]es, agreeably to Monsieur Duprat. According to the Muscogulges account of themselves, they arrived from the South-West, beyond the Mississipi, some time before the English settled the colony of Carolina and built Charleston; and their story concerning their country and people, from whence they sprang, the cause of leaving their native land, the progress of their migration, &c. is very similar to that celebrated historian's account of the Natches, they might have been included as allies and confederates in that vast and powerful empire of red men. The Muscogulges gradually pushing and extending their settlements on their North-East border, until the dissolution of the Natches empire; being then the most numerous, warlike and powerful tribe, they began to subjugate the various tribes or bands (which formerly constituted the Natches) and uniting them with themselves, formed a new confederacy under the name of the Muscogulges.

The Muscogulge tongue being now the national or sovereign language, the Chicasaws, Chactaws, and even the remains of the Natches, if we are to credit the Creeks and traders, being dialects of the Muscogulge; and probably, when the Natches were sovereigns, they called their own the national tongue, and the Creeks, Chicasaws, &c. only dialects of theirs. It is uncertain which is really the mother tongue.

As for those numerous remnant bands or tribes, included at this day within the Muscogulge confederacy, who generally speak the Stincard language, (which is radically different from the Muscogulge) they are, beyond a doubt, the shattered remains of the various nations who inhabited the lower or maritime parts of Carolina and Florida, from Cape [466] Fear, West to the Mississipi. The Uches and Savannucas is a third language, radically different from the Muscogulge and Lingo, and seems to be a more Northern tongue; I suppose a language that prevailed amongst the numerous tribes who formerly possessed and inhabited the maritime parts of Maryland and Virginia. I was told by an old trader that the Savannuca and Shawanese speak the same language, or very near alike.

CHAP. IX.

AFTER my return from the Creek nation, I employed myself during the spring and fore part of summer, in revisiting the several districts in Georgia and the East borders of Florida, where I had noted the most curious subjects; collecting them together, and shipping them off to England. In the course of these excursions and researches, I had the opportunity of observing the new flowering shrub, resembling the Gordonia *, in perfect bloom, as well as bearing ripe fruit. It is a flowering tree, of the first order for beauty and fragrance of blossoms: the tree grows fifteen or twenty feet high, branching alternately; the leaves are oblong, broadest towards their extremities, and terminate with an acute point, which is generally a little reflexed; they are lightly serrated, attenuate downwards and sessile, or have very short petioles; they are placed in alternate order, and towards the extremities of the twigs are crouded together, but stand more sparsedly below; the flowers are very large, expand themselves perfectly, are of a snow-white colour, and ornamented with a crown or tassel of gold coloured refulgent stamina in their centre; the inferior petal or segment of the corolla is hollow, formed like a cap or helmet, and entirely includes [468] the other four, until the moment of expansion; its exterior surface is covered with a short silky hair; the borders of the petals are crisped or plicated: these large, white flowers stand single and sessile in the bosom of the leaves, which being near together towards the extremities of the twigs, and usually many expanded at the same time, make a gay appearance; the fruit is a large, round, dry, woody apple or pericarp, opening at each end oppositely by five alternate fissures, containing ten cells, each replete with dry woody cuniform seed. This very curious tree was first taken notice of, about ten or twelve years ago, at this place, when I attended my father (John Bartram) on a botanical excursion; but, it being then

* On first observing the fructification and habit of this tree, I was inclined to believe it a species of Gordonia, but afterwards, upon stricter examination, and comparing its flowers and fruit with those of the Gordonia lasianthus, I presently found striking characteristics abundantly sufficient to separate it from that genus, and to establish it the head of a new tribe, which we have honoured with the name of the illustrious Dr. Benjamin Franklin. Franklinia Alatamaha.

late in the autumn, we could form no opinion to what class or tribe it belonged.

We never saw it grow in any other place, nor have I ever since seen it growing wild, in all my travels, from Pennsylvania to Point Coupe, on the banks of the Mississipi, which must be allowed a very singular and unaccountable circumstance; at this place there are two or three acres of ground where it grows plentifully.

The other new, singular and beautiful shrub *, now here in full bloom, I never saw grow but at two other places in all my travels, and there very sparingly, except in East Florida, in the neighbourhood of the sea-coast.

* I gave it the name of Bignonia bracteata extempore.

H AVING now completed my collections in Georgia, I took leave of these Southern regions, proceeding on my return to Charleston. Left Savanna in the evening, in consequence of a pressing invitation from the honourable Jonathan Bryan, Esq. who was returning from the capital, to his villa, about eight miles up Savanna river; a very delightful situation, where are spacious gardens, furnished with variety of fruit trees and flowering shrubs; observed in a low wet place at the corner of the garden, the Ado (Arum esculentum) this plant is much cultivated in the maritime parts of Georgia, and Florida, for the sake of its large Turnip-like root, which when boiled or roasted, is excellent food, and tastes like the Yam; the leaves of this magnificent plant are very large, and of a beautiful green colour, the spatha large and circulated, the spadix terminates with a very long subulated tongue, naked and perfectly white: perhaps this may be the Arum Colocasia. They have likewise, another species of the esculent Arum, called Tannier, which is a large and beautiful plant, and much cultivated and esteemed for food, particularly by the Negroes.

At night, soon after our arrival, several of his servants came home with horse loads of wild pigeons (Columba migratoria) which it seems they had collected in a short space of time at a neighbouring Bay swamp: they take them by torch light; they have particular roosting places, where they associate in incredible multitudes at evening, on low trees [470] and bushes, in hommocks or higher knolls in the interior parts of vast swamps. Many people go out together on this kind of sport, when dark; some take with them little fascines of fat Pine splinters for torches; others sacks or bags; and others furnish themselves with poles or staves; thus accoutered and prepared, they approach their roosts, the sudden blaze of light confounds, blinds and affrights the birds, whereby multitudes drop off the limbs to the ground, and others are beaten off with their staves, which by the sudden consternation, are entirely helpless, and easily taken and put into the sacks. It is chiefly the sweet small acorns of the Quercus phillos, Quercus aquatica, Quercus sempervirens, Quercus flammula, and others, which induce these birds to migrate in the autumn to those Southern regions; where they spend their days agreeably, and feast luxuriously, during the rigour of the colds in the North, whither they return at the approach of summer to breed.

Set off next day, and crossed the river at Zubley's ferry, about fifty miles above Savanna, and in three days after arrived at Charleston.

Observed, by the way near Jacksonsburg Ponpon, growing plentifully in good moist ground, usually by the banks of canals, Aster fructicosus. It is a most charming autumnal flowering shrub, it will rise to the height of eight or ten feet, when supported by neighbouring trees.

After a few days residence in Charleston, I set off on my return to my native land, crossed Cowper river, about nine miles above the city, where the water was a mile wide, and the ferry-house being on the opposite shore, I hoisted my travelling blanket on a pole for a signal, which being white, [471] the people soon came to me and carried me safe over. In three days more easy travelling, I crossed Winyaw bay, just below Georgetown, and in two days more, got to the West end of Long bay, where I lodged at a large Indigo plantation. Set off early next morning, and after crossing over the sand ridges, which afford little else but Quercus pumila, Myrica cerifera, Cassine, Sideroxilon and Andromeda entangled with various species of Smilax, got on the bay, which is a hard sand beach, exposed for the distance of fifteen miles to the continual lash of the Atlantic ocean; at about low water mark, are cliffs of rocks of the helmintholithus, being a very firm concrete or petrifaction, consisting of various kinds of seashells, fine sand and pulverized shells; there is a reef of these rocks, thirty or forty yards farther out than low water mark, which lift their rugged backs above water, and brave the continual strokes of the waves, which, however, assisted by the constant friction of the sands, make continual inroads upon them, bore them into holes and cavities, when tempestuous seas rend them to pieces, scattering the fragments over the sandy shore. It is pleasant riding on this clean hard sand, paved with shells of various colours.

Observed a number of persons coming up a head which I soon perceived to be a party of Negroes: I had every reason to dread the consequence; for this being a desolate place, and I was by this time several miles from any house or plantation, and had reason to apprehend this to be a predatory band of Negroes: people being frequently attacked, robbed, and sometimes murdered by them at this place; I was unarmed, alone, and my horse tired; thus [472] situated every way in their power, I had no alternative but to be resigned and prepare to meet them, as soon as I saw them distinctly a mile or two off, I immediately alighted to rest, and give breath to my horse, intending to attempt my safety by flight, if upon near approach they should betray hostile designs, thus prepared, when we drew near to each other, I mounted and rode briskly up, and though armed with clubs, axes and hoes, they opened to right and left, and let me pass peaceably, their chief informed me whom they belonged to, and said they were going to man a new quarter at the West end of the bay, I however kept a sharp eye about me, apprehending that this might possibly have been an advanced division, and their intentions were to ambuscade and surround me, but they kept on quietly and I was no more alarmed by them. After noon, I crossed the swash at the east end of the bay, and in the evening got to good quarters. Next morning early I set off again, and soon crossed Little River at the boundary; which is on the line that separates North and South Carolina; in an old field, on the banks of this river, a little distance from the public house, stands a single tree of the Magnolia grandiflora, which is said to be the most northern settlement of that tree. Passed this day over expansive savannas, charmingly decorated with late autumnal flowers, as Helianthus, Rudbeckia, Silphium, Solidago, Helenium, Serratula, Cacalia, Aster, Lillium Martagon, Gentiana caerulia, Chironia, Gentiana saponaria, Asclepias coccinea, Hypericum, Rhexea pulcherima, &c. &c.

Observed likewise in these Savannas abundance of the ludicrous Dionea muscipula (Dioneae, Ellis [473] epis. ad Linnaeum, miraculum naturae, folia biloba, radicalia, ciliata, conduplicanda, sensibilia, insecta incarcerantia. Syst. vegetab. p. 335.

This wonderful plant seems to be distinguished in the creation, by the Author of nature, with faculties eminently superior to every other vegetable production *; specimens of it were first communicated to the curious of the old world by John Bartram, the American botanist and traveller, who contributed as much if not more than any other man towards enriching the North American botanical nomenclature, as well as its natural history.

After traversing these ample savannas I gradually ascended sand hills to open Pine forests; at evening got to Old town near Brunswick, where I lodged. Brunswick is a sea-port town on the Clarendon, or Cape Fear river, about thirty miles above the capes; it is about thirty years since this was the seat of government, when Arthur Dobbs, Esq. was governor and commander in chief of the province of North Carolina. Continued up the West side of North West of Cape Fear river, and rested two or three days at the seat of F. Lucas, Esq. a few miles

* See some account of it in the introduction.

above Livingston's creek, a considerable branch of the North West. This creek heads in vast swamps, in the vicinity of the beautiful lake Wakamaw, which is the source of a fine river of that name, and runs a South course seventy or eighty miles, delivering its waters into Winyaw bay at George-town. The Wakamaw lake is twenty six miles in circuit, the lands on its Eastern shores are fertile and the situation delightful, gradually ascending from pleasing eminences; bounded on the North-West coast by vast rich swamps, fit for the production of Rice: [474] the lake is twelve miles West from Esq. Moores, whose villa is on the banks of the North West.

Proceeding again up the North West, crossed Carver's creek, and stopped at Ashwood, the ancient seat of Colonel William Bartram; the house stands on the high banks of the river, near seventy feet in height, above the surface of the water; this high bluff continues two or three miles on the river, and commands a magnificent prospect of the low lands opposite, when in their native state, presenting to the view grand forests and expansive Cane meadows; the trees which compose these forests are generally of the following tribes, Quercus tinctoria, Querc. alba, Querc. phillos, Querc. aquatica, Querc. hemispherica, Fraxinus excelsior, Platanus occidentalis, Liriodendron tulipifera, Liquid-amber styraciflua, Ulmus, Telea, Juglans hickory, Juglans cinerea, Juglans nigra, Morus rubra, Gleditsia triacanthus, Hopea tinctoria, Nyssa aquatica, Nyssa sylvatica, Carpinus and many more; the Cupressus disticha as stately and beautiful as I have seen any where. When these lands are cleared of their timber and cultivated, they produce abundantly, particularly, Wheat, Zea, Cotton, Hemp, Flax, with variety of excellent vegetables. This perpendicular bank of the river, by which the waters swiftly glide along, discovers at once the various strata of the earth of this low maritime country. For the most part the upper stratum consists of a light, sandy, pale, yellowish mold or loam, for ten or twelve feet in depth (except the flat level land back from the rivers, where the clays or marle approach very near the surface, and the ridges of sand hills, where the clays lie much deeper) this sandy mold or loam lays upon a deep bed of black, or dark slate coloured saline and sulphureous earth, [475] which is composed of horizontal thin flakes or laminae, separable by means of very thin, almost imperceptible veins or strata of fine micaceous particles, which drain or percolate a clear water, continually exuding, or trickling down, and forming little rills and diminutive cataracts, being conducted by perpendicular chinks or fissures; in some places, a portion of this clear water or transparent vapour, seems to coagulate on the edges of the veins and fissures, leaving a reddish curd or jelly-like substance sticking to them, which I should suppose indicates it to spring from a ferruginous source, especially since it discovers a chalybeate scent and taste: in other places these fissures shew evidently a crystallization of exceeding fine white salts, which have an aluminous or vitriolic scent: there are pyrites, marcasites, or sulphureous nodules, shining like brass, of various sizes and forms, some single and others conglomerated: other places present to view, strata of heterogenous matter, lying between the upper loamy stratum and the bed of black saline earth, consisting of various kinds of sea shells, some whole, others broken to pieces, and even pulverized, which fill up the cavities of the entire shells, and the interstices betwixt them: at other places we observe, two or three feet below the surface or virgin mold, a stratum of four, five or six feet in depth, of brownish marle, on a bed of testaceous rocks; a petrifaction composed apparently of various kinds of sea shells, belemnites, sand, &c. combined or united with a calcareous cement: these masses of rocks are in some places detached by veins and strata of a heterogenous earth, consisting of sea shells and other marine productions, as well as terrestrial, which seem to be fossil or in some degree of petrifaction, or otherwise [476] transmuted, particularly those curious productions called birds bills or sharks teeth (dentes carchariae) belemnites, &c. loosely mixed with a desiccated earth composed of sand, clay, particles of marle, vegetable rubbish, &c. And again we observe shells, marcasites, belemnites, dentes carchariae, with pieces of wood transmuted, black and hard as sea coal, singly interspersed in the black vitriolic strata of earth; when this black earth is exposed to the sun and dry air, the little thin laminae separate, and soon discover a fine, white crystallization, or aluminous powder, but this very soon disappears, being again incorporated with the general mass, which gradually dissolves or falls like quick-lime, and appears then a greyish, extremely fine, dry micaceous powder, which smells like gun-powder.

The North West of Cape Fear, here at Ashwood, is near three hundred yards over (when the stream is low and within its banks) and is eighty or ninety miles above the capes. Observed growing hereabouts a great variety of very curious and beautiful flowering and sweet scented shrubs, particularly Callicarpa, Æsculus pavia, floribus coccineis, caule suffructicoso, Æsculus sylvatica, floribus ex albo et carneo eleganter variegatis, caule arboreo, Ptelea trifoliata, Styrax, Stewartia, Fothergilla, Amorpha, Myrica, Stillingia fructicosa, foliis lanceolatis, utrinque glabris, fructu tricocco. Olea Americana, foliis lanceolato-ellipticis, baccis atro-purpureis (Purple berried bay.) Catesby. Ilex dahoon, Cassine Yapon, Azalea, varieties, Kalmea,

Cyrilla, Liquid amber peregrinum, Sideroxilon, Andromeda lucida, &c.

Leaving Ashwood, and continuing up the West side of the river, about forty miles, in the banks [477] of a creek, five or six feet below the sandy surface, are to be seen projecting out many feet in length, trunks of trees petrified to very hard stone; they lie between the upper sandy stratum and the common bed of blackish vitriolic earth; and these stone trees are to be seen in the same situation, sticking out of the perpendicular banks or bluffs of the river in this region: there are several trunks of large trees with their bark, stumps of their limbs and roots, lying petrified on the sand hills and Pine forests, near the road about this creek, not far from the saw-mills.

Crossed Rock-fish, a large branch of the North West, near its mouth or confluence, and at evening arrived at Cross-Creeks, another very considerable branch of the river, flowing in through its West banks: this creek gave name to a fine inland trading town, on some heights or swelling hills, from whence the creek descends precipitately, then gently meanders near a mile, through lower level lands, to its confluence with the river, affording most convenient mill-seats; these prospects induced active, enterprising men to avail themselves of such advantages pointed out to them by nature, they built mills, which drew people to the place, and these observing elegible situations for other profitable improvements, bought lots and erected tenements, where they exercised mechanic arts, as smiths, wheelwrights, carpenters, coopers, tanners, &c. And at length merchants were encouraged to adventure and settle; in short, within eight or ten years from a grist-mill, saw-mill, smith-shop and a tavern, arose a flourishing commercial town, the seat of government of the county of Cumberland: the leading men of the county, seeing plainly the superior advantages of this situation, on the banks [478] of a famous navigable river, petitioned the Assembly for a charter to empower them to purchase a district, sufficient for founding a large town, which being granted, they immediately proceeded to mark out its precincts, and named the new city Cambelton, a compliment to - - - - - - - - Cambel, Esq. a gentleman of merit, and a citizen of the county. When I was here about twenty years ago, this town was marking out its bounds, and there were then about twenty habitations, and now there are above a thousand houses, many wealthy merchants, and respectable public buildings, a vast resort of inhabitants and travellers, and continual brisk commerce by waggons, from the back settlements, with large trading boats, to and from Wilmington, the seaport and flourishing trading town on the Clarendon, about forty miles above the

[XII.] *Andromeda pulverulenta*

capes, which is about one hundred miles below this town. The Clarendon or Cape Fear river has its source in the Cherokee mountains, where its numerous confederate streams unite, after leaving the first ridges of the mountains, it assumes the name of Haw river, and coursing the hilly fertile country, above one hundred and fifty miles, receives through its West banks the West branch, called Deep river, and after this union, takes the name of the North-West of Cape Fear, from whence down to Cambelton, about eighty miles, it is navigable for perriauguas of considerable burthen.

Observed near Cambelton a very curious scandent Fern (Pteris scandens) rambling over low bushes, in humid situations, the lower larger fronds were digitated, or rather radiated, but towards the tops or extremities of the branches they became trifid, hastated, and lastly lanceolate; it is a delicate plant, of a yellowish lively green, and would be an ornament in a garden.

[479] Set off again from Cambelton, continuing yet up the North West about sixty miles, crossed over this branch, and soon after crossed the Roanoke, and then rested a few days at Mr. Lucas', a worthy old gentleman, a planter on Meherren river. Observed strolling over his fences and stables, a very singular and useful species of the Gourd (Cucurbita laginaria) their necks or handles are above two feet in length, and not above an inch in diameter; their bellies round, which would contain about a pint; they make excellent ladles, funnels, &c. At a little distance from Mr. Lucas', at the head of a swamp near the high road, I observed a very curious species of Prinos, which grows seven or eight feet high, the leaves broad, lanceolate, sharply serrated, nervous, and of a deep green colour; but its striking beauty consists in profuse clusters of fruit, collected about the cases or origin of the last spring's shoots; these berries are nearly round, about the size of middling grapes, of a fine clear scarlet colour, covered or invested with an incarnate mist or nebulae.

Being now arrived on the South border of Virginia, and the hoary frigid season far advanced, I shall pass as speedily as possible from hence to Pennsylvania, my native country; since those cultivated regions of Virginia and Maryland, through which I design to travel, have been over and over explored, and described by very able men in every branch of natural history.

After leaving Meherren, I soon arrived at Alexandria in Virginia, a fine city on the West banks of the Patowmac, about the 26th of December, having had excellent roads, and pleasant, moderate weather, neither snow nor ice to be seen, ex-[480]cept a slight fall of snow from a flying cloud, the day before I reached this place, but this evening

it clouding up from the West, the wind North-East and cold. Next
morning the snow was eight or ten inches deep on the ground, and
the wind shifting to North West, cleared up intensely cold; I however
set off and crossed the river just below the falls, and landed at
George-town in Maryland. The snow is now deep every where around,
the air cold to an extreme, and the roads deep under snow or slippery
with ice; rendered the travelling uncomfortable.

Being now arrived at Wright's ferry on the Susquehanna, I began
anxiously to look towards home, but here I found almost insuperable
embarrassments; the river being but half frozen over, there was no
possibility of crossing here, but hearing that people crossed at Anderson's, about five miles above, early next morning I set off again up the
river, in company with several travellers, some for Philadelphia; arriving at the ferry, we were joined by a number of traders, with their
pack-horses loaded with leather and furs, where we all agreed to
venture over together, and keeping at a moderate distance from each
other, examining well our icy bridge, and being careful of our steps,
we landed safe on the opposite shore, got to Lancaster in the evening, and next morning set forward again towards Philadelphia, and
in two days more arrived at my father's house on the banks of the
river Schuylkill, within four miles of the city, January 1778.
[481]

AN
ACCOUNT

OF THE
PERSONS, MANNERS, CUSTOMS

AND

GOVERNMENT

OF THE

MUSCOGULGES OR CREEKS,

CHEROKEES, CHACTAWS, &c.

ABORIGINES OF THE CONTINENT OF

NORTH AMERICA.

———————

BY WILLIAM BARTRAM.

———————

PHILADELPHIA:
PRINTED BY *JAMES & JOHNSON.*
M,DCC,XCI.

PART IV.

CHAP. I.

DESCRIPTION OF THE CHARACTER, CUSTOMS AND PER-
SONS OF THE AMERICAN ABORIGINES, FROM MY OWN
OBSERVATIONS, AS WELL AS FROM THE GENERAL
AND IMPARTIAL REPORT OF ANCIENT, RESPECTABLE
MEN, EITHER OF THEIR OWN PEOPLE, OR WHITE
TRADERS, WHO HAVE SPENT MANY DAYS OF THEIR
LIVES AMONGST THEM.

PERSONS AND QUALIFICATIONS.

THE males of the Cherokees, Muscogulges, Siminoles, Chicasaws, Chactaws and confederate tribes of the Creeks, are tall, erect,
and moderately robust, their limbs well shaped, so as generally to
form a perfect human figure; their features regular, and countenance
open, dignified and placid; yet the forehead and brow so formed, as to
strike you instantly with heroism and bravery; the eye though rather
small, yet active and full of fire; the pupil always black, and the nose
commonly inclining to the aquiline.

Their countenance and actions exhibit an air of magnanimity, superiority and independence.

Their complexion of a reddish brown or copper colour; their hair
long, lank, coarse and black as a raven, and reflecting the like lustre
at different exposures to the light.

[484] The women of the Cherokees are tall, slender, erect and of
a delicate frame, their features formed with perfect symmetry, their
countenance cheerful and friendly, and they move with a becoming
grace and dignity.

The Muscogulge women, though remarkably short of stature, are
well formed; their visage round, features regular and beautiful; the
brow high and arched; the eye large, black and languishing, expres-

306

sive of modesty, diffidence, and bashfulness; these charms are their defensive and offensive weapons, and they know very well how to play them off. And under cover of these alluring graces, are concealed the most subtile artifice; they are however loving and affectionate: they are I believe the smallest race of women yet known, seldom above five feet high, and I believe the greater number never arrive to that stature: their hands and feet not larger than those of Europeans of nine or ten years of age; yet the men are of gigantic stature, a full size larger than Europeans; many of them above six feet, and few under that, or five feet eight or ten inches. Their complexion much darker than any of the tribes to the North of them, that I have seen. This description will I believe comprehend the Muscogulges, their confederates, the Chactaws, and I believe the Chicasaws (though I have never seen their women) excepting however some bands of the Siminoles, Uches and Savannucas, who are rather taller and slenderer, and their complexion brighter.

The Cherokees are yet taller and more robust than the Muscogulges, and by far the largest race [485] of men I have seen * their complexions brighter and somewhat of the olive cast, especially the adults; and some of their young women are nearly as fair and blooming as European women.

The Cherokees in their dispositions and manners are grave and steady; dignified and circumspect in their deportment; rather slow and reserved in conversation; yet frank, cheerful and humane; tenacious of the liberties and natural rights of men; secret, deliberate and determined in their councils; honest, just and liberal, and are ready always to sacrifice every pleasure and gratification, even their blood, and life itself, to defend their territory and maintain their rights. They do homage to the Muscogulges with reluctance, and are impatient under that galling yoke. I was witness to a most humiliating lash, which they passively received from their red masters, at the great congress and treaty of Augusta, when these people acceded with the Creeks, to the cession of the New Purchase; where were about three hundred of the Creeks, a great part of whom were warriors, and about one hundred Cherokees.

The first day of convention opened with settling the preliminaries, one article of which was a demand on the part of the Georgians, to a territory lying on the Tugilo, and claimed by them both, which it

* There are however, some exceptions to this general observation, as I have myself witnessed. Their present grand chief or emperor (the Little Carpenter, Atta-kul-kulla) is a man of remarkable small stature, slender, and delicate frame, the only instance I saw in the nation; but he is a man of superior abilities.

seems the Cherokees had, previous to the opening of congress, privately conveyed to the Georgians, unknown to the Creeks, which the Georgians mentioning as a matter settled, the Creeks [486] demanded in council, on what foundation they built that claim, saying they had never ceded these lands. The Georgians answered, that they bought them of their friends and brothers the Cherokees. The Creeks nettled and incensed at this, a chief and warrior started up, and with an agitated and terrific countenance, frowning menaces and disdain, fixed his eyes on the Cherokee chiefs, asked them what right they had to give away their lands, calling them old women, and saying that they had long ago obliged them to wear the petticoat; a most humiliating and degrading stroke, in the presence of the chiefs of the whole Muscogulge confederacy, of the Chicasaws, principal men and citizens of Georgia, Carolina, Virginia, Maryland and Pennsylvania, in the face of their own chiefs and citizens, and amidst the laugh and jeers of the assembly, especially the young men of Virginia, their old enemy and dreaded neighbour: but humiliating as it really was, they were obliged to bear the stigma passively, and even without a reply.

And moreover, these arrogant bravos and usurpers, carried their pride and importance to such lengths, as even to threaten to dissolve the congress and return home, unless the Georgians consented to annul the secret treaty with the Cherokees, and receive that territory immediately from them; as acknowledging their exclusive right of alienation, which was complied with, though violently extorted from the Cherokees, contrary to right and sanction of treaties; since the Savanna river and its waters were acknowledged to be the natural and just bounds of territory betwixt the Cherokees and Muscogulges.

The national character of the Muscogulges, when ["478" = 487] considered in a political view, exhibits a portraiture of a great or illustrious heroe. A proud, haughty and arrogant race of men; they are however, brave and valiant in war, ambitious of conquest, restless and perpetually exercising their arms, yet magnanimous and merciful to a vanquished enemy, when he submits and seeks their friendship and protection: always uniting the vanquished tribes in confederacy with them; when they immediately enjoy, unexceptionably, every right of free citizens, and are from that moment united in one common band of brotherhood: they were never known to exterminate a tribe, except the Yamasees, who would never submit on any terms, but fought it out to the last, only about forty or fifty of them escaping at the last decisive battle, who threw themselves under the protection of the Spaniards at St. Augustine.

According to their own account, which I believe to be true, after their arrival in this country, they joined in alliance and perpetual amity, with the British colonists of South Carolina and Georgia, which they never openly violated; but on the contrary, pursued every step to strengthen the alliance; and their aged chiefs to this day, speak of it with tears of joy, and exult in that memorable transaction, as one of the most glorious events in the annals of their nation.

As an instance of their ideas of political impartial justice, and homage to the Supreme Being, as the high arbiter of human transactions, who alone claims the right of taking away the life of man: I beg leave to offer to the reader's consideration, the following event, as I had it from the mouth of a Spaniard, a respectable inhabitant of East Florida.

[488] The son of the Spanish governor of St. Augustine, together with two young gentlemen, his friends and associates, conceived a design of amusing themselves in a party of sport, at hunting and fishing. Having provided themselves with a convenient bark, ammunition, fishing tackle, &c. they set sail, directing their course South, along the coast towards the point of Florida, putting into bays and rivers, as conveniency and the prospect of game invited them; the pleasing rural, and diversified scenes of the Florida coast, imperceptibly allured them far to the south, beyond the Spanish fortified post. Unfortunate youth! regardless of the advice and injunctions of their parents and friends, still pursuing the delusive objects, they enter a harbour at evening, with a view of chasing the roe-buck, and hunting up the sturdy bear, solacing themselves with delicious fruits, and reposing under aromatic shades, when alas! cruel unexpected event, in the beatific moments of their slumbers, they are surrounded, arrested and carried off by a predatory band of Creek Indians, proud of the capture, so rich a prize; they hurry away into cruel bondage the hapless youth, conducting them, by devious paths through dreary swamps and boundless savannas, to the Nation.

At that time the Indians were at furious war with the Spaniards, scarcely any bounds set to their cruelties on either side: in short, the miserable youth were condemned to be burnt.

But, there being English traders in these towns, who learning the character of the captives, and expecting great rewards from the Spanish governor, if they could deliver them; they petitioned the Indians on their behalf, expressing their wishes to obtain [489] their rescue, offering a great ransom, acquainting them at the same time, that they were young men of high rank, and one of them the governor's son.

Upon this, the head men, or chiefs of the whole nation, were con-

vened, and after solemn and mature deliberation, they returned the
traders their final answer and determination, which was as follows.

"Brothers and friends. We have been considering upon this business concerning the captives.—And that, under the eye and fear of
the Great Spirit. You know that these people are our cruel enemies,
they save no lives of us red men, who fall in their power. You say that
the youth is the son of the Spanish governor, we believe it, we are sorry
he has fallen into our hands, but he is our enemy; the two young
men (his friends) are equally our enemies, we are sorry to see them
here: but we know no difference in their flesh and blood; they are
equally our enemies, if we save one we must save all three; but we
cannot do it, the red men require their blood to appease the spirits
of their slain relatives; they have entrusted us with the guardianship
of our laws and rights, we cannot betray them.

However we have a sacred prescription relative to this affair; which
allows us to extend mercy to a certain degree: a third is saved by lot;
the Great Spirit allows us to put it to that decision; he is no respecter
of persons." The lots are cast. The governor's son was taken and burnt.

If we consider them with respect to their private [490] character or
in a moral view, they must, I think, claim our approbation, if we divest
ourselves of prejudice and think freely. As moral men they certainly
stand in no need of European civilization.

They are just, honest, liberal and hospitable to strangers; consid-
erate, loving and affectionate to their wives and relations; fond of
their children; industrious, frugal, temperate and persevering; charita-
ble and forbearing. I have been weeks and months amongst them and
in their towns, and never observed the least sign of contention or
wrangling: never saw an instance of an Indian beating his wife, or
even reproving her in anger. In this case they stand as examples of
reproof to the most civilized nations, as not being defective in justice,
gratitude and a good understanding; for indeed their wives merit their
esteem and the most gentle treatment, they being industrious, frugal,
careful, loving and affectionate.

The Muscogulges are more volatile, sprightly and talkative than
their Northern neighbours, the Cherokees; and, though far more distant from the white settlements than any nation East of the Mississipi
or Ohio, appear evidently to have made greater advances towards the
refinements of true civilization, which cannot, in the least degree, be
attributed to the good examples of the white people.

Their internal police and family economy is what at once engages
the notice of European travellers, and incontrovertibly places these
people in an illustrious point of view; their liberality, intimacy and

friendly intercourse one with another, without any restraint of cere-
monious formality, as if they were even insensible of the use or
necessity of associating [491] the passions or affections of avarice,
ambition or covetousness.

A man goes forth on his business or avocations, he calls in at another
town, if he wants victuals, rest or social conversation, he confidently
approaches the door of the first house he chooses, saying "I am
come;" the good man or woman replies, "You are; its well." Immediately victuals and drink are ready; he eats and drinks a little, then
smokes Tobacco, and converses either of private matters, public talks
or the news of the town. He rises and says, "I go;" the other answers,
"You do!" He then proceeds again, and steps in at the next habitation
he likes, or repairs to the public square, where are people always conversing by day, or dancing all night, or to some more private assembly,
as he likes; he needs no one to introduce him, any more than the blackbird or thrush, when he repairs to the fruitful groves, to regale on
their luxuries, and entertain the fond female with evening songs.

It is astonishing, though a fact, as well as a sharp reproof to the
white people, if they will allow themselves liberty to reflect and form
a just estimate, and I must own elevates these people to the first rank
amongst mankind, that they have been able to resist the continual
efforts of the complicated host of vices, that have for ages overrun
the nations of the old world, and so contaminated their morals; yet
more so, since such vast armies of these evil spirits have invaded this
continent, and closely invested them on all sides. Astonishing indeed!
when we behold the ill, immoral conduct of too many white people,
who reside amongst them: notwithstanding it seems natural, eligible
and even easy for these simple, illiterate people, to put in practice
those beautiful [492] lectures delivered to us by the ancient sages and
philosophers, and recorded for our instruction.

I saw a young Indian in the Nation, who when present, and beholding the scenes of mad intemperance and folly acted by the white men
in the town, clap his hand to his breast, and with a smile, looking
aloft as if struck with astonishment, and wrapt in love and adoration to the Deity, as who should say, O thou Great and Good Spirit,
we are indeed sensible of thy benignity and favour to us red men, in
denying us the understanding of white men. We did not know before
they came amongst us that mankind could become so base, and fall so
below the dignity of their nature. Defend us from their manners, laws
and power.

The Muscogulges, with their confederates, the Chactaws, Chicasaws,
and perhaps the Cherokees, eminently deserve the encomium of all

nations, for their wisdom and virtue in resisting and even repelling the greatest, and even the common enemy of mankind, at least of most of the European nations, I mean spirituous liquors.

The first and most cogent article in all their treaties with the white people, is, that there shall not be any kind of spirituous liquors sold or brought into their towns; and the traders are allowed but two kegs (five gallons each) which is supposed to be sufficient for a company, to serve them on the road, and if any of this remains on their approaching the towns, they must spill it on the ground or secrete it on the road, for it must not come into the town.

On my journey from Mobile to the Nation, just after we had passed the junction of the Pensacola [493] road with our path, two young traders overtook us on their way to the Nation. We enquired what news? They informed us that they were running about forty kegs of Jamaica spirits (which by dashing would have made at least eighty kegs) to the Nation; and after having left the town three or four days, they were surprised on the road in the evening, just after they had come to camp, by a party of Creeks, who discovering their species of merchandize, they forthwith struck their tomahawks into every keg, giving the liquor to the thirsty sand, not tasting a drop of it themselves, and they had enough to do to keep the tomahawks from their own skulls.

How are we to account for their excellent policy in civil government: it cannot derive its influence from coercive laws, for they have no such artificial system. Divine wisdom dictates and they obey.

We see and know full well the direful effects of this torrent of evil, which has its source in hell, and we know surely, as well as these savages, how to divert its course and suppress its inundations. Do we want wisdom and virtue? let our youth then repair to the venerable councils of the Muscogulges.

CHAP. II.

Of their government and civil society.

THE constitution or system of their police is simply natural, and as little complicated as that which is supposed to direct or rule the approved economy of the ant and the bee, and seems to be nothing more than the simple dictates of natural reason, plain to every one, yet recommended to them by their wise and virtuous elders as divine, because necessary for securing mutual happiness: equally binding and effectual, as being proposed and assented to in the general combination: every one's conscience being a sufficient conviction (the golden rule, do as you would be done by) instantly presents to view, and produces a society of peace and love, which in effect better maintains human happiness, than the most complicated system of modern politics, or sumptuary laws, enforced by coercive means: for here the people are all on an equality, as to the possession and enjoyments of the common necessaries and conveniencies of life, for luxuries and superfluities they have none.

This natural constitution is simply subordinate, and the supreme, sovereign or executive power resides in a council of elderly chiefs, warriors and others, respectable for wisdom, valour and virtue.

At the head of this venerable senate, presides their mico or king, which signifies a magistrate or chief ruler: the governors of Carolina, Georgia, &c. are called mico; and the king of England is called [495] Ant-apala-mico-clucco *, that is the great king, over or beyond the great water.

The king although he is acknowledged to be the first and greatest man in the town or tribe, and honoured with every due and rational mark of love and esteem, and when presiding in council, with a humility and homage as reverent as that paid to the most despotic monarch in Europe or the East, and when absent, his seat is not filled by any other person, yet he is not dreaded, and when out of the council, he associates with the people as a common man, converses with them, and they with him in perfect ease and familiarity.

The mico or king, though elective, yet his advancement to that

* Clucco signifies great or excellent.

supreme dignity must be understood in a very different light from the elective monarchs of the old world, where the progress to magistracy is generally affected by schism and the influence of friends gained by craft, bribery and often by more violent efforts; and after the throne is obtained, by measures little better than usurpation, he must be protected and supported there, by the same base means that carried him thither.

But here behold the majesty of the Muscogulge mico, he does not either publicly or privately beg of the people to place him in a situation to command and rule them. No, his appearance is altogether mysterious, as a beneficent deity he rises king over them, as the sun rises to bless the earth!

No one will tell you how or when he became their king; but he is universally acknowledged to be the greatest person among them, and he is lo-[496]ved, esteemed and reverenced, although he associates, eats, drinks and dances with them in common as another man, his dress is the same, and a stranger could not distinguish the king's habitation, from that of any other citizen, by any sort of splendor or magnificence: yet he perceives they act as though their mico beheld them though invisible. In a word, their mico seems to them, the representative of Providence or the Great Spirit, whom they acknowledge to preside over and influence their councils and public proceedings. He personally presides daily in their councils, either at the rotunda or public square: and even here his voice in regard to business in hand, is regarded no more, than any other chief's or senator's, any other than in his advice as being the best and wisest man of the tribe, and not by virtue of regal prerogative. But whether their ultimate decisions require unanimity, or only a majority of voices, I am uncertain, but probably where there is a majority, the minority voluntarily accede.

The most active part the mico acts, is in the civil government of the town or tribe, here he has the power and prerogative of calling a council, to deliberate on peace and war, or all public concerns, as enquiring into, and deciding upon complaints and differences, but he has not the least shadow of exclusive executive power. He is complimented with the first visits of strangers, giving audience to ambassadors, with presents, and he has also the disposal of the public granary.

The next man in order of dignity and power, is the great war chief, he represents and exercises the dignity of the mico, in his absence in council; his voice is of the greatest weight, in military affairs: his power and authority are entirely independent [497] of the mico, though when a mico goes on an expedition, he heads the army, and is there the war chief: there are many of these war chiefs in a town or tribe, who are captains or leaders of military parties; they are elderly men, who in their youthful days, have distinguished themselves in war by valour, subtilty and intrepidity; and these veteran chiefs, in a great degree, constitute their truly dignified and venerable senates.

There is in every town or tribe a high priest, usually called by the white people jugglers, or conjurers, besides several juniors or graduates. But the ancient high priest or seer, presides in spiritual affairs, and is a person of consequence; he maintains and exercises great influence in the state; particularly in military affairs, the senate never determine on an expedition against their enemy without his counsel and assistance. These people generally believe that their seer has communion with powerful invisible spirits, who they suppose have a share in the rule and government of human affairs, as well as the elements; that he can predict the result of an expedition, and his influence is so great, that they have been known frequently to stop, and turn back an army, when within a days journey of their enemy, after a march of several hundred miles, and indeed their predictions have surprized many people. They foretell rain or drougth, and pretend to bring rain at pleasure, cure diseases, and exercise witchcraft, invoke or expel evil spirits, and even assume the power of directing thunder and lightning.

These Indians are by no means idolaters, unless their puffing the Tobacco smoke towards the sun, [498] and rejoicing at the appearance of the new moon,* may be termed so, so far from idolatry are they, that they have no images amongst them, nor any religious rite or ceremony that I could perceive; but adore the Great Spirit, the giver and taker away of the breath of life, with the most profound and respectful homage. They believe in a future state, where the spirit exists, which they call the world of spirits, where they enjoy different degrees of tranquility or comforts, agreeable to their life spent here: a person who in this life has been an industrious hunter, provided well for his family, an intrepid and active warrior, just, upright, and done all the good he could, will, they say, in the world of spirits, live in a warm, pleasant country, where are expansive, green, flowery savannas and high forests, watered with rivers of pure waters, replenished with deer, and every species of game; a serene, unclouded and peaceful sky; in short, where there is fulness of pleasure, uninterrupted.

They have many accounts of trances and visions of their people, who have been supposed to be dead, but afterwards reviving have related their visions, which tend to enforce the practice of virtue and the moral duties.

Before I went amongst the Indians I had often heard it reported

* I have observed the young fellows very merry and jocose, at the appearance of the new moon, saying, how ashamed she looks under the veil, since sleeping with the sun these two or three nights, she is ashamed to shew her face, &c

that these people, when their parents, through extreme old age, become decrepit and helpless, in compassion for their miseries, send them to the other world, by a stroke of the tomahawk or bullet. Such a degree of depravity and species of impiety always appeared to me so incred-[499]ibly inhuman and horrid, it was with the utmost difficulty that I assumed resolution sufficient to enquire into it.

The traders assured me they knew no instance of such barbarism, but that there had been instances of the communities performing such a deed at the earnest request of the victim.

When I was at Mucclasse town, early one morning, at the invitation of the chief trader, we repaired to the public square, taking with us some presents for the Indian chiefs. On our arrival we took our seats in a circle of venerable men, round a fire in the centre of the area; other citizens were continually coming in, and amongst them I was struck with awe and veneration at the appearance of a very aged man; his hair, what little he had, was as white as snow; he was conducted by three young men, one having hold of each arm, and the third behind to steady him. On his approach the whole circle saluted him, "welcome," and made way for him: he looked as smiling and cheerful as youth, yet stone-blind by extreme old age; he was the most ancient chief of the town, and they all seemed to reverence him. Soon after the old man had seated himself I distributed my presents, giving him a very fine handkerchief and a twist of choice Tobacco; which passed through the hands of an elderly chief who sat next to him, telling him it was a present from one of their white brothers, lately arrived in the nation from Charleston: he received the present with a smile, and thanked me, returning the favour immediately with his own stone pipe and catskin of Tobacco, and then complimented me with a long oration, the purport of which was the value he set on the friendship of the Carolinians: he said, [500] that when he was a young man they had no iron hatchets, pots, hoes, knives, razors nor guns, but that they then made use of their own stone axes, clay pots, flint knives, bows and arrows; and that he was the first man who brought the white peoples goods into his town, which he did on his back from Charleston, five hundred miles on foot, for they had no horses then amongst them.

The trader then related to me an anecdote concerning this ancient patriarch, which occurred not long since.

One morning after his attendants had led him to the council fire, before seating himself he addressed himself to the people after this manner—

"You yet love me; what can I do now to merit your regard? nothing; I am good for nothing; I cannot see to shoot the buck or hunt up the sturdy bear; I know I am but a burthen to you; I have lived long enough; now let my spirit go; I want to see the warriors of my youth in the country of spirits; (baring his breast) here is the hatchet, take it and strike." They answered with one united voice, "We will not; we cannot; we want you here."

CHAP. III.

OF THEIR DRESS, FEASTS AND DIVERTISEMENTS.

THE youth of both sexes are fond of decorating themselves with external ornaments. The men shave their head, leaving only a narrow crest or comb, beginning at the crown of the head, where it is about two inches broad and about the same height, and stands frizzed upright; but this crest tending backwards, gradually widens, covering the hinder part of the head and back of the neck; this lank hair behind is ornamented with pendant silver quills, and then jointed or articulated silver plates, and usually the middle fascicle of hair, which being by far the longest, is wrapped in a large quill of silver, or the joint of a small reed, curiously sculptured and painted, the hair continuing through it terminates in a tail or tassel.

Their ears are lacerated, separating the border or cartilaginous limb, which at first is bound round very close and tight with leather strings or thongs, and anointed with fresh bear's oil, until healed; the weight of the lead, extends this cartilage an incredible length, which afterwards being craped, or bound round in brass or silver wire, extends it semicircularly like a bow or crescent; and it is then very elastic, even so as to spring and bound about with the least motion or flexure of the body; this is decorated with soft white plumes of heron feathers.

A very curious diadem or band, about four inches broad, and ingeniously wrought or woven, and [502] curiously decorated with stones, beads, wampum, porcupine quills, &c. encircles their temples, the front peak of which is embellished with a high waving plume, of crane or heron feathers.

The cloathing of their body is very simple and frugal. Sometimes a ruffled shirt of fine linen, next the skin, and a flap, which covers their lower parts, this garment somewhat resembles the ancient Roman breeches, or the kelt of the Highlanders; it usually consists of a piece of blue cloth, about eighteen inches wide, this they pass between their thighs, and both ends being taken up and drawn through a belt round their waist, the ends fall down, one before, and the other behind, not quite to the knee; this flap is usually plaited and indented at the ends, and ornamented with beads, tinsel lace, &c.

The leg is furnished with cloth boots; they reach from the ancle to the calf, and are ornamented with lace, beads, silver bells, &c.

And the stillepica or moccasin defends and adorns the feet; they seem to be an imitation of the ancient buskin or sandal; these are very ingeniously made of deer skins, dressed very soft, and curiously ornamented according to fancy.

Besides this attire, they have a large mantle of the finest cloth they are able to purchase, always either of scarlet or blue colour; this mantle is fancifully decorated, with rich lace or fringe round the border, and often with little round silver, or brass bells. Some have a short cloak, just large enough to cover the shoulders and breast; this is most ingeniously constructed, of feathers woven or placed in a natural imbricated manner, usually of [503] the scarlet feathers of the flaningo, or others of the gayest colour.

They have large silver crescents, or gorgets, which being suspended by a ribband round the neck, lie upon the breast; and the arms are ornamented with silver bands, or bracelets, and silver and gold chains, &c. a collar invests the neck.

The head, neck and breast, are painted with vermilion, and some of the warriors have the skin of the breast, and muscular parts of the body, very curiously inscribed, or adorned with hieroglyphic scrolls, flowers, figures of animals, stars, crescents, and the sun in the centre of the breast. This painting of the flesh, I understand, is performed in their youth, by picking the skin with a needle, until the blood starts, and rubbing in a blueish tinct, which is as permanent as their life. The shirt hangs loose about the waist, like a frock, or split down before, resembling a gown, which is sometimes wrapped close, and the waist encircled by a curious belt or sash.

The dress of the females is somewhat different from that of the men; their flap or petticoat, is made after a different manner, is larger and longer, reaching almost to the middle of the leg, and is put on differently; they have no shirt or shift but a little short waistcoat, usually made of callico, printed linen, or fine cloth, decorated with lace, beads, &c. They never wear boots or stockings, but their buskins reach to the middle of the leg. They never cut their hair, but plait it in wreathes, which is turned up, and fastened on the crown, with a silver broach, forming a wreathed top-knot, decorated with an incredible quantity of silk ribbands, of various co-[504]lours, which stream down on every side, almost to the ground. They never paint, except those of a particular class, when disposed to grant certain favours to the other sex.

But these decorations are only to be considered as indulgencies on particular occasions, and the privilege of youth; as at weddings, festivals, dances, &c. or when the men assemble to act the war farce, on the evening immediately preceding their march on a hostile expedition; but usually they are almost naked, contenting themselves with the flap and sometimes a shirt, boots and moccasins; the mantle is seldom worn by the men, except at night, in the winter season, when extremely cold, and by the women at dances, which serves the purpose of a veil, and the females always wear the jacket, flap, and buskin, even children as soon or before they can walk, whereas the male youth go perfectly naked until they are twelve or fifteen years of age.

The junior priests or students, constantly wear the mantle or robe, which is white, and they have a great owl skin cased and stuffed very ingeniously, so well executed, as almost to represent the living bird, having large sparkling glass beads, or buttons fixed in the head for eyes: this insigne of wisdom and divination, they wear sometimes as a crest on the top of the head, at other times the image sits on the arm, or is borne on the hand. These bachelors are also distinguishable from the other people, by their taciturnity, grave and solemn countenance, dignified step, and singing to themselves songs or hymns, in a low sweet voice, as they stroll about the towns.

These people like all other nations, are fond of [505] music and dancing: their music is both vocal and instrumental; but of the latter they have scarcely any thing worth the name, the tambour, rattle-gourd, and a kind of flute, made of a joint of reed or the tibia of the deers leg: on this instrument they perform badly, and at best it is rather a hideous melancholy discord, than harmony; it is only young fellows who amuse themselves on this howling instrument, but the tambour and rattle, accompanied with their sweet low voices, produces a pathetic harmony, keeping exact time together, and the countenance of the musician, at proper times, seems to express the solemn elevated state of the mind; at that time there seems not only a harmony between him and his instrument, but instantly touches the feelings of the attentive audience, as the influence of an active and powerful spirit; there is then an united universal sensation of delight and peaceful union of souls throughout the assembly.

Their music, vocal and instrumental, united, keeps exact time with the performers or dancers.

They have an endless variety of steps, but the most common, and that which I term the most civil, and indeed the most admired and practised amongst themselves, is a slow shuffling alternate step; both feet move forward one after the other, first the right foot foremost, and next the left, moving one after the other, in two opposite circles, i. e. first a circle of young men, and within a circle of young women moving together opposite ways, the men with the course of the sun, and the females contrary to it, the men strike their arm with the open hand, and the girls clap hands, and raise their shrill sweet voices, answering an elevated shout of the men at [506] stated times of termination of the stanzas; and the girls perform an interlude or chorus separately.

They have songs to accompany their dances, of different classes, as martial, bacchanalian and amorous, which last I must confess, are extravagantly libidinous, and they have moral songs, which seem to be the most esteemed and practised, and answer the purpose of religious lectures.

Some of their most favorite songs and dances, they have from their enemy, the Chactaw; for it seems this people are very eminent, for poetry and music; every town amongst them strives to excel each other in composing new songs for dances; and by a custom amongst them, they must have at least one new song, for exhibition, at every annual busque.

The young mustee, who came with me to the Mucclasses from Mobile, having Chactaw blood in his veins from his mother, was a sensible young fellow, and by his father had been instructed in reading, writing and arithmetic, and could speak English very well. He took it into his head, to travel into the Chactaw country: his views were magnanimous, and his designs in the highest degree commendable, nothing less than to inform himself of every species of arts and sciences, that might be of use and advantage, when introduced into his own country, but more particularly music and poetry: with these views he privately left the Nation, went to Mobile, and there entered into the service of the trading company to the Chactaws, as a white man; his easy, communicative, active and familiar disposition and manners, being agreeable to that people, procured him access every where, and favored his subtilty and artifice: at length, however, the Chactaws hearing of his lineage and consangui-[507]nity with the Creeks, by the father's side, pronounced him a Creek, and consequently an enemy and a spy amongst them, and secretly resolved to dispatch him. The young philosopher got notice of their suspicions, and hostile intentions, in time to make his escape, though closely pursued, he however kept a head of his sanguinary pursuers, arrived at Mobile, and threw himself under the protection of the English, entered the service of the trader of Mucclasse, who was then setting off for the Nation, and notwithstanding the speed with which we travelled, narrowly escaped the ardor and vigilance of his pursuing enemies, who surprised a company of emigrants, in the desarts of Schambe, the very night after we met them, expecting to intercept him thereabout.

The young traveller, having learned all their most celebrated new songs and poetry, at a great dance and festival in the Mucclasse, a day or two after our arrival; the youth pressed him, to give out some of his new songs, he complied with their entreaties, and the songs and dance went round with harmony and eclat; their being a young Chactaw slave girl in the circle, who soon after, discovered very affecting sensations of affliction and distress of mind, and before the conclusion of the dance, many of her companions complimented her with sympathetic sighs and tears, from their own sparkling eyes. As soon as I had an opportunity, I enquired of the young Orpheus, the cause of that song being so distressing to the young slave. He replied, that when she was lately taken captive, her father and brothers were slain in the contest, and she understanding the sense of the song, called to remembrance the tragical fate of her family, and could not forbear weeping at the recital.

[508]   The meaning of the chorus was,

> All men must surely die,
> Tho' no one knows how soon,
> Yet when the time shall come,
> The event may be joyful.

These doleful moral songs or elegies, have a quick and sensible effect on their passions, and discover a lively affection and sensibility; their countenance now dejected, or again, by an easy transition, becomes gently elevated, as if in solemn address or supplication, accompanied with a tremulous, sweet, lamentable voice; a stranger is for a moment lost to himself as it were, or his mind, associated with the person immediately affected, is in danger of revealing his own distress unawares.

They have a variety of games for exercise and pastime; some particular to the men, some to the female sex, and others wherein both sexes are engaged.

The ball play is esteemed the most noble and manly exercise; this game is exhibited in an extensive level plain, usually contiguous to the town: the inhabitants of one town play against another, in consequence of a challenge, when the youth of both sexes are often engaged, and sometimes stake their whole substance. Here they perform amazing feats of strength and agility; the game principally consists in taking and carrying off the ball from the opposite party, after being hurled into the air, midway between two high pillars, which are the goals, and the party who bears off the ball to their pillar wins the game; each person having a racquet or hurl, which is an implement of a very curious construction, somewhat resembling a ladle or little hoop-net, with a handle near three feet in [509] length, the hoop and handle of wood, and the netting of thongs of raw hide, or tendons of an animal.

The foot-ball is likewise a favorite, manly diversion with them. Feasting and dancing in the square, at evening ends all their games.

They have besides, feasts or festivals almost for every month in the year, which are chiefly dedicated to hunting and agriculture.

The busk or feast of first fruits is their principal festival; this seems to end the last, and begin the new year.

It commences in August, when their new crops of Corn are arrived to perfect maturity: and every town celebrates the busk separately, when their own harvest is ready.

If they have any religious rite or ceremony, this festival is its most solemn celebration.

When a town celebrates the busk, having previously provided themselves with new clothes, new pots, pans and other household utensils and furniture, they collect all their worn out clothes and other despicable things, sweep and cleanse their houses, squares, and the whole town, of their filth, which with all the remaining grain and other old provisions, they cast together in one common heap, and consume it with fire; after having taken medicine, and fasted for three days, all the fire in the town is extinguished; during this fast they abstain from the gratification of every appetite and passion whatever. A general amnesty is proclaimed, all malefactors may return to their town, and they are absolved from their crimes, which are now forgotten, and they restored to favor.

[510] On the fourth morning, the high priest, by rubbing dry wood together, produces new fire in the public square, from whence every habitation in the town is supplied with the new and pure flame.

Then the women go forth to the harvest field, and bring from thence new Corn and fruits, which being prepared in the best manner, in various dishes, and drink withal, is brought with solemnity to the square, where the people are assembled, apparelled in their new clothes and decorations. The men having regaled themselves, the remainder is carried off and distributed amongst the families of the town. The women and children solace themselves in their separate families, and in the evening repair to the public square, where they dance, sing and rejoice during the whole night, observing a proper and exemplary decorum; this continues three days, and the four following days they receive visits, and rejoice with their friends from neighbouring towns, who have purified and prepared themselves.

CHAP. IV.

CONCERNING PROPERTY, AGRICULTURE, ARTS AND MANUFACTURES.

IT has been said by historians, who have written concerning the customs and usages of the aborigines of America, that they have every thing in common, and no private property; which are terms in my opinion too vague and general, when applied to these people. From my own frequent opportunities of observation, and the information of respectable characters, who have spent many years amongst them, I venture to set this matter in a just view before my readers.

I shall begin with the produce of their agricultural labours.

An Indian town is generally so situated, as to be convenient for procuring game, secure from sudden invasion, a large district of excellent arable land adjoining, or in its vicinity, if possible on an isthmus betwixt two waters, or where the doubling of a river forms a peninsula; such a situation generally comprises a sufficient body of excellent land for planting Corn, Potatoes, Beans, Squash, Pumpkins, Citruls, Melons, &c. and is taken in with a small expence and trouble of fencing, to secure their crops from the invasion of predatory animals. At other times however they choose such a convenient fertile spot at some distance from their town, when circumstances will not admit of having both together.

[512] This is their common plantation, and the whole town plant in one vast field together, but yet the part or share of every individual family or habitation, is separated from the next adjoining, by a narrow strip, or verge of grass, or any other natural or artificial boundary.

In the spring, the ground being already prepared, on one and the same day, early in the morning, the whole town is summoned, by the sound of a conch shell, from the mouth of the overseer, to meet at the public square, whither the people repair with their hoes and axes, and from thence proceed to their plantation, where they begin to plant, not every one in his own little district, assigned and laid out, but the whole community united, begins on one certain part of the field, where they plant on until finished, and when their rising crops are ready for dressing, and cleansing, they proceed after the same order, and so on day after day, until the crop is laid by for ripening. After the feast of the busk is over, and all the grain is ripe, the whole town again assemble, and every man carries of the fruits of his labour, from the part first allotted to him, which he deposits in his own granary; which is individually his own. But previous to their carrying off their crops from the field, there is a large crib or granary, erected in the plantation, which is called the king's crib; and to this each family carries and deposits a certain quantity, according to his ability or inclination, or none at all if he so chooses, this in appearance seems a tribute or revenue to the mico, but in fact is designed for another purpose, i. e. that of a public treasury, supplied by a few and voluntary contributions, and to which every citizen has the right of free and e-[513]qual access, when his own private stores are consumed, to serve as a surplus to fly to for succour, to assist neighbouring towns, whose crops may have failed, accommodate strangers, or travellers, afford provisions or supplies, when they go forth on hostile expeditions, and for all other exigencies of the state; and this treasure is at the disposal of the king or mico; which is surely a royal attribute to have an exclusive right and ability in a community to distribute comfort and blessings to the necessitous.

As to mechanic arts or manufactures, at present they have scarcely any thing worth observation, since they are supplied with necessaries, conveniencies and even superfluities by the white traders. The men perform nothing except erecting their mean habitations, forming their canoes, stone pipes, tambour, eagles tail or standard, and some other trifling matters, for war and hunting are their principal employments. The women are more vigilant, and turn their attention to various manual employments; they make all their pottery or earthen-ware, moccasins; spin and weave the curious belts and diadems for the men; fabricate lace, fringe, embroider and decorate their apparel, &c. &c.

C H A P . V .

OF THEIR MARRIAGE AND FUNERAL CEREMONIES.

As to their marriage ceremonies they are very simple, yet differ greatly in the various nations and tribes. Amongst some of the bands in the Muscogulge confederacy, I was informed the mystery is performed after the following manner. When a young man has fixed his affections, and is determined to marry, he takes a Cane or Reed, such as they stick down at the hills of their Bean vines for their support: with this (after having obtained her parents or nearest relations consent) he repairs to the habitation of his beloved, attended by his friends and associates, and in the presence of the wedding guests, he sticks his Reed down, upright in the ground, when soon after his sweet-heart comes forth with another Reed, which she sticks down by the side of his, when they are married; then they exchange Reeds, which are laid by as evidences or certificates of the marriage, which is celebrated with feasting, music and dancing: each one of their relations and friends, at the wedding, contributes something towards establishing the new family. As soon as the wedding is over, the town is convened, and the council orders or recommends a new habitation to be constructed for the accommodation of the new family; every man in the town joins in the work, which is begun and finished in a day's time.

The greatest accomplishments to recommend a young man to his favourite maid, is to prove himself a brave warrior, and a cunning, industrious hunter.

[515] They marry only for a year's time, and, according to ancient custom, at the expiration of the year they renew the marriage; but there is seldom an instance of their separating after they have children. If it should happen, the mother takes the children under her own protection, though the father is obliged to contribute towards their maintainance during their minority and the mother's widowhood.

The Muscogulges allow of polygamy in the utmost latitude; every man takes as many wives as he chooses, but the first is queen, and the others her handmaids and associates.

It is common for a great man amongst them, who has already half a dozen wives, if he sees a child of eight or nine years of age, who pleases him, and he can agree with her parents or guardians, to marry her and take her into his house at that age.

Adultery is always punished with cropping, which is the only corporal punishment amongst them, and death or out-lawry for murder, and infamy for less crimes, as fornication, theft, &c. which produces such repeated marks and reflections of ridicule and contempt, that generally ends in voluntary banishment; and these renegades and vagabonds are generally the ruffians who commit depredations and murders on the frontiers.

The Muscogulges bury their deceased in the earth; they dig a four square deep pit under the cabin or couch which the deceased laid on, in his house, lining the grave with Cypress bark, where they place the corps in a sitting posture, as if it were alive; de-[516]positing with him his gun, tomahawk, pipe and such other matters as he had the greatest value for in his life time. His eldest wife, or the queen dowager, has the second choice of his possessions, and the remaining effects are divided amongst his other wives and children.

The Chactaws pay their last duties and respect to the deceased in a very different manner. As soon as a person is dead, they erect a scaffold eighteen or twenty feet high, in a grove adjacent to the town, where they lay the corps, lightly covered with a mantle; here it is suffered to remain, visited and protected by the friends and relations, until the flesh becomes putrid, so as easily to part from the bones, then undertakers, who make it their business, carefully strip the flesh from the bones, wash and cleanse them, and when dry and purified by the air, having provided a curiously wrought chest or coffin, fabricated of bones and splints, they place all the bones therein; which is deposited in the bone-house, a building erected for that purpose in every town. And when this house is full a general solemn funeral takes place. When the nearest kindred or friends of the deceased, on a day appointed, repair to the bone-house, take up the respective coffins, and following one another in order of seniority, the nearest relations and connections attending their respective corps, and the multitude following after them, all as one family, with united voice of alternate Allelujah and lamentation, slowly proceeding on to the place of general interment, where they place the coffins in order, forming a pyramid *; and last-[517]ly, cover all over with earth, which raises a

* Some ingenious men, whom I have conversed with, have given it as their opinion, that all those pyramidal artificial hills, usually called Indian mounts were raised on this occasion, and are generally sepulchres. However I am of a different opinion.

conical hill or mount. When they return to town in order of solemn procession, concluding the day with a festival, which is called the feast of the dead.

The Chactaws are called by the traders flats, or flat-heads, all the males having the fore and hind part of their skulls, artificially flattened, or compressed, which is effected after the following manner. As soon as the child is born, the nurse provides a cradle or wooden case, hollowed and fashioned, to receive the infant, lying prostrate on its back, and that part of the case where the head reposes, being fashioned like a brick mould. In this portable machine the little boy is fixed, a bag of sand being laid on his forehead, which by continual gentle compressure, gives the head somewhat the form of a brick from the temples upwards, and by these means they have high and lofty foreheads, sloping off backwards. These men are not so neat in the trim of their heads, as the Muscogulges are, and they are remarkably slovenly and negligent in every part of their dress; but otherwise they are said to be ingenious, sensible and virtuous men; bold and intrepid, yet quiet and peaceable, and are acknowledged by the Creeks to be brave.

They are supposed to be most ingenious and industrious husbandmen, having large plantations, or country farms, where they employ much of their time in agricultural improvements, after the manner of the white people; by which means their territories are more generally cultivated, and better inhabited than any other Indian republic that we know of; the number of their inhabitants is said to greatly exceed the whole Muscogulge confederacy, although their territories are not a fourth part as ex-[518]tensive. It appeared to me from observation, and what information I could get, that the Indians entertain rational notions of the soul's immortality, and of a future state of social existence; and accordingly, in order to inculcate morality, and promote human happiness, they applaud praiseworthy actions, as commendable and necessary for the support of civil society, and maintaining the dignity and strength of their nation or tribe, as well as securing an excellent and tranquil state and degree in the world of spirits, after their decease. And they say the Great Spirit favours all good and brave men.

CHAP. VI.

LANGUAGE AND MANNERS.

THE Muscogulge language is spoken throughout the confederacy, (although consisting of many nations, who have a speech peculiar to themselves) as also by their friends and allies, the Natches. The Chicasaw and Chactaw the Muscogulges say is a dialect of theirs.

This language is very agreeable to the ear, courteous, gentle and musical: the letter R is not sounded in one word of their language: the women in particular speak so fine and musical, as to represent the singing of birds; and when heard and not seen, one might imagine it to be the prattling of young children: the men's speech is indeed more strong and sonorous, but not harsh, and in no instance guttural, and I believe the letter R is not used to express any word, in any language of the confederacy.

The Cherokee tongue on the contrary, is very loud, somewhat rough and very sonorous, sounding the letter R frequently, yet very agreeable and pleasant to the ear. All the Indian languages, are truly rhetorical, or figurative, assisting their speech by tropes, their hands, flexure of the head, the brow, in short, every member, naturally associate, and give their assistance to render their harangues eloquent, persuasive and effectual.

The pyramidal hills or artificial mounts and highways, or avenues, leading from them to artificial [*520*] lakes or ponds, vast tetragon terraces, chunk yards * and obelisks or pillars of wood, are the only monuments of labour, ingenuity and magnificence, that I have seen worthy of notice, or remark. The region lying between Savanna river and Oakmulge, East and West, and from the sea coast to the Cherokee or Apalachean mountains, North and South, is the most remarkable for their high conical hills, tetragon terraces and chunk yards; this region was last possessed by the Cherokees, since the arrival of the Europeans, but they were afterwards dispossessed by the Muscogulges,

---

* Chunk yard, a term given by the white traders, to the oblong four square yards, adjoining the high mounts and rotunda of the modern Indians.—In the center of these stands the obelisk, and at each corner of the farther end stands a slave post or strong stake, where the captives that are burnt alive are bound.

and all that country was probably many ages preceding the Cherokee invasion, inhabited by one nation or confederacy, who were ruled by the same system of laws, customs and language; but so ancient, that the Cherokees, Creeks, or the nation they conquered, could render no account for what purpose these monuments were raised. The mounts and cubical yards adjoining them, seemed to have been raised in part for ornament and recreation, and likewise to serve some other public purpose, since they are always so situated as to command the most extensive prospect over the town and country adjacent. The tetragon terraces, seem to be the foundation of a fortress, and perhaps the great pyramidal mounts, served the purpose of look out towers, and high places for sacrifice. The sunken area, called by white traders the chunk yard, very likely served the same conveniency, that it has been appropriated to by the more modern and even present nations of Indians, that is, the place where they burnt and [521] otherwise tortured the unhappy captives, that were condemned to die, as the area is surrounded by a bank, and sometimes two of them, one behind and above the other, as seats, to accommodate the spectators, at such tragical scenes, as well as the exhibition of games, shews and dances. From the river St. Juans, Southerly to the point of the peninsula of Florida, are to be seen high pyramidal mounts, with spacious and extensive avenues, leading from them out of the town, to an artificial lake or pond of water, these were evidently dignified in part, for ornament or monuments of magnificence, to perpetuate the power and grandeur of the nation, and no considerable one neither, for they exhibit scenes of power and grandeur, and must have been public edifices.

The great mounts, highways and artificial lakes up St. Juans on the East shore just at the enterance of the great Lake George, one on the opposite shore, on the bank of the Little Lake, another on Dunn's Island, a little below Charlotteville, and one on the large beautiful island just without the Capes of Lake George, in sight of Mount Royal, and a spacious one on the West banks of the Musquitoe river near New Smyrna, are the most remarkable of this sort that occurred to me; but undoubtedly many more are yet to be discovered farther South in the peninsula, however I observed none Westward, after I left St. Juans on my journey to little St. Juan, near the bay of Apalache.

But in all the region of the Muscogulge country, South-West from the Oakmulge River quite to the Tallapoose, down to the city of Mobile, and thence along the sea coast, to the Mississipi, I saw no signs of mountains or highways, except at Taensa, [522] where were several inconsiderable conical mountains, and but one instance of the tetragon terraces which was at the Apalachucla old town, on the West banks of that river; here were yet remaining conspicuous monuments, as vast four square terraces, chunk yards, &c. almost equalling those eminent ones at the Oakmulge fields; but no high conical mounts. Those Indians have a tradition that these remains are the ruins of an ancient Indian town and fortress. I was not in the interior parts of the Chactaw territories, and therefore am ignorant whether there are any mounts or monuments there.

To conclude this subject concerning the monuments of the Americans, I deem it necessary to observe as my opinion, that none of them that I have seen discover the least signs of the arts, sciences, or architecture of the Europeans or other inhabitants of the old world: yet evidently betray every sign or mark of the most distant antiquity.

FINIS.

COMMENTARY

COMMENTARY

T̶HE INTRODUCTION is interesting as a specimen of a philosophical discourse such as was more or less characteristic of eighteenth-century works on natural history.

[*xiii–xxv*] The technical plant names mentioned here are evidently derived almost wholly from the works of Linnaeus. The *Species plantarum* (1753; 1762–63) and one or more editions of the *Systema naturae* (1758, 1766, etc.) must have been familiar to Bartram from the days of his youth. The Academy of Natural Sciences of Philadelphia possesses at least three Linnaean works formerly belonging to him: the *Species plantarum*, 2d ed. (1762–63), the *Systema vegetabilium* (1774), presented to him in 1782 by Doctor Keilman, of Sweden, and the *Systema naturae* (1758), presented in 1808 by Dr. Thomas T. Hewson, of Philadelphia. Bartram's comments [*xix*] on the capture of insects by pitcher-plants (*Sarracenia*) prompted Croom to remark (1848: 97): "The manner in which they are imprisoned was first distinctly explained by William Bartram."

[*xxv–xxxi*] The observations on Mosquito River (Lagoon), Florida, belong to some period covered neither by the *Travels* (1773–77) nor by his journey to Florida in company with his father (1765–66). At the conclusion of this joint trip, however, he had remained in the province for a year or so; at first endeavoring to raise rice and indigo on the St. John's, and later apparently having some sort of association with J. G. W. De Brahm, His Majesty's surveyor-general for the Southern District of North America. This association is referred to in a footnote on page 144 of the *Travels*. De Brahm prepared a map of East Florida that was based upon surveys made from 1766 to 1770. When Bartram writes (p. 144) of having been on the Mosquito River "about ten years ago," the date of his retrospect is obviously not the year of publication of the *Travels* (1791), but a considerably earlier period when he was composing the manuscript. The date of the Mosquito River observations was "late in December" [*xxviii*], and the year was doubtless 1766.

[*xxxiv*] Bartram's ideal of an Indian commissioner, as expressed here, seems to have been eventually realized in large measure in the

able Colonel Benjamin Hawkins (1754–1816), whose *Sketch of the Creek Country, in 1798 and 1799* (1848) and whose letters (1916) form such valuable documents for a study of the Creeks and their neighbors. Unfortunately, a commissioner of Hawkins' type was quite exceptional.

Part I

[1–3] Bartram's weakness in chronology is evident at the very start, when he fixes the time of his departure from Philadelphia as "April, 1773." The actual date was apparently *March 20* [1] of that year (cf. W. Bartram, 1943: 172). The *South-Carolina Gazette* (no. 1946: [3], April 5, 1773) announces the arival at Charleston on *March 31* of two brigantines from Philadelphia: the *Prince of Wales* (Thomas Mason, master) and the *Charles-Town Packet* (Sam. Wright, master). Our author's Revolutionary sympathies may have deterred him from mentioning the name of the former vessel (Harper, 1953: 575–576). A letter of *April 1, 1773*, from Lionel Chalmers to John Bartram (in Darlington, 1849: 464) shows that William was in Charleston on the preceding day.

[4] Our traveler may have left Charleston on *April 11* or *12* on one of two schooners that sailed for Savannah on those dates; they were the *Savannah-Packet* and the *Betsy & Polly* (*South-Carolina Gazette*, no. 1947, April 12, 1773, and no. 1948, April 19, 1773). A letter of recommendation from Governor Wright (W. Bartram, 1943: 172) bears the date of *April 22*, but was perhaps written just a week previously. The country seat of Benjamin Andrew was in the Midway district of Liberty County (Jones, 1891: 2).

[5–6] According to Bartram's report to Fothergill (1943: 134), his departure from Savannah took place on *April 16*. The road from Savannah as far as Midway coincided rather closely with the present main highway leading southwestward (Route 17). From Midway a side road extends eastward to Sunbury on the Medway or Midway River (map of Liberty County, 1939). The inlet by which Sunbury is reached lies between Ossabaw (not St. Helena) and St. (not South) Catherine's Islands.

The island now visited by Bartram was Colonel's Island—not St. Catherine's, as indicated in the table of contents (cf. J. E. Le Conte, 1855; Jones, 1878: 169). St. Catherine's is altogether inaccessible to either a pedestrian or an equestrian. Among the trees listed here,

1. Certain dates are printed in italic to give the reader extra assistance in following Bartram's chronology.

Magnolia pyramidata is of particular interest; this is the first occurrence of the name in the literature, but no description accompanying the name is supplied until page *408* (see Annotated Index).

[*9–12*] For a further account of the exceptional character of the people of St. John's Parish (or Liberty County), see Joseph Le Conte (1903: 4 ff.).

[*12–15*] Bartram's route from the Midway district to Darien is rather puzzling, but it may be tentatively defined somewhat as follows: south along the Barrington Road to Bull Town Swamp at the southern border of Liberty County; then for several additional miles on the same road along the boundary between Long and McIntosh Counties (see soil map of the latter county, 1932); then 3 miles southeastward to the vicinity of Jones (Station), where he may have lost his way toward night in a westerly branch of Mortar Swamp; then, on the next day, 5 miles eastward, across "a considerable branch of Sapello river" to South Newport, where "a small plantation" belonging to a McIntosh was located; then "seven or eight miles" southward along the present U. S. Highway 17 to "Sapello bridge," which was doubtless at or near the present Eulonia; then, continuing southward along the same highway, a dozen miles more to Lachlan McIntosh's home in Darien on the banks of the Altamaha. Just such a route through McIntosh County as is here outlined is shown by Harris (1748, 2: map opposite p. 323).

The identity of the first McIntosh encountered, "the venerable grey-headed Caledonian" at South Newport, is eventually revealed in a letter of May 31, 1796, from Bartram to Lachlan McIntosh (New York Hist. Soc.): "Please give my respects also, to Good old Don[d] McAntosh, at the Swamp, between Sapello & the great swamp, where I had Shelter during a tremendous Thunder Storm."

[*16*] Bartram's route from Darien to Fort Barrington was probably very nearly identical with the one shown on the soil map of McIntosh County (1932), by way of Chisholm Swamp, McClendon School, and Cox. The "two new beautiful shrubs" (*Franklinia*, Pl. III, and *Pinckneya*) had been discovered on October 1, 1765, by John and William Bartram (cf. J. Bartram, 1942: 31, 66; Harper and Leeds, 1938) in the same spot where William now notes them again. This spot is believed to be a sand-hill bog on the north side of the road at a point about 1.7 miles northwest of Cox. There is considerable doubt as to whether these shrubs were actually in bloom at the time of Bartram's present visit, which was probably about *April 24 or 25* (cf. W. Bartram, 1943: 174). The flowers were more likely to have been found on a visit later in the season.

At Fort Barrington (deserted save for a small fishing club) part of the old earthen ramparts, including two of the corner bastions, were still in evidence in 1940.

[17–26] The events and observations set forth in these pages must actually belong to some later trip rather than to the present one, in the last few days of April. According to Bartram's report to Fothergill (1943: 135), his present excursion south of the Altamaha took him merely to the site of Brunswick. He could scarcely have gone as far as the St. Mary's, returned to Darien, where he "tarried a few days" [26], and still have managed to set off from this last point for Savannah by May 1, as he reports to Dr. Fothergill. Moreover, the "diminutive but elegant Kalmia" (K. hirsuta), whose flowers are described on page 18, does not ordinarily bloom in southeastern Georgia before the second week of May. This Kalmia had probably been known to the Bartrams on their Florida journey of 1765–66 (cf. J. Bartram, 1942: 92). The trip to the St. Mary's is much more likely to have taken place in the summer of 1776 (Harper, 1953: 573–574).

The route southward from Fort Barrington may be traced on the Early map of Georgia (1818) and on the Everett City, Hortense, Nahunta, and Boulogne quadrangles. It is indicated as the "Post Road" on the first three of these quadrangles, and as the "Old National Highway" on the Boulogne quadrangle. In the entire distance of about 60 miles between the Altamaha and the St. Mary's, Mt. Pleasant is practically the only village on this route. In 1936 the Post Road passed through an almost unbroken forest, and in northwestern Camden County it seemed to be nearly abandoned. Except for a certain amount of lumbering or turpentining in the bordering pine barrens, some sections of the road must have still appeared then very much as they did in Bartram's time. This was familiar ground to our traveler, from having passed over it with his father in 1765.

[18] The "hillocks of fresh earth, thrown up in great numbers in the night," were doubtless not the mounds in front of the Gopher Turtles' burrows (fig. 5) (which very rarely have a fresh appearance), but the heaps of soil pushed out on the surface from the excavations of the Georgia Pocket Gopher (Geomys pinetis pinetis) (fig. 4). This note, and the one on page 7 concerning a "ground-rat," are apparently the first references to Geomys in Georgia or anywhere else in the country (cf. Harper, 1952: 35).

The cowpen was probably one of two visited by the Bartrams in 1765 (cf. J. Bartram, 1942: 32, 67). It may have been on one of the headwaters of Turtle River, a little east of the present Waynesville,

Brantley County. Perhaps "Carney's Cowpens," shown in this vicinity on the Early map of 1818, are identical.

[19] The "beautiful species of Lupin" (*Lupinus villosus*) (fig. 6) still grows on the sand hills along the Post Road southeast of Waynesville.

[20] There were two possible ferry crossings of the Satilla ("St. Ille's")—at Burnt Fort and at Owen's Ferry (Boulogne quadrangle). It was apparently the latter that had been utilized by the Bartrams in 1765 (J. Bartram, 1942: 33, 67–68), and William had a distinct penchant for retracing his earlier route. Thus we may assume that he turned from his general southerly course at a point (marked "Mersells's" on the Early map) about 4 miles west-northwest of Owen's Ferry. This ferry is called "Brown's Ferry" on the Early map. It has been discontinued in recent years. After crossing the river here, Bartram doubtless took the road marked "Old National Highway" on the Boulogne quadrangle and followed it for about 15 miles to the St. Mary's at King's Ferry.

[20–23] The stirring adventure with the "intrepid Siminole," at a distance of "eight or ten miles" north of the St. Mary's, took place presumably somewhere in the vicinity of Bullhead Creek. Little did this son of the wilderness realize how the world of science and literature was destined to benefit by his forbearance! And it may be added that if Bartram had been other than a Quaker, he might not have survived.

[24–26] This is the most celebrated early account of Okefinokee Swamp, and it has often been quoted. It is possible that the inhabitants were, as Bartram says, a fugitive remnant of the ancient Yamasees. The St. Mary's River enters the ocean between Cumberland and Amelia Islands—not, as Bartram says, between Amelia and Talbot ("Talbert") Islands.

"The name of this great swamp is supposed to be derived from the Hitchiti dialect of the Muskhogean tongues, according to which it would mean 'trembling water.' The form of the name as it has come down to us would confirm this view, but logically the alternative supplied by Hawkins is better. He says that the swamp was called 'O-ke-fin-o-cau' or 'E-cun-fin-o-cau, from E-cun-nau, earth; and Fin-o-cau, quivering.' 'The first,' he adds, 'is the most common amongst the Creeks. It is from Ooka a Chactau word for water, and Fin-o-cau, quivering.' (Hawkins, 1848: 21.) The words for water in Choctaw and Hitchiti are almost identical, and Hawkins evidently was not familiar with the latter language. In spite of the preference Hawkins attributes to the Indians, 'quivering water' seems a less sensible designation than 'quivering earth,' because there is nothing peculiar in the quivering of water. It would quiver in a desert oasis or in a mountain pond as much as in a swamp, but the term 'quivering earth' would apply distinctively to a region like the Okefinokee. In Creek this would be Ikan-finoka as above given. In Hitchiti, however, it would be yakni finoki. Linguistically each of these latter interpretations nevertheless labors under the difficulty of accounting for the disappearance of an 'n.'" (J.R.S.) [1]

"The story of the lost tribe of the Okefinokee appealed strongly to later historians and persons of literary instincts. The English poetess, Mrs. Hemans, made it the subject of her poem, 'The Isle of Founts,' which begins:

> Son of the stranger! wouldst thou take
>   O'er yon blue hills thy lonely way,
> To reach the still and shining lake
>   Along whose banks the west-winds play?
> —Let no vain dreams thy heart beguile,
> Oh! seek thou not the Fountain-Isle."   (J.R.S.)

"The Yamasee were not exterminated in the wholesale manner which Bartram represents. They indeed lost heavily in wars with the English and Creeks and still more, probably, from epidemics of European origin, but they disappeared mainly because they split into a number of bands which were absorbed into other tribes. One such band seems to have remained on the Oklawaha and was absorbed by the Seminole. The noted chiefs Jumper and Alligator were said to have been descended from them. Another group went to West Florida, a Yamasee band appears at Mobile, and still another among the Upper Creeks, or possibly some of these were identical, since it is difficult to trace their movements. Finally, Yamasee entered into the make-up of the Yamacraw tribe which played such a conspicuous part in early Georgia history." (J.R.S.)

[28–32] Since Bartram here supplies so few details in regard to his journey to Augusta, his report to Fothergill (1943: 135–137, 174–176) will be drawn upon for the itinerary. The departure from McIntosh County took place on *May 1, 1773*, and Savannah was reached on *May 3*. The route from this point to Augusta was familiar to Bartram from his journey with his father in 1765. It may be traced with the help of Thomas Wright's map of 1763 (*Crown Coll.*, ser. 3, 3: 141, 1915), the Campbell map of 1780, the Faden map of South

1. Notes thus initialed are by John R. Swanton. See Preface, above, p. x.

Carolina (1780), the map in Hammond's *South Carolina* (1883), and modern topographic maps and county soil maps. Much of the old highway is now little used, and some of it has been quite abandoned or obliterated. In recent times it has been known as the "Old Augusta Road" (fig. 20) or the "Old Stage-coach Road."

On *May 4* Bartram and his companion proceeded 15 miles from Savannah and stopped at a public house that may have been Dacre's Tavern, near the Chatham-Effingham county boundary (Campbell map). On the following day they arrived at Ebenezer, and on *May 6?* they may have reached Mount Pleasant (the present Cedar Bluff Landing—Shirley quadrangle). The next night's lodging may have been at Black Creek Landing, about 3 miles from the southeastern corner of Screven County. On *May 8?* they turned northwestward, paused only briefly at the delightful Blue Springs (fig. 29) on Beaverdam Creek, and camped perhaps on Big Branch, 3 or 4 miles west of the present Millhaven (Hilltonia quadrangle). The next day's course led them across Brier Creek at the present Thompson's Bridge, past Marshman's Ponds and the present settlement of Shell Bluff (Green's Cut quadrangle), and apparently across McBean Creek, a little above the mouth of which they crossed the Savannah River to Galphin's store at Silver Bluff, in the present Aiken County, S.C. (Augusta quadrangle). On *May 14*, after a stay of probably several days at this place, the journey was continued upstream about 12 miles on the Carolina side to Fort Moore; here the river was recrossed, and in another 3 miles Augusta was reached.

In these pages [28–32] Bartram recognizes and describes some of the major subdivisions of the Coastal Plain of Georgia, with notes on the physiography and vegetation of each. This pioneer work seems to antedate by many decades (possibly a century or more) any similar study of this region. It may be of interest to compare his classification with that of R. M. Harper (1906: frontisp.; 1918: map, p. 704; 1922: 98–108, map on p. 99; 1930: 6, fig. 1). Bartram's first division [28–30] apparently comprises both the Coast Strip and the Flat Pine Lands of the modern classification. He omits the Altamaha Grit Region (or Rolling Wire-Grass Country), having barely skirted its northeastern border. The next division [30–31] is apparently the Lime-Sink Region, and the following one [31–32], with "a stratum of redish brown tough clay," the Southern Red Hills. The Fall-Line Sand Hills do not seem to have been distinguished from the adjacent divisions. The country between Augusta and the mountains [32] is the Piedmont Region.

Lyell remarks (1849, *1*: 257): "Bartram has, with his usual accuracy, alluded to these steps, or succession of terraces, as an important geographical feature of the country."

[*33–35*] While awaiting the arrival of the Indians at Augusta, Bartram (1943: 137–138) made a trip of several days (perhaps about *May 16* to *19*) to Wrightsborough and return. This place, about 35 miles west-northwest of Augusta, was then a newly founded Quaker settlement, and so it was naturally of interest to Bartram. He does not refer to this little excursion in the *Travels*.

The Treaty of Augusta was presumably concluded on *June 3, 1773* (Thomas, 1899: 639). The area ceded by the Indians is shown on the Purcell map of about 1776 and on a map (pl. 8) in the *Fifth Annual Report of the Bureau of American Ethnology* (1887).

Bartram's report to Fothergill (1943: 138–144) supplies many details of the tour with Col. Barnet's party to the Little, Broad, and Tugaloo Rivers that do not appear in the *Travels*. It was obviously not "about the middle of . . . May" [*34*] when this party set out. The date was *June 7*, according to the original account. The caravan proceeded over the lower trading path leading toward the Ogeechee and more westerly rivers. The first night's camp was evidently made at Spirit Creek (Hephzibah quadrangle), on the present Route 1. From this point the route was probably by the present McDuffie Road and its continuation, the Gibson Road (Harlem quadrangle), passing Leitner's, Burch's, Arrington's, and Hobbs's Mills. Just beyond the last-mentioned point, at the junction of Brier and Sweetwater Creeks, the main trading path continued westward, while a branch diverged northward about 15 miles to Wrightsborough, by way of the present Thomson (Purcell map of about 1776).

[*36*] After a stay of some days in this settlement, the party may have proceeded on *June 21* (W. Bartram, 1943: 139). Perhaps the route may be best deciphered from the more or less contemporary Purcell map, which very likely utilized the surveys made by Col. Barnet's party. Bartram's own account cannot be taken too literally. Here and there, along the south side of Little River, one may still find traces of the old Cherokee trail that Col. Barnet probably followed. At a point about 8 miles northwest of Wrightsborough, the trail crosses Williams Creek a little above its mouth (Crawfordville quadrangle). Bartram errs in calling this "the north branch of Little River," as he does in placing Wrightsborough "upon the head of Little River" (1943: 139).

Bartram's description of the "sublime forest" at this point induces a melancholy reflection on the extent of the destruction that has taken place in our Southeastern forests. Nothing in the whole region today can compare with this primeval stand of timber.

[37] The "magnificent monuments of . . . the ancient inhabitants of these lands" have proved a distinct puzzle, for Indian mounds are scarcely discoverable along Little River, despite the earnest search of amateur archaeologists. However, the late T. G. Macfie pointed out to me, on his farm just west of the junction of Little River and Williams Creek, certain features that may have formed the basis of Bartram's account. One of these is a large wooded mound bordering the river bottom; it is about 35–40 feet in height and about 150 by 60 yards in horizontal dimensions. It appears to be largely if not entirely a natural formation, although a pool at its northern base suggests a possible excavation for the purpose of adding material to the mound. This is what Bartram may have mistakenly described as a "stupendous conical pyramid, or artificial mount of earth." A little farther back from the river, in an open field on some elevated ground, is a "sunken area," more or less rectangular in form, perhaps a couple of acres in extent and several feet below the general level. But here again there seems to be no particular evidence of artificial formation. The very lack of any other known features along Little River answering at all to Bartram's description tends to fix upon this area as the location of his "magnificent monuments." It might be worth while for a professional archaeologist to inspect the area, if only for a negative result.

[38] From this point the old Cherokee trail continues westward along the ridge bordering Little River on the south. A very clear though abandoned remnant of it was pointed out to me by A. F. Bramlitt at Ficklin, on the boundary between Wilkes and Taliaferro Counties; it appears as a "sunken road" at right angles to, and west of, the railroad track. To judge by the Purcell map, the trail continued on the south side of the river to the vicinity of Edgewood Crossroads, then crossed the South and North Forks in the vicinity of Lyneville. From that locality it probably paralleled White's Creek on the northeast side until it reached the Buffalo Lick (fig. 7) at the head of that creek in extreme southeastern Oglethorpe County, half a mile southeast of Philomath (Crawfordville quadrangle).

[39] Bartram unfortunately placed the Buffalo Lick on the headwaters of the Ogeechee River instead of Little River, but the authoritative Purcell map, and each one of half a dozen or more later maps that show it at all, place it correctly in southeastern Oglethorpe County. This spot was located in 1934 by Arthur N. Leeds and myself

in the course of a very interesting search, the details of which are too lengthy to be given here. It answers to Bartram's description in occupying "several acres of ground"; in lying "at the foot of the S. E. promontory of the Great Ridge"; and in that its soil is a "tenacious fattish clay, which all kinds of cattle lick into great caves." In 1934 even the tradition of its having been a Buffalo lick had been lost, but it was still known as a former Deer lick. Half a century previously, according to Carl Wright, the owner of the land, there was a knee-deep depression, about a rod in diameter, where the earth had been licked away. This depression was still visible in 1934, though no longer so deep; and Mr. Wright's cattle still licked the ground thereabouts.

Two samples of earth from the Buffalo Lick were kindly supplied by John R. Swanton, of the Bureau of American Ethnology, and analyzed through the courtesy of J. E. Underwood and Rudolf Lehmann, of the Pennsylvania Salt Manufacturing Company. One sample was obtained from the surface of the lick; the other, from a foot below the surface. The analysis revealed only traces of sodium and the sulphate radical; a small amount of calcium; and large amounts of ferric oxide and aluminum oxide. The only combination of these constituents known to furnish an agreeable taste to animals, as Edgar T. Wherry informs me, is sodium sulphate. Perhaps a larger amount was available in Bartram's day, but has leached out since that time.

[40–41] Between the Buffalo Lick and Philomath another sunken section of the old Cherokee trail was pointed out to me by Mr. Wright. A boundary line shown on the Purcell map, extending from the Buffalo Lick to the mouth of Tugaloo River, is evidently the route followed and surveyed by Col. Barnet's party. At first it runs northwestward, zigzagging about the heads of streams on each side of the Broad-Oconee divide, to a point that was no doubt Cherokee Corner (Early map of 1818), on the boundary between Clarke and Oglethorpe Counties, about 9 miles southeast of Athens on Route 78. The branch of Broad River on which the party camped [41] may have been Buffalo Creek.

[42] The point at which the banks of the Oconee were reached was probably a few miles below the present Athens.

[43–44] The adventure with the "gold-fish" (Notropis lutipinnis) (fig. 8) may have taken place in the present Madison County, on any one of various headwaters of Broad River.

From the Buffalo Lick to the Tugaloo River, Bartram's original account (1943: 140–143) appears to be rather confused, while the narrative in the Travels [40–45] is so brief as to provide very little help in working out the itinerary. Probably the best clues are furnished by the Purcell map and Hall's county map of Georgia (1895). The original boundary of Wilkes County, from the Buffalo Lick to the Savannah River, as shown on the latter map, apparently coincided approximately with the boundary of the lands ceded by the Indians in 1773. On the assumption that Col. Barnet's party followed and marked this boundary line, their course from Cherokee Corner would have been northward through eastern Clarke County and western Madison County, and then northeastward through northern Madison County, southeastern Franklin County, and central Hart County. Present towns, villages, or other features on or near this route are: Winterville and New Grove Church, Clarke County (soil map of Clarke County, 1930); Neese, Ila, and junction of Hudson and Broad Rivers, Madison County (soil map of Madison County, 1921); Royston, Franklin County; and Bowersville, Hart County. According both to Bartram's original account and to the Purcell map, the course from the last-mentioned point should have led to the Savannah River at the mouth of the Tugaloo rather than at the mouth of Lightwood Log Creek (soil map of Hart County, 1933). The latter point is indicated on Hall's county map of 1895 and on a map of 1887 (*Fifth Ann. Rept. Bur. Am. Ethnol.:* pl. 8).

[44–47] While Bartram states in his report to Fothergill (1943: 143) that the party reached the mouth of the Tugaloo and there marked a "Line Tree" (as indicated on the Purcell map), he makes the curious mistake in the *Travels* of calling this the "Little river." The incident of an Indian capturing a "Trout" with a reed harpoon is placed near the mouth of the Tugaloo in the former account (1943: 144), but apparently on a branch of Broad River in the *Travels* [44]. Adair (1775: 403) refers to the use of the same sort of harpoon by Indians on the Savannah River.

The "great piles of a porous friable white rock" near Augusta [45] are further described elsewhere (1943: 138).

From the Tugaloo River to Augusta the route, as Bartram says, was "generally through the low lands on the banks of the Savanna" (cf. Goff, 1954: 128–129, map). While no details are given as to the return route from Augusta to Savannah, it probably did not deviate far from the path of the upward journey in May. The return to Savannah may have taken place about the *middle of July 1773*.

[48–56] In this brief chapter of nine pages Bartram passes over the entire period from *July 1773* to *March 1774*, without giving us any very clear or detailed account of his whereabouts and activities during the greater part of that time. He merely remarks [48] that he "spent the remaining part of this season in botanical excursions to the low countries, between Carolina and East Florida." However, in his report to Fothergill (1943: 144) he tells how he set off "from Savannah by land for the Alatamaha"; was "taken ill with a violent Fever" at Darien; did not recover his health for several weeks; and then made a second effort to proceed to Florida. (See also W. Bartram, 1943: 181.) Evidence on this point is furnished by a letter of *August 15, 1773*, from James Spalding, of Frederica, to his agent in Florida, Charles McLatchie (Bartram Papers, *4:* 103); it tells of shipping to him a trunk and a box belonging to Bartram. But apparently Bartram did not follow his goods to Florida until the following spring. When Thomas Lamboll, of Charleston, wrote to him in Savannah on *November 9, 1773* (Bartram Papers, *4:* 68), he remarked that the bearer, a Mr. Andrews, had seen Bartram in Savannah (apparently a very short time previously).

It should be possible to ascertain the date of the excursion up the Altamaha by means of the "almost total autumnal eclipse" of the moon described on page 51. According to information kindly supplied to Mr. Leeds by Dr. James Stokley (*in litt.*, February 12, 1935) from Oppolzer's *Canon der Finsternisse,* no eclipse of the moon was visible in Georgia during the summer or fall of 1773 or 1774. There was a partial eclipse on August 11, 1775, but during the summer and fall of that year Bartram was engaged in his journey to the Mississippi and return. I. Bernard Cohen, of the History of Science Department at Harvard, writes me (June 3, 1941) that Bartram could have seen the partial phases of a total eclipse on July 31, 1776. We are thus forced to conclude that the Altamaha voyage took place not in 1773 but in 1776! As Bartram tells us on page *467,* he spent "the spring and fore part of summer" of the latter year "in revisiting the several districts in Georgia and the East borders of Florida." July 31 is not exactly an "autumnal" date; on the other hand, "the divine hymns of the feathered songsters" [50] might not have been impressive much later in the season. This is but one of several instances in the *Travels* where events are related out of their proper chronological sequence. Bartram suffered either from a faulty memory or from an indifference to dates—if not from both!

The voyage up the Altamaha, for a distance of "fifty miles above the white settlements," may have extended to the general vicinity of the present Doctortown, Wayne County, or even farther, to Beards Bluff, Long County, where a Revolutionary outpost was maintained in 1776.

[54] "The Creek Confederation owed, if not its origin, at least its

complexity to union between the true Muskogee and several mutually related tribes in southern Georgia which called themselves Atcik-hata but are usually known to ethnologists as Hitchiti or Hitchiti-speaking people from the name of their most prominent tribe. The Muskogee and the Hitchiti were still at war when De Soto passed through their country in 1540. The 'Oakmulge fields' were on the east side of Ocmulgee River opposite Macon where are two remarkable groups of mounds recently made the subject of archeological investigation and now incorporated into the Ocmulgee National Monument. Since the Hitchiti at one time lived here and the Muskogee higher up the same river, it is possible that the tradition recorded by Bartram has an historical basis." (J.R.S.)

[55] "These 'Savannahs' were a part of the Shawnee who settled on and gave their name to Savannah River near the end of the seventeenth century. They aided the English in 1681 in driving from that river another tribe called Westo which is believed to have been a part of the Yuchi. So far were they from being driven off by the Creeks that a considerable body retired to the Chattahoochee and thence to the Tallapoosa where they lived in intimate contact with the other elements in the confederation and became particularly attached to the Tukabahchee, the Indians of the leading war town of the Upper Creeks. Other bands of Savannah Shawnee moved to Pennsylvania in several different emigrations but apparently wholly of their own volition.

"The Ogeechee proper were Yuchi, but see Comments for page 66.

"Wapoo is the name of a creek on the landward side of Edisto Island. No one else seems to have applied the name to a tribe, and Bartram may have done so simply because he knew that some of the Indians of this coast country, usually called by ethnologists Cusabo, afterwards went to Florida. The remainder were given a reservation on Palawana Island where they gradually faded from history.

"Santee. This tribe, which gave its name to Santee River, was connected with the Catawba and therefore belonged in the great Siouan stock. About 1716 the South Carolina colonists, assisted by the Cusabo Indians, attacked them and captured a considerable number which they sent as slaves to the West Indies. The remainder retired among the Catawba.

"Yamasee. See Comments for page 26. The Creeks claim too much here. They themselves were rather more than passive allies of the Yamasee when the latter attacked the outposts of South Carolina in 1715 and only turned against them after the English had driven them to Florida.

"Utinas. They were one of the leading tribes of Florida also called Timucua, a name afterwards extended to cover all the related tribes of northern Florida and a corner of Georgia. The Utina lived between the Suwannee and Santa Fe rivers until attacked and destroyed along with their allies by the English and Creeks. At no time can they be said to have 'cramped' the English colonists.

"By Icosans Bartram probably means the Coosa Indians of South Carolina who gave their name to Coosawhatchie River—and who are to be distinguished carefully from the Coosa of Alabama, a division of the Upper Creeks from whom the River Coosa derives its name. Some of them may have joined the Yamasee and have been 'driven out' in the same sense as were the Yamasee. Part may have gone with the Cusabo to Palawana Island, part are said by Adair to have settled among the Catawba, and a part appear to have retired among the Creeks.

"Paticas. Patica was the name of two Timucua towns on the lower course of St. Johns River. Their relations with the English were the same as those above indicated for the Utinas." (J.R.S.)

[55] For an account of Indian depredations in Georgia during the winter of 1773–74, see Jones (1883, 2: 132–135).

Part II

Part II, dealing with Bartram's Florida experiences, includes his observations on Seminoles, Alligators, and some birds and plants of exceptional interest. This may well be regarded as the most important section of the *Travels*.

[57] The point on the Altamaha at which Bartram embarked for Frederica must have been Darien, where he no doubt visited his friend Lachlan McIntosh. Perhaps it was here that he left his horse (Bartram Papers, 1: 78) for the period of his absence in Florida. Very likely Henry Laurens, as an old friend of Bartram's, had provided him with a letter of introduction to his agent on Broughton Island. For an account of the plantation life of James Spalding and others on St. Simon's Island, see Cate (1930: 51–62) and Cate, Colquitt, and McCarty (1940: 25–29).

[58–62] The road taken by Bartram from Frederica to the south end of St. Simon's Island is shown on an old map of that island which probably dates from Oglethorpe's time. A copy has been kindly furnished by Mrs. Margaret Davis Cate. One of the principal features is a "road newly opened from the camp and fort to Frederica." The fort (presumably Fort St. Simons) is at the extreme south end of the island. The road closely skirts the salt marshes of the southeastern portion of the island, passing by the Bloody Marsh where Oglethorpe defeated the Spaniards in 1742. This old military road is now very largely abandoned, but traces of it are still discernible. The habitation of Bartram's "sylvan friend" was doubtless near the cove or inlet at the southwestern corner of the island.

"Two sections of the water battery of Fort Frederica are in a fair state of preservation and are owned by the Colonial Dames" (Cate, Colquitt, and McCarty, 1940: 35). Ruins of the "officers barracks" and the nearby moat, now dry, are still in evidence. For a plan of Frederica, see Crown Collection (ser. 3, 3: 139–140, 1915).

Bartram's list of "shell-fish" [60] may be compared with Lyell's list (1849, 1: 254) of mollusks on an outlying portion of St. Simon's Island.

[63–65] "Little St. Simon's," where Bartram was put ashore, is obviously a *lapsus calami* for Cumberland Island. The spot where he landed was on the western side, bordering Cumberland River or Sound, and probably some miles from the south end. The fort was Fort William (Harris, 1748, 2: map opposite p. 323; Faden's Atlas, pl. 43, 1776), where Bartram's friend, John Stuart, at this time the Superintendent of Indian Affairs, had been in command in former years.

[65–69] After landing at the north end of Amelia Island, Fla., Bartram crossed the present Clark's Creek (Fernandina quadrangle), or Anderson's Creek of Faden's Atlas of 1776 (pl. 43), or Egan's Creek, as it is still called to some extent. On the south side of the mouth of this creek, adjoining Amelia River, was the "New Settlement" (the present Old Fernandina). This was presumably the headquarters of Lord Egmont's plantation. According to George E. Wolff, a local historian, the Egmont indigo plantation was in the northeastern part of the present Fernandina.

At Fernandina and vicinity there were, in 1940, remnants of one large sand mound and three shell mounds—presumably Bartram's "Ogeeche mounts." The sand mound was on the grounds of Public School No. 1, on the north side of Atlantic Avenue near 12th Street. A large part of it had been removed in building the school or grading the grounds. The remnant rose perhaps 10 feet above the general level; its original extent was scarcely determinable. This is apparently the mound described by Brinton (1859: 166–167). He estimated its height at 20 to 35 feet, and reported that human bones and various utensils were disinterred in abundance.

Tom O'Hagan, keeper of the Amelia Island Lighthouse, which stands on an eminence between Fernandina and the sea, pointed out the location of the shell mounds. One was about 200 yards south of the lighthouse and contained skeletons, but had been removed for road material. It was about 10 feet high and half an acre in extent. Another stood about ⅜ mile to the east, across the marsh bordering Clark's Creek. The third was about a mile south of the first, on the west side of the creek.

"Ogeechee mounts. As stated above [p. 347] the Ogeechee tribe was a band of Yuchi and this may have been the one which afterwards removed to Florida and settled at Spring Garden by Woodruff Lake. Possibly these Indians stopped upon the Georgia coast long enough to leave a memory of themselves there though they could hardly have remained for a sufficient length of time to erect mounds of any magnitude. However, the Ogeechee mentioned here may have been Indians from the mouth of Ogeechee River belonging to the Guale tribe which later settled in Florida north of St. Augustine. The Quaker Dickenson visited their towns in 1699. As to their 'destruction' we may say that myth makers have destroyed more tribes than America ever contained." (J.R.S.)

For a further account of the subsidence of the Georgia coast [69], see Lyell (1845, 1: 131; 1849, 1: 249–250), who quotes Bartram with approval.

[70] "Amelia Narrows" was the present Kingsley Creek, and "Fort George's sound" was probably the present Nassau Sound (Fernandina quadrangle). The evening's camp was probably made at the north end of Talbot Island. Faden's Atlas of 1776 (pl. 43) shows here a "Small Spring"—perhaps Bartram's "well of fresh water." The only other suitable campsite in this vicinity would have been on Black Hammock Island, on the west side of Sawpit Creek. The inland passage to the St. John's was by way of this creek and Sister Creek (Mayport quadrangle). The "Cow-ford" was at the site of the present Jacksonville. The "large . . . plantation near the ferry" was Pottburg (W. Bartram, 1943: 145), probably the present Arlington, on the east side of the St. John's opposite Jacksonville (Jacksonville quadrangle).

[73–96] The account that Bartram here gives of his voyage up the river to Spalding's Lower Store can not be altogether reconciled with that in his report to Fothergill (1943: 145–146). It may be well to utilize both in working out the itinerary. The late Francis C. Pyle has made an interesting study (1939) of this itinerary, basing it solely upon the *Travels*.

[73–77] "It was now about the middle of April," 1774 [73]. According to the earlier account, the first night's camp above the Cow-ford was made on the west side of the river, probably at the present Ortega or vicinity. The next day Bartram proceeded 5 miles, apparently re-crossing the river to the vicinity of Goodby's Creek (Orange Park quadrangle). Hereabouts Greenwood's plantation was familiar to him from visits in 1765 and 1766 (J. Bartram, 1942: 36, 47, 89). This was perhaps the plantation he now "wanted to reach." Since 1766, how-ever, it might have changed hands and become the Marshall planta-tion.

[78–79] The next plantation after Marshall's may have been at New Switzerland Point or vicinity, in St. John's County. Francis Philip Fatio had received a grant here in 1772 (Mowat, 1943: 70), and he may have been Bartram's nameless host. (In the earlier account only one of these two plantations is mentioned, and there seem to be other omissions as well.) Apparently Bartram continued to coast the eastern shore of the river. From New Switzerland Point to Fort Picolata is about a dozen miles—a suitable distance for a morning's sail with a favorable breeze.

Bartram's account of the conference with the Indians at St. Augus-tine evidently refers to the same affairs that are discussed by Mowat (1943: 24) in the following words:

"A major threat of war came early in 1774, shortly before Tonyn's arrival. Georgia was threatened with hostilities on the part of the Creeks, and letters from [Superintendent John] Stuart and from Sir James Wright, governor of Georgia, caused the Council to meet four times in February to discuss the province's defenses. . . . However, the danger passed, and the new governorship was inaugurated peace-fully. The Oconee king and some of his followers attended Tonyn's inauguration [on March 9] and were greatly impressed, and several Indians who arrived too late for the ceremony, including the Cow Keeper and Long Warrior, heard a friendly talk from the new governor on March 13, 1774."

While Bartram was passing the site of his old plantation near Pico-lata Creek, where tragic failure had overtaken him in 1766, what poignant feelings he must have experienced! He could scarcely have failed to step ashore for at least a brief view of the ruins. But what-ever his emotions, there was no intimate to whom he might unburden them.

[80–85] All trace of old Fort Picolata has now disappeared, and its exact location is no longer known. Its general site, however, was that of the present settlement of Picolata, St. John's County. Accord-ing to the report to Fothergill (1943: 146), Rollestown or Villa Real was reached the next day after Picolata, but several days are required for this part of the journey in the Travels. In the former account,

Bartram passed the fort and "got 2 Miles farther" before stopping to camp. If this was at "a little lagoon, under an elevated bank, on the West shore of the river" [81], it may have been at the mouth of Clark's Creek, Clay County (U. S. Coast and Geodetic Survey Chart, St. John's River, Hibernia to Racy Point, 1938). Here winds kept him in port a great part of the next day. The size he attributes to a live oak—"fifty paces . . . from the trunk . . . to the extremity of the limbs" [85]—is impossible. It was probably meant for the distance between the extremities of limbs on opposite sides of the tree. The great oak at Hibernia, a few miles downstream, was of approximately this size in 1940.

[85–88] The next night's camp, at an unspecified distance upstream, but at "a good harbour on the East shore," was probably somewhere between Tocoi Creek and Racy Point (U. S. Coast and Geodetic Survey Charts, St. John's River, Hibernia to Racy Point, 1938, and Tocoi to San Mateo, 1933). The "still lagoon" [85] suggests the cove at the mouth of Tocoi Creek.

[88–93] The former masses of water lettuce (*Pistia stratiotes*) on the St. John's have been largely replaced by water hyacinth (*Eichhornia crassipes*), introduced from the tropics about 1884 (Blatchley, 1902: 204 ff.; Gowanloch, 1945: 339). Bartram now kept "along the West or Indian shore," and the logical place to have crossed, to shorten distances along the curving river, would have been between Racy Point on the east shore and Nine Mile Point on the west shore. The "long point of land" that he doubled [90] was doubtless Forrester Point, on the east shore 3 miles north of Palatka. Above this point, however, the river is only slightly rather than "surprisingly" widened. The marshy west side of this expansion is shown on the Palatka quadrangle. The promontory and Indian settlement [92] were at the site of the present Palatka. Bartram was due to return to this village in the fall for a feast of watermelons and oranges [303].

"Oranges and melons came of course from the Old World. Potatoes had been introduced from South America. Corn, beans, pumpkins, squashes and tobacco were cultivated in the Southeast when it was first visited by Europeans." (J.R.S.)

[93–95] Charlotia or Rollestown was located on the east shore midway between the present East Palatka and San Mateo. The site is now a flat-topped bluff rising about 20 feet above the river, and partly wooded with live oaks and cabbage palmettoes. The abundant shells exposed in the face of the bluff are principally *Viviparus georgianus*, with some *Pomacea paludosa*. In the edge of the river I noticed in

1940 some detached pieces of a sort of shell conglomerate; these probably represented Bartram's "lower stratum" of "horizontal masses of a pretty hard rock, composed almost entirely of the above shell." No trace of the ancient settlement seems now discoverable. Modern structures in 1940 consisted of a dwelling at each end of the bluff and a tower for electric power lines near the middle.

[96] The "little remote island," "about seven miles higher up," was Murphy's Island (Palatka quadrangle). Spalding's Lower Store, our traveler's particular destination and headquarters for some months to come, was at the present Stokes Landing on the west side of the St. John's, 6 miles southwest of Palatka. According to local tradition (fide A. M. Thomas), the site was in a grove of live oaks about a hundred yards due west of the landing, where some ancient bricks from a chimney or a well have been excavated. An archaeological survey at this site has revealed some Seminole pottery (Goggin, 1949: 37).

[97–98] Bartram's important voyage up the St. John's, from Spalding's Lower Store to Lake Beresford and return, is described in Chapters 4 and 5. It is here made to appear as if it preceded the journey to the Alachua Savanna, which is described in Chapter 6. This, however, is the wrong sequence. It is evident from the report to Fothergill (1943: 146) that the latter journey was commenced in *April* (probably in the latter part of the month, a few days after his arrival at the Lower Store). Furthermore, in a letter written to his father from Charleston on March 27, 1775 (Bartram Papers, *1:* 78), William indicates that the trip to the Alachua Savanna came first, and covered a period of "a week or ten days." Thus there was ample time for the completion of this trip before Bartram started on his voyage up the St. John's "about the middle of May" [98].

The present account must be considered a composite one of two trips up the St. John's to the vicinity of Lake Beresford: the first one in *May and June,* the second in *August and September 1774.* These two trips are described separately in the report to Fothergill (1943: 150–154, 161–163, 185–187, 191–192).

[98] Mount Hope was a shell mound at Beecher Point on the east side of the St. John's at the north end of Little Lake George (cf. Wyman, 1875: 40; J. Bartram, 1942: 38, 70). The mound has been removed for road material. The indigo plantation there was owned by John Tucker (W. Bartram, 1943: 150; Mowat, 1943: 60–61).

[99–101] Mount Royal (fig. 9) is 3 or 4 miles farther upstream, at Fruitland Cove. The "fifteen years ago" must be in reference to the time when this portion of the *Travels* was being written (say 1780), for the previous visits to this place had been in 1765 and 1766 (J. Bartram, 1942: 38, 45). The day's journey was about a dozen miles.

[*101–105*] Bartram's course lay apparently between the two large islands at the north end of Lake George—Hog Island on the west and Drayton's Island on the east (map of Ocala National Forest, 1938; U. S. Coast and Geodetic Survey Chart, St. John's River, Palatka to Lake George, 1938). The night was spent at the south end of the latter. It is actually about 3 miles long and half as wide. In the Contents (p. iv), and nowhere else, Bartram refers to Drayton's Island as the "Isle Edelano."

[*106*] The island near the river's entrance, "about half a mile in the lake," has seemingly disappeared from recent maps. Wyman, as late as 1868 (p. 463), apparently refers to it as "Rope's Island, right bank, entrance of Lake George." Perhaps it has been overtaken by the advancing delta and is no longer an island. It is identical with the "Isle of Palms," described on page *157*.

[*110*] The channel and the island here mentioned were probably Blue Creek and Blue Island (U. S. Coast and Geodetic Survey Chart, St. John's River, Palatka to Lake George, 1938).

[*111–113*] Spalding's Upper Store was at the site of the present Astor, on the west side of the St. John's, about 5 miles above Lake George.

[*114–116*] In the report to Fothergill (1943: 151–154), Bartram refers to his companion on this part of the trip merely as "one of the men" (presumably a white trader), and indicates that they remained together until their return to the Upper Store. In the *Travels,* on the other hand, the companion is transformed into an Indian who deserted with a "terrible whoop" on the first day! An original draft of a portion of the *Travels* (Hist. Soc. Pennsylvania) corresponds closely with the account published in 1791.

The first night's camp was apparently at Manhatten or vicinity, on the west side no more than 3 miles above the Upper Store. The 90-foot palms noted on this section of the river were royal palms (*Roystonea elata*). The present description validates the name ("Palma Elate" = *P. elata*) provided on page iv of the Contents (Harper, 1946*a*). They have not been reported so far north in Florida by subsequent observers, and it is presumed that they did not survive the "freeze" of 1835 (Cooper, 1861: 440). It is astonishing that John Bartram made no reference to them in passing this point in 1765 and 1766.

[*116–117*] "The little lake" was the present Lake Dexter. The "little promontory" on the west shore was a shell mound at the spot marked "Idlewild Dock" on the river chart (although no dock is there). It is more appropriately referred to by Wyman (1875: 35–36) as "Bartram's Mound" (cf. Blatchley, 1902: map facing p. 196). Most of the shells have been removed for road material. The river is here contracted to a width of perhaps 125 yards.

This spot (fig. 10) may be considered justly celebrated as the scene of the most thrilling of all Bartram's zoological experiences, providing him with the principal basis for his immortal account of the Alligator and its bellowing. Although he has been much criticized for this account by some who lacked his advantages of observation, he has been quite thoroughly vindicated of late (Harper, 1930: 52–57, fig. 3; W. Bartram, 1943, 128, 186, fig. 24).

[118–121] Bartram's drawing of an Alligator (fig. 12) represents it with considerable accuracy as it appears in the act of bellowing. In the Okefinokee Swamp of Georgia I have seen the "tail brandished high" and have fairly felt how "the earth trembles with his thunder." If I have missed the "clouds of smoke" (poetic license for vapor) issuing from his nostrils, it may be because my observations have been far more limited than Bartram's. The turmoil of water as two rivals clash is wonderful to behold. There is every reason to believe that Alligators, before they had become cowed by firearms, were given to just such attacks on human beings as our author describes, especially during the mating season in the spring; in fact, there are well-authenticated accounts of such attacks (though perhaps on a smaller scale) in Okefinokee Swamp more than a century after Bartram's time.

[122–123] His description of the astonishing drive for fishes, which "threw my senses into such a tumult," receives corroboration through Audubon (1827: 273–275) and more particularly through Allen Chesser (in Harper, 1926: 417–418), who assuredly had never read a line of either Bartram or Audubon but had been assiduously reading the book of nature during a long lifetime spent in Okefinokee Swamp. As late as 1939 a spot in Lake Dexter, near the river's entrance, was known as "the striking ground," from the numbers of Large-mouthed Bass (or "Trout") that break the surface (or "strike") there. In the report to Fothergill (1943: 152) Bartram speaks of the Trout "continually striking at small young fish . . . of a bright silver colour"; these were no doubt the Florida Lesser Shad, or Shadine (*Signalosa petensis vanhyningi*).

[124] This is one of the earliest notices of the Florida Wood Rat (*Neotoma floridana floridana*) in the literature. Perhaps the very earliest mention of it is by John Bartram (1766: 30).

[125] The "Battle lagoon," where Bartram had gone fishing the

previous evening, appears on the river chart as "Mud Lake" (fig. 10). It opens out on the west side of the St. John's just above Lake Dexter.

[126–128] There is a little uncertainty concerning some of the details of Bartram's observations on the nests, eggs, and young of the Alligator. In evaluating them, however, we are still handicapped by lack of full information on this creature's life history (cf. Kellogg, 1929: 12–14; Harper, 1930: 63; McIlhenny, 1935). Furthermore, the present chapter seems to combine the events of two trips up the river, which are related separately in the report to Fothergill (1943); and some of the conditions described here (broken eggshells, and young ones swimming about) would apply only to the period of the later trip. The first trip was commenced "about the middle of May" (p. 98), and fresh, high nests of the Alligators [127] were perhaps not to be seen till a month or so later. But Bartram's description of them could easily have been based upon what he found on a later trip, in August. He apparently erred in believing that the Alligators "commonly lay from one to two hundred eggs in a nest" [127], for the maximum complement of an individual is now believed to be little more than forty. The eggs seem to be laid in a single group, perhaps several layers deep, but not in detached layers, separated by nest material, as Bartram states [127], unless perchance in the old days of superabundance and rivalry more than one individual did occasionally deposit eggs in a single nest. If the incubation period is approximately two months (say July 1 to September 1), and if the young leave the mother in about four months after hatching (McQueen and Mizell, 1926: 51), Bartram could scarcely have seen the brood following the mother Alligator [126] on the first trip in May. The number of young ones ("one hundred or more") was obviously too large, unless two or more broods happened to be combined, as indeed Bartram suggests [127].

[128] The account of 20-foot Alligators is perhaps not altogether improbable, even though, in these modern days of excessive hunting, they no longer arrive within several feet of that length. On this point the testimony of Lyell (1849, 1: 251) is interesting:

"When I first read Bartram's account of alligators more than twenty feet long, and how they attacked his boat and bellowed like bulls, and made a sound like distant thunder, I suspected him of exaggeration; but all my inquiries here [in Georgia] and in Louisiana convinced me that he may be depended upon."

It is well to remember, however, that Bartram is none too accurate in his general statements of dimensions and distances.

[130] The "rattling in the throat for near a minute" is scarcely

comprehensible unless it refers to a series of successive inhalations, for each separate inhalation should last for no more than a very few seconds (Harper, 1930: 55).

[*130–140*] Bartram's progress along this section of the St. John's (fig. 11) was apparently very leisurely. The distance from Lake Dexter to Lake Beresford is not more than a dozen miles in an air line (soil map of Lake County, northern sheet, 1928), and perhaps 18–20 miles by the windings of the river; yet, in covering this course, he spent parts of either two or three days, according to the several versions in the *Travels* (*130–140*) and in the report to Fothergill (1943: 152–153, 162–163). As already pointed out, the present account is apparently a composite one of two separate river trips, and consequently there are difficulties in interpreting the itinerary correctly.

The first night's camp [*134–136*] was perhaps at Mosquito Grove— a place most fittingly named, according to Bartram's account of it. This point is half a dozen miles above Lake Dexter. The weird and startling cries of the Florida Barred Owl (*Strix acclamator georgica*), with which Bartram was serenaded this night, are well calculated to make a memorable impression upon a solitary traveler in the wilderness. This bird seems much more vociferous than the northern subspecies (*S. a. acclamator*).

The description of the second night's lodging-place [*138–139*] applies fairly well to St. Francis—a shell bluff on the west side about midway between Lakes Dexter and Beresford. (See also W. Bartram, 1943: 162, 191–192.) This bluff has a frontage of about 250 yards along the St. John's River and St. Francis Dead River (U. S. Coast and Geodetic Survey Chart, St. John's River, Lake George to Lake Harney, 1928). It has a maximum width of about 200 feet, and a height of about 12 feet at the outer edge. Furrows on the grassy surface indicate cultivation in times past. Presumably this cultivation has obliterated for the present all signs of the graves of the vanquished Yamasees, which should make this spot one of exceptional archaeological interest. Most unfortunately, removal of the entire mound for road-building material had commenced in 1940. This mound was excavated and described by Wyman (1875: 33–35) under the name of "Old Town." Without the advantage of access to Bartram's manuscript, he did not realize that this was the burial place of the Yamasees, which he looked for elsewhere in vain (1875: 36).

"The tumuli mentioned may have been centuries older than the supposed encounter for which, incidentally, I know no other authority." (J.R.S.)

The "high bluff" with "grand Magnolia, glorious Palms," and other trees [139–140] was doubtless the present Hawkinsville, on the west side a mile above Crow's Bluff. This is a shell bluff, extending for probably half a mile along the river and reaching a height of perhaps 15 feet above it. Inland from it are "high open Pine forests." About 3 miles farther upstream the "branch of the river" [140] opening to view is the outlet of Lake Beresford. The "delightful little bluff" on the right hand of this branch [140] is on Huntoon Island.

[140–142] The principal season for Florida hurricanes, such as the one here described, is the early fall. The present one was doubtless encountered on Bartram's second trip to this point, in late August or September, and not on his first trip, about the first of June.

[143–144] According to local information, the Beresford plantation was near the present Beresford Station, which is on the east side of the lake toward the north end. This makes the right distance of "about four miles" [145] from the plantation house to Blue Springs. Lord Beresford's manager here was apparently a Mr. Bernard (letter from William Bartram, July 15, 1774, to Lachlan McIntosh; Dreer Coll., Scientists, 1). The circumstances of Bartram's trip to the Mosquito River are discussed above, page 335.

[144] The "spacious Indian mound" near New Smyrna was the famous Turtle Mound (cf. Small, 1923: 199–204, fig.).

[145–146] The "vast fountain of warm . . . mineral water" was the present Blue Springs, on the east side of the St. John's a few miles from Orange City, Volusia County. The outlet creek runs about half a mile before joining the river. The immediate surroundings, aside from some boathouses, a dwelling, and a clearing near the mouth of the creek, did not seem in 1939 to have changed greatly since Bartram's time. However, Alligators and large fishes were no longer "numerous in the bason." Other descriptions of Blue Springs are by John Bartram (1942: 40), William Bartram (1943: 154), and Wyman (1875: 23–24). This was the southernmost point reached by our traveler during his entire journey of 1773–77.

The orange grove where the first night of the downstream journey was spent was probably at St. Francis or vicinity. The high soaring of the Florida Sandhill Crane is a most interesting sight, but one only occasionally observed.

[147–148] This is the technically valid original description of the Florida Limpkin—*Tantalus pictus* (fig. 15) or—in current nomenclature—*Aramus guarauna pictus* (Bartram) (cf. Harper, 1942d: 219). The first mention of this bird occurs in Bartram's report to Fothergill (1943: 153). He shot one on his journey up the St. John's after spending a night at St. Francis, and apparently ate this specimen (the type!) on the same day at Hawkinsville, for he speaks of "finishing a small but savory repast on some Trout & a broiled bird." The account in the *Travels* is introduced while Bartram is passing down the river in the vicinity of St. Francis.

[*148–149*] The "two . . . species" of "Spanish curlews" are merely the adult and the immature, respectively, of a single species—the White Ibis (*Eudocimus albus*).

[*149–150*] This account of the "wood pelican"—Wood Ibis (*Mycteria americana*)—has been criticized by Audubon (1835: 128) and defended by Bryant (1859: 16). While there is justice in the remarks of both, Bartram no doubt faithfully set down his own observations.

[*150–152*] Concerning the identification of Bartram's "Vultur sacra," Cassin wrote (1853: 60): "There is no more inviting nor more singular problem in North American Ornithology." Until the report to Fothergill became available, it was not known that Bartram had actually had a specimen in his hands. This circumstance lends much greater credibility to his account than had been previously admitted. His description applies very satisfactorily to the King Vulture (*Sarcoramphus papa*) except in one particular. In that species the tail is black, whereas Bartram describes it as white, tipped with dark brown or black. We may consider this a slip due to imperfect memory, and we may conclude that the King Vulture actually occurred in Florida in Bartram's time, although it has not been definitely recorded since then. Certain severe freezes in subsequent years may have brought about a local extinction of the bird. In 1835, for example, a severe northwest wind blew for 10 days, and the thermometer dropped to 7°; the St. John's River was partly frozen, and "all" fruit was killed to the ground (J. L. Williams, 1837: 18). If the royal standard of the Muscogulges was made up of the white tail-feathers of some bird for display in peaceable negotiations (pp. 151, 454–455), that bird was probably the adult Southern Bald Eagle (*Haliaeetus leucocephalus leucocephalus*), and Bartram must have erred in identifying the feathers as those of his "Vultur sacra." The brown-tipped feathers with which the standard was furnished when carried to battle [*151*] may have belonged to the subadult Golden Eagle (*Aquila chrysaëtos canadensis*). This entire case has been more fully discussed elsewhere (Harper, 1936).

[*152*] The expression "coped," applied here to the "carrion crow" or Black Vulture (*Coragyps atratus*), is apparently used in the sense of "hooded," in reference to the "ruff or tippet . . . in which he can

conceal his neck and head at pleasure." The present account, in connection with the name "Vultur atratus," proposed on page 289,
constitutes the technically valid original description of this species
(Harper, 1942d: 212).

[152–156] In descending the river from the previous night's camp
at St. Francis or vicinity, Bartram once more passed his "Battle
lagoon" (or "Mud Lake" of the river chart) [153] just before reaching
Lake Dexter. The details of the leisurely tour which he now undertook about this lake cannot be traced very exactly. The distance from
the river's entrance to the narrow east end is a little more than 3 miles,
and the "Orange grove bluff" on which he camped may have been
on Spring Garden Creek, which enters the lake from the east. In two
places [154, 155] he refers to a "river" which may have been this
creek. The "traces of the habitations of the ancients" may have been
a sand mound, a causeway, and a shell heap on Tick Island, described
by Moore (1894: 48–50).

The fish described on pages 153–154 as the "yellow bream or sun
fish," and named "Cyprinus coronarius" in a footnote, is identifiable
as the Warmouth (fig. 13), known until recently as *Chaenobryttus
gulosus* (Cuvier, 1829). The current name is *Chaenobryttus coronarius*
(Bartram) (Harper, 1942a).

[154] There is difficulty in reconciling the occurrence of the "blue
linnet" or Indigo Bunting (*Linaria cyanea*) and of the "golden icterus"
—presumably the Baltimore Oriole (*Icterus galbula*)—in this part of
Florida at the time of Bartram's first trip, which was presumably early
June, for the breeding ranges of both lie considerably to the north.
If it was on the occasion of his second trip, in the early fall, they might
have been passing on their migration, but they would be less likely
to have been in song at that time.

[155] The figure and descriptive notes on the plate facing this page,
together with the seven words in the text, constitute the original
reference for Bartram's "Ixea caelestina," now known as *Salpingostylis
caelestina* (Bartram) Small. It was not rediscovered till about 156
years later (Small, 1931)! According to Dr. Small (p. 158), "Bartram's
original station appears to have been somewhere near Lake George."
The type locality can now be fixed quite definitely as near the shore
of Lake Dexter, Volusia County, Florida. It has become evident that
Bartram's original discovery of this elegant species dates back to his
first Florida trip in 1765–66, and probably to the spring of the latter
year. In writing to him on February 16, 1768, Peter Collinson (Bartram
Papers, 3: 73) acknowledges the receipt of a painting of *Ixia*. Still
more important evidence is an addendum to a letter from John Bartram

to Benjamin Rush, December 5, 1767 (Rush Corr., *23: 3*). This consists of a delightful descriptive essay by William on the "Purple Flower'd Ixia of Sᵗ Johns Rivʳ Eᵗ Florida." Aside from the intrinsic interest of the subject, this document is of special significance in being perhaps the earliest example of a nature essay by William that has survived to the present day.

The "good harbour, under the high banks of the river," where Bartram camped the following night, may have been at Orange Bluff (or Bluffton) on the east side at the outlet of Lake Dexter. Although this place was only about 3 miles above Spalding's Upper Store, he speaks of spending still another night en route, at some point on the east bank.

[156] The "Eastermost channel" between the Upper Store and Lake George was presumably the main river. There is a smaller channel on the west for part of the distance, known as Blue Creek (indicated but not named on soil map of Lake County, northern sheet, 1928; named by Moore, 1894: second map following p. 130).

[157] The "Isle of Palms" has been previously mentioned on pages *102* and *106*.

[157–168] In this passage occurs a considerable discrepancy between the *Travels* and the report to Fothergill. According to the latter (1943: 154, 163), the return from the first trip up the St. John's was by way of the eastern shore of Lake George, and the return from the second trip by way of the western shore. On the latter occasion Bartram visits only one of the two great springs on the west side of the lake. This is Silver Glen Spring, which he compares with Salt Springs, having visited the latter on the first ascent of the river (1943: 161–162). The report to Fothergill is believed to represent the true course of events.

As stated previously, the account in the *Travels* of a trip on the St. John's is actually a composite one of two separate trips. The resulting literary exigencies have evidently misplaced the present description [160–168] of "Six mile Springs"—or Salt Springs, as they are now known—and their surroundings.

In his approach to the springs [157], Bartram may have passed the southwestern corner of Lake George at some distance offshore, and may have thus failed to notice the mouth of Juniper Creek (map of Ocala National Forest, 1938). According to the original account (1943: 163), the night's camp on the lake shore was "about 2 miles" south of the outlet of Silver Glen Spring—or "Johnsons Springs," to use his own words. This is presumably where the adventure with the Wolf took place [158–159].

On the following morning [159] Bartram ignores the outlet of Silver Glen Spring and transports himself hurriedly to the mouth of Salt Springs Run ("the little river, descending from Six mile Springs," 160), toward the northwest corner of the lake. This runs a course of 4 or 5 miles from the head of the springs, which lies just east of Lake Kerr, Marion County. Salt Springs (fig. 16) had been first visited by both Bartrams on January 24, 1766 (J. Bartram, 1942: 44). This is particularly noteworthy as the spot where William then discovered the rare yellow anise (*Illicium parviflorum*). It now gave him delight to revisit the "alluring scene" and the "odoriferous Illisium groves" [160]. The springs in 1939 were still environed with a grove containing some of the trees he mentions, although the undergrowth had been cleared from a considerable space. A stone's throw north of the springs, however, there was a low hammock remaining in a good natural condition and containing plentiful specimens of the *Illicium*. The "chain of shallow ponds" [161] lies on the northeastern side of Lake Kerr and practically forms a part of it. The "endless wild desert" [163–165] is evidently a portion of the "Florida scrub"—an extremely interesting plant association virtually confined to this state (cf. R. M. Harper, 1915: 142–144; 1921: 209–211). A very large proportion of the entire area between Lake George and the Ocklawaha River is occupied by "scrub."

The "amazing crystal fountain" (Salt Springs) [165] consists of half a dozen "boils" arising in a basin about 40 yards in width. Some of the rocky chasms through which the water wells up may be as much as 30 feet deep (Cooke, 1939: 90). After nearly two centuries of disintegration, the limestone rocks no longer project above the water, as reported by both Bartrams; the uppermost are nearly a foot beneath the surface. Furthermore, the ebullition of the waters no longer has its pristine force, gushing out "two or three feet above the common surface" [166]. In 1788 Michaux (1889: 36) reported the ebullition as "more than half a foot." According to local information secured in 1940 by my companion, E. Perot Walker, the force of the waters was considerably greater 20 years previously. In 1940 the "boils" did not seem to well up more than a couple of inches above the general surface. The water of Salt Springs "has the composition of diluted sea water" (Cooke, 1939: 90); this probably accounts for the presence here of certain fishes of salt or brackish waters that are mentioned by Bartram [166] as well as of enormous Blue Crabs (*Callinectes sapidus*). Although Salt Springs have become a somewhat populous watering-place, a modicum of their original charm remained in 1939 and 1940.

[*160, 165, 166*] It was from Bartram's description of Salt Springs and its outlet that Coleridge drew much of the imagery of the immortal "Kubla Khan," as Lowes (1927: 366), Fagin (1933: 145–147), and J. K. Wright (1956) have remarked. Thus Salt Springs Run becomes the archetype of "Alph, the sacred river."

[*168–169*] The "Rocky Point" on the northwestern part of Lake George still bears that name (map of Ocala National Forest, 1938); it is barely 2 miles from the mouth of Salt Springs Run, but perhaps Bartram was estimating "nine miles" from the head of the run. "The island in the bay" where he spent the night was doubtless Drayton's Island. The gentleman at Mount Royal was Mr. Kean, as stated on page 98.

The "Voyage to the Upper Store" was performed "in less then Three Weeks," as Bartram writes in his manuscript account of his journey to Alachua (Hist. Soc. Pennsylvania). His return to Spalding's Lower Store from this first river trip seems to have taken place in *early June 1774;* from his second trip, approximately in *September 1774* (W. Bartram, 1943; 187, 192). As we have already seen, the *Travels* treats both trips as one.

[*170–174*] The trip to the Alachua Savanna, described in the present chapter, was evidently the first of Bartram's longer excursions from Spalding's Lower Store, and not the second, as indicated here. The start was made in *April* (W. Bartram, 1943; 146)—probably in the latter part of that month—and the date of the return probably fell within the *first part of May 1774.*

A particularly difficult point to identify on the present route was the "Halfway pond" [*174*] (fig. 17). But this and other puzzles have been solved with the enthusiastic cooperation of E. W. Watkins and Randall Wells, of Palatka, T. H. Hubbell and H. B. Sherman, of Gainesville, and other friends.

The "old trader" [*170*], frequently mentioned but not named in this and the following chapter, was probably Job Wiggens (cf. pp. 156, 305). Apparently much of what Bartram learned about the Seminoles, and other matters as well, came through this "old interpreter . . . often my travelling companion, friend and benefactor." Posterity may be accordingly grateful to the latter.

The route to the Alachua Savanna extends from the site of the Lower Store at the present Stokes Landing southwestward about 4 miles through dry pine barrens to Camp Branch (not mentioned in the *Travels*) (Palatka and Interlachen quadrangles). The "higher and drier knolls" [*171*] constitute an area of the highly interesting "Florida scrub" (cf. R. M. Harper, 1915: 142–144; 1921: 209–211), which may

still be found on the road west of Rodman, about a mile east of Deep
Creek. Some of the plants mentioned toward the bottom of page *171*,
as well as the birds and lizards mentioned on page *172*, are more or
less characteristic of the "scrub." This particular bit of "scrub" is the
type locality of the Florida Jay—the "Corvus Floridanus" of Bartram.

There seems to be a certain amount of confusion at this point in the
narrative. (A sentence or two in the original draft [MSS. Div., Hist.
Soc. Pennsylvania] have been deleted here.) Immediately after listing
the birds and lizards of the dry "scrub" [*172*], Bartram makes an
abrupt and puzzling transition in the following words: "After passing
over this extensive, level, hard, wet savanna." This "savanna" is evidently located between Camp Branch and the "scrub," and is described in the report to Fothergill (1943: 146) as "Bay gales." To
this habitat, rather than to the "scrub," belong some of the plants
mentioned on page *171*, including *Gordonia, Magnolia,* and probably
the "Andromeda nitida."

The "fine brook or rivulet" [*172*] was Deep Creek. The old crossing
was probably at or near the present bridge. According to E. W.
Watkins, the old trail from Deep Creek to Kenwood (2.5–3 miles west)
is represented by the road nearest to the now abandoned Ocklawaha
Valley Railroad on its north side (Interlachen quadrangle). This
passes through an extensive baygall ("bay-gale," *173*). Beyond Kenwood the old trail evidently extended to the present Johnson (about
7 miles northwest), perhaps in a rather direct course, passing north
of Hewitt Lakes and across Little Cabbage Creek. Along this part
of the route are to be found "the expansive airy Pine forests, on
parallel chains of low swelling mounds, called the Sand Hills" [*173*],
and "the sparkling ponds and lakes . . . on every side" [*174*].

[*174–179*] A mile and a half west of Johnson, in southwestern
Putnam County, is the southern end of Cowpen Pond (or Lake) (fig.
17). This attractive body of water is the "Half-way pond" of Bartram.
Together with its environs, it seems to have inspired one of the loftiest
passages he ever penned. This was included in his original draft of
the *Travels* (Journey to the Great Alachua Savanna; MSS. Div., Hist.
Soc. Pennsylvania), but unfortunately was omitted from the published
work. The deletion was presumably due to some unsympathetic
editor.

At the south end of the pond, and separated from it by a narrow
strip of land, is a deep, circular "sink-hole" [*174*] about 200 yards
in diameter. This is known at present as "Drummer's Pond." On
the east side of the sink-hole are extensive deposits of marl and
sand, which have been mined for some years for the production of

kaolin. Some of the deposits that are left are of a rocklike hardness, and in Bartram's poetic view this formation might easily have appeared as "a point of flat rocks" [174]. At least nothing so resembling rock seems to be known at any other lake in this section of the state. Adjoining the pond and the sink-hole is a grove of live-oaks, which would have made a fine camp-site for the traders.

The several fishes described here are, for the most part, identifiable, as will be seen from the index. Bartram's color descriptions of fresh specimens are valuable today. His account of "the great soft shelled tortoise" [177–178] applies in most respects to the Southern Soft-shelled Turtle (Amyda ferox). However, the tubercles on the head and neck and a fifth claw on each hind foot (as shown in the accompanying plates) do not fit; they may be regarded either as representing individual variations or as inaccuracies on Bartram's part (cf. Harper, 1940: 717). On the other hand, Conrad (1846: 46) presents a hearsay report of a soft-shelled turtle, with five claws to each foot, in the Manatee River, Fla.

In referring to the "lofty roosts" [179] of the Florida Sandhill Cranes, Bartram must have erred, through a defect of either eyesight or memory. At least these birds are not known at present to alight in trees.

[179–183] The route westward "for five or six miles" from Cowpen ("Half-way") Pond no doubt approximated the present Atlantic Coast Line as far as the vicinity of Hawthorn (Hawthorn quadrangle), where the hills rise to about 150 feet—a higher elevation than Bartram had encountered elsewhere on his way from the St. John's. But the "heaps or piles of rocks" he reports [180] are not apparent today. The "rapid brook" flows into the northwestern corner of Little Orange Lake ("a vast and beautiful lake," 180).

From the vicinity of Hawthorn the old trail, probably coinciding more or less with present roads, extends southwestward for about 4 miles to Lochloosa Creek ("another large deep creek of St. Juan's," 180), crossing it a little more than a mile above its mouth in Lochloosa Lake. It then continues southwestward for half a dozen miles, passing north of Watson's Prairie and approaching Orange Lake ("a great lake, many miles in length," 181–182) at its northwestern corner. Here a tributary creek, the River of Styx, courses through "a vastly extensive and sedgy marsh" [181]. The present crossing is by a recently constructed causeway and bridge, from which Orange Lake is easily visible.

The "sandy hills" [181] or "sand hills" [182], where Bartram reports "the great land tortoise, called gopher," are evidently located along his route between Lochloosa Creek and the River of Styx, in southeastern Alachua County. Accordingly the type locality of the species (*Gopherus polyphaemus*) (fig. 5) may be restricted a little further to this particular area (cf. Harper, 1940: 695). The account given on pages *182–183*, in connection with the proposal of the name "Testudo Polyphaemus" on page *18*, constitutes the type description of the Gopher Turtle. Its remarkable ability to carry a "man standing on its back" [*183*] has been abundantly verified.

[*183–184*] From the River of Styx to Tuscawilla Lake ("the great and beautiful lake of Cuscowilla," *183*) is no more than 3 miles in a direct line; thus Bartram's distance of "eight or nine miles" [*184*] is much overestimated. The "large artificial mound of earth" [*184*] was pointed out to me by E. W. Watkins; it stands on the summit of a ridge on the north side of the lake, at a point about ⅗ mile east of the center of Micanopy (Arredondo quadrangle). Its height in 1940 (after having been ploughed over for an indefinite period) was about 4 feet; its diameter, about 25 yards. About the turn of the century it was approximately twice as high, as Z. C. Herlong informed me.

"Here we note again the mythizing of the Yamasee. They were not the ancient inhabitants of Florida but of southern Georgia." (J.R.S.)

[*184–186*] The distance from the mound to the site of ancient Cuscowilla is not "near a mile" [*184*], but "about a quarter of a mile," as Bartram states in the report to Fothergill (1943: 147). The "pretty brook of water" [*184*], now altered by ditching and doubtless reduced in flow, enters the lake from the north about a quarter of a mile east of Micanopy. Z. C. Herlong informed me that at its source, in the eastern part of Micanopy, there was formerly a pond, which has now completely disappeared. We learn on a later page [*192*] that the town stood "upon a high swelling ridge of sand hills, within three or four hundred yards" of the lake.

"For the history of the Cuscowilla Indians and incidentally the beginnings of the Seminole Nation see pages 380–381. In the early part of the eighteenth century they lived upon the Oconee River and were known as the Oconee tribe. Their chief, Cowkeeper, was at that time constantly leading raiding parties against the Spaniards and Spanish Indians in Florida. Subsequently he and his people moved to the Creek towns on the Chattahoochee where part continued as late as 1799. Before that time, however, the chief and another part of the tribe moved to the Alachua country where Bartram found them in the town of Cuscowilla. Cowkeeper and his tribe retained, partly from this priority, the primacy also in the Seminole Nation and all of the head chiefs of the Seminole until the removal were descended from Cowkeeper in the female line." (J.R.S.)

In December 1765 Cowkeeper had visited St. Augustine with his family and attendants. Governor "Grant made him a Great Medal Chief and loaded him with presents and provisions." (Mowat, 1943: 23.)

His Indian name is given as "Ahaya" (John Stuart to Earl of Halifax, British Colonial Office Records, 5/66, pp. 5–6) (*fide* Howard Sharp, *in litt.*, June 21, 1944).

"Bartram's description of slavery among the Indians seems to be somewhat overdone at this place, and, indeed, on page 213 he partially contradicts himself." (J.R.S.)

On one of Bartram's own diagrams (1943: fig. 21) of the Alachua Savanna (fig. 18) the extreme right-hand portion, including the store (E), Cuscowilla (B), and Tuscawilla Lake (C), is oriented by approximately 90° from the proper compass directions. The sun must have been totally obscured by clouds while Bartram was getting his bearings in that locality!

[187–189] The destination for which the party of traders now set out was apparently the store on the southern border of the Alachua Savanna (erroneously represented on one of Bartram's diagrams as located on the eastern border; on the other, at the southeastern corner). According to Z. C. Herlong, the store was close to a spring about half a mile west of Chacala Pond ("a little lake," *189*) (Arredondo quadrangle). An old man who moved to the spring about 1850 is said to have built his house in part out of the remains of the store. An Indian field extended from the spring to Chacala Pond; this was perhaps the site of the "plantations" mentioned on page 193. The route to this place from Cuscowilla was nearly northward, on the east side of Grass, Sawgrass, and Burnt Ponds. The "savanna or bay-gale" [*187*] through which it passed is still in evidence.

The Alachua Savanna (or Payne's Prairie, as it is now generally called) was until comparatively recent years, as in Bartram's time, an intermittent lake (Sellards, 1914: 134–147). Drainage now prevents it from being more than a marsh. In its broader aspects it has probably much the same appearance as when it made such a memorable impression upon Bartram. Of course much of the surrounding forest has been cleared; and a road on a causeway now bisects the savanna. Grazing cattle and feeding herons are still a prominent feature of the landscape. But the Seminole, the Wolf, the Deer, and the Sandhill Crane have departed.

This ecstatic description of the savanna was utilized for specimen pages in James and Johnson's prospectus of the *Travels*, issued in 1790. It may be doubted whether a finer passage could have been selected. The choice may have been Bartram's own, revealing his fond recollection of life among the Seminoles. (Harper, 1946b: 35.)

One of Bartram's two sketches of the Alachua Savanna shows the water chinquapin ("Nymphea nilumbo," *189*) in Chacala Pond. This sketch bears a statement that the savanna is "above 60 miles in circumferance"; actually it is scarcely half of that. It covers probably 23 or 24 square miles.

[*190*] The remark concerning Florida Sandhill Cranes alighting on palms or pines, in repetition of a similar comment on page *179*, is rather incomprehensible today.

[*191*] For an account of "the late treaty of St. Augustine," see pages 78–79 and Commentary thereon.

[*195*] This description of "several large snakes" is apparently a composite one of two different species (cf. W. Bartram, 1943: 222).

[*196–199*] The tour of the Alachua Savanna, on which Bartram and the "old trader" (Job Wiggens?) now set out, took them at first toward its southwestern corner, at a distance of half a dozen miles from their camp near Chacala Pond (Arredondo quadrangle). The site of "the ancient Alachua" [*198*] was perhaps somewhere near the center of the southern border of the savanna. Here is "the most elevated eminence" [*198*] on this border, the altitude reaching 90–100 feet above the sea. The night's camp was apparently made before they reached the southwestern corner, for on the following morning their course was west for a time before they turned northwest [*199*].

"The 'famous and powerful' Alachua tribe was the Potano which was encountered by De Soto in 1539 and possibly by Narváez eleven years earlier. In 1565 Laudonnière's Frenchmen assisted the Utina in an attack upon these people, and the Spaniards found them difficult to subdue." (J.R.S.)

[*199*] This account of the Florida Wolf ("lupus niger") should apparently be recognized as the valid original description of that animal, with the Alachua Savanna as the type locality (Harper, 1942c).

[*200–203*] The adventure with the Deer took place apparently along the northwestern border of the savanna. To judge by the report to Fothergill (1943: 149, 184), the nesting of the Florida Sandhill Crane was observed at or near the Bivans Arm of the savanna, about 2 miles south-southwest of the present Gainesville. This is no doubt the "extensive grassy cove of the savanna" mentioned on page 202.

The "swift running brook of clear water" [202–203] is the present Sweetwater Branch, arising in the vicinity of Gainesville and entering the savanna at one of its northernmost points. The next brook crossed [203] was a short one at Oliver Park.

[203–207] The Alachua Sink (or "Great Sink" of Bartram) (fig. 18) is situated on the northeastern border of the savanna, about 3 miles south-southeast of Gainesville. The wooded knolls on its border, described by Bartram [204] as "fifty or sixty feet" high, are apparently only "thirty or forty feet" (Sellards, 1914: 135). The dry sink-holes or "infundibuliform cavities" are a noteworthy feature of the area. The rare soapberry (*Sapindus marginatus*) still grew there in 1939. Alligators were no longer in particular evidence at the Sink. Its surface was almost entirely concealed by masses of water hyacinth. From the knolls above the Sink an impressive view was obtained of the wide savanna.

[207–208] From the Alachua Sink the party seems to have approximately retraced its course to the previous night's camp, somewhere near the southwestern corner of the savanna. The "wet morass" they repassed was the Bivans Arm. The ulcers noted on the cattle and horses may have been similar to those that afflict human beings who have frequent contact with swamp waters in certain sections of the Southeast. Some toxic organism in the water may be the causative agent.

[208–209] The next night's camp was doubtless at the store near Chacala Pond; this was not quite at "the East end of the savanna" [208], although Bartram so represents it on one of his diagrams. The following day's route may be determined better, perhaps, from the report to Fothergill (1943: 150, 185) than from the *Travels*. According to the former, the party first skirted the savanna for about 4 miles, and apparently left it somewhere near the middle of its eastern border. The "old Spanish highway" [208], into which they then came, was obviously not the main road from St. Augustine to Pensacola, which lay probably a dozen miles farther north, running approximately west-northwest from Melrose toward the natural bridge over the Santa Fe River. It was rather one of several southern branches or offshoots from that road, marked "Path to Latchua" on the Purcell map of about 1779 (Boyd, 1938: 8th pl. following p. 24); beyond the limits of that map it probably passed west of Lake Newnan, crossed Prairie Creek, and continued south to Cuscowilla. Bartram's party may have crossed this highway about 1.5 miles south of Prairie Creek, leaving it on the "left hand" [209] and continuing northeastward to "a sandy ridge" a mile southwest of the present Rochelle

(Hawthorn quadrangle). From the vicinity of Rochelle they probably followed approximately the present course of the Atlantic Coast
Line to Lochloosa Creek ("a large creek of excellent water," 209).
It was probably about midway between this creek and Hawthorn that
they "fell into the old trading path" that they had followed on the
outward journey. The "Halfway Pond," as previously pointed out, was
the present Cowpen Pond in Putnam County. From that point to
Spalding's Lower Store they doubtless retraced their former route.
The date of their return was probably in the *first part of May 1774.*

[215] As previously explained (pp. 353, 363), a voyage up the
St. John's to Lake Beresford and return intervened between the
horseback trips to the Alachua Savanna and to the Suwannee River.
Apparently this voyage was begun about the *middle of May* and
completed in *early June 1774.*

The present journey to the Suwannee River must have been undertaken about the *middle of June 1774.* It seems to have lasted about
25 days. At its conclusion Bartram sent an account of it to his friend
Lachlan McIntosh, dating his letter *July 15* (Dreer Coll., Scientists, 1).
Not one of his three accounts of this journey (letter to McIntosh;
report to Fothergill; and *Travels*) agrees any too well with the others,
especially in the matters of camping places and daily progress.

[216] These brief observations on geographical variation in size
among horses, deer, and other animals preceded by nearly a century
an outstanding contribution on the subject by J. A. Allen (1871). He,
like Bartram, made comparisons between Florida animals and those
of more northern states. Bartram's early recognition of this phenomenon is commented on by both Allen (1876*a*: 28–29; 1876*b*: 177) and
Coues (1876: 101–102).

[216–218] The first day's journey, to the Cowpen Pond ("Half-way
Pond") in Putnam County, presumably followed the same route that
Bartram had taken on the earlier trip to the Alachua Savanna. It is
difficult to say where the road and the party divided the next day,
"within a few miles of Cuscowilla" [216]. Perhaps it was a mile or so
east of the River of Styx and north of Orange Lake. From this point
the most direct route to the southern border of the Alachua Savanna
would have crossed the River of Styx about 3 miles above its mouth
(Hawthorn quadrangle) and passed a little north of Lowman Pond
(Arredondo quadrangle). "The old Spanish highway" [217] is not the
one shown on the Purcell map of about 1779, but a more southerly
one, passing by the Alachua Savanna and Talahasochte on the
Suwannee River to St. Mark's on Apalachee Bay. I have found no
map that shows it. After passing along the southern border of the

Alachua Savanna, the trading path continued about 4 miles westward to Kanapaha Sink ("a beautiful little lake," *217*). Groves of ancient live oaks still bordered the sink in 1940 at this secluded and attractive spot. A road shown on the Arredondo quadrangle, extending from the southwestern corner of the Alachua Savanna to this point, and then 5 or 6 miles west-southwest to Archer (beyond the quadrangle), probably approximates the old trail. On the way to Archer the road passes "over sandy, gravelly ridges" [*217–218*] about 30 feet higher than Kanapaha Sink. The "little lakes or ponds" [*218*] probably constitute what is now known as "Watermelon Pond." In dry seasons it consists of a series of ponds; in wet seasons it is said to extend for about 8 miles in a SE–NW direction. The eastern end lies about 5 miles west of Archer (soil map of Alachua County, 1954). In his report to Fothergill (1943: 155) Bartram refers to it as "Generals Pond."

[*218*] The episode of the hawk and the Coachwhip is reflected in three of Coleridge's poems, as Fagin (1933: 139–141) has pointed out. A very similar occurrence, involving a Red-shouldered Hawk and a Lindheimer's Rat Snake in Texas, has been described by G. G. Williams (1951).

[*220*] The "cavities or sinks in the surface of the earth" are characteristic of the Peninsular Lime-Sink Region, which includes the territory along Bartram's route from the Alachua Savanna to the vicinity of Bronson, Levy County (R. M. Harper, 1914: 314–319). The sinks here mentioned were probably a few miles north of the present Bronson. The night's camp was probably not far from either the Little Wacasassa River or the Big Wacasassa River—small, sluggish streams which flow southward about 2 and 4 miles, respectively, west of Bronson. One of them must have been the "rapid rivulet" [*222*] crossed the next morning, for there are practically no other streams for miles in any direction.

[*221*] Bartram's remarks on the Florida Sandhill Crane (fig. 14) and its "seraphic music in the etherial skies" constitute one of his finest appreciations of bird life. They are particularly appropriate in the case of this very "human" bird.

[*221–224*] The day's journey from the vicinity of Big Wacasassa River seems to have extended at first for about 10 miles in a west-southwesterly direction to Long Pond ("a beautiful sparkling lake," *222*), whose northern end is about 2 miles south of Chiefland, Levy County. The area here traversed and described [*223*] is evidently, in part at least, the Gulf Hammock Region, and perhaps in part the Middle Florida Flatwoods (R. M. Harper, 1914: 302–313, and Generalized Soil Map of Florida, 1925). The "savanna and fields of

Capola" [223] were apparently about Long Pond. From this point to Talahasochte on the Suwannee River is a distance of about 10 miles in a northwesterly direction. The "sublime forest" of "stately Pine trees" [224] seems to have been largely cleared, but the "dark groves" nearer the river were still delightful in 1940, though recently lumbered to some extent.

[224–226] The determination of the site of Talahasochte is a matter of considerable interest. It was on the eastern bank of the river, "three or four miles" above Manatee Spring [230]. It is only at intervals of several miles that a bluff suitable for the location of a town occurs. The first such bluff above Manatee Spring is at New Clay Landing, about 3 miles upstream, and about 6 miles in an air line south of Oldtown. At the very edge of the river the bluff is only about 10 feet high, but it rises to perhaps twice that height at a distance of a stone's throw or so from the river. The next suitable bluff is said to be at Ross Landing, about 3 miles farther upstream; and there is a local tradition, according to McQueen Chaires, of Oldtown, that this was the village site. One difficulty in accepting New Clay Landing as the site of Talahasochte is indicated by John M. Goggin (*in litt.*, November 6, 1950): "Manatee Springs was clearly occupied by the Seminoles as indicated by potsherds of their types. However, at New Clay Landing the sherds are of earlier types, dating from the Weeden Island period, and definitely prehistoric."

The "Andrew Jackson Highway," which was perhaps imposed upon the "Old Spanish Highway," is said to have crossed the river at this point. The Suwannee is by no means so "pellucid" at present as Bartram reported it [224]. Its waters are only moderately clear, and quite dark. Long after Bartram's time, Forbes (1821: 130) and Shepard (1833: 167) agreed that the Suwannee was a clear stream. On the other hand:

"I have known that river since 1902, and have crossed it at various places from Fargo to its mouth, and have never seen anything but coffee-colored water in it. It looks as if the Okefinokee might be discharging more water into it now than 150 years ago." (R. M. Harper, *in litt.*, February 21, 1951.)

The Suwannee appears to be about 160–170 yards wide at New Clay Landing. The assertion of the Indians and traders [224–225] that it lacks tributaries does not accord with the facts. The more important of the affluents are Suwannoochee Creek and the Alapaha, Withlacoochee, and Santa Fe Rivers. But Bartram was appoximately correct in his remarks [225–226] on the general scarcity of smaller surface streams in the country adjoining the Suwannee on the east.

The local karst topography is discussed by R. M. Harper (1914: 314–315).

[227] "The 'considerable town of the Siminoles' at the bay of Calos was probably occupied by some of the Calusa Indians, not by the Seminole proper." (J.R.S.)

[230–232] Manatee Spring (fig. 19), still bearing the same name that Bartram used, is situated on the east side of the Suwannee at a point about 7 miles west of Chiefland, Levy County. As Bartram remarks in the report to Fothergill (1943: 158), though not in the *Travels,* the spring is about 300 yards distant from the river. This clearly distinguishes it from Fannin Spring, near Oldtown, since the latter is much closer to the river. The intermittent nature ascribed by Bartram to the ebullition is apparently less definite at the present time. The basin is about 80–90 feet in diameter. The outlet is perhaps 60 feet wide, has a strong current, and is well filled with dense beds of aquatic plants. In its pellucid waters fishes in considerable numbers and variety may be seen, but Manatees and Alligators are no longer in evidence. The "high woodland hills" [231] immediately adjacent to the spring are probably less than 10 feet in height. Manatee Spring was a secluded spot in 1940, still retaining much of its original charm despite some recent lumbering in the fine forest surrounding it. A few simple old cabins nearby did not particularly mar the scene, but this historic spring should be preserved from further encroachments of civilization. "It is now included in an undeveloped State Park" (Boyd, 1951: 10).

[232–235] On the day's excursion west of the Suwannee, the party seems, according to the report to Fothergill (1943: 159), to have followed the Indian trading path for a mile and a half up the river before turning westward. Continuing "five or six miles" [233] in this direction, they may have arrived near the headwaters of California Creek—a likely location for "the most extensive Cane-break" [233]. After turning northward for "eight or nine miles" [235], they doubtless reached the general vicinity of the present Oldtown. Bartram makes a curious mistake in referring to this place as "not more than thirty miles from St. Marks," for the actual distance in an air line is about 85 miles. A large part of the day's journey must have been within the boundaries of the Oldtown Hammock, which is indicated on R. M. Harper's Generalized Soil Map of Florida (1925). Most of the trees mentioned on page 233 are characteristic of hammocks.

[236] A much more detailed description of the calumet ceremony is provided by John Bartram (1942: 51). This description is repeated, in slightly paraphrased form, by Mowat (1943: 21–22), who gives

references to Bartram and also to the Journals of the East Florida Council (Colonial Office papers 5/570: 33). Neill (1955b: 84) errs in crediting the description solely to the latter source.

[238–240] Bartram's report to Fothergill (1943) and his *Travels* differ considerably in the narrative of the return journey to the St. John's. In attempting to trace his itinerary according to each account, it seems that we must make allowance, among other things, for considerable inaccuracy in the statement of distances. The "encampment in the forest about twelve miles from the river" [238] was presumably at Long Pond, near Chiefland.

A particular effort has been made to locate the Alligator Hole [238–240], as a place of exceptional interest. Fortunately Bartram made a sketch of this sink (1943: fig. 30), and it has been preserved in the British Museum. Fortunately, also, Horton H. Hobbs, Jr., of the University of Florida, while pursuing his investigations on crawfishes, had become familiar with a great many sinks in northern Florida. After examining a copy of Bartram's sketch, he conducted us to Blue Sink, in the pine forests a mile north of Newberry in Alachua County. It proved to bear a remarkably close resemblance to the sketch, particularly in the number and position of the semicylindrical hollows in the walls of the sink. Although the distance of about 23 miles from Talahasochte is greater than one would suppose from Bartram's narrative, it does not seem that there could be anywhere else in Florida a sink corresponding so very closely to his sketch. Thus we may at least provisionally consider that the Blue Sink is the Alligator Hole.

The sink is roughly elliptical, with horizontal dimensions of about 21 by 26 yards. Bartram was such a poor recorder of distances that his "sixty yards" [238] need not be taken seriously. The sides, for the most part, are of vertical rock, but at the north end a steep slope permits at least a partial descent toward the bottom. The blue water is now about 40 feet below the general surface, but about 1895, according to J. R. Fowler, it was within 12 or 15 feet of the surface. From the sink the land dips down toward the south through a slight vale or depression, in the direction of the shallow basin of the Wacasassa River. Consequently this would have been a more likely place for the eruption of the waters, as stated in the *Travels*, than for their disappearance, as stated in the report to Fothergill (1943: 161). If the Alligator Hole were actually only "about nine miles" [239] from Talahasochte, it might be looked for in north central Levy County, but the sinks thereabouts seem to be of quite a different type, with sloping sides of earth or crumbling rock.

[*240*] The "encampment," as previously stated, was presumably at Long Pond, about 10 miles southeast of Talahasochte.

[*242-243*] The "remarkable barren plains . . . joined with infinite savannas and ponds," were perhaps what is now known as "Sand Prairie." According to Albert Johnson, this area lies between Manatee Spring and Long Pond and is a noted place for ducks.

[*244-245*] A more detailed and extremely interesting account of the seven young warriors appears in the report to Fothergill (1943: 160).

[*246*] The walls of the sink here described, with "perpendicular tubes" and "excavated semicircular niches," bear considerable resemblance to those of the Alligator Hole or Blue Sink.

[*248*] The camping place "at a savanna, about twelve miles distance from this," was possibly near the Wacasassa River. The "Long Pond," now revisited, has already been frequently mentioned.

[*249*] The next camp, near the "bird isle," may have been somewhere about Watermelon Pond, 5 miles west of Archer in Alachua County. Bartram furnishes here an interesting illustration of his lack of uniformity in nomenclature. With one exception, the herons mentioned on this page appear under different names from those listed on page 293 (see Annotated Index, under Ardea).

[*251*] The encampment "near the banks of savannas and ponds" may have been at Kanapaha Sink, where the party had stopped on the westward journey. The next camp, on a creek near Cuscowilla, was possibly at the River of Styx, which flows into the northwestern corner of Orange Lake. From this point to the Lower Store on the St. John's, presumably the party's previous route was retraced, by way of Cowpen (or "Half-way") Pond. The date of the return was probably a few days prior to *July 15, 1774.*

[*252-254*] The "little voyage" up the St. John's to Lake George apparently took place in the *latter part of July, 1774.* The location of Mount Royal has been previously stated. The "Great Springs" were Salt Springs, visited and described on an earlier trip. The "long point of flat rocks" [253] may have been Lake George Point, opposite Drayton's Island and about 2 miles southeast of Georgetown. Dr. William Stork, mentioned here, published *A Description of East-Florida,* three editions of which (1766, 1769, and 1774) contained also John Bartram's journal of his journey on the St. John's in 1765–66. The "old deserted plantation, the property of a British gentleman" [253], was apparently somewhere along the eastern shore of Lake George. The "beautiful isle in sight of Mount Royal" [254] was doubtless Drayton's Island.

[*255–263*] "My late companion, the old trader" [*257*], was doubtless Job Wiggens (cf. p. 305). The rattlesnake killed and decapitated here [*261*] may be the one of whose head Bartram made a drawing (1943: fig. 41), which is now preserved in the British Museum.

[*265–266*] These page numbers seem to have been inadvertently omitted in the pagination. The narrative is continuous from the bottom of page *264* to the top of page *267*.

[*267*] It will be noted that Bartram offers no personal observations on the alleged power of snakes to fascinate their victims. This myth is still believed in by many poorly informed persons. In a paper on the same subject (1799*b*) Barton quotes both from the *Travels* and from a manuscript of Bartram's.

[*268–269*] This is apparently Bartram's only reference to a visit to Sapelo Island on the coast of McIntosh County, Georgia. He does not indicate its proper place in his itinerary. He may have gone there with his friends the McIntoshes in the latter part of 1773 or sometime in 1776.

[*270*] John Bartram made journeys to the Catskill Mountains in 1742, 1744, and 1753. It was on the last occasion that William (then 14) accompanied his father. The name "Giliad" does not seem to have been preserved to the present day for any summit in the Catskills. However, the locality of the rattlesnake episode was probably between North and South Mountains, close to North and South Lakes, about 2 miles northwest of Palenville, Greene County, N. Y. (cf. Bartram Papers, *1:* 35).

[*270–271*] The adventure with the Rattlesnake at Picolata on November 21, 1765, with all its interesting details, is tersely covered by prosaic John Bartram (1942: 35) in the following words: "Killed A monstrous rattlesnake."

[*272–276*] The snakes of these pages are identified or discussed in the Annotated Index. If the suggested identifications are correct, Bartram's accounts of the following species preceded their eventual description and technical naming by others: Diamondback Rattler [*267*], Four-lined Chicken Snake [*275*], and Pine Snake [*276*]. Bartram's account of the last became the basis of Daudin's *Coluber melanoleucus* (Harper, 1940: 718–720).

[*276–280*] These pages furnish doubtless the best account of American frogs and toads that had appeared up to 1791. Mark Catesby's work (1730?–1748), though lavishly illustrated, was of a cruder sort. L. A. G. Bosc, who made extensive natural history investigations about Charleston, S.C., from 1796 to 1798, was better trained in herpetology than any of his predecessors in America (cf. Harper, 1940: 706–709, portrait). His researches on frogs and toads were published in Daudin (1800; 1802; 1803, 8), in Sonnini and Latreille (1801), and in the *Nouveau Dictionnaire d'histoire naturelle* (1803–1804). Most of Bartram's species are identifiable, as will be seen from the Annotated Index. He was apparently the original discoverer and describer of the Southern Bullfrog (1), the Georgia Tree-Frog (provided No. 2 is properly so identified), the Southern Tree-Frog (4), the Southern Cricket Frog (5), the Little Tree-Frog (6), and the Southern Leopard Frog (7). He neglected a golden opportunity in not providing them with technical names. His account of "the largest frog" (276–277) was made the basis of Daudin's *Rana grunniens* (Harper, 1940: 704–706). He refers to a common defense reaction of the Southern Toad in his remark that "when irritated, they swell and raise themselves up on their four legs" [279]. As yet, however, very few additional observations on this interesting performance have been published (cf. Harper, 1934: 614, lower fig.).

[280–281] Among the half dozen lizards briefly noticed by Bartram, the Green Lizard (*Anolis carolinensis*) and the Pine Lizard (*Sceloporus undulatus undulatus*) were given technical names by others in subsequent years. The former had already been figured and described by Bartram's notable predecessor, Mark Catesby. Several of the others had been named by Linnaeus in 1758 or 1766.

[281] Bartram's account of the Gopher Turtle (pp. 18, 182–183), which he named *Testudo Polyphaemus*, constitutes the valid original description of this species. His large, fresh-water tortoise, with elevated carapace, is evidently the Florida Terrapin, not technically named until 39 years later by Le Conte.

[281–284] The present list of mammals is considerably more complete than that furnished in the report to Fothergill (1943: 164). The latter, however, includes several important species that are omitted from the present list: the Florida Cougar, the Bison, and apparently the Ocelot. A majority of Bartram's mammals had not been validly described previously, and if he had supplied binominal nomenclature and descriptive notes throughout, many of the names so proposed would have been valid today. Only two of his mammal names— "lupus niger" [199] and "lepus minor" [284] appear to meet the test of binominalism.

[284–288] These pages deserve attention as containing the first serious American contribution to the fascinating subject of bird migration. Bartram's field experience over some 14 degrees of latitude and

18 or 20 degrees of longitude in eastern North America gave him a broader and better comprehension of this phenomenon than a more sedentary observer would be likely to attain.

[288–302] The present list of birds, together with some miscellaneous observations scattered through other pages of the *Travels*, establish Bartram's reputation as the foremost American ornithologist up to his time. Coues says (1884: xvii): "I consider it [the *Travels*] the starting-point of a distinctively American school of ornithology." He designates the years 1791–1800 as the "Bartramian period" of that science in this country. And further (1875: 340): "If Wilson was the father of American Ornithology, as he has been styled, Bartram, back to whom the pedigree of many names is traceable, was certainly the grandfather of that vigorous offspring. His statement of United States' birds is one of the earliest of those which are of any special account, and which treat exclusively of this subject, while its extent and general pertinence entitle the author to rank among the fathers." In similar vein Stone writes (1932: 21): "This was a landmark in the progress of American ornithology next in importance to the work of Catesby and the first ornithological contribution, worthy of the name, written by a native American."

A considerable proportion of the bird names employed in the *Travels* are there introduced into the literature for the first time, and so must be considered from the point of view of zoological nomenclature. Coues (1875) has provided identifications of most of the names in Bartram's list. At the same time he has pointed out the need of recognizing such of these names as are binominal, are accompanied by descriptions, and have priority. His views, however, met with little acceptance on the part of his contemporaries, and the validity of the Bartramian names seems not to have been seriously reconsidered from the time of the adoption of the International Rules of Zoological Nomenclature in 1906 almost to the present day. Recently (1940: 694–695; 1942d) I have reopened the question and advocated the resurrection of a considerable number of Bartram's names. References to these cases will be found in the Annotated Index, which includes identifications of the bird names insofar as they can be provided at present. While these agree in the main with those made by Coues in 1875, the enormous progress in ornithological knowledge since that time has permitted a certain extension and modification of his findings. Coues himself might have gained additional light by a thorough search through the works of Bartram's friends, Edwards and Wilson. He seems to have overlooked entirely Bartram's large nomenclatural debt to the former.

In these pages it is apparent that Bartram's interest in zoology lagged somewhat behind that in botany. He unquestionably had a much greater fund of ornithological information than he has here imparted. He could very readily have added descriptions that would have lifted many of his names out of the category of *nomina nuda*. If he had been technically trained in zoology and its nomenclature, he would have applied exclusively binominal names (instead of the frequent polynomials) to his animals, and thereby would have become the author of many more valid names than can now be credited to him. Moreover, he could have supplied vastly more information of great interest and value on the habits and distribution of the many species met with in his extensive journeys. But before we pass judgment on this score, let us consider what readers he might have counted upon in providing literature of this sort. In a list of "all living zoologists" published by F. A. A. Meyer in 1794, the sole American included was William Bartram!

It is strange that Bartram did not manage to include in his list of birds several species that he himself had sent to Edwards, with subsequent publication in the latter's *Gleanings* (1758–64). These omissions were the Black-Throated Blue, Magnolia, Chestnut-Sided, and Worm-Eating Warblers, and apparently the Veery.

[303–304] The Indian town where the feast of watermelons and oranges was held was doubtless at the site of the present Palatka, county seat of Putnam County. The distance from the Lower Store (at the present Stokes Landing) is about 6 miles in an air line. The overland route probably went close to the present Penial and Palmetto School (Palatka quadrangle).

[305] The "numerous islands" in the St. John's were Stokes Island and the Seven Sister Islands. The "high bluff" was probably the present Buffalo Bluff.

[306] The departure downstream was probably not "about the last of September," as stated here. Bartram's report to Fothergill (1943: 163) extends his stay on the St. John's at least to about November 10, when the weather was turning cold and flights of migratory fowl were passing overhead. The Marshall plantation may have been in the vicinity of Goodby's Creek, on the east side of the river about 8 miles above Jacksonville. The route from the St. John's to St. Simon's Island, Ga., represented a retracing of the southward passage during the previous spring (pp. 63–72).

Broughton Island is in the lower course of the Altamaha River just below Darien, Ga. The settlement of New Hope was on the south side of the Altamaha opposite Broughton Island, at the head of a tidal channel known as "Wally Leg" (map of Glynn County, 1938).

[307] The inland passage from Broughton Island to Sunbury on the Medway River, in Liberty County, extended along the inner side of Sapelo and St. Catherine's Islands. One would judge from the present account that Bartram returned to Charleston, S.C., sometime in the autumn of 1774. However, he must have lingered at various points along the way for longer periods than are here indicated. For he wrote to his father from Charleston on March 27, 1775 (Bartram Papers, 1: 78), announcing his arrival at that point only two days previously!

Part "II" [= III]

[308] From this point on Bartram apparently does not succeed in recording a single date correctly. The year dates are advanced from one to three years, and even the months are not invariably correct. His excursion to the Cherokee nation took place in the *spring and early summer of 1775*—not 1776. The letters mentioned below (the first two still extant in the Bartram Papers, 4: 29, 56) furnish indisputable evidence on this point.

On April 14, 1775, Hy. Kelly, in Charleston, gives Bartram an order for plants, with the prospect of their being shipped from Pensacola, Fla.

On April 18, 1775, John Lewis Gervais, in Charleston, gives Bartram a letter of introduction to Major Andrew Williamson at Whitehall, S.C. In it he mentions Bartram's plan for a visit to the Cherokee nation.*

On April 30, 1775, the trader George Galphin, at Silver Bluff, S.C., supplies Bartram with a letter of recommendation to his western representatives (original among Darlington Papers, New-York Hist. Soc.). Soc.).

The absence of any reference to the Revolutionary War in the *Travels* is a subject of common remark. As a Quaker, Bartram was naturally averse to discussing such topics. Moreover, he departed on

---

* There is no evidence that Bartram went by way of Williamson's home, which seems to have been in the present Newberry County in upper South Carolina. The very next year Williamson was destined to lead an expedition against the Cherokees whom Bartram visited on such friendly terms. The map of his route published by Drayton (1821, 2: facing p. 343) gives an excellent indication of Bartram's route from Fort Prince George on the Keowee River, S.C., to the valley of the Little Tennessee River, N.C. Williamson bore the nickname of "Cow-driver." (Cf. Schoepf, 1911, 2: 197; J. Johnson, 1851: 142–152.) Bartram's Cherokee friends of 1775 might have had hard thoughts of him the following year if they had known that he had any relations with Williamson.

his long journey to the Carolina mountains and to the Mississippi about two weeks before the news of the Battle of Lexington reached Charleston (on May 8, 1775) (Drayton, 1821, *1:* 246).

In setting out from Charleston on *April 22, 1775* (not 1776), he doubtless proceeded about 11 miles up the northeast side of the Ashley River and crossed that stream on a ferry at the site of the present Drayton Hall (Ravenels quadrangle). Thence his course was about 6 miles southwest to Rantowle's Creek, and another mile to Wallace River. From this point the old Charleston-Savannah road doubtless approximated very closely the present Route 17 as far as Jacksonboro on the Edisto River (Cottageville quadrangle). For once Bartram seems to underestimate a distance; for Jacksonboro is at least 35 miles from Charleston by his route. From Jacksonboro to Pocotaligo, Jasper County (Yemassee quadrangle), there were alternative roads. Bartram may have taken the more southerly one by way of Ashepoo and Gardens Corner. This was probably the road that had been followed by his father and himself in 1765. In order to have arrived within 15 miles of Three Sisters Ferry on the second night, he must have reached Allison's (Faden map of 1776) in the vicinity of the present Ridgeland, Jasper County. But that would have involved a day's journey of approximately 45 miles, instead of the "thirty" he records. Presumably an extra day, not accounted for here, was spent on the road. In that case the second night may have been passed at Gardens Corner or vicinity in Beaufort County.

[*309*] The Three Sisters (more generally known as Two Sisters or merely Sisters) Ferry is about 15 miles west of Ridgeland, Jasper County, S.C., and about 3 miles east of Clyo, Effingham County, Ga. (Campbell map of 1780; Faden map of 1780; White, 1849, map; Hammond, 1883, map). It was still in use in the early part of the present century (R. M. Harper, 1905: 148, fig. 2), but is now abandoned. Michaux (1889: 9–10, 12) botanized in this vicinity on April 25 and 26 and May 13, 1787. In 1809 Alexander Wilson crossed the river at this point (Ord, 1825: cix). *Dirca palustris* still grew there in 1939.

The "delightful habitation" was very likely at ancient Mount Pleasant (Campbell map of 1780), which is said by Mr. R. B. Mallory to be the present Cedar Bluff Landing, Effingham County (Shirley quadrangle).

[*312*] To this day Negroes remain adept at improvising songs as they work.

[*313–314*] The route from this point to Silver Bluff was doubtless over roads already traveled by Bartram, either with his father in 1765 or with young John McIntosh in 1773. Of two alternative routes, one crossed Brier Creek near its mouth; the other, at the present Thompson's Bridge (Green's Cut quadrangle). Both routes are described in the Comments on John Bartram's diary of 1765–66 (1942: 64–66). In the same place are some further remarks on Galphin and his establishment at Silver Bluff.

[*315–316*] Fort Moore was situated at the now abandoned Sandbar Ferry, 3 miles southeast of Augusta. The tales told to Bartram concerning the erosion of the bluff and the shifting of the river bed were perhaps exaggerated. However, cattle in recent years are said to have fallen occasionally over the bluffs in this vicinity.

Fort Moore is of much interest from the fact that Bartram's renowned predecessor, Mark Catesby, sojourned there for some time in the 1720's, and made excursions thence toward the mountains in company with Indians to hunt for Buffaloes and other wild beasts.

[*318–319*] The fossil oyster shells here described by Bartram may still be found at the site he mentions—Shell Bluff, Burke County, about 7 miles east of McBean (Green's Cut quadrangle). The bluff rises to a maximum height of about 150 feet above the river. The place had been visited and described by John Bartram in 1765 (1767: 167; 1942: 25). His was the first scientific account of these huge fossil oysters. It was not until many years later (in 1834) that they were given the name of *Ostrea georgiana* by T. A. Conrad. For further accounts of this area see Lyell (1845, *1:* 124, 126, 142) and Veatch and Stephenson (1911: 237–248, pl. 19, fig. A). As Bartram remarks, the cool and shady bluff is noteworthy for the occurrence of several northern-ranging plants not commonly found elsewhere in the Coastal Plain.

[*320–321*] Bartram's departure from Augusta doubtless took place during the *first week of May 1775*. The road he took to Fort James was evidently not on the immediate banks of the Savannah River. The nearest one on the west side, as indicated on either old or modern maps, appears to have kept at an average distance of 3 or 4 miles from the river. It is marked "Washington Road" and "Petersburg Road" on the Clark's Hill quadrangle. It led, until recently, through Martinez, Evens, Kiokee, and Eubank in Columbia County, and Double Branches, Kenna, Goshen, and Graball in Lincoln County (Clark's Hill, Appling, McCormick, and Crawfordville quadrangles); but parts of this route are now inundated by the Clark Hill Reservoir, whose construction was begun in 1946. The first night's stop, on Little River, may have been at the former Lockhart's Ferry near Eubank.

[*322*] The remarks on the bones of ancient Buffaloes and Elk constitute a definite record for these species in Lincoln County, Ga. This

is apparently the southernmost point established for the range of the Elk in the Eastern States (cf. Seton, 1929, 3: 10, map 1).

[323–324] The old ford across the Broad River was replaced, until recently, by a ferry about ⅜ mile from its mouth; the spot is now inundated by the Clark Hill Reservoir. (Mr. Clement E. Sutton, of Washington, Ga., suggested that Bartram, in order to find a ford, may have had to go 2 or 3 miles upstream to Milford Shoals.) No vestige seems to be left of Fort James. At its possible site, a quarter of a mile along the road northeast of the ferry, on the highest ground thereabouts, there stood in 1940 a solitary old house of a colonial type, occupied by Negroes. This spot answered fairly well to Bartram's description in that it was at least approximately equidistant from the Broad and the Savannah Rivers and from their junction. The town laid out at this site became known as Petersburg. "This was once among the most prosperous towns in Georgia; but it is now in a state of dilapidation" (White, 1849: 227). See also Jones (1878: 233–239).

[324–326] The Indian monuments here described were located on Rembert's Bottom on the west side of the Savannah about 3 miles north-northwest of the mouth of Broad River (soil map of Elbert County, 1928). The principal mound was noteworthy, and more or less unique in this region, in having a spiral path leading to the top. Bartram refers to it elsewhere (1853: 14) as the largest Indian mound he ever saw. White (1849: 230) writes as follows: "In 1848, accompanied by Captain Rembert, the author of this work visited these mounds. The large one corresponds exactly with Bartram's description of it, with this exception, that the sides and summit are covered with a growth of large cane, and several large trees. The smaller mounds have been almost destroyed. Captain Rembert has excavated the smaller mounds, and found human skeletons, jars, pipes, beads, breastplates, stone hammers, hatchets, arrow heads, &c., &c." The large mound was virtually destroyed by the freshet of 1908. On a visit in 1940 I did not even succeed in locating its exact site. For more recent archaeological information see M. W. Stirling (in Wetmore, 1948: 59).

[326–328] The point where Bartram crossed the Savannah River on *May 10, 1775*, was very likely at the site of the former Calhoun Ferry, about 7 miles upstream from the mouth of Broad River (Elberton quadrangle). Beyond that point his route may have led approximately through the present Calhoun Falls, Abbeville County, S.C. Efforts to locate the exact site of Loughabber, the seat of Alexander Cameron, the Tory, have so far been fruitless. It is shown on Carleton's map of 1806 at the junction of Bryan's Creek and Appletree Creek (which seem to have disappeared from modern maps). The latter stream appears on Hunter's map of 1730; and nearby is "Dividing Path"—which might have been a strategic location for Cameron's headquarters. According to Drayton (1821, *1*: 408), the plantation was "on Little River in the Long-Cane Settlement."

"Lochaber plantation was, by the best evidence, located in the upper valley of Little River not far from the Indian boundary which now serves as a county line between Anderson and Abbeville counties, and probably fairly near the Cherokee trail from Ninety-six to Keowee." (A. L. Pickens, *in litt.*, February 7, 1947.) (Abbeville quadrangle.)

[328–329] The journey of *May 15, 1775*, from Loughabber to Seneca, was in a general northwesterly direction, probably passing through or near the site of the present Anderson. The day's journey was perhaps nearer 35 miles than 45.

[329–330] The site of Seneca (kindly pointed out to me by the late William H. Mills) is on the Seneca River a mile south of Clemson College, in extreme southwestern Pickens County, S.C. It is about an equal distance north of the railroad connecting Pendleton and the present town of Seneca (Pickens quadrangle). The later Fort Rutledge, on a natural eminence overlooking the rich bottoms of the river, occupied approximately the same site. The other part of the Indian village was directly opposite, on the west bank. Just a little distance upstream was an old ford by which communication between the two parts of the village was maintained. As in Bartram's time, so in 1939 the "fruitful plains on the river" still yielded an abundant harvest of corn.

[330–332] The only road from Seneca to Fort Prince George that is shown on Mouzon's map of 1775 runs up the west side of the river. The distance is not far from Bartram's estimate of 16 miles. This upper part of the stream takes the name of Keowee River.

The site of the fort, on the east side of the river above the mouth of Crow Creek, was occupied in 1939 by a level cornfield. According to the owner, J. E. M. Steele, the fort was just west of a huge mulberry tree standing in this cornfield (fig. 24). The spot is some rods back from the river, on the south side of a road leading across Nimmons Bridge. There was an old ford at a shoal place in the river a hundred yards downstream.

In view of the recent bloody encounters between the Cherokees and the whites, and those that were destined to take place the very next year, it is evident that Bartram bore a sort of charmed existence in being able to travel as peacefully as he did among the wild inhabitants of the Carolina mountains.

Kulsage or Sugar Town was upstream from Fort Prince George and on the opposite side of the river (Mouzon map of 1775). Several Indian mounds are still in evidence across the river from the fort, at the site of Old Keowee, which had been destroyed in 1760.

[333–335] The date of Bartram's departure from Fort Prince George was apparently about *May 19;* his return to this point from his excursion in the North Carolina mountains was less than a month later. Probably the best clues to his route beyond this point are to be found in four old maps: the Hunter maps of 1730 and 1751, the Purcell map of about 1776 (Swanton, 1922: pl. 7), and a map showing the marches of Col. Andrew Williamson in 1776 against the Cherokees (in Drayton, 1821, 2: facing p. 343). These may be interpreted on modern topographic maps and maps of the National Forests.

Here, as elsewhere, Bartram makes the mistake of giving a river's width in a certain number of yards instead of in the same number of feet. His road seems to have extended in a general northwesterly direction from the fort to the present village of Salem, at a distance of half a dozen miles. The "very considerable elevation" [333] was probably the ridge between the Keowee and Little Rivers, with an altitude of a little over 1,000 feet (Pickens quadrangle). The "charming vale" may have been that of Little River in the vicinity of Salem. From this point the road runs southwestward over "the more lofty ridges" (about 1,200 feet in altitude) [334], crosses Tomassee Creek, and passes a little east of Tomassee Knob (Walhalla quadrangle; map of Nantahala National Forest, 1935). A mile or more south of this knob, and just south of the headwaters of "Occonne vale" [334], is Oconee Station. At about this point Williamson's and Bartram's route turned northwestward again, crossed "the upper end of the vale" [334], and within about 2 miles passed over the southern end of Station Mountain ("the top of the Occonne mountain," 335) at an altitude of about 2,000 feet.

[336–341] On the other side of this mountain the "rapid large creek" [337] was one of the headwaters of Chauga River—either Jerry Creek or Village Creek (Walhalla quadrangle). The "ample meadow" [337] may have been near the junction of these two creeks. There is a local tradition of an Indian trail passing near this point. The "gap or opening between other yet more lofty ascents" [338] must have been Rocky Gap in the Chattooga Ridge, situated about 7 miles west of Oconee Station and 3.5 miles southeast of the junction of War Woman

Creek with the Chattooga River. The "large rapid brook . . . turn-
ing to the left" [338] was Whetstone Creek, a tributary of the
Chattooga. The "main branch of Tugilo" was the Chattooga, which
Bartram evidently crossed near the mouth of War Woman Creek.

It is strange that he does not here mention War Woman Creek,
whose course he must have followed for about 10 miles, from its
mouth to the source of its uppermost headwater, his "Falling Creek."
Eventually, however, in his observations (1853: 32) on the Creek
and Cherokee Indians, he does speak of having crossed this creek.
On pages 338 and 339 he seems to proceed a little prematurely to
Mount Magnolia and Falling Creek. The latter is mentioned again,
and apparently then in proper sequence, on page 341.

Until within the memory of persons still living in 1939 (for example, Jeff Beck), a canebrake occupied the valley bottom along War
Woman Creek. Indian trails were in the habit of avoiding such
stream bottoms and following the adjacent ridges. After crossing the
winding lower course of this creek several times, Williamson's route
(and Bartram's likewise) evidently led along the ridges on the north
side. Thus when Bartram speaks of "descending the other side of the
mountain" [341] just before reaching Falling Creek, he must refer to
a prominent ridge on the north side of War Woman Creek and on
the southwest side of Tuckaluge Creek. This is named Beck Ridge
on the map of the Chattahoochee National Forest (1937).

On the same map Bartram's "Falling Creek" is named Martin
Creek. It is also known locally as Finnie's Creek. I was fortunately
directed to it by Jeff Beck, from his home on War Woman Creek.
The sources lie close to the 2,500-foot contour in Court House Gap,
on the north side of Pinnacle Knob, which rises some 400 feet higher
than the gap. After tumbling down about 500 feet in its course of 2
miles, the stream joins the main War Woman Creek at a point nearly 4
miles east of Clayton.

Late in a July afternoon I crossed an open glade on its lower course
and began a steep ascent through the shady forest encompassing the
little creek. Within a quarter of a mile or so along the trail I came to
the first of three cascades, rushing down through a dank, narrow
gorge, with potholes left high and dry in the rock walls above. I could
hardly look down to the bottom over the precipitous sides, thick with
Rhododendron maximum. An old wooden sluice at the base of the
fall somewhat marred the natural scenery. Just above is the second
cascade, so near as to form almost a part of the first, and like it hidden away in the dark recesses of the gorge.

Another quarter of a mile up the mountain and the third cascade (fig. 21) opens to view. This is obviously the "u[n]paralleled cascade" [341] that so enraptured Bartram. Over successive ledges and sloping buttresses of solid rock the waters drop and slide in a broader front than at the lower cascades, and collect in a wide, transparent, boulder-girt pool at the base. At one side, above the pool, is a cavernous recess in the rock, with a twilight atmosphere created by the dense overhanging rhododendrons. From the pool, as from the bottom of a well, one gazes far upward to a little patch of sky, closed in by the tops of mighty hemlocks and lesser beech, maple, and tulip trees. In this wondrously enchanting scene, only a few hundred feet above the hot valley, one finds himself suddenly in a fairly boreal environment. In the previous 164 years, apparently only one other (Hawkins, 1916: 16) had recognized this as a spot that had delighted the poetic soul of William Bartram. Hawkins made his journey in 1796.

The "Magnolia auriculata" that Bartram describes [339–340] still occurred in 1939 at its type locality, the cascades of "Falling Creek." Although he discovered it in 1775, his long delay in publishing the description enabled Walter in 1788 (p. 159) to anticipate him and to give the species the name of *Magnolia fraseri*. A figure of it forms the frontispiece to Walter's work. "Mount Magnolia" [338, 339] is presumably the present Pinnacle Knob, which overlooks the town of Clayton from the northeast. Sargent (in Michaux, 1889: 469) is in error in considering it "probably either Hogback or Whiteside" Mountains along the Macon-Jackson county boundary in North Carolina.

[342–345] From the cascades Bartram doubtless continued his ascent and passed through Court House Gap among "the steep rocky hills" [342], on the north side of Pinnacle Knob. This gap is about 400 feet higher than the one on the south side of Pinnacle Knob, where the present highway passes. Yet the old trail to Clayton from the east, up to about the time of the Civil War, is said to have passed through Court House Gap. One can only imagine that dense canebrakes and possibly boggy ground may have been deterrents in the case of the lower gap.

This route, across the divide between the waters of the Savannah and the Tennessee Basins, by way of the Court House Gap (fig. 22), is one of much historical significance. It was evidently the route of Sir Alexander Cuming and George Hunter (Hunter's map of 1730). Major Williamson and his troops in 1776 seem to have followed almost exactly Bartram's path of the previous year (Drayton, 1821, 2: map facing p. 343). Michaux (1889: 20) apparently did likewise in 1787, and Palisot de Beauvois in 1796.

This was so evidently the main-traveled route in the eighteenth century that one is tempted to speculate that De Soto may have passed over it in 1540. In fact, Meek (1839), Schoolcraft (1851–1857), and Brevoort (1865) indicate such an approximate route (Swanton *et al.,* 1939: map 2). On the other hand, Dr. Swanton suggests (*op. cit.:* 200–201; 1946: 47) that the Spanish cavaliers took a more difficult route by way of Highlands to Franklin, N.C.

The "pretty grassy vale" with its "delightful creek" [*342*] was presumably the valley of Stekoa Creek just north of Clayton in Rabun County, Ga. It was apparently on the slopes of this valley, perhaps not far from the present Clayton, that Bartram took refuge in "an Indian hunting cabin" [*343*]. "The ancient famous town of Sticoe" [*345*] must have been at or near the present Clayton (cf. Hunter's map of 1730; also town No. 11 in Swanton, 1922: pl. 7). However, I could secure no information there as to the presence of any nearby "Indian mount or tumulus and great terrace" [*345*]. The "spur of the mountains pushing forward" [*345*] may have been the southern spur of Black Rock Mountain extending to Clayton (Walhalla quadrangle). The place where the road forked was evidently the "dividings" of Hawkins (1916: 16). Here the "left hand path" [*345*] runs westward toward the headwaters of the Hiwassee River, while the one "to the right hand" goes northward toward Rabun Gap (cf. Swanton, 1922: pl. 7). The "delightful brook, water of the Tanase" [*345*], was evidently Black's Creek, just north of Mountain City and Rabun Gap (map of Chattahoochee National Forest, 1937). "The opening of the extensive and fruitful vale of Cowe" [*345*] is 1.5 miles north of this gap, where the Little Tennessee flows in from its sources in the mountains a few miles to the west and southwest.

[*345–346*] For the first few miles north of Rabun Gap Bartram's trail seems to have coincided more or less with the old road shown on the Walhalla quadrangle; this is not altogether the course of the present main highway. The "pretty silvery brook of water" [*345*] was probably Black's Brook, joining the Little Tennessee from the east between the above-mentioned Black's Creek and Darnell Creek (map of Chattahoochee National Forest, 1937). While the "hollow rocky grounds . . . arching over the river" [*346*] must have been on the adjacent portion of the Little Tennessee, I was unable to see or to learn anything of such a feature during a hasty journey in 1939. Michaux (1889: 20) seems to have visited this part of the river on June 16, 1787. He describes it as flowing among rocks that divide it into three or four channels, in such a manner that one can cross on the rocks, although the width of the stream above and below is about 60 feet. Perhaps Bartram crossed to the west side of the Little Tennessee [346] where the older road does, just above Mill or Darnell Creek (Walhalla quadrangle; map of Chattahoochee National Forest, 1937). About a mile farther downstream, on the east side of the river opposite Dillard, a huge Indian mound stands in a cultivated field. In 1939 it was about 100 feet in diameter and 15 feet in height. The sight of it may have inspired Bartram's remark on the "ruins" of the "towns of the a[n]cients" [346].

[347] A mile north of Dillard "the mountains recede, the vale expands," and "on the right hand a lofty pyramidal hill terminates a spur of the adjacent mountain." The "very beautiful creek" beyond this is Estatoah Creek, and the "u[n]paralleled waterfall" on the mountainside is Estatoah Falls. Even in their present shorn glory (for most of the water has been diverted for a power plant), the falls are stupendous. Two or three hundred feet of sheer sloping rock, over which the waters once thundered in volume, give a bare suggestion of the magnificence that Bartram beheld.

He seems to mention either one too many or one too few crossings of the river. The main path down the Vale of Cowee was evidently on the west side of the river (Hunter's map of 1730; *Crown Coll.*, ser. 2, 3: 35, 1910; Drayton, 1821, 2: map facing p. 343). The crossing in the vicinity of Estatoah Falls must have been from east to west, although the narrative seems to indicate the opposite. In this vicinity is the boundary between Georgia and North Carolina.

[349] The trader's house where Bartram spent the night was evidently somewhere in the vicinity of Tanyard Brook or Skeenah Creek (Cowee quadrangle).

[350] The town of Echoe was somewhere near the point where Cartoogechaye Creek joins the Little Tennessee (Mooney, 1900: 523). Nucasse was on the site of the present Franklin, N.C. Although Watauga Creek enters the river from the east, the Indian town of that name ("Whatoga") is shown on the west side by some authorities (Hunter's maps of 1730 and 1751; Swanton, 1922: pl. 7), probably about opposite the creek. On the other hand, Mooney (1900: pl. 3) places it on the east side. Perhaps this settlement, like Cowee, occupied both sides of the river.

[350–352] The venerable "chief of Whatoga" was apparently one of those in attendance at the treaty of Augusta in November, 1763. His name is revealed by Jones (1883, 2: 42): "Will, the head man of Whatoga, led the delegation from the Middle Settlement."

Cowee ("Cowe") was situated about the mouth of Cowee Creek, at the site of the present West's Mill, Macon County, N.C. The date of arrival here was about *May 22, 1775.*

[*353*] By "Jore mountain" Bartram refers primarily to the Nantahalas, which form the divide on the west side of the Vale of Cowee. But since he speaks of the range crossing the river in the vicinity of the town of Cowee, it may be considered to include Davis Bald, Leatherman Bald, Raven Mountain, and Cowee Bald, which form a ridge to the north of Cowee (Cowee quadrangle) (fig. 23).

[*354–358*] Bartram's account of his afternoon's excursion among the hills west of Cowee contains one of the most romantic and self-revealing passages in the entire book. The course taken by himself and the trader apparently led them westward about 1.5 miles to Rose Creek ("a brisk flowing creek," *354*), which enters the Little Tennessee from the south (map of Nantahala National Forest, 1938). This may well have been named from "the blooming mountain cluster Rose" encountered on the higher slopes. "The summit of this very elevated ridge" may have been the gap above the westerly headwater of Rose Creek. The "Jore village" [*355*] may have been somewhere in the vicinity of the present Burningtown (Hunter's map of 1751 [as "Hyoree"]; Cowee quadrangle), on the divide between Iotla and Burningtown Creeks. The village, however, was certainly not "many thousand feet higher" than the point from which it was viewed. The "fine little river" [*355*] that they crossed was doubtless Burningtown Creek, at a point perhaps 4 or 5 miles from its mouth. The "horse-stamp" [*355*] may have been somewhere near the mouth of Parrish Creek. The return to Cowee may have been by way of the present Parrish, a mile northeast of Burningtown. It was perhaps in this vicinity that Bartram was privileged to gaze upon the Cherokee "hamadryades" in the unconscious enjoyment of their strawberry picnic—a scene that he proceeded to paint in indelible words (cf. Harper, 1939*c:* 64). The course from "these Elysian fields" to Cowee may have led "obliquely" across the ridge between Horton and Roper Knobs.

[*359–362*] The date of departure westward from Cowee was apparently about *May 24, 1775.* According to the Contents (p. viii), Bartram "set off from Whatoga to the Overhill towns"; and this suggests that his course lay up the valley of Iotla Creek. The "Jore village," as already stated, may have been at or near the present Burningtown. The yaupon was here far inland from its natural range, and it must have been introduced and cultivated by the Cherokees. It is very doubtful if it can have survived in that spot to the present day without the care of the Indians. The "Jore" [*360*], "down the vale about two miles" to the westward of the village, must have been Burningtown Creek. From this vicinity the course led southward up "Roaring creek" (Falls Creek), past Burningtown Falls, where the water was "dashing and roaring over rocky precipices." The "two or three ascents or ridges" were apparently eastern spurs of Wayah Bald. A trail over the 3,300-foot divide, shown on the Cowee quadrangle, is probably more or less identical with Bartram's route. On the south side of this divide the trail makes a junction with the road passing eastward down the valley of Wayah Creek ("the trading path from the Overhills to Cowe"). It was apparently at or near this junction that Mr. Gallahan took his leave. Either the "large creek" in a "stony narrow vale" or "another noisy brook" [361] was Wayah Creek; it is difficult to account for both of these streams.

The point where Bartram encountered the Cherokee youth and his dogs was apparently near the head of Wayah Creek (Nantahala and Wayah Bald quadrangles). To ascend "the most elevated peak" of the Nantahalas meant a digression of something more than a mile northward from Wayah Gap to Wine Spring Bald (5,445 feet).

[363–364] The descent westward from Wayah Gap was down the valley of Jarrett Creek. It may be noted that Bartram refers to this descent as "remarkably gradual" for "two or three miles." This may be considered a strong argument in favor of the route through Wayah Gap rather than one through Burningtown Gap (5 miles to the north), for on the west side of the latter gap the descent is much more abrupt (Wayah Bald quadrangle). The latter route seems to be the one shown on Hunter's map of 1751. The steep part of the path, where the micaceous deposits were found, is apparently about halfway down the five-mile-long valley of Jarrett Creek. (I have not had an opportunity to investigate this portion of Bartram's route.) The "large creek or river" [364] crossed the next day was doubtless the Nantahala River, although the distance to it was far less than "eight or ten miles." Perhaps this distance was meant to represent the entire day's journey. The point of crossing was probably in the vicinity of Aquone near the mouth of Choga Creek.

[364–365] Beyond the Nantahala the most probable route for Bartram was up the valley of Choga Creek and across the divide (at Old Road Gap) to Junaluska Creek (Wayah Bald quadrangle). For it was on this route that he would have been most likely to meet Atakullakulla, coming by way of the present Robbinsville and Andrews from his home town of Chotte, above Fort Loudon on the Little Tennessee River in Monroe County, Tenn. (Hunter's map of 1751; Swanton, 1922: pls. 6, 7).

Ata-kullakulla (*ca.* 1700–1780), as the grand chief of the Cherokees, was certainly known to Bartram by reputation, and was immediately recognizable by his "remarkable small stature" [*485*]. A modern writer would have made much more of this encounter; in particular, he would have dwelt upon Ata-kullakulla's voyage to England as a member of Sir Alexander Cuming's delegation in 1730, his dining with the King of England, and the portrait that Hogarth had painted of him in court costume! (Cf. Mooney, 1900: 40, 42, 510; J. P. Brown, 1938: pl. facing p. 40, and 1957; Swanton, 1946: pl. 8, left-hand fig.) But in the democratic view of a Quaker perhaps these circumstances added little or nothing to Ata-kullakulla's stature and did not affect the simple "friend and brother" relationship here proclaimed. Possibly Bartram had heard from John Stuart himself how the latter's life had been saved through the friendship and intervention of Ata-kullakulla during the disastrous retreat from Fort Loudon in 1760 (Mooney, 1900: 43–44; Arthur, 1914: 569). Momentous events were now brewing. Stuart and his deputy, Alexander Cameron, in behalf of the British government, were about to instigate the Cherokees to attacks on the frontier settlements of the American Revolutionists (Mooney, 1900: 47, 48). But Ata-kullakulla remained steadfast in his devotion to the American cause (Mooney, 1900: 54).

[*366*] It was apparently in the valley of Junaluska Creek, not far from the present Andrews, in Cherokee County, that Bartram made his serious decision to return, and so faced eastward again. The date of the return to Cowee was perhaps about *May 27, 1775.*

[*371–373*] The journey from Cowee to Keowee (fig. 24), presumably by the same route by which he had come, may have taken place approximately on *May 29* and *30.* The ancient stone "altars" or "ovens" that Bartram reported about Keowee should be of much archaeological interest, if discoverable. Mr. Chas. N. Wilson, formerly of Greenville, S.C., who, at my suggestion, very kindly searched the area and made local inquiries, was unable to find any trace or even tradition of the "altars." The sojourn at Seneca apparently occurred during the *early part of June,* and that at Fort James during the middle of that month.

In his conference with the Indian chiefs at Seneca, Cameron may have already been paving the way to stirring them up against the Revolutionists. A month previously news of the Battle of Lexington had reached Charleston, and in consequence he may have received special instructions from Superintendent Stuart. By the following September he had retreated from Loughabber and had gone among the Cherokees (Drayton, 1821, *1:* 408).

[373–374] Many of the Cherokee towns listed here may be located on one or another of the following maps: Hunter, 1730 and 1751; Mouzon, 1775; Romans, 1776; Drayton, 1821, 2: facing p. 343; Mooney, 1900: pl. 3; Swanton, 1922: pl. 7; *Crown Coll.*, ser. 2, 3: 34–35, 1910. This list should be compared with a similar list of Cherokee towns in Drayton (1821, 1: 428). It was furnished by Richard Pearis to W. H. Drayton in 1775. The number of men in the 43 towns is given as 2,021.

[375–376] To go from Fort James to one of the nearest points on the upper Broad River where Bartram had passed with Col. Barnet's party just two years previously (e.g. the vicinity of the junction with Hudson River; Carnesville quadrangle), and return would have involved a journey of approximately 50 miles. It is unfortunate that Bartram has left us no details of that excursion.

The site of Fort Charlotte, opposite the mouth of Broad River, was later occupied by the town of Vienna. The latter name appears on maps as late as 1841, but it has disappeared from recent maps. The farm of M. St. Pierre, reached on *June 22, 1775*, was presumably at, or in the vicinity of, the French settlement of New Bordeaux, on the site of the present Bordeaux on Little River in McCormick County, S.C. (Faden Atlas of 1776: pl. 39; McCormick quadrangle). According to Castiglioni (1790, 1: 284), French Protestants had established this settlement, but abandoned it during the Revolution. The distance from Fort Charlotte is little more than half the "twenty miles" indicated by Bartram. The next stop, "nine or ten miles farther down the river," may have been in the vicinity of Benningsfield Creek, west of Plum Branch, Edgefield County, S.C. "Six miles farther down the river" may have brought the party to a ferry in the vicinity of the recent Price Ferry (the "Hughchee" of Faden's map of 1776), about 5 miles above the mouth of Little River (site now obliterated by the Clark Hill Reservoir). The route from this point to the "Flat-rock" (which lay probably at an air distance of 30 miles to the southwest) is a matter of conjecture; it may, however, have passed through Bartram's old stamping-ground at Wrightsborough, McDuffie County, Ga.

[376–377] Both the Faden Atlas of 1776 (pl. 39) and the Romans map of the same year show a junction of roads a little east of Rocky Comfort Creek in the present Warren County, Ga. One (probably that traveled by Bartram) comes from Little River on the northeast; the other, from Augusta on the east. This was the logical rendezvous for Bartram's party and for the traders coming from Augusta. Inquiry in Warren County in 1940 led me to Camak, whence I was conducted by

C. P. Lazenby to a granite outcrop (fig. 25) on his father's property
a mile to the northwest, on a headwater of Middle Creek (map of
Warren County, 1939). Although there are several other granite outcrops within a few miles, this is the one to which the name "Flat Rock"
seems to be particularly applied at the present day, and it is quite
possibly the area visited by Bartram. Taitt's map of 1772 shows the
main road that extended from Augusta southwest to the Chattahoochee, as crossing the headwaters of Brier Creek, which lie actually
within 2 miles of this Flat Rock. Taitt is in error in indicating a further
extension of Brier Creek to the north, under the name of Sweetwater
Branch. The "Dancing Hill" of his map may be identical with Bartram's
"Flat-rock." Camak is said by the residents to be on the old road
from Augusta to Milledgeville. It is also a point on the present Georgia
Railroad, which seems to have been laid down on the old Indian
trading-path for most of the distance between Augusta and Macon.

Bartram's description of the "expansive clean flat or horizontal rock"
and the "delightful rivulet of excellent water" fits the place admirably.
On the other hand, Middle Creek is tributary to Little River, and the
nearest headwater of the "Great Ogeche" is about 2 miles to the
south. This, however, would not be the first time that Bartram was
confused in regard to these two river systems (cf. 39). The Flat Rock
in 1940 was still a most inviting spot, and it served as a favored picnic
ground. Here grow many of the characteristic plants of the Georgia
granite outcrops, of which Dr. Rogers McVaugh has made an in-
tensive study (1943). Among them are *Sedum pusillum, Diamorpha
cymosa, Phacelia dubia, Silene caroliniana, Nothoscordium bivalve,
Oxytria crocea, Opuntia* sp., *Cheilanthes lanosa,* and *Asplenium
platyneuron.* The low woods that closely invest the rock exposures
include *Pinus taeda, Ulmus alata, Celtis tenuifolia* var. *georgiana,* and
Liquidambar styraciflua, with *Rhododendron canescens, Vaccinium
elliottii,* and *Callicarpa americana* among the shrubbery. I did not
locate on April 28 the "species of Ipomea" that Bartram found in
bloom at a date two months later. It is identified by Bayard Long and
the late Dr. F. W. Pennell as standing cypress (*Gilia rubra*).

Another spot that might be investigated as the possible site of
Bartram's Flat Rock is the Brinkley Place Flat Rock, situated 1¾
miles west of Camak (*Geol. Survey Georgia Bull.* 9-A: 227–229, 1902).

[*377 ff.*] Bartram's course from this point southwestward to the
Chattahoochee was the great Indian trading-path, which followed the
Fall-Line Sand Hills. It is remarkable that no historian or geographer
seems to have attempted to trace this historic route in all its details.
Goff (1954: 128–129, map) has indicated it roughly, but without the

benefit of Taitt's map he has doubtless placed it too far south between Columbia and Baldwin Counties. The route is indicated, though none too well, on the Purcell map of about 1776; also on Thomas Wright's map of Georgia and Florida, 1763 (*Crown Coll.*, ser. 3, *3:* 141, 1915). But by far the most detailed and most accurate of contemporary maps is that which David Taitt prepared during his journey of 1772, and which has only recently become available, although his journal was published as long ago as 1916. It is very evident that his route across both Alabama and Georgia was identical for the greater part of the way with that of Bartram. It has thus proved enormously useful in determining a large and difficult section of Bartram's travels. I was first made acquainted with it by the late Dr. Charles C. Harrold, and subsequently a photographic copy of the original in the William L. Clements Library at the University of Michigan was very kindly furnished to the American Philosophical Society.

Of all possible routes across the state, this one along the Fall-Line Sand Hills doubtless encounters the minimum number of streams or swamps. There is a definite physiographic reason for the location of this great Indian highway.

[379] The Flat Rock is apparently little more than 5 or 6 miles from any point on Rocky Comfort Creek where the party is likely to have crossed, and it is doubtful if as many as "two considerable rivulets" would have been passed on the way. Furthermore, this would seem to have been altogether too short a distance for a day's journey. It is also a remarkable fact that Bartram mentions here no crossing of the "Great Ogeche," which he could not possibly have avoided. One is thus led to suspect that he somehow confused the Ogeechee River itself with Rocky Comfort Creek, and that the party encamped on the banks of the river on the first night after leaving Flat Rock (perhaps *June 29, 1775*). Taitt's map indicates that from the vicinity of the last-mentioned spot the path closely approximated the line of the Georgia Railroad southwestward to Sparta, in central Hancock County. The "two considerable rivulets" crossed by Bartram were presumably Rocky Comfort Creek (perhaps including its tributary, Whetstone Creek) and Long Creek (map of Warren County, 1939). The crossing of the Ogeechee was probably at or near Mayfield, Hancock County. From the Flat Rock to this point is about a dozen miles —a very short day's journey.

In the vicinity of Sparta the path turned more to the south, away from the line of the present railroad. It crossed two headwaters of Big Buffalo Creek (soil map of Hancock County, 1909; map of Hancock County, 1952) and then Little Buffalo Creek at a point 3.5

miles northeast of Shelba, Hancock County (Milledgeville quadrangle). Passing through Shelba, it continued southwest for about
a dozen miles to Rock Landing on the Oconee River, meanwhile
crossing Town Creek at a point approximately east of Milledgeville.
Rock Landing (reached on *July 1, 1775*) is about 4 miles below
Milledgeville, near the mouth of Camp Creek (a westerly tributary).
The day's journey, if from the Ogeechee, would have been about 35–
40 miles. It is more likely, however, that two days were required to
cover this distance, for the progress on each of several following
days is recorded as "about twenty miles."

[*380–381*] The ethnological importance of this passage is indicated
by Swanton, who says (1922: 180–181):

"Almost all that is known of later Oconee history [after 1695] is
contained [in this account]. The removal of this tribe from the Oconee
River took place . . . just after the Yamasee outbreak of 1715, and
the movement into Florida about 1750. . . . Bartram's narrative gives,
not merely the history of the Oconee, but a good account also of the
beginnings of the Seminole as distinct from the Creeks." (See also
Commentary for pages *54* and *184*.)

"For the origin of the word Tomoco or Timucua see the discussion
of Utina in the Commentary for page 55. The Calloosas or Calusa
lived along the southwestern coast of the Florida peninsula between
Charlotte Harbor and the Florida Keys. This was the tribe which
gave Ponce de Leon such a rough reception and was responsible for
his death." (J.R.S.)

[*381*] The route between the Oconee River at Rock Landing and
the Ocmulgee River at the present Macon is indicated on land-lot
maps of this section furnished to Charles C. Harrold by the Division
of State Parks, Historic Sites, and Monuments in 1938; here it is
marked in part as "Garrison Road" and in part as "Hawkins' Trail."
It takes a fairly direct course, apparently passing through no town
or village marked on current maps (of Baldwin County, 1952; Jones
County, 1952; and Bibb County, 1953). It is apparently more or less
identical with State Highway 49. The same route is indicated on the
map in White (1849); and an intermediate point shown there is
Wallace, on the west side of Commissioners Creek in southeastern
Jones County. At the western end the Garrison Road passes close to
the reconstructed Fort Hawkins, which overlooks Macon from the
east.

Taitt's map (1772) indicates a width of 350 feet for the Oconee,
which is better than Bartram's 250 yards. Similarly, he gives 300 feet
for the Ocmulgee, in contrast to Bartram's 300 or 400 yards. (The

figures given in Taitt's journal vary greatly from those on his map.) It is strange that Bartram passes by the remarkable Ocmulgee mounds (fig. 26) with so little notice. They are doubtless the most remarkable structures of their kind in the entire Southeast. They are comprised within the recently established Ocmulgee National Monument. For further descriptions see White (1854: 275) and "Ocmulgee National Monument" (National Park Service, Washington, 1951: 6 pp., 5 figs., 1 map).

The crossing of the Ocmulgee, according to Dr. Harrold, was a little upstream from the Spring Street bridge at Macon. This point was passed apparently on *July* 3. "Stony Creek," 6 miles to the west, was doubtless the present Rocky Creek. The old road followed by Taitt and Bartram is supposed to have crossed this creek about a hundred yards north of the present Columbus Road (Route 80).

[382] The Great and Little Tobosochte of Bartram (the Large and Little Tobasaughkee of Taitt's map) are apparently Tobesofkee and Echeconnee Creeks, respectively, of current maps. The old road, known here as the Federal or Wire Road, but marked Knoxville Road on the map of Bibb County (1953), crosses the latter stream at a point 3 miles south of the present main highway (Route 80). It then continues about 10 miles west-southwest to Knoxville and Roberta (map of Crawford County, 1939).

The "large brook called Sweet Water" is a place of particular interest as the type locality of Bartram's *Hydrangea quercifolia*. Baldwin (in Darlington, 1843: 61) places it "about six miles north easterly" from the Creek Agency on the Flint River. On the Purcell map (Swanton, 1922: pl. 7) it is named the "Sweetwater" and shown as a tributary of the Flint River, in a position corresponding rather definitely to that of the present Culpeper Creek (map of Crawford County, 1939). On the other hand, there is a modern "Sweetwater Creek," arising 2½ miles northeast of Knoxville and flowing into Echeconnee Creek, a tributary of the Ocmulgee. The weight of evidence from the Purcell map and from Baldwin is in favor of Culpeper Creek as Bartram's "Sweet Water." The distance by road from this creek to the Flint River is about 8 miles. Although grazing and other agricultural operations seem to have brought about a local extinction of the *Hydrangea* in the vicinity of Knoxville, Dr. Harrold showed me some flowering specimens on June 11 on Rocky Creek, just west of Macon. In 1812 Baldwin had found it "very abundant."

[383] From Knoxville southwestward the old and the new roads seem to coincide as far as the Flint River. This stream was crossed apparently on *July* 5. Taitt's map gives a width of 450 feet for the

river, but his journal says 200 feet. This may be compared with Bartram's 250 yards and my own estimate of 200 feet.

Not many years later this locality became famous as the site of the Creek Agency, headquarters of the renowned Col. Benjamin Hawkins (1754–1816), able Superintendent of Indian Affairs (cf. Jones, 1878: 241–244; Pound, 1951). A monument marking his lonely grave, on a little elevation just east of the river and about a quarter of a mile southeast of the highway bridge, is the only present vestige of the Creek Agency (map of Crawford County, 1939).

From the Flint River to the Chattahoochee Bartram's route is probably represented fairly well by a road shown on the map in White (1849); it passes through Holt's Shop (just beyond Patsiliga Creek in northern Taylor County) and Fort Perry (in northern Marion County), crosses Pine Knot Spring or Creek (near the Chattahoochee-Marion county boundary), and continues along the south side of Upatoi Creek. Practically the same route is shown on the Early map of 1818 and on the Tanner map of 1841. (See also map of Taylor County, 1951; map of Marion County, 1950; and map of Chattahoochee County, 1939.) The "large and deep creek" beyond the Flint River was doubtless Patsiliga Creek. The lovely *Hypericum aureum* (now known as *H. frondosum* Michx.), discovered there by Bartram, still flourished in the vicinity in 1939.

[384] One of the creeks passed the next day was probably Whitewater Creek, in western Taylor County.

[384–386] It is interesting that when John Lyon (MS), the Philadelphia horticulturist, was passing through this identical part of Georgia in July 1803, the horses of his party were attacked by "a large species of fly," just as those in Bartram's party had been 28 years previously.

[387] The Pintchlucco may have been the present Pine Knot Creek. From this point on, the path roughly parallels Upatoi Creek, at an average distance of about 2 miles to the south (soil map of Chattahoochee County, 1924; Columbus quadrangle).

[388–389] The point of departure for the day's journey (apparently of *July 11*), "nine or ten miles" from the Chattahoochee, was perhaps the site of the present Ochillee, on Ochillee Creek, Chattahoochee County. The course at first was a little south of west, approximating the present "First Division Road" of the Fort Benning Military Reservation. After passing the head of Gilbert Creek, the path probably turned nearly southward along the ridge west of that creek, and reached the Chattahoochee at the present Chambers Landing, opposite the "Uche town." Taitt's map indicates a width of 400 feet for the river at this point, compared with Bartram's 300 or 400 yards. Uchee was just below the mouth of Uchee Creek, in Russell County, Ala. (soil map of Russell County, 1913).

"The form of the name Chattahoochee given by Bartram, 'Chata Uche,' leads to the suspicion that he supposed that the river derived its name from the name of the Yuchi tribe by him spelled 'Uche,' and such an error at any rate has been perpetuated by some later writers. This is wholly erroneous. The word Chattahoochee signifies 'incised or sculptured rocks' and was given on account of certain rock formations near Columbus, Georgia. The origin of the name Uche is unknown, but that tribe did not settle upon the Chattahoochee River until a comparatively late date. When first brought to the attention of Europeans this tribe was entirely independent of the Creeks and was living in eastern Tennessee whence they drifted south in the seventeenth century in several successive waves. Although these bands gradually came together and had united with the Creeks by the middle of the century following, they preserved their autonomy and their language, and they still preserve them. See Speck (1909)." (J.R.S.)

"Bartram is correct in stating that the Yuchi language is entirely distinct from the Creek, but in identifying it with Shawnee his informants led him widely astray. It happened that about the time when the Yuchi and Shawnee entered the Creek Confederation a band of each became very close friends, but while Yuchi forms a stock by itself Shawnee is a dialect of the great Algonquian family which once occupied the greater part of our northeastern territory and the eastern interior of Canada." (J.R.S.)

[389] The journey to the "Apalachucla town" extended about 8 miles to the south-southwest. This town was situated 1.5 miles below the mouth of Ihagee Creek, on the west side of the Chattahoochee. All the mounds about it have been ploughed away, as Mr. Peter A. Brannon informed me. The "great Coweta town" was at the approximate site of Phoenix City, opposite Columbus, Ga. The principal Indian towns along this section of the Chattahoochee are shown on Taitt's map.

Swanton, after quoting Bartram's account of Apalachicola, says (1922: 133) that while it "apparently throws a great deal of light upon the history of the Apalachicola, it actually introduces many perplexities."

"The Apalachucla town actually belonged to the Atcik-hata or Hitchiti group though Bartram, on page 463, has mistakenly classed it with the Muskogee-speaking towns. Actually Kasihta was the leading peace town of the Lower Creeks, and it is unlikely that such leadership as is here indicated would have been bestowed upon a town of an alien group. However, Apalachicola was also called 'Talwa Thlako' or Big Town, and very likely took a leading part in bringing the Atcik-hata into the confederation. For this reason it perhaps enjoyed some distinction among the towns devoted to peace. In spite of Bartram's assertion, however, councils, even for the purpose of making peace, were not always held there. Bartram is quite correct in stating that Coweta was the leading war town." (J.R.S.)

A most interesting episode, pertaining apparently to this part of the *Travels,* is related elsewhere by Bartram (1853: 37–39). Here he tells of a visit to a private, well-organized plantation "belonging to a chief of the town of the Apalachians, about six miles from the town, on or near the banks of the river . . . He is called the *Bosten* or Boatswain by the traders." As Bartram remarks in the *Travels* [389], his time here "was employed in excursions round about this settlement."

[390] The "ancient Apalachucla," a mile and a half below the new town, was apparently in the vicinity of the present Burr's Landing (soil map of Russell County, 1913).

"This slaughter of traders may have taken place just before the English and Creek attack upon the Apalachicola in 1707–08. It could not have been at the outbreak of the Yamasee War because the Apalachicola were then on Savannah River." (J.R.S.)

[392] "How Bartram derived the idea that the Cherokee were dominated by the Creeks or stood in fear of them is a mystery, since they had rather recently won a considerable victory over the latter and pushed them out of the Tennessee Valley. The Chickasaw were usually on friendly terms with the Creeks, particularly those of the town of Kasihta, but they were in no way intimidated by them and also won a rather striking engagement about twenty years after this time." (J.R.S.)

[395] The "stoloniferous shrub" discovered in the vicinity of "Apalachucla" was the white buckeye (*Aesculus parviflora*). It was technically named in 1788 by Walter, whose description is much less complete than Bartram's.

[396] We come here to another point where it is virtually impossible to reconcile Bartram's chronology. The last previous date given by him is *July 1,* at the Oconee River, Ga. The next ten days of travel, duly accounted for in the narrative, brought the party to the Chattahoochee and "Apalachucla town" presumably on *July 11.* Yet after continuing here "about a week" [389], they set off westward on "July

13th"! Perhaps our most feasible procedure is to accept this last date provisionally, at the same time reducing the stay at "Apalachucla" from "about a week" to two days. (However, see Commentary for pp. *403–404*.)

Peter A. Brannon's description (1939) of Bartram's route through Alabama has been very helpful, and personal discussions with him in Montgomery have likewise been profitable. In the absence of any details in the *Travels* concerning the route to Talasse, we may have recourse to the maps of Taitt (1772), Purcell (about 1776), and Early (1818), and the Geological Map of Alabama (1894). The last fortunately shows the Old Federal Road of 1805, which was evidently laid down upon the Indian trading-path that provided a route for Bartram across the greater part of the state.

In leaving "Apalachucla" on *July 13, 1775*, Bartram's party doubtless proceeded northward and came into the western road somewhere between Uchee, near the mouth of Uchee Creek, and the present Nuckolls, about 8 miles farther upstream (soil map of Russell County, 1913; Seale quadrangle). At about the latter point a branch diverged northeastward across Uchee Creek to the towns a little higher up the Chattahoochee. The main path went almost due west from this point at least as far as the present village of Uchee in Russell County, meanwhile passing through Sand Fort. From Uchee, according to Brannon (1939), it continued westward through Old Fort Bainbridge, Creek Stand, Warrior Stand, Old Fort Hull, and Persimmon Creek (Geol. Map of Alabama, 1894), whence Bartram diverged to the right toward Talasse. On the other hand, Taitt's map indicates a course northwest from the vicinity of Uchee to "halfway house" (which appears to have been in the approximate location of the present Society Hill), and thence down Uphapee Creek—first on the north side, then on the south side—to Talasse. A similar route is shown on the Purcell map of about 1776 and is indicated by Hawkins in 1799 (in Swanton, 1922: 244), who speaks of a trading-path crossing Opintlocco Creek twice. Talasse was on the east bank of the Tallapoosa River just above the mouth of Uphapee Creek, in extreme northwestern Macon County, Alabama. It would appear quite likely that Taitt, Bartram, and Hawkins all followed much the same course.

The journey from Talasse to Coolome, a distance of perhaps 25 miles along the left or south bank of the Tallapoosa, could have been accomplished in a single day (say *July 16, 1775*). Otasse is shown on Taitt's map as just below the mouth of Calebee Creek. Ancient Coolome was situated on a wide level area by the river a mile north of Cooks Station and 9 or 10 miles east-northeast of Montgomery, in

Montgomery County. Dr. R. P. Burke kindly conducted us to the site. It is marked by a wooded mound approximately 100 feet in diameter and 13 feet in height, set in the midst of grazing land. There is another and smaller mound in the woods at the edge of the river bluff. Taitt's map places Germany's plantation some little distance east of Coolome. He gives (1916: 501) a width of 200 yards for the Tallapoosa at this point.

[397–398] The day's journey (*July 19?*) of "about eighteen miles" led in a southwesterly direction through or near the present Mytilene, Oak Grove Church, and Pinedale, and across Catoma Creek toward Snowdoun, in Montgomery County. The latter part of this journey was along the route of the later Old Federal Road. Natural prairies or "great plains" (now greatly modified by agriculture) occupy considerable areas south of Catoma Creek. They form a part of the Black Belt of Alabama (cf. R. M. Harper, 1913: 84–91). The night's camp was probably in the vicinity of Snowdoun. It was evidently in the same vicinity that the "litter of young wolves" was encountered. Howell (1921: 32) misplaces this locality "on the Tallapoosa River, near Coolome."

The next day's march, southwestward along the line of the Old Federal Road, should have led to the headwaters of Big Swamp Creek, in southeastern Lowndes County. The "considerable creeks" [398] passed in the meantime would have been Pintlalla and Pinchony Creeks. The crossing of the latter was about 1.5 miles northwest of the settlement of Pintlalla (soil map of Montgomery County, 1926). Here, on the west side of the creek, appears a sunken vestige of the old road, passing diagonally beneath the bridge on the present highway and reaching the creek a few yards downstream from the bridge. Hereabouts is the supposed site of Manac's Tavern, a former landmark.

[399] The black soil gives this region the name of Black Belt. The limestone rock is Selma Chalk (R. M. Harper, 1913: 84). Beyond Big Swamp Creek the route passed close to Fort Deposit and half a dozen miles northwest of Greenville.

[400] Bartram is quite mistaken as to the distance of this section of the trail from the Alabama River; it is approximately 35 miles instead of "two or three." Probably he actually had in mind some of the upper tributaries of the Escambia-Conecuh system, such as the sources of Persimmon and Pigeon Creeks, hereabouts "bearing away Southerly." The forest "which continued above seventy miles" obviously required several days to traverse; it must have extended across the Blue Marl Region, the Southern Red Hills, and the Lime Hills

(cf. R. M. Harper, 1943: 65, fig. 4) to a point somewhere on the Monroe-Conecuh county boundary, which is formed by the Old Federal Road.

[401] "We now enter a very remarkable grove of Dog wood trees." To judge by the position of this passage in Bartram's narrative, we might assume that the dogwood forest was located along the above-mentioned county boundary. However, this is quite likely one of the points where we must make some allowance for the author's penchant for inexact orientation. For J. B. Little (1885: 71) refers to an area near Fort Bibb, which was established on the Federal Road in the northwestern part of Butler County in 1818, in the following words:

"The level portion of low, flat land between Reddock and Pine Barren Creeks, was originally covered with a pine forest and a dense undergrowth of dogwood. From the thickness of the undergrowth, this section of the county was called Dogwood Flat, but the name was afterward changed, and is now known as Pine Flat. The soil of Pine Flat is a brown loam."

This area is approximately a dozen miles west of Greenville.

[402–403] Since Bartram's party had left the headwaters of Big Swamp Creek about *July 21*, the route for several days had been along the divide between the Alabama and the Escambia-Conecuh Basins. If they had continued along the line of the later Old Federal Road (fig. 27), they would have crossed the Escambia River on the Monroe-Conecuh county boundary, about 3 miles north of Escambia County. At a point so close to its source, this must be a rather small stream. Instead, however, of crossing here, the party evidently turned southward on the east side of the river for a considerable distance, and then "forded the river Schambe about fifty yards over." If Bartram made his usual mistake in regard to the width of rivers, the "fifty yards" should have been nearer 50 feet. Romans (1776: 303) gives a width of "about 60 feet" at a still lower crossing. Taitt's map shows alternative paths in this section, one on each side of the Escambia River (or, as he calls it, the "Weewa Oaka or Little Scambia"). The "very different" landscape in which Bartram now found himself was the Southwestern Pine Hills (cf. R. M. Harper, 1913: 113–123, frontisp.). Chestnut trees no longer occur naturally so far south in Alabama.

[403–404] From the crossing of the Escambia the route seems to have continued southwestward along the divide to a point about midway between Perdido and Stockton, Baldwin County, where it makes a junction with an east-west road between these two points. Bartram here turned westward along the latter road. Two or three miles west of the junction, where the road begins to descend the western slope of the ridge, is an area answering well to his description of "heights . . . encumbered with pebbles, fragments and cliffs of rusty ferrugineous rocks." It is now known as Gopher Hill, from the numbers of Gopher Turtles formerly found thereabouts. Bartram's course presently turned toward the northwest and brought him to "Taensa" on the eastern channel of the Mobile Delta (fig. 28). This place was apparently at or near the mouth of Hall's Creek, about 4 miles north of Stockton (*Crown Coll.*, ser. 3, *1*: 48, 1915; soil map of Baldwin County, 1912; Tensaw quadrangle). Taitt's map of 1772 shows this side path extending northwestward from the main trading-path on the divide and crossing the "Taensa old fields." The distance from Taensa to Mobile, by the meandering channels of the delta, is somewhat more than "thirty miles." The date of arrival at Mobile was presumably about *July 26, 1775*. However, the first date mentioned by Bartram after his arrival is "July 31st, 1778" [= 1775], and this may have been the very day of arrival, or possibly the day thereafter. The chronology would work out much better if we assumed that "July 13th" [*396*], when Bartram started westward from the Chattahoochee, was a slip for July 18.

[*405*] The "Taensa bluff" reached on or soon after *August 5* is probably the same place as the "Taensa" where Bartram first arrived at the Mobile Delta [*403*]. Hamilton (1897: 194) can scarcely be right in placing it at "modern Stockton." The Crown Collection map (ser. 3, *2*: 93, 1915) indicates that "Major Robert Farmer's plantation" was located approximately at Hall's Creek, a mile or so northeast of Bryant's Landing. Walter B. Jones, of the Geological Survey of Alabama, has noted (MS) "mounds of earth" in this vicinity on a local map. This area is of particular interest as the type locality of *Myrica inodora*.

Taitt's map of 1772, considered by itself, might be misleading, for it places "Major Forman" about 7 miles farther north, in the vicinity of Pierce's Landing, at the mouth of Major's Creek, 4 miles west of the settlement of Tensaw (soil map of Baldwin County, 1912; Tensaw quadrangle). As a matter of fact, the Crown Collection map also shows two land lots (39 and 40) in the vicinity of Pierce's Landing as belonging to Major Farmar. Evidently he had holdings in different places.

[*406*] The "East channel" up which Bartram sailed joins the Alabama River about a mile below Major's Creek. The names "Tensaw Lake," "Big Beaver Creek," "Bear Creek," and "Little Bear Creek" are

applied to successive portions of this channel (Tensaw quadrangle). The type locality of *Oenothera grandiflora* is "a few miles above Taensa," i.e. along the east channel between Hall's Creek and the Alabama River. This name may have been originally proposed by Bartram and submitted with the specimens he forwarded to Dr. Fothergill. At any rate, the name was applied by Solander, who worked on Bartram's material in London, and it was published in Aiton (1789, 2: 2), with the remark, "*Introd.* 1778, by John Fothergill, M.D." A copy of this volume of Aiton's *Hortus kewensis* was acquired by Bartram's friend, Benjamin Smith Barton, in 1790, and is now in the library of the Academy of Natural Sciences of Philadelphia.

[407–409] The bluff at which Bartram landed, "above ten miles" upstream from Taensa, may have been at Pierce's Landing. The landing the next noon may have been at or near the Boatyard Lake, on the Alabama River about midway between Pierce's Landing and the Cutoff. This, then, would be the type locality of *Prunus nemoralis* and *Magnolia pyramidata*.

From this point Bartram probably continued several miles upstream to the Cutoff and passed through it from its eastern end to its western end at its confluence with the Tombigbee. This is apparently the river junction to which he refers, rather than that of the Alabama and the Tombigbee about 4 miles to the south.

It is difficult, at least for one who has not been on the Tombigbee, to attempt to trace the voyage up this river. The "large lagoon," "just within its capes," may have been a bayou on the west side, opposite the Cutoff (soil map of Washington County, 1919; Tensaw quadrangle). Or perhaps it was Bates Lake, a little more than a mile farther upstream. The "high steep bluff," with "extensive old plantations" [409], was possibly McIntosh Landing, on the west side 7 or 8 miles above the Cutoff.

[410–411] Canes (*Arundinaria gigantea*) of the size described by Bartram seem no longer discoverable (R. M. Harper, 1928: 73). However, Lyell (1849, 2: 63) saw 30-foot canes on the Tombigbee, and Hamilton (1897: 226) reports a cane in colonial times that was over 47 feet long. The total voyage up the Tombigbee may not have extended more than 15 or 20 miles above the Cutoff.

[411–412] The horseback journey of perhaps "thirty miles" up the river from Major Farmar's plantation may have taken Bartram to the vicinity of the present Mt. Pleasant, in southwestern Monroe County. The creek that "swam" the horses may have been Little River.

[*413*] It was probably at least mid-August, and perhaps later, when Bartram returned to Mobile. He does not fully account for the passage of time in this region.

A number of early naturalists testify to the non-native status of the honey bee in America; e.g. Collinson to John Bartram, 1768? (Bartram Papers, *3:* 80); Nuttall (1951: 61); Charles Pickering to John Torrey, 1828 (Torrey-Redfield Coll.).

[*414–415*] The voyage from Mobile to Pensacola apparently began on or about *September 3, 1775*. The first day's run was down the bay to Mobile Point; that of the second day, along the coast of the Gulf of Mexico to Pensacola, Fla. Governor Chester gave Bartram the following permit to travel and collect in West Florida (Bartram Papers, *1:* 79):

West Florida   By His Excellency Peter Chester Esquire Captain
EMBOSSED   General and Governor in Chief in and over the Prov-
SEAL   ince of West Florida and the Territories depending
               thereon in America   Chancellor and Vice Admiral
               of the same &ca. &ca.

To all to whom these Presents shall come or may in any wise concern

Greeting.

Know ye that William Bartram Botanist having requested my Leave and Licence to Travel through the different parts of this Province under my Government, in order to make Botanical and other Observations I do hereby permit him to Travel in and over the said Province for the purpose of Collecting Rare and useful productions in Botany and Natural History. And I do here Command all His Majesty's Servants and Subjects within this Province that they do not interrupt him in his lawful proceedings, but that they be aiding and assisting to him as becometh all encouragers of useful Discoveries

> Given under my hand and Seal at Arms at Pensacola the
> Fifth day of September in the Year of our Lord one Thou-
> sand seven Hundred and Seventy Five and in the Fifteenth
> Year of His Majestys Reign

PTR C CHESTER

By His Excellency's Command.
    Alexr. Macullagh./. D. Sec.y.

[*416*] An interesting view of old Pensacola appears in Roberts (1763: pl. facing p. 11).

[417] On this page occurs a curious example of an apparently misplaced observation by Bartram. His description of "Saracinia lacunosa" applies to the hooded pitcher-plant, currently known as *Sarracenia minor*. This species, however, does not occur in the Pensacola area! (Cf. Wherry, 1935: 16–17; Merrill, 1945: 31–32.) The return to Mobile was apparently on *September 6, 1775*.

[418–419] On the subject of Bartram's illness at Mobile and farther west, Mark F. Boyd writes (June 26, 1939):

"It does not appear likely to me that he had any systemic infection, or systemic disease, but rather more probable that the difficulty with his eyes might be attributable to some powerful irritant. Wonder whether he might have been mixed up with poison ivy?"

The late Dr. E. P. Darlington suggested the possibility of scarlet fever, which is apt to affect the eyes, and which was formerly more virulent than nowadays. The apparently permanent injury to Bartram's left eye, resulting from this illness [421], must have detracted from his subsequent ability in distinguishing the characters of live, wild birds, especially without the benefit of field glasses. In a letter accompanying his lengthy observations on the Creek and Cherokee Indians, written in 1789, he says (1853: 9): "My weakness of sight, I hope, will plead for me, when I assure you I have been obliged to write the greater part of this with my eyes shut, and that with pain." This last incident bespeaks remarkable fortitude.

The farm "about six miles below the town" was probably on the north side of Dog River (soil map of Mobile County, 1911; Hollingers Island quadrangle). The next stop was perhaps somewhere in the vicinity of Bellefontaine or Fowl River, and the third stop on Mon Louis Island (Cedar Point quadrangle). The "channel Oleron" was the present Grant's Pass or Pass aux Herons, between Cedar Point on the mainland and Dauphin Island. The course to the westward lay through Mississippi Sound. The lower course of Pearl River forms the boundary between Louisiana and Mississippi. The French gentleman's habitation was presumably somewhere in the vicinity of its mouth, at a distance of about 90 miles west of Mobile Bay. The proprietor's name was possibly M. de la Gauterais (cf. Romans, 1776: 211).

[420–423] "Pearl Island" was apparently not the present Pearl River Island, which lies at the mouth of that river on the north side of Lake Borgne. According to the topographic map (Rigolets quadrangle), the latter island consists wholly of salt marsh. The site of Mr. Rumsey's plantation was more likely an area bounded on the south by The Rigolets, on the east by West Pearl River, on the north by Salt Bayou, and on the west by Lake Pontchartrain. This is marked "I[sle] des Petites Coqilles" on a *Crown Collection* map (ser. 1, 2: 1, 1907), and "Prevost Island" on the Rigolets quadrangle. It seems to contain a central portion of higher land than salt marsh. Bartram's stay here "of four or five weeks" apparently extended to about the *middle of October, 1775.*

[*423–425*] The distance across Lake Pontchartrain from The Rigolets to Pass Manchac, following the north shore, is about 50 miles.

[*425–426*] The "straits that communicate to the Lake Mauripas" are the present Pass Manchac (Pontchatoula quadrangle). Bartram's description does not fit the present topography very well. The point where the "right hand channel" (the present North Pass) diverges is only 1.5 miles from Lake Pontchartrain, instead of "six or eight miles." The winding course of the North Pass is about 8 miles in length, instead of "three or four miles." The channels do not reunite, but enter Lake Maurepas at points about 2 miles apart. Taitt's map (1772) and the *Crown Collection* map (ser. 2, 3: 72, 1910) do not substantiate Bartram's description. The latter must have trusted to a faulty memory. The distance around the north shore of Lake Maurepas to the mouth of the Amite River is about 10 miles (Pontchatoula and Springfield quadrangles). The tortuous course of this river is approximately double the air distance between given points. Taitt's map indicates a width of 260 feet near the river's mouth, gradually lessening to 200 feet a few miles below the junction with the Iberville River or Bayou Manchac. The plantation of the Scotch gentleman was probably in the vicinity of Head of Island or French Settlement (Denham Springs quadrangle).

[*427–428*] The head of navigation on the Bayou Manchac was probably near the halfway point between the Amite and the Mississippi Rivers (the total air distance being about 15 miles), or perhaps a little below the junction with Bayou Fountain (Baton Rouge quadrangle) (cf. *Crown Coll.*, ser. 3, 2: 71, 1915; Kniffen, 1935: 464, fig. 1).

"Small boats continued to ply this route [Bayou Manchac] until 1814, when Andrew Jackson, for strategic purposes, constructed an earthwork dam to sever water connection between the Manchac and the Mississippi" (Kniffen, 1935: 462).

Manchac was on the north side of the bayou at its western end, a mile south of the present Burtville. The site is marked "Ft. Bute" on Taitt's map. Bartram's fascination at his first sight of the mighty Mississippi may be readily imagined. It was one of the great moments in his travels. The date seems to have been approximately *October 21, 1775.*

The topographic map (Baton Rouge quadrangle) indicates that the height of the banks is nearer 15 than "fifty feet." Opposite Ft. Bute, on the south side of the Bayou Manchac, a "Spanish Post" is marked on Taitt's map.

[429–430] The gentleman from Baton Rouge, Bartram's traveling companion on the Mississippi, was William Dunbar (1749–1810). He arrived in America in 1771, and two years later he "established a plantation in the British province of West Florida near Baton Rouge." Subsequently he moved to Natchez, Mississippi. His broad scientific interests brought him the friendly regard of President Jefferson. The latter appointed him to explore the Ouachita River in 1804–05 and suggested his participation in the western expedition that was eventually conducted by Zebulon M. Pike in 1806–07. Fifteen of his letters to Jefferson are preserved in the Library of Congress. "He corresponded with, and held as his close friends, Sir William Herschel, Bartram, Hunter, Rittenhouse, and Rush." (*Dict. Am. Biog.*, 5: 507–508; Mrs. Rowland, 1930; C. Johnson, 1943: *passim.*) Alexander Wilson wrote to Bartram on September 2, 1810: "Mr. Dunbar, of Natchez, remembered you very well, and desired me to carry his good wishes to you" (Ord, 1825: clxiii).

Baton Rouge is about 15 miles upstream from Bayou Manchac, not "more than forty miles." "Alabama" was apparently in the vicinity of the present Burtville or Gardere. The "friend's habitation" [430] was in the vicinity of Baton Rouge.

[430–431] "Point Coupe" was in the same or approximately the same location as the present Pointe Coupee, on the west side of the Mississippi in Point Coupee Parish, about 35 miles upstream from Baton Rouge (Taitt's map of 1772; Swanton, 1922: pl. 5; Bayou Sara quadrangle). The "White cliffs" or "Brown's cliffs" were in the vicinity of the present Port Hudson, on the east side of the river, about 23 miles above Baton Rouge. The cliffs, however, have receded a considerable distance to the eastward from their position in Bartram's day (Lyell, 1849, 2: 138–141). The plantation owned by Governor Browne was near Port Hickey, a mile or so farther downstream.

[431] "August 27, 1787," should read *October 27, 1775!* The "small rivulet" was evidently the one flowing southward through Port Hickey (Bayou Sara quadrangle). It was farther from the river in 1775 than at present. The "White plains" are in the vicinity of Plains, half a dozen miles east-northeast of Port Hickey.

[432] As Lyell points out (1849, 2: 138–141), the course of the Mississippi changes fairly rapidly. Drastic changes in shore lines and islands on this part of the river since 1836 are shown on the New

Roads quadrangle (1939). Thus it seems impossible to identify the particular island where Bartram's Bear sought refuge. It may have been one of four shown on Taitt's map of 1772 within a few miles downstream from False River, an ancient oxbow of the Mississippi. A single island (Browne's) is shown in approximately the same location on a map in the *Crown Collection* (ser. 3, 2: 100, 1915).

[433] This page seems to furnish still another example of a misplaced observation (cf. Commentary for 417). The description of a "muscle" with "horns or protuberances" applies to *Elliptio spinosus* of the Altamaha River in Georgia—a species quite unknown elsewhere (Goodrich, 1930: 140). The "geese" and "brant" observed here, being merely winter visitors, furnish ample proof that the date was not "August" [431].

[433–434] An account of the relations between the French and the Natchez, very similar to the one given here by Bartram, is furnished by Stiggins (in Swanton, 1922: 314–315). The establishment at Natchez was destroyed in 1730, according to Thomassy (1860: map following p. 226).

"The Natchez massacre of 1729 created a profound impression throughout this part of America and became the basis for stories that verge upon the mythic. See Bureau of American Ethnology Bulletin 43, 1911." (J.R.S.)

[435–436] Lyell, who examined these same cliffs at Port Hudson (1849, 2: 137–142), quotes the present account with approval, and remarks concerning the fossil forest that Bartram "had commented with his usual sagacity on the magnitude of the geographical changes implied by its structure."

[437–438] The return journey from Baton Rouge to Mobile began apparently on *November 10, 1775*. Essentially the same route was pursued as on the westward journey. The "island of Orleans" was presumably in the vicinity of Head of Island (Denham Springs quadrangle). The date "November 13th, 1777," when Lake Maurepas was passed, may be considered correct as to the month and day. Mobile was reached apparently on or about *November 16, 1775*. The next ten days were evidently spent in packing up specimens and preparing for the next stage of the journey.

[440–441] "November 27th 1777," the date of departure from Mobile, is probably correct except as to year. During his voyage to the Mississippi Bartram had probably left his horse with Major Farmar at the latter's plantation on the eastern channel of the Mobile Delta. In the absence of any geographical details concerning the first part of his journey northeastward from the Mobile Delta, we can only assume that it covered practically the same ground as his journey in the opposite direction during the previous July, i.e. the line of the Old Federal Road of 1805.

[442] Bartram's highest latitude in Alabama was approximately 32° 30' N., along the Tallapoosa River.

[443–444] The name "Deadman's Creek" might seem to suggest the modern Murder Creek, whose headwaters the party would have passed along the Monroe-Conecuh county boundary in the vicinity of Midway; but the incident from which the latter derived its name is said to have occurred about 1805 (Hodgson, 1824, 1: 143). At an average rate of progress of 20 miles per day, this point would have been reached in three or four days from the Mobile Delta. The "large deep creek," which Bartram and the young Mustee crossed by means of a raft, was perhaps Catoma Creek, several miles northeast of Snowdoun in Montgomery County; this is the largest stream along that part of the route, and it is about a day's journey from the Tallapoosa River.

[445] The point where the Tallapoosa was reached (about *December 4, 1775*), opposite the town of Savannuca (Taitt's map of 1772), was probably in the vicinity of Judkins Ferry, 8 miles northeast of Montgomery (soil map of Elmore County, 1914).

[446] Mucclasse was a mile or two downstream from Savannuca, on the north side of the river.

"The Mucclasse or Muklasa Indians spoke a dialect related either to Alabama or to Koasati." (J.R.S.)

[447] Alabama, the site of Fort Thoulouse, was at the upper junction of the Coosa and Tallapoosa Rivers, 4 miles southwest of Wetumpka in Elmore County. Taitt's map exhibits at this point a symbol similar to the one at Ft. Bute on the Mississippi, but there is no accompanying name. Tuckabatche was on the west bank of the Tallapoosa opposite the mouth of Uphapee Creek, at a distance of 21–22 miles due east of Mucclasse.

"Tuckabatche (or Tukabahchee) was the head war town of the Upper Creeks, corresponding to Coweta among the Lower Creeks with which it was on most intimate terms. The two refused to side with the hostiles in the Creek-American War. The town of Tukabahchee was located in the bend of Tallapoosa where it turns west, and its site has been indicated by a marker. Ottasse or Attasse, or, as the ethnologists spell the name, Atasi, was ordinarily on terms of the closest intimacy with Tukabahchee although they divided in the Creek War. By some it was considered a branch of the larger town, but this is probably erroneous." (J.R.S.)

[449] To reach the old town of Coolome and James Germany's

plantation, which lay a little to the eastward (Taitt's map), involved recrossing the Tallapoosa to the south side. This was familiar ground to Bartram from his visit during the previous July.

[*450*] His course to Tuckabatche was probably along the north side of the Tallapoosa, after having crossed it once more in the vicinity of Coolome. Taitt (1916: 501) had taken exactly this course on February 12, 1772. Bartram's remark on continuing "up" the river from Tuckabatche is rather confusing, for the well-known "Attasse," "Atasi," or "Ottasse" was half a dozen miles downstream, on the south side of the Tallapoosa just below the mouth of Calebee Creek (soil map of Macon County, 1905). This site is plainly indicated on Taitt's map and practically all the other old maps of that area. Swanton (1922: 265, pl. 2) has located another "Atasi" several miles upstream from Tuckabatche, on the east side of the Tallapoosa, perhaps on the basis of Bartram's statement. It does not seem at all likely, however, that there should have been at one time two towns of the same name only 10 miles or so apart. It is perhaps best to consider that Bartram's "up the river" was a slip for "down the river."

"From the wording here it would appear that Atasi was up stream from Tukabahchee at this time, but this is contrary to the location given in all other sources, and Bartram may actually have doubled back along the south side of the Tallapoosa from Tukabahchee." (J.R.S.)

[*456–457*] "What Bartram describes here was probably merely an abandoned Creek square ground belonging perhaps to some town other than Atasi but not necessarily abandoned very long. Indeed I doubt whether the 'ignorance' of the Atasi Indians regarding its origin was as wide spread as Bartram would have us believe. His remarks regarding this 'monument' are typical of his treatment of aboriginal remains in the territory through which he passed, and his obsession regarding their high antiquity was partly responsible for the similar obsession which afflicted later writers of the latter part of the eighteenth century and the first part of the nineteenth, and for the myth of that 'mysterious race of mound builders.'" (J.R.S.)

Bartram's account of the Indian towns along the Tallapoosa [*445–457*] gives little intimation of the drunkenness and general disorderliness that were so prevalent during Taitt's sojourn three years earlier. His Quaker philosophy evidently enabled him to look chiefly upon the brighter side of human nature, and less upon the baser side.

[*457*] The date of departure from Attasse was *January 2, 1776*, not "1778." In the absence of any information to the contrary, we may assume that Bartram now retraced the course of his journey west-

ward from the Chattahoochee during the previous July. Taitt (1916: 545) shows that Chiaha ("Chehaw" or "Geehaws") was about 3 miles below the Uchee town, which in turn was just below the mouth of Uchee Creek in Russell County, Ala. (soil map of Russell County, 1913). Thus Chiaha was approximately opposite Cody Landing (Columbus quadrangle). "Usseta" or Kasihta must have been at Cody Landing or near vicinity. This was apparently not the main Kasihta town (which was farther upstream), but one of its branch villages. Taitt's map indicates that he crossed the Chattahoochee at approximately the same point as Bartram.

"In his list of Creek towns on pages 462–464 Bartram evidently identifies Usseta with Kasihta, but the towns usually called 'point towns' were Chiaha, Osochi, and Okmulgee. It is possible that Bartram intended the second of these instead of Kasihta in this place. In his list Osochi appears under the name 'Hooseche.' The differences in language would apply in either case, and he could have passed between either pair." (J.R.S.)

"There is every reason to suppose that they ['point towns'] derived their name from the fact that they were located on a point of land running into the Chattahoochee, or in other words on the inside of a sharp bend. It is the point below Ft. Mitchell in Russell Co., Ala." (John R. Swanton, in litt., November 12, 1941.)

[458–460] Going northward half a dozen miles or so from the Chattahoochee, and meanwhile crossing Oswichee Creek, Bartram would have come to the east-west trading path paralleling Upatoi Creek on its south side. From this point to Warren County, Ga., he doubtless retraced his course of the preceding June and July. The crossing of the Ocmulgee was at the present Macon; that of the Oconee, at Rock Landing 4 miles below Milledgeville; and that of the Ogeechee, probably at or near the present Mayfield. On the early use of skin boats for crossing rivers in the Southeast, see Neill (1954). The dejection felt by Bartram at the Ocmulgee may have been due to Revolutionary War news imparted by the two companies of westward-bound traders who were encountered at that point (Harper, 1953: 573). The "waters of great Ogeche" [459], on which the party camped the last night before reaching the main river, were doubtless Little Ogeechee Creek, several miles northeast of Sparta, Hancock County.

[460] From the Ogeechee to Augusta the route was probably by way of the present Warrenton, Warren County; thence through southern McDuffie and western Richmond Counties (Hobbs', Arrington's, Burch's, and Leitner's Mills—Harlem quadrangle), and onward

through northern Richmond County across Spirit, Butler, and Rocky
Creeks (Hephzibah quadrangle). The latter part of this route had
been covered in June, 1773, when Bartram accompanied Col. Barnet's
party in its survey of the "new purchase" [34]. The entire route across
Georgia is indicated on Taitt's map (1772). The sojourn at Augusta
was apparently from about *January 14 to 18, 1776.*

[*460–462*] In leaving Augusta, Bartram doubtless crossed the Savannah River at the Sandbar Ferry, 3 miles below the town, and continued about 10 miles down the Carolina side to Silver Bluff. There
he doubtless had many matters to communicate to his friend George
Galphin besides the affair of the unhappy trader of Mucclasse [*462*].
From Silver Bluff to Savannah the route was probably more or less
identical with that pursued (in the reverse direction) by himself and
young John McIntosh in May 1773 (see Commentary for *28–32*). The
"Great Springs" were the present Blue Springs on Beaverdam Creek
(fig. 29), 5 miles southeast of Hilltonia in Screven County (cf. J. Bartram, 1942; 27, 65, fig. 14; W. Bartram, 1943: 136, 175). As probably the most attractive spot along the entire route between Augusta
and Savannah, it well deserves the very pleasing description here provided. The "Cassine" or yaupon (*Ilex vomitoria*), perhaps introduced
and cultivated there by the Indians, does not seem to have survived to
the present day. Savannah was reached probably about the *last of
January 1776.*

[*462–464*] The locations of most of the Creek towns listed here have
been worked out with the aid of *Bureau of American Ethnology Bulletin, 30* (1907, 1910), Gatschet (1884, 1888), Swanton (1922), and
other sources, including particularly the maps of Taitt (1772) and
Purcell (about 1776). (See Annotated Index.) Among the towns
which Bartram locates on the Flint River [*464*], Cuscowilla, Talahasochte, Caloosahatche, St. Marks, and probably others were not on
this river but in Florida.

"By 'Stinkard' in his list of Creek towns Bartram means towns speaking dialects of Alabama or Koasati among the Upper Creeks and dialects of Hitchiti among the Lower Creeks. His classification is generally correct, but there are some errors. For one thing he repeats his
error (see Comments for p. 389) of stating that the Yuchi spoke the
same language as the Shawnee, telling us that the 'Savannuca'
spoke the 'Uche tongue' and the 'Uche' the 'Savannuca tongue.' There
was at one time a town of Chickasaw Indians among the Creeks of
Coosa River, but the dialect which Bartram attributes to the Abacooche and in part to the Natche town was undoubtedly Natchez,
though some Chickasaw may have mingled with these Indians. Apala-

chucla or Apalachicola was an Atcik-hata or Hitchiti town, not of the Muskogee connection as he gives it. And finally I am of the opinion that the Osochi or 'Hooseche' Indians originally, and perhaps in Bartram's time, spoke Timucua." (J.R.S.)

[465] On the origin and migration of the Creeks see also W. Bartram (1853: 12 and 1943: 171) and Swanton (1946: 22–27, map 10).

"Here Bartram recognizes the distinctive character of the Natchez language, but what he says regarding the ancient 'empire' of the Natchez and its subsequent break-up is pure romance. The legends of nearly all southeastern tribes indicated an origin toward the northwest rather than southwest, but Du Pratz, Milfort, and other writers have screwed this around so as to mean southwest, with the evident desire to tie them to the glamorous Aztec empire." (J.R.S.)

[467–468] The effect upon William Bartram of the course of the Revolutionary War, and his curious failure to mention it in his *Travels*, have been the subject of a certain amount of comment and speculation. His actual return to Philadelphia just a year previous to the date given in the *Travels* has not hitherto been taken into account in this speculation.

During 1775 there had occurred the Battles of Lexington, Bunker Hill, Fort Ticonderoga, Crown Point, and Quebec—all far from the territory Bartram was exploring. During the summer and fall of 1776 General Howe defeated the American forces under Washington in a series of engagements about New York City. During the following December and January Washington turned the tables upon the British at Trenton and Princeton in New Jersey. Just at that time Bartram reached his home in West Philadelphia after nearly four years of wandering in the South. Eight months later, in September 1777, Howe defeated the Americans on the Brandywine. The approach of the British Army is said to have hastened the death of John Bartram on the 22d of that month—just four days before the British entered Philadelphia (Darlington, 1849: 44).

Meanwhile, in the South, the British had failed in an attack on Charleston in June 1776. Early in that year there had been skirmishes at Savannah and on the St. Mary's River (Jones, 1883, 2: 224–227, 233–234). It was not until December 1778 that the British captured Savannah. During the next two years they swept up through South and North Carolina.

Thus William Bartram apparently did not come into actual contact with any of the Revolutionary warfare during his long southern peregrinations. Unquestionably, however, the spirits of the peace-minded Quaker were greatly perturbed and depressed by the news from the North. Perhaps this explains, at least in part, the meager account he has provided of his last season's field work "in Georgia and the East borders of Florida."

It would appear that his activities during a portion of 1776 took a strikingly new turn, if we may credit the following passage in the biographical sketch by Ord? (1832: iii):

"In 1776, just at the commencement of the Revolutionary War, and while on his return from Florida to Georgia, Mr. Bartram volunteered and joined a detachment of men, raised by Gen. Lochlan [sic] McIntosh, to repel a supposed invasion of that state from St. Augustine by the British; he was offered a lieutenant's commission if he would remain, but the report which led him to volunteer his services having proved false, the detachment was disbanded, and Mr. Bartram resumed his travels."

There seems to be no good reason for questioning the trustworthiness of this statement (especially if it may be ascribed to a man of Ord's standing), despite Bartram's lifelong Quakerism and his devotion to the principles of peace, as expressed, for example, in the following of his own words: "I profess myself of the Christian Sect of the People called Quakers, & consequently am against War & violence, in any form or maner whatever" (MS, Hist. Soc. Pennsylvania).

Aside from the reference to the blooming of *Franklinia* (fig. 3) on the Altamaha, very little definite information can be gleaned concerning the extent of Bartram's excursions during the spring and summer of 1776. He would be quite likely to have at least called at the homes of Benjamin Andrew in the Midway district of Liberty County, of Lachlan McIntosh at Darien, and of James Spalding on St. Simon's Island, although various circumstances connected with the Revolution may have taken each one of these gentlemen away. Presumably Andrew was busy in the council of the patriots in Savannah, while McIntosh had taken a command in the Army. Spalding, as a loyalist, had perhaps already moved to Florida. Even if these friends were absent, Bartram doubtless would have been entertained by any members of their families remaining at home. It is possible that after finding *Franklinia* in bloom near Fort Barrington, he continued on an overland journey from the Altamaha to King's Ferry on the St. Mary's. On pages 17–27 the incidents of this journey are placed (apparently out of chronological sequence) in the spring of 1773. Perhaps this is as far as he went in 1776 on "the East borders of Florida."

Certain circumstances of the encounter with the "intrepid Siminole" [20–21] may be worthy of comment. If this actually took place in 1776, it may have been during Bartram's term of military service under his friend McIntosh. McCall (1816, 2: 84) speaks of "bodies of observation" that "were kept in motion" at that period between the Revolutionary outposts on the Altamaha and the Satilla. Who knows but that McIntosh may have utilized Bartram's knowledge of the country and his peaceful reputation to send him on a scouting trip in the direction of the British forces as far as the St. Mary's? It may have been with the deliberate intention of enhancing his peaceful appearance that he now went "unarmed" [21], whereas he ordinarily carried a fusee on his travels. It was only natural for a Quaker to omit from the book any direct reference to his own Revolutionary activities (cf. Harper, 1953).

Another event obviously described out of sequence is the eclipse of the moon, which Bartram observed on a voyage up the Altamaha [51]. This must have taken place on *July 31, 1776*, instead of in the summer of 1773 (cf. Commentary for p. 51). Thus a little more of his time during 1776 may be accounted for. Perhaps even the Altamaha voyage was undertaken as part of his scouting for McIntosh.

Bartram's long delay in bringing out the *Travels* enabled his kinsman, Humphry Marshall, to publish the first valid description of *Franklinia alatamaha* in his *Arbustrum Americanum* of 1785. Marshall indicates, however, that the name had already appeared in Bartram's horticultural catalogue; hence it has been credited to "Bartram ex Marshall" (E. L. Little, Jr., 1945: 503; Merrill, 1945: 18), although the catalogue of about 1783 lists the species merely as "Alatamaha." (One of the two known copies of this catalogue is preserved among the Bartram Papers, *1*: 86.) It now seems likely that Bartram's first sight of the blossoms was sometime in the summer of either 1773 or 1776 rather than in April 1773. This involves a revision of an opinion previously expressed (Harper and Leeds, 1938: 3). The horticulturist who reported the recent flowering of the species in April had evidently confused it with *Gordonia lasianthus*.

It has long been thought that *Franklinia* was last seen in the wild in 1790, by Moses Marshall; but this date must now be advanced to 1803 (John Lyon's MS Journal, June 1, 1803).

The other "new, singular and beautiful shrub" found near Fort Barrington was Georgia bark (*Pinckneya bracteata*).

[469–470] It was evidently on some date near, or prior to, *October 30, 1776*, that Bartram had left the lower Altamaha River in Georgia for the last time. For on that day his friend James Bailley addressed a letter (Bartram Papers, *1*: 2) to him from Broughton Island, containing the following passage: "And write me before you leave Charleston and likeway upon your arrival in Philadelphia." It was perhaps in *early*

November, 1776, that Bartram departed from Savannah on his home-
ward journey of some 800 miles. The villa of Jonathan Bryan, the
Revolutionary patriot, was at the mouth of Pipemaker's Creek, on the
south side (Campbell map of 1780; soil map of Chatham County,
1911). It is possible that Bryan and Bartram had become acquainted
while jointly concerned in the defense of the southern frontier of
Georgia against the British in the summer of 1776 (cf. White, 1849;
125). The present brief account of "wild pigeons" constitutes one of
the principal records we have of the former occurrence in Georgia of
the now extinct Passenger Pigeon (cf. Greene *et al.*, 1945: 45).

[*470–471*] Zubley's Ferry was about 2 miles above Purysburgh, S.C.,
and about 20 miles (not "fifty") above Savannah (Campbell map of
1780; Early map of 1818). To reach it, our traveler took the familiar
road to Ebenezer, but turned off to the river several miles south of
that point. Though the ferry has long since been abandoned, the old
roadway leading to it on the Carolina side is still plainly visible. The
route taken from the vicinity of Purysburgh to Charleston was probably more or less identical with the one that Bartram had traveled with
his father in 1765 (cf. J. Bartram, 1942: 21–23). Jacksonburgh was the
present Jacksonboro on the Edisto or Ponpon River.

Just why Bartram should have gone "nine miles" above Charleston
to cross the Cooper River instead of using the Hobcaw Ferry at the
city is not apparent. Since he usually overestimated distances, he may
have crossed from the vicinity of the present U. S. Navy Yard to
Thomas Island, where the river is about ⅔ mile wide (Charleston
quadrangle). Some of the old maps (Jefferys, 1776; Faden, 1780) show
a road extending from about that point along the north side of the
Wando River. Bartram may have rejoined the more frequented road
in the vicinity of Awendaw. He would then have proceeded toward
Georgetown by way of Cochran's Ferry on the Santee, which was
located a mile or so upstream from the modern bridge on Route 17.

The reason for crossing Winyah Bay below Georgetown, instead of
at or a little above the city, where the ferries were located, is likewise
not apparent. But there was evidently a regular crossing of the bay
below the town, for it is shown on Hunter's map of 1730 and Schoepf
(1911, 2: 163) took such a route in 1784. From this vicinity to Cape
Fear River in North Carolina he traveled a familiar route, having
been over it with his father in 1765 (cf. J. Bartram, 1942: 18–19). The
road followed the highest part of the neck of land between the Waccamaw River and the ocean as far as Murrell's Inlet. Several miles
beyond that point it turned to the hard sands of the ocean beach and

so continued for about 15 miles, past the present Myrtle Beach, to the Lewis Swash (the present Singleton Swash) (soil map of Horry County, 1924). The rocks on the beach are low-lying beds of coquina —certainly not "cliffs." They had been remarked upon in 1765 by John Bartram (1942: 14). There is an exposure of these rocks at Hurl Rock Beach, a mile southwest of Myrtle Beach. The encounter with the "party of Negroes" must have taken place not very far from Myrtle Beach.

[472–473] The "swash at the east end of the bay" was doubtless the Lewis Swash of the old maps. Here the road turned obliquely inland and crossed White Point Creek at a point nearly a mile from the sea. This portion of the road has been abandoned but is still evident. From the vicinity of White Point Creek to Little River the road was probably more or less identical with the main road shown on the soil map of Horry County (1924). The more recently constructed paved highway (Route 17) does not follow this route exactly. Bartram may have lodged that night with Captain Ross at Little River, as he and his father had done on August 10, 1765.

Venus' fly-trap (*Dionaea muscipula*) still abounds in the wet pine barrens of southwestern Brunswick County. Although the elder Bartram may have been the first to send specimens of this remarkable plant abroad, he was apparently not its discoverer. Probably the first announcement of its discovery was made in a letter written by Governor Arthur Dobbs from Brunswick, N.C., on April 2, 1759, to Peter Collinson in London (original in Collinson's smaller volume, p. 254, Linnaean Society of London; copy kindly furnished by the late Charles B. Montgomery). On the distribution of the species see Coker (1928) and R. M. Harper (1928b).

From the state boundary near Little River Bartram's road (now known as the Old Georgetown Road) apparently extended through the present Calabash, Shallotte, and Supply (soil map of Brunswick County, 1937). From the last point he may have taken a road that extended nearly to the present Southport and then turned northward along the west side of Cape Fear River to Brunswick. Or he may have taken a more direct road that is shown on the Mouzon map of 1775 and the Price and Strother map of 1808; this apparently passed through the present Bolivia. Old Town was at the mouth of Old Town Creek, on the west side of Cape Fear River about 7 miles south of Wilmington. The Lucas place was perhaps in southern Bladen County, 2 or 3 miles north of East Arcadia, and across the river from Indian Wells (Price and Strother map of 1808; soil map of Bladen County, 1914). Lake

Waccamaw had doubtless become familiar to Bartram during his residence at Ashwood on the Cape Fear River from 1761 to 1765 and
from 1770 to 1772.

[474–476] Ashwood was on the right bank of the river about 5 miles
northeast of Council, Bladen County. The site is now marked merely
by a cellar excavation, in which a few chimney bricks may be seen.
On one side is the wooded river bluff; on the other, wide, level cultivated fields. A fine spring, that doubtless served the household in by-
gone days, issues from the steep bluff a little below its top. The bluff
was originally about 60 feet high, but the river has been raised 8 or
10 feet by the construction of locks. The river is nearer 300 feet in
width than "three hundred yards" [476]. The trees, shrubs, and fossils
of this area were discussed at length by John Bartram (1942: 15–18)
as well as by his son. The property was still owned in 1940 by a descendant of Col. Bartram's—David Gillespie Robeson.

William's return to Ashwood on the present occasion could scarcely
fail to have been a melancholy one. The time was probably *late November* or *early December 1776*. His uncle, Col. William Bartram, had
died in 1770; the latter's wife, in 1772; and their son, William Bartram, Jr., M.D., in 1771. Their daughter Sarah, who had married General Thomas Brown, survived till 1779, and was doubtless present to
welcome the traveler. Another daughter, Mary, who married Thomas
Robeson, was probably also in the neighborhood.

The warm feeling that William had for his uncle was revealed when
he wrote of him as "beloved & esteemed for his patriotic Virtues, in
defending & supporting the Rights of Man. & particularly, the Poor,
abandoned, & the Stranger; His House was open, & his Table free, to
his neighbour, the oppressed & the stranger." (Delafield Coll.; J. Bartram, 1942: 81.)

[476–478] The list of "flowering" shrubs at Ashwood was doubtless
based upon long previous experience there rather than upon the
present winter visit. The creek on which the petrified trees were noted
was no doubt Willis' Creek, a westerly tributary of the Cape Fear
River in extreme southwestern Cumberland County. These trees had
also been observed by John Bartram (1942: 17–18). The late H. A.
Rankin, of Fayetteville, kindly conducted me to the spot in 1939 and
pointed out some of the trees. The route from Ashwood to this creek is
probably represented fairly well on the Price and Strother map of
1808. It seems to have passed through the present Elizabethtown and
Tarheel, but between Dublin and the river. Apparently the same road
is shown on the soil map of Bladen County (1914); for the most part

it lies within a mile or two of the river. In the vicinity of Ashwood a section of the old highway or "Stage-coach Road" may be seen just east of Route 87. On the south side of Willis' Creek, also, there is a disused old road a little east of Route 87 and roughly parallel to it; this, in Mr. Rankin's opinion, may have been the main highway in Bartram's time. The soil map of Cumberland County (1922) shows what may have been a further section of this old road; it extends most of the way from Willis' Creek northward to a point near the mouth of Rockfish Creek, and it is closer to the river than Route 87.

Mr. Rankin believed that the old road crossed Rockfish Creek (7 miles below Fayetteville) a very short distance above its mouth and then continued a little way along a hogback ridge between the river and the creek. About a mile and a half to the northwest the old road crossed Carver's Branch a hundred yards or so east of Route 87; a remnant of it was still visible there in 1939. Cross Creek flows through the present Fayetteville and joins the Cape Fear River at that point. Bartram's reference to being there "about twenty years ago" doubtless harks back to the days of his trading venture in 1761–65. The name of the town was changed from Cross Creek to Fayetteville in 1784 (Henderson, 1923: 122).

[479–480] Little more than conjectures can be made concerning the route from Cambelton (the present Fayetteville) to the Meherrin River in Virginia. However, the Mouzon map of 1775, the Purcell map of about 1776, Faden's map of the marches of Cornwallis (in Schenck, 1889: facing p. 16), and Price and Strother's map of 1808 seem to furnish good clues. Apparently the route extended for "about sixty miles" north-northwest through or near the present Manchester, Spout Springs, Jonesboro, Sanford, and Pittsboro, and across Cane Creek in extreme southern Alamance County (soil map of Alamance County, 1901). A gap in this part of the text narrative is supplied by a few words in the Contents (p. x): "Deep River—crosses Haw River." The former river lies, in part, between Chatham and Lee Counties; the latter, between Alamance and Orange Counties. On the north side of Cane Creek was the Quakers Meeting House of Mouzon's map. Hereabouts the road turned northeastward (perhaps along the Old Woody's Ferry Road) to Hillsboro, Orange County, and Oxford, Granville County (the latter marked as "Harris Burgh" on Mouzon's map). Beyond that point it passed between Island and Nutbush Creeks in northern Vance County and crossed the Roanoke at some ferry (perhaps Royster's) in south central Mecklenburg County, Va. (Mouzon and Faden maps). Still continuing northeastward, it may have crossed

COMMENTARY

the Meherrin River in the vicinity of Ogburn, Mecklenburg County,
and then passed through the present Kenbridge, Lunenburg County,
and Blackstone, Nottoway County (Purcell map).

As a possible clue to Mr. Lucas' location on the Meherrin River,
I learned of a Lucas' Ford on a small tributary of the river about 2.5
miles north or northwest of Safford's Bridge, which spans the river in
the vicinity of Ogburn.

After leaving the Meherrin River and arriving in the vicinity of
the present Blackstone, Bartram would have come into an old colonial
trail running east-northeast about 50 miles to Petersburg (Purcell
map). A roadside marker in Blackstone calls attention to this trail,
which doubtless approximated Route 460. From Petersburg to Alexandria (*December 26*) the route was presumably by way of Richmond
and Fredericksburg, but from Georgetown, Md., to the Susquehanna
River it is highly problematical. For some reason Bartram apparently
sought to avoid a direct course to Philadelphia through populous
Baltimore and Wilmington. Wright's Ferry (*Trans. Am. Philos. Soc.,
1:* pl. 7, fig. 1, 1771) was between the present Wrightsville and
Columbia, Pa., and Anderson's Ferry was "five miles above," at
Marietta. The final stage of the long journey, after Lancaster, was
probably through Coatesville and West Chester. A likely stopping-
place, on the last night, was the home of his second cousin, Humphry
Marshall (author of the *Arbustrum Americanum*, 1785), who lived at
Marshallton, 4 miles west of West Chester.

Those who have taken Bartram's dates literally have believed that
he returned to his father's house only to find it bereft of its owner.
However, since he returned in *January* (perhaps about the *2d*) *1777,*
there remained eight full months in which these two rare spirits were
able to confer on William's wonderful new experiences and discoveries in the Southland. It is pleasant to believe that the elder
Bartram's earlier doubts as to William's worth and ability were at
last happily dissolved. For surely, in listening to the tales of persevering endeavor and high adventure among primitive scenes and
peoples, and in scanning the field journals brought back, he must
have realized that his truly talented son had now attained full stature.
His cup would no doubt have filled to the brim if he had lived to see
the publication of the *Travels.*

For the years 1773 to 1777, we have, thanks to the *Travels,* more
detailed information about William Bartram's activities than for any
other period of his life. The soul-stirring experiences of those years
were in great contrast to his sedentary occupations during most of the
other years.

Part IV

[481–522] These pages, devoted to an exposition of the persons, manners, customs, government, arts, and languages of the southeastern Indians, may be profitably compared with another and later treatise by Bartram on the same subjects. The manuscript of the latter was composed in 1789, in answer to numerous queries placed before our author by his ambitious friend Benjamin Smith Barton. Barton doubtless kept the manuscript in his possession till his death in 1815. Its whereabouts and ownership up to the middle of that century remain unknown. In the meantime, however (evidently at some date prior to 1835), John Howard Payne, author of "Home, Sweet Home," made a copy of Bartram's manuscript, and likewise copies of the accompanying original drawings, in a quarto composition book. This "commonplace book" was found among Payne's effects after his death at Tunis in 1852; it is now preserved at the Historical Society of Pennsylvania.

Some 60 years after its composition by Bartram, the original manuscript was dramatically discovered in Mobile, Alabama, where it had been shipped as mere extra filling for a box of books! It presently came into the hands of E. G. Squier, who published it in *Transactions of the American Ethnological Society, 3,* 1853. And now the manuscript seems to have disappeared once more, no one knows where! Among the drawings copied by Payne, there is one of a public square and house in a Creek village; this was not included in the drawings published by Squier.

The publication of 1853 includes the original queries as well as the answers. It goes somewhat further than the present pages [481–522] in discussing certain topics, such as the history, origin, migrations, artistic accomplishments, religious ideas, medical usages, and agricultural practices of the Creeks, Cherokees, and other southern tribes. It is thus obvious that Bartram profited from his friend's queries to the extent of providing more comprehensive or more encyclopedic information on various ethnological topics than he had when merely writing without this external stimulus.

[484] "What Bartram says regarding the shortness of Creek women seems to be borne out, at least in part, by later investigations." (J.R.S.)

[485–486] "Bartram seems to have misinterpreted entirely the attitude of the Cherokee and Creeks toward each other. The former were by no means 'submissive' to the latter, whom they had defeated signally and pushed out of their former territories on the Tennessee and the upper valley of the Coosa. One suspects that he has transferred the common story regarding relations between the Iroquois and Delaware out of its proper setting." (J.R.S.)

[487] "On the Yamasee see Comments for page 26. The Creeks were by no means always friends of the British colonists. They gave at least tacit support to the Yamasee in 1715 in their struggle with the South Carolinians." (J.R.S.)

[490] "Here Bartram pays a well deserved tribute to the more highly developed social institutions of the Creeks." (J.R.S.)

[490–493] Bartram's laudatory account of the temperate and moral conduct of the Creeks scarcely accords with Taitt's description (1916) of the debauchery in their Alabama towns in 1772.

[495] "The mystery surrounding the accession of a mico is contributed entirely by Bartram, but he is quite right in stating that the position was not much sought after. This was because of the onerous obligations which a mico was obliged to assume along with the dignity." (J.R.S.)

[497] "This 'high priest' was the official known to the Creeks as hilis haya or 'medicine maker.'" (J.R.S.)

[498] "According to Creek belief there actually was a being corresponding rather closely with the Great Spirit of Indian romancers. He was called Hisagita-immisi, 'breath bearer,' and was regarded in later times, at least, as the presiding genius of the annual busk ceremony." (J.R.S.)

[499] For the identity of the blind old chief of Mucclasse, see the Annotated Index, under Chief(s).

In his monumental work (1946) on the material culture of the Indians of the Southeastern States, Dr. Swanton makes nearly 100 references to, or quotations from, Bartram. There is only a handful of other authorities—such as Adair, De Soto, Lawson, Du Pratz, and John Smith—of whom he makes equally extensive use. This is an indication of the importance of Bartram's works of 1791 and 1853 as ethnological source material.

ANNOTATED INDEX

ANNOTATED INDEX

$\mathbb{T}$HIS INDEX pertains only to that part of the present volume (pp. xli–lxi, 1–332) which represents Bartram's own *Travels*. The references are not to the pages of the present volume but to those of the original publication of 1791 (indicated in the present text of the *Travels* by italic numbers in square brackets). The entries include all names of plants, animals, minerals, persons, Indian tribes, and geographical areas or localities (such as towns, settlements, bodies of water, islands, and mountains), as well as other words of economic, social, or scientific interest. Such of these words as were misspelled in the original edition are inserted here, within parentheses and quotation marks, immediately after the corrected spelling (see the list of variant and incorrect spellings, below, pp. 695–700). Definitions or explanations of the index entries are supplied in all cases where such information has been deemed suitable. As a means of assembling Bartram's distributional data, particularly on plants and animals, geographical information is supplied with the page references wherever it has seemed useful. Cross-references are given for synonymous terms and variant spellings appearing in more than one place in the index. Wherever it has been possible, biographical notes have been added concerning the persons whose names are entered.

A primary object of this index is to translate Bartram's names of plants and animals into current nomenclature. The modern names supplied are usually synonyms of those he used, but this is not invariably the case, for occasionally he went astray in his determination or interpretation of a species. This could hardly have been otherwise in the then existing state of taxonomic knowledge. As a means of identifying or elucidating the names that Bartram applied to objects in the plant, animal, and mineral kingdoms, many of these names are here supplied with parenthetical references to pages or plates in the works of Catesby, Edwards, or Linnaeus, where the same objects had been earlier described or portrayed. It should be borne in mind that these were the principal authorities on which Bartram based his nomenclature. There are also occasional references of this sort to other early authors, as well as references to more recent authors who have discussed the nomenclature of Bartram's species. A certain number of Bartram's names remain unidentifiable: some are *nomina nuda,* and others are accompanied by inadequate or imperfect descriptions.

New generic and specific names, proposed by Bartram in the *Travels* under the binomial system, are indicated in this index by a prefixed asterisk; this applies whether they are nomenclaturally valid or merely *nomina nuda.*

When two or more localities in a given state are mentioned consecutively under a single index entry, the name of the state is generally given only with the first of these localities. Where modern names of localities differ from the names employed by Bartram, the former are generally substituted in the index references, e.g. Cowpen Lake instead of "Half-way Pond." The modern names are necessarily used in the many cases where Bartram supplied no names at all for his localities.

The botanical nomenclature herein employed is that of Gray's *Manual,* eighth edition (Fernald, 1950), for such species as are treated in that work. For southern species not included in Gray's *Manual,* Small (1933) is utilized as the primary authority. However, if the genera to which these southern plants belong are included in Gray's *Manual,* and if the generic names there employed differ from Small's usage, preference is given to Gray. In general, the names of fishes are according to Fowler (1945); of amphibians and reptiles, according to Schmidt (1953); of birds, according to the *Check-list* of the American Ornithologists' Union, fifth edition (1957); and of mammals, according to Miller and Kellogg (1955). However, a number of bird names that were proposed by Bartram and that I consider valid under the International Rules of Zoological Nomenclature, are given preference over the synonymous names in the A.O.U. *Check-list.*

Those who have suggested identifications of Bartramian species or have contributed other information utilized in this index are indicated at the appropriate place by the insertion of their initials within parentheses. Although most of them are mentioned in the Preface (pp. viii–x), their names are repeated here for convenience of reference:

Sherman C. Bishop *	Andrew L. Pickens
John W. Cadbury III	H. A. Rankin *
Ezra T. Cresson, Jr.*	James A. G. Rehn
Horton H. Hobbs, Jr.	H. Radclyffe Roberts
Frank Morton Jones	David R. Sumstine
Arthur N. Leeds *	John R. Swanton
Bayard Long	Louise F. A. Tangier
Richard A. McLean	Henry K. Townes
Francis W. Pennell *	Edgar T. Wherry

* Deceased.

"Aazalea." *See* Azalea.

Abacooche (properly Abihkutci): a former Upper Creek town on Tallaseehatchee Creek, 5 miles east of Coosa River, in Talladega County, Ala. (Taitt, map of 1772, and 1916: 508, 532; *Bur. Am. Ethnol. Bull., 30*, Pt. I: 2, 1907; Swanton, 1922: 252–253, pl. 2; Talladega quadrangle); listed, 463.

Aborigines of North America, general account of, 481–522.

Acer glaucum (cf. Marshall, 1785: 2): probably red maple (*A. rubrum* L. var.); on St. John's River above Lake Dexter, Fla., 130; along upper Savannah River, Ga., 320; on Amite River, La., 425.

Acer negundo (or "nigundo"): ash-leaved maple (*A. negundo* L.); on St. John's River above Lake Dexter, Fla., 130; near Alachua Savanna, 187; on Amite River, La., 425.

Acer rubrum (cf. Catesby, 1731, *1:* 62, pl. 62): red maple (*A. rubrum* L. vars.); on Colonel's Island, Ga., 6; in coastal swamps, 29; on lower St. John's River, Fla., 84; on the St. John's above Lake Dexter, 130; near Alachua Savanna, 187; near Three Sisters Ferry, S.C., 309; along upper Savannah River, Ga.–S.C., 320, 327; near Wayah Gap, N.C., 362; on Amite River, La., 425. *See also* Maple, Scarlet.

Acer (or "Acher") saccharinum (or "sacharinum"): in these cases, probably not *A. saccharinum* L., but sugar maple (*A. saccharum* Marsh.) (*cf.* Rush, 1793: 64); of Virginia and Pennsylvania, xvi; along upper Savannah River, Ga., 320; near Oconee Station, Oconee County, S.C., 335; on Oconee (= Station) Mountain, 337.

Acer striatum, s[eu] Pennsylvanicum: probably mountain maple (*A. spicatum* Lam.); on Oconee (= Station) Mountain, S.C., 337; near Wayah Gap, N.C., 362.

A. *striatum* Du Roi is considered (*Index Kewensis*) a synonym of *A. spicatum. A. Pennsylvanicum* Marsh. (not L.) is evidently the same species.

"Acher." *See* Acer saccharinum.

Aconitum napellus: not the European *A. napellus* L., but probably clambering monkshood (*A. uncinatum* L.); in the Broad River region, Ga., 45; along upper Savannah River, 321.

"Aconitum napellus. Wild. p. 1233" (Bartram to Muhlenberg, September 6, 1810; Muhlenberg Letters: 137).

Actaea: probably white baneberry (*A. pachypoda* Ell.); along upper Savannah River, Ga., 321.

Adam's needle. *See* Palmetto royal.

Adansonia digitata: baobab tree (*A. digitata* L.); in the tropics, xiv.

Adder. *See* Asp.

"Ado," "Adoe." *See* Eddo.

Adonis, 313; son of, 447.

Adultery: Indians given to, 213; punishment for, among Muscogulges, 515.

Adventurers, a company of, bound for West Florida, 366, 375, 376.

Aesculus: buckeye (*Aesculus* sp.); at the White Cliffs, La., 436.

Aesculus or Pavia, a species of, with white flowers: white buckeye (*Ae. parviflora* Walt.) (cf. R. M. Harper, 1928: 257); described, from Chattahoochee River, Ala., viii, 395.

Aesculus *alba: *nomen nudum*—white buckeye (*Ae. parviflora* Walt.); in Monroe or adjacent county, Ala., 401; on upper Tensaw River, 408.

"He [Bartram] says his Aesculus alba (p. 401, 408) is the Aesculus parviflora of Walter" (B. S. Barton, MS, September 2, 1805).

Aesc[ulus] *arborea: *nomen nudum*—perhaps Carolina buckeye (*Ae. sylvatica* Bartr., *q.v.*); about Wrightsborough, Ga., 36.

Aesc[ulus] *Florid[a]: perhaps Carolina buckeye (*Ae. sylvatica* Bartr., *q.v.*) (cf. Fernald, 1944: 48; Merrill, 1945: 22); described, in Monroe or adjacent county, Ala., 401.

Aesculus pavia (or "parva"): for the most part red buckeye (*Ae. pavia* L.), but the records from the Piedmont of Georgia and South Carolina may have been based upon red forms of Carolina buckeye (*Ae. sylvatica* Bartr.) (cf. Coker and Totten, 1937: 305): on Colonel's Island, Ga., 7; about Wrightsborough, 36; on the Great Ridge, 41; near Salt Springs, Fla., 164; near Alachua Savanna, 187, 198; near Three Sisters Ferry, S.C., 309; at Shell Bluff, Ga., 318; along upper Savannah River, 320, 327; on Oconee (= Station) Mountain, S.C., 337; along Chattahoochee River, Ala., 393; in Butler, Monroe, or adjacent counties, 400, 401; on upper Tensaw River, 408; described, along Cape Fear River, N.C., 476.

Aesculus pavia, a new species of, with larger flowers and broader leaves: perhaps a red form of Carolina buckeye (*Ae. sylvatica* Bartr., *q.v.*); described, along Keowee River, S.C., 328–329.

Aesculus *sylvatica: Carolina buckeye (*Ae. sylvatica* Bartr.; syn., *Ae. neglecta* Lindley) (cf. Fernald, 1944: 47; Merrill, 1945: 22); on the Great Ridge, Ga., 41; along upper Savannah River, 320, 327; near Oconee Station, Oconee County, S.C., 335; described, along Northwest Cape Fear River near Ashwood, 5 miles northeast of Council, Bladen County, N.C., 476. *See also* Pavia sylvatica.

"[Bartram says] that his Aesculus sylvatica, p. 320, 327, 333, 335, 393 is the yellow flowered Aesculus or flava of Aiton" (B. S. Barton, MS, September 2, 1805). *Ae. neglecta* not having been described till 1826, Bartram was obviously unable to identify his species with it.

Aesculus *sylvatica, s[eu] *Virginiana: Carolina buckeye (*Ae. sylvatica* Bartr.) (cf. preceding entry); along Chattahoochee River, Ala., 393.

"Virginiana" is merely an alternative name (Merrill, 1945: 22).

Aesculus *Virginica: *nomen nudum*—buckeye (*Aesculus* sp.); of the Northern States, xvi.

"Aesculus Pavia I never saw farther N⁰ than Cape-Fear N⁰ Carolina about Lat. 33. But, Esculus Virginica as far as 37. & another species which I shall denominate Æsculus [*]oboriginea, as far N⁰ as Redstone & Ahlegany, which seem to be of a middle or doubtful liniage between AEs. virginica s. [*]occidentalis. & AEs. hypocastanum, the pericarpium being prickly like the oriental & the Flower & leaves, bearing a nearer resemblance to the Oriental species than any we have yet the knowledge of." (W. Bartram, notes on back of a letter of September 12, 1795, from B. S. Barton; Bartram Papers, *1:* 9.)

The distribution here assigned to *Ae. virginica* suggests that it is identical with *Ae. pavia.* The characters given for *Ae.* "*oboriginea*" indicate that it is synonymous with *Ae. glabra* Willd. While William Bartram is not known to have been in western Pennsylvania, John Bartram may have found "*oboriginea*" there (Redstone Creek and Allegheny River).

Afric, sooty sons of, 312.

Agate. *See* Jasper or agate.

Agave: undetermined; near Long Pond, Levy County, Fla., 248.

Agave Virginica: rattlesnake-master (*A. virginica* L.); in Warren County, Ga., 379.

Agave vivipara: in this case, not *A. vivipara* L., but another wild century-plant (*A. neglecta* Small) (Small, 1923: 27–28; 1933: 320); described, on Mosquito River, Fla., xxvii.

The figure referred to by Small is evidently one on the map preceding the Introduction in the *Travels.*

"Agave vivipara, Wild. 4ᵗʰ Ed. p. 193" (Bartram to Muhlenberg, September 6, 1810; Muhlenberg Letters: 137).

Agriculture: of the ancients, regulated by bird migration, 285; neglected at Tangipahoa River, La., 425; consultations about, at Attasse, Ala., 454; festivals dedicated to, 509; among American aborigines, 511–513.

Alabama (state): tree growth compared with that in Georgia and Carolina, 400.

Alabama (in Louisiana): a former town of Alibamu Indians, on the east bank of Mississippi River, apparently in the vicinity of the present Burtville or Gardere, East Baton Rouge Parish, La. (*Bur. Am. Ethnol. Bull., 30,* Pt. I: 43, 1907; Swanton, 1922: pl. 1; Baton Rouge quadrangle); visited, 429.

Alabama (in Alabama): apparently identical with Tuskegee, a former Upper Creek town in the fork of the Coosa and Tallapoosa Rivers, about 4 miles southwest of Wetumpka, Elmore County, Ala. (*Bur. Am. Ethnol. Bull., 30,* Pt. II: 853, 1910; Taitt, 1916: 541; Swanton, 1922: 197, 209–210, pls. 2, 6, 8, 9; Wetumpka quadrangle); visited, 447; listed, 463.

The site is marked as "Old Fort Jackson" on the Geological Map of Alabama, 1894.

"The 'Alabama town' here mentioned was actually the town of the Tuskegee or Taskigi Indians who spoke Alabama or a closely related dialect. The settlements to which the name Alabama strictly belonged were some miles below the junction of the Coosa and Tallapoosa." (J.R.S.)

Alabama (or "Coosau" or Mobile) River: the largest river of Alabama, formed near the center of the state by the junction of the Coosa and the Tallapoosa, and taking a southwesterly course to the Mobile Delta; a branch of, 396; crossing tributaries of, 398; a road leading near (in this case "Alabama" is perhaps a slip of the pen for "Escambia"), 400; an arm of the Mobile River, 408; emigrants from Georgia bound for, 443; formed by the junction of the Coosa and the Tallapoosa, 447. *See also* Coosa River.

Alachua: in the following cases, evidently the district about and including the Alachua Savanna (the present Payne's Prairie), Alachua County, Fla.; 223; trading at, 97, 98; citizens of, 191; Creeks migrating from Georgia to the plains of, 380. *See also* Cuscowilla or Alachua ("Allachua").

Alachua (or ancient Alachua town): the ancient capital of the Alachua tribe, situated probably at about the middle of the southern border of Alachua Savanna, in Alachua County, Fla. (Arredondo quadrangle); abandoned by the Indians, 193; its site visited, 198.

Alachua roads: extending from St. John's River to Alachua Savanna; journey along, 216.

Alachua Savanna: the present Payne's Prairie, a marshy expanse covering about 20 square miles south of Gainesville, Alachua County, Fla. (Arredondo quadrangle) (fig. 18); 225, 238; encampment on, 185; described, 187–190; unhealthfulness of, 193; returned to, 194; tour about, 196–208; its accommodations for human inhabitants and domestic animals, 251.

Alachuas. *See* Indians—Alachuas or Oconees.

Alatamaha. *See* Altamaha.

A[lauda] campestris, gutture flavo, the sky lark (cf. Catesby, 1730?
1: 32, pl. 32): Northern Horned Lark (*Eremophila alpestris alpestris*
(L.)); listed, 290 *bis.*

Alauda magna, the great meadow lark (cf. Catesby, 1730? *1*: 33, pl.
33): Eastern Meadowlark (*Sturnella magna magna* [L.]); listed,
290 *bis.*

Alauda ("aluda") maxima: Eastern Meadowlark (*Sturnella magna
magna* [L.]); resident in Pennsylvania, 286.

A[lauda] migratoria, corpore toto ferrugineo, the little brown lark:
American Pipit (*Anthus rubescens rubescens* [Tunstall]); listed,
290 *bis.*

Edwards received a specimen from Bartram, describing and
figuring it (1760, *2:* 185, 220, pl. 297) as "Lark from Pennsylvania"
—"Alauda Pensilvanica."

Alcea, a plant allied to, with flowers of a damask rose color: perhaps
fen rose (*Kosteletzkya virginica* [L.] Presl); described, on Drayton's
Island, Fla., 105.

Alcedo alcyon, the great crested king-fisher (cf. Catesby, 1731, *1:*
69, pl. 69): Eastern Belted Kingfisher (*Megaceryle alcyon alcyon*
[L.]); listed, 289 *bis.*

Alder: *Alnus rugosa* (Du Roi) Spreng.; at Macon, Ga., 459.

"Alegany." *See* Alleghany.

Aletris: star-grass (*Aletris* sp.); near Long Pond, Levy County, Fla.,
248.

Alexandria in Virginia; arrived at, 479.

Alga; on plains near Suwannee River, Fla., 243.

Allagae (more usual spelling: Ellijay): one of several former Cherokee
towns of this name, probably the one on the headwaters of Keowee
River, S.C. (Mooney, 1900: 517); listed, 374.

Alleghany ("Alegany") mountains. *See* Cherokee or Alleghany mountains.

Alligator(s) (or "allegator" or crocodile[s]): American Alligator
(*Alligator mississipiensis* [Daudin]) (fig. 12); in the Coastal Plain,
not seen above Augusta, Ga., 46; on lower St. John's River, Fla.,
78, 90; voice, at Drayton's Island, 106; in Blue Springs, 145; young
as food of Wood Ibis, 150; not molesting "Trout" in Salt Springs,
168; at Alachua Savanna, 190, 193; in Alachua Sink, 206; in Manatee
Spring, 231; in the Alligator Hole, 238; tortured by traders at Watermelon? Pond, Alachua County, 250; as a species of lizard, 280;

at head of Mobile Delta, Ala., 408; on Amite River, La., 426; exposure to, 445. *See also* Crocodile(s).

Alligator-Hole: a sink-hole, probably the one now known as Blue Sink, a mile north of Newberry, Alachua County, Fla.; visited and described, with an account of an eruption there, 238–240.

Almond, sweet: *Prunus communis* (L.) Fritsch; compared with tallow nut, 115.

Almond tree (Amygdalus communis): *Prunus communis* (L.) Fritsch; soil adapted for, 337. *See also* Amygdalus communis.

Altamaha (or "Alatamaha" or "Alatahama") River: one of the principal rivers of Georgia, formed by junction of the Oconee and the Ocmulgee, and discharging into the Atlantic near Darien; xv, 324, 340, 379; Fort Barrington on, 10; set off for settlements on, 12; road along, 16; crossed at Fort Barrington, 17; returned to, 26; divide between Savannah and Altamaha Basins, 35, 39, 42; a trip up, 48–56; description of, 52–54; excursions about, and descent of, 57; south channel of, 60; rice-growing on, 66; flowers noticed at, 171; descent of, 268; Spoonbill ranging north to, 293; Alachua settlements extending from, 381; Ocmulgee a branch of, 381.

Altars or sepulchres; of the ancients, near Keowee, S.C., 372.

"Aluda." *See* Alauda maxima.

Amalthea[']s horn, or cornucopia: the horn of plenty (Webster); compared with the leaves of *Sarracenia flava*, xviii.

Amaryllis: a genus of bulbous plants (family Amaryllidaceae), in Bartram's time having wider limits than at present and including *Zephyranthes* and other current genera; in the tropics, xv.

Amaryllis atamasco (cf. Catesby, 1748, 2, appendix: 12, pl. 12): atamasco lily (*Zephyranthes atamasco* [L.] Herb.); about St. Mary's River, Ga.–Fla., 24; west of Deep Creek, Putnam County, Fla., 173; in Levy County, 224.

Ambassadors (Indian), audience to, 454, 496.

Amelia Island: the northeasternmost island on the coast of Florida; at the mouth of St. Mary's River, 26; crossing from Cumberland Island to, 64–65; fertility and favorable situation of, 66; leaving, 72.

Amelia Narrows: the present Kingsley Creek, on the west side of Amelia Island, Fla. (Romans' map of 1772; Fernandina quadrangle); passing, 70.

America, North: largest animal in, 264; largest snake in, 267, 276; birds wintering in southern regions of, 286; birds of, 288–302; French coming to, 419, 433; Irishman coming to, 460.

Amite (or "Amete") River: in southwestern Mississippi and southeastern Louisiana, emptying into Lake Maurepas; ascent and description of, 425–427; Iberville channel flowing into, 429; descent of, 437.

Ammunition (or "amunition"); presented by Mr. Marshall, 77; Bartram furnished with, 252; Spaniards provided with, 488.

Amnesty, proclaimed at the busk, 509.

Amorpha: lead plant (*Amorpha* sp.); along Chattahoochee River, Ala., 394; along Cape Fear River, N.C., 476.

Ampelis garrulus, crown bird, or cedar bird: in this case, not Bohemian Waxwing (*Bombycilla garrula* [L.]), but Cedar Waxwing (*B. cedrorum* Vieillot); listed, 290 *bis;* account of, 298.

Amusements; of American aborigines, 505–509.

Amygdalus communis: almond (*Prunus communis* [L.] Fritsch); proposed culture in Georgia, 460. *See also* Almond.

Amyg[dalus] Persica. *See* Peaches.

A[nas] bucephala, the bull-neck and buffaloe head (cf. Catesby, 1732, *1:* 95, pl. 95; Linnaeus, 1758: 125; Linné, 1766: 200): presumably Bufflehead (*Bucephala albeola* [L.]), although this species is otherwise accounted for as *Anas rustica* (p. 294) and as *Anas minor picta* (p. 295); listed, 294.

　Coues (1875: 356) identifies "A. bucephala" as the American Goldeneye (*Bucephala clangula americana* [Bonaparte]), but if this is what Bartram had in mind, he confused both the technical name and one of the common names ("buffaloe head"). On the margin of page 125 of Bartram's own copy of the *Systema* of 1758, he has written, opposite *Anas bucephala,* "Buffels head Duck." Linnaeus himself bestowed three different names on the Bufflehead.

A[nas] caudata, the sprig tail duck: Pintail (*Anas acuta* L.); listed, 294.

A[nas] discors, the blue winged teal: Blue-winged Teal (*Anas discors* L.); listed, 295.

Anas fera torquata major . . . the great wild duck, called duck and mallard: Common Mallard (*Anas platyrhynchos platyrhynchos* L.), female and male; listed, 294.

A[nas] fistulosa, whistling duck: perhaps either American Goldeneye (*Bucephala clangula americana* [Bonaparte]) or Baldpate (*Mareca americana* [Gmelin]); listed, 295.

　This name of Bartram's bears a suspicious resemblance to Edwards' two species of "Whistling Duck" or "Anas fistularis," etc. (1751, *4:* 193–194, 247–248, pls. 193–194). These, however, are actually tree-ducks of the genus *Dendrocygna,* unknown in Pennsylvania.

A[nas] leucocephala, the black white faced duck: perhaps the female of either the Greater Scaup Duck (*Aythya marila nearctica* Stejneger) or the Lesser Scaup Duck (*Aythya affinis* [Eyton]); listed, 294. *See also* Anas subcerulea.

A[nas] *migratoria, the least green winged teal: *nomen nudum*— Green-winged Teal (*Anas carolinensis* Gmelin); listed, 295.

A[nas] minor picta, the little black and white duck called butterback (cf. Edwards, 1747, 2: 100, 128, pl. 100; Trumbull, 1888: 83): Bufflehead (*Bucephala albeola* [L.]), male; listed, 295. *See also* Anas bucephala; Anas rustica.

A[nas] nigra maxima, the great black duck (cf. Edwards, 1750, 3: 155, pl. 155, and 1751, 4: 246, as "Anas, Canadensis, major, niger"): probably Surf Scoter (*Melanitta perspicillata* [L.]); listed, 294.

A[nas] *principalis, maculata, the various coloured duck, his neck and breast as tho' ornamented with chains of beads (cf. Edwards, 1747, 2: 99, 128, pl. 99, as "Dusky *and* Spotted Duck" or "Anas, fuscus, maculatus"): Harlequin Duck (*Histrionicus histrionicus* [L.]), male; listed, 295.

"The *Newfoundland* Fishers call it the *Lord,* for what Reason I cannot tell; but I suppose the Reason of this Name may be from the Likeness of a Chain it has about its Neck, seeing the wearing of Gold Chains is an antient Mark of Dignity in *Europe*" (Edwards, 1747, 2: 99). Bartram's name "principalis" must refer to the word *"Lord"* in Edwards' account.

A[nas] rustica, the little brown and white duck (cf. Catesby, 1732, 1: 98, pl. 98; Linnaeus, 1758: 125; Linné, 1766: 201): Bufflehead (*Bucephala albeola* [L.]), female; listed, 294. *See also* Anas bucephala; Anas minor picta.

On the other hand, the "Little Brown and White Duck" of Edwards (1750, 3: 157, pl. 157) is evidently a female Harlequin Duck.

Anas sponsa, the summer duck: Wood Duck (*Aix sponsa* [L.]); listed, 295.

A[nas] *subcerulea, the blue bill: doubtless composite, including both Greater Scaup Duck (*Aythya marila nearctica* Stejneger) and Lesser Scaup Duck (*Aythya affinis* [Eyton]); listed, 294. *See also* Anas leucocephala.

[Anastasia Island.] *See* St. Anastatius Island.

Ancients, their notions on bird migration, 285. *See also* Indians, Indian country, etc.

Anderson's ferry on the Susquehanna: at Marietta, Lancaster County, Pa. (L.F.A.T.); crossed river there on ice, 480.

Andrew ("Andrews"), Hon. B[enjamin]: a member of the Georgia

Assembly and a plantation proprietor in the Midway district of Liberty County; acquaintance with, 4; entertained by, 11–12; recommending Bartram to L. McIntosh, 15.

This gentleman was born in South Carolina about 1730, and settled in the Midway district in 1754. He allied himself with the Revolutionists in the struggle with Great Britain. In 1777 he became president of the Executive Council of Georgia, and in 1780 a member of the Continental Congress. For further information see Jones (1891: 1–4).

Andromeda(s): in Bartram's usage, a collective genus, more or less equivalent to the present ericaceous tribe Andromedeae, including *Leucothoë, Pieris, Chamaedaphne, Oxydendrum, Lyonia*, and probably other genera of the current manuals—and even *Cyrilla* (Cyrillaceae); on Colonel's Island, Ga., 6; in Lime-Sink Region, Ga.–S.C., 30; on St. Simon's Island, Ga., 61; near Orange Lake, Fla., 181; near Alachua Savanna, 187; in Escambia or adjacent county, Ala., 403; on Long Bay, S.C., 471.

Andromeda of Florida, called Pipe-stem Wood . . . Andromeda formosissima. *See* Andromeda formosissima.

Andromeda arborea (cf. Catesby, 1731, *1*: 71, pl. 71): sour-wood (*Oxydendrum arboreum* [L.] DC.); in Southern Red Hills, Ga., 32; near Alachua Savanna, Fla., 187; along upper Savannah River, Ga.–S.C., 327; in Warren County, Ga., 378.

Apparently this species no longer occurs so far south and east as the Alachua Savanna.

And[romeda] axillaris ("axilaris"): presumably fetter-bush (*Leucothoë axillaris* [Lam.] D. Don); near Palatka, Fla., 303.

And[romeda] calyculata: undetermined (certainly not *Chamaedaphne calyculata* [L.] Moench); near Palatka, Fla., 303.

Andromeda ferruginea ("ferruginia" or "ferruginae"): stagger-bush or "poor grub" (either *Lyonia ferruginea* [Walt.] Nutt. or *L. fruticosa* [Michx.] G. S. Torr.); about St. Mary's River, Ga.–Fla., 24; west of Spalding's Lower Store, Fla., v, 171; on plains near Suwannee River, 242.

Andromeda *formosissima: pipewood (*Leucothoë acuminata* [Ait.] G. Don) (cf. Darlington, 1843: 124; Elliott, 1817, *1*: 488; Merrill, 1945: 22); about St. Mary's River, Ga.–Fla., 24; near Deep Creek, Putnam County, Fla., v, 172; near Palatka, 303.

In Michaux's journal for May 1, 1788 (1889: 35), there is a record of "Andromeda formosissima" on the St. John's River, perhaps at Rollestown, just above East Palatka. Very likely Michaux had secured the name from Bartram.

Andromeda lucida: *nomen nudum*—a homonym and perhaps a synonym of *A. lucida* Lam. (1783) (= next entry); along Cape Fear River, N.C., 476.

Andromeda nitida (cf. Marshall, 1785: 8): hoorah bush (*Lyonia lucida* [Lam.] K. Koch); in Liberty County, Ga., 10; about St. Mary's River, Ga.–Fla., 24; in Putnam County, Fla., 171, 172, 303; near Suwannee River, 242.

Andromeda *pulverulenta: *Zenobia pulverulenta* (Bartr. ex Willd.) Pollard (cf. Fernald, 1940: 472–473; Merrill, 1945: 22); figured on plate facing page 476.

The name *Andromeda pulverulenta* appears only on the plate, and it is not accompanied by a description. Willdenow (1799: 610), whose name is based upon Bartram's plate, gives the habitat as "Florida"—perhaps outside the known range of the species. Since Bartram's plate is inserted opposite his list of plants about Ashwood, that may be considered the type locality. Ashwood is on the Northwest Cape Fear River, 5 miles northeast of Council, Bladen County, N.C.; it lies in the lower half of the Coastal Plain, rather than "near the inner border of the Coastal Plain," as Fernald (1940: 472) has it. I have collected specimens in the same county, 2 miles east of White Lake, May 21, 1939.

And[romeda] *viridis ("virides"): *nomen nudum*—undetermined; near Palatka, Fla., 303.

Anemone hepatica: hepatica (*Hepatica americana* [DC.] Ker); at Falling Creek, Rabun County, Ga., 342.

Anemone thalictroides: rue anemone (*Anemonella thalictroides* [L.] Spach); at Falling Creek, Rabun County, Ga., 342.

Angel, guardian; protected by, 158.

Angelica lucida (or "luceda" or "lucido") or Nondo . . . [or] White Root (cf. Linnaeus, 1753: 251; Gray, 1841: 25): *Ligusticum canadense* (L.) Britt.; in Broad River region, Ga., 45; along upper Savannah River, 321; at Loughabber, S.C., 327; near Wayah Gap, N.C., 362.

"*Angelica lucida*. this celebrated plant is badly de[s]cribed by Botanests, if known at all   I suppose it to be the plant mentioned by Clayt. Flor. virginica. Imperatoria licida canadensis. Tourn. Inst. p. 317. Angelica lucida canadensis fortasse vulg. Belly-ach. Root. Clayt. In Virginia, Carolina, Georgia Nondo, Belly-Ach. Root. White-Root." (Bartram to Muhlenberg, September 6, 1810; Muhlenberg Letters: 137.)

Anguis fragilis. *See* Snake, glass.

Animals: eggs of, compared with seeds of plants, xxii; disseminating seeds of plants, xxiii; instinct in, compared with reason in man, xxv; bones at Charlotia, Fla., 94, and on Drayton's Island, 103; those of the elevated interior larger than those of the flat country along the coast, 216; scarce in southwestern Alachua County, Fla., 218; collected by Bartram, 261; figures of, tattooed on Indians, 503.

Animals, aquatic, in subterranean waters of Florida, 226.

Animals, domestic, accommodations for, on Alachua Savanna, Fla., 251.

Animals, predatory, protection of Indian crops against, 511.

Animal creation, peaceable disposition of, 268.

Animal productions, of middle region of Georgia, 45–46.

Aniseed, or anise seed: *Pimpinella anisum* L.; compared with *Angelica lucida*, 327, and with a *Collinsonia*, 412.

Annona: in this case, northern pawpaw (*Asimina triloba* [L.] Dunal); near Wayah Gap, N.C., 362. *See also* Annona glabra, Annona triloba.

Annona, a very curious species of, with long, extremely narrow leaves (not the "Anona pygmea" of pl. facing p. 18) (cf. Exell, 1927: 65–67): dwarf pawpaw (*Asimina pigmea* [Bartr.] Dunal); described, from south of Altamaha River, in Wayne County, Ga., 18. *See also* Annona pigmea, Annona pygmea.

As indicated above, this is Exell's interpretation. It may be objected, however, that the flowers are not very close to those of *Asimina triloba* in size and perhaps not in color (see the comparison made by Bartram on p. 18). There is no doubt some confusion in Bartram's treatment.

Annona, a dwarf decumbent (Annona *pigmea): dwarf pawpaw (*Asimina pigmea* [Bartr.] Dunal) (cf. Exell, 1927: 65–69, pl. 581, upper fig.; Merrill, 1945: 23); described, west of Spalding's Lower Store, Putnam County, Fla., and "at Alatamaha" River, Ga., 171. Spelled "Annona pygmea" in Contents (p. v). *See also* preceding entry; Annona pygmea.

The description on page 171 may be considered the type description; but the reference to what was "already noticed" virtually makes the description on page 18 part of the original; and this is supplemented by Bartram's manuscript, as published by Exell (1927: 65). Bartram's specimen No. 22 in the British Museum, from "the hard sandy level humid Plains of Et. Florida. Lat. 30," may be considered the type specimen. It was probably collected in the vicinity of Rodman, Putnam County, Fla. According to Exell, *Asimina angustifolia* A. Gray is a synonym.

Annona, with large, white, sweet-scented flowers: pawpaw (probably

Asimina incana [Bartr.] Exell) (cf. Exell, 1927: 67); at Charlotia, Fla., 95. *See also* next two entries.

Annona, a new species of (Annona *incana ["incarna"]): showy pawpaw (*Asimina incana* [Bartr.] Exell) (cf. Exell, 1927: 67–69, pl. 581, lower fig.; Merrill, 1945: 23); described, from vicinity of Rodman, Putnam County, Fla., 171. Spelled "Annona incana" in Contents (p. v). *See also* next entry.

Annona, a new species of, with large white fragrant flowers: identical with the "Anona grandiflora" of the plate facing page 20, i.e. showy pawpaw (*Asimina incana* [Bartr.] Exell); south of Altamaha River, Ga., 18. *See also* two preceding entries; Annona grandiflora.

Annona *alba: *nomen nudum*—pawpaw (*Asimina* sp.); near Palatka, Fla., 303.

Annona glabra: in these cases, not *Annona glabra* L., but probably northern pawpaw (*Asimina triloba* [L.] Dunal); near Oconee Station, S.C., 335; along Chattahoochee River, Ala., 393. *See also* Annona, Annona triloba.

An[n]ona *grandiflora: showy pawpaw (*Asimina incana* [Bartr.] Exell) (cf. Exell, 1927: 67–69; Merrill, 1945: 22); figured on plate facing page 20. The name is preoccupied in Lamarck (1786). *See also* Annona, a new species of (two entries).

Annona *incana (or "incarna"). *See* Annona, a new species of (Annona incana).

Annona *pigmea. *See* Annona, a dwarf decumbent.

Annona pygmea: presumably dwarf pawpaw (*Asimina pigmea* [Bartr.] Dunal); near Orange Lake, Fla., 181. *See also* next entry.

An[n]ona pygmea (not the narrow-leaved "Annona" described on p. 18; not the "Annona pigmea" described on p. 171; not the "Annona pygmea" of p. 181) (cf. Exell, 1927: 67, 69): pawpaw (*Asimina secundiflora* Shuttleworth); figured on plate facing page 18.

There is perhaps some question as to the correctness of this interpretation by Exell; he finds no descriptive matter in Bartram pertaining to the figured species.

An[nona] triloba ("Antrilobe"—a misprint) (cf. Catesby, 1747, 2: 85, pl. 85): northern pawpaw (*Asimina triloba* [L.] Dunal); flowers compared with those of *Asimina pigmea*, 18. *See also* Annona, Annona glabra.

"Anona." *See* Annona.

A[nser] aliis ceruliis, the blue winged goose (cf. Edwards, 1750, 3: 152, pl. 152, and 1751, 4: 246, as "Blue-winged Goose" or "Anser, Canadensis, alis coeruleis"): Blue Goose (*Chen caerulescens* [L.]); listed, 294.

Bartram doubtless introduced this name from Edwards without realizing its probable identity with his "Anser branta grisea maculata."

A[nser] branta, corpore albo, remigibus nigris, the white brant goose: either Lesser Snow Goose (*Chen hyperborea hyperborea* [Pallas]) or Greater Snow Goose (*Ch. h. atlantica* Kennard), or a composite of both (cf. Harper, 1942*d*: 219); listed, 294.

A[nser] branta grisea ("grisca") maculata, the great particoloured brant, or grey goose: probably Blue Goose (*Chen caerulescens* [L.]); listed, 294.

The "grey or Brant Goose" of Bartram's drawing ("Tab. IV") in the British Museum (reproduced in W. Bartram, 1943: fig. 16) is evidently an adult Blue Goose.

Anser Canadensis, the Canadian goose: Common Canada Goose (*Branta canadensis canadensis* [L.]); listed, 294. *See also* Geese.

A[nser] fuscus maculatus, the laughing goose (cf. Edwards, 1750, 3: 153, pl. 153, and 1751, 4: 246); White-fronted Goose (*Anser albifrons* [Scopoli]); listed, 294.

Ant(s): as food of toads, 280; economy of, 494.

Ant-apala-mico-clucco; king of England called, 495.

Anthemis nobilis: chamomile (*A. nobilis* L.); usefulness, xvii.

"Antrilobe." *See* Annona triloba.

Apalachee ("Apalache," "Apalachi," "Apalatche," or "Aplatchi"), Bay of: a portion of the Gulf of Mexico adjacent to the west coast of Florida (in Bartram's usage having a greater extent than the present Apalachee Bay); Suwannee River discharging into, 26; St. Marks on, 94, 208, 215; Talahasochte near, 97; Alachua settlements extending to, 381; murders committed there by Seminoles, 438; Suwannee River near, 521.

"Apalachean" or "Apalachian" mountains. *See* Appalachian mountains.

Apalachean Old Fields (cf. Boyd, 1938: pl. 5): an area of Indian settlement near the present Tallahassee, Leon County, Fla.; vestiges of Spanish settlement at, 233.

Apalachicola ("Apalachucla") River: in Bartram's usage, primarily the Chattahoochee River (which forms part of the boundary between Georgia and Alabama), but probably including the present Apalachicola River in Florida, which is formed by the junction of the Chattahoochee and the Flint; 233, 416, 522; Uchees on the main branch of, 211; tributaries of, 396.

Apalachicola ("Apalachucla") or Chattahoochee ("Chata Uche") River: Chattahoochee River; crossed at Chehaw and Usseta, 457; list of towns on, 463–464. *See also* Chattahoochee or Apalachicola.

Apalachicola ("Apalachucla") (new town): capital of the Creek
Confederacy, situated on the west side of Chattahoochee River, 1.5
miles below Ihagee Creek, Russell County, Ala. (Taitt's map of
1772, as "Pallachicola"; Early's map of 1818, as "Pal-la-choo-chee";
Swanton, 1922: 134, pl. 2; soil map of Russell County, Ala., 1913);
visited and described, 389–391; cane swamps near, 395; set out from,
396; listed, 463. See also Commentary for p. 389.

Apalachicola ("Apalachucla") (old town): a former Lower Creek town
on the west side of Chattahoochee River in the vicinity of Burr's
Landing, about 3 miles below Ihagee Creek, Russell County, Ala.;
ruins visited and described, 390–391; terraces, chunk yards, etc.,
at, 522.

Apis bombylicus. See Bumblebee.

"Aplatchi." See Apalachee, Bay of.

Appalachian ("Apalachean" or "Apalachian") mountains: the Blue
Ridge; 42, 288, 299, 447; Elk in, 46. See also Cherokee or Appalachian Mountains.

Apple tree(s): Pyrus malus L.; Hercules club resembling, 88; planted
at Fort Thoulouse, Ala., 447.

Apricot: Prunus armeniaca L.; in temperate zone, xv.

Araneus *saliens: some species of jumping spider (family Salticidae)
(S.C.B.); described, on Mosquito River, Fla., xxix–xxxi. (Cf. W. Bartram, 1943: 167.)

Ardea alba: American Egret (Casmerodius albus egretta [Gmelin]):
nesting at Watermelon? Pond, Alachua County, Fla., 249. See also
Ardea immaculata.

A[rdea] alba minor, the little white heron (cf. Catesby, 1731, 1: 77,
pl. 77): either immature Little Blue Heron (Florida caerulea
caerulea [L.]) or Snowy Egret (Leucophoyx thula thula [Molina]);
listed, 293.

Ar[dea] caerulea ("cerulea") (cf. Catesby, 1731, 1: 76, pl. 76): Little
Blue Heron (Florida caerulea caerulea [L.]); nesting at Watermelon? Pond, Alachua County, Fla., 249. See also Ardea purpurea
cristata.

A[rdea] *clamator, corpore subceruleo, the quaw bird, or frogcatcher:
Black-crowned Night Heron (Nycticorax nycticorax hoactli
[Gmelin]) (cf. Barton, 1799a: 18); listed, 293.

Ardea herodias, the great bluish grey crested heron: Great Blue Heron
(Ardea herodias herodias L.); listed, 293.

A[rdea] *immaculata, the great white river heron (cf. Barton, 1799a:
20): nomen nudum—American Egret (Casmerodius albus egretta
[Gmelin]); listed, 293. See also Ardea alba.

A[rdea] maculata cristata, the speckled crested heron, or crabcatcher (cf. Catesby, 1731, *1:* 79, pl. 79): probably Yellow-crowned Night Heron (*Nyctanassa violacea violacea* [L.]); listed, 293.

A[rdea] *mugitans, the marsh bittern ("bitern"), or Indian hen: *nomen nudum*—American Bittern (*Botaurus lentiginosus* [Rackett]) (cf. Harper, 1942d: 219); listed, 293.

A[rdea] *parva, the least brown and striped bittern ("bitern"): *nomen nudum*—Eastern Least Bittern (*Ixobrychus exilis exilis* [Gmelin]); listed, 293.

A[rdea] purpurea cristata, the little crested purple or blue heron: Little Blue Heron (*Florida caerulea caerulea* [L.]); listed, 293. *See also* Ardea caerulea.

Ar[dea] stellaris cristata ("crestata") (cf. Catesby, 1731, *1:* 79, pl. 79; Jefferson, 1782: 126): probably Yellow-crowned Night Heron (*Nyctanassa violacea violacea* [L.]); nesting at Watermelon? Pond, Alachua County, Fla., 249.

Ar[dea] stellaris maxima: probably Ward's Heron (*Ardea herodias wardi* Ridgway); nesting at Watermelon? Pond, Alachua County, Fla., 249.

A[rdea] subfusca stellata ("stillata"), the little brownish spotted bittern ("bitern") (cf. Catesby, 1731, *1:* 78, pl. 78): probably an immature Night Heron (either *Nycticorax nycticorax hoactli* [Gmelin] or *Nyctanassa violacea violacea* [L.]); listed, 293.

A[rdea] varia ("varra") cristata, the grey white crested heron: possibly Louisiana Heron (*Hydranassa tricolor ruficollis* [Gosse]); listed, 293.

Ar[dea] violacea: Yellow-crowned Night Heron (*Nyctanassa violacea violacea* [L.]); nesting at Watermelon? Pond, Alachua County, Fla., 249.

A[rdea] violacea ("violacca"), the crested blue bittern ("bitern"), (called poor Jobe): Yellow-crowned Night Heron (*Nyctanassa violacea violacea* [L.]); listed, 293.

Ar[dea] virescens: Eastern Green Heron (*Butorides virescens virescens* [L.]); nesting at Watermelon? Pond, Alachua County, Fla., 249.

A[rdea] virescens ("viriscens"), the green bittern ("bitern") or poke: Eastern Green Heron (*Butorides virescens virescens* [L.]); listed, 293.

A[rdea] virescens ("viriscens") minor, the lesser green bittern ("bitern"): presumably not different from the preceding species (*Butorides virescens virescens* [L.]), unless in the variations of plumage with age; listed, 293.

Arena (cf. Linné, 1768, *3:* 196): sand; in middle (Piedmont) region of Georgia, 45.

Areopagus. *See* Square, public, or areopagus.

Arethusa ("Arethuza") (cf. Catesby, 1730?, *1:* 58, pl. 58): in this case, probably spreading pogonia (*Cleistes divaricata* [L.] Ames); at Falling Creek, Rabun County, Ga., 342.

Arethusa *pulcherrima ("pulcherima"): *nomen nudum* (Merrill, 1945: 33)—either swamp pink (*Arethusa bulbosa* L.) or a species of some related genus, such as *Pogonia;* beauty of, xviii.

Aristolochia ("Aristalocha" or "Aristalochia") frutescens, s[eu] odoratissima (cf. Catesby, 1730? *1:* 29, pl. 29): not *A. odoratissima* L., but perhaps Dutchman's pipe (*A. durior* Hill; syn., *A. frutescens* Marsh.); near Oconee (= Station) Mountain, S.C., 337; near Wayah Gap, N.C., 362.

Arrows; armed by Indians with scales of Gars, 176. *See also* Bows and arrows.

Arrowheads, in Screven or Burke Counties, Ga., 462.

Arsenal, at Pensacola, Fla., 416.

Artisans, in party setting out from Augusta, Ga., 35.

Arts, among American aborigines, 513.

Arum, esculent, called Tannier: the edible root or stem of any of several related aroids, including the taro (*Colocasia antiquorum* Schott) (Webster); cultivated in Georgia, 469.

Arum Colocasia: taro (*Colocasia antiquorum* Schott); 469.

Arum esculentum. *See* Eddo.

Arum triphyllum: jack-in-the-pulpit (*Arisaema triphyllum* [L.] Schott); along upper Savannah River, Ga., 321.

Arundo gigantea. *See* Cane(s), Reeds or Canes.

Asafoetida ("Assafetida"), Gum; compared with *Cleome lupinifolia,* 425.

Asclepias: one or more species of milkweed (*Asclepias* or related genera); in Warren County, Ga., 379.

Asclepias *carnosa: *nomen nudum* (Merrill, 1945: 33)—a milkweed (*A. humistrata* Walt.); near Suwannee River, Fla., 242.

   "*Asclepias carnosa,* A. humistrata of Walter" (Bartram to Muhlenberg, September 6, 1810; Muhlenberg Letters: 137).

Asclepias *coccinea: *nomen nudum* (Merrill, 1945: 33)—a milkweed (perhaps *A. lanceolata* Walt.); in Brunswick County, N.C., 472.

   "*Asclepias coccinia.* perhaps Walters A. lanciolata. differs little from Wildenow's A. curassavica" (Bartram to Muhlenberg, September 6, 1810; Muhlenberg Letters: 137).

Asclepias ("Assclepias") *fragrans: *nomen nudum* (Merrill, 1945: 33)—a milkweed (perhaps *Podostigma pedicellata* [Walt.] Vail) (cf. Elliott, 1817, *1:* 326); probably on the Brantley-Glynn county boundary, Ga., 19.

"This little obscure plant almost hid in the grass. perfumes the savanas. perhaps Walters. *A. pedicellata*" (Bartram to Muhlenberg, September 6, 1810; Muhlenberg Letters: 137).

Ash: *Fraxinus* spp.; formerly growing where salt marshes are, 69; near Charlotia on St. John's River, Fla., 93; on Salt Springs Run, 160; mats made of splints of, 369; on Oconee River, Ga., 379; in Butler or adjacent county, Ala., 400; on lower Tombigbee River, 410. *See also* Fraxinus.

Ashwood: the former seat of Colonel William Bartram (uncle of the naturalist) on the west side of Cape Fear River, 5 miles northeast of Council, in Bladen County, N.C. (soil map of Bladen County, 1919); stay at, 474–476.

Asia; 14.

Asilus, species of: deer-flies (genus *Chrysops*, family Tabanidae); tormented by, in Taylor County, Ga., viii, 385–386.

Asp or adder of the Old World: Common Viper (*Vipera berus* [L.]); compared with Ground Rattler, 274.

"Assafetida." *See* Asafoetida.

"Assclepias." *See* Asclepias.

Aster: aster (*Aster* spp.); near Suwannee River, Fla., 243; along upper Savannah River, Ga., 321; in Brunswick County, N.C., 472.

Aster *fructicosus (or "fruticosus"): *nomen nudum* (Merrill, 1945: 33)—climbing aster (*A. carolinianus* Walt.); near Jacksonboro, S.C., ix, 470.

Astronomers; in party setting out from Augusta, Ga., 35; taking observations on Broad River, 41.

Astronomy, of the ancients, 285.

Ata-kullakulla ("Ata-cul-culla" or "Atta-kul-kulla") or Little Carpenter: emperor or grand chief of the Cherokees; meeting with, near Nantahala River, N.C., 364–365; small stature of, 485.

This famous Cherokee was born about 1700. His home town was Chotte, half a dozen miles up the Tennessee River from Fort Loudon, Tenn. (Hunter's map of 1751). He was one of the chiefs taken to England by Sir Alexander Cuming in 1730. He is said to have been made second in authority under Oconostota in 1738. Through his influence a peace treaty was made with Governor Glenn, of South Carolina, in 1755, and another one was signed at Charleston in 1761. He saved the life of Capt. John Stuart in 1760 after Fort Loudon had been captured and most of the garrison had been massacred. Although most of the Cherokees sided with the British during the Revolution, Ata-kullakulla maintained friendship with the Americans. He died probably about 1780. (Cf. Mooney,

1900: 40–44, 54, 510; *Bur. Am. Ethnol. Bull., 30,* Pt. I: 115, 1907; Arthur, 1914: 569; Brown, 1938: pl. facing p. 40, and 1957; Swanton, 1946: Pl. 8.)

Atlantic Ocean: entering, 1; aspect during and after a storm, 2–3; the Altamaha entering, 53; coastal islands as an advance on, 68; navigation from Flint River to, 384; lash of, 471. *See also* Great water, Ocean.

Attasse. *See* Otasse.

Augusta, Ga.; treaty of, 9, 33–34, 485; set off for, 28; village and environs described, 32; arrival at, 33; vegetation in vicinity of, 34; Col. Barnet's party setting off from, 35; friable white rock near, 45; Alligator not seen above, 46; return to, 46; trading path to the Creek Nation from, 54, 376; road from Savannah to, 313, 461; superseding Fort Moore, S.C., 316; site described, 316–317; seat of government removed to, 317; set off from, 320; region north of, 335; Indian traders from, 377, 458; water chinquapin at, 409; prepare to set off to, from Mobile, 438; traders bound for, from Alabama, 447, 450; set off for, from Otasse, 457; arrived at, 460; left, 460.

The town of Augusta was marked out in 1735 and garrisoned the next year. At first it was inhabited principally by Indian traders and storekeepers. It soon became a great trading center, visited annually by more than 2,000 pack-horses and 600 men. Boats made trips to Charleston, and after Savannah was founded, to that city. During the Revolution, in 1779, Augusta was captured by the British. (White, 1849: 513–514.)

Auris marina (cf. Linné, 1767, *1,* Pt. II: 1256, reference under *Haliotis tuberculata*): apparently intended to designate some limpetlike gastropod mollusk (R.A.M.); on St. Simon's Island, Ga., 60. *See also* Haliotis auris marina.

Axes; used in felling cypresses, 92; Negroes armed with, 472; used on Indian plantations, 512; stone axes formerly used by the Creeks, 500.

Azalea (or "Aazalea"): azalea (*Rhododendron* spp.); in Lime-Sink Region, Ga., 31; in Southern Red Hills, 32; along upper Savannah River, 320; in Oconee County, S.C., 334; various species near Oconee (= Station) Mountain, 337; in Vale of Cowee, Ga., 346; near Cowee, N.C., 357; in Monroe or adjacent county, Ala., 401; in Escambia or adjacent county, 403; on upper Tensaw River, 408; at Macon, Ga., 459; varieties along Cape Fear River, N.C., 476.

Azalea, fiery: probably showy azalea (*Rhododendron speciosum* [Willd.] Sweet) (E.T.W.) (cf. Gray, 1841: 25–26); described, between Little and Broad Rivers, Ga., vii, 322–323.

Azalea, flaming: probably flame azalea (*Rhododendron calendula-*

ceum [Michx.] Torr.); along Keowee River, S.C., 328; on Oconee (= Station) Mountain, 336.

Azalea, sweet: azalea (*Rhododendron* sp.); on St. Simon's Island, Ga., 61.

Azalea *coccinea (or "coccinia") (cf. Elliott, 1817, *1*: 239): *nomen nudum* (Merrill, 1945: 33)—probably showy azalea (*Rhododendron speciosum* [Willd.] Sweet); xvi, xvii; at Shell Bluff, Ga., 319.

Azalea *flammea: *nomen nudum* (Merrill, 1945: 34)—probably either flame azalea (*Rhododendron calendulaceum* [Michx.] Torr.) or showy azalea (*R. speciosum* [Willd.] Sweet) (cf. Gray, 1841: 25–26); along upper Savannah River, Ga.–S.C., 327. (Cf. Rehder, 1921: 127, 129.)

Azalea *flammula: *nomen nudum* (Merrill, 1945: 34)—probably flame azalea (*Rhododendron calendulaceum* [Michx.] Torr.); at Falling Creek, Rabun County, Ga., 342.

Azalea *nuda: *nomen nudum* (Merrill, 1945: 34)—probably pink azalea (*Rhododendron nudiflorum* [L.] Torr.); in coastal swamps, 29.

Azalea *rosea: *nomen nudum* (Merrill, 1945: 34)—azalea (*Rhododendron* sp.); xvi.

Azalea viscosa (cf. Catesby, 1730? *1*: 57, pl. 57): swamp azalea (*Rhododendron viscosum* [L.] Torr.); in coastal swamps, 29.

Babel, ancient: the Babylonian city of biblical renown; 391.

Bacon, at Mobile Bay, Ala., 419.

Bahama Islands: expeditions of Florida Indians to, 227; governor of, 431.

Bahama white rock: limestone; 318.

Bailey's [or Baillie's?], Mr.: a place at or near the present Eulonia, McIntosh County, Ga.; stopped at, 15.

There were intermarriages between the Baillie and McIntosh families.

Bailey [Baillie, or Bailley], James: Henry Laurens' agent on Broughton Island, Ga.; received by, 57.

On October 30, 1776, this gentleman wrote a sort of farewell letter to Bartram from Broughton Island (Bartram Papers, *1*: 2); it is signed "James Bailley."

Ball play: a man's game among the Indians, closely resembling the modern lacrosse; among the Alachuas, 198; among the Cherokees, 369–371; among Indians, 508–509.

Baltimore bird, both species of the (oriolus, Linn. [,] icterus, Cat.) (cf. Catesby, 1730? *1*: 48, 49, pls. 48, 49; Linnaeus, 1758: 108; Linné,

1766: 162): Baltimore Oriole (*Icterus galbula* [L.]) and Orchard Oriole (*I. spurius* [L.]); account of, 302. *See also* Oriolus Baltimore, Oriolus (icterus minor), Oriolus spurius.

Bands or bracelets, silver, worn by Indians, 503.

Banquet, at Cuscowilla, Fla., 191, 194.

Barilla: probably saltwort (*Salsola kali* L.); on salt marshes in Georgia, 68.

Bark (of trees), Cherokee rotundas roofed with, 368.

Bark(s) (or "barke") (boat(s) or canoe[s]); on lower St. John's River, Fla., 76; on the St. John's at St. Francis, 139; on Lake Beresford, 143; on Lake George, 253; presented to Job Wiggens, 305; reeds as masts for, 410; sailing from Pensacola to Mobile, 415; Tangipahoa River, La., navigable for, 424; on Ocmulgee River, Ga., 459; on coast of Florida, 488. *See also* Boat, trading; Canoe(s); Vessel(s).

Barnet, Col[onel]; charged with survey of lands ceded by Indians at treaty of Augusta, and inviting Bartram to accompany him, 34; salmon trout presented to, 44. *See also* Colonel, the.

No additional biographical information concerning a Col. Barnet seems discoverable. It is possible that this name represents a misspelling of "Bartlett." Jones says (1883, 2: 131): "Col. Bartlett and Messrs. Young, Holland, and Maddox were appointed Commissioners . . . to negotiate sales" of land in the New Purchase. See also McCall (1816, 2: 6) and Stevens (1859, 2: 84).

Barracks, at Pensacola, Fla., 416.

Barrels, for pitch, 419.

Barrington. *See* Fort Barrington.

Bartram, John: father of William Bartram; advantages enjoyed under, xiii; journey into Florida with, 55; Mount Hope named by, 98; calling a Florida shrub the tallow nut, 115; attending him on a botanical excursion (in 1765–66), 468; first to communicate Venus' fly-trap to the Old World, 473. *See also* Father [of William Bartram].

John Bartram's chief fame rests upon his founding of the first true botanical garden in America. He corresponded with some of the principal men of learning abroad, including Linnaeus, Gronovius, Catesby, Fothergill, and Peter Collinson, and he was the friend of such Americans as Benjamin Franklin, Cadwallader Colden, John Clayton, and Alexander Garden. He was one of the nine original members of the American Philosophical Society, and he took an active part in its early meetings (Van Doren, 1943: 279–288). He was a member of the Royal Academy of Sciences of Stockholm, but not a Fellow of the Royal Society of London (cf. p. xiii). In

1765 he was appointed botanist to the King of England. Journals of several of his exploratory trips for plants have been published; particularly the journey to Lakes Onondaga and Ontario (1751) and the one to the Carolinas, Georgia, and Florida (1767, 1769, 1942). For accounts of his life see, among others, W. Bartram (1804*b*), Darlington (1849), Earnest (1940), J. Bartram (1942), and Mrs. Cheston (1953).

Bartram, William (1739–1823) (author of the *Travels*); received by the Cowkeeper at Cuscowilla and given the name of Puc Puggy, 185; received by the White King at Talahasochte, 238; travels from New England to the Mississippi and Florida, 288; malady in eyes, 418–421, 436.

Bartram, Colonel William: half-brother of John Bartram; Ashwood the seat of, 474.

This William Bartram (1704–1770) spent his early years in Pennsylvania and in North Carolina, where his father (also named William) was killed by White Oak Indians. He went to North Carolina for the second time about 1726, and spent the remainder of his life at Ashwood on the Northwest Cape Fear River in Bladen County. He was a colonel of militia and a representative in the North Carolina Assembly for many years. His nephew William pays a feeling tribute to his patriotic virtues and his hospitality (in a partly unpublished manuscript in the Delafield Collection). The younger man had spent a number of years (1761–65, 1770–72) at Ashwood or vicinity, while engaged in unprofitable trading ventures. The Ashwood property was still owned in 1940 by a lineal descendant of the colonel, David Gillespie Robeson. (For a further account, see J. Bartram, 1942: 80–81.)

*Bartramia *bracteata: Georgia bark (*Pinckneya bracteata* [Bartr.] Raf.; syn., *P. pubens* Michx.) (cf. Harper, 1942*b*: 6–7; Merrill, 1945: 23–24); pleasing figure, xviii. *See also* Bignonia bracteata; Shrubs, two new beautiful.

Bartsia ("Bartsea"): in this case, Indian paint-brush (*Castilleja coccinea* [L.] Spreng.) (F.W.P.); pleasing figure, xviii.

Baskets: of strawberries, 358; manufactured by Alibamu Indians, 429.

Bass: perhaps Black Sea-bass (*Centropristis striatus* [L.]); at Cape Hatteras, N.C., 2; about Georgia coastal islands, 67.

Bass, spotted: perhaps Calico Bass (*Pomoxis nigro-maculatus* [Le Sueur]); at Salt Springs, Fla., 166.

Bats: winged mammals of the order Chiroptera; of Florida, Pennsylvania, Virginia, and Europe, 283; near Clayton, Ga., 344.

Bat, great. *See* Caprimulgus lucifugus.

Batata(s): sweet potato(es) (*Ipomoea batatas* [L.] Poir.); usefulness, xvii; on hammock land, 65; at Palatka, Fla., 93; land fit for, at Lake Beresford, 144; on old Spanish plantations near Suwannee River, 233; on St. John's River, 254; on lower Tombigbee River, Ala., 409; on Escambia River, Fla., 416; at Mobile Bay, Ala., 419; near The Rigolets, La., 422; at Tangipahoa River, 425. *See also* Convolvulus batata, Potatoes.

Baton Rouge (or "Batonrouge"), now called New-Richmond: the present Baton Rouge, capital of Louisiana; voyage to, 429; friend (doubtless William Dunbar—see Commentary) at, 429–436; curious vine found there, 436.

Battle, between the Cherokees and the Carolinians: at The Narrows, near Mulberry Creek, about 3 miles south of Otto, Macon County, N.C. (Cowee quadrangle) (A.L.P.); described, 348. *See also* Middleton, "General."

  This battle had taken place on June 10, 1761 (cf. Carroll, 1836, *1:* 467, 474, and *2:* 530; Jones, 1883, *2:* 8, 14, etc.; Mooney, 1900: 44).

Battle Lagoon: the present Mud Lake, on the west side of St. John's River just above Lake Dexter, Fla. (U. S. Coast and Geodetic Survey Chart, Lake George to Lake Harney, 1928) (fig. 10); Alligators in, 117–126; passed by, 153.

Bay of Apalachee ("Apalache," "Apalachi," "Apalatche," or "Aplatchi"). *See* Apalachee, Bay of.

Bay of Pearls: apparently off the mouth of Pearl River, between Lake Borgne, La., and Mississippi Sound, Miss.; 429; sailed through, 437.

Bay St. Louis: an arm of Mississippi Sound, between the present cities of Bay St. Louis and Pass Christian, Miss.; passing by, 437.

Bays: probably red bays (*Persea borbonia* [L.] Spreng.); at Hawkinsville on St. John's River, Fla., 140; at Long Pond, Levy County, 243.

Bay, Big: the Creek name for *Magnolia grandiflora* signifying, 232.

Bay, Purple berried. *See* Olea Americana (Purple berried bay) Catesby.

Bay(s), Red (cf. Catesby, 1731, *1:* 63, pl. 63): either *Persea borbonia* (L.) Spreng. or *P. b.* f. *pubescens* (Pursh) Fern. (which Bartram did not definitely differentiate); at St. Francis on St. John's River, Fla., 139; at New Smyrna, 144; on Salt Springs Run, 160; about Alachua Savanna, 198; near Suwannee River, 224. *See also* Bay(s), Sweet; Laurus Borbonia.

  Bartram apparently used the names "Red Bay" and "Sweet Bay" as synonyms.

Bay(s) (or bay trees), Sweet: either *Persea borbonia* (L.) Spreng. or *P. b.* f. *pubescens* (Pursh) Fern.; in Liberty County, Ga., 11; on St.

Simon's Island, 58, 59, 61; formerly growing where salt marshes are, 69; at Nassau Sound, Fla., 70. *See also* Bay(s), Red; *Laurus Borbonia.*

Bay, dwarf Sweet (Laurus Borbonia): in this case, *Persea humilis* Nash; near Salt Springs, Fla., 164.

Bay-gall ("bay-gale"): a low, swampy area, sometimes covered with water, and containing a dense growth of mostly evergreen trees and shrubs, among which one or more bays (*Gordonia, Magnolia,* or *Persea*) are generally present (cf. W. Bartram, 1943: 146, 196; Torrey, 1894: 159–160; R. M. Harper, 1914: 203, 248, 283, etc.); west of Deep Creek, Putnam County, Fla., 173; near Alachua Savanna, 187, 197.

The use of this vernacular term seems to be more or less restricted to Florida.

Bay swamp: probably very similar to bay-gall (*q.v.*); near lower Savannah River, Ga., 469.

Beads: Cherokee girls ornamented with, 370; on breech-clout and boots, 502, as head ornaments, 502, and on waistcoat among Indians, 503.

Beans: according to Bartram himself (1853: 48), this term probably applies to various species of *Phaseolus;* at Palatka, Fla., 93, 304; at Cuscowilla, 193; at Watauga, N.C., 350; near Cowee, 354; near The Rigolets, La., 422; cultivation by Indians, 511.

Dolichos, mentioned by Bartram (1853: 48) along with *Phaseolus,* probably refers to cowpeas (*Vigna sinensis* Endl.). According to J. G. Smith (1899: 5), cowpeas have been cultivated in the South at least since the middle of the eighteenth century.

Beans, French (Phaseolus ["phaccolus"]): *Phaseolus* sp.; time for planting, 288.

Bean vines: *Phaseolus* sp.; reeds for support of, 514.

Bear(s): Florida Bear(s) (*Euarctos americanus floridanus* [Merriam]) (certainly this form in Florida, and probably in southeastern Georgia and southern Alabama); feeding on saw-palmetto, and displaying affection, on Mosquito River, Fla., xxv–xxvi; on Colonel's Island, Ga., 7; skin on St. Simon's Island, 60; on Jekyl and Cumberland Islands, 63; on Drayton's Island, Fla., 103; at Lake Dexter, 124; pulling to pieces a nest of the Florida Wood Rat, 125; bear's oil in repast at Cuscowilla, 186; depredations near Alachua Savanna, 194; hides traded by Seminoles, 211, 214; bear's oil bartered by Indians to Spaniards in Cuba, 227; in Suwannee River region, 235; several killed by White King and his retinue, 235; royal feast of, 236; ribs in repast at Talahasochte, 241; cakes fried in bear's oil, 241; account of, 282; hunting ground for, in Alachua region, 380; plentiful in Florida, 392; in Baldwin or adjacent county, Ala., 412; on coast of Florida, 488. *See also* the two following entries.

Bear(s): in the following cases, either Florida Bear(s) (*Euarctos americanus floridanus* [Merriam]) or Eastern Black Bear(s) (*E. americanus americanus* [Pallas]), local specimens not being available for more exact determination; in middle region of Georgia, 46; scarce near Muscogulge towns, 210; skin used for tobacco pouch, 453; in paintings at Otasse, Ala., 455; hunting of, 500; Indians' ears anointed with bear's oil, 501. *See also* preceding and following entries.

Bear(s): in the following cases, Louisiana Bear(s) (*Euarctos americanus luteolus* [Griffith]); crossing the Mississippi, La., 433; crossing the Amite River, 437. *See also* the two preceding entries.

Beasts: mammals; of Florida and Carolina, 281.

Beavers: Carolina Beavers (*Castor canadensis carolinensis* Rhoads); in Florida and Georgia, 281.

Beaver, big: as Indian name for Manatee, 232.

Bedding, spread on bank of Amite River, La., 436.

Bee(s) (or honey bees): *Apis mellifera* L.; hibernating Parrakeets compared with bees in a hive, 301; introduced from Europe, and ranging from Nova Scotia to East Florida, but few or none to the westward, 413 (cf. Jefferson, 1782: 133); economy of, 494.

Bees, humble: bumblebees (*Bombus* spp.); compared in size with horse-flies, 385. *See also* Bumblebee.

Bee-hives: on St. Simon's Island, Ga., 60; cypress knees serving for, 91.

Bee tree: a hollow tree in which bees have stored honey; cut down, 305.

Bees-wax: bartered by Indians to Spaniards in Cuba, 227; compared with wax of *Myrica inodora*, 406.

Beech: *Fagus grandifolia* Ehrh. var. *caroliniana* (Loud.) Fern. & Rehd.; in Butler or adjacent county, Ala., 400. *See also* Fagus, Fagus sylvatica.

Beef: production in Georgia, 311; repast of dried beef, 344. *See also* Cattle, Neat's tongue.

Belemnites (or "bellemnites"): some fossil cephalopod mollusk; at Silver Bluff, S.C., 314; along Cape Fear River, N.C., 475, 476 (in the latter locality probably *Belemnitella americana* Morton—cf. Stephenson, 1912: 149).

Bell, on horses in a caravan, 441.

Belt(s) (or sash): worn by Indians, 503; made by Indian women, 513.

Bermudian white rock: limestone; 318.

Betula lenta: in this case, probably river birch (*B. nigra* L.); along Chattahoochee River, Ala., 393.

Betula nigra: in these cases, black birch (*B. lenta* L.); on Oconee (= Station) Mountain, S.C., 337; near Wayah Gap, N.C., 362.

Bidens frondosa: beggar-ticks (*B. frondosa* L.); along upper Savannah River, Ga., 321.

Big Island: a former Cherokee town on an island of this name in Little Tennessee River a short distance below the mouth of Tellico River, in Monroe County, Tenn. (Romans' map of 1776, as "Mialago"; Mooney, 1900: 508; Loudon quadrangle); listed, 374.

Bignonia: in this case, probably the "Bignonia bracteata" of p. 468, which is Georgia bark (*Pinckneya bracteata* [Bartr.] Raf.); on Altamaha River, Ga., 48.

Bignonia: in this case, any one of several species, now placed in the genera *Bignonia, Campsis,* or *Gelsemium;* on upper Tensaw River, Ala., 408.

Bignonia *bracteata (cf. description, without a name, p. 16): Georgia bark (*Pinckneya bracteata* [Bartr.] Raf.; syn., *P. pubens* Michx.) (cf. Harper, 1942b: 6–7; Merrill, 1945: 23–24); on Altamaha River, Ga., and in East Florida, 468. *See also* Bartramia bracteata; Bignonia (first entry); Shrubs, two new beautiful.

Bignonia (or "Bignonea") crucigera: trumpet flower (*B. capreolata* L.); in Liberty County, Ga., 10; in coastal swamps, 29; on St. Simon's Island, 59; on lower St. John's River, Fla., 87; on the St. John's above Lake Dexter, 136; in Oconee County, S.C., 334; in Monroe or adjacent county, Ala., 401.

Bignonia radicans: trumpet creeper (*Campsis radicans* [L.] Seem.); in coastal swamps, 29; on lower St. John's River, Fla., 87; near Wayah Gap, N.C., 362; in Monroe or adjacent county, Ala., 402.

Bignonia sempervirens (cf. Catesby, 1730? *1:* 53, pl. 53): yellow jessamine (*Gelsemium sempervirens* [L.] Ait. f.); in Liberty County, Ga., 10; in coastal swamps, 29; on St. Simon's Island, 59; in Oconee County, S.C., 334; near Wayah Gap, N.C., 362; in Monroe or adjacent county, Ala., 402. *See also* Jasmine, yellow; Jessamine, yellow.

Biloxi: on the coast of Mississippi, in the present Harrison County; pass by, 437.

Birds: attributes of, xxxi–xxxiii; not numerous in forests, but near habitations, 20; hymns of feathered songsters on Altamaha River, 50; Mayflies as food for, 81; melody of feathered songsters ceasing at end of day, 82; summons of the gentle monitors of the meads and groves, 100; winged inhabitants of the groves, 106; as prey of the "trout," 109; of Florida, 147–152; merry, at Salt Springs, 166; be-

tween Orange and Tuscawilla Lakes, 183; shot by Indian lads near
Alachua Savanna, 194; preyed on by snakes, 195; Seminoles as free
as birds of the air, 212; charmed by rattlesnakes, 267; devoured by
Pine Snake, 276; note of Little Tree-frog compared with chattering
of young birds, 278; of Carolina, Florida, and the Northern States,
284–302; migration of, 284–288; list of birds seen from Pennsylvania
to Florida, 288–302; tuneful tribes, 309; melody of feathered songsters, 343; afraid to chirp during approach of thunderstorm, 343;
shouts of tenants of the groves and meads, 344; singing merrily, 387;
Muscogulge women's speech likened to singing of birds, 519.

Birds, soft billed: probably identical with the "slender-billed birds"
of Edwards (1764, 3: 334) and W. Bartram (1943: 166, 197)—i.e.
wood warblers (family Parulidae) and a few other small birds;
migrations of, 287.

Birds' bills or sharks' teeth (dentes carchariae): fossil sharks' teeth
(cf. Stephenson, 1912: 122–143); along Cape Fear River, N.C., 476.

Bird isle (cf. "Bird Island pond," p. vi): perhaps Watermelon Pond,
5 miles west of Archer, Alachua County, Fla. (the "Generals Pond"
of W. Bartram, 1943: 155, 188); described, 249–250.

Biscuit; repast of, 344, 361.

Bittern(s): in the following cases, probably some of the smaller
herons, such as Night Herons (*Nycticorax* and *Nyctanassa*) and
Eastern Green Herons (*Butorides*) (cf. Catesby, 1731, 1: 78–80);
screaming of, at Lake Dexter, Fla., 124; compared with Limpkin,
148; cooked for supper, 249.

Bittern ("bitern"), crested blue. *See* Ardea violacea.

Bittern ("bitern"), green. *See* Ardea virescens.

Bittern ("bitern"), least brown and striped. *See* Ardea parva.

Bittern ("bitern"), lesser green. *See* Ardea virescens minor.

Bittern ("bitern"), little brownish spotted. *See* Ardea subfusca stellata.

Bittern ("bitern"), marsh. *See* Ardea mugitans.

Blacks, a boat rowed by three, 429. *See also* Negro(es), Negro
slave(s), Slaves (Negro).

Black-bird(s): probably some species of the genus *Quiscalus;* depredations near Alachua Savanna, Fla., 194 (in this case probably
Florida Grackles (*Quiscalus quiscula quiscula* [L.]); mentioned,
491.

Blackbird, crow. *See* Gracula purpurea.

Black drink. *See* Cassine (or black drink).

Blacksmith, at Charlotia, Fla., 95.

Blanket(s): spread by a fire, 50, on the ground, 135, and under oaks,
137; for bedding, 158; Seminoles in want of, 257, 260; hoisted for a
signal, 470.

Blockhouse. *See* Fortress or blockhouse.

Blue bill. *See* Anas subcerulea.

Blue bird, motacilla sialis: Eastern Bluebird (*Sialia sialis sialis* [L.]); resident in Pennsylvania, 286. *See also* Motacilla sialis.

Bluff, Orange grove, on the little lake: doubtless Orange Bluff (or Bluffton), at the outlet of Lake Dexter, Volusia County, Fla.; camped at, 153.

Boat(s): on Altamaha River, Ga., 17, 57; in Georgia coastal waters, 68; on St. John's River, Fla., 66, 76, 94, 98, 137; at Lake Dexter, 155; on Lake George, 157; at Manatee Spring, 231; bound for Pearl River, La.–Miss., and for Perdido River, Ala.–Fla., 413; voyage to the Mississippi in, 423–427; on the Mississippi, 429, 430, 434; set off from Mobile in, 440. *See also* Bark(s), Canoe(s), Vessel(s).

Boat, portable leather, used in crossing Ocmulgee River, Ga., 458, 459.

Boat, pleasure-, at Amelia Island, Fla., 70.

Boat, sail-, on St. John's River, Fla., 72.

Boat(s) (or bark), trading: on Tensaw River, Ala., 405; sailed in, from Mobile to Pearl River, 418–420; on the Mississippi, La., 437; on Cape Fear River, N.C., 478.

Bomble bee. *See* Bumblebee.

Bone-house, for depositing bones of the deceased in Choctaw towns, 516.

Booby. *See* Pelecanus sula.

Boots: worn by Indians, 502, 504; not worn by Indian women, 503.

Botanist: to the King of Great Britain, xiii; information useful to, xiv.

Botanists, European, a species of *Stewartia* new to, 334.

Botanist and traveler, American: John Bartram (*q.v.*); 473.

Bows and arrows: used by Indians at Palatka, Fla., 92, and near Alachua Savanna, 194; formerly used by the Creeks, 500. *See also* Arrows, Arrow-heads.

Bowl, used in eating at Watauga, N.C., 351.

Bracelets, Cherokee youths ornamented with, 370. *See also* Bands or bracelets.

Brandy, 61, 112.

Brant: probably either Lesser Snow Geese (*Chen hyperborea hyperborea* [Pallas]) or Blue Geese (*Chen caerulescens* [L.]); on the Mississippi, La., 433.

Brant, great particoloured. *See* Anser branta grisea maculata.

Brass: sulphurous nodules compared with, 475; wire in ears of Indians, 501; bells on mantle of Indians, 502.

Bread, in feast at Talahasochte, Fla., 236.

Bream: various fishes of the bass family (Centrarchidae), such as Copper-nosed Bream (*Lepomis macrochirus purpurescens* Cope),

Red-breasted Bream (*L. auritus* [L.]), Shell-cracker Bream (*L. microlophus* [Günther]), and Warmouth (*Chaenobryttus coronarius* [Bartram]); at Salt Springs, Fla., 166, 168; in Alachua Sink, 205; in Suwannee River, 228; in Blue Springs, Screven County, Ga., 461.

Bream, golden, or sunfish: Warmouth (*Chaenobryttus coronarius* [Bartram]) (cf. Harper, 1942*a*) (fig. 13); at Cowpen Lake, Putnam County, Fla., 176. *See also* Bream, yellow.

Bream, great black or blue: Copper-nosed Bream (*Lepomis macrochirus purpurescens* Cope); described, at Cowpen Lake, Putnam County, Fla., 176.

Bream, great yellow or particoloured: Shell-cracker Bream (*Lepomis microlophus* [Günther]); described, at Cowpen Lake, Putnam County, Fla., 176–177.

Bream, red bellied: Red-breasted Bream (*Lepomis auritus* [L.]); at Cowpen Lake, Putnam County, Fla., 176. *See also* Red-belly.

Bream, silver or white: undetermined; at Cowpen Lake, Putnam County, Fla., 176.

Bream, yellow, or sun fish, Cyprinus coronarius: Warmouth (*Chaenobryttus coronarius* [Bartram]; syn., *C. gulosus* [Cuv.]) (cf. Harper, 1942*a*) (Pl. VIII*b*); described, at Lake Dexter, Fla., 153–154. *See also* Bream, golden.

Breeches, 445; breech-clout resembling Roman breeches, 502.

Breech-clout, trader and Indians clothed with, 446.

Brick, buildings of, at Mobile, Ala., 404.

Bridge, across Iberville channel, La., 428.

Bridge, raccoon: a tree felled across a creek; 445.

Brig [*Prince of Wales*], bound for Charleston, 1.

Brigantine Charleston Packet, embarked on, 1.

British colonists, in alliance with Muscogulges, 487.

British gentleman, plantation of, on Lake George, Fla., 253.

British government, planters under, 253.

British settlement, on the Mississippi, La., 405.

Broad River: an important tributary of the Savannah in northeastern Georgia; 316, 320, 324; encamped on a branch of, 41, 43; survey of, 41; cray-fish and "gold-fish" in a branch of, 43–44; surrounding country described, 45; crossed, 46, 323; excursion up, 375.

Bromelia Ananas: pineapple (*Ananas sativus* Schult. f.); *Tillandsia lingulata* resembling, 62.

Brooch ("broach"), silver. *See* Silver.

Brook, swift running, flowing into Alachua Savanna, Fla.: Sweetwater Branch, on the north side of the savanna (Arredondo quadrangle); came to, 202.

Brook, water of the Tennessee ("Tanase"): the present Black's Creek, just north of Rabun Gap, Ga. (Walhalla quadrangle; map of Chattahoochee National Forest, 1937); crossed, 345.

Broom-Pine. *See* Pine, Broom- .

Broughton (or "Broton") Island: an island about 6 square miles in extent, in the mouth of Altamaha River, opposite Darien, McIntosh County, Ga. (soil map of McIntosh County, 1932); canoe obtained at, 48; location of, 53; returned to, 55; stopping at, 57; meeting Henry Laurens at, 306–307.

Brown[e], Governor [Montfort], of West Florida and the Bahama Islands; Brown[e]'s Cliffs on the Mississippi named in honor of, 431; meeting with, 431.

Browne was lieutenant governor under Governor George Johnstone and took over the government on Johnstone's departure in 1767, serving till 1769. In 1768 he made a trip to the Mississippi and sent a glowing description of the country to the secretary of state. He had holdings of land near Mobile and near Baton Rouge. "In 1774 he was appointed governor of the Bahamas. He paid a brief visit to West Florida in 1775 to attend to his private affairs and no doubt to further his land schemes. When the Bahamas were taken over by the Americans in 1776," he was made prisoner but later exchanged. He returned to the Bahamas as governor in 1778 but was recalled in 1779. "He returned to America in 1782 seeking his fortune again and not without success in the British Army." (C. Johnson, 1943: 61–62, 64.)

"The plantation owned by Gov. Brown[e] is located near what is called Port Hickey on the maps. On either side of Gov. Brown[e]'s plantation, the land was owned by Peter and Daniel Hickey, who apparently afterwards owned Gov. Brown[e]'s place (property map at the State Land Office)." (Clair A. Brown, *in litt.*, July 24, 1941.)

His holdings on the Mississippi are shown in the Crown Collection of Photographs of American Maps (ser. 3, 2: 100, 1915). They included the present Port Hudson, and extended west about to Fancy Point and east-southeast for perhaps 4 or 5 miles.

Brown[e]'s Cliffs. *See* White Cliffs.

Brunswick, N.C.: formerly the capital of the colony, but long since deserted; situated in Brunswick County on the west side of the estuary of Cape Fear River, 5.5 miles south of Town Creek; location of, 473.

The site is now marked by a small monument erected by the Colonial Dames.

Bryan, Jonathan: a prominent citizen and Revolutionary patriot of Georgia; visit to his plantation, 469–470.

Bryan was born on September 12, 1708, and lived in various places in South Carolina until 1752, when he came to Georgia. He was presently appointed a Judge of the General Court and a royal counsellor of the colony. In 1774 and 1775 he became embroiled with Governor Tonyn of Florida over an attempt to lease the Apalachee Old Fields from the Creek Indians. At the commencement of the Revolution he was active in the cause of liberty and became a member of the Council of Safety, the Convention, and the State Congress. He was made prisoner by the British and sent to New York. He was finally exchanged and returned to Georgia, where he continued an active and determined patriot. He was a friend of the Wesleys and of George Whitefield. He died in March 1788. (White, 1849: 124–126 and 1854: 366; Mowat, 1943: 88–90; Screven, 1956.)

"He may justly be styled one of the principal Founders and Fathers of Georgia" (Harden, 1913, *1:* 257).

His plantation ("Brampton") was just below the mouth of Pipemaker's Creek, about 3 (not "eight") miles above Savannah (Campbell map of 1780; soil map of Chatham County, 1914; *Georgia Hist. Quart.,* 27 [1]: 28–55).

Buck: Virginia White-tailed Deer (*Odocoileus virginianus* [Boddaert]); on Cumberland Island, Ga., 65; at Alachua Savanna, Fla., 207; in paintings at Otasse, Ala., 455; hunting of, 500. See also Cervus sylvaticus, Deer, Roebuck, Venison.

Buckskin(s): skins of Virginia White-tailed Deer (*Odocoileus virginianus* [Boddaert]); heavier among the Upper Creeks and Cherokees than among the Seminoles or in the low country of Carolina, 216; traded by Seminoles, 257. See also Deer.

Buffalo ("buffaloe"): American Bison (*Bison bison bison* [L.]); bones of, between Little and Broad Rivers, Ga., 322.

Buffalo (Urus): American Bison (*Bison bison bison* [L.]); no longer seen in middle region of Georgia, 46.

Buffalo ("buffaloe") head. See Anas bucephala.

Buffalo Lick, Great: near the present Philomath, Oglethorpe County, Ga.; set off for, 35; visited and described, 39; set off from, 40; at extremity of the Great Ridge, 42.

Buildings: at Manchac, La., 428; of a trader at Muclasse, Ala., 446; in public square at Otasse, described, 453–456.

Bull: *Bos taurus* L.; contrasted with the ox, 186; voice compared with that of the Bullfrog, 277. See also Beef, Bullocks, Calf, Cattle, Cows, Ox.

Bullet, 498.

Bull frog (Northern): *Rana catesbeiana* Shaw; voice compared with that of Southern Bullfrog and with that of a bull, 277.

Bull-neck. *See* Anas bucephala.

Bullocks: *Bos taurus* L.; served in banquet at Cuscowilla, Fla., 191.

Bumblebee ("bomble bee, apis *bombylicus"): *nomen nudum—
Bombus* sp.; captured by a jumping spider, at Mosquito River, Fla.,
xxx. *See also* Bees, humble.

Busk (or "busque"): a solemn annual festival of the Creeks (and also
of the Choctaws, according to Bartram), a feast of first fruits (cf.
Bur. Am. Ethnol. Bull. 30, Pt. I: 176–178, 1907); new songs at
busks of the Choctaws, 506; described, 509–510; mentioned, 512.

Buskin(s), ancient, or sandal: Indian moccasin resembling, 502; worn
by Indian women, 503, 504.

Butcher bird, bluish grey (lanius): Loggerhead Shrike (*Lanius ludovicianus ludovicianus* L.); in Putnam County, Fla., v, 172. *See also*
Lanius garrulus.

Butcher-bird, little black capped, of Florida. *See* Lanius garrulus.

Butcher-bird, little grey, of Pennsylvania. *See* Lanius griseus.

Butter; 19, 311, 349.

Butterback. *See* Anas minor picta.

Butterflies: diurnal Lepidoptera (division Rhopalocera); fishes likened
to, 167; hunting of, 188.

Butterfly, black, with yellow stripes and crimson spots: Zebra Butterfly (*Heliconius charithonius* [L.]) (F.M.J. and J.W.C. III); on
Mosquito River, Fla., xxviii.

Butterfly, with forked tail, blue stripes, and blue and crimson circles:
perhaps *Papilio marcellus* Cramer, though the description is not
accurate for this species (F.M.J. and J.W.C. III); on Mosquito
River, Fla., xxviii.

Butterfly, white, with black crescents and blue and crimson orbs: the
nearest approach to this description is *Ascia monuste* (L.) (J.W.C.
III); on Mosquito River, Fla., xxix.

Buzzard, turkey, Vultu[r] aura: Turkey Vulture (*Cathartes aura
septentrionalis* Wied); compared with King Vulture, 150. *See also*
Vultur aura, Vultures.

Cabbage tree: cabbage palmetto (*Sabal palmetto* [Walt.] Lodd.);
contrasted with royal palm, 115. *See also* Corypha palma, Palm(s),
Palm tree(s).

Cabins (buildings), Indian; on Tallapoosa River, Ala., 445.

Cabin(s) (or "cabbins") or couch or sophas: "a sort of sofa raised
about two feet above the common ground" in public or private
buildings of the Indians (W. Bartram, 1853: 38, 54); at Watauga,
N.C., 351; in Cherokee rotundas, 369; in rotunda and other buildings at Otasse, Ala., 451, 452, 455; grave dug beneath, 515.

Cables; made of long moss, 88.

Cacalia: undetermined; near Suwannee River, Fla., 242; in Brunswick County, N.C., 472.

The "Cacalia" of the Contents (p. v) refers to the next entry.

Cacalia *heterophylla: garberia (*Garberia heterophylla* [Bartr.] Merrill & F. Harper; syn., *G. fruticosa* [Nutt.] A. Gray) (cf. Merrill, 1945: 24); described, near Salt Springs, west side of Lake George, Marion County, Fla., 164.

"*Cacalia fruticosa*. I doubt if Michaux or Lyon saw it, I believe neither of them asscended the River S^t. Juan as high as where it grows, in the sandy barens." (Bartram to Muhlenberg, September 6, 1810; Muhlenberg Letters: 137.) (Michaux did, however, reach Lake George.)

Cacalia, another species than C. heterophylla: undetermined; described, near Salt Springs, Fla., 164.

Cacalia suffruticosa: "doubtless *Garberia fruticosa*" [= *G. heterophylla* (Bartr.) Merrill & F. Harper] (Small, 1923: 28); on Mosquito River, Fla., xxviii.

Bartram may have had in mind the Linnaean species of this name, which, however, is a South American plant.

Cactus: in these cases, prickly pear (*Opuntia* spp.); various species on plains near Suwannee River, Fla., 242; near Long Pond, Levy County, 248.

Cactus cochenellifer (or "cochinellifer") (cf. Linnaeus, 1753: 468): the cochineal plant of Mexico (*Nopalea cochenillifera* [L.] Salm-Dyck); in the tropics, xv; on Mosquito River, Fla., xxviii (in the latter case a misidentification of some species of prickly pear [*Opuntia*]) (cf. Small, 1923: 28).

Cactus grandiflora (cf. Linnaeus, 1753: 467): night-blooming cereus (*Selenicereus grandiflorus* [L.] Brit. & Rose); in the tropics, xiv.

Cactus melo-cactus: "Turk's head" (*C. melocactus* L.); in the tropics, xiv.

Cactus opuntia: in this case not *C. opuntia* L., but a composite description of scrub prickly-pear (*Opuntia ammophila* Small) and another species; near Salt Springs, Fla., v, 162–163.

"In recording it in his narrative, he [Bartram] confused the vegetative parts of this plant and the large fruits of the prickly-pear of the coastwise kitchenmiddens" (Small, 1933: 907).

"Calamut." *See* Calumet.

Calandra *pratensis, the May bird (cf. Wilson, 1808, *1*: 54; Stone, 1913: 348; Harper, 1942*d*: 217): *nomen nudum*—Dickcissel (*Spiza americana* [Gmelin]); listed, 291.

Calf (or calves): *Bos taurus* L., young; preyed upon by Cougar, 46, and by Bears, 282; on lower Savannah River, Ga., 310; at Fort Moore, S.C., 316; at Natchez, Miss., 434. *See also* Beef, Bull, Bullock, Cattle, Cows, Ox.

Calico ("callico"), waistcoat made of, 503.

"Callicanthus." *See* Calycanthus.

Callicarpa (cf. Catesby, 1736, 2: 47, pl. 47): French mulberry (*C. americana* L.); on Colonel's Island, Ga., 6; cultivated by the ancients near Little River, 38; on St. Simon's Island, 58; at Charlotia, Fla., 95; on St. John's River above Lake George, 114; near Salt Springs, 164; between Orange and Tuscawilla Lakes, 183; near Alachua Savanna, 187; in Levy County, 221; near Three Sisters Ferry, S.C., 309; along upper Savannah River, Ga., 321; near The Rigolets, La., 421; at the White Cliffs, 436; at Blue Springs, Screven County, Ga., 461–462; along Cape Fear River, N.C., 476.

"Calloosas." *See* Indians—Caloosas.

Caloosahatche (cf. *Bur. Am. Ethnol. Bull., 30*, Pt. I: 196, 1907): a former Seminole town, presumably on Caloosahatchee River in southern Florida, rather than on Flint River, Ga., as indicated by Bartram; listed, 464.

Calos, Bay of: San Carlos Bay or vicinity, at mouth of Caloosahatchee River, Fla.; Spaniards trading at, 227.

Calumet (or "calamut") or great pipe of peace, the imperial (or royal) standard, or eagle's tail; at feast at Talahasochte, Fla., 236; described, 151, 454–455; made by Indian men, 513. *See also* Standard, royal.

Calves. *See* Calf.

Calycanthean groves: presumably woods in which sweet shrub (*Calycanthus floridus*) grows; at Keowee, S.C., 331.

Calycanthus (or "Callicanthus"): sweet shrub (*C. floridus* L.) or perhaps, in part, some other species of the same genus; xvi; in Liberty County, Ga., 10; in Southern Red Hills, 32; about Wrightsborough, 36; between Little and Broad Rivers, 322; along upper Savannah River, Ga.–S.C., 327; in Oconee County, S.C., 334; on Oconee (= Station) Mountain, 336; near Cowee, N.C., 357; in Monroe or adjacent county, Ala., 402.

Calycanthus (or "Callicanthus") floridus (cf. Catesby, 1730? *1*: 46, pl. 46): sweet shrub (*C. floridus* L.); xvii; at Shell Bluff, Ga., 318; at Falling Creek, Rabun County, Ga., 342.

Cambel (properly Campbell?), ———, Esq., city of Cambelton, N.C., named for, 478.

Cambelton (properly Campbelton?): name of a new city founded near Cross Creeks—the present Fayetteville, N.C.; 478; set off from, 479.

Cambelton was perhaps about midway between Cross Creeks and the Cape Fear River (H.A.R.). The Price and Strother map of 1808 (J. Bartram, 1942: map 2) shows "Campbelton" on the opposite (east) bank of Cape Fear River from Fayetteville.

Camellia: probably the common camellia (*C. japonica* L.); in the tropics, xiv.

Cameron, (Alexander): Deputy Commissioner of Indian Affairs, with a seat at Loughabber, apparently in the northern part of the present Abbeville County, S.C.; visit to, 326–328; holding a congress at Seneca, 372.

Like his chief, John Stuart, Cameron was a Tory in the Revolution. "Mr. [W. H.] Drayton while at the Congaree Store, wrote on the 26th of September [1775] to Mr. Alexander Cameron, Deputy Superintendent in the Cherokee Nation, requesting him in the name of the Colony, to remove from the Cherokees, to whom he had retreated from Lochaber, his plantation on Little River in the Long-Cane Settlement" (Drayton, 1821, *1:* 408). Cameron declined, and eventually incited the Cherokees to unite with him in warring upon the Revolutionists (J. Johnson, 1851: 56).

"Cana." *See* Canna.

Canaanites: a biblical people; high places and sacred groves of, 368.

"Canabis." *See* Cannabis.

Canada, 199, 298; plants common in, 337.

"Cancer, Squilla": on the assumption that the comma was inserted through accident or error, this becomes "Cancer Squilla" (cf. Linné, 1767, *1*, Pt. II: 1051), a stomatopod crustacean of an undetermined species; on St. Simon's Island, Ga., 60.

Cancer *macrourus. *See* Cray-fish.

Candles, made of berries of *Myrica inodora,* 406.

Cane(s) (or Reed[s]): one or both species of *Arundinaria*, small cane (*A. tecta* [Walt.] Muhl.) and giant cane (*A. gigantea* [Walt.] Chapm.); matts of, at Palatka, Fla., 304; on upper Tensaw River, Ala., 406; along the Mississippi, La., 432; used in making a raft, 444; for fuel and light in rotunda at Otasse, Ala., 450–451; in marriage ceremony of Muscogulges, 514. *See also* Reeds or Canes.

Canes (Arundo gigantea): giant canes (*Arundinaria gigantea* [Walt.] Chapm.); in coastal swamps, 29; on Patsiliga Creek, Taylor County, Ga., 383.

Cane brake(s) (or "Cane-break" or Cane meadows): a more or less dense and extensive growth of canes (*q.v.*); west of Suwannee River, Fla., 233–234; in Warren County, Ga., 377, 379; west of Oconee River, 381; west of Ocmulgee River, 382; west of Flint River, 384, 385, 387; west of Chattahoochee River, Ala., 394; in Monroe or adjacent county, 402; in Escambia or adjacent county, 402; in northwestern Florida, 416; on the White Plains, La., 431; in Screven County, Ga., 461; along Cape Fear, N.C., 474. *See also* Cane swamp(s).

Cane forests: probably of giant cane (*Arundinaria gigantea* [Walt.] Chapm.); near Port Hudson, La., 431.

Cane pastures: more or less identical with cane meadows (see above); in southern Alabama, 443.

Cane swamp(s): damp areas grown with one or both species of *Arundinaria*, small cane (*A. tecta* [Walt.] Muhl.) and giant cane (*A. gigantea* [Walt.] Chapm.); south of Altamaha River, Ga., 19; in Lime-Sink Region, 31; about Wrightsborough, 36; near Little River, 38; near the Buffalo Lick, 39; along Oconee River, 43; along Chattahoochee River, Ala., 395; between Chattahoochee and Tallapoosa Rivers, 396; near Stockton, 403. *See also* Cane brake(s).

Canna ("Cana") Indica: apparently red canna (*C. indica* L.), although this is a very early date for the introduction of an East Indian species; on Amite River, La., 426.

Canna ("Cana") lutea (cf. P. Miller, 1768): golden canna (*C. flaccida* Salisb.); at Lake Dexter, Fla., 155.

Cannabis ("Canabis"): a genus of Urticaceae, comprising hemp (*C. sativa* L.); usefulness, xvii.

Cannon: at Apalachean Old Fields, Fla., 233; at Pensacola, 416; on Mobile Bay, Ala., 418.

Canoe(s): in Bartram's time, probably chiefly or entirely dugouts; in Okefinokee Swamp, Ga., 26; on Altamaha River, 48; in Georgia coastal waters, 68; mentioned, 90; made of cypress trunks, 92; fishing from, 108–109; Alligators attacking, 119–121, 126; on St. John's River, Fla., 134–136, 303; used by Florida Indians in expeditions to Bahamas and Cuba, 227; on Suwannee River, 228, 232, 235; Savannah River navigable for, 316; on Little Tennessee River, N.C., 349, 354; on Chattahoochee River, Ga.–Ala., 388; endeavor to procure, 405; on Tensaw River, Ala., 405; reeds as masts for, 410; French escaping from Natchez, Miss., in, 434; on Tallapoosa River, Ala., 446; made by Indian men, 513. *See also* Bark(s); Vessel(s).

Cantharides: a preparation of blister beetles (*Cantharis vesicatoria* [L.]), used as a rubefacient and vesicatory (Webster); as a remedy, 420.

Cape Canaveral: on the East Coast of Florida, in Brevard County; 144.

Cape Fear: in Brunswick County, N.C., south of Wilmington; 299, 465–466.

Cape Fear (or Clarendon) River: the Northwest Cape Fear River, arising in north central North Carolina and entering the ocean about 25 miles south of Wilmington; a lake near, 409; journey along, 473, 476–479; course of, 478. *See also* North West of Cape Fear River.

Cape Henlopen: in Sussex County, Del.; sail by, 1, 2.

Capes of St. Mary: the opposing tips of Cumberland Island, Ga., and Amelia Island, Fla.; 66.

Capola: an old Spanish settlement in the vicinity of Long Pond, Levy County, Fla.; 223–224, 233.

Capon (traders' name): a former Seminole Town, whose location is uncertain, though placed by Bartram on the Flint River, Ga.; listed, 464.

Capparis: caper bush (*C. spinosa* L.); proposed culture in Georgia, 460.

C[aprimulgus] Americanus, night hawk, or whip poor will (cf. Linnaeus, 1758: 193): composite, including both Eastern Nighthawk (*Chordeiles minor minor* [Forster]) and Eastern Whip-poor-will (*Caprimulgus vociferus vociferus* Wilson) (cf. Barton, 1799*b*: 208; Wilson, 1812, 5: 80–81); listed, 292. *See also* Night hawk.

Caprimulgus *lucifugus, the great bat, or chuck wills widow (cf. Catesby, 1730? 1: 8, pl. 8): Chuck-will's-widow (*Caprimulgus carolinensis* Gmelin); listed, 292. *See also* Whip-poor-will.

Caprimulgus rufus. *See* Whip-poor-will, Caprimulgus rufus.

Capsicum: bird pepper (*C. frutescens* L. var.) (cf. Bailey, 1935, *1*: 659); near Nassau Sound, Fla., 71.

    Curtiss (1879: 118) reports *C. frutescens* from practically the same area where Bartram was.

Captain: of a vessel in Georgia, 63–64; of the fort on Cumberland Island, 65; of a boat going from Mobile to Pensacola, 414, 415, and from Mobile to Pearl River, 418–420.

Caravan: setting out to survey the New Purchase, Ga., 35; of traders, setting out from Flat Rock, 378; of traders, at Apalachicola, Ala., 395.

Carduelis ("Carduelus") Americanus, the goldfinch (cf. Catesby,

1730? *1:* 43, pl. 43): Eastern Goldfinch (*Spinus tristis tristis* [L.]); listed, 291.

C[arduelis] ("Carduelus") pinus, the lesser goldfinch: Northern Pine Siskin (*Spinus pinus pinus* [Wilson]); listed, 291.

C[arduelis] ("Carduelus") *pusillus ("pusilus"), the least finch: perhaps Common Redpoll (*Acanthis linaria linaria* [L.]); listed, 291.

Carduus: thistle (*Cirsium* sp.); along upper Savannah River, Ga., 321.

Carica papaya: papaya or custard-apple (*C. papaya* L.); beauty of, xvii; on St. John's River at Charlotia, Fla., 94; described, on the St. John's above Lake Dexter, iv, 131–132.

"First noticed in Florida in 1774 by William Bartram" (Sargent, 1902, *14:* 7).

Carnation: *Dianthus armeria* L.; *Cacalia heterophylla* likened to, 164.

Carolina: either North Carolina or South Carolina, or both; 46, 48, 154, 172, 216, 220, 241, 303; various trees of, xv–xvi; exploration of, 1; acquaintance in, 3; sea-coast islands of, 9; maritime parts of, 19, 23; coastal swamps in, 29; unsafe to travel in the northwest of, 55; colony established by the English, 55; planters along the coast of, 69; settlers leaving Charlotia for, 95; rivers of, 225; snakes of, 273–276; frogs of, 276–280; lizards of, 280–281; tortoises of, 281; beasts of, 281–284; birds of, 284–302; Catesby's history of, 299; tree growth in Alabama and Carolina compared, 400; landscape of southern Alabama and Carolina compared, 402; method of making pitch in, 419; decision to return to, 436; vegetation of Louisiana and Carolina compared, 436; Indians from maritime parts of, 465; settled by English, 465; citizens of, at Augusta, Ga., 486; governor of, 494. *See also* North Carolina, South Carolina.

Carolina, (South); 316, 324; crossed Savannah River into, 326.

Carolinians, (South); Ogeechee Indians slain by, 66; keeping a garrison at Fort Moore, S.C., 316; battle between Carolinians and Cherokees in Vale of Cowee, N.C., 348; Indians driven away by, 380; friendship of an old chief for, 499.

Carpenters; repairing Bartram's boat, 76; at Cross Creeks, N.C., 477.

Carpets. *See* Matts or carpets.

Carpinus: probably blue beech (*C. caroliniana* Walt.) rather than hop hornbeam (*Ostrya virginiana* [Mill.] K. Koch—formerly known as *Carpinus ostrya*); about Wrightsborough, Ga., 36; on St. Simon's Island, 58; along upper Savannah River, 320; along Chattahoochee River, Ala., 393; on Amite River, La., 425; along Cape Fear River, N.C., 474.

Carpinus betula: not *C. betula* L., but blue beech (*C. caroliniana* Walt.); on Colonel's Island, Ga., 6.

C[arpinus] ostrya: hop hornbeam (*Ostrya virginiana* [Mill.] K. Koch); on Colonel's Island, Ga., 6.

Carver's Creek: a small westerly tributary of Cape Fear River in the vicinity of Council, Bladen County, N.C. (soil map of Bladen County, 1914); crossed, 474.

Caryophyllata (cf. Linnaeus, 1753, *1:* 500–501): presumably avens (genus *Geum*); a new species of, 43. *See also* Geum odoratissimum.

Caryophyllus ("Caryophylus") aromaticus: clove tree (*Eugenia aromatica* [L.] Baill.); in the tropics, xiv. *See also* Cloves.

Cassine: yaupon (*Ilex vomitoria* Ait.); on Colonel's Island, Ga., 6; on St. Simon's Island, 58; near Salt Springs, Fla., 164; west of Spalding's Lower Store, 171; about Alachua Savanna, 198, 202; near Suwannee River, 242; Painted Bunting among, 299; on upper Tensaw River, Ala., 408; at Blue Springs, Screven County, Ga., 462; on Long Bay, S.C., 471. *See also* two following entries.

Cassine (or black drink): a drink made from the leaves of yaupon (*Ilex vomitoria* Ait.); at feast at Talahasochte, Fla., 236; at Otasse, Ala., 450–453.

For an account of the ceremonial use of this drink see Gatschet (1888, 2: 87–91).

Cassine (or "Casine") °yapon: *nomen nudum* (Merrill, 1945: 34)— yaupon (*Ilex vomitoria* Ait.); occurrence at Jore village, N.C., and its use as a drink by the Indians, 359; along Cape Fear River, 476.

"Ilex cassine of Walt. The true Yapon or Cassine held in sacred veneration by the Muscogulges, or Creeks, & by all the Indians of Florida & Louisiana." (Bartram to Muhlenberg, November 29, 1792; Muhlenberg Letters: 25.)

"[Bartram says] that his Cassine Yapon, p. 357, Irish edition, is the Ilex vomitoria of Aiton" (B. S. Barton, MS, September 2, 1805; Delafield Coll.).

Castle at St. Augustine: Castillo de San Marcos; built of coquina, 80. For further accounts see J. Bartram (1942: 33, 52–53, 78, figs. 26, 28) and Chatelain (1941: 59–75, frontisp., maps 5, 6, 9, 12, 22).

Castor cauda lanciolata. *See* Muskrat.

Cat: Wildcat (*Lynx rufus* subsp.); a cat skin of tobacco, 499.

Cats: *Felis catus* L.; sick after eating lizards, 172.

Cat Island, La.: between Mississippi and Chandeleur Sounds; passing by, 437.

Catalpa (cf. Catesby, 1730, *1:* 49, pl. 49): catalpa (*C. bignonioides* Walt.); in Liberty County, Ga., 10.

Cat-bird (muscicapa vertice nigro) (cf. Catesby, 1731, *1:* 66, pl. 66):

Catbird (*Lucar carolinensis* [Linné]) (cf. Harper, 1942*d*: 215–216); account of, 299–301. *See also* Lucar lividus.

Caterpillar ("catterpillar"), common grey . . . (Phalena *periodica): *nomen nudum*—probably Tent Caterpillar (*Malacosoma americana* [Fabricius]); on Amelia Island, Fla., and in the Northern States, 66.

Catesby, Mark: author of *The Natural History of Carolina, Florida and the Bahama Islands* (1730?–1748); birds mentioned or figured by, 8, 148–149, 284; on bird migration, 284; the Pewit of, 287; mistakes in his accounts of certain birds, 299–300; a *Robinia* figured by (in 2, appendix: 20, pl. 20), 335; "purple berried bay" of, 476.

Catesby (1682–1750) was probably Bartram's most noted predecessor in the annals of American natural history. Although an Englishman, he had spent a considerable period in America (about 1712–19 in Virginia, 1722–25 in South Carolina, and 1725–26 in the Bahamas). (For biographical information, see Darlington, 1849: 319; Stone, 1905*a*, 1929; Mrs. Allen, 1937, 1951: 463–478; W. H. Miller, 1948.)

Catfish: various members of the family Ameiuridae, probably including such species as Southern Channel Cat (*Ictalurus lacustris punctatus* [Rafinesque]), Southeastern Yellow Cat (*Ameiurus natalis erebennus* Jordan), and other species of the latter genus; at Salt Springs, Fla., 166; at Cowpen Lake, Putnam County, 176; in Alachua Sink, 205; in Blue Springs, Screven County, Ga., 461.

Cathead Creek: a northerly tributary of Altamaha River near Darien, Ga. (soil map of McIntosh County, 1932); rice plantations on, 16.

Catskill Mountains: in Greene, Ulster, and Delaware Counties, N.Y., reaching an altitude of more than 4,000 feet; journey to, and Rattlesnake in, 270.

Cattle: *Bos taurus* L.; south of Altamaha River, Ga., 19; at the Buffalo Lick, 39; on Altamaha River, 49; on St. Simon's Island, 58; on Georgia coastal islands, 67; eating long moss, 88; on and about Alachua Savanna, Fla., 188, 190, 197, 207–208; range for, near Suwannee River, 235; on lower Savannah River, Ga., 310–311; pasturage for, near Oconee (= Station) Mountain, S.C., 338; in Vale of Cowee, N.C., 349; canes as food for, 377; pasture for, in northwestern Florida, 416; Scotch grass fed to, 430. *See also* Beef, Bull, Bullocks, Calf, Cows, Neat's tongue, Ox, Steers.

Causeway, west of Suwannee River, Fla., 234.

Cedar berries (Juniperus *Americana): red cedar (*Juniperus virginiana* L.); food of birds, 298. *See also* Cedar, red; Juniperus Americana.

Cedar, Red: *Juniperus* sp.; at Huntoon Island on St. John's River, Fla., 140.

Cedar, Red (Juniperus *Americana): *Juniperus virginiana* L.; on Savannah River above Fort James, Ga., 325. *See also* Cedar berries, Juniperus Americana.

Cedar, white (Cupressus thyoides): *Chamaecyparis thyoides* (L.) BSP.; a species of cypress resembling, 411. (This species is probably white cedar itself.)

Cedar bird. *See* Ampelis garrulus.

Cedar Point: perhaps the present Zinder Point, at the east side of the St. John's entrance into Lake George, Fla. (U. S. Coast and Geodetic Survey Chart, St. John's River, Palatka to Lake George, 1938); roving from, 107; arrived at, 156.

Celtis: hackberry (*Celtis* sp.); in coastal swamps, 29; about Wrightsborough, Ga., 36.

Cepa. *See* Onions.

Cephalanthus (or "Cephalanthos"): button-bush (*C. occidentalis* L.); on Colonel's Island, Ga., 7; along upper Savannah River, 321.

Cercis (or "Cercea" or "Circis"): redbud (*C. canadensis* L.); on Colonel's Island, Ga., 6; in lower Coastal Plain, 29; in Southern Red Hills, 32; about Wrightsborough, 36; near Alachua Savanna, Fla., 187; along upper Savannah River, Ga., 320; along Chattahoochee River, Ala., 394; in Lowndes or Butler Counties, 399.

C[erthia] *picta, blue and white striped or pied creeper (cf. Edwards, 1760, 2: 190, 220, pl. 300): *nomen nudum*—Black and White Warbler (*Mniotilta varia* [L.]); listed, 289 *bis*.

The "blue" of the description is more properly blue-black. Edwards received a specimen from Bartram.

C[erthia] pinus, the pine creeper: Northern Pine Warbler (*Dendroica pinus pinus* [Wilson]); listed, 289 *bis*.

This is the Pine Creeper of Catesby (1731, *1:* 61, pl. 61), not of Edwards (1760, *2:* 139–141, pl. 277), the latter being the principal basis of *Certhia pinus* Linné (1766: 187). The former is the Northern Pine Warbler; the latter, the Blue-Winged Warbler, which is accounted for on page 292 as "P. aureus alis ceruleis." J. A. Allen (1876a: 26–27) and Coues (1876: 101) were too hasty in identifying Bartram's *Certhia pinus* as the latter species.

Certhia *rufa, little brown variegated creeper: *nomen nudum*—Brown Creeper (*Certhia familiaris americana* Bonaparte) (cf. Harper, 1942d: 214); listed, 289 *bis*.

Cervus *sylvaticus. The American deer: Virginia White-tailed Deer

(*Odocoileus virginianus* [Boddaert]); at Lake George, Fla., 110. *See also* Deer, Roebuck.

On various other pages (e.g. 188, 200) there are references to Deer with apparently sufficient descriptive matter to validate the name *sylvaticus*. However, it is antedated by *Cervus virginianus* Boddaert (1784).

Chactaws. *See* Indians—Choctaws.

Chains, silver and gold, worn by Indians, 503.

Chain-carriers, in surveying party in upper Georgia, 35.

Chairs, stuffed with long moss, 88.

Chalk: on the White Plains, La., 431; at the White Cliffs, 435.

Chalmers (or "Chalmer"), Doctor Lionel: a physician of Charleston, S.C.; conference with, 3, 307.

"Dr. Lionel Chalmers . . . was for many years the leader of scientific activity in South Carolina . . . A graduate of Edinburgh, he was for forty years a physician in Charleston. He recorded observations on meteorology from 1750 to 1760 . . . and published also valuable papers on pathology. He was the host and patron of many naturalists, such as the Bartrams." (Goode, 1888: 36.) He acted as agent for Dr. John Fothergill, of London, in supervising the southern travels of William Bartram from 1773 to 1777. He died in 1777, at the age of 62. (See also Darlington, 1849: 464–465; Kelly and Burrage, 1920: 204; W. Bartram, 1943: 134, 172, 200.)

Chamaerops ("Chamerops"), dwarf creeping: saw palmetto (*Serenoa repens* [Bartr.] Small); fruit eaten by Bears in Florida, xxv. *See also* Corypha obliqua; Corypha repens; Palmetto; Palmetto, dwarf; Palmetto, saw.

Chameleon, green: *Anolis carolinensis* (Voigt); prey of Rough Green Snake and Swallow-tailed Kite, 275. *See also* Lizard, green.

Chaplets, in sanctuary at Otasse, Ala., 454.

Character, of American aborigines, 483–493.

C[haradrius] ("Charadrus") *maculatus, the great field spotted plover (cf. Edwards, 1750, 3: 140, pl. 140, and 1751, 4: 245, as "spotted Plover" or "Pluvialis viridis maculatus ventre nigro, Canadensis"): *nomen nudum*—probably American Golden Plover (*Pluvialis dominica dominica* [Müller]), although the symbol * is erroneous in this case; listed, 296.

C[haradrius] ("Charadrus") *minor, the little sea side ring necked plover: *nomen nudum*—perhaps composite, including Semipalmated Plover (*Charadrius semipalmatus* Bonaparte), Wilson's Plover (*C.*

wilsonia wilsonia Ord), and Piping Plover (*C. melodus* Ord); listed, 296.

Charadrius ("Charadrus") vociferus, the kildea or chattering plover (cf. Catesby, 1731, *1*: 71, pl. 71): Killdeer (*Charadrius vociferus vociferus* L.); listed, 296.

Chariot; of Governor Chester, 414.

Charleston, S.C.; embarked for, 1; arrived at, 2; forwarding collections to, 28, 48, 97; Creeks sending deputies to, 55; caged Rice-birds in, 297; arrival at, and excursions about, 307; set off from, 308; road from, to Cherokee country, 317; John Stuart residing in, 327; cheese obtained in, 344; coming from, 351; horses from Vale of Cowee sold in, 356; impressions of its inhabitants, 360; flowering season in Charleston and the North Carolina mountains compared, 363; journeys to and from, 365; education of halfbreed children in, 449; built by English, 465; return to, from Georgia, 469; arrived at, 470; set off from, 470; coming from, 499; white people's goods introduced from, 500.

For contemporary accounts of Charleston, see Schoepf (1911, *2*: 164–223) and Carroll (1836, *1*: 501–533).

Charlotia: also known as Rollestown, a settlement founded about 1764 by Denys Rolle on the St. John's River between the present East Palatka and San Mateo, Putnam County, Fla. (Palatka quadrangle); arrival at and description of, 93–96; a pawpaw growing near, 171; Indian town on the St. John's below, 304.

"Rolles Town, Mount Royal, and three or four others of less note have seen too many wretches fall victims to hunger and ill usage. . . . Rolles Town in particular has been the sepulchre of above four hundred such victims." (Romans, 1776: 270.)

At various times 200 whites were brought in, but difficulties arose. Rolle went over in person and settled the whole again with 150 Negroes under different overseers. In 1782 there were 79 working Negroes, 27 children, 200–300 cattle, 100 hogs, and many oxen. 15,000 trees were tapped for turpentine (Shelburne Papers *66*: 685–688).

"Lord Rolle obtained a grant of land on the St. John's, which he named Charlotia. To this place he transported nearly three hundred miserable females, who were picked up about the purlieus of London. His object was to reform them, and make of them good members of society. They all died in a few years." (Williams, 1837: 188.)

The locality, nearly deserted by 1939, was still known to some as Rollestown; but it is named "Rivercrest" on the chart of St.

John's River (Palatka to Lake George, 1938). *See also* Rolle, Denys.

Charlotteville: a variant spelling of Charlotia (*q.v.*); iv; great mound near, 521.

Chat, yellow breasted (oenanthe, Cat[esby,] motacilla trochilus, Linn.) (cf. Catesby, 1730, *1:* 50, pl. 50): Yellow-breasted Chat (*Icteria virens virens* [L.]); account of, 302. *See also* Garrulus australis, Motacilla trochilus.

Chattahoochee ("Chata Uche"): a former Lower Creek town on the Chattahoochee River in western Georgia, probably in Troup County (Swanton, 1922: pl. 2); listed, 463.

Chattahoochee ("Chata Uche") or Apalachicola ("Apalachucla"): a river (the Chattahoochee) arising in northeastern Georgia, forming the boundary between Alabama and Georgia in the lower half of its course, and taking the name of Apalachicola below the junction with the Flint; Flint River an arm of, 384; Pintchlucco a branch of, 387; crossed, 388. *See also* Apalachicola, Commentary for p. 388.

Chatuga: a Cherokee town, apparently on the upper Tellico River, Monroe County, Tenn. (Romans' map of 1776, as "Chattoogee"; Mooney, 1900: 536; Swanton, 1922: pl. 7, as "Chatiqui"); listed, 373.

Checlucca-ninne (properly Tcułako-nini): a former Okfuskee settlement on Chattahoochee River in western Georgia, probably in Troup County (Swanton, 1922: 249, pl. 2, as "Chułakonini"); listed, 463.

Cheese; in Georgia, 19, 311; repast of, 344, 349, 361.

Chehaw (properly Chiaha): a former Creek town on the west bank of Chattahoochee River, 3 or 4 miles below the mouth of Uchee Creek, in Russell County, Ala. (Taitt, 1916: 545 [but not the editorial footnote]; Swanton, 1922: 169, pl. 2, as "Chiaha [5a]"; Columbus, Ga., quadrangle); crossed river at, 457; listed, 464.

Chelone: turtle-head (probably *C. glabra* L.); along the upper Savannah River, Ga., 321.

Chelowe (properly Chilhowee); a former Cherokee town on Tellico River, Monroe County, Tenn., near the North Carolina boundary (Mooney, 1900: pl. 3; *Bur. Am. Ethnol. Bull., 30,* Pt. I: 267, 1907); listed, 373.

Cherokees. *See* Indians—Cherokees.

Cherokee country: in Bartram's usage, parts of northwestern South Carolina, northern Georgia, western North Carolina, and eastern Tennessee; road to, from Charleston, 317; Jore mountain highest land in, 353, 361; yaupon in, 359; return from, 375.

Cherokee or Alleghany ("Alegany") or Appalachian ("Apalachean") mountains: the Blue Ridge; as boundary of the Piedmont, 32; the Great Ridge a projection of, 42; source of Altamaha River in, 52; Indigo Bunting in, 299; sources of Savannah River in, 316; in South Carolina, 337; Mount Magnolia in, 338; project for going beyond, 372; source of Coosa River in, 408; source of Cape Fear River in, 478; mounds, terraces, and chunk yards in region south of, 520.

Cherokee River: Little Tennessee River in Georgia, North Carolina, and Tennessee (perhaps including also the upper part of the main Tennessee River); course of, 339. *See also* Tennessee River.

Cherokee tongue, Indian speaking only in, 362.

Cherries: *Prunus* spp.; in Pennsylvania, 298.

Cherries, bird: perhaps *Prunus pensylvanica* L. f.; compared with berries of *Myrica inodora*, 405.

Chesapeake ("Chesapeak"), bay of; navigation in, 68.

Chest; forwarded from Savannah to St. John's River, Fla., 64; on an island in the St. John's, 96.

Chester, Governor [Peter]: Governor of West Florida; meeting with, 414–415; his palace, 416 (cf. Roberts, 1763: pl. facing p. 11).

Governor Chester arrived in West Florida in 1770 and continued in office "until the province was lost to Spain in 1781. . . . One of the main problems which faced Chester was that of Indian relations. . . . His administration was lethargic. Apparently he never visited the western part of the province during his stay of eleven years in West Florida. He quarreled with the military and his attitude toward the assembly was overbearing and high-handed. With his secretary, Philip Livingston, Junior, he was charged with grave irregularities in office and the home government was investigating his conduct at the time of the fall of the province." (C. Johnson, 1943: 76.)

Chestnut(s) ("chesnut[s]"): *Castanea dentata* (Marsh.) Borkh.; live-oak acorns eaten like chestnuts by Indians, 85; Cherokee habitations roofed with bark of, 367; in Butler or adjacent county, Ala., 400; in Escambia or adjacent county, 403; compared in taste with water chinquapin, 409. *See also* Fagus castanea.

Chewase: an unidentified Cherokee town on a branch of Tennessee River—perhaps at the present Robbinsville, Graham County, N.C. ("Chewochee" on Hunter's map of 1751); listed, 373.

Chewe: a former Cherokee town on Cheoah River, about Robbinsville, Graham County, N.C. (Nantahala quadrangle) (cf. "Cheowe" on Hunter's map of 1730; Mooney, 1900: 538, pl. 3); listed, 373.

Chickasaw ("Chicasaw") River. *See* Tombigbee or Chickasaw River.

Chickasaw territories: including parts of northern Alabama, northern Mississippi, and western Tennessee; 408.

Chickens: *Gallus gallus* (L.); prey of Four-lined Chicken Snake, 276; notes compared with those of a frog, 278. *See also* Cock; Fowl, common domestic; Hen(s).

Chicken bird. *See* Lucar lividus.

Chief(s), (Indian); at feast at Talahasochte, Fla., 236; functions and attributes of war chiefs, 496–497; a blind old chief at Mucclasse, Ala., 499.

The story told by the blind old chief is strongly reminiscent of Adair's account (1775: 277) of the "wolf-king" of Mucclasse returning from Charleston with a back-load of English goods. John Ellis, in a letter to Alexander Garden, April 8, 1761 (J. E. Smith, 1821, *1*: 508), refers to the relations of the "wolf king" with the people of Georgia. Gordon (in Mereness, 1916: 385) mentions an aged "Wolf King" who visited Pensacola in 1764 and spoke of his experiences in Georgia and Carolina; he then looked a hundred years old. In a communication to Governor James Wright, of Georgia, and to John Stuart, Superintendent of Indian Affairs, the Wolf King proposes a cessation of trade for two years to bring the rebellious and murderous Indians to humility (Shelburne Papers 60: 93–95). The document is dated at Mucclasse, April 29, 1766, and signed by James Germany, interpreter. Taitt (1916: 509–510, 541) records his dealings with the Wolf King of Mucclasse in 1772. Fagin (1933: 185–186) is inclined to consider Bartram's account the inspiration for Mrs. Hemans' poem, "The Aged Indian."

China brier (Smilax pseudo China; Smilax aspera, etc.): *Smilax pseudo-china* L. or *S. bona-nox* L. (cf. Fernald, 1944: 32–38); contee made from, 241. *See also* Contee; Smilax, pseudo China.

"All of the southeastern Indians made flour out of the roots of the China briar or *Smilax*, but when the Seminole Indians reached southern Florida they found the Indians employing the roots of the *Zamia integrifolia*. They gave the same name, kunti, to this that they had employed for the roots of the China briar, and when they wished to distinguish the two called the *Zamia* kunti hatki, 'white kunti,' and the *Smilax* kunti tcati, 'red kunti.' Clay MacCauley (1887) describes the method of extracting the flour of the *Zamia*." (J.R.S.) (Cf. W. Bartram, 1943: 169–170; Porcher, 1869: 616–617; Hedrick, 1919: 538; Small, 1933: 311; Fernald and Kinsey, 1943: 140–142.)

Chinese language, 458.

Chinese screens, 132.

Chionanthus: old man's beard (*C. virginica* L.); on Colonel's Island, Ga., 7; about St. Mary's River, Ga.–Fla., 24; in coastal swamps, 29; in Lime-Sink Region, 30; in Southern Red Hills, 32; near Deep Creek, Putnam County, Fla., v, 172; along upper Savannah River, Ga., 321.

Chipping bird. *See* Passer domesticus.

Chironia: marsh pink (*Sabatia* spp.); beauty, xviii; in Brunswick County, N.C., 472.

Chironia *pulcherrima ("Pillcherima"): *nomen nudum*—marsh pink (*Sabatia* sp.); probably on the Brantley-Glynn county boundary, Ga., 19.

    "*Chironia*. There are in the moist Savanas of Carolina & Florida many species of this charming plant, there called Savana Pinks. perhaps this species may be Walters. *C. dodecandra*[.]" (Bartram to Muhlenberg, September 6, 1810; Muhlenberg Letters: 137.)

Chockeclucca (properly Tcahki łako): a former Okfuskee settlement on Chattahoochee River in western Georgia, perhaps in Heard County (Swanton, 1922: 249, pl. 2, as "Chakiłako"); listed, 463.

Chote (other spellings: Chota, Echota, Itsati): a former Cherokee town on Sautee Creek, White County, Ga., where a great mound existed (Hunter's map of 1730; Mouzon's map of 1775; Mooney, 1900: 523, 527, pl. 3; Dahlonega quadrangle); listed, 374.

Chote (more properly Echota or Itsati) great: an important former Cherokee town on the south side of Little Tennessee River, a short distance below Citico Creek, in Monroe County, Tenn. (Hunter's map of 1751; Mooney, 1900: pl. 3; *Bur. Am. Ethnol. Bull., 30*, Pt. I: 413, 1907; Swanton, 1922: pls. 6, 7; Loudon quadrangle); listed, 373.

    It was the ancient capital and sacred "peace town" of the nation; likewise the home town of the noted chief Ata-kullakulla (*q.v.*).

Christians, several among Alachua Indians, 186.

Chrysocoma: some species of *Elephantopus, Vernonia,* or related genus; near Suwannee River, Fla., 242.

Chuaclahatche: a former Upper Creek town, apparently on the present Chewockeleehatchee Creek in northeastern Macon County, Ala. (Taitt's map of 1772, as "half way house"; Geol. Map of Alabama, 1894; Swanton, 1922: 245); listed, 463.

Chuck-will's-widow. *See* Caprimulgus lucifugus, Whip-poor-will.

Chunk yard. *See* Indian country, etc.

Church bells, at Apalachean Old Fields, Fla., 233.

Cicadae, or locusts: cicadas (family Cicadidae); noise of, 274.

Circaea ("Circea"): probably enchanter's nightshade (*C. quadrisulcata* [Maxim.] Franch. & Sav. var. *canadensis* [L.] Hara); along upper Savannah River, Ga., 321.

Circus: in this case, probably equivalent to chunk yard; at Sticoe, Rabun County, Ga., 345.

Cistus: probably rock-rose (*Helianthemum* spp.); near Suwannee River, Fla., 242; near Long Pond, Levy County, 248.

Citra (lapsus for Citrus?), ambrosial: perhaps orange (*Citrus* sp.); on Isle of Palms, Lake George, Fla., 157.

Citron, great sweet scented: *Citrus medica* L.; proposed culture in Georgia, 461.

Citruels or Citruls: watermelons (*Citrullus vulgaris* Schrad.); at Cuscowilla, Fla., 193; at Palatka, 303–304; cultivation by Indians, 511. See also Cucurbita citrullus; Melons; Watermelons.

Citrus: a genus of Rutaceae, comprising the oranges, lemons, limes, etc.; in the tropics, xv.

Citrus aurantium: bitter-sweet orange (*C. aurantium* L.); in the tropics, xv; near Alachua Savanna, Fla., 187; proposed culture in Georgia, 460.

Citrus limon: lemon (*C. limonia* Osbeck; syn., *C. medica* var. *limon* L.); proposed culture in Georgia, 461.

Citrus *verrucosa: *nomen nudum* (Merrill, 1945: 34)—undetermined; proposed culture in Georgia, 461.

Clams: probably including such species as the Hard Clam (*Venus mercenaria* L.) and the Soft Clam (*Mya arenaria* L.); about Georgia coastal islands, 68.

Clams (or clam shells), little (or small or white), called les coquilles ("coquelles" or "coqueles"): probably pelecypod mollusks of the genus *Rangia* (family Mactridae); at The Rigolets, La., 421; at Tangipahoa River, 424; on the White Plains, 431.

　　Prof. Clair A. Brown (*in litt.*, July 24, 1941) refers to the "little clams" on the White Plains as *Rangia* shells, but adds that he has not been able to locate them in that area. Conrad (1834a: 126–128) discusses the deposits of *Rangia cyrenoides* Des Moulins along the Gulf of Mexico between Mobile Bay and the Mississippi River.

Clarendon, or Cape Fear River. See Cape Fear River.

Clennuse: a former Cherokee town, at the site of the present Murphy, Cherokee County, N.C. (Mooney, 1900: 535, pl. 3, as "Tlanusiyi"; cf. "Connusse" and "Quanasse" in this vicinity on Hunter's map of 1730); listed, 373.

Cleome *lupinifolia: spider-flower (*Cleome* sp. or *Neocleome* sp.) (cf. Merrill, 1945: 24–25); described, at mouth of Tangipahoa River, La., 425.

"*Cleome lupinifolia* most like C. 5phylla Wild." (Bartram to Muhlenberg, September 6, 1810; Muhlenberg Letters: 137).

Clethra: latherbush (probably *C. alnifolia* L.); about St. Mary's River, Ga.–Fla., 24; near Deep Creek, Putnam County, Fla., 172.

Clethra alnifolia (cf. Catesby, 1731, *1:* 66, pl. 66): latherbush (*C. alnifolia* L.); on Colonel's Island, Ga., 6.

Cliffs, high painted, on the Mississippi: probably the White Cliffs, near Port Hudson, La. (Bayou Sara quadrangle); passed under, 432. *See also* White Cliffs.

Climate, favorable for crops in Suwannee River region, Fla., 234.

Clinopodium ("Olinopodium"): basil (*Clinopodium* sp.); near Suwannee River, Fla., 242.

Clitoria (or "Clitorea"): butterfly pea (*C. mariana* L.); at Lake Dexter, Fla., 155; west of Deep Creek, Putnam County, 173; near Lake Lochloosa, 181; described, at Long Pond, Levy County, 243.

Cloak, worn by Indians, 502.

Clothes (or "cloths"): fire for drying, 387; removed in crossing a creek, 445; refitted with, at Augusta, 460; old exchanged for new at the busk, 509, 510.

Clothing (or "cloathing"): purchased by the Seminoles, 212; procured from Bear and Deer, 214; of Indians, 502–504.

Cloves: dried flower buds of an East Indian tree (*Eugenia aromatica* [L.] Baill.); a plant smelling like, 43; compared with *Illicium*, 442. *See also* Caryophyllus.

Cluale (properly Hoɫiwahali): a former Upper Creek town on the north side of Tallapoosa River, south of Ware, Elmore County, Ala. (Swanton, 1922: 257, pl. 2; soil map of Elmore County, 1914); listed, 463.

Clubs; Negroes armed with, 472.

Coach-whip snake. *See* Snake, coach-whip.

Coal, on an island in Mississippi River, 433.

Cochineal, Suwannee River region suitable for production of, 234.

Cochineal insect: *Coccus cacti* L. (J.W.C. III); described, near Salt Springs, Fla., 163.

Cochleae ("Cochlae" or "Cochlea") (cf. Linné, 1767, *1:* 1073): gastropod mollusks (class Gastropoda); various species on St. John's River at Charlotia, 93, and above Lake George, Fla., 114.

The molluscan names on page 93 seem to represent a curious mixture of typographical errors and nomenclatural confusion. At least most of them are probably not to be regarded as normal binomials, consisting of a generic and a specific name. The second term of the combination, in most cases, seems to be a generic name, while the first term may serve to designate a supergeneric grouping: *Cochlea* for gastropods, *Concha* for pelecypods, and *Haliotis* for limpetlike gastropods (R.A.M.). With this interpretation, and with typographical errors corrected, the names might stand as follows: Cochleae, Cochlea Helix, Cochlea labyrinthus, Cochlea Voluta; Concha Mytilus, Concha Ostrea, Concha Pecten; Haliotis Auris marina, Haliotis Patella.

Coch[lea H]elix ("Cochelix"): apparently intended to designate some gastropod mollusk of the genus *Helix;* on St. John's River at Charlotia, Fla., 93. See note under Cochleae.

Coch[lea] *labyrinthus (cf. *Buccinum labyrinthus* Gmelin, 1790): *nomen nudum*—some undetermined gastropod mollusk, perhaps *Viviparus georgianus* (Lea); on St. John's River at Charlotia, Fla., 93. See note under Cochleae.

Coch[lea] voluta: apparently intended to designate some gastropod mollusk of the genus *Voluta,* but actually perhaps *Pomacea paludosa* (Say); on St. John's River at Charlotia, Fla., 93. See note under Cochleae.

Cock, domestic: *Gallus gallus* (L.); crowing compared with that of Wild Turkey, 83. *See also* Chickens; Fowl, common domestic; Hen(s).

Cocos nucifera: coco palm (*C. nucifera* L.); in the tropics, xv.

Cod. See Trout, Sea- .

Coffee: *Coffea* spp.; brought by Indians from Cuba, 227; breakfasting on, 349.

Coffins, used by Choctaws, 516.

Colchicum: autumn crocus (*Colchicum* spp.); elegance, xviii.

Collar, worn by Indians, 503.

Collars [horse?], stuffed with long moss, 88.

Collections: of seeds and roots, 210; placed on board a vessel on St. John's River, 305; shipped to Liverpool, 306–307; completed in Georgia, 469.

Collinsonia, a species of: apparently stone-root (*Micheliella anisata* [Sims] Briq.) (cf. Mohr, 1901: 15); as a febrifuge, in Baldwin or adjacent county, Ala., 411–412.

"*Collinsonia.* Not, mentioned by Walt or Wild." (Bartram to Muhlenberg, September 6, 1810; Muhlenberg Letters: 137.)

Colonel, the: Colonel Barnet; settling a controversy between surveyors and Indians, 40. *See also* Barnet, Colonel.

[Colonel's Island.] *See* Island near Sunbury, Ga.

Colonies, Northern British (of America), emigrants from, in Mobile, 404.

Colts: *Equus caballus* L., young; preyed on by Cougar, 46. *See also* Horse(s).

Columba Caroliniensis, the turtle dove (cf. Catesby, 1730? *1:* 24, pl. 24): Eastern Mourning Dove (*Zenaidura macroura carolinensis* [L.]); listed, 290 *bis*. *See also* Dove; Dove, turtle.

C[olumba] migratoria, the pigeon of passage or wild pigeon (cf. Catesby, 1730? *1:* 23, pl. 23): Passenger Pigeon (*Ectopistes migratorius* [L.]); listed, 290 *bis*. *See also* Pigeon, wild.

C[olumba] passerina, the ground dove: Eastern Ground Dove (*Columbigallina passerina passerina* [L.]); listed, 290 *bis*. *See also* Doves, Catesby's ground.

Colymbus (cf. Colymbus *colubrinus, p. 295): probably Florida Water-turkey (*Anhinga anhinga colubrina* [Bartram]; syn., A. a. *leucogaster* [Vieillot]); at Watermelon? Pond, Alachua County, Fla., 249.

Colymbus arcticus, the great speckled diver (cf. Edwards, 1750, *3:* 146, pl. 146; and 1751, *4:* 246; Linnaeus, 1758, *1:* 135): presumably Pacific Loon (*Gavia arctica pacifica* [Lawrence]); listed, 295.

If Bartram merely took this name from the literature, it applies best to the Pacific Loon (a subspecies occurring rarely on the coast of Eastern North America). However, any observations of his own are much more likely to have been on the Red-throated Loon (*Gavia stellata* [Pontoppidan]) than on the Pacific Loon. These two species were more or less confused by Edwards, and also by Linnaeus in 1758.

C[olymbus] auritus et cornutus, the little eared brown dobchick ("dobekick") (cf. Edwards, 1750, *3:* 145, pl. 145, and 1751, *4:* 246): American Horned Grebe (*Podiceps auritus cornutus* [Gmelin]); listed, 295.

Colymbus cauda elongata. *See* Snake Birds.

C[olymbus] *colubrinus, cauda elongata, the snake bird of Florida: Florida Water-turkey (*Anhinga anhinga colubrina* [Bartram]; syn., A. a. *leucogaster* [Vieillot]); listed, 295. *See also* Colymbus, Snake Birds.

The partial description on page 295, together with the full description on pages 132–133 (where the only technical name applied is the polynomial "Colymbus cauda elongata"), seems to validate the name *colubrinus*. The place where the full description is inserted in Bartram's narrative suggests the designation of the St. John's River just above Lake Dexter as the type locality.

C[olymbus] *Floridanus, the great black cormorant of Florida, having a red beak: Florida Cormorant (*Phalacrocorax floridanus floridanus* [Bartram]); syn., *Carbo floridanus* Audubon) (cf. Harper, 1942d: 219–220); listed, 295.

Colymbus *migratorius, the eel crow (cf. "Corvus aquaticus" in Linné, 1766, *1*: 216–217): *nomen nudum*—Double-crested Cormorant (*Phalacrocorax floridanus migratorius* [Barton]; syn., *Carbo auritus* Lesson); listed, 295.

Barton (1799a: 17) makes it plain that this is the Double-crested Cormorant, and his description of the "Colymbus migratorius of Bartram" validates the specific name. The type locality is "the neighbourhood of Philadelphia." On eels as the food of this bird, see Bent (1922: 248).

C[olymbus] minor fuscus, little crested brown dobchick ("dobekick") (cf. Catesby, 1732, *1*: 91, pl. 91; Linnaeus, 1758, *1*: 136): doubtless Pied-billed Grebe (*Podilymbus podiceps podiceps* [L.]), although not crested; listed, 295.

"Dobekick" is evidently a typographical error for "dobchick." Catesby writes "Dopchick"; Edwards, "Dob-chick." In Bartram's own copy of the *Systema* of 1758, he has written on the margin of page 136, "Pied Bill Dobchick."

C[olymbus] *musicus, the great black and white pied diver or loon: *nomen nudum*—Common Loon (*Gavia immer* [Brünnich]); listed, 295. *See also* Loons.

Commelina: day-flower (*Commelina* sp.); along upper Savannah River, Ga., 321.

Compass, involved in a controversy with an Indian chief, 40.

Conch shell(s): in these cases, perhaps one or more species of the gastropod genus *Busyon* (R.A.M.) (cf. Wyman, 1875: 56–57); full of black drink at Otasse, Ala., 452; sounded as a signal in an Indian town, 512.

Concha mytilus ("mytulus"): apparently intended to designate some pelecypod mollusk of the genus *Mytilus* or a related genus (R.A.M.); on St. John's River at Charlotia, Fla., 93. See note under Cochleae.

Conc[ha] ostrea ("Concostrea"): apparently intended to designate some species of oyster (probably *Ostrea virginica* Gmelin); on St. John's River at Charlotia, Fla., 93. See note under Cochleae.

Conc[ha] pecten ("peeton"): apparently intended to designate some

species of scallop (genus *Pecten*) (R.A.M.); on St. John's River at
Charlotia, Fla., 93. See note under Cochleae.

Concha *venerea: *nomen nudum*—possibly Hard Clam (*Venus* sp.);
on St. Simon's Island, Ga., 60.

Concubine, fleeing from a prince of Talahasochte, 244.

Congress of Augusta. See Augusta.

Conisca: an unidentified Cherokee town on a branch of Little Tennessee River, but perhaps identical with Connuca on Cartoogeechaye
Creek, near Franklin, N.C. (Hunter's map of 1730; Cowee quadrangle); listed, 373.

Conjurers. See Priest, high.

Contee ("conte"): a jelly made from China brier (apparently either
Smilax pseudo-china L. or *S. bona-nox* L.); at Talahasochte, Fla.,
241; manufacture described, 241. See also China brier; Smilax,
pseudo China.

Convallaria ("Convalaria"), perfumed: perhaps Alleghanian lily-of-
the-valley (*C. montana* Raf.), though apparently not otherwise recorded from so far south; between Little and Broad Rivers, Ga.,
322.

Convallaria ("Convalaria") majalis: not *C. majalis* L., but Alleghanian
lily-of-the-valley (*C. montana* Raf.) (cf. Gray, 1841: 28; Fernald,
1944: 12–14); xvii; at Falling Creek, Rabun County, Ga., 342; near
Wayah Gap, N.C., 362. See also Lily of the valley.

Convallaria ("Convalaria") racemosa: false Solomon's seal (*Smilacina
racemosa* [L.] Desf.); along upper Savannah River, Ga., 321.

Convolvulus (or "Convolvulous"): a genus of Convolvulaceae, comprising the bindweeds and—in Linnaean usage—the sweet potato
and other species now placed in different genera; usefulness, xvii;
various species on St. John's River above Lake Dexter, Fla., 136;
west of Deep Creek, Putnam County, 173; near Lake Lochloosa,
180.

Convolvulus, with large, white, sweet-scented flowers: probably moon
flower (*Calonyction aculeatum* [L.] House); on Lake George, Fla.,
253. See also next entry.

Convolvulus, or perhaps an Ipomoea ("Ipomea"), with a white flower
and a thin tube: moon flower (*Calonyction aculeatum* [L.] House);
on St. John's River above Lake Dexter, Fla., 136–137. See also preceding entry.

Convolvulus, palmated: perhaps a morning-glory, *Operculina dissecta*
(Jacq.) House; at Long Pond, Levy County, Fla., 243. See also
next entry.

Convolvulus, palmated leaved (Convol. dissectus): a morning-glory, *Operculina dissecta* (Jacq.) House (cf. W. Bartram, 1943: 201, fig. 15; Merrill, 1945: 25); described, on Drayton's Island in Lake George, Putnam County, Fla., 104. *See also* preceding entry.

Convolvulus batata (cf. Catesby, 1736, 2: 60, pl. 60): sweet potato (Ipomoea batatas [L.] Poir.); near Alachua Savanna, Fla., 193; on upper Savannah River, S.C., 375. *See also* Batata(s), Potatoes.

Convol[vulus] dissectus. *See* Convolvulus, palmated leaved.

Coolome (more properly Kolomi or Kulumi): a former Upper Creek town on both sides of Tallapoosa River, about 10 miles east-north-east of Montgomery, Ala. (Taitt's map of 1772; Early's map of 1818; Swanton, 1922: 267–268, pls. 2, 7, and 1946: 146–147); visited and described, 396–397; called at, 449; leaving, 450; listed, 462.

The old town was on the south side of the river, near the present Cook's Station (soil map of Montgomery County, 1930); the new town was on the opposite bank. There is an account of Coolome in Hawkins (1848: 33–34).

Cooper ("Cowper") River: arising in Berkeley County, S.C., about 45 miles north of Charleston, and emptying into Charleston Harbor; crossed, 470.

Coopers, at Cross Creeks, N.C., 477.

Coosa ("Coosau") River: formed by the junction of the Oostanaula and Etowah Rivers at Rome, Ga., and uniting with the Tallapoosa in central Alabama to form the Alabama River; course of, 408; confluence with the Tallapoosa, 447; list of Creek towns on, 463. *See also* Alabama (or "Coosau") River.

Coosauda (properly Koasati): a former Upper Creek town, ¼ mile below Fort Thoulouse in the forks of the Coosa and Tallapoosa Rivers, and about 4 miles southwest of Wetumpka, Elmore County, Ala. (Taitt, map of 1772, and 1916: 536–537; Purcell map of about 1776; Wetumpka quadrangle); listed, 463.

Not below the lower forks of the rivers, as indicated by Swanton (1922: pl. 2).

Coot enrobed in blue: perhaps Purple Gallinule (*Porphyrula martinica* [L.]); at Salt Springs, Fla., 160. See remark under Rallus major subceruleus.

Coot, great blue or slate coloured, of Florida. *See* Fulica Floridana.

Coots, laughing: presumably American Coots (*Fulica americana americana* Gmelin); at Lake Dexter, Fla., 118. *See also* Fulica Floridana.

Copper belly: probably Red-bellied Water Snake (*Natrix erythrogaster erythrogaster* [Forster]); in Florida and Carolina, 276.

Coquilles ("coquelles"). *See* Clams, little.

Corallinus (cf. Corallina, Linné, 1767, *1*, Pt. II: 1304): coral?; on St. Simon's Island, Ga., 60.

Coralloides (cf. Linnaeus, 1753, *2*: 1141, 1145, 1151, 1154): some undetermined lichen; near Suwannee River, Fla., 243.

Coreopsis alternifolia (cf. Elliott, 1823? *2*: 413; Small, 1933: 1444); a composite, *Actinomeris alternifolia* (L.) DC.; along upper Savannah River, Ga., 321.

Coreopsis bidens (cf. Elliott, 1823? *2*: 430; Small, 1933: 1453): beggarticks (*Bidens* sp.); on floating islets in St. John's River, Fla., 130.

Cormorant. *See* Snake Birds.

Cormorant, great black, of Florida. *See* Colymbus Floridanus.

Corn: maize (*Zea mays* L.); on Colonel's Island, Ga., 6; plantations in Liberty County, 10; on hammock land, 65; at Mount Royal, Fla., 100; land fit for, at Lake Beresford, 144; a granary for, at Cuscowilla, 192; at Cuscowilla, 193; Bears and Raccoons fond of, 194; at an Indian village east of Alachua Savanna, 209; plantations near Talahasochte, 226; ridges on old Spanish plantations near Suwannee River, 233; on St. John's River, 254; at Palatka, 304; at Watauga, N.C., 350; fed to Bartram's horse, 351; plantations near Cowee, 354; plantations on Escambia River, Fla., 416; harvested at time of the busk, 509–510; cultivation by Indians, 511. *See also* Zea.

Corn cakes: cornbread, or corn pones (made of *Zea mays* L.); hickory milk an ingredient in, 38; in repast at Cuscowilla, Fla., 186, and at Talahasochte, 241; breakfasting on, 349; in repast at Watauga, N.C., 351.

Corn field(s); patroled by Indians at night, 194; opposite Fort Moore, S.C., 316.

Corn flour: cornmeal (made of *Zea mays* L.); mixed with flour from China brier, 241; eaten during fasting at Otasse, Ala., 456.

Corn, Indian: maize (*Zea mays* L.); on St. Mary's River, Ga.–Fla., 23; on Savannah River above Fort James, Ga., 325; on Savannah River, S.C., 375.

Corn meal: meal made of *Zea mays* L.; at Mobile Bay, Ala., 419.

Corn thief. *See* Sturnus predatorius.

Corn (Zea): maize (*Z. mays* L.); on lower St. John's River, Fla., 77, 92, 93; Suwannee River region suitable for, 234; on lower Tombigbee River, Ala., 409; near The Rigolets, La., 422; on Mississippi River, 430. *See also* Zea.

Cornus alba: probably silky dogwood (*C. amomum* Mill.; syn., *C. alba* Walt.); on Colonel's Island, Ga., 6; along upper Savannah River, 321.

"[Bartram says] that his Cornus alba, p. 321 is the Cornus alba of other botanists" (B. S. Barton, MS, September 2, 1805; Delafield Coll.).

Cornus Florida (cf. Catesby, 1730? *1:* 27, pl. 27): flowering dogwood (*C. florida* L.); on Colonel's Island, Ga., 6; in Southern Red Hills, 32; near Broad River, 44; near Alachua Savanna, Fla., 187; near Three Sisters Ferry, S.C., 309; at Shell Bluff, Ga., 318; along upper Savannah River, 320; in Oconee County, S.C., 334; near Wayah Gap, N.C., 362; in Warren County, Ga., 378; along Chattahoochee River, Ala., 394; in Montgomery or Lowndes Counties, Ala., 398; in southern Lowndes County, 399. *See also* Dog-wood.

Cornus sanguinea (cf. Walter, 1788: 88; Elliott, 1817, *1:* 209): not *C. sanguinea* L., but probably either silky dogwood (*C. amomum* Mill.) or stiff dogwood (*C. foemina* Mill.); on Colonel's Island, Ga., 6; along upper Savannah River, 321.

"He [Bartram] says his Cornus sanguinea, p. 321, is our common Red Willow, or (—— sericea)" (B. S. Barton, MS, September 2, 1805; Delafield Coll.).

Corvus *carnivorus, or raven: *nomen nudum*—Northern Raven (*C. corax principalis* Ridgway); resident in Pennsylvania, 286; listed, 290. *See also* Corvus maritimus.

C[orvus] cristatus, s[eu] pica glandaria, the blue jay (cf. Catesby, 1730? *1:* 15, pl. 15): Northern Blue Jay (*Cyanocitta cristata bromia* Oberholser); listed, 290. *See also* Corvus glandarius.

C[orvus] *Floridanus, pica glandaria minor, the little jay of Florida: Florida Jay (*Aphelocoma floridana* [Bartram]; syn., *A. coerulescens* [Bosc]; cf. Harper, 1942d: 213); listed, 290. *See also* Jay without a crest; Pica glandaria cerulea non cristata.

The use of the symbol ¶ in this place is erroneous.

Corvus *frugivora, or crow (or C. *frugivorus, the common crow): *nomen nudum*—probably composite, including Eastern Crow (*C. brachyrhynchos brachyrhynchos* Brehm) and Fish Crow (*C. ossifragus* Wilson); resident in Pennsylvania, 286; listed, 290.

The two species were always confused until distinguished by Wilson (Ord, 1815: 325).

Corvus glandarius s[eu] corvus cristatus, or blue jay: not the European *C. glandarius* L., but Northern Blue Jay (*Cyanocitta cristata bromia* Oberholser); resident in Pennsylvania, 286. *See also* Corvus cristatus.

C[orvus] *maritimus, the great sea-side crow, or rook: *nomen nudum* —either Northern Raven (*C. corax principalis* Ridgway) or some otherwise undescribed and presumably extinct species or subspecies of Florida (cf. Harper, 1942d: 213); listed, 290. See also Corvus carnivorus.

Corylus: hazelnut (Corylus sp.); along upper Savannah River, Ga., 320.

Corypha *obliqua: "The more or less erect form [of saw palmetto (Serenoa repens [Bartr.] Small)] whose stem has left the ground" (Small, 1930b: 61) (cf. Merrill, 1945: 25); described, on St. Simon's Island, Ga., 61. See also Chamaerops, Corypha repens, Palmetto.

This form is not now recognized as distinct from Serenoa repens.

Corypha *palma (or great Cabbage Palm): nomen nudum—cabbage palmetto (Sabal palmetto [Walt.] Lodd.); on Colonel's Island, Ga., 6; in coastal swamps, 29; on St. Simon's Island, 61; on St. John's River near Charlotia, 93, above Lake George, 114, and above Lake Dexter, Fla., 131; near Alachua Savanna, 187; in Levy County, 222. See also Cabbage tree; Palm(s); Palm tree(s).

Corypha pumila (cf. Small, 1930b: 61): dwarf or blue-stem palmetto (Sabal minor [Jacq.] Pers.; syn., Corypha pumila Walt.); in coastal swamps, 29; on St. Simon's Island, Ga., 61; on St. John's River near Charlotia, Fla., 93.

The "very dwarf species of Palmetto (Corypha pumila stipit. serratis)" (p. 170) is evidently a different species. See Palmetto, a very dwarf species of.

Corypha *repens . . . (Dwarf Saw Palmetto): saw palmetto (Serenoa repens [Bartr.] Small) (cf. Small, 1930b: 61; Merrill, 1945: 25); described, on St. Simon's Island, Ga., 61; on St. John's River at Charlotia, Fla., 94; near Suwannee River, 242. See also Chamaerops; Corypha obliqua; Palmetto; Palmetto, dwarf; Palmetto, saw.

Cos (cf. Linné, 1768, 3: 61–64): probably sandstone; in the middle region of Georgia, 45.

Cotton: for the most part, at least, upland cotton (Gossypium hirsutum L.); on St. Mary's River, Ga.–Fla., 23; on hammock land, 65; on Georgia coastal islands, 67; at Mount Royal, Fla., 100; land fit for, at Lake Beresford, 144; dyed with red bay, 162; Suwannee River region suitable for, 234; on St. John's River, 254; dress of, 313; near The Rigolets, La., 422; on the Mississippi, 430; along Cape Fear River, N.C., 474.

Cotton, annual: upland cotton (Gossypium hirsutum L.); described, 67.

Cotton, West-Indian (or perennial): probably sea-island cotton (Gossypium barbadense L.); described, on Georgia coastal islands, 67; at Lake George, Fla., 253.

This is valuable and apparently overlooked evidence on the date of introduction of sea-island cotton into North America (cf. J. Bartram, 1942: 15, 85; *U. S. Dept. Agric., Farmers Bull., 302:* 26, 1907; Watt, 1907: 272).

Coturnix. *See* Tetrao minor.

Couch. *See* Cabin(s) or couch.

Council: with Indians at Cuscowilla, Fla., 190–191; at Talahasochte, 237–238; of chiefs and warriors, 494, 495, 496; ordering a new habitation for a new family, 514.

Council-house (or "counsel-house" or town-house): at Cuscowilla, Fla., 191; at Talahasochte, 227, 236; at Spalding's Lower Store, 257, 260; at Seneca, S.C., 329; at Sticoe, Rabun County, Ga., 345; described, at Watauga, N.C., 350; of Cherokees, described, 367. *See also* Rotunda, Town house.

Cows (or kine): *Bos taurus* L.; on lower Savannah River, Ga., 310–311; Scotch grass fed to, 430. *See also* Bull, Bullocks, Calf, Cattle, Neat's tongue, Ox, Steers.

Cowskin, whip of, 440.

Cowee ("Cowe"): a former Cherokee town on the Little Tennessee River, at the present West's Mill, Macon County, N.C.; situation, 345; journey to, 349, 352; visited and described, 352–353, 366–371; excursion from, 354–358; set off from, 359; path from Overhills to, 360; return to, 366; ball-play at, 369; listed, 373.

Cowee ("Cowe"), Vale of: valley of Little Tennessee River, from its source near Rabun Gap, Ga., to the vicinity of West's Mill, Macon County, N.C.; passage through, 345–353; northern end described, 352–358.

The "Vale of Keowe" (p. 354) is a *lapsus calami* for Vale of Cowee.

Coweta town, great: a former Lower Creek town on the west side of the Chattahoochee, at the approximate site of Phoenix City, Lee County, Ala. (Taitt's map of 1772; Early's map of 1818; *Bur. Am. Ethnol. Bull., 30,* Pt. I: 669, 1907); nature of, 389; listed, 463. *See also* Comments for page 389.

Cow-ford: on St. John's River at the site of the present Jacksonville, Fla.; passage to, 66; arrived at, 72; mentioned, 74; passing, 306.

Cowkeeper: a Seminole chief at Cuscowilla, Fla.; a trader delegated to treat with, 170; reception by, and conference with, 184–186. See Commentary for p. 184.

Cow-pen: south of Altamaha River, Ga., 18; producing milk, butter, and cheese, 19; on lower Savannah River, 310.

Cowpen bird. *See* Sturnus stercorarius.

Cowper River. *See* Cooper River.

Crabs: probably various species, but perhaps principally Blue Crabs (*Callinectes sapidus* Rathbun); about Georgia coastal islands, 68.

Crab, wild (*Pyrus coronaria*): in this case, not *P. coronaria* L., but perhaps narrow-leaved crab apple (*P. angustifolia* Ait.) (cf. R. M. Harper, 1928: 200); in Montgomery or Lowndes Counties, Ala., 398. *See also* Pyrus coronaria.

Crabcatcher. *See* Ardea maculata cristata.

Cradle, of Choctaw infants, 517.

Crane(s): Florida Sandhill Cranes (*Grus canadensis pratensis* Bartram) (fig. 14); on Altamaha River, Ga., 49; resting on cypresses, 91; on Alachua Savanna, Fla., 188, 201–202; behavior at sunrise, 245; feathers as head ornaments among Indians, 502.

Even if these cranes formerly alighted in trees, as Bartram reports, they are no longer known to do so.

Crane(s), savanna: Florida Sandhill Crane(s) (*Grus canadensis pratensis* Bartram); at Cowpen Lake, Putnam County, Fla., 179; at Alachua Savanna, 190. *See also* Grus pratensis.

Crane, savanna (Grus pratensis): Florida Sandhill Crane (*G. canadensis pratensis* Bartram) (cf. Harper, 1942d: 218–219); behavior near Lake Dexter, Fla., 146–147; described, from the vicinity of the present Bronson, Levy County, 220–221.

The last-mentioned locality constitutes the type locality. The nearest approach to a type specimen is Bartram's drawing in the British Museum (fig. 14).

Crane, whooping (Grus *alba ["alber"]) (cf. Catesby, 1731, *1*: 75, pl. 75): *nomen nudum—Grus americana* (L.); on the Mississippi in the vicinity of Port Hudson, La., 433. *See also* Grus clamator.

Cray-fish: *Cambarus* spp.; south of Altamaha River, Ga., 20; fed upon by White Ibis and Limpkin, 148.

Cray-fish (Cancer *macrourus*): *nomen nudum—Cambarus* sp.; behavior in a branch of Broad River, Ga., 43–44.

Creek; none between Alachua Savanna and Suwannee River, Fla. [except Wacasassa River], 225.

Creek, a very beautiful, with a waterfall upon it, on the side of the Vale of Cowee: Estatoah Creek and Falls, in extreme northern Rabun County, Ga. (map of Chattahoochee National Forest, 1937); described, 347.

Creek, a few miles from Cuscowilla; probably Lochloosa Creek, Alachua County, Fla.; camp at, 251.

Creek, large, of excellent water: Lochloosa Creek, Alachua County, Fla.; came to, 209.

Creek, a large deep, of St. Juan's: Lochloosa Creek, Alachua County, Fla.; crossing, 180.

Creek, a large deep, a branch of the Alabama: apparently Catoma
Creek, Montgomery County, Ala.; passage of, by a raft, 443–445.

Creek, a large and deep, a branch of the Flint: Patsiliga Creek, Taylor County, Ga.; camp near, 383.

Creek, on west side of Cape Fear River, about 40 miles above Ashwood: probably Willis Creek, entering the river at the southern
boundary of Cumberland County, N.C. (soil map of Cumberland
County, 1922); petrified trees on, 477.

Creeks. See Indians—Creeks.

Creek Nation. See Indians—Creeks.

Creeper, blue and white striped or pied. See Certhia picta.

Creeper, little brown variegated. See Certhia rufa.

Creeper, pine. See Certhia pinus.

Creeper, yellow throated. See Parus griseus.

Crescents, tattooed on Indians, 503.

Crescents or gorgets, silver, worn by Indians, 503.

Crib, king's. See King's crib.

Crickets: probably Black Field Crickets (Gryllus assimilis Fabricius)
(J.A.G.R.); note compared with that of Little Tree-frog, 278; size
compared with that of metamorphosed toads, 280.

Crickets, sand: perhaps mole-crickets (Gryllotalpa or related genus)
(J.A.G.R.); in Alachua County, Fla., 218.

Crickets, savanna. See Frog, diminutive species of.

Crinum: a genus of Amaryllidaceae, comprising swamp lilies; in the
tropics, xv.

Crinum, perfumed: probably swamp lily (C. americanum L.); at Lake
George, Fla., 157.

Crinum, called . . . White Lilly: probably swamp lily (C. americanum L.) (cf. Darlington, 1843, 345); on St. Simon's Island, Ga.,
59.

"Crinum——I cant find this charming plant, neither Wildenow
or Walter has it under this name; perhaps a Pancratium. the infundibuliform Nectarium, that characterises this genus might have
escaped my notice. Perhaps Mr. Elliott could procure for you a
specimin & some Roots, as Buffort [Beaufort, S.C.] is but a days
journey from St. Simons, where I found it. The inhabitants call it
White-Lilly." (Bartram to Muhlenberg, September 6, 1810; Muhlenberg Letters: 137.)

Crinum *floridanum: nomen nudum—swamp lily (C. americanum
L.); xvii.

Crocodile(s) (or "crocadiles" or "crocodile alligator" or "allegators"):
American Alligator(s) (Alligator mississipiensis [Daudin]) (fig.
12); at Nassau Sound, Fla., 71; on lower St. John's River, 88, 89;

general account of, at Lake Dexter, including numbers, roaring, attacks on man and fish, nests, eggs, and young, 117–130, 153; crocodile a term synonymous with alligator, 90; on the St. John's above Lake Dexter, 134–136, 138; their thunder as presage of a storm, 140; at Salt Springs, 166, 167; taking prey by surprise, 168; in lakes in Putnam County, 174; at Cowpen Lake, Putnam County, 175; at Alachua Sink, 205–206; in Alachua County, 250; at Lake Pontchartrain, La., 424. See also Alligator(s).

Cropping (of ears); as punishment for adultery, 515.

Cross beak. See Loxia rostro forficato.

Cross beak, blue. See Loxia cerulea.

Cross-Creeks: a small westerly tributary entering Cape Fear River at the present Fayetteville, N.C. (soil map of Cumberland County, 1925), and a town of the same name on this stream; arrived at, 477; town described, 477–478.

   The town was at the junction of Cross and Blount's Creeks, about 1 mile from the river (H.A.R.).

Croton: a genus of Euphorbiaceae, comprising the crotons; at The Rigolets, La., 421.

Crow: Corvus sp.; 148. See also Corvus frugivora.

Crows: either Florida Crows (Corvus brachyrhynchos pascuus Coues) or Fish Crows (C. ossifragus Wilson), or both; imagined presence on floating islands in St. John's River, Fla., 90; depredations near Alachua Savanna, 194, 201.

Crow, carrion. See Vultur atratus; Vulture, coped.

Crow, common. See Corvus frugivora.

Crow, eel. See Colymbus migratorius.

Crow, great sea-side. See Corvus maritimus.

Crown bird. See Ampelis garrulus.

Crucifixes, silver; worn by Alachua Indians, 186.

Crying bird (Ephouskyca), Tantalus *pictus: Florida Limpkin (Aramus guarauna pictus [Bartram]) (cf. Harper, 1942d: 219) (fig. 15); on Altamaha River, Ga., 49; described, from Florida and Georgia, 147–148. See also Tantalus pictus.

Cuba: expeditions of Florida Indians to, 227; trade with Spaniards of, 227.

Cuckoo of Carolina. See Cuculus Caroliniensis.

Cuckoo (Cuculus *Caroliniensis): nomen nudum—Yellow-billed Cuckoo (Coccyzus americanus americanus [L.]); near Lake Lochloosa, Fla., 181. See also Cuculus Caroliniensis.

Cuculus *Caroliniensis, the cuckoo of Carolina (cf. Catesby, 1730? 1: 9, pl. 9): nomen nudum—Yellow-billed Cuckoo (Coccyzus americanus americanus [L.]); listed, 289 bis. See also preceding entry.

Cucumber: *Cucumis sativus* L.; fruit of palmetto royal compared with, 72; fruit of pawpaw compared with, 171.

Cucumber tree (Mag[nolia] acuminata): *M. acuminata* L.; *M. pyramidata* resembling, 340. *See also* Magnolia acuminata.

Cucurbita: a genus of Cucurbitaceae, comprising the gourds, pumpkins, and squashes; faculty of tendrils, xxi.

Cucurbita citrullus (or "citrulus"): watermelon (*Citrullus vulgaris* Schrad.; syn., *Cucurbita citrullus* L.); in the tropics, xv; at Palatka, Fla., 93; near Alachua Savanna, 193. *See also* Citruel, Watermelons.

Cuc[urbita] lagenaria (or "laginaria"): gourd or calabash (*C. lagenaria* L.); near Alachua Savanna, Fla., 193; on Meherrin River, Va., x, 479.

Cuc[urbita] melopepo: bush pumpkin or squash (a variety of *C. pepo* L.) (cf. Bailey and Bailey, 1930: 191); near Alachua Savanna, Fla., 193.

Cuc[urbita] pepo: field pumpkin (*C. pepo* L.); near Alachua Savanna, Fla., 193.

Cucurbita *peregrina. *See* Squash, Wild.

Cucurbita verrucosa (cf. Jefferson, 1782: 68): cymling, a scalloped summer squash (*C. pepo* var. *condensa* Bailey; syn., *C. verrucosa* L.); at Palatka, Fla., 93; near Alachua Savanna, 193.

Culex. *See* Mosquitoes.

Cumberland, county of, N.C.; Cross Creeks the seat of government, 477.

Cumberland Island: the southernmost island on the coast of Georgia, in Camden County; game on, 63; passing by, 63. *See also* Little St. Simon's [Island].

Cunhutke (properly Kan-hatki): a former Upper Creek town on the north side of Tallapoosa River in Elmore County, Ala., just below Coolome and apparently identical with White Ground (Taitt, map of 1772, and 1916: 537, as "white ground"; Swanton, 1922: 269–270, pl. 2); listed, 463.

The site was probably about 2 miles upstream from Judkins Ferry (soil map of Elmore County, 1911).

Cupressus disticha (cf. Catesby, 1730? *1:* 11, pl. 11): either river cypress (*Taxodium distichum* [L.] Richard) or pond cypress (*T. ascendens* Brongn.), or both, the two not being differentiated by Bartram; of Carolina and Florida, xv; in Liberty County, Ga., 10; about St. Mary's River, Ga.–Fla., 24; in coastal swamps, 29; Wild Turkeys on, 83; described, on lower St. John's River, Fla., 90–91; on Amite River, La., 425; along Cape Fear River, N.C., 474. *See also* Cypress, Cypress swamp(s).

Cupressus thyoides. *See* Cedar, white.

Cur-dog: *Canis familiaris* L.; young Wolf compared in size with, 398. *See also* Dog(s).

Curlews: in this case, probably chiefly Hudsonian Curlews (*Numenius phaeopus hudsonicus* Latham); near Amelia Island, Fla., 70.

Curlews: in this case, probably White Ibises or "Spanish Curlews" (*Eudocimus albus* [L.]); imagined presence on floating islands in St. John's River, Fla., 90.

Curlew, dusky and white Spanish. *See* Tantalus fuscus.

Curlew, lesser field. *See* Numenius minor campestris.

Curlew, great sea coast. *See* Numenius magnus rufus.

Curlew, sea side lesser. *See* Numenius cinereus.

Curlews, Spanish: White Ibises (*Eudocimus albus* [L.]); on Altamaha River, Ga., 49; at Nassau Sound, Fla., 71.

Curlews, Spanish, Tantalus albus, Numenius ("Numinus") albus Cat-[esby] (cf. Catesby, 1732, *1*: 82, pl. 82): adult White Ibises (*Eudocimus albus* [L.]); described, from Florida, 148–149. *See also* Tantalus alber, Tantalus fuscus.

Curlews, Spanish, Tantalus *versicolor, Numenius ("Numinus") fuscus Cat[esby] (cf. Catesby, 1732, *1*: 83, pl. 83): immature White Ibises (*Eudocimus albus* [L.]); described, from Florida, 148–149. *See also* Tantalus fuscus.

Curlew, white Spanish. *See* Tantalus alber.

Currants; *Vitis corinthiaca* for, 460.

Cuscowilla (or Alachua ["Allachua"]): a former Seminole town near the northwestern corner of Tuscawilla Lake, about a quarter of a mile east of the center of the present Micanopy, Alachua County, Fla.; set off for, 170; high forests of, 179; conference with, and entertainment by, Indians at, 184–186; cattle there compared with those of Pennsylvania, 190; town and environs described, 191–194; a baygall near, 197; Indians setting off for, 207; road to, 216; compared with Talahasochte, 227; mentioned, 251; founded by Creeks from Georgia, 380; listed, 464.

  In the last reference, Bartram is in error in placing Cuscowilla on the Flint River, unless possibly there was an older town of the same name on that river.

Cuscowilla, lake of: the present Tuscawilla Lake, near Micanopy, Alachua County, Fla. (Arredondo and Williston quadrangles); v; forest near, 183; Indian mound and village near, 184. *See also* Lake, a large and beautiful.

Customs, of American aborigines, 485–493.

Cydonia: a genus of Malaceae, including the quince (*C. oblonga* Mill.); in temperate zone, xv.

Cygnus ferus, the wild swan: Whistling Swan (*Olor columbianus* [Ord]); listed, 294.

Cynips. *See* Gnats (cynips).

Cypress (or cypress tree[s] [Cupressus disticha]): either river cypress (*Taxodium distichum* [L.] Richard) or pond cypress (*T. ascendens* Brongn.), or both, the two not being differentiated by Bartram; on Altamaha River, Ga., 49; formerly growing where salt marshes are, 69; on lower St. John's River, Fla., 90, 93; cypress knees described, 91; house built of, 95; on the St. John's above Lake Dexter, 137; Wood Ibis on, 150; bark covering roofs at Cuscowilla, 192; canoes made of, on Suwannee River, 227; Parrakeets said to hibernate in, 301; timber for the West-India market, 312; houses in Uchee town and at Coolome, Ala., roofed with cypress bark or shingles, 388, 397; buildings of, at Mobile, 404; on upper Tensaw River, 407; on lower Tombigbee River, 410; boat made of, 430; stumps in the White Cliffs, La., 435; grave lined with cypress bark, 515. *See also* Cupressus disticha.

Cypress, a species of, resembling white cedar (Cupressus thyoides): probably identical with white cedar (*Chamaecyparis thyoides* [L.] BSP.); in northern Baldwin County, Ala., 411.

Cypress swamp(s): low area(s), either alluvial or nonalluvial, containing a growth of cypress; at Lake George, Fla., 106; at Lake Dexter, 116, 122; at Lake Pontchartrain, La., 424; near the White Cliffs, 435.

Cyprinus coronarius. *See* Bream, yellow.

Cypripedium: lady's slipper (*Cypripedium* sp.); at Falling Creek, Rabun County, Ga., 342.

Cypripedium calceolus: a European species of lady's slipper (*C. calceolus* L.); pleasing figure, xviii.

Cyrilla: tyty (*C. racemiflora* L.); v; in Lime-Sink Region, Ga., 30; on St. Simon's Island, 61; along Cape Fear River, N.C., 476.

Cyrilla (or "Cyrella") racemiflora: tyty (*C. racemiflora* L.); on Colonel's Island, Ga., 6; in Liberty County, 10; about St. Mary's River, Ga.–Fla., 24; near Deep Creek, Putnam County, Fla., 172.

Dance(s); by Seminoles at Spalding's Lower Store, Fla., 255, 260, 263; among Indians, 504, 521; at Mucclasse, Ala., 507.

Dance, ball-play; among the Cherokees, 369–371.

Dancing; at Talahasochte, Fla., 236; at Mucclasse, Ala., 446; at Alabama, Ala., 447; among Indians, 505–506, 509; at the busk, 510; at a Muscogulge marriage, 514.

Daphne: a genus of ornamental shrubs, of the family Thymelaeaceae; xvi.

Darien (or "Darian"): a settlement in McIntosh County, Ga., near the mouth of Altamaha River, at the site of the present Darien; road to, 12, 13; mentioned, 53.

Darts: spear-heads?; in Screven or Burke Counties, Ga., 462.

Dartmouth: name of a town planned at the junction of the Broad and Savannah Rivers, in Elbert County, Ga.; 324, 326, 328; return to, 366, 372, 373, 375.

   "Petersburg is at the junction of the Savannah and Broad Rivers. This was once among the most prosperous towns in Georgia; but it is now in a state of dilapidation." (White, 1849: 227.) Perhaps the name was changed from Dartmouth to Petersburg on account of the attitude of the Earl of Dartmouth toward the Revolutionists.

   The site is now inundated by the Clark Hill Reservoir.

Dartmouth, earl of: William, second Earl of Dartmouth (1731–1801); a town named in his honor, and a grant obtained by him for the Indian trading company of Georgia, 324.

   In 1765 and 1766 he was president of the board of trade and foreign plantations; in 1772 he held the same office and also that of secretary for the colonies; and in 1775 he became lord privy seal. The next year he advocated the employment of force against the American colonies. Dartmouth College was named after him. Among his papers are many letters from America relating to the struggle for independence. (*Encyclopaedia Britannica*.)

Dates: *Phoenix dactylifera* L.; reported (erroneously) in Okefinokee Swamp, Ga., 25.

Daucus: carrot (*Daucus carota* L.); time for planting, 288.

Dauphin Island: at the west side of the entrance to Mobile Bay, Ala.; passed, 414, 419, 438.

Deadman's Creek: possibly the present Murder Creek, in Conecuh and Escambia Counties, Ala. (see Commentary); leaving, 443.

Death, as punishment for murder, 515.

Deep River: an upper tributary of Cape Fear River, in central North Carolina; x, 478.

Deer (or "dear" or fawns or roebuck or Cervus sylvaticus): Virginia White-tailed Deer (*Odocoileus virginianus* [Boddaert]); on South Mosquito River, Fla., xxv; on Colonel's Island, Ga., 7; fawns preyed upon by great grey eagle, 8; in McIntosh County, 13; south of Altamaha River, 19; at the Buffalo Lick, 39; physic-nut used as a charm in pursuit of, 41; on St. Simon's Island, 58, 63; on Jekyl and Cumberland Islands, 63; eating long moss, 88; on Drayton's Island, Fla., 103; at Lake George, 110; dressed skins dyed with red bay, 162; at Cowpen Lake, Putnam County, 179; on or about Alachua Savanna, 188, 194, 197, 200–201; scarce near Muscogulge towns, 210; hides traded by the Seminoles, 211, 214; Creek name for, 216; skins bartered by Indians to Spaniards in Cuba, 227; range for, near Suwannee River, 235; fawn-skin presented by a family of Talahasochte, 244; fawns prey of Wildcat, 282; bones of, between Little and Broad Rivers, Ga., 322; near Cowee, N.C., 356; hunting ground for, in Alachua region, Fla., 380; plentiful in Florida, 392; in Baldwin or adjacent county, Ala., 412; chaplets of Deer's hoofs, 454; in world of spirits, 498; Indian moccasins made of skins, 502; Indian flute made of tibia, 505. *See also* Buck; Buckskin(s); Cervus sylvaticus; Roebuck; Venison.

Delaware [River and Bay]; sail down, 1.

Delphinium: larkspur (*Delphinium* spp.); along upper Savannah River, Ga., 321; between Little and Broad Rivers, 322; at Loughabber, S.C., 328; *Gilia rubra* resembling, 376; at Flat Rock, Ga., 377. *See also* Larkspur.

Delphinium peregrinum: larkspur (*Delphinium* sp.)—not the European *D. peregrinum* L.; in the Broad River region, Ga., 45.
  "*Delphinium peregrinum,* I believe a nondescript" (Bartram to Muhlenberg, September 6, 1810; Muhlenberg Letters: 137).

Deluge, at the Alligator Hole, Fla., 239.

Demere, Capt. Raimond, his property on St. Simon's Island, Ga., 58.
  Demere was an officer under General Oglethorpe at the Battle of Bloody Marsh (1742) (Mrs. Cate, 1943: 148, 150).

Desert, an endless wild, near Salt Springs, Fla.: the Florida "scrub" (cf. R. M. Harper, 1915: 142–144); described, 163–165.

Desert ("desart"), solitary: rocky ridges in the vicinity of the present Archer, Alachua County, Fla.; described, 218. *See also* Plains, barren.

Diadem(s): of Cherokee youths, 370; as head ornament among Indians, 501–502; made by Indian women, 513.

Dianthus: in this case, probably one of the catchflys, *Silene baldwinii* Nutt. (E.T.W.); near Suwannee River, Fla., 242.

Dionaea (or "Dionea") muscipula: Venus' fly-trap (*D. muscipula* Ellis); motion and volition, xx–xxi; in Brunswick County, N.C., ix, 472; communicated to Old World by John Bartram, 473.

Dioscorea ("Discorea") bulbifera: wild yam-root (*Dioscorea* sp.)— not the Asiatic *D. bulbifera* L.; at Mobile, Ala., 438–439.

Diospyros: persimmon (*D. virginiana* L.); cultivated by the ancients near Little River, Ga., 38; along upper Savannah River, 320; in Warren County, 378.

Diospyros Virginiana. *See* Persimmon.

Diospyros *Virginica (lapsus for "Virginiana") (cf. Catesby, 1738, 2: 76, pl. 76): persimmon (*D. virginiana* L.); on St. John's River above Lake Dexter, Fla., 131. *See also* Persimmon.

Dirca palustris: leatherwood (*D. palustris* L.); at Three Sisters Ferry, Ga., vii, 309; at Shell Bluff, 319.

"Discorea." *See* Dioscorea.

Disease, called water-rot or scald; afflicting cattle and horses on Alachua Savanna, Fla., 207–208.

Diver, great black and white pied. *See* Colymbus musicus.

Diver, great speckled. *See* Colymbus arcticus.

Dobbs, Arthur, Esq.: a former governor of North Carolina; 473.

Dobbs had a sustained interest in botanical subjects. He wrote two letters to John Bartram from abroad in 1749 and 1751, and two others from Brunswick, N.C., in 1760 and 1761 (Bartram Papers, 3: 100–103). He also wrote from Brunswick to Peter Collinson concerning Venus' fly-trap on April 2, 1759, and on January 24, 1760. In the former letter he says: "We have a kind of Catch *Fly Sensitive which closes upon anything that touches it.* It grows in this latitude 34 but not in 35°." (Original in Collinson's smaller volume, p. 254, Linnaean Society of London; copy kindly furnished by the late Chas. B. Montgomery.) This constitutes apparently the first announcement of the discovery of the famous *Dionaea muscipula*. The other letter to Collinson is quoted in part by Brett-James (1925: 265).

Dobbs became governor in 1754, and he died in office on March 28, 1765, a few months before John Bartram's visit to Brunswick. There are a few references to him in the journal of Lord Adam Gordon (Mereness, 1916: 401, 402). Dobbs published a book (1744) on the Hudson Bay region, and he is credited with the discovery of the pollination of flowers by insects (Grant, 1949).

Dobchick ("dobekick"), little crested brown. *See* Colymbus minor fuscus.

Dobchick ("dobekick"), little eared brown. *See* Colymbus auritus et cornutus.

Dodecatheon meadia ("Dodecathean meadea") (cf. Catesby, 1748, 2, appendix: 1, pl. 1): shooting-star (*D. meadia* L.); at Shell Bluff, Ga., 319.

Dog(s): *Canis familiaris* L.; Florida Wolves compared with, 199;

controlling a troop of horses, 222–223; cur dog compared in size with Florida Wildcat, 282; terrified at noise of Gray Foxes, 282; attending a young Indian, 361. See also Cur-dog.

Dog-wood, Cornus Florida (cf. Catesby, 1730? 1: 27, pl. 27): flowering dogwood (C. florida L.); in Butler or adjacent county, Ala., 400; a remarkable grove of, in northwestern Butler County, 401. See also Cornus florida.

Dolichos: probably cowpea (Vigna sinensis Endl.); varieties planted near Alachua Savanna, Fla., 193.

Dotterel ("dotrill"). See Morinella Americana.

Dove: probably Eastern Mourning Dove (Zenaidura macroura carolinensis [L.]); at Lake Dexter, Fla., 154.

Doves, Catesby's ground (cf. Catesby, 1730? 1: 26, pl. 26): Eastern Ground Doves (Columbigallina passerina passerina [L.]); on Colonel's Island, Ga., 8. See also Columba passerina.

Dove, turtle: Eastern Mourning Dove (Zenaidura macroura carolinensis [L.]); in Liberty County, Ga., 11; feeding on Hercules' club, 88. See also Columba Caroliniensis.

Drawings, of curious objects, 48.

Dress, of American aborigines, 501–504.

Drink, black. See Cassine (or black drink).

"Drink, thin": some sort of Indian beverage; served at Cuscowilla, Fla., 184.

Drosera rotundifolia ("Drossea rotundiflolia"): round-leaved sundew (D. rotundifolia L.); an insect-catcher, xx.

Drum: at Talahasochte, Fla., 236; used by Seminoles, 245.

Drum [a fish]: probably either Red Drum (Sciaenops ocellata [L.]) or Black Drum (Pogonias cromias [L.]); about Georgia coastal islands, 67; at Salt Springs, Fla., 166.

Duck(s): species of Anatidae; at Lake Beresford, Fla., and vicinity, 144; young preyed upon by Soft-shelled Turtle, 178; in Suwannee River region, 235; in paintings at Otasse, Ala., 455.

Duck, black white faced. See Anas leucocephala.

Duck, great black. See Anas nigra maxima.

Duck, great fishing. See Mergus major.

Duck, little black and white. See Anas minor picta.

Duck, little brown and white. See Anas rustica.

Duck, round crested. See Mergus cucullatus.

Duck, sprig tail. See Anas caudacuta.

Duck, summer. See Anas sponsa.

Duck, various coloured. See Anas principalis, maculata.

Duck, whistling. See Anas fistulosa.

Duck, great wild, called duck and mallard. *See* Anas fera torquata major.

Dunn's Island: the present Murphy's Island in St. John's River near the mouth of Dunn's Creek, Putnam County, Fla. (Palatka quadrangle); great mound on, 521.

Dunn's Lake: the present Crescent Lake, in Putnam and Flagler Counties, Fla.; Rolle's grant lying on, 95.

Du Pratz ("Duprat"), [Le Page]: author of *Histoire de la Louisiane* (3 vols. Paris, 1758); his account of the Natchez, 465.

"Dyospyros." *See* Persimmon.

Eagle: in this case, any species of the genera *Haliaeetus* or *Aquila;* eyes of a Cherokee chief compared with, 352.

Eagles: in this case, Southern Bald Eagles (*Haliaeetus leucocephalus leucocephalus* [L.]); nesting in cypresses, 91.

Eagle's tail or standard. *See* Calumet.

Eagle, bald (falco leucocephalus): adult Southern Bald Eagle (*Haliaeetus leucocephalus leucocephalus* [L.]); on Colonel's Island, Ga., 8; victimizing the Fish Hawk, 8; at Alachua Savanna, Fla., 199. *See also* Falco leucocephalus.

Eagle, fishing. *See* Falco piscatorius.

Eagle, great grey: immature Southern Bald Eagle (*Haliaeetus leucocephalus leucocephalus* [L.]); on Colonel's Island, Ga., 8. *See also* Eagle, bald; Falco leucocephalus; Falco maximus; Falco regalis.

Eagle, white, Vultura sacra: presumably King Vulture (*Sarcoramphus papa* [L.]), although in this case there is some possibility of confusion with the Southern Bald Eagle (*Haliaeetus leucocephalus leucocephalus* [L.]) (cf. Harper, 1936: 382–383); imperial standard made of its tail feathers, 454–455. *See also* Vultur sacra; Vulture, painted.

Ears: cropping of, threatened against a trader at Mucclasse, Ala., 448–449; ornaments of, among Indians, 501; adultery punished by cropping of, 515.

Earthen-ware; manufactured by Alibamu Indians, 429. *See also* Indian country, etc.; Pottery (or earthen-ware).

East Lake: Lake Dexter, on St. John's River, Lake and Volusia Counties, Fla.; Sandhill Cranes at, 147; passage of, 155.

Echeta (properly Hitchiti): a former Lower Creek town on the east side of Chattahoochee River, 4 miles below Chiaha, i.e. near the Chattahoochee-Stewart county boundary, Ga. (*Bur. Am. Ethnol. Bull., 30,* Pt. I: 551, 1907; Swanton, 1922: 177, pls. 2, 9); listed, 464.

The present Hitchitee Creek joins the Chattahoochee in extreme northwestern Stewart County. This is approximately the site of "Hitchiata" as shown on Taitt's map of 1772.

Echinitis: undetermined (presumably some marine invertebrate); on St. Simon's Island, Ga., 60.

Echium: perhaps false gromwell (*Onosmodium virginianum* [L.] A. DC.); near Long Pond, Levy County, Fla., 248.

Echoclucco, Creek name for horse, 216.

Echoe: a former Cherokee town on the west side of Little Tennessee River, between the present Leeds and Cartoogechaye Creek, Macon County, N.C. (Hunter's maps of 1730 and 1751; Romans' map of 1776; Mooney, 1900: 523, pl. 3); arrived at, 350; listed, 373.

Eclipse, of the moon, on Altamaha River, Ga., 51.

For the date, see Commentary for p. 51.

Eddo ("Ado" or "Adoe") (Arum esculentum): taro (*Colocasia antiquorum* Schott) or a related species; description, cultivation, and utilization, in Georgia, ix, 469.

Edelano, Isle: Drayton's Island, in Lake George, Fla., iv. See Commentary for p. 102.

Edwards, [George]: a British naturalist, particularly known for his *Natural History of Birds* (4 vols. 1743–1751) and his *Gleanings of Natural History* (3 vols. 1758–1764); birds figured in his works, 284; on bird migration, 284.

Edwards was born in 1693 and died in 1773. Coues (1884: xiv) characterized his *Natural History* as "a treatise which easily ranks among the half-dozen greatest works of the kind of the Pre-Linnaean epoch." His total contributions to North American ornithology were of such importance that Coues proposed the name "Edwardsian period" for the years 1748–1758. In the *Gleanings* Edwards presented descriptions and plates of about 23 birds, the specimens of which had been contributed from Pennsylvania by William Bartram. About half of these accounts became the bases for names that were subsequently proposed by Linnaeus and by Gmelin and are still in current use. A letter from Edwards to William has been published (Darlington, 1849: 419–420).

Egan, (Stephen) (cf. Mowat, 1943: 70): Lord Egmont's agent on Amelia Island, Fla.; hospitality of, 65–66; shooting a Pelican, 70; departed for St. Augustine, 72.

Egmont [John James Percival], Lord: owner of a plantation on Amelia Island, Fla., 64, 66.

He was elected a trustee of Georgia in 1749. There is a biographical sketch in Stevens (1847, *1:* 474).

Elk: Eastern Elk or Wapiti (*Cervus canadensis canadensis* [Erxleben]); a few in Appalachian Mountains, 46; bones of, between Little and Broad Rivers, Ga., 322.

Ellis, [John]: a London merchant and crown agent for West Florida; referred to, 472.

Ellis (1710–1766) corresponded with Linnaeus, the Duchess of Portland, Dr. Alexander Garden of Charleston, and others on botanical subjects. He described *Dionaea* in a letter to Linnaeus in 1768, on the basis of specimens brought to England in that year by William Young. For biographical notes, see J. E. Smith (1821, *1*: 79 ff.) and Barnhart (1923).

Elm(s): *Ulmus* spp.; near Charlotia on St. John's River, Fla., 93; near Lake Lochloosa, 181; on Oconee River, Ga., 379; in Pennsylvania, 459; at Macon, Ga., 459. *See also* Ulmus.

Elysian fields: of Alachua, Fla., 188; near Cowee, N.C., 358.

Elysian ("Elisian") springs: Salt Springs, Marion County, Fla.; left, 168.

Elysium ("Elisium"); a portion of St. John's River above Lake Dexter, Fla., so characterized, 146.

Emberiza ciris (or "Ceris"). *See* Linaria ciris, Painted finch.

E[mberiza] *livida, the blue or slate coloured rice bird: *nomen nudum* —perhaps the Rusty Blackbird (*Euphagus carolinus* [Müller]), male and female, or perhaps the male Eastern Cowbird (*Molothrus ater ater* [Boddaert]), in either adult or postjuvenal plumage; listed, 291.

Bartram does not account for the Rusty Blackbird unless by this reference. The symbol † fits this species, but not the Cowbird. Catesby's figure and description of the Cowbird (1730? *1*: 34, pl. 34), which were familiar to Bartram, represent only the female. This may have led Bartram to regard the male as a different species —"the blue or slate coloured rice bird." It is scarcely likely that Alexander Wilson was correct in writing to John Abbot on January 23, 1812 (Torrey-Redfield Coll.) that "the slate-coloured rice bird is a species of Grosbeak"—that is, if he had Bartram's bird in mind. Bartram accounts for the Blue Grosbeak as *Loxia cerulea* (p. 290 bis). Wayne remarks (1910: 108, 111, 132) on the predilection of all three species for rice plantations in South Carolina.

Emberiza oryzivora, (1) the rice bird (cf. Catesby, 1730? *1*: 14, pl. 14; Edwards, 1760, *2*: 173, 220, pl. 291, upper and lower figs.; W. Bartram, 1943: fig. 36): Bobolink (*Dolichonyx oryzivorus* [L.]), either female in any plumage or male in winter plumage; listed, 291. *See also* Rice bird.

Edwards received specimens from Bartram.

E[mberiza] *varia, (2) the pied rice bird: *nomen nudum*—male Bobolink (*Dolichonyx oryzivorus* [L.]) in breeding plumage; listed, 292.

Emigrants from Georgia; met in southern Alabama, 443; captured by Choctaws, 446, 507.

Emperor. *See* Ata-kullakulla.

Empetrum: rosemary (*Ceratiola ericoides* Michx.); west of Spalding's Lower Store, Fla., 171; near Orange Lake, 181; near Suwannee River, 242; near Long Pond, Levy County, 248.

Empetrum album: in this case, not the Old World *E. album* L., but rosemary (*Ceratiola ericoides* Michx.); v (cf. p. 171).

England; Denys Rolle set sail from, 94; Mica nitida exported to, 363; specimens shipped to, 467.

England, king of. *See* King of England.

English (people): in Carolina, alliance with the Creeks, 55; former cultivation of St. Simon's Island, Ga., 62; in Mobile, Ala., 404; finding no honeybees at Mobile, 413; buildings by, at Manchac, La., 428; compared with French as colonists, 435; settling Carolina, 465; a mustee under their protection, 507.

English gentleman, owner of a plantation; at Mount Hope on St. John's River, Fla., 98; at Lake Beresford, 114.
    The first of these was John Tucker (De Brahm's map of 1771–1774?; W. Bartram, 1943: 150, 185; Mowat, 1943: 60, 61).

English gentleman at Pearl Island, La. *See* Rumsey, Mr.

English (language), spoken by an Indian on St. John's River, 75, and by a mustee in Alabama, 506.

English traders. *See* Traders, English.

Ephemera: probably Mayflies (family Ephemeridae), and perhaps the species *Hexagenia orlando* Traver (H.H.H., Jr.); myriads on lower St. John's River, Fla., life history, and reflections on, 80–83.

Ephemera, great yellow, called May fly: probably *Hexagenia limbata* (Guerin) (E.T.C., Jr.); food of Rice-birds, 297.

Ephouskyca (or "Ephouskyka"). *See* Crying bird; Tantalus pictus.

Epigaea: trailing arbutus (*E. repens* L.); at Falling Creek, Rabun County, Ga., 342.

Equipage; horses laden with, 215; repaired at Apalachicola, Ala., 395.

Erie, region of [Lake]; various trees of, xvi.

Eryngium: button snakeroot (*Eryngium* sp.); in Warren County, Ga., 379.

Erythrina ("Erythryna") (cf. Catesby, 1736, 2: 49, pl. 49): cardinal

spear (*E. herbacea* L.); v; near Long Pond, Levy County, Fla.,
248.

Erythrina (or "Erythryna") corallodendrum: not the West Indian *E.
corallodendron* L., but cardinal spear (*E. herbacea* L.); on Mosquito River, Fla., xxviii; described, near Salt Springs, 162, 164.

   According to Small (1923: 28), the reference on page xxviii is
to red cardinal (*E. arborea* [Chapm.] Small).

Erythronium *maculatum: *nomen nudum* (Merrill, 1945: 34)—
adder's tongue (*E. ?americanum* Ker); at Falling Creek, Rabun
County, Ga., 342.

Escambia ("Schambe" or "Shambe") River: arising in south central
Monroe County, flowing southward across southwestern Conecuh
County and western Escambia County, Ala., and then across extreme western Florida into Escambia Bay near Pensacola; forded,
402; plantations on, 416; bloody field of, 438; emigrants in deserts
of, 507.

Estatoee ("Estotowe"): a former Cherokee town on the Tugaloo
River below the junction of the Chattooga and Tallulah Rivers, in
Oconee County, S.C. (Hunter's map of 1730; Mouzon's map of
1775; *Bur. Am. Ethnol. Bull., 30*, Pt. I: 439, 1907); listed, 374.

Estatoee ("Estotowe") great: a former Cherokee town, perhaps the
one on the headwaters of Keowee River in northwestern Pickens
County, S.C. (Mouzon's map of 1775; Drayton, 1821, 2: map facing
p. 343; Hammond, 1883: map; Mooney, 1900: pl. 3; *Bur. Am. Ethnol.
Bull., 30*, Pt. I: 439, 1907); listed, 374.

Eto-mico: the Creek name for *Persea borbonia*, 232.

[Eufaula.] *See* Ufale.

Euonymus ("Evonimus"): strawberry bush (probably *E. americanus*
L.); along upper Savannah River, Ga., 320; near Wayah Gap, N.C.,
362.

Euonymus ("Euonismus") Americana: strawberry bush (*E. americanus* L.); near Oconee (= Station) Mountain, S.C., 337.

Eupatorium: some undetermined species of *Eupatorium* (family Compositae); along upper Savannah River, Ga., 321; in Warren County,
378.

Eupatorium scandens: climbing hemp-vine (*Mikania scandens* [L.]
Willd.); on St. John's River above Lake Dexter, Fla., 136.

Euphorbia: spurge (species of *Euphorbia* or of related genera); various species, near Suwannee River, Fla., 242; in Warren County,
Ga., 379.

Euphorbia picta: probably painted leaf (*E. heterophylla* L.); on St.
Simon's Island, Ga., 59.

   "I have sent . . . a Specimin of Euphorbea picta. if it is the

Euphorb. heterophylla of Linn. Spec. plant. it is there very illy defined, that comes nearest to ours of any in his catalogue, but there is no notice take[n] of the brylliant red painted leave emediately under the Umbels. I believe ours is a new Species—" (Bartram to Muhlenberg, September 8, 1792; Muhlenberg Letters: 21.)

Europe: the *Meleagris* of, 14; cheese supplied from, 19; shipment of collections to, 48, 306–307; trade produce shipped from St. John's River to, 97; countries of, 251; honey bees imported from, 413; navies of, 415; monarch in, 495.

Europeans: animals frightened away by invasion of, 46; arrival in Georgia, 520; no signs of their arts, sciences, or architecture in ancient American monuments, 522.

European military architects; traces of fortresses by, at Silver Bluff, S.C., 315.

European bats, compared with American, 283.

European civilization, Indians in no need of, 490.

European nations, liquors as enemy of, 492.

European travellers, their notice of Indians, 490.

European women, complexion compared with that of Cherokees, 485.

Evonimus. *See* Euonymus.

Eyes, malady in, 418–421, 436.

Fagus: beech (*F. grandifolia* Ehrh. var. *caroliniana* [Loud.] Fern. & Rehd.); at the White Cliffs, La., 436. *See also* Fagus sylvatica.

Fagus castanea ("castania"): chestnut (*Castanea dentata* [Marsh.] Borkh.); of Virginia and Pennsylvania, xvi; about Wrightsborough, Ga., 36; near Broad River, 44; along upper Savannah River, Ga.–S.C., 327; near Stockton, Ala., 403. *See also* Chestnut(s).

Fagus pumila, s[eu] *Chinkapin (cf. Catesby, 1730? *1:* 9, pl. 9): Piedmont chinquapin (*Castanea pumila* [L.] Mill.); about Wrightsborough, Ga., 36; along upper Savannah River, Ga.–S.C., 327.

"Chinkapin" is "merely an alternate name" or possibly "only . . . the vernacular name" (Merrill, 1945: 25).

Fagus sylvatica: in these cases, not the European *F. sylvatica* L., but American beech (*F. grandifolia* Ehrh.; in the more southern localities, var. *caroliniana* [Loud.] Fern. & Rehd.); of Virginia and Pennsylvania, xvi; in coastal swamps, 29; about Wrightsborough, Ga., 36; near Little River, 37; on lower St. John's River, Fla., 84, 90; near Lake Lochloosa, 181; between Orange and Tuscawilla Lakes, 183; near Alachua Savanna, 187, 198; west of Suwannee River, 233; near Three Sisters Ferry, S.C., 309; along upper Savannah River, Ga.–S.C., 327; along Chattahoochee River, Ala., 393; near The Rigolets, La., 421. *See also* Beech, Fagus.

F[alco] Aquilinus, cauda ferrug[inea], great eagle hawk: not *F. aquilinus* Gmelin (1788), but Eastern Red-tailed Hawk (*Buteo jamaicensis borealis* [Gmelin]); listed, 290. *See also* Falco major cauda ferruginea.

Falco columbarius, the pidgeon hawk (cf. Catesby, 1730? *1:* 3, pl. 3): Eastern Pigeon Hawk (*F. columbarius columbarius* L.); resident in Pennsylvania, 286; listed, 290.

　　Bartram erred as to its status in Pennsylvania.

Falco furcatus, the forked tail hawk, or kite (cf. Catesby, 1730? *1:* 4, pl. 4): Swallow-tailed Kite (*Elanoïdes forficatus forficatus* [L.]; syn., *F. furcatus* L. [1766]); listed, 290. *See also* Hawk or kite, forked tailed.

F[alco] gallinarius, the hen hawk: not *F. gallinarius* Gmelin (1788), but probably either a species of *Buteo* or Cooper's Hawk (*Accipiter cooperii* [Bonaparte]); listed, 290.

F[alco] *glaucus, the sharp winged hawk, of a pale sky-blue colour, the tip of the wings black: White-tailed Kite (*Elanus glaucus glaucus* [Bartram]; syn., *E. leucurus majusculus* Bangs and Penard) (cf. Harper, 1942*d:* 212); listed, 290.

Falco leucocephalus, or bald eagle (cf. Catesby, 1730? *1:* 1, pl. 1): adult Northern Bald Eagle (*Haliaeetus leucocephalus alascanus* C. H. Townsend); resident in Pennsylvania, 286; listed, 290. *See also* Eagle, bald; Eagle, great grey; Falco maximus; Falco regalis.

Falco *major cauda ferruginea ("ferruginio"): *nomen nudum*—Eastern Red-tailed Hawk (*Buteo jamaicensis borealis* [Gmelin]); resident in Pennsylvania, 286. *See also* Falco Aquilinus.

Falco *maximus, or great grey eagle: *nomen nudum*—immature Northern Bald Eagle (*Haliaeetus leucocephalus alascanus* C. H. Townsend); resident in Pennsylvania, 286. *See also* Falco regalis.

F[alco] niger, the black hawk (cf. Edwards, 1743, *1:* 4, pl. 4, and 1747, *2:* 125, as "Black Hawk *or* Falcon" or "Falco, niger, *Americanus*"): not *F. niger* Gmelin (1788), but Duck Hawk (*F. peregrinus anatum* Bonaparte); listed, 290.

Falco *piscatorius, or fishing-hawk (or "fishing eagle") (cf. Catesby, 1730? *1:* 2, pl. 2): Osprey (*Pandion haliaetus carolinensis* [Gmelin]); described, on Colonel's Island, Ga., 8; victimized by Bald Eagle, 8; listed, 290.

Falco *pullarius, the chicken hawk: *nomen nudum*—some undetermined hawk, of the genera *Accipiter* or *Buteo;* resident in Pennsylvania, 286; listed, 290.

F[alco] *ranivorus, the marsh hawk: *nomen nudum*—Marsh Hawk (*Circus cyaneus hudsonius* [L.]); listed, 290.

The engraving of this species in Edwards (1760, 2: pl. 291) was made from a drawing by Bartram.

Falco *regalis, the great grey eagle: *nomen nudum*—immature Northern Bald Eagle (*Haliaeetus leucocephalus alascanus* C. H. Townsend); listed, 290. *See also* Falco maximus.

F[alco] sparverius, the least hawk or sparrow hawk (cf. Catesby, 1730? *1*: 5, pl. 5): Eastern Sparrow Hawk (*Falco sparverius sparverius* L.); listed, 290.

F[alco] *subcerulius, the sharp winged hawk, of a dark or dusky blue colour: Mississippi Kite (*Ictinia subcerulia* [Bartram]; syn., *I. misisippiensis* [Wilson]) (cf. Harper, 1942d: 212); listed, 290.

Falling Creek: the present Martin Creek, 3 miles northeast of Clayton, Rabun County, Ga.; cascades of, 339, 341.

Falls, on the Potomac: either Little Falls, or both Little Falls and Great Falls, respectively 3 and 12 miles above Georgetown, D.C.; crossed river below, 480.

Farm(s): on St. Simon's Island, Ga., 60; on Lake Beresford, Fla., 140–144; on Mobile Delta, Ala., 403; of Governor Chester, near Pensacola, Fla., 415; below Mobile, Ala., 418, 419.

Farmar ("Farmer"), Major [Robert]: proprietor of a plantation on the Tensaw River, Ala.; invitation from, 405; furnishing horses and a Negro, 411; took leave of, 440.

For the location of Major Farmar's holdings along the Tensaw River, see Commentary for pp. 403–407.

Major Farmar, with two British regiments, took possession of Mobile from the French in 1763, and he remained in command there for a number of years. "He gave but three months' shrift to those inhabitants who preferred emigration to taking the oath of allegiance to King George." He was 45 years of age at this time. Aubry, the French governor at New Orleans, wrote of him: "This governor of Mobile is an extraordinary man. . . . It is said that the English ministry sent him to Mobile to get rid of him, because he was one of the hottest in the opposition." (Hamilton, 1897: 177, 191, 193–194.) There is a letter from him to Colonel Amherst, November 17, 1763, in the Clements Library (Amherst Papers, 7: 42); it deals with military matters. A feud in which he engaged with Governor George Johnstone "ended in a court-martial for him in 1768, which after many delays resulted in an acquittal." Later he was elected to the assembly. (C. Johnson, 1943: 51, 98.)

Fast, or fasting: to avert sickness, at Otasse, Ala., 455; at the busk, 509.

Father [of William Bartram]: John Bartram (1699–1777); journeys to

Catskill Mountains and to Florida with, 270; arrived at his house on the Schuylkill, Pa., 480. *See also* Bartram, John.

Fawns. *See* Deer.

Feast(s), or feasting; at Talahasochte, Fla., 235–236; at Mucclasse, Ala., 446; of American aborigines, 509–510; at a Muscogulge marriage, 514; of the dead, 517.

Feathers: Seminole warriors ornamented with, 244; pipe adorned with, 351; Indian cloak made of, 502.

Felis cauda truncata. *See* Wild cats.

"Felix." *See* Filix.

Fellow traveller(s). *See* Traveller(s), fellow.

Fern, scandent (Pteris *scandens*): climbing fern (*Lygodium palmatum* [Bernh.] Sw.) (cf. Merrill, 1945: 33); described, near Cambelton (= Fayetteville), N.C., 478. *See also* Filix scandens.

   Filix scandens Bartram and *Pteris scandens* Bartram are preoccupied in *Lygodium* by *Ophioglossum scandens* Linnaeus (1753).

Ferrum: iron; in the middle region of Georgia, 45.

Ferry: at Fort Barrington, Ga., 16; on Satilla River, 17; at the Cowford on St. John's River, Fla., 72–73; at Fort Moore, S.C., 315; at Anderson's (= Marietta, Pa.) on Susquehanna River, 480. *See also* Three Sisters.

Ferry-house, on Cooper River, S.C., 470.

Festivals, among Indians, 504.

Fever(s): at Charlotia on St. John's River, Fla., 95; ill with, 411, 413, 418–421.

Ficus: a genus of Moraceae, comprising the figs; in temperate zone, xv.

Ficus carica. *See* Fig(s).

Field fare: not the European Fieldfare (*Turdus pilaris* L.), but Robin (*Turdus migratorius* subspp.); breeding range of, 301. *See also* Robins, Robin redbreast, Turdus migratorius.

Fig(s) (Ficus carica), or fig trees: *Ficus carica* L.; on St. Simon's Island, Ga., 62; likened to fruit of *Carica papaya*, 132; at Palatka, Fla., 304; soil adapted for, 337; on upper Tensaw River, Ala., 407; near The Rigolets, La., 423; proposed culture in Georgia, 460.

Fig, common dwarf Indian: prickly pear (*Opuntia* sp.); compared with *Opuntia ammophila*, 163.

Filbert: *Corylus* sp.; compared in size with nut of water chinquapin, 409.

Filix ("Filex") *osmunda: *nomen nudum*—either cinnamon fern (*Osmunda cinnamomea* L.) or royal fern (*O. regalis* L.) (E.T.W.) (cf. Merrill, 1945: 33); near Deep Creek, Putnam County, Fla., 173.

Filix ("Felix") *scandens, perhaps species of Trichomanes: climbing fern (*Lygodium palmatum* [Bernh.] Sw.) (cf. Merrill, 1945: 33); described, on the Great Ridge, in Oglethorpe County, Ga., 41. *See also* Fern, scandent.

This record is of particular interest in being the first mention of the species in the literature (A.N.L.).

Finch, least. *See* Carduelis pusillus.

Finch, painted. *See* Linaria ciris.

Finch, purple. *See* Fringilla purpurea.

Finch creeper, various coloured little. *See* Parus varius.

Fire(s); annual firing of the deserts [Florida "scrub"], 164, and of forests in Carolina and Florida, 225; keeping down magnolias, 172; persecuting power of, 242; extinguished and produced anew at the busk, 510.

Fish: as food of the fishing-hawk, 8; Mayflies as food for, 81, 83; as prey of "trout," 109; devoured by Alligators at Lake Dexter, Fla., 123; Snake Birds feeding on, 133; sought by Alligator, 135; at Lake Beresford and vicinity, 144; in Blue Springs, 145; preyed upon by Warmouth, 154; in and near Salt Springs Run, 159–160; behavior at Salt Springs, 166–168, and at Cowpen Lake, Putnam County, 175–177, 179; preyed upon by Soft-shelled Turtle, 178; driven on shore of Alachua Savanna by Alligators, 193; in Tuscawilla Lake, 193; in Alachua Sink, 205–206; in Kanapaha Sink, 217; in Suwannee River and vicinity, 224, 235; in subterranean waters of Florida, 226; dry fish bartered between Indians and Spaniards in Cuba and at Bay of Calos, Fla., 227; behavior in Suwannee River, 229–230; in Manatee Spring, 231; in Alligator Hole, 238; in repast at Talahasochte, 241; in Long Pond, Levy County, 248; at Sapelo Island, Ga., 268; squamae of, 335. *See also* Bass, Bream, Catfish, Drum, Flounder, Gar, Gold-fish, Grouper, Mud fish, Mullet, Rock[fish], Shark, Sheepshead, Skate, Skipjack, Sting-ray, Trout, Whiting.

Fish hooks, presented to Indians, 244.

Fish pond (traders' name) (cf. Taitt's map of 1772, as "Athlagulga or Fishpond"; Hawkins, in Swanton, 1922: 276, as "Thlot-lo-gul-gau"): a former Upper Creek town on Elkahatchee Creek, near the Coosa-Tallapoosa county boundary, Ala. (Dadeville or Wetumpka quadrangles); listed, 463.

Fishermen: on Cumberland Island, Ga., 64; sharks and rays troublesome to, 68.

Fishing: in Liberty County, Ga., 11; on Sapelo Island, 268; at Tangipahoa River, La., 425; on Amite River, 437.

Fishing-hawk. *See* Falco piscatorius.

Fishing tackle; 252, 488.

Flag (emblem), on chief's house at Cuscowilla, Fla., 184.

Flags (plants): *Iris* spp.; 178.

Flamingo ("flaningo"): *Phoenicopterus ruber* L.; Indian cloak made of flamingo feathers, 503. *See also* Phoenicopterus ruber.

Flap: in these cases, apparently a breech-clout; worn by Indians, 502, 504.

Flap or petticoat; worn by Indian women, 503, 504.

Flat-rock: perhaps the present Lazenby's Flat Rock, a mile northwest of Camak, Warren County, Ga. (fig. 25); a rendezvous for traders and Indians, 376–377; 384, 395.

Flax: *Linum* sp.; Suwannee River region suitable for, 234; along Cape Fear River, N.C., 474.

Flies: species of the order Diptera; 167.

Flies, biting, burning, or stinging, several species of: probably all horseflies (family Tabanidae); tormenting horses in Taylor County, Ga., 384–386.

    The larger species, including the "hippobosca" and the one of a dusky color with a green head, were probably members of the genus *Tabanus*. The species of "asilus or smaller biting flies" were probably members of the genus *Chrysops*. (H.K.T.)

Flint River: a river of southwestern Georgia, joining the Chattahoochee to form the Apalachicola; 25; list of Cherokee towns on, 374 (in this case mentioned by mistake for the Chattahoochee); fording, 383; tributaries of, 384; list of Lower Creek towns on, 464.

    The last-mentioned list (with the exception of "Forks") appears to be of Florida towns, not on the Flint River.

Flora: a sort of indigo, 77; the bounteous kingdom of, 156.

Florida(s): groves in, xv; cypress in, xv; various trees of, xvi; exploration of, 1; acquaintance in, 3; sojourn in, 15; hunting grounds in, bordering Okefinokee Swamp, 26; set off for, from Savannah, 57; planters along coast of, 69; lakes of, 147; Chuck-will's-widow in, 154; Wolves of, 199; travels in, 210; savannas of, 221; rivers of, 225; *Smilax* in, 241; blooming realms of, 253; snakes of, 273–276; frogs of, 276–280; lizards of, 280–281; tortoises of, 281; beasts of, 281–284; birds of, 284–302; claimed by Tomocos, Utinas, Caloosas, Yamasees, and other ancient tribes, 380; held by Yamasees, 392; Indians from maritime parts of, 465; revisiting eastern borders, 467; eddo in, 469; mounds of, 521.

Florida, point of: either the peninsula or the southern tip of it; expeditions of Indians by canoe to, 227; travels to, 287, 288, 488.

Florida, East: that part of the present Florida situated east of the Apalachicola River (cf. Romans' map of 1776); excursions between Carolina and, 48; Spaniards in, 55; resolve to travel into, 56; embark for, 63; a passenger for, 64; disturbances between Lower Creeks and white inhabitants of, 78; a pawpaw in, 171; Soft-shelled Tortoise in, 177; rocks forming the foundation of, 205; Spanish settlements in, 208–209; possessed by the Seminoles, 211; colony of, established by Spaniards, 216; Coach-whip in, 220; plants common in, 232; former journey to, 270; Cottonmouth Moccasins in, 272; travels into, 381; Lower Creeks in, 391; water chinquapin in, 409; honey bees in, 413; *Illicium* in, 442; Georgia bark in, 468; a Spaniard in, 487.

Florida, West: that part of the present Florida situated west of the Apalachicola River, plus a strip of territory extending west along the Gulf Coast to the Mississippi (cf. Romans' map of 1776); possessed by the Seminoles, 211; Otter and Beavers in, 281; adventurers bound for, 366, 375; trading path for, 397; no honey bees in, 413; researches on natural history of, 415; late governor of, 431.

Floridans. *See* Indians—Floridans.

Flounder: in this case, perhaps some species of *Paralichthys*; about Georgia coastal islands, 67.

Flounder: in this case, perhaps Southern Hog-choker (*Trinectes maculatus fasciatus* [Lacepède]); at Salt Springs, Fla., 166.

Flour; made of roots of China brier, 241.

Flowers; drawing some, 260; tattooed on Indians, 503.

Flute(s); used by Seminoles, 245; used by Indians, 505.

Flycatcher, black cap. *See* Muscicapa nunciola; Pewit.

Flycatcher, brown and greenish. *See* Muscicapa rapax.

Flycatcher, great crested yellow bellied. *See* Muscicapa cristata.

Flycatcher, little domestic. *See* Muscicapa cantatrix.

Flycatcher, golden crown. *See* Parus aurio vertice.

Flycatcher, golden winged. *See* Parus alis aureis.

Flycatcher, green black throated. *See* Parus viridis.

Flycatcher, little olive cold. *See* Muscicapa subviridis.

Flycatcher, little red eye'd. *See* Muscicapa sylvicola.

Foot-ball, as an Indian game, 509.

Forks (traders' name): a former Seminole town, perhaps at junction of Flint and Chattahoochee Rivers (cf. Romans' map of 1776); listed, 464.

Fornication: Indians given to, 213; infamy as punishment for, 515.

Fort, at south end of Cumberland Island, Ga.; walking to, 64–65.

This was Fort William (J. Johnson, 1851: 106; Mrs. Cate, 1943: 137).

Fort, ancient; on Altamaha River opposite Darien, Ga., 53.

Recent archaeological excavations at the supposed site of Bartram's "tetragon terrace" on Evelyn plantation have yielded nothing of interest (Margaret Davis Cate, *in litt.*, July 28, 1946). This plantation adjoins Santo Domingo Park on the south.

Fort Barrington: on the northeast side of Altamaha River, about 14 miles northwest of Darien, Ga.; travels toward, 10; road to, 12, 16; crossed river at, 17; a pawpaw growing near, 171.

It has been stated that this frontier fort was burned by a British force in 1777 (Siebert, 1928: 232) or in March, 1778 (Mowat, 1943: 121). On the other hand, Margaret Davis Cate informs me (*in litt.*, July 28, 1946) that there is nothing in the Colonial Records to indicate that the fort was ever burned. During the Revolution it was renamed Fort Howe, and as such it was occupied by an American force as late as April and May, 1778.

The location and a plan of the fort are shown by De Brahm (1849: pls. [5], [6]).

Fort Charlotta (or "Charlotte"): on the Carolina side of Savannah River, in McCormick County, opposite the mouth of Broad River; 324; rendezvous at, 375; set out from, 375.

Fort Conde: a fortress at Mobile, Ala. (cf. Hamilton, 1897: map opposite p. 134); Taensa above, 403; described, 404.

Fort George Island: a Florida coastal island on the north side of the mouth of St. John's River; 306.

Fort George's sound: the present Nassau Sound, Fla. (Fernandina quadrangle); sailing across, 70.

Fort James[,] Dartmouth: at the junction of Broad and Savannah Rivers, in southeastern Elbert County, Ga.; journey to, 320, 322; arrival at, and description of, 323; set off for, 372; Fort Charlotte near, 375.

Fort Louis de la Mobile: a French fortress on Mobile River, Ala., established in 1702 and abandoned in 1711 (Hamilton, 1897: map opposite p. 86; *Crown Coll.*, ser. 3, *1*: 48, 1915); possible traces of, on lower Tombigbee River, 410.

As Hamilton remarks (1897: 240), Bartram places this fort too far upstream.

Fort Moore, S.C.: on Savannah River about 3 miles below Augusta, Ga.; site described, 315–316.

Fort Ninety Six: at or near the present Ninety Six, Greenwood County, S.C.; road to, 317.

Fort Picolata: on east side of St. John's River, at the present settlement of Picolata, Fla. (Purcell map of about 1779; soil map of St. John's County, 1917); description of, 80; distance from St. Augustine, 208; a Rattlesnake at, 270–272.

The exact site of this ancient little fort is no longer ascertainable. Here, in November 1765, Governor James Grant and Superintendent John Stuart had concluded a treaty with the Indians. John Bartram, who was present with his son, described (1942: 35, 51) both the fort and the picturesque ceremonies connected with the treaty. The fort was "abandoned in 1769" (Mowat, 1943: 27). For further information on Picolata, see Vignoles (1823: 67), Fairbanks (1858: 144), Chatelain (1941: 78, 83, 90–92, 166–167 [note 85]), and J. Bartram (1942: 35, 98, fig. 25).

Fort Prince George[,] Keowee ("Keowe"): on east side of Keowee River, about 3 miles south of Ellenburg, Pickens County, S.C. (fig. 24); set out for, 328; arrived at, 330; serving as a trading house, 332; set off from, 333.

No vestige remains of this fort, which figured in various campaigns against the Cherokees. A cornfield now occupies the ancient site.

Fort St. Mark's: at the site of the present St. Mark's, Wakulla County, Fla.; in Bay of Apalachee, 215. See also St. Mark's.

F[or]t Thoulouse: a former French fort, in the present Elmore County, Ala., just above the junction of the Coosa and Tallapoosa Rivers, and 4 miles southwest of Wetumpka (Swanton, 1922: 209–210, pl. 9; Wetumpka quadrangle); 408; traces of, described, 447.

The site is marked as "Old Ft. Jackson" on the Geological Map of Alabama (1894).

Fortifications; at Apalachean Old Fields, Fla., 233.

Fortress or blockhouse at Pensacola, Fla. (cf. Roberts, 1763: pl. facing p. 11); described, 416.

Fortress at Natchez, Miss.; established by the French, 433.

Fortress, ancient, on west side of Mobile Bay, Ala.; vestiges of, 418.

Fortress, ancient French, Thoulouse. See Fort Thoulouse.

Fortress of Spaniards; below Manchac, La. (cf. Romans' map of about 1772), 428; at Pointe Coupée (cf. Thomassy, 1860: map following p. 226), 434.

Fossils, in middle region of Georgia, 45.

Fothergill, Dr. [John], of London; exploring the southern colonies at his request, 1; wrote to, 56; a merchant in Liverpool a friend of, 307; instructions of, 307; specimens forwarded to, from Mobile, 438.

This noted Quaker physician (1712–1780) deserves great credit as the Maecenas who subsidized Bartram's southern travels of 1773–77 and thus enabled him to secure his priceless records of eighteenth-century American natural history. While acquiring fame and fortune from his London practice, he indulged his taste for botany and horticulture. On his estate at Upton, in Essex, he cultivated plants from all parts of the world in the most ample horticultural buildings that had been seen up to that time. In 1765 he leased Lea Hall, in Cheshire, to which he retreated each summer. Miller's *Gardeners Dictionary* was produced under his patronage. He is commemorated in the genus *Fothergilla*, proposed by Murray for a group of North American shrubs. A number of his letters to John and William Bartram were published by Darlington (1849). Still others are preserved at the Historical Society of Pennsylvania. Probably through his friendship with John Bartram, Fothergill was one of the first foreigners to be elected (in 1770) a member of the American Philosophical Society.

For additional information, see Lettsom (1784), Darlington (1849: 333–335), Fox (1919), and Brett-James (1925: 105–108).

Fothergilla: a genus of Hamamelidaceae, comprising three species of witch alders; in the Lime-Sink Region, Ga., 31; along Cape Fear River, N.C., 476.

Fothergilla gardeni ("gardini"): dwarf witch-alder (*F. gardeni* Murr.); on Colonel's Island, Ga., 6.

Fountain, a vast, of mineral water: the present Blue Springs, on the east side of St. John's River, near Orange City, Volusia County, Fla.; visited and described, 145–146. *See also* Springs.

Fowls, aquatic: probably herons, etc.; at Lake George, Fla., 105.

Fowl, common domestic: *Gallus gallus* (L.); hatching a Wild Turkey's egg, 14. *See also* Chickens, Cock, Hen(s).

Fowl, sea: shore birds (order Charadriiformes) and the like; on St. Simon's Island, Ga., 63; near Amelia Island, Fla., 70; at Nassau Sound, 71.

Fowl, [water]: ducks (family Anatidae) and the like; seized by Soft-shelled Turtle, 178.

Fowling; on Amite River, La., 437.

Fox(es) (or foxes "of the smaller red species"): Gray Foxes (*Urocyon cinereoargenteus* subspp.); on Colonel's Island, Ga., 7; account of, in Carolina and Florida, 282; in paintings at Otasse, Ala., 455.

Fragaria: strawberry (*Fragaria* sp.); in Oconee County, S.C., 334. *See also* Strawberry.

France; an immigrant from, 419.

Frankincense; resin of *Silphium* tasting like, 399.

Franklin, Dr. Benjamin; *Franklinia* named in honor of, 467.

Franklin (1706–1790) was a founder of the University of Pennsylvania and of the American Philosophical Society, a member of the Continental Congress, Commissioner to France, an early investigator of electricity, a particular friend of the Bartrams, etc., etc. William Bartram had originally intended to dedicate the *Travels* to Franklin, but the latter's death intervened (Harper, 1946).

Franklinia (or Franklinia Alatamaha): Franklin tree (*F. alatamaha* Bartr. ex Marsh.) (cf. Little, 1945: 503; Merrill, 1945: 18) (fig. 3); in the temperate zone, xvi; described, from McIntosh County, Ga., 467–468. *See also* Gordonia, a species of.

This famous tree has never been found in the wild except at or near the type locality, and it has not been seen there since 1803, but it persists in cultivation. For accounts of it, see Castiglioni (1790, 2: 243, pl. 12), Lyell (1849, 1: 261), Wherry (1928), Barnhart (1933), Jenkins (1933; 1943), and Harper and Leeds (1938).

Fraxinus: ash (*Fraxinus* spp.); on lower St. John's River, Fla., 84, 90; west of Suwannee River, 233; along upper Savannah River, Ga.-S.C., 327; near Wayah Gap, N.C., 362; near Stockton, Ala., 403; on Amite River, La., 425. *See also* Ash.

Fraxinus *aquatica: *nomen nudum* (Merrill, 1945: 34)—perhaps water ash (*F. caroliniana* Mill.); on Colonel's Island, Ga., 6; about St. Mary's River, Ga.–Fla., 24; on St. John's River above Lake Dexter, Fla., 130.

"A small Tree, grows in Water or wet swamps" (Bartram to Muhlenberg, September 6, 1810; Muhlenberg Letters: 137).

Fraxinus excelsior (or "excelcior" or "exelsior"): in these cases, not the Old World *F. excelsior* L., but white ash (*F. americana* L.); of the Northern States, xvi; on Colonel's Island, Ga., 6; in the lower Coastal Plain, 29; about Wrightsborough, 36; on St. John's River at Charlotia, Fla., 94, and above Lake Dexter, 130; near Alachua Savanna, 187; near Three Sisters Ferry, S.C., 309; near Oconee Station, Oconee County, 335; along Iberville Canal, La., 427; along Cape Fear River, N.C., 474.

"Fraxinus excelsior is F. Americana. Hort. Kew[s]. (our great White-Ash.) I called it so from its magnitude & usefullness[.]"

(Bartram to Muhlenberg, September 6, 1810; Muhlenberg Letters: 137.)

Frederica: a fort and settlement on the northwest side of St. Simon's Island, Ga.; arrival of a vessel and of Bartram at, 57; return to, 61; ruins of town and fort, 62; return of vessel to, 97; set sail for, 306; arrival at, 306.

Frederica was settled in 1739, and was the favorite residence of General Oglethorpe, the founder of Georgia. This was the base from which he attacked and defeated the Spaniards at the Battle of Bloody Marsh. For further accounts, see Jones (1878: 45–136), Mrs. Cate (1930: 54–62; 1943: 117–122), and "Fort Frederica National Monument" (U.S. Dept. Interior, 8 pp., 1944). A plan of Frederica is shown in the *Crown Coll.* (ser. 3, *3:* 139, 140, 1915).

French: an ancient fort on Altamaha River, Ga., supposedly their work, 53; buildings at Mobile, Ala., 404; families at Taensa Bluff, 405; name for *Myrica inodora*, 405; ancient fortress of, on lower Tombigbee River, 410; at Mobile, 413; artificial bank on the Mississippi, La., constructed by, 428; settlement at Pointe Coupée (*q.v.*) on the Mississippi, 430; settling at Natchez and elsewhere on the Mississippi, 433–435; apple trees planted by, at Fort Thoulouse, Ala., 447.

French gentleman; sailed with, from Mobile to Pearl River, 418–420; proprietor of a plantation on Mobile Bay, 419; adventures on the Mississippi, 433–434. *See also* St. Pierre, Mons.

French gentlemen; residents of Mobile and owners of farms on the delta, 404.

Frenchman; master of a farm below Mobile, Ala., 418.

Frigate ("frigat") bird. *See* Pelecanus aquilus.

F[ringilla] canabina, the hemp bird: in this case, not the European *F. cannabina* L., but probably Eastern Purple Finch (*Carpodacus purpureus purpureus* [Gmelin]) (females and immature males), as suggested by Stone (1913: 345); listed, 291.

In Alexander Wilson's own copy of the *Travels* (but not certainly in his script), an annotation indicates that this is the Purple Finch (presumably the female or immature male). Barton (1799a: 9, 10, 14, 20) seemed to think it might be the Greater Redpoll.

Fringilla erythrophthalma, the towhe bird (cf. Catesby, 1730? *1:* 34, pl. 34): in this case, Red-eyed Towhee (*Pipilo erythrophthalmus erythrophthalmus* [L.]); listed, 291. *See also* Towhee bird.

F[ringilla] fusca, the large brown white throat sparrow: not *F. fusca* Mueller (1776), but White-throated Sparrow (*Zonotrichia albicollis* [Gmelin]); listed, 291.

Edwards' "White-throated Sparrow" (1760, 2: 198, 220, pl. 304), upon which Gmelin (1789) based the name *Fringilla albicollis*, was "taken from a neat drawing in colours, done by Mr. William Bartram of Philadelphia."

F[ringilla] purpurea, the purple finch (cf. Catesby, 1730, 1: 41, pl. 41): Eastern Purple Finch (*Carpodacus purpureus purpureus* [Gmelin]); listed, 291. See also Fringilla canabina.

F[ringilla] *rufa, the red, or fox-coloured ground or hedge sparrow: *nomen nudum*—Eastern Fox Sparrow (*Passerella iliaca iliaca* [Merrem]); listed, 291.

Fritillaria: a genus of Liliaceae, comprising the fritillaries; elegance, xviii.

Frogs: in Bartram's usage, including not only the true frogs (Ranidae) but also the tree-frogs (Hylidae) and the toads (Bufonidae); Mayflies as food for, 81; croaking on lower St. John's River, Fla., 88; imagined presence on floating islands in the St. John's, 89; shot with bows and arrows by Indians, 92; as food of "trout," 109, of Wood Ibis, 150, of King Vulture, 152, and of Soft-shelled Turtle, 178; at Lake Dexter, 154; social converse of, in southwestern Alachua County, 218; of Florida and Carolina, 276–280. See also Tree frogs.

Frog, bell: either Green Tree-frog (*Hyla cinerea cinerea* [Schneider]) or Georgia Tree-frog (*H. gratiosa* Le Conte); account of, 277.

Frog, diminutive species of, called savanna crickets: Little Tree-frog (*Hyla ocularis* Bosc and Daudin) (cf. Harper, 1939*b*); account of, 278.

Frog, a beautiful green: Green Tree-frog (*Hyla cinerea cinerea* [Schneider]); account of, 277.

This and the "bell frog" mentioned on the same page are evidently identical, unless the latter is the Georgia Tree-frog.

Frog, a less green: perhaps Southern Tree-frog (*Hyla squirella* Bosc); account of, 278.

Frog, a little grey speckled: Florida Cricket Frog (*Acris gryllus dorsalis* [Harlan]) (in Florida) or Southern Cricket Frog (*A. g. gryllus* [Le Conte]) (in Carolina); account of, 278.

Frogs, high land, called toads, of two species, red and black: color phases of the Southern Toad (*Bufo terrestris* [Bonnaterre]); account of, 279–280.

Frogs, land: Southern Toads (*Bufa terrestris* [Bonnaterre]); preyed on by snakes, 195.

Frog, largest, in Florida and Carolina: Southern Bullfrog (*Rana grunniens* Daudin; syn., *R. grylio* Stejneger) (cf. Harper, 1940: 704–706); account of, 276–277.

Frog, shad: in Pennsylvania, Northern Leopard Frog (*Rana pipiens pipiens* Schreber), and in the South, Southern Leopard Frog (*R. p. sphenocephala* Cope); account of, 278–279.

Frogcatcher. *See* Ardea clamator.

Fruits; harvested at the busk, 510.

Fulica *Floridana, the great blue or slate coloured coot of Florida: *nomen nudum*—American Coot (*Fulica americana americana* Gmelin); listed, 296. *See also* Coots, laughing.

Funeral ceremonies: among American aborigines, 515–517; among Muscogulges, 515–516; among Choctaws, 516–517.

Fungus called Jew's ears: *Auricularia auricula-judae* (L.) Berk.— (F.W.P.; D.R.S.); in Catskill Mountains, N.Y., 270.

Furniture, old exchanged for new at the busk, 509.

Furs (or "furrs"): bartered by Indians to Spaniards in Cuba, 227; traded by Seminoles, 257; horses loaded with, 457, 480.

Fusahatche (properly Fus-hatchee): a former Upper Creek town on the north side of Tallapoosa River in Elmore County, Ala., 2 miles below Hołiwahali (Swanton, 1922: 269, pl. 2) or ¾ mile above Kolomi (Taitt, 1916: 537); listed, 463.

    The site was apparently in the vicinity of Ware Ferry (soil map of Elmore County, 1911).

Fusee (or fuzee or gun or piece): a flintlock gun; equipped with, 74, 76, 252; use for protection against Alligators and Bears, 119–125; kept under Bartram's head at night, 136; near Alachua Savanna, 195.

Gale on the Atlantic, damage from, 2. *See also* Hurricane, Storm, Tempest.

Galega: probably devil's shoestring (*Tephrosia* sp.); near Suwannee River, Fla., 243.

Galahan (or "Gallahan"), Mr.: chief trader at Cowee, N.C.; hospitality and character of, 353; accompanying Bartram toward Overhill towns, 359; conducting Bartram to the chief of Cowee, 366; attending a festival at Cowee, 369; waiting for, at Keowee, S.C., 372.

Galphin ("Golphin"), G[eorge]: an influential and wealthy trader, with a store at Silver Bluff on the Carolina side of the Savannah River a dozen miles below Augusta; his establishment visited, and letters of recommendation obtained from, 313–315; his aid solicited for a trader at Mucclasse, Ala., 449, 462.

    Galphin had settled at Silver Bluff in 1734. He built up a large Indian trade, and had agents as far away as Alabama. He eventually became Assistant Superintendent of Indian Affairs. He was devoted to the American cause during the Revolution and is said to have contributed $20,000 toward equipping the fleet under John Paul Jones. His store, or "Fort Galphin," was taken by the British, but was recovered by American troops in 1780; no vestige of it seems now to remain. Some of his descendants were living in the vicinity in 1939.

A letter of Galphin's, dated April 30, 1775, and recommending Bartram to his western agents, is among the Darlington Papers.

For additional information, see J. Bartram (1942: 64–65, 88, figs. 12–13), J. Johnson (1851: 356), Jones (1883, 2: 136–138), and Miss Williams (1905).

Gambling, Indians fond of, 213.

Game: protection on Georgia coastal islands, 67; Florida abounding in, 211.

Games; among Indians, 213, 508–509, 521.

Gannet (or "ganet"): Wood Ibis (*Mycteria americana* L.); at Alachua Savanna, Fla., 190; on the Mississippi near Anchor, La., 433. *See also* Pelican, solitary; Pelican, wood; Tantalus Ichthyophagus; Tantalus loculator.

Gar (or "garfish" or "garr"): either Eastern Long-nosed Gar (*Lepisosteus osseus osseus* [L.]) or Eastern Short-nosed Gar (*Cylindrosteus platostomus platyrhincus* [De Kay]), or both; in Blue Springs, Fla., 145; in Salt Springs, 166; in Alachua Sink, 205, 206; in Blue Springs, Screven County, Ga., 461.

Gar ("garr"), great brown spotted: Eastern Long-nosed Gar (*Lepisosteus osseus osseus* [L.]); described, at Cowpen Lake, Putnam County, Fla., 175–176.

Garcinia mangostana: mangosteen (*G. mangostana* L.), a Malayan fruit of the family Guttiferae; in the tropics, xv.

Gardenia ("Gardinia"): a genus of Rubiaceae, including the Cape jasmine (*G. jasminoides* Ellis), an Asiatic plant; in the temperate zone, xvi.

It is difficult to understand how this name comes to appear in a list of predominantly native plants; perhaps Bartram had some different plant in mind.

Garrison, at Pensacola, Fla., 416.

Garrulus *australis, the yellow breasted chat: nomen subnudum— Yellow-breasted Chat (*Icteria virens virens* [L.]); listed, 290 *bis. See also* Chat, yellow breasted; Motacilla trochilus.

Geese: perhaps chiefly Canada Geese (*Branta canadensis canadensis* [L.]); at Lake Beresford and vicinity, Fla., 144; in Suwannee River region, 235; on the Mississippi near Anchor, La., 433. *See also* Anser Canadensis.

Gentiana *caerulea ("caerulia"): *nomen nudum* (Merrill, 1945: 34)—
gentian (*Gentiana* sp.); in Brunswick County, N.C., 472.

Gentiana saponaria (cf. Catesby, 1731, *1:* 70, pl. 70): soapwort
gentian (*G. saponaria* L.); in Brunswick County, N.C., 472.

George-town, in Maryland: the present Georgetown, in the District of
Columbia; landed at, 480.

Georgetown, S.C.: identical with the present city of the same name;
passed, 471; mouth of Waccamaw River at, 473.

Georgia; exploration of, 1, 4; acquaintance in, 3; sea-coast islands of,
9; sojourn in, 15; maritime parts of, 19, 23; succession of physiographic and floral areas from the sea coast to Augusta, 28–32;
coastal swamps in, 29; merchants of, demanding lands from Indians,
33; founded by Oglethorpe, 62; inhabitants, soil, and marine products of coastal islands, 66–69; return to, 77; settlers leaving Charlotia for, 95; Crying Bird in, 147; a pawpaw in, 171; return of
schooner to, 210, 251; size of animals in, 216; Coachwhip in, 220;
Indian stores in, 228; Rattlesnake in, 267; seacoast of, 268; Beavers
present and Muskrats absent, 281; birds of, 287–302; watermelons
in, 303; set sail for, 306; crossed Savannah River into, 309, 376;
favorable site of Augusta in, 316, 317; Georgia side of Savannah
River, 316, 318; Indian trading company of, 324; a new magnolia in,
340; Dartmouth in, 366; lower districts of, 381; tree growth compared with that of Alabama, 400; vegetation compared with that of
Louisiana, 436; emigrants from, 438, 443; travels through, 458–462;
Irishman settling in, 460; revisiting, 467; completed collections in,
469; citizens of, at Augusta, 486; British colonists of, 487; governor
of, 494.

Georgians; demand for Indian territory, 485–486.

Gerardia: false foxglove (*Gerardia* spp.); near Suwannee River, Fla.,
242; near Long Pond, Levy County, 248; in Warren County, Ga.,
379.

Gerardia ("Gerardea") *flammea: probably the scrophulariaceous
plant currently known as *Macranthera flammea* (Bartr.) Pennell
(cf. Merrill, 1945: 25–26); described, in Baldwin or adjacent county,
Ala., 412.

Pennell (1935: 414) discusses this case in detail. Evidently Bartram's account is somewhat confused; at least the habitat assigned
does not fit *Macranthera,* but *Clinopodium coccineum,* which bears
some resemblance to the other plant (cf. R. M. Harper, 1928: 313).

Germany, James: the principal trader of Coolome, Ala.; consult with,
396; tarried with, 449; character and status of, 449. *See also* Trader,
at Coolome, Ala.

About 1763 Germany had been sent by Major Robert Farmar, in

command at Mobile, to Fort Thoulouse to keep possession (Hamilton, 1897: 182). In 1766, acting as an interpreter, he prepared a communication from the Wolf King of Mucclasse to Governor James Wright, of Georgia, and to Superintendent John Stuart (Shelburne Papers, *60:* 93–95). Taitt mentions (1916: 501, 509, 510, 527, 540, 541) his relations with Germany in 1772.

Geum: avens (*Geum* sp.); in Oconee County, S.C., 334.

Geum *odoratissimum, a new species of Caryophyllata: *nomen subnudum*—undetermined (cf. Merrill, 1945: 26); near Broad River, Ga., 43.

"I know not whether Michaux or Lyon saw it" (Bartram to Muhlenberg, September 6, 1810; Muhlenberg Letters: 137).

Gilead ("Giliad"), peak of: in the Catskill Mountains, N.Y.; a (Timber) Rattlesnake on, 270.

Probably this peak was the present South Mountain, about 2 miles northwest of Palenville, Greene County, N.Y. (cf. Bartram Papers, *1:* 35).

Ginseng (Panax): *Panax quinquefolius* L.; compared with *Angelica lucida*, 327. *See also* Panax.

Glarea (cf. Linné, 1768, *3:* 197): apparently very fine sand; in the middle region of Georgia, 45.

Glass-snake. *See* Snake, glass.

Gleditsia: either honey locust (*G. triacanthos* L.) or water locust (*G. aquatica* Marsh.) (probably the former in the first two of the following cases); on Oconee River, Ga., 379; along Chattahoochee River, Ala., 394; near The Rigolets, La., 421.

Gleditsia monosperma (cf. Catesby, 1730, *1:* 43, pl. 43; Walter, 1788: 254): water locust (*G. aquatica* Marsh.); on St. John's River above Lake Dexter, Fla., 131.

Gleditsia triacanthos (or "triacanthus"): honey locust (*G. triacanthos* L.); about Wrightsborough, Ga., 36; cultivated by the ancients near Little River, 38; on St. John's River above Picolata, Fla., 84, and above Lake Dexter, 131; along upper Savannah River, Ga., 320; along Mississippi River, La., 432; along Cape Fear River, N.C., 474.

Globularia: not the Old World genus of this name, but probably a species of *Petalostemum* (family Leguminosae) (F.W.P.); near Suwannee River, Fla., 242.

"*Globularia,* I am not certain this is the Family that this singular plant belongs to. The Fructification is a compact elyptical head imbricated, resembling Xyris; some of the species are singularly beautiful in respect to their multifid foliage." (Bartram to Muhlenberg, September 6, 1810; Muhlenberg Letters: 137.)

Gloriosa superba: climbing lily (*G. superba* L.); in the tropics, xiv.

Glycine: in this case, perhaps groundnut (*Apios americana* Medic.); near Lake Lochloosa, Fla., 181.

Glycine apios: groundnut (*Apios americana* Medic.); in coastal swamps, 29; on St. John's River above Lake Dexter, Fla., 136; along upper Savannah River, Ga., 321.

Glycine (or "Glycene") frutescens: American wisteria (*Wisteria frutescens* [L.] Poir.); in Liberty County, Ga., 10; in coastal swamps, 29; on St. John's River above Lake Dexter, Fla., 136; near Cowee, N.C., 357; in Monroe or adjacent county, Ala., 402.

Gnaphalium: everlasting (*Gnaphalium* sp.); at Lake Dexter, Fla., 155; near Suwannee River, 243.

Gnats (cynips): in this case, doubtless not hymenopterous gall-midges (genus *Cynips*), but probably gnats (order Diptera) of some undetermined family (E.T.C., Jr.); persecuted by, in southwestern Georgia, 386.

God (or synonymous terms); boundless palace of the sovereign Creator, xiv; display of the Almighty hand, xiv; favors of the great Author, xvi; the great Creator revealing useful plants, xvii; power, wisdom, and beneficence of the Supreme Creator and Sovereign Lord of the universe, xxiii; incense we can offer to the Almighty, xxxiv; will of the Almighty and injunction of the Great Spirit, 21; guidance of a divine and powerful preceptor, 22; thanks to the Almighty, the Creator and Preserver, 47; relying on our God, 52; works and power of the Creator, 57; Creator supreme, almighty, 59; power, majesty, and perfection of the great Almighty Creator, 73; glory of the Creator's works, 82; servants of the Most High, 100; homage to the great Creator, 100; Seminole guarded by the Deity, 107; the sun as minister of the Most High, 158; under the care of the Almighty, 158; wisdom and power of the supreme author of nature, 189; nature at the command of the Supreme Creator, 229; thunder and lightning under direction of the Great Spirit, 259; thanksgiving to the Supreme Creator and preserver, 269; corn given by the Great Spirit only for food to man, 351; the Good Spirit spoke, 365; homage to the Supreme, 452; blowing smoke toward the Great Spirit, 453; sabbath sacred to the Great Spirit, 457; distinguished by the Author of nature, 473; homage to the Supreme Being, 487; eye and fear of the Great Spirit, 489; love and adoration to the Deity, 492; Great and Good Spirit, 492; representative of Providence or the Great Spirit, 496; adore the Great Spirit, 498; the Great Spirit favors all good and brave men, 518.

Godwit, great red breasted. *See* Numenius pectore rufo.

Godwit, greater. *See* Numenius Americana.

Godwit, white. *See* Numenius, alba varia.

Gold chains; worn by Indians, 503.

Goldfinch. *See* Carduelis Americanus; Oriolus spurius.

Goldfinch, lesser. *See* Carduelis pinus.

Gold-fish: Bartram's Minnow (*Notropis lutipinnis* [Jordan and Brayton]); behavior and description of, in a branch of Broad River, Ga., 43–44. (Cf. W. Bartram, 1943: 180, fig. 11.)

Golphin. *See* Galphin.

Goose, blue winged. *See* Anser aliis ceruliis.

Goose, Canadian. *See* Anser Canadensis.

Goose, grey. *See* Anser branta grisea maculata.

Goose, laughing. *See* Anser fuscus maculatus.

Goose, tame: derived chiefly from the wild Graylag Goose (*Anser anser* [L.]); compared in size with a Pelican, 70.

Goose, white brant. *See* Anser branta.

Gopher. *See* Tortoise, great land.

Gordonia: red or loblolly bay (*G. lasianthus* [L.] Ellis); v; in the Lime-Sink Region, Ga., 30; about lakes in Putnam County, Fla., 174.

Gordonia, a species of, Franklinia Alatamaha ("Alatahama"): Franklin tree (*Franklinia alatamaha* Bartr. ex Marsh.) (cf. E. L. Little, Jr., 1945: 503; Merrill, 1945: 18); described, near Fort Barrington, McIntosh County, Ga., 16. *See also* Franklinia.

Gordonia lasianthus (or "Lacianthus" or "Lascanthus") (cf. Catesby, 1730, *1*: 44, pl. 44); red or loblolly bay (*G. lasianthus* [L.] Ellis); of Carolina and Florida, xvi; on Colonel's Island, Ga., 6; in Liberty County, 10; flowers compared with those of *Franklinia*, 16; about St. Mary's River, Ga.–Fla., 24; on St. John's River near Charlotia, Fla., 93; described, at Salt Springs, 161–162; west of Spalding's Lower Store, 171; *Franklinia* resembling, 467.

Gorgets, Cherokee youths ornamented with, 370. *See also* Crescents or gorgets.

Gossypium: a genus of Malvaceae, comprising the cottons; usefulness, xvii. *See also* Cotton.

Gourd (Cucurbita lagenaria [or "laginaria"]): gourd or calabash (*Lagenaria vulgaris* Ser.); on Meherrin River, Va., x, 479. *See also* Cucurbita lagenaria.

Government and civil society; of American aborigines, 494–500.

Governors of Carolina, Georgia, etc., called mico, 494.

Governor of Cuba, presenting an Indian with tobacco, 227.

Governor of East Florida: Patrick Tonyn (1725–1804); holding a council with the Lower Creeks, 78–79; Seminole horses to be purchased for, 215; a young man in service of, 215.

Colonel Tonyn arrived as governor in March 1774, and the council here referred to took place very shortly afterward. He also "had a talk with the Indians on the 26th of November, 1775, at Picolata." (Forbes, 1821: 23.) He had a plantation at the site of the present Green Cove Springs (W. Bartram, 1943: 150, 224). His rather turbulent career as the last British governor of Florida (1774–1784) is sketched by Mowat (1943: 83–149). A map of the Georgia and Florida coast (*Catalogue of the De Renne Library 3*: 1207) shows a Fort Tonyn on the St. Mary's River, probably at the site of the present King's Ferry. American soldiers marched against this fort in 1778.

Governor of West Florida and the Bahama Islands. *See* Browne, Governor Montfort.

Governor [of Georgia]. *See* Wright, Sir James.

Governor of North Carolina. *See* Dobbs, Arthur.

Governor, Spanish, of St. Augustine; son captured and executed by Creeks, 488–489.

Gracula *purpurea, the lesser purple jackdaw, or crow blackbird (cf. Catesby, 1730? *1*: 12, pl. 12): *nomen nudum*—if restricted to the breeding bird of southeastern Pennsylvania, this name applies to Stone's Grackle (*Quiscalus quiscula stonei* Chapman) (cf. Harper, 1942*d*: 213–214); listed, 289 *bis*.

Gracula quiscula, the purple jackdaw of the sea coast: not *G. quiscula* L., but Atlantic Boat-tailed Grackle (*Cassidix mexicanus torreyi* Harper)—this subspecies at least for the most part (cf. Harper, 1942*d*: 213); listed, 290.

The use of the symbol ¶ in this place is erroneous.

Grain, old, burned at the busk, 509.

Granadilla, Passiflora incarnata, called May-Apple: may-pop (*P. incarnata* L.); at Lake Dexter, Fla., 155.

Granary (or granaries); private and public, at Cuscowilla, Fla., 194; public, at disposal of the mico, 496; of Indians, 512–513.

Grant, Governor [James], of Florida; a (Diamondback) Rattlesnake served at his table, 271.

Grant (1720–1806) was a British soldier. He took part in campaigns in Flanders (1747–48) and in Ireland, in the French and Indian War (1758), in the war with the Cherokees (1760 and 1761), and in the Revolutionary battles of Long Island, Brandywine, and Germantown. He served as governor of Florida from 1764 to 1771, and departed for England in 1772 on account of bad health. His colonial rule was arbitrary, but he encouraged the cultivation of rice and indigo, and he directed the construction of the King's Highway from New Smyrna and St. Augustine to the St. Mary's River. He also promoted John Bartram's exploration of the St. John's River. (Cf. J. Bartram, 1942: 89; Romans, 1776: 223; Forbes, 1821: 171; Carroll, 1836, *1*: 466–475; Fairbanks, 1858: 170–171; Tucker, 1929; Mowat, 1943: 14–33; *New Inter. Encycl.*)

Grant, Dr.: a physician of the garrison at Mobile, Ala.; return to Mobile with, 413.

Grapes: *Vitis* sp.; compared in size with *Ilex* berries, 479.

Grapes, European wine: *Vitis vinifera* L.; compared with grapes in South Carolina, 329.

Grape vines: *Vitis* spp.; magnitude on lower St. John's River, Fla., 86–87; near The Rigolets, La., 423; used on a raft, 444–445.

Grape vines (Vitis *campestris) of a peculiar species: possibly fox grape (*V. labrusca* L.) (B.L.); described, in Butler or adjacent county, Ala., 400.

"Vitis campestris, Cherokee grape, Vines spred over shrubs. said to be excellent for Wine." (Bartram to Muhlenberg, September 6, 1810; Muhlenberg Letters: 137.)

Apparently not the muscadine (*V. rotundifolia* Michx.) as suggested by Fernald (1944: 48) (cf. Merrill, 1945: 32–33).

Grape vines (Vitis vinifera): in this case, not the cultivated grape of Europe (*V. vinifera* L.), but some native species of *Vitis;* along Keowee River, S.C., 329.

Grass, jointed decumbent: undetermined; on St. John's River above Lake Dexter, Fla., 130.

Grass, a fine short: undetermined; near Orange Lake, Fla., 181.

Grasshoppers. *See* Locusta.

Grave(s): of Yamasees on St. John's River, Fla., 139; of Indians in Vale of Cowee, N.C., 348; among Muscogulges, 515.

Great Hammock (traders' name): a former Seminole town, whose location is uncertain, though placed by Bartram on the Flint River; listed, 464.

Great Island (traders' name): a former Seminole town, whose location is uncertain, though placed by Bartram on the Flint River; listed, 464.

Great Lake: Lake George, the largest lake on St. John's River, about 18 miles south of Palatka, Fla.; crossing, 98; channels to, 156; re-entering, 168; shells in rocks on, 180. *See also* Lake George.

Great Ridge: the height of land between the Altamaha and the Savannah Basins, in northeastern Georgia; Buffalo Lick on, 35, or at foot of, 39; a north course up, 41; description of, 41–42.

Great water: Atlantic Ocean; 495. *See also* Atlantic Ocean, Ocean.

Greeks; a colony at New Smyrna, Fla., 144; origin of war among, 392–393.

Grist-mill; at Cross Creeks, N.C., 477. *See also* Mills, Saw-mills.

Grouper ("Grooper"): probably some species of *Epinephilus* or related genus (family Serranidae); about Georgia coastal islands, 67.

Grouse ("grous") of Pennsylvania. *See* Tetrao urogallus.

Gruel; made of corn flour and eaten during fasting at Otasse, Ala., 456.

Grus *alba ("alber"). *See* Crane, whooping.

Grus *clamator, vertice papilloso, corpore niveo remigibus nigris, the great whooping crane (cf. Catesby, 1731, *1:* 75, pl. 75): Whooping Crane (*Grus americana* [L.]); listed, 292–293. *See also* Crane, whooping.

G[rus] *pratensis, corpore cinereo, vertice papilloso, the great savanna crane: Florida Sandhill Crane (*Grus canadensis pratensis* Bartram) (cf. Harper, 1942*d:* 218–219) (fig. 14); listed, 293. *See also* Crane(s); Crane(s), savanna.

The wrong symbol is employed here.

Guide(s); in party setting out from Augusta, Ga., 35; obtained at Coolome, Ala., 397.

Guilandina dioica: Kentucky coffee-tree (*Gymnocladus dioica* [L.] K. Koch); of the Northern States, xvi.

The words "Kentuke coffe tree" are written (presumably by Bartram) beside this name in his copy of Linné's *Systema Vegetabilium* (1774).

Guineas, three, paid for a boat, 73.

Gulf ("gulph") [of Mexico], Indians crossing by canoe, 227.

Gull, great grey. *See* Larus griseus.

Gull, great white. *See* Larus alba.

Gull, little white river. *See* Larus alba minor.

Gun(s): of an Indian, 115; Wolf killed with butt of, 398; not formerly owned by the Creeks, 500; buried with the dead among Muscogulges, 516. *See also* Fusee, Piece(s).

Guns, swivel, at Fort James, Ga., 323.

Gun-men or warriors; 500 in Uchee town, Ala., 388. *See also* Warriors.

Gun-powder, 476.

Habitation(s): in Vale of Cowee, N.C., 349; at Watauga, 350; at Cowee, 354; of Cherokees, described, 367; on Mobile Delta, Ala., 404, 407; in Pensacola, Fla., 416; on Tangipahoa River, La., 424; at Manchac, 428; on the Mississippi, 430; in Baton Rouge, 436; of the Muscogulges, 446; of the Muscogulge king, 496; erected by Indian men, 513. *See also* House(s).

Hair; dressing of, among Indians, 501, 503.

Halesia (or "Halesa"): silverbell trees (*Halesia* spp.); in lower Coastal Plain, 29; in Southern Red Hills, 32; about Wrightsborough, Ga., 36; on the Great Ridge, 41; on St. Simon's Island, 58; at Lake George, Fla., 157; between Orange and Tuscawilla Lakes, 183; near Three Sisters Ferry, S.C., 309; along upper Savannah River, Ga., 320; in Oconee County, S.C., 334; at Falling Creek, Rabun County, Ga., 342; near Wayah Gap, N.C., 362; along Chattahoochee River, Ala., 394; in Monroe or adjacent county, 401, 402; in Escambia or adjacent county, 403; on upper Tensaw River, 408; near The Rigolets, La., 421; at the White Cliffs, 436.

The records from the Piedmont and the Blue Ridge doubtless pertain to *H. carolina* L., while those from the Coastal Plain may pertain to any one of three species.

Halesia diptera: two-winged silverbell (*H. diptera* Ellis); on Colonel's Island, Ga., 6; near Salt Springs, Fla., 164; near Alachua Savanna, 187; in Levy County, 221; on Oconee (= Station) Mountain, S.C., 337; a new species or variety of, on lower Tombigbee River, Ala., 410.

The record from Oconee Mountain, S.C., is very questionable, since this species is known to extend only very slightly into the Piedmont from the Coastal Plain.

Halesia tetraptera (or "taetraptera") (cf. Catesby, 1731, *1*: 64, pl. 64): four-winged silverbell (*H. carolina* L.; syn., *H. tetraptera* L.); on Colonel's Island, Ga., 6; in Liberty County, 10; near Salt Springs, Fla., 164; near Alachua Savanna, 187; on Oconee (= Station) Mountain, S.C., 337.

Half-way Pond: the present Cowpen Pond, in southwestern Putnam County, Fla. (fig. 17); environs and fauna described, 174–179; proceed from, 179; camped at, 209, 216.

Haliotis auris marina: apparently intended to designate some limpet-like gastropod mollusk (R.A.M.); on St. John's River at Charlotia, Fla., 93. *See also* Auris marina, and note under Cochleae.

Hal[iotis] patella: an undetermined marine shell; on St. John's River at Charlotia, Fla., 93.

Halmea spuria: a probable misprint for Kalmia spuria (*q.v.*).

Hamadryades, Cherokee maidens as, 357.

Hamamelis (cf. Catesby, 1748, 2, appendix: 2, pl. 2): witch hazel (*H. virginiana* L.); along upper Savannah River, Ga., 321; near Oconee (= Station) Mountain, S.C., 337.

Hammock(s) ("hommock[s]"): "in general . . . a comparatively dense forest composed mostly of trees other than pines, not subject to inundation . . . in a region where open pine forests or prairies predominate" ([R. M. Harper, in] *New Intern. Encycl.,* 1915); "hommocky" land on Amelia Island, Fla., 65; at Lake Dexter, 117; on St. John's River at Hawkinsville, 140; at Lake Beresford, 142; near Alachua Savanna, 187; "hommocky" points at Tuscawilla Lake, 193; "hommocky" country in Florida, 211; in Levy County, 221, 222, 223, 224; in Alachua County, 249; near Palatka, 303; in Escambia or adjacent county, Ala., 402; Passenger Pigeons roosting in, 470.

Handkerchief; presented to a blind old chief, 499.

Hanger: a short, usually slightly curved sword (Webster); for each ranger at Fort James, 324.

Hang nest. *See* Oriolus Baltimore.

Hares: perhaps including both the Eastern Cottontail (*Sylvilagus floridanus mallurus* [Thomas]) and the Carolina Marsh Rabbit (*S. palustris palustris* [Bachman]); on Colonel's Island, Ga., 7.

Hatchet(s): iron ones not formerly owned by the Creeks, 500; of an Indian chief, 500.

Haw River: an upper tributary of Cape Fear River, in north central North Carolina; x, 478.

Hawk: any of various species of the families Accipitridae or Falconidae; Soft-shelled Turtle's beak likened to a hawk's bill, 178; encounter with a Coachwhip Snake, 218–219.

Hawk, black. *See* Falco niger.

Hawk, chicken. *See* Falco pullarius.

Hawk, great eagle. *See* Falco Aquilinus.

Hawk or kite, forked tailed: Swallow-tailed Kite (*Elanoïdes forficatus forficatus* [L.]); feeding on Rough Green Snake and Chameleon, 275. *See also* Falco furcatus.

Hawk, hen. *See* Falco gallinarius.

Hawk, kite. *See* Milvus.

Hawk, least. *See* Falco sparverius.

Hawk, marsh. *See* Falco ranivorus.

Hawk, pidgeon. *See* Falco columbarius.

Hawk, sharp winged. *See* Falco glaucus, Falco subcerulius.

Hawk, sparrow. *See* Falco sparverius.

Hay; grass fit for, in Oconee County, S.C., 334.

Hedera arborea: pepper vine (*Ampelopsis arborea* [L.] Koehne); on St. John's River above Lake Dexter, Fla., 136; near Alachua Savanna, 187.

Hedera *carnosa: probably Virginia creeper (*Parthenocissus quinquefolia* [L.] Planch.) (cf. Merrill, 1945: 26); described, near Long Pond, Levy County, Fla., 243.

Hedera quinquefolia ("quinquifolia"): Virginia creeper (*Parthenocissus quinquefolia* [L.] Planch.); on St. John's River above Lake Dexter, Fla., 136; near Alachua Savanna, 187.

Hedysarum: in this case, probably bush clover (*Lespedeza* sp.) or beggar's-ticks (*Desmodium* spp.); near Suwannee River, Fla., 243.

Heifer. *See* Cattle.

Helenium: sneezeweed (*Helenium* spp.); near Suwannee River, Fla., 242; in Brunswick County, N.C., 472.

Helianthus: sunflower (*Helianthus* spp.) or some related plant; near Lake Lochloosa, Fla., 180; near Suwannee River, 242; along upper Savannah River, Ga., 321; in Brunswick County, N.C., 472.

Helmintholithus: in this case, coquina; on Long Bay, S.C., 471.

Helonias: perhaps crow poison (*Zigadenus densus* [Desr.] Fern.); near Long Pond, Levy County, Fla., 248.

Hematites, along Upatoi Creek, Chattahoochee County, Ga., 387.

Hematopus ostrealegus, the will willet or oister catcher: in this case, not the European Oyster-catcher (*Haematopus ostralegus ostralegus* L.), but the American Oyster-catcher (*H. palliatus palliatus* Temminck); listed, 296.

There is some possibility here of confusion with the Eastern Willet (*Catoptrophorus semipalmatus semipalmatus* [Gmelin]), to which the name "will willet" might seem to be more naturally applied (cf. Trumbull, 1888: 164–165). This common and conspicuous bird is omitted from the list presented on pages 289–296.

Hemlock spruce (P[inus] abies): either Canada hemlock (*Tsuga canadensis* [L.] Carr.) or Carolina hemlock (*T. caroliniana* Engelm.); near Aquone, N.C., 364. *See also* Pinus abies, Pinus canadensis.

Hemp: *Cannabis sativa* L.; along Cape Fear River, N.C., 474.

Hemp bird. *See* Fringilla canabina.

Hen(s), domestic: *Gallus gallus* (L.); compared in size with Limpkin, 147; Catbirds a vexation to, 300. *See also* Chickens; Cock; Fowl, common domestic.

Hen, Indian. *See* Ardea mugitans.

Heracleum *maximum: cow parsnip (*H. maximum* Bartr.; syn., *H. lanatum* Michx.) (cf. Fernald, 1944: 50; Merrill, 1945: 26); described, near Clayton, Rabun County, Ga., 344.

Herbaceae ("herbaccae" or "herbacia"): herbaceous plants; along upper Savannah River, Ga., 321; in Warren County, 378–379.

Herons: various species of the family Ardeidae; at Nassau Sound, Fla., 71; imagined presence on floating islands in St. John's River, 90; feathers as head ornaments among Indians, 501, 502.

Heron, great bluish grey crested. *See* Ardea herodias.

Heron, little crested purple or blue. *See* Ardea purpurea cristata.

Heron, grey white crested. *See* Ardea varia cristata.

Heron, speckled crested. *See* Ardea maculata cristata.

Heron, great white river. *See* Ardea immaculata.

Heron, little white. *See* Ardea alba minor.

Hibernian: Irishman; 353.

Hibiscus, with ovate lanceolate leaves and large incarnate flowers: perhaps swamp rose-mallow (*H. moscheutos* L.); described, on Drayton's Island, Fla., 105.

Hibiscus coccineus: "blazing star" (*H. coccineus* Walt.); described, on Drayton's Island, Fla., 104–105.

Hibiscus, procumbent species of: probably *H. aculeatus* Walt.; south of Altamaha River, Ga., 19.

Hibiscus, shrub (perhaps Hibisc. spinifex): *Pavonia spinifex* (L.) Cav.; described, on Drayton's Island, Fla., 104.

"*Hibiscus spinifex,* I cant find it in Wild. or Walter" (Bartram to Muhlenberg, September 6, 1810; Muhlenberg Letters: 137).

Hibiscus (or "Hybiscus") spinifex: a mallow (*Pavonia spinifex* [L.] Cav.); on St. John's River above Lake Dexter, Fla., 114; near Salt Springs, 164.

These occurrences tend to confirm Small's belief (1933: 853) that the species is native, not introduced.

Hickory (or "Hiccory") or Hickories: *Carya* spp.; near Broad River, Ga., 44; on St. John's River near Charlotia, Fla., 93; at Lake Beresford, 142; near Salt Springs, 164; at Silver Bluff, S.C., 315; on Oconee River, Ga., 379; in Butler or adjacent county, Ala., 400. *See also* Juglans.

Hickory ("hiccory"), shell-barked. *See* Juglans exaltata.

Hickory ground (traders' name): a former Upper Creek town, in 1772 and 1799 on east bank of Coosa River about 2 miles below the present Wetumpka, Elmore County, Ala. (Taitt, map of 1772, and 1916: 536; Swanton, 1922: 242, pl. 2; Wetumpka quadrangle); listed, 463.

Hickory ("Hiccory") milk: made from nuts of shell-bark hickory; used in Creek Indian cookery, 38.

Hides, an Indian family loaded with, 244.

Highlanders; kilt of, 502.

Hillaba (properly Hilibi): a former Upper Creek town on Hillabee Creek, probably near the Clay-Tallapoosa county boundary, Ala. (Taitt, map of 1772, and 1916: 530; *Bur. Am. Ethnol. Bull., 30*, Pt. I:

549, 1907; Swanton, 1922: 259, pl. 2, as "Hilibi (3)"; Ashland quadrangle); listed, 463.

Hippobosca: in this case, some species of horsefly (*Tabanus*); tormenting horses in Taylor County, Ga., 385.

Hirundo. See Swallows.

H[irundo] *cerdo, the chimney swallow: *nomen nudum*—Chimney Swift (*Chaetura pelagica* [L.]); listed, 292.

Barton (1799a: 17) refers to the "Chimney-Bird" by the name of *Hirundo pelasgia*, and adds (p. 18): "This is the Hirundo cerdo of Bartram. Travels."

Hirundo pelasgia, cauda aculeata, the house swallow: Barn Swallow (*H. rustica erythrogaster* Boddaert); listed, 292.

The technical nomenclature employed by Bartram suggests the Chimney Swift (*Chaetura pelagica*—*Hirundo pelagica* L., 1758; *H. pelasgia* L., 1766) (cf. Catesby, 1748, 2, appendix: 8, pl. 8); and Coues (1875: 352) so interprets this species as well as the "H. cerdo" a few lines below. But Bartram's account (1791: 287) and Wilson's reference (1812, 5: 42) to Bartram's observations show that the Barn Swallow was the species that the latter had in mind. It is referred to as "House Swallow" in Bartram's later diary (Stone, 1913: 349). See also Swallow, house.

H[irundo] purpurea, the great purple martin (cf. Catesby, 1730, 1: 51, pl. 51): Purple Martin (*Progne subis subis* [L., 1758]; syn., *Hirundo purpurea* L. [1766]); listed, 292.

H[irundo] riparia vertice purpurea, the bank martin: doubtless composite, including Bank Swallow (*Riparia riparia riparia* [L.]) and Tree Swallow (*Iridoprocne bicolor* [Vieillot]); listed, 292. See also Martin, bank.

"Hirundo riparia" should apply only to the Bank Swallow, but "vertice purpurea" applies rather to the Tree Swallow. Bartram did not distinguish the Tree, Cliff, or Rough-winged Swallows. They were described years later by others.

Historians; on the aborigines of America, 511.

Hiwassee ("Hiwasse"): a former Cherokee town on the Hiwassee River at the junction of Peachtree Creek, Cherokee County, Tenn. (Mooney, 1900: 512, pl. 3; Swanton, 1922: pl. 7, as "Haywassee"; Nantahala quadrangle); listed, 373.

Hoes: Negroes armed with, 472; iron hoes not formerly owned by the Creeks, 500; used on Indian plantations, 512.

Hogehege River: the middle and lower portions of the Tennessee River (Swanton, 1922: pl. 4); 339.

Holston ("Holstein") River: arising in southwestern Virginia and joining the Clinch in eastern Tennessee to form the Tennessee River;
339.

Ho[l?]mes, D., principal trader at Keowee, S.C., 332. *See also* Trader,
at Keowee, S.C.

Hominy ("hommony" or "homony"): a food prepared from corn;
hickory milk an ingredient in, 38; cooked with acorn oil by Indians,
85; in repast at Cuscowilla, Fla., 186, and at Watauga, N.C., 351.

"Hommock(s)." *See* Hammock(s).

Honey: on St. Simon's Island, Ga., 60, 61; in repast at Cuscowilla, Fla.,
186; traded by Seminoles, 212; bartered by Indians to Spaniards in
Cuba, 227; honeyed water in feast at Talahasochte, 236; contee
sweetened with, 241; an Indian family loaded with, 244; secured
from a bee tree, 305.

Hooseche (properly Osochi): a former Lower Creek town on the west
side of Chattahoochee River, 2 miles below the mouth of Uchee
Creek, Russell County, Ala. (*Bur. Am. Ethnol. Bull., 30*, Pt. II: 161,
1910; Swanton, 1922: 166, pls. 2, 9; Taitt's map of 1772, as "Wari-
sia"); listed, 464.

Hopea tinctoria (or "tinctorea") (cf. Catesby, 1730, *1:* 54, pl. 54):
horse sugar (*Symplocos tinctoria* [L.] L'Hér.); about St. Mary's
River, Ga.–Fla., 24; in lower Coastal Plain, 29; in the Lime-Sink Region, 30; on St. John's River above Lake Dexter, Fla., 131; near Salt
Springs, 164; near Alachua Savanna, 187; along upper Savannah
River, Ga.–S.C., 327; near Wayah Gap, N.C., 362; along Chattahoochee River, Ala., 393; along Cape Fear River, N.C., 474.

Horn Island, La.: between Mississippi Sound and Gulf of Mexico;
pass by, 437.

Horse(s): *Equus caballus* L.; purchased in Savannah, Ga., 5; south of
Altamaha River, 17, 19; of a Seminole, 21; start a journey with, 28;
riding and pack-horses in Col. Barnet's party, 35; at the Buffalo
Lick, 39; on St. Simon's Island, 58, 60; on Georgia coastal islands,
67; compared in size with Alligator, 128; Seminole ("Siminole")
horses on Alachua Savanna, Fla., 188, 201; Indians on horseback,
190; about Alachua Savanna, 194, 196, 197, 200, 203, 207; Wolves
feeding on carcass of, 199; horses of the true Seminole breed ridden
by Indians of Cuscowilla, 207; diseased on Alachua Savanna, 207;
driven by traders, 208; at Halfway Pond, 209; Seminole horses described and compared, 215–216; riding and pack-horses on trip to
Talahasochte, 215, 218; Seminole horses to be purchased for the
governor, 215; Andalusian breed brought by Spaniards to Florida,

216; several troops of Seminole horses near Long Pond, Levy County, one under control of a dog, 222–223; hunted by traders near Talahasochte, 229; crossing Suwannee River, 232; pack-horses of chief trader, 237, 238; near the Alligator Hole, 239; belonging to a family of Talahasochte, 244; searching for, at Long Pond, Levy County, and vicinity, 248–249; water and pasture for "our creatures," 251; sold by Seminoles in St. Augustine, 255; pack-horse men at Spalding's Lower Store, 255; collected by Seminoles at this store, 263; set off from this store on Seminole horses, 303; transported across St. John's River, 304–305; stable and provender for, 309; for each ranger at Fort James, Ga., 324; Bartram's only companion, 341; sinking under its rider, 343; turned out in meadows, 344; feet dyed with strawberry juice, 346; steed turned out to graze, 347; cared for by Indians at Watauga, N.C., 350, 351, 352; at a horse-stamp near Cowee, 355–356; turned to graze, 361; a company of Cherokees on horseback, 364; of Indian traders, 377–378; method used by traders in breaking, 377–378; cane as food for "our quadrupeds," 379; excellent food for, on Patsiliga Creek, Taylor County, Ga., 384; tormented by heat and flies, 384–386; driven across Chattahoochee River, 388; feeding in cane swamps along the Chattahoochee, Ala., 395; hunted up, 402; furnished by Major Farmar, 411; Scotch grass fed to, 430; set off with, to the White Plains, La., 431; in caravan leaving Taensa, Ala., 440, 441, 443; exchange of, 441–443; with emigrants from Georgia, 443; swimming a creek in Montgomery County, Ala., 444–445; escaping from Choctaws with, 446; in a caravan leaving Otasse, 457; crossing Ocmulgee River, 458, 459, and Ogeechee River, Ga., 460; horse-loads of Wild Pigeons, 469; on Long Bay, S.C., 472; pack-horses crossing Susquehanna River, Pa., on ice, 480; formerly none among Creeks, 500. *See also* Colts.

Horse-hair; long moss resembling, 88.

Horse-stamp: probably something in the nature of a horse corral, analogous to a cowpen; near Cowee, N.C., 355–356.

Hortus Siccus: herbarium specimens of dried plants; sent to Charleston, 48.

Hothletega (properly Hoƚi-taiga): a former Okfuskee settlement on Chattahoochee River in western Georgia, probably in Troup County (Swanton, 1922: 249, pl. 2); listed, 463.

House(s): on St. John's River at Charlotia, Fla., 95; dwelling-house at Lake Beresford, 143; in Cuscowilla, described, 191–192; farm house in South Carolina, 326; in Vale of Cowee, N.C., 349; at Echoe, 350; mansion-house on Savannah River, S.C., 375; in Uchee town, Ala., described, 388; in Mobile, 404; on lower Tombigbee River, 410; at Lake Pontchartrain, La., 424; at Cambelton, N.C., 478; cleaned at the busk, 509. *See also* Habitation(s), Public house.

Humble bees. *See* Bees, humble.

Humble plant (Mimosa pudica): *M. pudica* L.; compared with sensitive briar, 24; as a weed on the Mississippi, 430.

Hummingbird: Ruby-throated Hummingbird (*Archilochus colubris* [L.]); on St. Simon's Island, Ga., 61. *See also* Trochilus colubris.

Hunters: in party setting out from Augusta, Ga., 35; going out to Oconee River, 42; bringing in venison and Turkeys, 45, and a Savanna Crane, 220.

Hunting: by inhabitants at Tangipahoa River, La., 425; festivals dedicated to, 509; a principal employment of Indian men, 513.

Hurl(s). *See* Rackets or hurl(s).

Hurricane; oak thrown down by, 74; at Lake Beresford, Fla., 141–143; near Clayton, Ga., 343; between Flint and Chattahoochee Rivers, 386. *See also* Gale, Storm, Tempest.

Hyacinthus: a genus of Liliaceae, comprising the hyacinths; in the tropics, xv.

"Hybiscus." *See* Hisbiscus spinifex.

Hydrangea: hydrangea (*Hydrangea* sp.); along upper Savannah River, Ga.–S.C., 327.

Hydrangea ("Hydrangia"), new species of: *Hydrangea quercifolia* (*q.v.*); viii.

Hydrangea (or "Hydrangia") *quercifolia: oak-leaved hydrangea (*H. quercifolia* Bartr.) (cf. Merrill, 1945: 26); pleasing figure, xviii; described, from Sweet Water Brook (probably Culpeper Creek), Crawford County, Ga., 382–383; figured on pl. facing p. 382; on upper Tensaw River, Ala., 408.

Hydrastis, new species of: false bugbane (*Trautvetteria carolinensis* [Walt.] Vail) (Gray, 1841: 2); described, along Jarrett Creek, near Aquone, N.C., 364.

"Hydrastis, every way larger than H. canadensis" (Bartram to Muhlenberg, September 6, 1810; Muhlenberg Letters: 137).

Hydrocotyle ("Hydrocotile") *fluitans: *nomen nudum* (Merrill, 1945: 34)—water pennywort (*Hydrocotyle* sp.); on floating islets in St. John's River, Fla., 130.

"*Hydracotyle fluitans* differs little if any from H. umbellata. except being every way larger, and its growing with other floating plants in Rivers and stagnate ponds" (Bartram to Muhlenberg, September 6, 1810; Muhlenberg Letters: 137).

Hypericum: St. John's-wort (*Hypericum* sp.); in Brunswick County, N.C., 472.

Hypericum *aureum: golden St. John's-wort (*H. frondosum* Michx.) (cf. Merrill, 1945: 27); described, from Patsiliga Creek, Taylor County, Ga., 383.

Bartram's name is preoccupied in Loureiro (1790).

"*Hypericum aureum*. a splended shrub, Lyon saw it, he shewed me specimins of it[.]" (Bartram to Muhlenberg, September 6, 1810; Muhlenberg Letters: 137.)

Hypoxis: star-grass (*Hypoxis* sp.); near Long Pond, Levy County, Fla., 248.

Hyssopus: a genus of Labiatae, comprising the hyssop (*H. officinalis* L.); usefulness, xvii.

Iberville canal (or "channel"): the present Bayou Manchac, La., separating East Baton Rouge Parish on the north from Iberville and Ascension Parishes on the south (soil map of East Baton Rouge Parish, 1905; Baton Rouge quadrangle); ascent of, 427; bridge over, 428.

Ibis (or Egyptian Ibis): *Threskiornis aethiopicus aethiopicus* (Latham); compared with Wood Ibis, 150, 293.

Ice, in Maryland and on Susquehanna River, 480.

Icterus, golden: presumably Baltimore Oriole (*Icterus galbula* [L.]); at Lake Dexter, Fla., 154. See also Baltimore bird, Oriolus Baltimore.

The occurrence of this species and of the Indigo Bunting at this locality in summer does not seem very probable.

Icterus minor. See Oriolus (icterus minor); Oriolus spurius.

Idolatry, not observed among Indians, 497–498.

Ilex: perhaps American holly (*I. opaca* Ait.); near Suwannee River, Fla., 243.

Ilex angustifolium: perhaps narrow-leaved dahoon holly (*I. cassine* var. *angustifolia* Willd.); about St. Mary's River, Ga.–Fla., 24.

Ilex aquifolium: American holly (*I. opaca* Ait.); on Colonel's Island, Ga., 6; in Lime-Sink Region, 30; on St. Simon's Island, 58; on lower St. John's River, Fla., 84; near Salt Springs, 164; near Suwannee River, 242; near Three Sisters Ferry, S.C., 309.

Ilex dahoon: dahoon or cassena (*I. cassine* L.); along Cape Fear River, N.C., 476.

Ilex myrtifolium: myrtle-leaved holly (*I. myrtifolia* Walt.); near Suwannee River, Fla., 242.

Ilex varietas: in Bartram's usage, *Ilex* was apparently equivalent to the current section *Aquifolium* of the genus *Ilex* (yaupons and hollies); on Colonel's Island, Ga., 6.

Illicium: anise trees, constituting a genus of aromatic shrubs or trees in the family Magnoliaceae, with two species in the Southeastern United States and five in Asia; in the tropics, xiv.

Illicium (or "Illisium"): (in Alabama and probably in Georgia) purple anise (*I. floridanum* Ellis); on Altamaha River, Ga., 48; in Escambia or adjacent county, Ala., 403; on upper Tensaw River, 408; in southern Alabama, ix, 442; range of, 442.

The record from Lake George, Fla., included in the statement of range on page 442, pertains to the yellow anise (*I. parviflorum* Michx.).

Illicium ("Illisium"): in this case, yellow anise (*I. parviflorum* Michx.); at Salt Springs, Fla., vi, 160. (Cf. J. Bartram, 1942: 74.)

Illicium ("Illisium") Floridanum: in the following cases, purple anise (*I. floridanum* Ellis); beauty and fragrance, xvii; in Monroe or adjacent county, Ala., 402, 443.

Illicium ("Illisium") Floridanum: in this case, yellow anise (*I. parviflorum* Michx.); at Salt Springs, Fla., 165.

Illinois, region of, various trees of, xvi.

India pictures, 132.

Indian(s) (tribes not specified): capacity for civilization, and welfare of, xxxiii–xxxiv; inhabiting Colonel's Island, Ga., 5; a peculiar race in Okefinokee Swamp, 25; chiefs delegated to assist surveyors, 34; in party setting out from Augusta, 35; cultivating certain trees for their fruits, 38; instance of sagacity, 39–40; chief heading Col. Barnet's party, 40; using the physic-nut as a charm, 41; catching a Salmon Trout in Broad River region, 44; taking leave at Savannah River, 45; James Spalding's connections with tribes of East Florida, 58; plundering stores in Florida, 63–64; as hunter for a plantation on St. John's River, 75, 76; utilization of live-oak acorns, 85; hunters burning savannas, 107; a young Indian accompanying Bartram on upper St. John's, 114–115; running a gauntlet between, 125; actions of a chief compared with those of an Alligator, 130; a camping place of, on St. John's River, 134; name for the Limpkin, 147; setting "deserts" on fire, 152; party at Spalding's Upper Store, 156; utilization of Gars, 176; avenue of travelers near Alachua Savanna, 189; driving cattle on Alachua Savanna, 190; chiefs, senators, warriors, and young men assembled for council at Cuscowilla, 191; abandoning Alachua town, 193; visiting traders on Alachua Savanna, 207; name for a disease of cattle and horses, 207; at Lochloosa Creek, Alachua County, 209; horses to be purchased of, 215; proprietor of a troop of horses near Talahasochte, 223; their account of Suwannee River, 224–225; expeditions in canoes from Florida to Bahamas and Cuba, 227; fishing in Suwannee River, 228; chiefs at Talahasochte engaged with chief trader, 228; killing a Manatee and their name for it, 231–232; crossing Suwannee River in canoe, 232, 235; their accounts of Spanish settlements, 233; pathway of, on Spanish causeway, 234; seats in council house assigned to Indians of other towns, 236; observing the eruption at the Alligator Hole, 238–239; on a hunt near Long Pond, Levy County, 244; providing a feast of watermelons and oranges at Palatka, 303–304; George Galphin's trade with tribes of the South and Southwest, 314; *Angelica lucida* sold to Indians of Florida, 327; a prospective guide at Keowee, S.C., 333; relations with white traders, 353; use of yaupon by Southern Indians, 359; rendezvous at Flat Rock, Ga., 376; causes of their migrations, 391–392; origin of war among, 392–393; chewing resin of *Silphium*, 399; drying and storing grapes for provisions, 400–401; presents for, 440; red men conducting Bartram over the Tallapoosa and to Mucclasse, Ala., 446; guarding a trader's store at Mucclasse, 447; the aged not put to death, 498–500; division of labor among men and women, 513.

Indians—Alabama: Alibamu, a Muskhogean tribe of the Creek Confederacy formerly dwelling in southern Alabama, but about 1763 a portion of the tribe removed to the banks of the Mississippi (*Bur. Am. Ethnol. Bull.*, 30, Pt. I: 43–44, 1907; Swanton, 1946: 86–88); 429.

"These Alabama Indians . . . afterward moved farther west and the greater part of them finally reached the neighborhood of the Trinity River in Texas where their descendants still live, occupying a reservation in Polk County near Livingston" (J.R.S.).

Indians—Alachuas or Oconees ("Ocones"): Lower Creeks or Seminoles, formerly living on Oconee River, Ga., and migrating to the Alachua region of Florida (*Bur. Am. Ethnol. Bull.*, 30, Pt. I: 34, 1907, and Pt. II: 105, 1910; Swanton, 1946: 165); their customs tinctured with Spanish civilization, 186; Cuscowilla the capital of, 191; numbers and activities of the ancient Alachuas (actually the Potano—see Commentary), 198; vanquishing other Florida tribes and attacking the Spanish, 380–381. *See also* Indians—Seminoles.

Indians—Caloosas ("Calloosas"): a tribe of southwestern Florida (*Bur. Am. Ethnol. Bull.*, 30, Pt. I: 195–196, 1907; Swanton, 1946: 101–102; Neill, 1955a); claiming Florida but vanquished by Alachuas, 380–381. See Commentary for p. 380.

Indians—Cherokees (including "Overhill Indians"): a tribe occupying, in Bartram's time, upper Georgia, northwestern South Carolina, western North Carolina, and eastern Tennessee (cf. *Bur. Am. Ethnol. Bull., 30*, Pt. I: 245–249, 1907; Swanton, 1922: 213, 253, and 1946: 110–115); introduction to the chiefs, 9; at treaty of Augusta, 33; on bad terms with whites, 55; route into Cherokee country, 307; set off for Cherokee nation, 308; Mr. Cameron a deputy commissioner for, 326; Bartram's business in Cherokee country, 327; town of Seneca ("Sinica") described, 329–330; war between Cherokees and Carolinians, 330; ill-treated by Virginians, 331; jealous of white travelers, 331; former population in Vale of Keowee, S.C., 332; battle between Cherokees and Carolinians in Vale of Cowee, N.C., 348; trader married to a Cherokee woman, 349; girls with strawberries in Vale of Cowee, 349; hospitality and character of chief of Watauga, 350–352; maidens gathering strawberries near Cowee, 357–358; skirmishes of Overhill Indians with Virginians, 359; meeting with a young fellow, 361–362; meeting with a company led by Ata-kullakulla, near Nantahala River, 364–365; conducted to chief of Cowee, 366; habitations, council house, rotunda, festivals, and games at Cowee, 367–371; congress with Lower Cherokees at Seneca, S.C., 372; list of towns in Cherokee nation, 373–374; forced into alliance with Muscogulges, 392 (see Commentary for this page); rotunda compared with that of Upper Creeks, 450; general account of, 481–522; character, customs, and persons of, 483–492; language of, 519; in Georgia, preceded by mound-builders, 520.

The "Overhill Indians" were those living in extreme southwestern North Carolina and adjacent parts of Tennessee and Georgia (cf. Swanton, 1922: pl. 7). The Overhill towns listed by Bartram (pp. 373–374) were apparently mainly, if not wholly, in Tennessee.

Indians—Chickasaws ("Chicasaws"): a tribe closely related to the Choctaws, with their principal territory in northern Mississippi and western Tennessee (cf. *Bur. Am. Ethnol. Bull., 30*, Pt. I: 260–262, 1907; Swanton, 1946: 116–119); bringing the Chickasaw plum from beyond the Mississippi, 38; compelled by Muscogulges to sue for peace, 392 (see Commentary for this page); trade with, 404; a dialect of Chickasaw spoken at Abacooche, Ala., 463; their language as a dialect of Muscogulge, 465, 519; character, customs, and persons of, 483–484, 492.

Indians—Choctaws ("Chactaws") or Flatheads: a tribe occupying principally middle and southern Mississippi, but extending also into adjacent parts of Alabama and Louisiana; located near Muscogulges, 210; band of Seminoles destined against those of West Florida, 255, 257; George Galphin's trade with, 314; rivalry with Muscogulges, 392; Swanson and McGillivray's trade with, 404; interpreter for, 418; maritime settlements of, 437; conflict with Creeks, 438; a Choctaw slave, 440; apprehensions toward, 442; capturing emigrants in Alabama, 446, 507; their language as a dialect of Muscogulge, 465, 519; general account of, 481–522; character, customs, and persons of, 483–484, 492; eminent for poetry and music, 506; a Mustee with Choctaw blood, 506; a Choctaw slave girl at Mucclasse, Ala., 507; flattened heads of, 517; attributes of, 517; plantations, numbers, and territories of, 517; territories of, 522. Also mentioned in Contents (Pt. III, Ch. v), viii.

The Choctaws were pre-eminently agriculturists. Although of the same linguistic stock as the Creeks, their customs, social organization, and physical characteristics were very different. They were constantly at war with the Creeks and the Chickasaws (*Bur. Am. Ethnol. Bull., 30*, Pt. I: 288–289, 1907; Swanton, 1922: 420–421, and 1946: 121–123).

Indians—Creeks (or Creek Confederacy or Creek Nation or Muscogulges), including Upper and Lower Creeks (but see separate entries for Alachuas and Seminoles or Lower Creeks): a tribe occupying, in Bartram's time, chiefly the basins of the Chattahoochee and Alabama Rivers and northern Florida (cf. *Bur. Am. Ethnol. Bull., 30*, Pt. I: 362–365, 1907; Swanton, 1922, and 1946: 153–154); introduction to the chiefs, 9; a Creek at Fort Barrington, Ga., 17; legendary account of Okefinokee Swamp, 26; conquering and nearly exterminating the Yamasees, 26; at treaty of Augusta, 33; making hickory ("Hiccory") milk from hickory nuts, 38; trading path from Augusta to Creek Nation, 54; settling on Ocmulgee River after migrating from beyond the Mississippi, 54; subduing the surrounding tribes, 54; making alliance with English in Carolina and driving Spaniards into their fortifications in Florida, 55; Ogeechee Indians slain by, 66; conquering Yamasees on St. John's River, 139; constructing their royal standard of King Vulture feathers, 151; Cowkeeper's head ornamented in the Creek mode, 185; subduing ancient Floridans and driving Spaniards into St. Augustine, 208–209; relations with white people, 210; disposition and manners of Muscogulges, 210–211, 213; their name for horse, 216; Choctaw horses among Upper Creeks, 216; their names for *Magnolia grandiflora* and *Persea borbonia*, 232; friendly talks from Creek Nation, 251; treaty with Creek Nation at Picolata, Fla., 270; route into regions of, 307; George Galphin's trade with, 314; cession of lands to discharge their debts, 324; use of yaupon by, 359; journey through territories of, 366; habitations compared with those of Cherokees, 367; trading path from Augusta to, 376; traders bound for Creek Nation, 377; inhabitants of Oconee town moving into Upper Creeks, 380; migration from Georgia into Florida, 380–381; Upper Creeks confederated with Alachuas, 380–381; relations of Uchees with, 389; Uchee language different from Muscogulge, 389; tradition concerning a sunken yard at Apalachicola, Ala., 390; wars with Yamasees, Spaniards, Cherokees, Chickasaws, and Choctaws, 392; Otasse a Muscogulge town, 396; trade with, 404; habitations compared with those of French at Mobile, 404; leaving Creek Nation, 411, 413; conquering Alabama nation, 429; journey through Creek Nation, 438; conflict with Choctaws, 438; a Mustee Creek, 440, 443, 446; approach to Creek Nation, 443; nuptials of a Creek girl, 446; mode of habitations of, 446; a chief's conflict with a trader at Mucclasse, 448–449; treating Bartram with friendship, 449; Creek woman the wife of a trader at Coolome, 449; chiefs and warriors at Otasse, 450–454; king in ceremony in rotunda at Otasse, 452–453; ignorance concerning purpose of a pine pillar, 456; keeping the Sabbath at Otasse, 457; Muscogulge language, 458; traders bound to the Nation, 458; list of towns and tribes in Creek Confederacy, 462–464; towns in Alabama speaking Muscogulge, 462–464; population, derivation, migration, languages, and relations with other tribes, 464–466; return from Creek Nation, 467; general account of, 481–522; character, customs, and persons of, 483–493; capture and burning of Spanish youths by, 488–489; majesty of the mico, 495; a trader setting off for the Nation, 507; a Mustee with Creek blood, 507; marriage ceremonies of, 514–515; dress, numbers, and territories compared with those of Choctaws, 517; language of, 519; in Georgia, preceded by mound-builders, 520.

Indians—Floridans, ancient, or Yamasees; mound made by, near Tuscawilla Lake, Fla., 184; subdued by Creeks, 208, or Alachuas, 380. *See also* Indians—Yamasees.

Indians—Icosans: probably the Coosa tribe of South Carolina (Swanton, 1922: 22, 56); warred upon by Creeks, 55. See Commentary for p. 55.

Indians—Natchez ("Natches"): a tribe formerly living about the present Natchez, Miss. (*Bur. Am. Ethnol. Bull., 30,* Pt. II: 35–36, 1910; Swanton, 1922: 312–316, and 1946: 158–161); relations with French, 433–434; relations with Muscogulges, and Du Pratz's account of, 464–465; speaking the Muscogulge language, 519.

Indians—Ogeechee ("Ogeeche"): a tribe presumably occupying the region of Ogeechee River in Georgia, but perhaps confused by Bartram with the Yamasees (cf. Swanton, 1922: 312); warred upon by Creeks, 55; driven from Ogeechee River to Amelia Island, Fla., 66. See Commentary for p. 66.

Indians—Otasses (properly Atasi): inhabitants of the Upper Creek town of Otasse on the Tallapoosa River, Ala. (Swanton, 1922: 265–266); belonging to the snake family or tribe, 455.

Indians—Overhill. *See* Indians—Cherokees.

Indians—Paticas: a Carolina tribe, probably one of the Yamasee bands (Swanton, 1922: 22); warred upon by Creeks, 55. See Commentary for p. 55.

Indians—Santees: a tribe, probably Siouan, formerly residing on the middle Santee River, S.C. (*Bur. Am. Ethnol. Bull., 30,* Pt. II: 461, 1910); warred upon by Creeks, 55. See Commentary for p. 55.

Indians—Savannas or Savan(n)ucas: a branch of the Shawnee tribe residing in South Carolina (principally on Savannah River near Augusta), part of them moving to Chattahoochee River in 1715, as a result of the Yamasee War (Swanton, 1922: 317–320, and 1946: 184); warred upon by Creeks, 55; Uchee language called Savanna or Savanuca tongue, a dialect of Shawanese, 389; persons of, 484. See Commentary for p. 55.

Indians—Seminoles ("Siminoles") or Lower Creeks: an offshoot of the Creek Confederacy, occupying (in Bartram's time) mainly northern Florida east of the Apalachicola River (*Bur. Am. Ethnol. Bull., 30,* Pt. II: 500–502, 1910; Swanton, 1922: 398–414, pl. 1, and 1946: 181–182; Neill, 1956); encounter with a fierce Seminole, 20–23; disturbances between white inhabitants and, 78; robbing the traders, 79; Talahasochte a town of, 97; hunting and resting, 107; relations with white trader, and moral conduct of, 111–113; their customs tinctured with Spanish civilization, 186; hunting on Alachua Savanna, 188; relations of Seminole girls with white traders, 194–195; disposition and manners of, 211–214; a town of, on Bay of Calos, Fla., 227 (see Commentary for this page); sovereigns in Suwannee River region, 234; a party of warriors at Long Pond, Levy County, 244–245; their songs described, 245; friendly talks from their towns, 251; bacchanalian party, and adventure with Rattlesnake, at Spalding's Lower Store, 255–263; departure from Spalding's Lower Store, 303; those in East Florida joined by kindred from Apalachicola, Ala., 391; intended journey through their territories frustrated, 438; speaking the Muscogulge and Stinkard tongues, 464; list of their towns on Flint River, 464; character and persons of, 483–484. *See also* Indians—Alachuas, Indians—Creeks, Commentary for p. 184.

Indians—Shawanese: Shawnee; Uchee language a dialect of Shawanese, 389; Shawanese language similar to Savannuca, 466. *See also* Indians—Savannas; Commentary for pp. 388–389.

Indians—Taensas: a small tribe, related to the Natchez, that migrated from the Mississippi to the Mobile region early in the eighteenth century, but departed for Louisiana in 1764, after the British had taken over their territory from the French (*Bur. Am. Ethnol. Bull., 30*, Pt. II: 668–669, 1910; Swanton, 1922: 128, and 1946: 188–189); ancient town of, on Tensaw River, Ala., 405.

"In 1682 La Salle found them living on Lake St. Joseph in the northeastern part of the territory now embraced in Louisiana. Later, in 1706, they abandoned this site and moved farther down the Mississippi and ultimately to Mobile Bay, but returned to Louisiana in 1764, where they occupied several successive sites but gradually died out." (J.R.S.)

Indians—Tangipahoa ("Taensapaoa"): an extinct tribe, formerly living on the river of the same name in Louisiana (*Bur. Am. Ethnol. Bull., 30*, Pt. II: 685, 1910); 424.

Indians—Tomocos: Timucua, an ancient tribe of Florida (*Bur. Am. Ethnol. Bull., 30*, Pt. II: 752, 1910; Swanton, 1922: 320–398, and 1946: 193–194); claiming Florida, but vanquished by Alachuas, 380–381. See Commentary for p. 55 (Utinas).

Indians—Uchees ("Uches") (properly Yuchi): a tribe residing in early colonial times in the Savannah River region of Georgia and South Carolina, but migrating in the eighteenth century west to the Chattahoochee and Tallapoosa Rivers and south into Florida (*Bur. Am. Ethnol. Bull., 30*, Pt. II: 1003–1007, 1910; Swanton, 1922: 286–312, and 1946: 212–215); a populous town of, on the Chattahoochee, 211; ferrying traders' merchandize over this river, 388; Uchee tongue spoken at Savannuca, Ala., 463; their language formerly prevailing in Maryland and Virginia, 466; persons of, 484. See Commentary for pp. 388–389.

Indians—Utinas: a Florida tribe, apparently identical with the Timucua (*Bur. Am. Ethnol. Bull., 30*, Pt. II: 876–877, 1910; Swanton, 1922: 320–321, 330, and 1946: 201–202); warred upon by Creeks, 55; claiming Florida, but vanquished by Alachuas, 380–381. See Commentary for p. 55.

Indians—Wapoos: a tribe formerly living on Wapoo Creek and adjacent coast of South Carolina (*Bur. Am. Ethnol. Bull., 30*, Pt. II: 912, 1910; Swanton, 1922: 23); warred upon by Creeks, 55. See Commentary for p. 55.

Indians—Yamasees (or "Yamases"): a tribe formerly inhabiting parts of Georgia, South Carolina, and Florida (*Bur. Am. Ethnol. Bull., 30*,

Pt. II: 986–987, 1910; Swanton, 1922: 80–109, and 1946: 208–211); a fugitive remnant in Okefinokee Swamp, Ga., 26; warred upon by Creeks and sheltered by Spaniards in Florida, 55; slain by Creeks on St. John's River, 139; captives attending the Cowkeeper as slaves, 185; claiming Florida but vanquished by Alachuas, 380–381; conquered by Muscogulges, 392, 487; seeking protection of Spaniards, 487. See also Indians—Floridans; Commentary for p. 55.

Indian country, earthenware, fields, habitations, monuments, mounds, plantations, settlements, territories, towns, etc.: earthen vessels on Colonel's Island, Ga., 6; travels in Indian territories, 9; town, fields, and mounds near Fort Barrington, 17; traces of town, and monuments, near Little River, 37; old settlements near Little River, 38; field on Altamaha River, 50; fields and monuments on Ocmulgee River (the famous Macon mounds), 54; tumuli called Ogeechee mounts on Amelia Island, Fla., 66; Indian shore of St. John's River (the western shore), 90, 92, 96; settlement or village at the present Palatka, described, 92–93; earthenware at Charlotia, 94; town and tumuli at Charlotia, 95; journeys planned to towns in Florida, 97; old fields at Mount Royal, 99; a mound, remains of a town, earthenware, and old fields on Drayton's Island, 102–103; Indian coast of St. John's River, 114; sepulchres of Yamasees at St. Francis on St. John's River, 139; mount and avenue near New Smyrna, 144; fields and traces of habitations at Orange Bluff on St. John's River, 154; field at Salt Springs, 160; settlement of the ancients at Little Orange Lake, Alachua County, 180; mound, traces of town, and habitations near Tuscawilla Lake, 184; chief's house at Cuscowilla described, 184; fields near Alachua Savanna, 198; vestiges of town on border of Alachua Savanna, 199; village near present Rochelle, Alachua County, 209; trading path west of Suwannee River, 235; snagged sapling called an Indian ladder, 247; hunting tracks near Palatka, 303; visit to town on site of present Palatka, 303–304; mounts, terraces, etc., at Silver Bluff, S.C., 315; letters to agents in Indian territories, 320; grant for Indian trading company of Georgia, 324; monuments on Savannah River above Fort James visited and described, 324–326; alone in a wild Indian country, 331; mounts and terraces at Keowee, S.C., 332; remains of town, tumuli, terraces, orchards, etc., near the present Salem, Oconee County, 333–334; villages of the ancients near Oconee (= Station) Mountain, 338; hunting cabin near the present Clayton, Ga., 343–344: mount and terrace at ancient Sticoe, Rabun County, 345; towns of the ancients in Vale of Cowee, 346; graves in Vale of Cowee, N.C., 348; mount at Watauga, 350; villages and settlements in Vale of Cowee, 355;

council house of Cherokees standing on mount, 367; origin of the mounts, 367–368 (cf. Commentary for p. 456); altars, sepulchres, or ovens near Keowee, S.C., 372; fields and plantations on Oconee River, Ga., 379; town, mounds, and terraces at Ocmulgee Fields, 381; plantations on Chattahoochee River, Ala., 389; mounds or terraces at Apalachicola, Ala., 390; new land for plantations, 391; traders bound for towns in Creek Nation, 395; plantations and towns along Tallapoosa River, 396, 397, 449; mounds at Taensa Bluff, 405; ancient villages on lower Tombigbee River, 410; nearest town of the Seminoles, 438; cabins on Tallapoosa River, 445; fields on Ocmulgee River, Ga., 458; mounts at Blue Springs, Screven County, 462; arrow-heads, darts, knives, etc., in Screven or Burke Counties, 462; senates, 497; mounts supposedly constructed as sepulchres, 516; mounts, highways, artificial ponds, terraces, chunk yards, and obelisks, 519–522; scarcity of "mountains" (mounds) in Muscogulge country, 521–522; terraces, chunk yards, etc., at Apalachicola old town, Ala., and at Ocmulgee Fields, Ga., 522; no sign of European culture in Indian monuments, 522. *See also* Council-house, Earthen-ware, Habitation(s), House(s), Pots, Rotunda.

Indigo: one or more introduced and cultivated species of *Indigofera*— apparently chiefly *I. tinctoria* L., but probably also to some extent *I. suffruticosa* Mill. (*I. anil* L.); on Colonel's Island, Ga., 6; on St. Mary's River, Ga.–Fla., 23; on Amelia Island, Fla., 65; culture on Georgia coastal islands, 67; plantations on lower St. John's, 73, 76; that made in Florida compared with the Spanish and Prussian blue, 77; plantation at Mount Hope on St. John's River, 98; at Mount Royal, 100; ruined by hurricane at Lake Beresford, 143, 144; Suwannee River region suitable for, 234; at Lake George, 253; plantations on St. John's River, 254, on Savannah River, S.C., 375, on Escambia River, Fla., 416, near The Rigolets, La., 422, on the Mississippi, 430, and on Long Bay, S.C., 471.

" 'Indigo' not being now cultivated, the seed is difficult to obtain. . . . Further south . . . it has become in some measure naturalized—growing spontaneously about houses." (William Baldwin, Savannah, Ga., February, 1817; in Darlington, 1843: 205.)

Indigo, perennial ("pirennial"): probably wild indigo (*Indigofera caroliniana* Mill.); in Levy County, Fla., 223.

Indigofera: wild indigo (probably *I. caroliniana* Mill.); between Orange and Tuscawilla Lakes, Fla., 183.

Infamy, as punishment for crimes, 515.

Inhabitants, human: accommodations for, about Alachua Savanna, Fla., 251; their accounts of snakes, 274.

Insect(s): members of the class Insecta; infinite variety in middle region of Georgia, 46; prey of Six-lined Lizards, 172, and of Rough Green Snake, 275; amphibious insects in Suwannee River, Fla., 230; Little Tree-frogs taken for, 278; as food of toads, 280, and of swallows, 286; Catbird feeding on reptile insects (probably creeping or crawling forms), 300; silenced at approach of thunderstorm, 343.

Interpreter: young interpreter as companion on Suwannee River, Fla., 229; old interpreter (probably Job Wiggens) at conference with Seminoles at Spalding's Lower Store, 257, 258, 260–262; boat presented to old interpreter, Job Wiggens, 305; interpreter for Choctaw nation, 418. *See also* Trader, chief; Wiggens, Job.

Intoxication, at Spalding's Lower Store, Fla., 256.

Ipomoea ("Ipomea"): morning-glories (species of *Ipomoea* or related genera); west of Deep Creek, Putnam County, Fla., 173; near Lake Lochloosa, 181; at Lake George, 253. *See also* Convolvulus.

Ipomoea ("Ipomea"), with erect stem, pinnatifid leaves, and red flowers: standing cypress (*Gilia rubra* [L.] Heller) (B.L., F.W.P., E.T.W.); described, from Flat Rock, near Camak, Warren County, Ga., 376–377.

Ipomoea ("Ipomea") *erecta: probably standing cypress (*Gilia rubra* [L.] Heller) (cf. Merrill, 1945: 27); on St. Simon's Island, Ga., 59.
   A *nomen nudum* here, but perhaps validated by the description on pages 376–377, though Bartram himself does not connect the name with the description.

Ipomoea quamoclit ("Ipomea quamoclet"): cypress vine (*I. quamoclit* L.); compared with *Gilia rubra*, 377.

Ireland; native of, settling in Georgia, 460.

Iris versicolor: blue flag (*I. versicolor* L.); decoction of roots as a cathartic, 456.

Irish; in Mobile, Ala., 404.

Iron cannon, and iron pots or kettles for boiling tar; on Mobile Bay, Ala., 418–419.

Iron implements; not formerly owned by Creeks, 500.

Iron ore; in Levy County, Fla., 223; in Baldwin County, Ala., 403.

Isinglass, (Mica. S. vitrum Muscoviticum): muscovite, a form of mica; along Jarrett Creek, near Aquone, N.C., 363.

Islands; in St. John's River, Fla., 305.

Islands, floating, in St. John's River; formed of *Pistia stratiotes*, 88–90.

Island in the bay at Lake George, Fla.: Drayton's Island (soil map of Putnam County, 1919); camped at, 169.

Island, large, without the capes of Lake George: Drayton's Island; great mound on, 521.

Island, large beautiful, in Lake George: Drayton's Island; description of, 102–106.

Island, near south end of Lake George, 106.

Islands, three in Lake George described, 102.

The first is Hog Island, and the second Drayton's Island. Chief Justice William Drayton had a grant of land on this island (Mowat, 1943: 70), and it obviously derived its name from him. Concerning the third island, see Commentary for p. 106.

Island in St. John's River, 7 miles above Charlotia, Fla.: the present Murphy's Island, 4 miles south of Palatka (Palatka quadrangle); traders and goods secreted on, 96.

Island near Sunbury, Ga.: Colonel's Island (map of Liberty County, 1939); exploration, flora, and fauna of, 5–9.

Islands, sea-coast; as an advance on Atlantic Ocean, 68; sailing past those of Florida and Georgia, 306. *See also* Georgia.

Isle in sight of Mount Royal: Drayton's Island, Putnam County, Fla.; camped on, 254.

Isle of Palms: in Lake George, Fla., near the entrance of St. John's River; visited and described, 157. See Commentary for p. 106.

Isthmus of Florida: in Bartram's usage, apparently the base of the Florida Peninsula, in the general latitude of Gainesville and Lake George; Spanish highway across, 208; mentioned, 226, 227.

Itea: Indian reed (*I. virginica* L.); on Colonel's Island, Ga., 6; in Liberty County, 10; about St. Mary's River, Ga.–Fla., 24.

Iva: marsh elder (probably *I. frutescens* L.); on Colonel's Island, Ga., 6.

Ivory; Manatee ribs compared with, 231.

Ixia ("Ixea"), cerulean: Bartram's celestial lily (*Salpingostylis caelestina* [Bartr.] Small); at Lake Dexter, Fla., 155.

Ixia ("Ixea") *caelestina: Bartram's celestial lily (*Salpingostylis caelestina* [Bartr.] Small) (cf. Merrill, 1945: 27); figured and described on plate facing p. 155. See also Commentary for this page.

Jackdaws: either Boat-tailed Grackles (*Cassidix mexicanus major* [Vieillot]) or Florida Grackles (*Quiscalus quiscula quiscula* [L.]), or both; imagined presence on floating islands in St. John's River, Fla., 90; depredations near Alachua Savanna, 194.

Jackdaw, lesser purple. *See* Gracula purpurea.

Jackdaw, purple, of the sea coast. *See* Gracula quiscula.

Jacket, worn by Indian women, 504.

Jacksonburg (or "Jacksonburg[,] Ponpon"): the present Jacksonboro on Edisto (or Ponpon) River, in Colleton County, S.C.; arrived at, 308; passed, 470.

Jacobea, Corymbous (Senecio Jacobea): ragwort (not the European *Senecio jacobea* L., but probably *S. glabellus* Poir.); on Drayton's Island, Fla., 105. *See also* Senecio Jacobea.

Jamaica; *Smilax aspera* in, 241.

Jamaica spirits: probably Jamaica rum; carried by traders to Creek Nation, 493.

Jasmine (or "Jasmin"), yellow: *Gelsemium sempervirens* (L.) Ait. f.; on St. Simon's Island, Ga., 61; at Charleston, S.C., and near Wayah Gap, N.C., 363; at Macon, Ga., 459. *See also* Bignonia sempervirens; Jessamine, yellow.

Jasper or agate; in Screven or Burke Counties, Ga., 462.

Jatropha ("Tatropha"): spurge nettle (*J. stimulosa* Michx.); near Long Pond, Levy County, Fla., 248.

Jay, blue. *See* Corvus cristatus; Corvus glandarius.

Jay, crested blue, of Virginia: Northern Blue Jay (*Cyanocitta cristata bromia* Oberholser); compared with Florida Jay, 172.

Jay without a crest (pica glandaria cerulea non crestata): Florida Jay (*Aphelocoma floridana* [Bartram]; syn., *A. coerulescens* [Bosc]) (cf. Harper, 1942*d:* 213); described, between Rodman and Deep Creek, Putnam County, Fla., 172. Listed in Contents (p. v) as "Pica glandaria non cristata." *See also* Corvus Floridanus; Pica glandaria cerulea non cristata.

Jay, little, of Florida. *See* Corvus Floridanus.

Jekyl Island: a coastal island opposite Brunswick, Ga.; a channel of Altamaha River passing its north end, 53; game on, 63.

Jessamine, yellow (Bignonia sempervirens) (cf. Catesby, 1730, *1:* 53, pl. 53): *Gelsemium sempervirens* (L.) Ait. f.; on Oconee (= Station) Mountain, S.C., 337; near Cowee, N.C., 357. *See also* Bignonia sempervirens; Jasmine, yellow.

Jew's ears. *See* Fungus called Jew's ears.

Johnsonia: a synonym of *Callicarpa* L. (*q.v.*), a genus including the French mulberry (*C. americana* L.); near Salt Springs, Fla., 164.

"Joco." Misprint for Toco (*q.v.*).

Jore mountain(s): including the Nantahalas, which bound the valley of the Little Tennessee on the west, and that portion of the Cowee Mountains that forms the boundary between Macon and Swain Counties, N.C. (Cowee quadrangle); closing the Vale of Cowee, 353; prospect of, 354, 355; determined to cross, 361; ascent of most elevated peak (Wine Spring Bald), 362; Cherokee towns near, 373.

Jore (River), a branch of the Tennessee ("Tanase"): probably the present Burningtown Creek, in extreme northern Macon County, N.C. (Cowee quadrangle); tributaries of, 360; passing, 366.

Jore village: a former Cherokee town on Iotla Creek, probably near the present site of Burningtown, Macon County, N.C. (*Bur. Am. Ethnol. Bull.*, *30*, Pt. I: 634, 1907; Cowee quadrangle); prospect of, 355; passed through, 359–360; listed, 373, 374.

The Jore of page 374 is presumably different from the one of page 373, but if so, its location is unknown.

Judaea ("Judea"); nations of, 368.

Jugglers. *See* Priest, high.

Juglans: a genus of Juglandaceae, in Bartram's usage including the hickories (*Carya*) as well as the walnuts (*Juglans*); at Shell Bluff, Ga., 318; various species along Chattahoochee River, Ala., 393; at White Cliffs, La., 436.

Juglans *acuminata: *nomen nudum* (Merrill, 1945: 34)—possibly pignut hickory (*Carya glabra* [Mill.] Sweet); in Southern Red Hills, 32.

Juglans alba (cf. Catesby, 1730?, *1*: 38, pl. 38): probably white-heart hickory (*Carya tomentosa* Nutt.); near Oconee Station, Oconee County, S.C., 335; on Oconee (= Station) Mountain, S.C., 337; near Wayah Gap, N.C., 362.

Juglans cinerea: not *J. cinerea* L. (unless on p. xvi), but possibly bitternut hickory (*Carya cordiformis* [Wang.] K. Koch); of Virginia and Pennsylvania, xvi; about Wrightsborough, Ga., 36; on St. John's River above Lake Dexter, Fla., 131; between Orange and Tusca-willa Lakes, 183; near Alachua Savanna, 187; at Alachua Sink, 204; along Cape Fear River, N.C., 474.

Juglans *exaltata, shell-barked hickory ("hiccory"): *nomen nudum* (Merrill, 1945: 34)—*Carya ovata* (Mill.) K. Koch; in lower Coastal Plain, 29; in Southern Red Hills, 32; about Wrightsborough, Ga., 36; near Little River, 37, where cultivated by the ancients, 38; near Three Sisters Ferry, S.C., 309; in Lowndes or Butler Counties, Ala., 399; along the Mississippi, La., 432.

Juglans hickory (or "hiccory") (cf. Merrill, 1945: 34): hickory (*Carya* spp.), the "hickory" apparently not being used as a specific name, but in apposition to *Juglans;* on lower St. John's River, Fla., 90; various species along upper Savannah River, Ga.–S.C., 320, 327, and near Oconee Station, Oconee County, S.C., 335; near Wayah Gap, N.C., 362; in Warren County, Ga., 378; along Chattahoochee River, Ala., 394; along Cape Fear River, N.C., 474.

Juglans nigra (cf. Catesby, 1731, *1*: 67, pl. 67): black walnut (*J. nigra*

L.); of Virginia and Pennsylvania, xvi; about Wrightsborough, Ga.,
36; near Little River, 37, where cultivated by the ancients, 38;
near Three Sisters Ferry, S.C., 309; near Oconee Station, Oconee
County, 335; near Wayah Gap, N.C., 362; along Chattahoochee
River, Ala., 394; in Lowndes or Butler Counties, 399; along Iberville Canal, La., 427; along the Mississippi, 432; along Cape Fear
River, N.C., 474. *See also* Walnut, Black.

Juglans pecan: pecan (*Carya illinoensis* [Wang.] K. Koch); of Virginia
and Pennsylvania (a case of erroneous distribution), xvi; at Mobile,
Ala., 438.

J[uglans] *rustica: *nomen nudum* (Merrill, 1945: 34)—presumably
some species of hickory (*Carya*); near Three Sisters Ferry, S.C.,
309.

Juniperus *Americana: *nomen nudum* (Merrill, 1945: 34)—either red
cedar (*J. virginiana* L.) or southern red cedar (*J. silicicola* [Small]
Bailey); on Colonel's Island, Ga., 6; at The Rigolets, La., 421. *See
also* Cedar berries; Cedar, Red.

Kalmia: a genus of Ericaceae, comprising the American laurels; xvi;
elegance, xviii; a shrub allied to, 321.

Kalmia (or "Kalmea"): in these cases, probably mountain laurel (*K.
latifolia* L.); in Vale of Cowee, Ga., 346; along Cape Fear River,
N.C., 476.

Kalmia: in this case, calico-bush (*K. hirsuta* Walt.); near Orange
Lake, Fla., 181. *See also* Kalmia ciliata.

Kalmia, a new: calico-bush (*K. hirsuta* Walt.); described, near Mount
Pleasant, Wayne County, Ga., 18. *See also* preceding entry; Kalmia
ciliata.

Kalmia angustifolia: undetermined (not *K. angustifolia* L.); on
Colonel's Island, Ga., 7; in Lime-Sink Region, 30.

Kalmia (or "Kalmea") *ciliata: calico-bush (*K. hirsuta* Walt.) (cf.
Merrill, 1945: 27–28); on Colonel's Island, Ga., 7; on St. John's
River at Charlotia, Fla., 94; west of Spalding's Lower Store, Putnam
County, v, 171; near Suwannee River, 242. *See also* Kalmia, a new.

Kalmia glauca: undetermined (not *K. glauca* Ait.); near Alachua
Savanna, Fla., 187.

Kalmia latifolia (cf. Catesby, 1747, 2: 98, pl. 98): mountain laurel (*K.
latifolia* L.); xvii; near Broad River, Ga., 44; on Oconee (= Station)
Mountain, S.C., 336; at Falling Creek, Rabun County, Ga., 342.

Kalmia ("Halmea") *spuria: *nomen nudum* (Merrill, 1945: 34)—tar-
flower (*Befaria racemosa* Vent.); near Palatka, Fla., 303. *See also*
Rhododendron spurium; Shrub, beautiful, allied to Rhododendron.

Kean: a gentleman at Mount Royal, Fla.; hospitality of, 98.

Kegs, of Jamaica spirits, 493.

Kelsall. *See* Spalding and Kelsall.

Keowee ("Keowe"): a former Cherokee town on the west side of Keowee River, in Oconee County, S.C., opposite Fort Prince George and about 3 miles south of Ellenburg (cf. Hunter's map of 1730; Mouzon's map of 1775; Mooney, 1900: 525, pl. 3); surroundings described, 330–332; mentioned, 339; return to, 371; antiquities near, 372; listed, 374.

Keowee ("Keowe") River: in Bartram's usage, the combined Keowee and Seneca Rivers, tributary to the Savannah in extreme northwestern South Carolina; set out for, 326; crossed branches of, 328; town of Seneca on, 329; crossed at Fort Prince George, 333; prospect of, 333; a branch of, 373. *See also* Savannah or Keowee River.

Keowee ("Keowe"), Vale of: valley of Keowee River, in Oconee and Pickens Counties, S.C.; described, 331–332. The reference on page 354 is a *lapsus calami* for Vale of Cowee (*q.v.*).

Kettles. *See* Iron cannon, and iron pots or kettles.

"Khamnus." Misprint for Rhamnus (*q.v.*).

Kids: *Capra hircus* L.; Deer compared with, 200.

Kildea. *See* Charadrius vociferus.

Kilt ("kelt") of the Highlanders; breech-clout resembling, 502.

Kine. *See* Cows.

King or mico: the Long Warrior a king, 257; in ceremony in rotunda at Otasse, Ala., 452–454. *See also* Mico or king.

King of England (or of Great Britain); botanist to, xiii; a grant obtained from, for the Indian trading company of Georgia, 324; called Ant-apala-mico-clucco, 494–495.

King bird. *See* Lanius tyrannus.

King's crib, serving as a public granary, 512–513.

King-fisher, great crested. *See* Alcedo alcyon.

King's tree; the Creek name for *Persea borbonia* signifying, 232.

Kiolege (properly Kealedji): a former Upper Creek town on a creek of the same name, which empties into the west side of Tallapoosa River in northeastern Elmore County, Ala. (Taitt, map of 1772, and 1916: 515–516, 528; *Bur. Am. Ethnol. Bull., 30*, Pt. I: 642, 1907; Swanton, 1922: 272, pl. 2); listed, 463.

This town was probably near the present Kowaliga, Elmore County (Dadeville quadrangle). It was "Scattered along the . . . Creek for the Space of Eight miles" (Taitt, 1916: 516).

Kite, forked tailed (or "forked tail"). *See* Falco furcatus; Hawk or kite.

Kite hawks. *See* Milvus.

Knives; of stone, in Screven or Burke Counties, Ga., 462; of flint, formerly used by Creeks, 500; of iron, not formerly owned by Creeks, 500.

Kulsage or Sugar Town: a former Cherokee town on Keowee River, near the present Fall Creek in Oconee County, S.C. (Mouzon's map of 1775; Mooney, 1900: 525; soil map of Oconee County, 1909); location, 331; listed, 374.

Lace; on breech-clout, boots, and mantle of Indians, 502; on waist-coat, 503; made by Indian women, 513.

Lacerta. *See* Lizards, slender, long-tailed.

Lactuca. *See* Lettuce.

Lake, a beautiful: Lake Beresford, Volusia County, Fla.; surroundings and hurricane there described, 140–143. *See also* Long Lake.

Lake, a beautiful little: Kanapaha Sink, in northwestern corner of Kanapaha Prairie, Alachua County, Fla. (Arredondo quadrangle); camped at, 217.

Lake, a beautiful sparkling: probably Long Pond, south of Chiefland, Levy County, Fla.; passed, 222.

Lake Borgne ("Borgone"): an arm of the Gulf of Mexico, in eastern Louisiana; 421.

Lake George: the largest lake on St. John's River, about 18 miles south of Palatka, Fla.; prospect of, 98; description and passage of, 101–106, 156–169; swamps below, 130; alone on, 158; Salt Springs discharging into, 165; fish in, 168; compared with Orange Lake, 182; crossed, 252; *Illicium* near, 442; great mounds at, 521. *See also* Great Lake.

Lake, a great: in this case, Orange Lake, in Alachua County, Fla. (Hawthorn and Citra quadrangles); described, 181–182.

Lake, a large and beautiful, near Cuscowilla: Tuscawilla Lake, near the present Micanopy, Fla. (Arredondo and Williston quadrangles); described, 192–193. *See also* Cuscowilla, lake of.

Lake, the little: in this case, Little Lake George on St. John's River, just above Welaka, Putnam County, Fla. (soil map of Putnam County, 1919); Mount Hope on, 98. *See also* Little Lake.

Lake, the little: in the following cases, Lake Dexter, in Lake and Volusia Counties, Fla.; surroundings described, 116–117; camped at, 153.

Lake, a little, adjoining Alachua Savanna: Chacala Pond, 3 miles north of Micanopy, Fla. (Arredondo quadrangle); described, 189.

Lake Maurepas (or "Mauripas"): a lake in southeastern Louisiana,

west of Lake Pontchartrain (Ponchatoula and Springfield quadrangles); passage of, 425, 437.

Lake Pontchartrain: an arm of the Gulf of Mexico, north of New
Orleans, La.; voyage through, 423–425, 437.

Lake, a vast and beautiful, west of Half-way Pond: Little Orange
Lake, in Alachua and Putnam Counties, Fla. (Hawthorn quadrangle); pass by, 180.

Lake Waccamaw ("Wackamaw" or "Wakama"): in Columbus County,
N.C., 30 miles west of Wilmington (soil map of Columbus County,
1919); water chinquapin in, 409; described, ix, 473–474.

Lambs: *Ovis aries* L.; prey of Gray Foxes, 283. *See also* Sheep.

Lancaster, Pa.; passed, 480.

Language; of American aborigines, 519; of Muscogulges, Natchez,
Chickasaws, Choctaws, and Cherokees, 519.

Lanius. *See* Butcher bird, bluish grey.

L[anius] garrulus, the little black capped butcher-bird of Florida: not
L. garrulus L., but Loggerhead Shrike (*L. ludovicianus ludovicianus*
L.); listed, 289 *bis*. *See also* Butcher bird, bluish grey.

Lanius *griseus* ("griscus"), the little grey butcher-bird of Pennsylvania: *nomen nudum*—probably Migrant Shrike (*L. ludovicianus
migrans* W. Palmer) (cf. B. S. Barton, 1799a: 11; Harper, 1942d:
214); listed, 289 *bis*.

L[anius] tyrannus, the king bird: Eastern Kingbird (*Tyrannus tyrannus* [L.]); listed, 289 *bis*.

Lantana (perhaps Lant. camerara): shrub verbena (*L. camara* L.);
described, on Drayton's Island, Fla., 103.
  "*Lantana*. Agrees nearest to L. camara, the flowers scarlet and
golden yellow in the same corymbe. but I think the jun[i]or shoots
are not aculiated as Wildenow saith[.]" (Bartram to Muhlenberg,
September 6, 1810; Muhlenberg Letters: 137.)

Lantana, balmy: probably shrub verbena (*Lantana camara* L.); on
Isle of Palms, Lake George, Fla., 157.

Lanthorns: lanterns; isinglass suitable for, 364.

Lark, great meadow. *See* Alauda magna.

Lark, little brown. *See* Alauda migratoria.

Lark, sky. *See* Alauda campestris.

Larkspur, garden: *Delphinium* sp.; compared with a wild *Delphinium*,
328. *See also* Delphinium.

Larus alba ("alber"), the great white gull: probably composite,
including adults of both Herring Gull (*L. argentatus smithsonianus*
Coues) and Ring-billed Gull (*L. delawarensis* Ord); listed, 295.
  The latter species was not differentiated till 1815.

Larus alba minor, the little white river gull: probably, for the most part, Common Tern (*Sterna hirundo hirundo* L.); listed, 295.

Larus *griseus ("griceus"), the great grey gull: *nomen nudum*— probably composite, including immature individuals of both Herring Gull (*L. argentatus smithsonianus* Coues) and Ring-billed Gull (*L. delawarensis* Ord); listed, 295.

Laura-cerasa. *See* Prunus laurocerasus.

Laurels: southern magnolias (*Magnolia grandiflora* L.); on St. John's River above Lake Dexter, Fla., 131; near Lake Lochloosa, 180; near Long Pond, Levy County, 222.

Laurel(s) (Magnolia grandiflora): southern magnolia(s) (*M. grandiflora* L.); on lower St. John's River, Fla., 74, 75; on Sapelo Island, Ga., 268.

Laurels, pyramidal: probably southern magnolias (*Magnolia grandiflora* L.); in Liberty County, Ga., 11.

Laurel Magnolia(s): southern magnolia(s) (*Magnolia grandiflora* L.); on lower St. John's River, Fla., 85, 90; those on the Mississippi and on the St. John's compared, 86; description of, 86; at Mount Royal, 99; compared with *Carica papaya*, 131; on the St. John's at St. Francis, 139; at Lake Dexter, 154; lacking about dwelling houses on the St. John's, 254.

Laurel tree(s) (Magnolia grandiflora): southern magnolia(s) (*M. grandiflora* L.); on Colonel's Island, Ga., 6; at Mucclasse, Ala., 446. *See also* Magnolias; Magnolia grandiflora.

Laurens (or "Lawrens"), Henry: a distinguished citizen of Charleston, S.C.; owner of a plantation at Broughton Island, Ga., 48; his agent on Broughton Island, 57; shipping rice and Bartram's collections to Liverpool, 306–307.

Laurens (1723–1792) later became president of the Continental Congress and an American commissioner at the Treaty of Paris. He was a friend of both Bartrams. On August 9, 1766, he had written to John Bartram, advising him of the distressing condition of William at his plantation on the St. John's (Darlington, 1849: 438–442).

Laurus: properly, a genus of Lauraceae, but in Bartram's usage practically equivalent to the family itself, including such currently recognized genera as *Cinnamomum, Lindera, Litsea, Persea,* and *Sassafras;* in Southern Red Hills, 32; on Altamaha River, Ga., 48; at White Cliffs, La., 436.

Laurus benzoin: probably spice-bush (*Lindera benzoin* [L.] Blume var. *pubescens* [Palmer & Steyerm.] Rehd.); on Altamaha River, Ga., 50; along Chattahoochee River, Ala., 393.

Laurus Borbonia (cf. Catesby, 1731, *1:* 63, pl. 63): red bay or sweet bay (either *Persea borbonia* [L.] Spreng. or *P. b.* f. *pubescens* [Pursh] Fern., which Bartram did not definitely differentiate); on Colonel's Island, Ga., 6; in lower Coastal Plain, 29; in Lime-Sink Region, 30; on Altamaha River, 50; on lower St. John's River, Fla., 84, 93, 94; near Alachua Savanna, 187, 202, 204; in Levy County, 221; Painted Bunting among, 299; near Three Sisters Ferry, S.C., 309; along Chattahoochee River, Ala., 393; near The Rigolets, La., 421; on Amite River, 425; along Iberville Canal, 427; along the Mississippi, 432; at Blue Springs, Screven County, Ga., 461. *See also* Bay(s), Red; Bay(s), Sweet; Bay, dwarf Sweet.

Laurus Borbonia or Red Bay: in this case, probably *Persea borbonia* (L.) Spreng.; at Manatee Spring, Fla., 232; Eto-mico the Creek name for, 232.

Laurus camphor[a]: camphor tree (*Cinnamomum camphora* [L.] Nees & Eberm.); in the tropics, xiv.

Laurus cinnamomum ("cinam."): cinnamon tree (*Cinnamomum zeylanicum* Nees); in the tropics, xiv.

Laurus Indica: undetermined; at Shell Bluff, Ga., 318.

Ordinarily this name should be equivalent to *Persea indica* (L.) Spreng., an ornamental shrub of the Azores, Canary, and Madeira Islands.

Laurus Persica: avocado (*Persea gratissima* Gaertn. f.); in the tropics, xiv.

Laurus sassafras (cf. Catesby, 1730, *1:* 55, pl. 55): sassafras (*Sassafras albidum* [Nutt.] Nees); in lower Coastal Plain, 29; near Three Sisters Ferry, S.C., 309; along Chattahoochee River, Ala., 393; near The Rigolets, La., 421; along Iberville Canal, 427; along the Mississippi, 432. *See also* Sassafras.

Lead, black (stibium): in this case, probably graphite; along Jarrett Creek, near Aquone, N.C., 364.

Leather; as cargo on St. John's River, 304; as freight in a traders' caravan, 445; horses loaded with, 457, 480; ferried across Ocmulgee River, 459; thongs in ears of Indians, 501.

Lechea: pinweed (*Lechea* sp.); near Suwannee River, Fla., 243.

Lemon: *Citrus limonia* Osbeck; scent of a *Collinsonia* compared with, 412.

Leontice thalictroides: blue cohosh (*Caulophyllum thalictroides* [L.] Michx.); at Falling Creek, Rabun County, Ga., 342.

Lepus minor. *See* Rabbit.

Lettuce ("lettice"), garden: *Lactuca sativa* L.; *Pistia stratiotes* resembling, 89.

Lettuce (lactuca): *Lactuca sativa* L.; time for planting, 288.

Lettuce, Indian: *Swertia caroliniensis* (Walt.) Ktze. (W. P. C. Barton, 1818, *2:* 103); described, from the Great Ridge, Ga., 42.

"Indian Lettuce. Michaux saw it & has named it in Flo. boreale. but I have not the Book." (Bartram to Muhlenberg, September 6, 1810; Muhlenberg Letters: 137.)

Levant trade, 460.

Lichen, near Suwannee River, Fla., 243.

Lightning: setting a pine tree ablaze, 13; at Lake Beresford, Fla., 141, 142; setting "deserts" on fire, 152; struck by, 386.

Lightwood: resinous pine wood; armed with a lightwood knot, 261.

"Light'ood knot" is still a very common expression in the South.

Ligustrum vulgare ("ruelgare"). *See* Privet.

Lilium ("Lillium"): probably leopard lily (*Lilium catesbaei* Walt.); near Long Pond, Levy County, Fla., 248.

Lilium ("Lillium") Martagon: lily (*Lilium* sp.)—not the Old World *L. martagon* L.; in Brunswick County, N.C., 472.

Lilium superbum: Turk's-cap lily (*L. superbum* L.); representing pride, xvii, and elegance, xviii.

Lily ("Lilly") of the valley: *Convallaria montana* Raf.; near Cowee, N.C., 354. *See also* Convallaria majalis.

Lily ("Lilly"), White. *See* Crinum.

Lime; fossil oyster shells burned to, 318.

Limes: *Citrus aurantifolia* (Christm.) Swingle; fruit of tupelo gum used instead of, 17.

Lime, Wild. *See* Tallow-nut.

Limodorum: in this case, not *Limodorum* L., but *Calopogon* R. Br., a genus of Orchidaceae, comprising the grass-pinks; beauty, xviii.

Limestone; not seen in middle region of Georgia, 45; on Altamaha River, 49; in Levy County, Fla., 223; at Manatee Spring, 232; at Blue Springs, Screven County, Ga., 461.

*Linaria ciris, the painted finch, or nonpareil: Eastern Painted Bunting (*Linaria ciris ciris* [L.]—formerly *Passerina ciris ciris* [L.]) (cf. Harper, 1942*d:* 216–217); listed, 291.

Linaria ciris (emberiza ciris Linn.) or painted finch, or nonpareil (cf. Catesby, 1730, *1:* 44, pl. 44): Eastern Painted Bunting; distribution of, 299. *See also* preceding entry, Nonpareil, Painted finch.

Linaria cyanea ("cianea") (tanagra Linn.) the blue linnet ("linet") (cf. Catesby, 1730, *1:* 45, pl. 45): Indigo Bunting (*Linaria cyanea* [L.]—formerly *Passerina cyanea* [L.]) (cf. Harper, 1942*d:* 216–217); account of, 299.

L[inaria] cyanea, the blue linnet: Indigo Bunting; listed, 291. *See also* preceding entry; Linnet, blue.

Linen (or "linnen"); dyed with red bay, 162; shirt of, worn by Indians, 502; waistcoat made of, 503.

Lingo (in the 1792 edition replaced by "Stincard"); ordinarily, a language or dialect, but in this case apparently some particular though undetermined language—or perhaps a misprint; 466.

Linnet, blue: Indigo Bunting (*Linaria cyanea* [L.]—formerly *Passerina cyanea* [L.]); at Lake Dexter, Fla., 154. *See also* Linaria cyanea.

Linum: a genus of Linaceae, comprising the flaxes; usefulness, xvii.

Liquidambar ("Liquid Amber" or "Liquid-amber"): sweet gum (*Liquidambar styraciflua* L.); in Liberty County, Ga., 10; on Altamaha River, 48; on lower St. John's River, Fla., 84, 94; at Lake Dexter, 154; near Lake Lochloosa, 181; between Orange and Tuscawilla Lakes, 183; near Alachua Savanna, 187, 198; at Alachua Sink, 204; at Manatee Spring, 232; west of Suwannee River, 233; along upper Savannah River, Ga., 320; on lower Tombigbee River, Ala., 410; at White Cliffs, La., 436. *See also* Liquidambar styraciflua; Sweet Gum.

Liquidambar ("Liquid-amber") peregrinum: sweet fern (*Comptonia peregrina* [L.] Coulter); along Cape Fear River, N.C., 476.

Liquidambar ("Liquid Amber" or "Liquid-amber") styraciflua (or "Styraciflua") (cf. Catesby, 1738, *2:* 65, pl. 65): sweet gum (*L. styraciflua* L.); of Virginia and Pennsylvania, xvi; on Colonel's Island, Ga., 6; in lower Coastal Plain, 29; near Little River, 37; on lower St. John's River, Fla., 90; in eastern Alabama, 394; near The Rigolets, La., 421; along Iberville Canal, 427; along the Mississippi, 432; along Cape Fear River, N.C., 474. *See also* Liquidambar, Sweet Gum.

Liquor(s); brought by Indians from Cuba, 227; Seminole warriors treated with, 245; consumed by Seminoles at Spalding's Lower Store, 255–257; Bartram refreshed with, 310; spirituous liquors as the common enemy of mankind, 492; prohibition of, in Indian towns, 492.

Liriodendron (or Liriodendron tulipifera) (cf. Catesby, 1730, *1:* 48, pl. 48): tulip tree (*L. tulipifera* L.); of Virginia and Pennsylvania, xvi; in Liberty County, Ga., 10; in lower Coastal Plain, 28; about Wrightsborough, 36; near Little River, 37; near Broad River, 44; near Three Sisters Ferry, S.C., 309; along upper Savannah River, Ga.–S.C., 320, 327; along Chattahoochee River, Ala., 393; along Iberville Canal, La., 427; along the Mississippi, 432; at White Cliffs, 436; along Cape Fear River, N.C., 474. *See also* Poplar.

Little Carpenter. *See* Ata-kullakulla.

Little Lake: the present Little Lake George, an expansion of St. John's

River just above Welaka, Putnam County, Fla. (soil map of Putnam County, 1919); the Ocklawaha joining the St. John's at, 182; great mound at, 521. *See also* Lake, the little.

Little River, Ga.: arising in Oglethorpe and Greene Counties and discharging into the Savannah (at the modern Clark Hill Reservoir) above Augusta; Wrightsborough on [a tributary of], 35; landscape and vegetation about, 36; plants about this river and on the Great Ridge compared, 41; rapid current of, 316; arrived at, 321; included in the New Purchase, 324.

Little River, north branch of: actually Williams Creek, a southerly tributary of Little River, on the Taliaferro-Warren county boundary, Ga.; crossed, 36.

Bartram's geographical confusion here is probably due to his placing Wrightsborough on Little River itself, instead of on Wrightsborough Creek.

Little river: in this case, not the river previously mentioned by that name, but Tugaloo River, which joins the Seneca to form the Savannah (cf. W. Bartram, 1943: 181; also Purcell map of about 1776); corner tree marked at its confluence with the Savannah, 45.

Little River, S.C.: an inlet of the ocean close to the North Carolina boundary; crossed, 472.

Little St. Juan River: Suwannee River, flowing across northern Florida, from Okefinokee Swamp, Ga., to Suwannee Sound, Gulf of Mexico; rising in Okefinokee Swamp, 26; Talahasochte on, 97, 208; trip to, 98, 215–251; descrpition of, 224–226; voyage down, 229–230; crossed, 232; mentioned, 249; journey to, 521.

Little St. Simon's [Island]: in this case, evidently a *lapsus* for Cumberland Island (*q.v.*), Ga.; put ashore on, 64.

Live oak(s). *See* Oak(s), Live.

Liverpool, England, a ship sailing for, 306–307.

Livingston, [Philip, Junior]: provincial secretary of West Florida; received by, 414–415; residence of, 416.

"He was a member of the famous Livingston family of New York." His name "is closely connected with many questionable deals. He was, by deputation from the patentee . . . provincial secretary. Chester soon made him a member of the council and receiver general. He acquired several other offices and in 1778 his enemies claimed that, either personally or by deputy, he held no less than nine. . . . It is not difficult to believe the charge made in 1778 that Livingston had by various means acquired the title to one hundred thousand acres." (C. Johnson, 1943: 130.)

Livingston's Creek: a westerly tributary of Cape Fear River in eastern Columbus County, N.C. (Price and Strother, map of North Carolina, 1808; soil map of Columbus County, 1919); 473.

Lizards: reptiles of the suborder Sauria; compared in shape with Alligator, 128; as food of King Vulture, 152; of Florida and Carolina, 280–281.

Lizards, blue bellied squamous: Pine Lizards (*Sceloporus undulatus undulatus* [Bosc and Daudin]) (cf. Harper, 1940: 712); in Florida and Carolina, 280.

Lizard, green, or little green chameleon: *Anolis carolinensis* (Voigt); account of, 280. *See also* Chameleon, green.

Lizard, large copper coloured: Broad-headed Skink (*Eumeces laticeps* [Schneider]); account of, 280–281.

Lizard, slender, of a fine blue colour: apparently a composite account, including the "striped" or Six-lined Lizard (already mentioned a few lines above) and one or two species of skinks (*Eumeces*) as well; in Florida and Carolina, 280–281.

The swiftness and the very long and slender tail apply better to *Cnemidophorus;* the blue color and the habitat about log buildings, to *Eumeces.* Among the skinks probably concerned, *E. inexpectatus* Taylor occurs in both Florida and Carolina; *E. fasciatus* (L.) in Carolina but not in Florida (Carr, 1940: 76).

Lizards, slender, long-tailed, called scorpions: Six-lined Lizards (*Cnemidophorus sexlineatus* [L.]); described, in Putnam County, Fla., 172. Listed in Contents (p. v) as "Lacerta."

Nowadays in the Southeast the vernacular name "Scorpion," as applied to lizards, seems to be restricted to the genus *Eumeces,* and particularly to the species *laticeps.*

Lizard, striped, called scorpion: Six-lined Lizard (*Cnemidophorus sexlineatus* [L.]); in Florida and Carolina, 280.

Lobelia: lobelia (*Lobelia* sp.); near Suwannee River, Fla., 242.

Lobelia cardinalis: cardinal flower (*L. cardinalis* L.); on Drayton's Island, Fla., 105.

Locusta, a species of: almost certainly the Green-striped Locust (*Chortophaga viridifasciata* [De Geer]) (H.R.R.); food of Ricebirds, 297.

Locustae: probably short-horned grasshoppers (family Locustidae), perhaps also including long-horned grasshoppers (family Tettigoniidae); prey of Six-lined Lizards, 172.

London, England, 438.

Long Bay: along the coast of Horry and Georgetown Counties, S.C.; passed, 471–472.

Long Lake: the present Lake Beresford, Volusia County, Fla.; described, 144. *See also* Lake, a beautiful.

Long Pond: an extensive pond still bearing that name, south of Chiefland, Levy County, Fla.; return to, 244; revisited and described, 248.

Long Warrior: a chief or king of the Seminoles, whose portrait serves as a frontispiece; conduct at Spalding's Lower Store, 257–260; departure of, 303.

Lonicera: coral honeysuckle (*L. sempervirens* L.) or other species of that genus; on St. Simon's Island, Ga., 61; at Falling Creek, Rabun County, 342; on upper Tensaw River, Ala., 408.

Lonicera sempervirens: coral honeysuckle (*L. sempervirens* L.); in Liberty County, Ga., 10; in coastal swamps, 29; in Oconee County, S.C., 334; in Monroe or adjacent county, Ala., 402.

Loons of various species: in Bartram's usage, apparently including cormorants (*Phalacrocorax floridanus* [Bartram] subspp.) as well as loons (*Gavia* spp.); at Nassau Sound, Fla., 71. See also Colymbus musicus, Snake Birds.

Lorimer, Dr. [John]: member of the council at Pensacola, Fla.; meeting with, 414, 415.

Romans (1776: 334) refers to "my very worthy friend Doctor J. *Lorimer*, at *Pensacola*." He was an early member of the American Philosophical Society. A letter of his, addressed to Dr. Hugh Williamson, and dated January 7, 1769, was published in the Society's *Transactions* (1: 250–254, 1771). In it he refers to having been "notified" in April, 1765, "as surgeon to the forces here at the war office." The letter deals mainly with the vegetable productions and climate of West Florida, currents in the Gulf of Mexico, and adjacent harbors. He reported in 1769 on a fever epidemic at Mobile (Hamilton, 1897: 205–208).

In 1766 he contested the election of one David Williams to the assembly and was seated in the latter's stead. He "was held in high esteem, served during one session as speaker *pro tempore* and was very active in the business of the house." In 1770 he was appointed deputy auditor general. (C. Johnson, 1943: 86–87, 90, 99, 225.)

Loughabber, the seat of Alexander Cameron: apparently in the northern part of the present Abbeville County, S.C.; left, 328. (*See* Commentary for pp. 326–328.)

Lower Creeks. *See* Indians—Alachuas; Indians—Creeks; Indians—Seminoles.

Loxia cardinalis, the red bird, or Virginia nightingale (cf. Catesby, 1730? 1: 38, pl. 38): Eastern Cardinal (*Richmondena cardinalis cardinalis* [L.]); listed, 290 *bis*.

L[oxia] cerulea, the blue cross beak (cf. Catesby, 1730? 1: 39, pl. 39): Eastern Blue Grosbeak (*Guiraca caerulea caerulea* [L.]); listed, 290 *bis*.

L[oxia] rostro forficato, the cross beak: Red Crossbill (*Loxia curvi-rostra* subspp.); listed, 290 *bis*.

This determination is based upon the fact that this species is much less rare in Pennsylvania than the White-winged Crossbill (*L. leucoptera* Gmelin). Bartram accounted for only one species.

*Lucar *lividus, apice nigra, the cat bird, or chicken bird: Catbird (*Lucar carolinensis* [L.]) (cf. Harper, 1942*d:* 215–216); listed, 290 *bis*. See also Cat-bird.

Lucas, Mr.: a planter on Meherrin River, Va.; stayed with, 479.

Lucas, F., Esq.: a settler on the west side of Cape Fear River, above Livingston's Creek, in Bladen or Columbus Counties, N.C.; stayed with, 473.

On the Price and Strother map of 1808 a Lucas is indicated some miles below Carver's Creek and across the river from Indian Wells.

Lupines ("Lupins"): *Lupinus* spp.; about St. Mary's River, Ga.–Fla., 24.

Lupine ("Lupin"), a beautiful species of (Lupinus *breunis): lady lupine (*Lupinus villosus* Willd.) (cf. Merrill, 1945: 28) (fig. 6); described, south of Altamaha River (probably along the Brantley-Glynn county boundary, southeast of Waynesville), Ga., 19. (*See* Commentary for this page.)

"Breunis" is possibly a misprint for "biennis."

Lupinus *breunis. *See* preceding entry.

Lupinus *filifolius: *nomen nudum* (Merrill, 1945: 34)—perhaps sand-hills lupine (*L. nuttallii* S. Wats.); near Suwannee River, Fla., 243.

"Lupinus filifolius, folioles very narrow like a thread, I believe not in Wild[.]" (Bartram to Muhlenberg, September 6, 1810; Muhlenberg Letters: 137).

Lupus niger. *See* Wolves (lupus niger).

Luscinia, s[eu] *philomela *Americana, the yellow hooded titmouse (cf. Catesby, 1730, *1:* 60, pl. 60; Harper, 1942*d:* 218): *nomen nudum* —probably Hooded Warbler (*Wilsonia citrina* [Boddaert]); listed, 292.

The technical names, "Luscinia, seu philomela," indicate Bar-tram's acquaintance with Sloane's great folio work (1707, 1725) on Jamaica, in which the same names occur on plate 259 of Volume 2.

Lutra. *See* Otter(s).

Lycium ("Lysium") *salsum: Christmas berry (*L. carolinianum* Walt.); at The Rigolets, La., 421. *See also* next entry.

Lycium *salsum (perhaps L. afrum Linn.): Christmas berry (*L. caro-linianum* Walt.) (cf. Merrill, 1945: 28); described, on St. Simon's Island, Ga., 59. *See also* preceding entry.

Hitchcock (1932: 224, 334–335) seems unduly conservative in excluding this as a doubtful species. The characters given by him (p. 207) for *L. halimifolium* do not correspond to Bartram's description.

Lynx. *See* Wild cat.

M'Gee, leader of a Georgia family; murder by Indians in Florida, and punishment of his murderers, 237.

McIntosh ("M'Intosh"), [Donald]: a settler in McIntosh County, Ga.; entertained by, 13. (See Commentary for this page.)

McIntosh ("M'Intosh"), John: son of Lachlan McIntosh; a companion in Bartram's travels, 15, 27, 35; in Colonel Barnet's party, 40; observing cray-fish and "gold-fish," 43.

John McIntosh (1748–1826) became a prominent soldier in the Revolution, attaining the rank of lieutenant-colonel. He made a gallant defense of Fort Morris, at Sunbury, and was captured at the Battle of Brier Creek, Ga. In the War of 1812 he served under Jackson at Mobile as a major-general. (*Appleton's Cyclopaedia*, 4: 124, 1888.) I was in error (in W. Bartram, 1943: 212) in considering John a son of William McIntosh.

McIntosh ("M'Intosh"), L[achlan]: the General McIntosh of Revolutionary fame; welcome by, 15; tarried with, 26.

Lachlan McIntosh (1725 or 1727–1806) accompanied his father, John More McIntosh, in emigrating in 1736 from Scotland to Georgia, where they settled near the mouth of the Altamaha River. He spent some early years in the counting-house of Henry Laurens in Charleston, but later returned to Georgia and became a land surveyor. During the Revolution he served both in the South and in the North. Meanwhile he mortally wounded the ambitious Button Gwinnett in a duel. After the war he lived in Georgia in retirement and comparative poverty. (Spalding, 1836.)

Evidence of Bartram's firm friendship with McIntosh may be found in letters he addressed to the latter on July 15, 1774, and May 31, 1796. The first (*Dreer Coll.*, Scientists, 1), in which he recounts his experiences on a trip he had just completed to the Suwannee River, commences as follows: "Being perticularly desireous of meriting your esteem and regar'd, I have a pleasure in every thing that I think may tend to your amusement." The second (New-York Hist. Soc.), in which he refers to McIntosh as "my venerated Friend," is one of the most touching that the naturalist ever penned.

There is further evidence of this friendship in Bartram's reported volunteering for military service under McIntosh in 1776 (Ord?

1832: iii). *See* Commentary for p. 467; also Jones, 1891: 139–154.

McIntosh ("M'Intosh"), Mrs. [Lachlan]: née Sarah Threadcraft; consent to the journey of her son John, 27.

McIntosh's ("M'Intosh's") Island: perhaps the present General's Island (soil map of McIntosh County, 1932); at the mouth of Altamaha River, Ga., 53.

McLatchie ("M'Latche"), C[harles]: agent at Spalding's Lower Store on St. John's River; hospitality of, 96; conferences with, 97; delegating a trader to treat with Indians at Cuscowilla, 170; conference of the Long Warrior and other Seminole chiefs with, 257–260; inviting Bartram on a visit to an Indian town, 303; taking leave of, 306.

On August 15, 1773, James Spalding wrote to McLatchie from Frederica, advising him of the shipment of a trunk and a box belonging to Bartram (Bartram Papers, 4: 103).

Mace: a spice made from nutmeg (*Myristica*); compared with *Illicium*, 442.

Magazine, in fortress at Pensacola, 416.

Magnolia(s): in at least most of the following cases, doubtless southern magnolias (*Magnolia grandiflora* L.); in Liberty County, Ga., 11; on lower St. John's River, Fla., 81; on Drayton's Island, 103, 169; at Lake George, 106; at Lake Dexter, 116, 117; at New Smyrna, 144; at Blue Springs, 146; at Salt Springs, 165; about lakes in Putnam County, 174; near Lake Lochloosa, 181; between Orange and Tuscawilla Lakes, 183; about Alachua Savanna, 198, 217; in Levy County, 220, 222, 223; near Suwannee River, 224, 233; in Escambia or adjacent county, Ala., 403; at White Cliffs, La., 436. *See also* Laurels, Laurel Magnolia(s), Laurel tree(s), Magnolia grandiflora, Magnolian groves.

Magnolia: in this case, probably either mountain Magnolia (*Magnolia fraseri* Walt.) or cucumber tree (*M. acuminata* L.); near Cowee, N.C., 357.

Magnolia, a species differing little from Magnolia glauca; doubtless white bay (*M. virginiana* L.) or some form thereof; described, at Salt Springs, Fla., 161.

Perhaps this is what Sargent has described as *M. virginiana* var. *australis*.

Magnolia, a new species of, in the maritime parts of Georgia: probably Bartram's magnolia (*M. pyramidata* Bartram) (cf. Harper, 1942*b*: 7–8; Merrill, 1945: 29); described, 340. *See also* Magnolia pyramidata.

Magnolia, glorious: southern magnolia (*Magnolia grandiflora* L.); xvii.

Magnolia(s), grand: southern magnolia(s) (*Magnolia grandiflora* L.); at Lake George, Fla., 102; on St. John's River above Lake Dexter, 137, and at Hawkinsville, 139; near Tuscawilla Lake, 192.

Magnolias, pyramidal: probably southern magnolias (*Magnolia grandiflora* L.); at Lake George, Fla., 157.

Magnolia, towering: southern magnolia (*Magnolia grandiflora* L.); at Salt Springs, Fla., 160.

Magnolia acuminata (cf. Catesby, 1748, *2*, appendix: 15, pl. 15): cucumber tree (*M. acuminata* L.); of Carolina and Florida, and of the Northern States, xvi; about Wrightsborough, Ga., 36; on the Great Ridge, 41; near Broad River, 44; along upper Savannah River, Ga.–S.C., 320, 327; near Oconee Station, Oconee County, S.C., 335; near Wayah Gap, N.C., 362. *See also* Cucumber tree.

Magnolia *auriculata (or "auriculato"): mountain magnolia (*M. fraseri* Walt.) (cf. Merrill, 1945: 28–29); along upper Savannah River, Ga., 320; described, at Falling Creek, 4 miles northeast of Clayton, Rabun County, 339–340, 342; along Jarrett Creek, near Aquone, N.C., 364. *See* Commentary for pp. 339–340; also next entry.

Magnolia auriculata: in the following cases, large-leaved magnolia (*M. macrophylla* Michx.) (cf. Merrill, 1945: 29, footnote); in Monroe or adjacent county, Ala., 402; on upper Tensaw River, 408.

The following statement, on p. 18 of the descriptive notes accompanying specimens and drawings that were sent by Bartram in 1788 to "Friend [Robert] Barclay" and are now preserved in the British Museum, helps to determine the species:

"I shall just observe that I discoverd, in the Creek Nation & Wt. of Georgia a Species of *Magnolia* (auriculata) very different from Mr. Frazers. The leaves of which were very large near 2 feet in length, the Flowers, white, Very large, & Fragrant & the Strobile or Seed Vessel 4.5 inches in length of a fine Crimson Color——"

Mohr (1901: 14) was correct in considering Bartram's species *M. macrophylla*. It was not until 12 years after the publication of the *Travels* that the tree was named by Michaux (1803, *1*: 327).

Magnolia glauca (cf. Catesby, 1730? *1*: 39, pl. 39): white bay (*M. virginiana* L.); on Colonel's Island, Ga., 6; in Liberty County, 10; about St. Mary's River, Ga.–Fla., 24; in Lime-Sink Region, 30; on Altamaha River, 50; description of a species differing little from it, 161.

Magnolia grandiflora (cf. Catesby, 1738, *2*: 61, pl. 61): southern magnolia (*M. grandiflora* L.); on the Mississippi and Altamaha Rivers and in Florida, xv; on Colonel's Island, Ga., 6; in Liberty County, 10;

in coastal swamps, 29; in Lime-Sink Region, 30; in Southern Red Hills, 32; formerly growing where salt marshes are, 69; Wild Turkeys on, 83; on St. John's River, Fla., below Palatka, iv, 84, above Lake George, 114, and near Huntoon Island, 141; near Alachua Savanna, 187; in Levy County, 221; at Manatee Spring, 232; the Creek name for, 232; near Three Sisters Ferry, S.C., 309; at Shell Bluff, Ga., 318; along Chattahoochee River, Ala., 393; in northwestern Butler County, 401; in Monroe or adjacent county, 402; on upper Tensaw River, 407–408; near The Rigolets, La., 421; along Iberville Canal, 427; along Mississippi River, 432; at Blue Springs, Screven County, Ga., 461; at Little River, S.C.–N.C., 472. See also Laurels, Laurel Magnolia(s), Laurel tree(s), Magnolia(s), Magnolian groves.

Magnolia grandiflora, depressed and degraded: probably more correctly identified in Bartram's report to Fothergill (1943: 146) as "short Magnolia glauca" [= M. virginiana L.] (cf. R. M. Harper, 1906: 239); in Putnam County, Fla., 171.

Nuttall (1822: 295) records from East Florida "a dwarf variety [of "Magnolia glauca"] not exceeding three or four feet."

Magnolia *pyramidata: a nomen nudum here, applied to some undescribed form of magnolia (cf. Harper, 1942b: 7–8); on Colonel's Island, Ga., 6.

Magnolia *pyramidata: Bartram's magnolia (cf. Harper, 1942b: 7–8; Merrill, 1945: 29); described, probably somewhere in vicinity of Boatyard Lake, 4 miles west of Tensaw, Ala. (soil map of Baldwin County, 1912; Tensaw quadrangle), 408. See also Magnolia, a new species of.

Magnolia tripetala (cf. Catesby, 1738, 2: 80, pl. 80): umbrella tree (M. tripetala L.); in Southern Red Hills, 32; on the Great Ridge, Ga., 41; along upper Savannah River, Ga.–S.C., 320, 327; compared with M. auriculata, 339.

Magnolian groves: probably consisting chiefly of southern magnolia (Magnolia grandiflora L.); on Altamaha River, Ga., 48.

Major. See Farmar, Major.

Mallard. See Anas fera torquata major.

Malva, blue flowered: undetermined; at Flat Rock, Ga., 377.

Malva, a climber, with broad hoary leaves and small greenish white flowers: undetermined; at Loughabber, S.C., 327.

"Malva volubilis. I belive a nondescrip. Lyon never found it." (Bartram to Muhlenberg, September 6, 1810; Muhlenberg Letters: 137.)

Malva, cerulean: undetermined; at cataracts of Augusta, Ga., 35; in Broad River region, 45.

Malva, with panicles of purple or blue flowers: undetermined; at Loughabber, S.C., 327.

"Malva paniculata. I know not whether Michaux has it. I have not his Book. I cant find any like it in Wildenow. I it is a very beautiful Plant. flowers large, deep blue or purple[.]" (Bartram to Muhlenberg, September 6, 1810; Muhlenberg Letters: 137.)

Malva *scandens: *nomen nudum* (Merrill, 1945: 34)—undetermined; on the Great Ridge, Ga., 41.

Man (or men): *Homo sapiens* L.; reason in, xxv; power and preeminence, 101; carried on back of Gopher Turtle, 183; disturbing game on Alachua Savanna, Fla., 188; ingenuity and labor, 193; Coachwhip snake familiar with, 220; bones of, between Little and Broad Rivers, Ga., 322.

Man of war bird. *See* Pelecanus aquilus.

Manakin: in Edwards' usage (1764, 3: 333), manakins were a heterogeneous group of birds, including not only those now known by that name, but also the Hoopoe, Cedar Waxwing, etc.; Catbird allied to, 300.

Manatee ("manate") or sea cow (Trichechus manatus): Florida Manatee (*T. manatus latirostris* [Harlan]); described, at Manatee Spring, Fla., 231–232.

Manatee ("Manate") Spring: on east side of Suwannee River, 7 miles west of Chiefland in Levy County, Fla. (fig. 19); visited and described, 230–232.

Manchac: a former British settlement on east bank of the Mississippi, just above Iberville Canal (the present Bayou Manchac), in East Baton Rouge Parish, La. (Baton Rouge quadrangle); projected trip to, 405, 413; set off for, 423; arrived at, 427, 428, 437; set off from, 429.

Manes; of a rattlesnake, appeased, 263.

Mankind: *Homo sapiens* L.; not attacked by Florida Bears, 282; predilection for society of each other, 360. *See also* Man.

Mantle (or robe); worn by Indians, 502, and their junior priests, 504; covering corpse among Choctaws, 516.

Manufactures, among American aborigines, 513.

Maple(s): probably red maple (*Acer rubrum* L. var.); on Salt Springs Run, Fla., 160; near Lake Lochloosa, 181; in Pennsylvania, 459.

Maple, Scarlet: probably red maple (*Acer rubrum* L. var.); on St. John's River near Charlotia, Fla., 93; in Butler or adjacent county, Ala., 400; at Macon, Ga., 459. *See also* Acer rubrum.

Marble; not seen in middle region of Georgia, 45.

Marcasites (or "markasites"): a mineral; at Silver Bluff, S.C., 314; along Cape Fear River, N.C., 475, 476.

Markers; in party setting out from Augusta, Ga., 35.

Marl ("marle"); in coastal swamps, and used as fertilizer, 30; along Cape Fear River, N.C., 474–476.

Marmalade, made from native plums, 423.

Marriage ceremonies: among American aborigines, 514–515; among Muscogulges, 514–515. See also Nuptials, Weddings.

Mars, sons of, 255.

Marsh, a vastly extensive and sedgy: River of Styx, flowing into the northwestern corner of Orange Lake, Alachua County, Fla. (Hawthorn quadrangle); crossed, 181.

Marshall, Mr. [Abraham]: plantation owner on lower St. John's River, Fla.; hospitality of, 76–77; called on, 306.
    The name of Marshall's plantation was "Satonia." His first grant was in 1773. (Mowat, 1943: 70.)

Martin, bank (hirundo riparia): Bank Swallow (Riparia riparia riparia [L.]); migrations of, 287. See also Hirundo riparia.
    These observations probably cover one or two additional species not named here.

Martin, great purple. See Hirundo purpurea.

Maryland; trees of, xvi; birds of, 288–302; tribes formerly inhabiting, 466; journey through, 479–480; citizens of, at Augusta, Ga., 486.

Mason, [Thomas]; captain of Prince of Wales, 1, 2.

Matts or carpets; made of splints, in Cherokee rotundas, 369.

Mattock, Jos.; founder of Wrightsborough, Ga., 35; hospitality of, 36.
    Elsewhere (1943: 139) Bartram spells this name as "Mattox." A Mr. "Maddox" (doubtless the same individual) is mentioned by McCall (1816, 2: 6), Stevens (1859, 2: 84), and Jones (1883, 2: 131) as one of the four commissioners appointed to negotiate sales of land in the New Purchase.

Mattresses ("mattrasses"), stuffed with long moss, 88.

May-Apple. See Granadilla.

May bird. See Calandra pratensis.

May fly. See Ephemera, great yellow.

Meal, made of roots of China brier, 241.

Meat, barbecued, an Indian family loaded with, 244.

Medeola ("Mediola"): Indian cucumber-root (M. virginiana L.); along upper Savannah River, Ga., 321.

Medicine: to avert sickness at Otasse, Ala., 455; at the busk, 509.

Mediterranean (Sea); fruits cultivated there, 460–461.

Medusa (cf. Linné, 1767, *1*, Pt. II: 1096): a jellyfish (phylum Coelenterata); on St. Simon's Island, Ga., 60.

Medway meeting. *See* Midway meeting.

Medway (nowadays sometimes spelled "Midway") River: a short coastal stream between Bryan and Liberty Counties, Ga. (map of Liberty County, 1939); Sunbury on, 5; branches of, 10.

Meherrin ("Meherren") River: arising in south central Virginia and joining the Blackwater in northeastern North Carolina; sojourn on, 479.

Melanthium: perhaps fly poison (*Amianthium muscaetoxicum* [Walt.] Gray); near Long Pond, Levy County, Fla., 248.

Meleagris: Eastern Wild Turkey (*Meleagris gallopavo americana* Bartram; syn., *M. g. silvestris* Vieillot); in Pennsylvania, 286; in Vale of Cowee, N.C., 348.

Meleagris *Americanus, the wild turkey: Eastern Wild Turkey (*M. gallopavo americana* Bartram; syn., *M. g. silvestris* Vieillot) (cf. Harper, 1942*d*: 216); listed, 290 *bis*. *See also* Turkey(s).

Meleagris ("mileagris") of Asia and Europe: presumably referring to a Himalayan tragopan, the *Meleagris satyra* of Linnaeus (1758, *1*: 157); size compared with that of American Wild Turkey, 14.

Meleagris occidentalis. *See* Turkey, wild (Meleagris occidentalis).

Melons, cultivation by Indians, 511.

Melons (Cucurbita citrullus): watermelons (*Citrullus vulgaris* Schrad.); at Palatka, Fla., 93.

Men. *See* Man, Mankind.

Merchants; at Pensacola, Fla., 416; at Cross Creeks, N.C., 477, 478.

Mergus (cf. Mergus cucullatus, p. 295): perhaps Hooded Merganser (*Lophodytes cucullatus* [L.]); nesting at Watermelon? Pond, Alachua County, Fla., 249.

M[ergus] cucullatus, the round crested duck (cf. Catesby, 1732, *1*: 94, pl. 94; Edwards, 1764, *3*: 316, 326, pl. 360): Hooded Merganser (*Lophodytes cucullatus* [L.]); listed, 295.

Mergus major pectore rufo, great fishing duck (cf. Edwards, 1747, *2*: 95, 128, pl. 95): Red-breasted Merganser (*Mergus serrator serrator* L.); listed, 295.

Merula *flammula, sand-hill redbird of Carolina: *nomen nudum*— Scarlet Tanager (*Piranga olivacea* [Gmelin]) (cf. Harper, 1942*d*: 214–215); listed, 290 *bis*.

M[erula] *Marilandica, the summer red bird (cf. Catesby, 1730, *1*: 56, pl. 56): *nomen nudum*—Summer Tanager (*Piranga rubra rubra* [L.]) (cf. Harper, 1942*d*: 214–215); listed, 290 *bis*. *See also* Redbird, summer.

Mexico, Indigo Bunting in, 299.

Mexico, bay of: Gulf of Mexico; St. Marks on, 235; navigation from Flint River to, 384.

Mica, in middle region of Georgia, 45.

Mica. S[eu] vitrum Muscoviticum. *See* Isinglass.

Mica nitida: perhaps talc or kaolin; along Jarrett Creek, near Aquone, N.C., 363.

Micaceous ("miceous") earth, along Jarrett Creek, near Aquone, N.C., 363.

Mice: in this case, at least for the most part, Cotton Mice (*Peromyscus gossypinus gossypinus* [Le Conte]); on Colonel's Island, Ga., 7.

Mice: in this case, House Mice (*Mus musculus* subspp.); in Charleston, S.C., 281.

    The white individuals, with red eyes, were albinos of this species.

Micos: Indian kings; assembling at Coweta town, Ala., 389.

Mico clucco the Long Warrior or King of the Seminoles ("Siminoles"); portrait, as frontispiece. *See also* Long Warrior.

Mico or king, functions and attributes, 494–497. *See also* King or mico.

Middleton, "General," commander of Carolinian auxiliaries: evidently Colonel Thomas Middleton (1719–1766), of South Carolina; Cherokees vanquished by, 330; in battle with Cherokees, 348.

    Colonel Middleton, in charge of a provincial regiment, was associated with Colonel James Grant, who was in command of the British regulars. The battle in the Vale of Cowee had taken place in June, 1761. (Carroll, 1836, *1:* 467, 474; *Appletons' Cyclopaedia;* Jones, 1883, *2:* 8, 14, etc.)

Midway ("Medway") meeting: a historic church of Liberty County, Ga., 5 miles north of Riceboro; attended service in, 9.

    The Midway Church was burned down by the British in 1778, but it was rebuilt in 1792. During the Civil War it was damaged and desecrated by Federal troops. It is now preserved as a Georgia shrine and landmark. (Cf. White, 1849: 377–378, and 1854: 518–519, figs.; Jones, 1889; Park, 1929; 348–361; Martin, 1936; Cate, Colquitt, and McCarty, 1940: 61–63.)

Mifflin, Thomas; dedication. (Cf. Harper, 1953: 575.)

Migration(s): of birds, 287; of Indians, 391–392; of Passenger Pigeons, 470.

Milk: at a cowpen south of Altamaha River, Ga., 19; in repast at Cuscowilla, Fla., 186; at plantation on Savannah River, Ga., 310–311; in repast at Watauga, N.C., 351.

Mills, built at Cross Creeks, N.C., 477. *See also* Grist-mill, Saw-mill(s).

Milvus, Kite Hawks: in Bartram's usage, a group comprising the subfamilies Elaninae, Perninae, and Milvinae in the family Accipitridae; diagnosis and list of, 290.

Mimosa, a species of: "Mimosa virgatia" (*q.v.*); viii.

Mimosa intsia: not *M. intsia* L., but sensitive briar (*Schrankia* sp.); in Levy County, Fla., 224.

Mimosa pudica. *See* Humble plant.

Mimosa sensitiva: in these cases, not *M. sensitiva* L., but probably sensitive briar (*Schrankia* sp.); in Levy County, Fla., 224, 248.

Mimosa sensitiva, a new species of: sensitive briar (*Schrankia* sp., perhaps *S. microphylla* [Dryand.] Macbr.); described, about St. Mary's River, Ga.–Fla., 24.

   "Mimosa procumbens   Walter dont mention it. I dont know if Michaux saw it." (Bartram to Muhlenberg, September 6, 1810; Muhlenberg Letters: 137.)

Mimosa virgata ("virgatia"): not *M. virgata* L., nor *Neptunia lutea* (Leavenw.) Benth. (as indicated by Merrill, 1945: 29), but a *Desmanthus* (Turner, 1951: 86) and probably *D. illinoensis* (Michx.) MacM.; described, at The Rigolets, St. Tammany Parish, La., 421–422.

Mink: for the most part, at least, Salt-marsh Mink (*Mustela vison lutensis* [Bangs]); in Florida and Carolina, 281.

Minnows, 167.

Minorquies: Minorcans; a colony at New Smyrna, Fla., 144.

Mississippi (or "Missiippi," "Missisipi," "Missisippi," "Mississipi") River, xv, 298, 339, 423, 430, 466; Chickasaw plum brought from beyond, 38; migration of Creeks or Muscogulges from beyond, 54, 465; inland navigation from Virginia to, 68; subsidence of land near, 69; magnolias on, 86; horses brought from beyond, 216; travels to, 288, 468; British settlement on, 405; passage to, 414; description of, 427–429; crossed, 432.

Mitchella repens (cf. Catesby, 1730? *1*: pl. 20): partridge berry (*M. repens* L.); at Falling Creek, Rabun County, Ga., 342.

Mobile "in West Florida" (now Alabama): on the site of the modern city at the head of Mobile Bay, Ala.; 443, 492, 506, 507, 521; adventurers bound for, 366; set off for, 397; proceeded for, 403; description of, 404; set off from, 405, 440; return to, 413, 417, 418; one beehive brought there from Europe, 413; set sail from, 414; papers left at, 414; anchor at, 438.

Mobile Bay (or "Bay of Mobile"): an arm of the Gulf of Mexico, in southwestern Alabama; approach, 403; capes at entrance to, 414, 415; voyage on, 418–419; West Cape of (probably Cedar Point), 438; entered, 438.

Mobile Point: a peninsula at the entrance to Mobile Bay, Ala., on the east side; spent night at, 414.

Mobile River: formed by junction of the Alabama and Tombigbee Rivers, and flowing through the Mobile Delta to Mobile Bay, Ala.; 398, 416; tributaries of, 396; eastern channel of, 403, 405–411; two large arms of, 408; capes of, 415; Alabama nation on, 429; *Illicium* on, 442. *See also* Alabama River.

Moccasins; of Cherokee youths, 370; worn by Indians, 504; made by Indian women, 513. *See also* Stillepica or moccasin.

Moccasin, harmless, with blotches of a deep nut brown: undetermined; described, from Carolina and Florida, 273–274.

The name, size, shape, reputation, and to some extent the colors, but not the habitat, fit the Southern Water Snake (*Natrix sipedon fasciata* [L.]). Possibly this species and the Corn Snake (*Elaphe guttata* [L.]) are here confused.

Moccasin snake, poisonous: Cottonmouth (*Agkistrodon piscivorus* [Lacepède]); account of, 272–273.

Mock-bird: Eastern Mockingbird (*Mimus polyglottos polyglottos* [L.]); compared with Catbird, 299.

Mock-bird (turdus polyglottos) (cf. Catesby, 1730? *1*: 27, pl. 27): Eastern Mockingbird (*Mimus polyglottos polyglottos* [L.]); song, xxxii; in Liberty County, Ga., 11; on Altamaha River, 51; on St. Simon's Island, 61; near Three Sisters Ferry, S.C., 309; near Clayton, Ga., 344; resident in Pennsylvania, 286. *See also* Turdus polyglottos.

Mole: including both Florida Mole (*Scalopus aquaticus australis* [Chapman]) and Howell's Mole (*S. a. howelli* Jackson); in Florida and Carolina, 283.

Moles: in this case, Florida Moles (*Scalopus aquaticus australis* [Chapman]); not found on Colonel's Island, Ga., 7.

Momordica: a genus of Cucurbitaceae, comprising the balsam-apples; faculty of tendrils, xxi.

Monarchs, of the Old World, 495.

Monuments. *See* Indian country, etc.

Moon: eclipse of, on Altamaha River, Ga., 51; silver queen of night, 190; soft light of full moon, 245; birds imagined going to, 285; Indians rejoicing at appearance of new moon, 498.

Moor fowl: Appalachian Ruffed Grouse (*Bonasa umbellus monticola* Todd); at Keowee, S.C., 331. *See also* Tetrao tympanus.

Moore, Esq.: a settler on west side of Cape Fear River, in Bladen or Columbus Counties, N.C.; 474.

A "Moor" is indicated hereabouts on the Faden map of 1776, and an "A. Moore" on the Price and Strother map of 1808.

Moral system; discussed, 52.

Morality, inculcated by Indians, 518.

Morinella °Americana, the turnstone or dotterel ("dotrill") (cf. Catesby, 1731, *1:* 72, pl. 72; Edwards, 1750, *3:* 141, pl. 141, and 1751, *4:* 245); *nomen nudum*—Ruddy Turnstone (*Arenaria interpres morinella* [L.]); listed, 294.

Mortars (apparently a sort of cannon), at Apalachean Old Fields, Fla., 233.

Mortar (or "morter") (a plastic building material); 388, 456.

Mortar, wooden, roots of China brier pounded in, 241.

Morus: a genus of Artocarpaceae, comprising the mulberries; usefulness, xvii.

Morus: in these cases, doubtless red mulberry (*M. rubra* L.); on lower St. John's River, Fla., 84; at Lake George, 157; in Levy County, 221; near Oconee Station, Oconee County, S.C., 335; near Wayah Gap, N.C., 362; along Chattahoochee River, Ala., 393, 394; in Lowndes or Butler Counties, 399; near The Rigolets, La., 421; at White Cliffs, 436. *See also* Morus rubra, Mulberry.

Morus: in this case, white mulberry (*M. alba* L.); proposed culture in Georgia, 460.

Morus alba. *See* Mulberry trees, European.

Morus rubra: red mulberry (*M. rubra* L.); on Colonel's Island, Ga., 6; in lower Coastal Plain, 29; about Wrightsborough, 36; cultivated by the ancients near Little River, 38; on St. John's River at Charlotia, Fla., 94, and above Lake Dexter, 131; near Salt Springs, 164; between Orange and Tuscawilla Lakes, 183; near Alachua Savanna, 187; at Alachua Sink, 204; near Three Sisters Ferry, S.C., 309; at Shell Bluff, Ga., 318; along upper Savannah River, 320; along Iberville Canal, La., 427; along the Mississippi, 432; along Cape Fear River, N.C., 474. *See also* Morus; Mulberry.

Mosquitoes ("musquetoes" or "musquitoes" or "musquitoes (culex)"): species of the family Culicidae, including such genera as *Culex, Anopheles,* and *Aëdes;* at Nassau Sound, Fla., 71; on St. John's River, 88, 135, 136; at Lake George, 158, 252; at Alachua Savanna, 193; at Half-way Pond, 216; at Kanapaha Sink, 217; efforts to extirpate, 254; persecuted by, 386; at Mobile Point, Ala., 414, 417; on Amite River, La., 426.

Mosquito ("Musquito" or "Musquitoe") River: Mosquito Lagoon, extending along the east coast of Florida from the vicinity of New

Smyrna to Merritt's Island; observations near, xxv–xxxi; New Smyrna on, 144; great mound (Turtle Mound) on, 521.

Moss: in Bartram's usage, either mosses (Musci) or lichens (Lichenes); between Little and Broad Rivers, Ga., 322.

Mosses, crustaceous: doubtless lichens (Lichenes); near Suwannee River, Fla., 243; on White Plains, La., 431.

Moss, long (Tillandsia ["Tillandsea" or "Tillansia"] usneascites [or "ulneadscites"]): long or Spanish moss (Tillandsia usneoides L.); description and utilization, on lower St. John's River, Fla., iv, 87; on cypresses, 91. See also Tillandsia usneascites.

Motacilla: a genus of passerine birds (in the family Motacillidae), now restricted to the wagtails, but formerly with much wider limits; Catbird distinguished from, 300.

M[otacilla] *Caroliniana, (reg[ulus] *magnus) the great wren of Carolina: Carolina Wren (Thryothorus ludovicianus ludovicianus [Latham]); listed, 291.

M[otacilla] *domestica (regulus *rufus) the house wren: nomen nudum—Eastern House Wren (Troglodytes aëdon aëdon Vieillot) (cf. Wilson, 1808, 1: 129; Coues, 1875: 351); listed, 291.

Barton (1799a: 15) is evidently in error in identifying this species with "The little Sparrow" of Catesby (1730? 1: 35, pl. 35), which may be the Eastern Field Sparrow (Spizella pusilla pusilla [Wilson]).

M[otacilla] *fluviatilis, the water wagtail: nomen nudum—Louisiana Water-thrush (Seiurus motacilla [Vieillot]); listed, 291.

M[otacilla] *palustris, (reg[ulus] *minor) the marsh wren: nomen nudum—Long-billed Marsh Wren (Telmatodytes palustris palustris [Wilson]); listed, 291.

Motacilla sialis, the blue bird. (Rubicula ["Rebicula"] Americana, Cat[esby]) (cf. Catesby, 1730, 1: 47, pl. 47): Eastern Bluebird (Sialia sialis sialis [L.]); listed, 291. See also Blue bird.

Motacilla trochilus. See Chat, yellow breasted.

Bartram is confused in citing this name, for the Motacilla trochilus of Linnaeus is not the "yellow brested Chat" or "Oenanthe americana pectore luteo" of Catesby, but a European bird, the Willow Warbler (Phylloscopus trochilus trochilus [L.]).

Mound ("mount"), a magnificent Indian: Mount Royal, at Fruitland Cove, between Welaka and Georgetown, Putnam County, Fla. (fig. 9); described, 99–100. See also Mount Royal.

The earliest description of this famous mound is apparently that by John Bartram, who visited it in company with his son in 1765 and 1766. Possibly he gave the name to this mound as he did to Mount Hope. It is about an eighth of a mile north of Fruitland Cove. In 1893, before being excavated by Moore, it was 16 feet in height and had a circumference of 555 feet. In 1939 and 1940 large trees were growing over its surface. The "highway" leading northward from the mound is still faintly discernible; it was probably of ceremonial significance. Instead of leading directly to a pond half a mile distant, as reported in some accounts, it seems to pass a little on one side, to the east.

For further accounts see J. Bartram (1769: 25–26; 1942: 38, 45, 74–75), W. Bartram (1853: 57–58, fig. 6; 1943: 150–151, 185–186), Brinton (1859: 168–169), Wyman (1875: 40), and Moore (1894: 16–35). The original sketch of Mount Royal by William Bartram is now lost, but there is fortunately a copy by John Howard Payne in his commonplace book (Hist. Soc. Pennsylvania). Moreover, the original was reproduced in 1848, and the reproduction is copied in the present volume (fig. 9).

Mount Hope: a shell bluff on Beecher Point, at the outlet of Little Lake George, Fla. (cf. J. Bartram, 1942: 38, 70); converted into an indigo plantation, 98.

Mount Magnolia: probably Pinnacle Knob (alt. 2,000 feet), 2 miles northeast of Clayton, Ga. (fig. 22) or perhaps one of the higher summits a mile or so northward (map of Chattahoochee National Forest, 1937); ascent and naming of, 338–342.

Mount Royal: a place at Fruitland Cove, between Welaka and Georgetown, Putnam County, Fla., deriving its name from a celebrated Indian mound there (soil map of Putnam County, 1919) (fig. 9); stayed at, 98; prospect of, 103; sailing to, 168–169; arrived at, 252, 254; mentioned, 521. See also Mound, a magnificent Indian.

M[oun]t Turtle: the modern Turtle Mound on the eastern shore of Mosquito Lagoon, 5 miles southeast of New Smyrna, Fla.; on map, facing page viii. For further accounts, see Brinton (1859: 78) and Small (1923: 199–204, fig.).

Mountain cock. See Tetrao lagopus, Tetrao urogallus.

Moyamensing ("Moyomensing"): a district in southern Philadelphia County, Pa.; cattle of, 190.

Mucclasse (properly Muklasa): a former Upper Creek town on north side of Tallapoosa River in Elmore County, Ala., about 3 miles below Coolome and apparently at or near the present Judkins Ferry (Taitt, map of 1772, and 1916: 509, 541; Bur. Am. Ethnol. Bull., 30, Pt. I: 955, 1907; Swanton, 1922: 207, pls. 2, 7, 8, 9, and 1946:

152–153; soil map of Elmore County, 1911); visit to, and Indian nuptials at, 446–449; returned to, 447; set off from, 449; a trader of, 462, 507; listed, 463; a blind old chief at, 499–500; came to, 506.

Mud fish: Bowfin (*Amia calva* L.); described, at Cowpen Lake, Putnam County, Fla., 176; in Alachua Sink, 205.

Mulberry (or "common wild Mulberry" or "native Mulberry" or "Mulberry trees"): red mulberry (*Morus rubra* L.); near Salt Springs, Fla., 164; in Levy County, 223; near Suwannee River, 224; European mulberry grafted on, 308; at Silver Bluff, S.C., 315; on Oconee River, Ga., 379; in Butler or adjacent county, Ala., 400; compared with *Halesia diptera*, 410. *See also* Morus, Morus rubra.

Mulberry trees, European (Morus alba): white mulberry (*M. alba* L.); orchard of, in South Carolina, 308.

Mullet: either Common Mullet (*Mugil cephalus* L.) or Silver Mullet (*M. curema* Valenciennes), or both; about Georgia coastal islands, 67.

Murder; death or outlawry as punishment for, among Mucogulges, 515.

Musa: a genus of Musaceae, comprising the bananas; usefulness, xvii.

Musa paradisiaca ("paradisica"): plantain banana (*M. paradisiaca* L.); in the tropics, xiv.

Musa sapientum; common banana (*M. paradisiaca* ssp. *sapientum* [L.] Kuntze); in the tropics, xiv.

Musci: flies; prey of Six-lined Lizards, 172.

Muscicapa: a genus of Old World flycatchers, in Linnaean usage having much wider limits than at present; Summer Redbird classed with, 302.

Muscicapa *cantatrix, the little domestic flycatcher or green wren (cf. Wilson, 1810, 2: 166): *nomen nudum*—Northern White-eyed Vireo (*Vireo griseus noreboracensis* [Gmelin]); listed, 290 *bis*.

M[uscicapa] ("Muscitapa") cristata, the great crested yellow bellied flycatcher (cf. Catesby, 1730, 1: 52, pl. 52): Northern Crested Flycatcher (*Myiarchus crinitus boreus* Bangs) (cf. Harper, 1942d: 214); listed, 289 *bis*.

Muscicapa ("Muscitapa") *nunciola, the pewit, or black cap flycatcher (cf. Catesby, 1730, 1: 53, pl. 53): Eastern Phoebe (*Sayornis phoebe* [Latham]); listed, 289 *bis*. *See also* Pewit.

This name, while perhaps nomenclaturally validated by the reference to Catesby on page 287, is antedated by the *Muscicapa phoebe* of Latham (1790).

M[uscicapa] ("Muscitapa") *rapax, the lesser pewit, or brown and greenish flycatcher (cf. Wilson, 1810, 2: 81): *nomen nudum*— Wood Pewee (*Contopus virens* [L.]); listed, 289 *bis*.

M[uscicapa] ("Muscitapa") *subviridis, the little olive col[oure]d flycatcher (cf. Wilson, 1810, 2: 77; Coues, 1875: 348): *nomen nudum*—Acadian Flycatcher (*Empidonax virescens* [Vieillot]), or perhaps a composite of several species of that genus (cf. Harper, 1942d: 214); listed, 289 *bis*.

M[uscicapa] *sylvicola, the little red eye'd flycatcher (cf. Catesby, 1730, *1*: 54, pl. 54): *nomen nudum*—Red-eyed Vireo (*Vireo olivaceus* [L.]); listed, 290 *bis*.

Muscicapa vertice nigro. *See* Cat-bird.

Muscle, with horns or protuberances; on an island near Anchor, La., 433.

    The description fits a unique species, *Elliptio spinosus* (Lea), described from Altamaha River, Ga., and unknown in the Mississippi. Goodrich (1930: 140) is probably correct in assuming that Bartram has here confused the two localities. (Cf. Tomkins, 1955.)

Muscogulge. *See* Indians—Creeks.

Muscogulge tongue, spoken by Seminoles, 464.

Muses, inspiring a Seminole, 107.

Music: after a feast at Talahasochte, Fla., 236; Seminoles entertaining with, 245; at Mucclasse, 446, and at Alabama, Ala., 447; among Indians, 505–506; at a Muscogulge marriage, 514.

Musicians, in Cherokee rotundas, 369–370.

Musket ("musquet"), report of, 75.

Musket ball, eggs of Gopher Turtle compared with, 183.

Muskrats (castor cauda lanceolata ["lanciolata"]): Common Muskrat (*Ondatra zibethicus zibethicus* [L.]); in northern parts of Carolina and Georgia, 281.

"Musquetoes" (or "musquitoes"). *See* Mosquitoes.

"Musquito" (or "Musquitoe") River. *See* Mosquito River.

Mustee [= métis]: a person of mixed white and Indian blood; a Mustee Creek as traveling companion of Bartram in Alabama, 440, 443–445; nuptials of, 446; learning Choctaw songs and poetry, 506–507.

Mustela: a genus of Mustelidae, comprising minks, weasels, etc.; species of Florida and Carolina, 281.

Myrica: one or more species of wax myrtle, perhaps chiefly *Myrica cerifera* L.; on Altamaha River, Ga., 48; on St. Simon's Island, 58; on upper Tensaw River, Ala., 408; at The Rigolets, La., 421; at Lake Pontchartrain, 423; along Cape Fear River, N.C., 476.

Myrica cerifera (cf. Catesby, 1731, *1*: 69, pl. 69): presumably wax myrtle (*M. cerifera* L.); on Colonel's Island, Ga., 6; in Liberty County, 10; about St. Mary's River, Ga.–Fla., 24; on Altamaha

River, Ga., 50; on St. John's River above Lake George, Fla., 114; at Lake George, 157; near Salt Springs, 164; near Orange Lake, 181; on Long Bay, S.C., 471. *See also* Myrtle(s).

Bartram did not distinguish the northern bayberry (*M. pensylvanica* Loisel.), and probably included it under the above designation.

Myrica cerifera, two or three varieties: wax myrtles, perhaps including *M. pensylvanica* Loisel. in addition to *M. cerifera* L. and *M. pusilla* Raf. (this last the "very dwarfish" one); near Suwannee River, Fla., 242.

Myrica °inodora: odorless wax myrtle (*M. inodora* Bartr.); described, on upper Tensaw River, near Hall's Creek, Ala. (soil map of Baldwin County, 1912; Tensaw quadrangle), 405–406.

Myrica, low: probably dwarf wax myrtle (*M. pusilla* Raf.); near Alachua Savanna, Fla., 187.

Myrica, odoriferous: probably wax myrtle (*M. cerifera* L.); on Sapelo Island, Ga., 268.

Myrtle(s): probably *Myrica cerifera* L.; in Liberty County, Ga., 11; on St. John's River at Huntoon Island, Fla., 140.

Myrtles (Myrica cerifera ["carefera"]): wax myrtle (*M. cerifera* L.); near Nassau Sound, Fla., 71.

Myrtus, broad leaved sweet: dune red bay (*Persea littoralis* Small) (Small, 1923: 28); on Mosquito River, Fla., xxviii.

Myrtus caryophyllata: clove tree (*Eugenia aromatica* [L.] Baill.); in the tropics, xiv.

Myrtus communis: the classic myrtle (*M. communis* L.); in the tropics, xiv.

Myrtus pimenta: allspice (*Pimenta officinalis* Berg); in the tropics, xiv.

Mytili ("Mytuli"), fresh-water: pelecypod mollusks, probably of the genus *Elliptio* (R.A.M.); on St. John's River above Lake George, Fla., 114.

Nae oche (usually spelled Nacoochee or Naguchee): a former Cherokee town near the junction of Sautee Creek and Chattahoochee River, in White County, Ga. (Hunter's map of 1730; Mouzon's map of 1775; Mooney, 1900: 526, pl. 3; Dahlonega quadrangle); listed, 374.

Mooney's statement and map do not appear to be accurate.

Narcissus: a genus of Amaryllidaceae, comprising the narcissi, daffodils, jonquils, etc.; in the tropics, xv.

Natche (properly Natchez): a former Natchez town on Tallasee-hatchee Creek, Talladega County, Ala., about 4 miles north of Sylacauga (Taitt, map of 1772, and 1916: 531–532; *Bur. Am. Ethnol. Bull.*, 30, Pt. II: 36, 1910; Swanton, 1922: 313, pls. 2, 7; Talladega quadrangle); listed, 463.

Natchez ("Natches"): an old settlement on the Mississippi in Adams County, Miss.; French settling at, 433–434. *See also* Indians—Natchez.

Nation. *See* Indians—Creeks.

Natives, entertaining French at Natchez, Miss., 433.

Natural history: attention to, 285; of North America, 473; every branch of, 479.

Natural productions: from sea coast to Augusta, Ga., 28–32; of Georgia, 47.

Naturalists: their classification of the Alligator, 280; undescribed birds left to future naturalists, 296; curious, 318.

Nature; works of, xiii, 338; as the work of God, xxiv; scene(s) of primitive (or rural or uncultivated) nature, 49, 107, 215, 243, 322, 360, 388; pursuit of new productions of, 73–74; primary productions of, 89; reviving at the appearance of the sun, 100; simple and necessary calls of, 111; face of, appearing again after a hurricane, 142; happy state of, before the fall, 168; awaking to life and activity, 246; furnishing toads with a long tongue, 280; repast presented from lap of, 348; cheerful countenance of, 387; all her various perfections, 415.

Neat's tongue; repast of, 361. *See also* Beef.

Nebuchadnezzar: the Biblical character, King of Babylon; Bartram's situation compared to his, 360.

Nectarine ("Nectarin"): *Amygdalus persica* L. var. *nucipersica* Schneid.; in temperate zone, xv.

Needles, presented to Indians, 244.

Negro(es): on a plantation on St. John's River, 75; felling cypresses, 92; furnished by Major Farmar, 411; manning a boat, 418, 423; tannier esteemed by, 469; apprehensions from a party of, on Long Bay, S.C., 471. *See also* Blacks, Slaves (Negro).

Negro slave(s): manning a boat, 70; at Lake Beresford, Fla., 143; as guide to Seneca, S.C., 328. *See also* Blacks, Slaves (Negro).

Nepenthes distillatoria: a pitcher plant (*N. distillatoria* L.) native to Ceylon; pleasing figure, xviii.

New England; various trees of, xvi; travels in, 288.

New Hope: a settlement on south side of Altamaha River in Glynn

County, Ga., opposite Broughton Island and at the source of a tidal channel known as "Wally Leg" (*fide* Mrs. G. V. Cate) (map of Glynn County, 1938); plantation at, 306.

The lower part of the Broadfield plantation was called New Hope (Mrs. Cate, 1930: 198).

New-Jersey: various trees of, xvi; iron ore in, 223; water chinquapin in, 409; white cedar of, 411.

New Mexico: including, under Spanish dominion, parts of the present Texas and other adjacent states; horses brought from, 216.

New Orleans, La.; 287, 298; travels to, 288.

New Purchase: in Bartram's usage, apparently consisting roughly of the basins of the Broad and Little Rivers, Ga., although the territory ceded by the Indians at Augusta in 1773 also extended farther south, between the Ogeechee and Altamaha Rivers on the west and the Savannah on the east (cf. Purcell map of about 1776; Royce, 1887: pl. 8, and 1899: 639, pl. 122; Phillips, 1902: pl. 1); boundaries of, 34, 324; productions of, 376; cession of, 485.

New-Richmond. *See* Baton Rouge.

New-Smyrna: on east coast of Florida, in the present Volusia County; on map facing page xii; history and description of, 144; a great mound near, 521.

New-York; various trees of, xvi; mentioned, 270; plants common in, 337.

Newport River, [North]: a coastal stream in Liberty County, Ga. (map of Liberty County, 1939); Sunbury near, 5; branches of, 10.

Newport [River, South]: a stream forming the boundary between Liberty and McIntosh Counties, Ga. (soil map of McIntosh County, 1932); crossing waters of, 12.

Nicotiana. *See* Tobacco.

Night hawk: in this case, either one of two species that Bartram confused—Eastern Nighthawk (*Chordeiles minor minor* [Forster]) and Eastern Whip-poor-will (*Caprimulgus vociferus vociferus* Wilson); near Clayton, Ga., 344. *See also* Caprimulgus Americanus.

Night hawk or whip-poor-will: an evident confusion of two distinct species, the former being the Florida Nighthawk (*Chordeiles minor chapmani* [Coues]), and the latter the Eastern Whip-poor-will (*Caprimulgus vociferus vociferus* Wilson) (cf. Wilson, 1812, 5: 80–81); compared with Chuck-will's-widow, 154. *See also* Whip-poor-will(s).

Nightingale. *See* Loxia cardinalis.

Nilaque: a former Cherokee town, identical with Big Island (*q.v.*).

Niowe: an unidentified Cherokee town on the headwaters of Tennessee River (*Bur. Am. Ethnol. Bull.*, *30*, Pt. II: 73, 1910); listed, 374.

Noddy. *See* Sterna stolida.

Noewe: an unidentified Cherokee town on the upper waters of Tennessee River, apparently in western North Carolina (*Bur. Am. Ethnol. Bull.*, *30*, Pt. II: 79, 1910); listed, 373.

Hunter's map of 1751 indicates such a town in the vicinity of the present Murphy, Cherokee County, N.C.

Nondo. *See* Angelica lucida.

Nonpareil (or "nonparel"): Painted Bunting (*Linaria ciris ciris* [L.] —formerly *Passerina ciris ciris* [L.]) (cf. Harper, 1942*d*: 216–217); in Liberty County, Ga., 11; on St. Simon's Island, 61; on Drayton's Island, Fla., 106; at Lake Dexter, 154. *See also* Linaria ciris; Painted finch.

North America: botanical nomenclature and natural history of, 473; aborigines of, 481.

North Carolina: trader from, 111; boundary, 472; travels through, 472–479; capital and governor of, 473. *See also* Carolina.

North West of Cape Fear River: the northwestern branch, or Northwest Cape Fear River, N.C.; journey up, 473–474; width, 476; a branch of, 477; course of, 478. *See also* Cape Fear River.

Northern States [of the United States]; cheese from, 19; Tent Caterpillar in, 66; Mole in, 283; birds not reaching, 289.

Nova-Scotia: Indigo Bunting in, 299; honey bees in, 413.

Nowe: an unidentified Cherokee town, on a branch of Little Tennessee River; listed, 373.

Nuanha (properly Nununyi): a former Cherokee town on the Oconalufty River, near the present Cherokee, Swain County, N.C. (Mooney, 1900: pl. 3; *Bur. Am. Ethnol. Bull.*, *30*, Pt. II: 98, 1910; Cowee quadrangle); listed, 373.

Nucasse: a former Cherokee town at the site of the present Franklin, Macon County, N.C. (Hunter's map of 1730; Romans' map of 1776; Mooney, 1900: 527, pl. 3; Cowee quadrangle); passed, 350; listed, 373.

Numenius, alba varia, the white godwit (cf. Edwards, 1750, *3*: 139, pl. 139): Marbled Godwit (*Limosa fedoa* [L.]), in juvenal plumage; listed, 293.

Numenius ("Numinus") albus. *See* Curlews, Spanish.

N[umenius] *Americana, the greater godwit (cf. Edwards, 1750, *3*: 137, pl. 137, and 1751, *4*: 245; Linnaeus, 1758, *1*: 146): *nomen nudum* —adult Marbled Godwit (*Limosa fedoa* [L.]); listed, 294.

N[umenius] *cinereus, the sea side lesser curlew: *nomen nudum*—probably Hudsonian Curlew (*Numenius phaeopus hudsonicus* Latham); listed, 294.

N[umenius] *fluvialis, the red shank or pool snipe: *nomen nudum*—perhaps including both Greater and Lesser Yellowlegs (*Totanus melanoleucus* [Gmelin] and *T. flavipes* [Gmelin]); listed, 294.

Numenius ("Numinus") fuscus. *See* Curlews, Spanish.

N[umenius] magnus rufus, the great sea coast curlew: probably Long-billed Curlew (*N. americanus americanus* Bechstein); listed, 294.

N[umenius] minor campestris, the lesser field curlew: perhaps Eskimo Curlew (*Numenius borealis* [Forster]); listed, 294.

N[umenius] pectore rufo ("ruso"), the great red breasted godwit (cf. Edwards, 1750, *3:* 138, pl. 138, and 1751, *4:* 245): Hudsonian Godwit (*Limosa haemastica* [L.]); listed, 293.

Nuptials, of Indians at Mucclasse, Ala., 446. *See also* Marriage ceremonies; Weddings.

Nuthatch. *See* Sitta.

Nuthatch, black capped, red bellied. *See* Sitta varia.

Nuthatch, grey black capped. *See* Sitta Europea.

Nux mosch[ata]: nutmeg (*Rees's Cyclopaedia,* 1st Am. ed., *26*); in the tropics, xiv.

Nyctanthes: a genus of Old World shrubs in the family Oleaceae, comprising jasmines, and in Linnaean usage including several species now referred to *Jasminum;* in the tropics, xiv.

Nymphs, Cherokee maidens as, 357.

Nymphaea (or "Nymphea"): probably water chinquapin (*Nelumbo lutea* [Willd.] Pers.); at Lake George, Fla., 108; at "Battle Lagoon," near Lake Dexter, 118; in Suwannee River, 228.

Nymphaea (or "Nymphea" or "Nyphaea") nelumbo ("nilumbo"): water chinquapin (*Nelumbo lutea* [Willd.] Pers.); at Lake George, Fla., 107; in Chacala Pond, Alachua County, 189; in Suwannee River, 230; described, near mouth of Tombigbee River, Ala.; also recorded from New Jersey, two lakes near Cape Fear River, N.C., Savannah River at Augusta, and East Florida, viii, 409.

Nympheum: presumably a temple of nymphs, i.e. a fountain; vi.

Nyssa (or "Nussa"): gum (*Nyssa* spp.); in lower Coastal Plain, 29; on Salt Springs Run, Fla., 160.

Nyssa aquatica (cf. Catesby, 1730, *1:* 41, pl. 41; Elliott, 1824, 2: 684): probably, for the most part, black gum (*N. sylvatica* Marsh. vars.) rather than tupelo gum (*N. aquatica* L.); of Carolina and Florida, xvi; about St. Mary's River, Ga.–Fla., 24; in coastal swamps, 29; on St. John's River near Charlotia, Fla., 93, and above Lake Dexter,

131; at Salt Springs, 161; on Amite River, La., 425; along Cape Fear River, N.C., 474.

Nyssa *coccinea, si[ve] *Ogeeche: tupelo gum (*N. ogeche* Bartr. ex Marsh.) (cf. E. L. Little, Jr., 1945: 503; Merrill, 1945: 30); described, from Altamaha River at Fort Barrington, McIntosh County, Ga., 17. *See also* Nyssa Ogeeche.

Nyssa multiflora (cf. Elliott, 1824, 2: 684): probably black gum (*N. sylvatica* Marsh. var.); on Amite River, La., 425.

N[yssa] *Ogeeche, si[ve] *coccinea: tupelo gum (*N. ogeche* Bartr. ex Marsh.) (cf. E. L. Little, Jr., 1945: 503; Merrill, 1945: 30); about St. Mary's River, Ga.–Fla., 24. *See also* Nyssa coccinea.

Nyssa sylvatica: black gum (*N. sylvatica* Marsh. vars.); about St. Mary's River, Ga.–Fla., 24; on St. John's River above Lake Dexter, Fla., 131; at Salt Springs, 161; near Deep Creek, Putnam County, 172; near Three Sisters Ferry, S.C., 309; along upper Savannah River, Ga.–S.C., 327; in Warren County, Ga., 378; west of Chatta-hoochee River, Ala., 394; near Stockton, 403. *See also* Sour Gum.

Nyssa *tupilo: *nomen nudum* (Merrill, 1945: 34)—gum (*Nyssa* sp.); on St. John's River near Charlotia, Fla., 93.

Oak(s): *Quercus* spp.; near Broad River, Ga., 44; on Altamaha River, 50; on St. Simon's Island, 58, 59; formerly growing where salt marshes are, 69; at Palatka, Fla., 92; on St. John's River near Charlotia, 93, at St. Francis, 138, at Hawkinsville, 140, and near Huntoon Island, 141; at Blue Springs, 146; near Tuscawilla Lake, 184; in Alachua County, 209, 218; near Long Pond, Levy County, 222, 244; near Suwannee River, 224, 233; at Silver Bluff, S.C., 315; matts made of splints of, 369; on Oconee River, Ga., 379; leaves compared with those of *Hydrangea quercifolia*, 383; in Montgomery County, Ala., 397; in Butler or adjacent county, 400. *See also* Oak forests, Oak tree.

In many cases the oaks of the above references (especially in Florida) were doubtless live oaks (*Q. virginiana* Mill.).

Oak, Black, Quercus *tinctoria (cf. Elliott, 1824, 2: 601): *nomen nudum* (Merrill, 1945: 34)—black oak (*Q. velutina* Lam.); of Virginia and Pennsylvania, xvi; in Southern Red Hills, 32; near junction of Little River and Williams Creek, Taliaferro County, Ga., 37, 38; near Three Sisters Ferry, S.C., 309. *See also* Quercus tinctoria.

Oaks, dwarf: *Quercus* sp.; at Lake Pontchartrain, La., 423. *See also* Querci, dwarf.

Oak(s), Live (or Live-oak[s]): chiefly *Quercus virginiana* Mill., but probably including some scrub live-oaks (*Q. v.* Mill. var. *maritima* [Chapm.] Sarg.), which Bartram did not differentiate; on Colonel's Island, Ga., 6; on Altamaha River, 50, 53; on St. Simon's Island, 58, 60, 61; *Tillandsia* parasitic on, 61; on Amelia Island, Fla., 65; at Nassau Sound, 70; on lower St. John's River, 74, 75, 81, 84; growth habit, 84–85; use of acorns by Indians, 85; on St. John's River at Charlotia, 94, and at Mount Royal, 99; on Drayton's Island, 103, 105; Bears and Turkeys fond of acorns, 103; at Lake George, 106, 157, and above it, 114; at Lake Dexter, 116, 117, and above it, 131, 132, 134, 137; on St. John's River at St. Francis, 139, and at Orange Bluff, 154; at Lake Beresford, 142, 143; at New Smyrna, 144; near Salt Springs, 160, 164; in Putnam County, 174; near Tuscawilla Lake, 183, 193; near Alachua Savanna, 189, 202, 204; at Kanapaha Sink, 217; in Levy County, 220, 223, 243; at Manatee Spring, 232; near the Alligator Hole, 238; lacking about dwelling houses on St. John's River, 254; at Spalding's Lower Store, 259; on Sapelo Island, Ga., 268; near The Rigolets, La., 421. *See also* Quercus sempervirens.

Oak, Live-, Quercus sempervirens: *Q. virginiana* Mill.; xvii. *See also* Quercus sempervirens.

Oak, Maryland Water. *See* Quercus aquatica.

Oak, Narrow-leaved Wintergreen. *See* Quercus dentata.

Oak, Red. *See* Quercus rubra.

Oaks, shrub, evergreen and deciduous, a great variety of: probably including such species as scrub oak (*Quercus myrtifolia* Willd.), Chapman's oak (*Q. chapmani* Sarg.), and scrub live-oak (*Q. virginiana* Mill. var. *maritima* [Chapm.] Sarg.); on plains near Suwannee River, Fla., 242.

Oak, Spanish. *See* Quercus sinuata.

Oak, Swamp White. *See* Quercus prinos.

Oak, Water-: either *Quercus hemisphaerica* Bartr. ex Willd. or *Q. nigra* L.; on Colonel's Island, Ga., 7.

Oak, Water, Quercus *Hemispherica: Darlington oak (*Q. hemisphaerica* Bartr. ex Willd.) (cf. Elliott, 1824, 2: 597–598); in Carolina, xv. *See also* Quercus dentata, Quercus hemispherica.

Oak, White-: *Quercus alba* L.; at Macon, Ga., used in making a boat, 458. *See also* Quercus alba.

Oak, Willow-leaved. *See* Quercus phellos.

Oak forests: *Quercus* spp.; along Oconee River, Ga., 43.

Oak tree: *Quercus* sp.; on lower St. John's River, Fla., 74.

Oakfuske, upper and lower: former Upper Creek towns on Tallapoosa River, Tallapoosa County, Ala., one (if not both) being on the west side at or near Young's Ferry, west of Dadeville (Taitt, 1916:

528–529; Swanton, 1922: 249, pl. 2; soil map of Tallapoosa County, 1909; Dadeville quadrangle); listed, 462.

Taitt's map of 1772 shows two unnamed village sites at this point; they may be upper and lower Oakfuske. Through error he places "Oakfuskee" at the site of lower Eufaula.

Oakfuske River. *See* Tallapoosa or Oakfuske River.

Oakmulge. *See* Ocmulgee.

Oaquaphenogaw, the great swamp and lake. *See* Okefinokee.

Oars or sculls, on a boat on Ocmulgee River, Ga., 458.

Oats: *Avena sativa* L.; on upper Savannah River, S.C., 375.

"Occone" or "Occonne." *See* Oconee mountain, Oconee town, Oconee vale.

Ocean [as a general term], 173, 181, 233, 335, 378.

Ocean: in this case, Gulf of Mexico; Amite River flowing into, 429.

Ocean, [Atlantic]: St. Mary's River entering, 26; off St. Simon's Island, Ga., 59, 61; prospect of, from Cumberland Island, 65, and from Sapelo Island, 268; Savannah River flowing into, 316. *See also* Atlantic Ocean, Great Water.

Ochre(or "Ochra"): in middle region of Georgia, 45; in Warren County, 378; along Upatoi Creek, Chattahoochee County, 387.

Ocklawaha ("Ockli-Waha") Great River: the present Ocklawaha River, arising in a group of lakes in central Florida, and entering St. John's River just below Little Lake George; connecting Orange Lake with the St. John's, 182.

Ocmulgee ("Oakmulge") fields: on the site of the present Ocmulgee National Monument, on east side of Ocmulgee River at Macon, Ga.; terraces, etc., at, 381, 522.

Ocmulgee ("Oakmulge") River: a large river of central Georgia, joining the Oconee to form the Altamaha; 25, 53, 382, 520, 521; crossed by trading path, 54; Indian fields and monuments on, 54; site of first settlement of the Creeks after migrating from beyond the Mississippi, 54; fording, 381; crossing, 458, 459.

Oconees ("Ocones"). *See* Indians—Alachuas or Oconees.

Oconee ("Occonne") mountain: the present Station Mountain (alt. 2,300 feet), a mile west of Tomassee Knob, Oconee County, S.C. (Walhalla quadrangle); ascent of, prospect from, and vegetation of, 334–337.

Oconee ("Ocone" or "Oconne") River: a large river of eastern Georgia, joining the Ocmulgee to form the Altamaha; hunters going out to, 42; joining the Ocmulgee, 53; crossed by trading path, 54; New Purchase touching on, 324; crossing branches of, 379; camped on, 379; fording, 381; crossed, 459.

Oconee ("Occonne") town: in this case, a former Indian town, at or near the present Oconee Station, Oconee County, S.C. (Walhalla quadrangle); ruins of, 335.

Oconee ("Ocone") town: in this case, a former Creek town at Rock Landing on east side of Oconee River, 5 miles below the present Milledgeville in Baldwin County, Ga. (Milledgeville quadrangle); evacuated by Indians, 380.

Oconee ("Occone"): in this case, a former Lower Creek town on east side of Chattahoochee River, just below the mouth of Hannahatchee Creek, near the present Omaha, Stewart County, Ga. (Taitt's map of 1772; Melish map of 1818; *Bur. Am. Ethnol. Bull., 30,* Pt. II: 105, 1910; soil map of Stewart County, 1916; Swanton, 1922: 181, pls. 2, 7, 9); listed, 464.

Oconee ("Occonne") vale: the valley of Oconee Creek, near Tomassee Knob, Oconee County, S.C. (Walhalla quadrangle); visited and described, 334.

Ocunnolufte: a former Cherokee town, probably on Oconalufty River, Swain County, N.C., at the present Birdtown, where there was formerly a considerable mound (Mooney, 1900: 517; Cowee quadrangle); listed, 373.

Oenanthe. *See* Chat, yellow breasted.

Oenothera *grandiflora: Bartram's evening primrose (*Oe. grandiflora* Ait.) (cf. Merrill, 1945: 30); described, along east channel of Mobile Delta, between Hall's Creek and Alabama River, Baldwin County, Ala., 406–407.

"This species seems to be known in the wild state only in the type region in Alabama where Bartram discovered it" (Small, 1933: 946).

Ogeechee ("Ogeeche"). *See* Indians—Ogeechee.

Ogeechee ("Ogeeche") limes; a name for *Nyssa ogeche* Bartr. ex Marsh., 17.

Ogeechee ("Ogeeche") mounts. *See* Indian country, etc.

Ogeechee ("Ogeche," "Ogechee," or "Ogeeche") River, or Great Ogeechee: one of the larger rivers of Georgia, situated between the Savannah and the Altamaha; 5; northern limit of *Nyssa ogeche,* 17; source of, 39; Ogeechee Indian settlements near, 66; rice-growing on, 66; New Purchase at head of, 324; a branch of, 376, 379; crossed, 460.

Oglethorpe (or "Oglethorp"), General [James Edward]; colony established in Georgia by, 13; former seat of, on St. Simon's Island, 58; founder of Colony of Georgia, 62.

Oglethorpe (1696–1785) founded the colony in 1732. He defended it against the Spaniards, and attacked the latter in their stronghold at St. Augustine in 1740. Two years later, at the decisive

Battle of Bloody Marsh on St. Simon's Island, he defeated the Spaniards and put an end to their hopes of conquest of the British colonies. In 1743 he returned to England. For biographical information, see Spalding (1840), White (1849: 461–465), Wright (1867), Ettinger (1936), and Mrs. Cate (1943).

Ohio, various trees of, xvi.

Ohio River: the chief eastern tributary of the Mississippi; the Tennessee ("Hogehege") flowing into, 339.

Oil, among provisions, 124.

Okefinokee ("Oaquaphenogaw" or "Ouaquaphenogaw"), a vast lake or marsh: a celebrated swamp covering nearly 700 square miles, chiefly in Charlton and Ware Counties, southeastern Georgia; legendary account of, 24–26; source of Suwannee River, 224.

Until its virtual destruction by fire in 1954–55, Okefinokee Swamp was one of the finest natural features of the Eastern States. Little known and largely unexplored till the present century, when severe inroads were made on its wealth of cypress and pine timber, it harbored a rich and extremely interesting fauna and flora. It became a national wild life refuge in 1936. Bartram here furnishes one of the earliest accounts of the swamp. For additional information, see McQueen and Mizell (1926); Harper (1927; 1934).

Old town: at the mouth of Old Town Creek, on the estuary of Cape Fear River, Brunswick County, N.C. (Price and Strother map of 1808); got to, 473.

Olea: in this case, olive (*O. europaea* L.); usefulness, xvii.

Olea Americana: devil-wood (*Osmanthus americana* [L.] Gray); on Colonel's Island, Ga., 6; about St. Mary's River, Ga.–Fla., 24; on St. John's River below Palatka, Fla., 84, and above Lake Dexter, 132; at Lake George, 157; near Salt Springs, 164; west of Spalding's Lower Store, 171; near Alachua Savanna, 187; at Manatee Spring, 232; near The Rigolets, La., 421.

Olea Americana (Purple berried bay) Catesby (cf. Catesby, 1731, *1*: 61, pl. 61): devil-wood (*Osmanthus americana* [L.] Gray); described, along Cape Fear River, N.C., 476.

Olea europaea ("europea"). *See* Olives.

Oleron Channel, or Pass au Oleron: the present Grant's Pass, between Dauphin Island and Cedar Point, Ala. (Cedar Point quadrangle); passage of, 419, 438.

This channel appears on various old maps (e.g. that of Darby and Tanner, 1821) as "Pass au Heron." It is close to "Isle au Heron." Bartram's spelling is perhaps a corruption; there is, however, an "Isle d'Oléron" off the coast of France.

"Olinopodium." *See* Clinopodium.

582   ANNOTATED INDEX

Olive(s): in these cases, *Olea europaea* L.; compared with fruit of tupelo gum, 17; proposed culture in Georgia, 460.

Olives: in this case, perhaps devil-wood or wild olive (*Osmanthus americana* [L.] Gray); in Alachua County, Fla., 218.

Olive, Indian. *See* Physic-nut.

Olives (Olea europaea ["europea"]): *O. europaea* L.; soil adapted for, 337.

Onions (cepa): *Allium cepa* L.; time for planting, 288.

Onocrotalus ("Onocratulus") *Americanus, the American sea pelican ("pelicane") (cf. Edwards, 1747, 2: 93, pl 93): *nomen nudum*— Eastern Brown Pelican (*Pelecanus occidentalis carolinensis* Gmelin); listed, 295.

Ophrys: probably either Small's twayblade (*Listera smallii* Wiegand) or ladies'-tresses (*Spiranthes* sp.); at Falling Creek, Rabun County, Ga., 342.

Ophrys *insectoria: *lapsus* for *O. insectifera* L. (1753, 2: 948), a European orchid (cf. Merrill, 1945: 34); pleasing figure, xviii.

Ophrys, spiral: probably ladies'-tresses (*Spiranthes* sp.); beauty, xviii.

Opossums (or "opossoms"): *Didelphis marsupialis* L. subspp.; on Colonel's Island, Ga., 7; on Drayton's Island, Fla., 103; in Florida and Carolina, 281.

    The form of Florida and the lower coast region of Georgia is *D. m. pigra* Bangs.

Orange(s) (or Orange grove[s] or Orangery or Orange tree[s]): either bitter-sweet oranges (*Citrus aurantium* L.) or sweet oranges (*C. sinensis* Osbeck); along Mosquito Lagoon, Fla., xxvii; reported in Okefinokee Swamp, Ga., 25; at Nassau Sound, Fla., 70; on St. John's River above Jacksonville, 74, 76, 81, at Palatka, 92, at Charlotia, 94, at Mount Hope, 98, and at Mount Royal, 99; at Lake George, 102, 106, 157, 253; Bears fond of, on Drayton's Island, 103; on St. John's River above Lake George, 111, 115; at Lake Dexter, 116, 124, 154, and above this lake, 131, 132, 134; compared with fruit of wild squash, 137; on St. John's River at St. Francis, 138, 139, at Hawkinsville, 140, and below Lake Beresford, 146; at New Smyrna, 144; at Blue Springs, 146; "Trout" stewed with orange juice, 158; at Salt Springs, 160, 165, 166; on Drayton's Island, 169; in Putnam County, 174; at Little Orange Lake, Alachua County, 180; near Tuscawilla Lake, 183, 192; about Alachua Savanna, 187, 198, 200, 204, 217; destruction of, along St. John's River, to make room for crops, 253–254; feast of, at Palatka, 303–304.

    According to Hume (1926: 45, 50), "the Spaniards brought the first bigarade [or bitter-sweet] oranges to America. The fruit was obtained by the Indians and they carried it about on their journeys. The seeds were dropped where the fruit was eaten, and finding in Florida . . . a soil and climate adapted to their growth, produced trees where they had been deposited. As a result, wild groves were formed on the shores of lakes and rivers. . . .

"The sweet orange was not so widely distributed throughout Florida as the sour [or bitter-sweet] orange; at least, it was not found so abundantly in the native woods. . . . The sweet orange, being less hardy, was not as capable of making a place for itself among the native trees as the sour variety."

Orange (Citrus aurantium): bitter-sweet orange (*C. aurantium* L.); Painted Bunting among, 299.

Oration, by a Cherokee chief at Cowee, N.C., 369.

Orchis: a genus of Orchidaceae, comprising certain orchids; usefulness, xvii.

Ordnance, pieces of; at ancient Fort Thoulouse, Ala., 447.

Oriolus Baltimore, Baltimore bird or hang nest (cf. Catesby, 1730, *1*: 48, pl. 48): Baltimore Oriole (*Icterus galbula* [L.]); listed, 290 *bis*. See also Baltimore bird; Icterus, golden.

Oriolus (icterus minor): Orchard Oriole (*Icterus spurius* [L.]); sexes alike in song and in care of eggs and young, and female more gaily dressed than male, xxxii. *See also* Baltimore bird.

Bartram is obviously misled here by Catesby (1730, *1*: 49, pl. 49), who represents a young male as an (adult) male, and an adult male as a female.

O[riolus] spurius, the goldfinch or icterus minor (cf. Catesby, 1730, *1*: 49, pl. 49): Orchard Oriole (*Icterus spurius* [L.]); listed, 290 *bis*.

Orleans, island of: on the west of Lake Maurepas, La., and presumably formed by branches of Amite River; 437.

Orpheus: a Thracian poet and musician, in Greek mythology; a Mustee Creek as, 507.

Oryza (cf. Catesby, 1730? *1*: pl. 14): rice (*O. sativa* L.); in temperate zone, xv; usefulness, xvii.

Oryza ("oryz") zizania: wild rice (*Zizania aquatica* L.); food of Rice-birds, 296–297.

Zizania L. is a generic name, and it is very doubtful if Bartram meant to use it here as a specific term.

Osgood, Rev. [John]: pastor of Midway Meeting, Liberty County, Ga.; sermon by, 9.

He was born in Dorchester, S.C., in 1710, and died on August 3, 1773, as stated on his tombstone in Midway Cemetery. He was a "dear and much honoured pastor" (White, 1854: 519). In the report to Fothergill (1943: 134) Bartram speaks of having "heard a good Sermon by Mr. Percey" in this meeting-house.

Ostrea (or ostreae): oyster(s) (fossil) (*Ostrea* spp.); at Silver Bluff, S.C., 314; in limestone in Black Belt of Alabama, 399. *See also* Oysters; Oyster shells.

Otasse (or "Attasse"; properly Atasi): a former Upper Creek town on south side of Tallapoosa River, just below the mouth of Calebee Creek, in Macon County, Ala. (Taitt, map of 1772, and 1916: 504, 540; Early's map of 1818; Geol. Map of Alabama, 1894; soil map of Macon County, 1905; *Bur. Am. Ethnol. Bull., 30,* Pt. I: 107, 1907; Swanton, 1922: 265–266, pls. 2, 7, 8, 9); passed by, 396; a caravan of traders preparing to start from, 447; sojourn at, and description of, 450–457; listed, 463.

Otasses. *See* Indians—Otasses.

Otter(s) (or otter [lutra]): *Lutra canadensis* (Schreber) subspp.; imagined presence on floating islands in St. John's River, Fla., 89; in Florida and Carolina, 281; skin used for tobacco pouch, 453.

The subspecies of Florida and southeastern Georgia is *L. c. vaga* Bangs; of South Carolina, *L. c. lataxina* F. Cuvier.

Ouaquaphenogaw. *See* Okefinokee.

Outlaws, in Georgia, 378.

Out-lawry, as punishment for murder, 515.

Ovens, of the ancients, near Keowee, S.C., 372.

Overhill towns (or Overhills): Cherokee settlements in extreme southwestern North Carolina and adjacent parts of Tennessee and Georgia (cf. Swanton, 1922: pl. 7); path from Sticoe to, 345; roads from, to Vale of Cowee, 350; journey toward, 359–366; path from, to Cowee, 360; roads to, 362; treaty to be convened in, 372; list of, 373–374.

The towns mentioned in the list were apparently mainly, if not wholly, in Tennessee.

Overseer, at Charlotia, Fla., 95.

Ovid: a Roman poet (43 B.C.–A.D. 17); 133.

Owls: in these cases, probably Florida Barred Owls (*Strix acclamator georgica* Latham) (cf. Harper, 1942d: 211); whooping of, at Lake Dexter, Fla., 124; screams of, above Lake Dexter, 135–136.

Owl, great (or great horned): Great Horned Owl (*Bubo virginianus virginianus* [Gmelin]); a great owl skin as insigne of junior priests among Indians, x, 504.

Owl, great horned. *See* Strix pythaules.

Owl, great horned white. *See* Strix maximus.

Owl, great white. *See* Strix arcticus.

Owl, little screech. *See* Strix assio.

Owl, sharp winged. *See* Strix peregrinator.

Owl, whooting. *See* Strix acclamator.

Ox: *Bos taurus* L.; contrasted with the bull, 186. *See also* Bull, Cattle.

Oysters: for the most part, at least, *Ostrea virginica* Gmelin; about Georgia coastal islands, 68; at Nassau Sound, Fla., 70; at Sapelo Island, Ga., 268.

Oyster banks: probably *Ostrea virginica* Gmelin; on Mississippi Sound, Miss. and Ala., 437, 438.

Oyster ("oister") catcher. *See* Hematopus ostrealegus.

Oyster shells, fossil: *Ostrea georgiana* Conrad; described, at Shell Bluff, Ga., 318.

Pack-horsemen: their compassion on horses tormented by flies, 384; at Taensa, Ala., 440.

Paint(s); supplied to Seminoles, 260; used by certain Indian women, 504.

Painted finch (Emberiza Ceris Linn.): Painted Bunting or Nonpareil (*Linaria ciris ciris* [L.]—formerly *Passerina ciris ciris* [L.]) (cf. Harper, 1942*d*: 216–217); on Colonel's Island, Ga., 8. *See also* Linaria ciris, Nonpareil.

Paintings and sculptures, in public square at Otasse, Ala., 455.

Palestine, nations of, 368.

Palm(s): in most or all of the following cases, cabbage palmettos (*Sabal palmetto* [Walt.] Lodd.); on St. Simon's Island, Ga., 60, 61; on Amelia Island, Fla., 65; at Nassau Sound, 70; compared with palmetto royal, 71; on St. John's River above Jacksonville, 74, 85, at Palatka, 92, and at Mount Royal, 99; at Lake George, 102, 106, 157; on Drayton's Island, 103; at Lake Dexter, 116, 117; on St. John's River above Lake Dexter, 131, 132, 137, at St. Francis, 138, and at Hawkinsville, 140; at New Smyrna, 144; at Blue Springs, 146; on Salt Springs Run, 160; at Salt Springs, 165; near Tuscawilla Lake, 183, 192; about Alachua Savanna, 188, 190, 198; in Levy County, 220, 222, 223, 244; lacking about houses on St. John's River, 254. *See also* Cabbage tree, Corypha palma, other entries under Palms, Palm tree(s).

Palm(s), exalted: either royal palms (*Roystonea elata* [Bartr.] F. Harper) or cabbage palmettos (*Sabal palmetto* [Walt.] Lodd.); at Salt Springs, Fla., 160; near Long Pond, Levy County, 245. *See also* Palma elata.

Palms of Florida: chiefly cabbage palmettos (*Sabal palmetto* [Walt.] Lodd.); xvi.

Palms, plumed: probably cabbage palmettos (*Sabal palmetto* [Walt.] Lodd.); in Liberty County, Ga., 11.

Palms, shadowy: cabbage palmettos (*Sabal palmetto* [Walt.] Lodd.); near Alachua Savanna, Fla., 217.

Palms, short: probably cabbage palmettos (*Sabal palmetto* [Walt.] Lodd.); near Alachua Savanna, Fla., 202.

Palm tree(s): cabbage palmettos (*Sabal palmetto* [Walt.] Lodd.); along Mosquito Lagoon, Fla., xxvii; on lower St. John's River, 84; near Long Pond, Levy County, 243.

Palm trees, of a different species from the cabbage tree: royal palms (*Roystonea elata* [Bartr.] F. Harper; syn., *R. regia* [HBK.] O. F. Cook) (cf. Harper, 1946*a*); described, on St. John's River between Astor and Lake Dexter, Lake and Volusia Counties, Fla., 115–116. *See also* next entry.

This description validates the name "Palma *Elate" (misprint for *elata*) in the Contents (p. iv).

Palma (or "Palm") *elata: royal palm (*Roystonea elata* [Bartr.] F. Harper); on St. John's River, Fla., below Palatka, 90, at Charlotia, 94, and near Huntoon Island, 141. *See also* preceding entry.

Palmetto: probably saw palmetto (*Serenoa repens* [Bartr.] Small); near Alachua Savanna, Fla., 187; canopy composed of leaves of, 304.

Palmetto, dwarf prickly fan-leaved: saw palmetto, (*Serenoa repens* [Bartr.] Small); on Colonel's Island, Ga., 7.

Palmetto, a very dwarf species of (Corypha pumila stipit. serratis): saw palmetto (*Serenoa repens* [Bartr.] Small); west of Spalding's Lower Store, Fla., 170. *See also* Corypha pumila.

Palmetto, dwarf creeping, with stipes serrated: saw palmetto (*Serenoa repens* [Bartr.] Small); near Orange Lake, Fla., 181.

Palmetto, Dwarf Saw. *See* Corypha repens.

Palmetto royal (Yucca gloriosa) or Adam's needle: perhaps not *Y. gloriosa* L., but Spanish dagger (*Y. aloifolia* L.) (cf. Curtiss, 1879: 118); described, near Nassau Sound, Fla., 71–72. *See also* Yucca gloriosa.

Palmetto, saw: *Serenoa repens* (Bartr.) Small; west of Deep Creek, Putnam County, Fla., 173. *See also* Chamaerops, Corypha obliqua, Corypha repens, other entries under Palmetto.

Pans; old exchanged for new at the busk, 509.

Panax ginseng (cf. Merrill, 1945: 34): ginseng (*P. quinquefolius* L.); near Wayah Gap, N.C., 362. *See also* Ginseng, Panax quinquefolium.

Perhaps "ginseng" is to be considered here not as a specific name but merely as a common name in apposition to *Panax*.

Panax quinquefolium ("quinquifolium"), or Ginseng: *P. quinquefolius* L.; in Oconee County, S.C., 334. See also Ginseng, Panax ginseng.

Pancratium *fluitans: *nomen nudum* (Merrill, 1945: 34)—spider lily (*Hymenocallis,* probably *H. coronaria* [Le Conte] Kunth) (cf. Le Conte, 1835: 145); at cataracts of Augusta, Ga., 35.

    "Pancratium fluitans, a very small species" (Bartram to Muhlenberg, September 6, 1810; Muhlenberg Letters: 137).

Pancratium, odorous: spider lily (*Hymenocallis* sp.); on Drayton's Island, Fla., 105.

Panicum *hirtellum. See Scotch grass.

Panther. See Tiger(s).

Papaver somniferum: opium poppy (*P. somniferum* L.); usefulness, xvii. See also Poppy flower.

Papilio: a Linnaean genus, originally including all the butterflies; a great variety in middle region of Georgia, 46.

Paroquets: Carolina Paroquets (*Conuropsis carolinensis carolinensis* [L.]); feeding on cypress seeds, 91–92. See also Parrakeet, Psittacus Caroliniensis.

Parrakeet ("parakeet") (Psittacus Caroliniensis ["psitlicus Carolini-enses"]): Carolina Paroquet (*Conuropsis carolinensis carolinensis* [L.]); account of, 301. See also Paroquets, Psittacus Caroliniensis.

Parrot of Carolina. See Psittacus Caroliniensis.

Partridge (of Pennsylvania). See Tetrao minor.

P[arus] alis aureis, the golden winged flycatcher (cf. Edwards, 1760, 2: 189, 220, pl. 299, as "Muscicapa alis aureis"): Golden-winged Warbler (*Vermivora chrysoptera* [L.]); listed, 292.

    Edwards received his specimen from Bartram, and his name became the basis for *Motacilla chrysoptera* L.

P[arus] aureus alis ceruleis. the blue winged yellow bird (cf. Edwards, 1760, 2: 139, pl. 277, upper fig., and p. 219, as "Certhia pinus"; Wilson, 1810, 2: 109, pl. 15; Harper, 1942d: 218): Blue-winged Warbler (*Vermivora pinus* [L.]); listed, 292.

    Edwards received his specimen from Bartram.

P[arus] aureus vertice rubro, the yellow red pole (cf. Edwards, 1758, 1: 99, pl. 256, and 1760, 2: 218, as "Avicula lutea vertice rubro"; Wilson, 1811, 4: 19): Yellow Palm Warbler (*Dendroica palmarum hypochrysea* Ridgway); listed, 292.

    Edwards received his specimen from Bartram.

P[arus] aurio vertice, the golden crown flycatcher (cf. Edwards, 1760,

2: 187, 220, pl. 298, as "Muscicapa aureo vertice"): Eastern Myrtle
Warbler (*Dendroica coronata coronata* [L.]), adult male in spring
plumage; listed, 292.

Edwards received his specimen from Bartram, and his name
became the basis of *Motacilla coronata* L.

P[arus] *cedrus, uropygio flavo, the yellow rump (cf. Catesby, 1730,
1: 58, pl. 58; Edwards, 1758, *1:* 97, pl. 255, and 1760, *2:* 218, as
"Muscicapa uropygio luteo"): Eastern Myrtle Warbler (*Dendroica
coronata coronata* [L.]), in winter plumage; listed, 292. *See also*
Yellow rump.

Edwards' name and plate were based upon a specimen of the
Magnolia Warbler (*Dendroica magnolia*) received from Bartram;
but the latter in subsequent years confused this species and the
Myrtle Warbler (Harper, 1942d: 218).

Parus cristatus, bluish grey crested titmouse (cf. Catesby, 1730, *1:*
57, pl. 57): not the European *P. cristatus* L., but Tufted Titmouse
(*P. bicolor* L.); listed, 292.

P[arus] *Europeus, the black cap titmouse: *nomen nudum*—perhaps
composite, including both Black-capped Chickadee (*Parus atricapillus atricapillus* L.) and Northern Carolina Chickadee (*P. carolinensis extimus* [Todd and Sutton]); listed, 292.

P[arus] griseus ("griccus") gutture luteo, the yellow throated creeper
(cf. Catesby, 1731, *1:* 62, pl. 62): not *P. griseus* Müller, but Yellow-
throated Warbler (*Dendroica dominica dominica* [L.]); listed, 292.

P[arus] *luteus, the summer yellow bird: *nomen nudum*—Eastern
Yellow Warbler (*Dendroica petechia aestiva* [Gmelin]); listed, 292.

P[arus] peregrinus, little chocolate breast titmouse: not *P. peregrinus*
L., but Bay-breasted Warbler (*Dendroica castanea* [Wilson]) (cf.
Wilson, 1810, *2:* 97); listed, 292.

P[arus] *varius, various coloured little finch creeper (cf. Catesby,
1731, *1:* 64, pl. 64; Wilson, 1811, *4:* 17): *nomen nudum*—Parula
Warbler (*Parula americana* [L.]); listed, 292.

P[arus] *viridis gutture nigro, the green black throated flycatcher
(cf. Edwards, 1760, *2:* 190, 220, pl. 300, upper fig., as "Muscicapa
viridis gutture nigro"): *nomen nudum*—Black-throated Green Warbler (*Dendroica virens virens* [Gmelin]); listed, 292.

Edwards received his specimen from Bartram, and his name
became the basis of *Motacilla virens* Gmelin.

Pass Aux Christian: in Bartram's usage, a part of Mississippi Sound,
apparently in the vicinity of Pascagoula, Miss.; got through, 438.

Pass au Oleron. *See* Oleron Channel.

P[asser] *agrestis, the little field sparrow (cf. Wilson, 1810, 2: 121): *nomen nudum*—Eastern Field Sparrow (*Spizella pusilla pusilla* [Wilson]); listed, 291.

Passer *domesticus, the little house sparrow or chipping bird: *nomen nudum*—Eastern Chipping Sparrow (*Spizella passerina passerina* [Bechstein]); listed, 291.

P[asser] *nivalis, the snow bird (cf. Catesby, 1730? 1: 36, pl. 36): *nomen nudum*—Slate-colored Junco (*Junco hyemalis hyemalis* [L.]); listed, 291.

P[asser] *palustris, the reed sparrow: *nomen nudum*—Swamp Sparrow (*Melospiza georgiana* [Latham]); listed, 291.

Passiflora incarnata. *See* Granadilla.

Pastinaca: parsnip (*Pastinaca sativa* L.); time for planting, 288.

Patella: an undetermined mollusk; on St. Simon's Island, Ga., 60.

"Patowmac." *See* Potomac.

Pavia *sylvatica: evidently an alternative name for *Aesculus sylvatica* Bartr. (*q.v.*), the Carolina buckeye; near Broad River, Ga., 44.

Pavilion, described, in Indian village at Palatka, Fla., 304. *See also* Shed or pavilion.

Peace, deliberations on, 496.

Peach(es), or Peach trees: *Prunus persica* (L.) Batsch; on St. Mary's River, Ga.–Fla., 23; on St. Simon's Island, Ga., 62; at Palatka, Fla., 304; orchards in Oconee County, S.C., 334, and at Sticoe, Rabun County, Ga., 345; on upper Tensaw River, Ala., 407; near The Rigolets, La., 423.

Peaches, (Amyg[dalus] Persica): *Prunus persica* (L.) Batsch; soil adapted for, 337.

Peacock: *Pavo cristatus* L.; compared in color with Warmouth, 154, and with Mudfish, 176.

Pearls, Bay of. *See* Bay of Pearls.

Pearl Island: apparently not the present Pearl River Island, La., lying off the mouth of Pearl River, but an area bounded on the south by The Rigolets, on the north by Salt Bayou, and on the east by West Pearl River (Rigolets quadrangle); an English gentleman on, and description of, 420–423; set off from, 423.

Pearl River: a river of central and southern Mississippi, its lower course forming the boundary between that state and Louisiana; settlements about, 405; boat bound for, 413, 418, 419, 420; tributaries of, 424.

Pear(s): *Pyrus communis* L.; compared with *Carica papaya*, 131; near The Rigolets, La., 423.

Peas: probably either cowpeas (*Vigna sinensis* Endl.) or the introduced English peas (*Pisum sativum* L.); at Palatka, Fla., 304; near The Rigolets, La., 422.

Peas (vitia sativa): English peas (*Pisum sativum* L.); time for planting, 288.

Pedicularis: probably wood betony (*Pedicularis canadensis* L.); near Long Pond, Levy County, Fla., 242, 248.

Pelicans: Eastern Brown Pelicans (*Pelecanus occidentalis carolinensis* Gmelin); described, at Nassau Sound, Fla., 70, 71.

Pelican ("pelicane"), American sea. *See* Onocrotalus Americanus.

Pelican, solitary, of the wilderness: Wood Ibis (*Mycteria americana* L.), perhaps in immature plumage; at Alachua Savanna, Fla., 190. *See also* Gannet; Pelican, wood; Tantalus Ichthyophagus; Tantalus loculator.

Pelican, wood (or wood-), Tantalus loculator (cf. Catesby, 1732, *1*: 81, pl. 81): Wood Ibis (*Mycteria americana* L.); on Altamaha River, Ga., 49; described, from Florida, 149–150. *See also* Gannet; Pelican, solitary; Tantalus Ichthyophagus; Tantalus loculator.

Pelecanus ("Pelicanus") aquilus, the frigate ("frigat") or man of war bird: not the South Atlantic *P. aquilus* L., but the West Indian Man-o'-war-bird (*Fregata magnificens rothschildi* Mathews); listed, 295.

P[elecanus] ("Pelicanus") sula, the booby: Booby (*Sula* sp.); listed, 295.

Pennsylvania: various trees of, xvi; name of Cougar in, 46; Tent Caterpillar in, 66; cattle in, 190; Wolves of, 199; iron ore in, 223; Wampum Snake in, 273; Bullfrog of, 277; Leopard Frog in, 278; bats in, 283; Ground Squirrel of, 284; birds of, 286–302; *Dirca* and *Dodecatheon* in, 319; plants common in, 337; white men of, 365; white cedar of, 411; Woodcock in, 459; travels in, 468; journey toward, 479; citizens of, at Augusta, Ga., 486.

Pensacola: an old Spanish settlement on Pensacola Bay, in northwestern Florida, taken over by the English in 1763; Spanish high road (or way) to, 232, 234; arrival at and description of, 414–417; a white man from, 445.

Pensacola, bay of: an arm of the Gulf of Mexico, adjacent to the city of Pensacola, northwestern Florida; Escambia River emptying into, 402.

Pensacola road: extending northward from Pensacola, Fla., along the west side of Escambia River (Taitt's map of 1772); junction of (in southwestern Alabama), 492–493.

Pentandra monogynia, Cl[ass] ("Bl."): a large group in the Linnaean classification of plants; *Pinckneya* referred to, 16.

Pepper; *Capsicum* as, 71; among provisions, 124.

Perdicium, silvery: pineland daisy (*Chaptalia tomentosa* Vent.) (cf. Elliott, 1823? 2: 460); at Lake Dexter, Fla., 155.

Perdido (or "Perdedo") River: forming the boundary between Baldwin County, Ala., and Escambia County, Fla.; boat going to, viii, 413.

Perreauguas (or "Perreaugues" or "perriaguas" or "pettiaugers"): apparently synonymous with pirogues—two-masted, flat-bottomed boats—although the "pettiaugers" made of cypress trunks must have been round-bottomed; in Georgia coastal waters, 68; made of cypress trunks, 92; on Escambia River, Fla., 416; on Tangipahoa River, La., 424; on rivers in Alabama, 447; on Cape Fear River, N.C., 478.

Persicaria *amphibia: *nomen nudum* (Merrill, 1945: 34)—smartweed (*Polygonum* sp.—section *Persicaria*); on floating islets in St. John's River above Lake Dexter, Fla., 130.

Persimmon ("Pesimmon") (Diospyros ["Dyospyros"] Virginiana): *D. virginiana* L.; food of Cedar-bird, 298. *See also* Diospyros.

Persons; of American aborigines, 483–485.

Petrella *pintada, the pintado bird: *nomen nudum*—perhaps the Pintado Petrel (*Daption capensis* [L.]), although there is no known North American record up to and including Bartram's time (Harper, 1942d: 220); listed, 295.

Perhaps Bartram mistook some gull in immature plumage for the "white and black Spotted Peteril" of Edwards (1747, 2: 90, pl. 90, lower fig., and p. 128, as "Petrella, media, maculata").

Pettiaugers. *See* Perreauguas.

Petticoat. *See* Flap or petticoat.

Pewit, or black cap flycatcher (cf. Catesby, 1730, 1: 53, pl. 53): Eastern Phoebe (*Sayornis phoebe* [Latham]); arrival in spring, 287. *See also* Muscicapa nunciola.

Pewit, lesser. *See* Muscicapa rapax.

Phaëthon ("Phaeaton") aethereus, the tropic bird: Red-billed Tropicbird (*Phaëthon aethereus* L.); listed, 295.

Phalaena ("Phalina"): a Linnaean genus originally comprising all the moths (except *Sphinx*); a great variety in middle region of Georgia, 46.

Phalaena *bombyca. *See* Silk-worms.

Phalaena ("Phalena") *periodica. *See* Caterpillar, common grey.

Pharsalia, Fields of: a district in Thessaly, Greece, around the town of Pharsalus; compared with Vale of Cowee, N.C., 354.

Phaseolus ("Phaciolus"): in this case, perhaps wild bean (*P. polystachios* [L.] BSP.); along upper Savannah River, Ga., 321.

Phaseolus ("phaccolus"). *See* Beans, French.

Pheasant of Pennsylvania. *See* Tetrao tympanus.

Philadelphia, Pa.: set sail from, 1; travelers bound for, 480; set out for, 480.

Philadelphus: syringa (*Philadelphus* sp.); in Vale of Cowee, N.C., 346; near Cowee, 357.

Philadelphus inodorus (or "inodorous") (cf. Catesby, 1738, 2: 84, pl. 84): syringa (*P. inodorus* L., or perhaps some subsequently described species of that genus); at cataracts of Augusta, Ga., 35; at Shell Bluff, 319; along upper Savannah River, 320; between Little and Broad Rivers, 322; in Oconee County, S.C., 334; on Oconee (= Station) Mountain, S.C., 336; at Falling Creek, Rabun County, Ga., 342.

Philomela (cf. *Luscinia seu Philomela* Sloane, 1725, 2: 307, pl. 259, fig. 3): possibly Nightingale (*Luscinia megarhynchos* Brehm); compared with Catbird, 299.

Philomela Americana. *See* Luscinia.

Philosophers, ancient, bird migration studied by, 285.

Philosophy, education in the schools of, 22.

Phlox: phlox (*Phlox* spp.); varieties of, at Lake Dexter, Fla., 155; west of Deep Creek, Putnam County, 173.

Phoenicopterus ruber, the flamingo (cf. Catesby, 1731, 1: 73, pl. 73): West Indian Flamingo (*P. ruber* L.); listed, 296.

Physic-nut, or Indian Olive: oil-nut (*Pyrularia pubera* Michx.); described, from the Great Ridge, Ga., 41; used as charm by Indians, 41.

    "*Physic-Nut.* Lyon told me he saw it in northern hilly parts of Georgia, but dont know its family[.]" (Bartram to Muhlenberg, September 6, 1810; Muhlenberg Letters: 137.)

    A possible reason for the present scarcity of this shrub is its rapid destruction by cattle (cf. Buckley, 1859: 290–291).

Physic pot; in sanctuary at Otasse, Ala., 454.

Physiologists: collecting data for, 23; reasoning of, 280.

Pica glandaria. *See* Corvus cristatus.

Pica glandaria cerulea non cristata, the little jay of East Florida: a synonym of Corvus Floridanus (*q.v.*); listed, 290, footnote. *See also* Jay without a crest.

Pica glandaria minor. *See* Corvus Floridanus.

Picolata. *See* Fort Picolata.

Picus, or woodpeckers of several species: birds now placed in various genera of the family Picidae; resident in Pennsylvania, 286.

P[icus] auratus, the gold winged woodpecker (cf. Catesby, 1730? *1*: 18, pl. 18): Northern Flicker (*Colaptes auratus luteus* Bangs); listed, 289 *bis*.

P[icus] erythrocephalus, red headed woodpecker (cf. Catesby, 1730? *1*: 20, pl. 20): Eastern Red-headed Woodpecker (*Melanerpes erythrocephalus erythrocephalus* [L.]); listed, 289 *bis*.

P[icus] Carolinus, the red bellied woodpecker (cf. Catesby, 1730? *1*: 19, pl. 19): Eastern Red-bellied Woodpecker (*Centurus carolinus carolinus* [L.]); listed, 289 *bis*.

P[icus] pileatus, the great red crested black woodpecker (cf. Catesby, 1730? *1*: 17, pl. 17): Southern Pileated Woodpecker (*Dryocopus pileatus pileatus* [L.]); listed, 289 *bis*.

Picus principalis, the greatest crested woodpecker, having a white back (cf. Catesby, 1730? *1*: 16, pl. 16): Ivory-billed Woodpecker (*Campephilus principalis* [L.]); listed, 289 *bis*.

    Coues remarks (1875: 347): "For 'white back' *read* 'white beak.'" This is by no means obligatory, although in accord with Catesby's "largest white-bill Woodpecker."

P[icus] pubescens, the least spotted woodpecker (cf. Catesby, 1730? *1*: 21, pl. 21): Northern Downy Woodpecker (*Dendrocopos pubescens medianus* [Swainson]); listed, 289 *bis*.

P[icus] varius, yellow bellied woodpecker (cf. Catesby, 1730? *1*: 21, pl. 21): Yellow-bellied Sapsucker (*Sphyrapicus varius varius* [L.]); listed, 289 *bis*.

P[icus] villosus, the hairy, speckled and crested woodpecker (cf. Catesby, 1730? *1*: 19, pl. 19): Eastern Hairy Woodpecker (*Dendrocopos villosus villosus* [L.]); listed, 289 *bis*.

Piece(s): gun(s); Alligator shot with, 121; discharged as a signal, 235; ready for Bears, 437. See also Fusee, Gun(s).

[Piedmont region], described, 32.

Pigs: *Sus scrofa* var.; prey of Wildcat, 282, and of Gray Foxes, 283. *See also* Swine.

Pigeons, wild (Columba migratoria) (cf. Catesby, 1730? *1*: 23, pl. 23): Passenger Pigeons (*Ectopistes migratorius* [L.]); many collected by torch light along Savannah River, Ga., 469–470. See also Columba migratoria.

Pilau ("pillo" or "pilloe"): a dish made of rice boiled with meat, etc. (Webster); made with Raccoons, 63, and with young waterfowl, 249.

Pines: *Pinus* spp.; in McIntosh County, Ga., 13; south of Satilla River, 20; on Altamaha River, 53; east of Alachua Savanna, Fla., 209; in southwestern Alachua County, 218; timber for the West-India market, 312.

Pine, Broom- (*P. palustris* L.): longleaf pine (*Pinus australis* Michx. f.); on Colonel's Island, Ga., 7; on St. Simon's Island, 58. *See also* Pines, lofty; Pines, long-leaved; Pinus palustris.

Pine forest(s): *Pinus* spp.; in McIntosh County, Ga., 14; south of Altamaha River, 17, 19; along St. Mary's River, Ga.–Fla., 26; in Southern Red Hills, 31; on St. Simon's Island, Ga., 58; at Mount Royal, Fla., 100; on St. John's River near St. Francis, 138, and at Hawkinsville, 140; near Lake Lochloosa, 180; near Orange Lake, 181; near Alachua Savanna, 189, 202, 208, 209, 217; in Levy County, 220; Cricket Frogs in, 278; near Palatka, 303; along lower Savannah River, Ga., 309, 310; between Chattahoochee and Tallapoosa Rivers, Ala., 396; in Brunswick County, N.C., 473; along Cape Fear River, N.C., 477.

Pine knots: more or less knotty sticks of pine (probably *Pinus australis* Michx. f.); fires made with, 387, 460.

Pine lands, savanna; near Alachua Savanna, Fla., 197.

Pines, lofty: probably longleaf pines (*Pinus australis* Michx. f.); at Cowpen Lake, Putnam County, Fla., 179; near Tuscawilla Lake, 184; at Alachua Savanna, 190.

Pine(s), long leaved (or Broom): longleaf pine(s) (*Pinus australis* Michx. f.); on St. John's River at Charlotia, Fla., 94; west of Deep Creek, Putnam County, 173; in Escambia or adjacent county, Ala., 402.

Pine, long-leaved (P[inus] palustris): longleaf pine (*P. australis* Michx. f.); in Lime-Sink Region, 30; a tall, ancient pillar of, at Otasse, Ala., 456–457. *See also* Pine, Broom- , Pinus palustris.

Pine, long-leaved Pitch- , or Broom-Pine, Pinus Palustris: longleaf pine (*P. australis* Michx. f.); on Colonel's Island, Ga., 6. *See also* Pinus palustris.

Pines (Pinus Palustris): longleaf pines (*P. australis* Michx. f.); near Salt Springs, Fla., 161.

Pine savannas: pine barrens; near Alachua Savanna, Fla., 208.

Pine splinters; used for torches, 470.
      This is still a common practice in the country districts of Georgia.

Pines, stately: probably longleaf pines (*Pinus australis* Michx. f.); in Levy County, Fla., 223, 224.

Pines, stately (Pinus palustris): longleaf pines (*P. australis* Michx. f.); on Altamaha River, Ga., 50.

Pine(s), terebenthine: probably longleaf pine(s) (*Pinus australis* Michx. f.); its top gilded by the sun, 245; between Flint and Chattahoochee Rivers, Ga., 386.

Pine tree(s): *Pinus* spp.; set ablaze by lightning, 13; near Cuscowilla, Fla., 193, 197; near Suwannee River, 242; on Mobile Bay, Ala., 419.

Pine trees (P[inus] palustri[s]): longleaf pines (*P. australis* Michx. f.); west of Spalding's Lower Store, Fla., 170.

Pine trees, scrubby: *Pinus* sp.; on the White Plains, La., 432.

"I suspect the scrubby pine to be either *Pinus taeda* or *Pinus palustris* [= *australis*]" (Clair A. Brown, *in litt.*, July 24, 1941).

Pine trees, shrubby: *Pinus* sp.; west of Deep Creek, Putnam County, Fla., 173.

Pine trees, three leaved: perhaps black pines (*Pinus serotina* Michx. f.); near Alachua Savanna, Fla., 187.

Pine, Wild. *See* Tillandsia lingulata.

Pine, yellow. *See* Pinus palustris.

Pintado bird. *See* Petrella pintada.

Pintchlucco (Creek): the present Upatoi Creek, an easterly tributary of the Chattahoochee on the boundary between Muscogee and Chattahoochee Counties, Ga. (Columbus quadrangle); camp on, 387.

Pin[us] abies: not the Old World *P. abies* L., but Canada hemlock (*Tsuga canadensis* [L.] Carr.); of the Northern States, xvi; on Oconee (= Station) Mountain, S.C., 337. *See also* Hemlock spruce, Pinus Canadensis.

Pin[us] balsamea ("balsamica"): balsam fir (*Abies balsamea* [L.] Mill.); of the Northern States, xvi.

Pin[us] Canadensis: Canada hemlock (*Tsuga canadensis* [L.] Carr.); of the Northern States, xvi. *See also* Hemlock spruce; Pinus abies.

P[inus] echinata: shortleaf pine (*P. echinata* Mill.); in lower Coastal Plain, 28.

Pin[us] larix: not the Old World *P. larix* L., but tamarack (*Larix laricina* [DuRoi] K. Koch); of the Northern States, xvi.

Pinus lutea: possibly slash pine (*P. elliottii* Engelm.), for the most part; on Colonel's Island, Ga., 6; in lower Coastal Plain, 28; in Warren County, 378; in Butler or adjacent county, Ala., 400.

Sargent synonymizes *lutea* Walt. with *palustris* Mill. (= *australis* Michx. f.), but Bartram more than once uses both names for pines in a single locality. The slash pine, however, is not likely to have occurred in Warren County, Ga.

Pinus palustris: longleaf pine (*P. australis* Michx. f.); described, in Warren County, Ga., 378.

Pinus palustris, Linn., the long-leaved Pitch pine, or yellow Pine: longleaf pine (*P. australis* Michx. f.); on lower Savannah River, Ga., 312. See also Pine, Broom- ; Pine(s), long leaved; Pines (Pinus Palustris); Pine(s), terebenthine; etc.

Pinus *phoenix: *nomen nudum* (Merrill, 1945: 34)—pine (*Pinus* sp.); of Carolina and Florida, xvi.

Pinus squarrosa ("squamosa" or "squarosa") (cf. Walter, 1788: 237; Elliott, 1824, 2: 633; Merrill, 1945: 34): shortleaf pine (*P. echinata* Mill.); on Colonel's Island, Ga., 6; in lower Coastal Plain, 28.

Pinus strobus: white pine (*P. strobus* L.); of the Northern States, xvi; on Oconee (= Station) Mountain, S.C., 337.

Pin[us] sylvestris: not the European *P. sylvestris* L., but an undetermined species of pine; on Oconee (= Station) Mountain, S.C., 337.

Pinus taeda (or "toeda"): loblolly pine (*P. taeda* L.); of Carolina and Florida, xvi; on Colonel's Island, Ga., 6; in lower Coastal Plain, 28; in Southern Red Hills, 32; described, in Warren County, 378; in Butler or adjacent county, Ala., 400; near Stockton, 403.

Pipe(s); smoked with Indians at Cuscowilla, Fla., 184; at feast in Talahasochte, 236; smoked at Watauga, N.C., 351; in ceremony in rotunda at Otasse, Ala., 453; buried with the dead among Muscogulges, 516.

Pipe of peace. See Calumet.

Pipe(s), stone; presented by a blind old chief, 499; made by Indian men, 513.

Pipe-stem wood. See Andromeda of Florida; Andromeda formosissima.

Pirates; Georgia coastal islands open to ravages of, 67.

Pistacia ("Pistachia"): pistachio tree (*P. vera* L.); proposed culture in Georgia, 460.

Pistia: water lettuce (*P. stratiotes* L.); at Lake Dexter, Fla., 118; floating fields (or islets) of, on St. John's River above Lake Dexter, 130, 132, and below Lake Beresford, 140; on Salt Springs Run, 160; on Suwannee River, 228.

Pistia stratiotes (or "stratoites"): water lettuce (*P. stratiotes* L.); described, and forming floating islands, on lower St. John's River, Fla., iv, 88–89; on Lake George, 106; on Suwannee River, 230.

Pistols, dragoon; two for each ranger at Fort James, Ga., 324.

Pisum: a genus of Leguminosae, comprising the garden or English peas; usefulness, xvii.

Pitch; varying methods of making, in Alabama and Carolina, 419.

Plains, barren, between Suwannee River and Long Pond: perhaps the present "Sand Prairie," Levy County, Fla.; visited and described, 242–243. See also Desert.

Plains, great: part of the Black Belt or central prairie region of Alabama, encountered by Bartram in Montgomery County (cf. R. M. Harper, 1913: 84–91, frontisp.); journey over, and description of, 397–399.

Plants; seeds of, compared with eggs of animals, xxii; specimens of, spread out to dry, 347. *See also* Specimens, Vegetables.

Plant, curious, of the verticillate order, with scarlet flowers: perhaps red basil (*Clinopodium coccineum* [Nutt.] Kuntze); described, at Pensacola, Fla., 417.

Plantago Virginica: hoary plantain (*P. virginica* L.); in Oconee County, S.C., 334.

Plantation(s): on Colonel's Island, Ga., 5–6; of [Donald] McIntosh, in McIntosh County, 13; one at Broughton Island, owned by Henry Laurens, 48; on Amelia Island, Fla., 64–65; on Georgia coastal islands, 67; on lower St. John's River, Fla., 74, 75, 76, 78, 306; of an English gentleman, on upper St. John's River, 114; at Lake Beresford, 141–144; near Alachua Savanna, 193–194; old Spanish, near Suwannee River, 233, 235; of Dr. Stork, and of a British gentleman, on Lake George, 253; orange groves destroyed on, 253–254; on St. John's River near Spalding's Lower Store, 305; on Broughton Island and at New Hope, Ga., 306; on lower Savannah River, 313; in Vale of Cowee, N.C., 350; at Watauga, 350, 352; near Cowee, 354; on Savannah River, S.C., 375, 376; along Tensaw River, Ala., 405, 406, 407; on lower Tombigbee River, 409, 410, 411; in Baldwin or adjacent county, 412; on Escambia River, Fla., 416; on Mobile Bay, Ala., 419; on Pearl River, Miss.–La., 418; at Lake Pontchartrain, La., 424; on Amite River, 426; on Mississippi River, 429, 430; of the French, at Natchez, Miss., 434; Indian, along Tallapoosa River, Ala., 449; near Augusta, Ga., 460; of an Indian town, its operation, 512–513; of Choctaws, 517. *See also* Corn, Indigo, Rice.

Plantation below the Cliffs: probably in the vicinity of the present Faulkner Lake, East Baton Rouge Parish, La. (Bayou Sara quadrangle); arrived at, 436.

Lyell (1849, 2: 143–145) gives an account of a visit to the same vicinity, and perhaps to the same plantation.

Planters, along the southern coasts, 69.

Plaster, not seen in middle region of Georgia, 45.

Platalea ajaja, the spoonbill: Roseate Spoonbill (*Ajaia ajaja* [L.]); listed, 293.

Platanus: sycamore (*P. occidentalis* L.); about Wrightsborough, Ga., 36; near Little River, 37; on lower Tombigbee River, Ala., 410; along Iberville Canal, La., 427.

Platanus occidentalis (or "occidentales") (cf. Catesby, 1730, *1*: 56, pl. 56): sycamore (*P. occidentalis* L.); of Virginia and Pennsylvania, xvi; in lower Coastal Plain, 29; near Three Sisters Ferry, S.C., 309; along Chatttahoochee River, Ala., 393; on Amite River, La., 426; along the Mississippi, 432; along Cape Fear River, N.C., 474.

Plover, chattering. *See* Charadrius vociferus.

Plover, great field spotted. *See* Charadrius maculatus.

Plover, little sea side ring necked. *See* Charadrius minor.

Plum ("Plumb"): in these cases, probably Chickasaw plum (*Prunus angustifolia* Marsh.); old orchards in Oconee County, S.C., 334, and at Sticoe, Rabun County, Ga., 345. *See also* Prunus Chicasaw.

Plums ("Plumbs") [cultivated]: probably *Prunus domestica* L.; near The Rigolets, La., 423.

Plums ("Plumbs"), a native species of, with crimson fruit, spiny branches, and serrated leaves; *Prunus* sp.; near The Rigolets, La., 423.

Perhaps the same as recorded by Mohr (1901: 551) from shell banks in Mobile County, Ala., under the name of *P. hortulana* Bailey.

Plum ("plumb"), ordinary: *Prunus domestica* L.; compared with tallow nut, 115.

Plum ("Plumb"), wild. *See* Prunus Indica.

Pocontallahasse (properly Pakan tallahassee): a former Upper Creek town on a creek of the same name (the modern Hatchet Creek, now part of Mitchell Lake), between Rockford and the Coosa River, Coosa County, Ala. (Taitt, map of 1772, and 1916: 534–535; *Bur. Am. Ethnol. Bull., 30*, Pt. II: 191, 1910—locality erroneous; Swanton, 1922: 273–274, pl. 2; Wetumpka quadrangle); listed, 463.

Poinciana pulcherrima ("pulcherima"): dwarf poinciana (*Caesalpinia pulcherrima* [L.] Swartz); in the tropics, xv.

Point[e] Coup[e]: probably at or near the site of the present Pointe Coupee, on the west bank of the Mississippi, in Pointe Coupee Parish, La. (Bayou Sara quadrangle); visit to, 430, 432–435; travels to, 468.

A map of 1731 (by Broutin), reproduced in Thomassy (1860, following p. 226), shows "Fort de la pointe Coupée" about 6 miles southeast of the present Pointe Coupee. But Swanton (1922: pl. 5) shows "Habitations de la Pointe Coupée" considerably northwest of the "Redoute.

Poke. *See* Ardea virescens.

Pole-cats: Florida Skunks (*Mephitis mephitis elongata* Bangs); on Colonel's Island, Ga., 7.

Polecat (putorius): Florida Skunk (*Mephitis mephitis elongata* Bangs); in Florida and Carolina, 281.

Polyanthus tuberosa. *See* Tube-rose.

Polygala, varieties: polygalas (*Polygala* spp.); near Suwannee River, Fla., 242.

Polygamy, among Muscogulges, 515.

Polymnia: bear-foot (*P. uvedalia* L.); near Lake Lochloosa, Fla., 180; between Orange and Tuscawilla Lakes, 183; in Warren County, Ga., 379.

Pomegranate(s): *Punica granatum* L.; on St. Simon's Island, Ga., 62; fruit of prickly pear compared with, 163.

Pomegranate ("Pomgranate") (Punica granatum): *P. granatum* L.; soil adapted for, 337.

Pompions: pumpkins—perhaps Seminole pumpkins or crookneck squashes (*Cucurbita moschata* Duchesne) (cf. Small, 1922: 1930a: 14; 1933: 1287); at Palatka, Fla., 93. *See also* Pumpkins.

Pond, a deep: perhaps the present Watermelon Pond, in southwestern Alachua County, 5 miles west-northwest of Archer, Fla. (soil map of Alachua County, 1954); encamped near, 249.

Ponpon River: Edisto River, S.C., Jacksonboro on, 308.

Pontchartrain. *See* Lake Pontchartrain.

Pony ("poney"), Indian: *Equus caballus* L.; furnished with, 460.

Poopoa Fort: the old fort of "St. Francisco de Pupa," at the present Bayard Point, Clay County, Fla., across St. John's River from Fort Picolata (Purcell map, about 1779; Vignoles, 1823: 67; Fairbanks, 1858: 144; Chatelain, 1941: 90–92, 166–167); 208.

Poor Jobe. *See* Ardea violacea.

Poplar: in these cases, perhaps tulip tree (*Liriodendron tulipifera* L.); wood compared with that of magnolia, 86; near Tuscawilla Lake, Fla., 192. *See also* Liriodendron.

Poppy flower, fringed: *Papaver somniferum* L.; *Cacalia heterophylla* likened to, 164. *See also* Papaver somniferum.

Populus: cottonwood (*Populus* sp.); on lower Tombigbee River, Ala., 410.

Populus heterophylla: swamp cottonwood (*P. heterophylla* L.); of Carolina and Florida, xvi; in lower Coastal Plain, 29; near Three Sisters Ferry, S.C., 309; along Chattahoochee River, Ala., 393.

Populus tremula ("trimula"): in this case, not the European *P. tremula* L., but perhaps Carolina poplar (*P. deltoides* Bartr. ex Marsh.); on Oconee (= Station) Mountain, S.C., 337.

Porcelain or China ware, Mica nitida exported for making, 363.

Porcupine: Canada Porcupine (*Erethizon dorsatum dorsatum* [L.]); quills as head ornaments among Indians, 502.

Porpoise(s): probably Bottlenose Dolphin(s) (*Tursiops truncatus* [Montague]) (cf. Kellogg, 1939: 82); in the Atlantic, 3; puffing noise of Soft-shelled Turtle likened to that of porpoise, 178.

Pots, old exchanged for new at the busk, 509.

Pots, clay, formerly used by the Creeks, 500.

Pots, iron, not formerly owned by the Creeks, 500.

Potato(es) (or "potatoe"): doubtless sweet potato(es) (*Ipomoea batatas* [L.] Poir.); potato house at Cuscowilla, Fla., 192; at Palatka, 304; cultivation by Indians, 511.

Potatoes, Convolvulus batata: sweet potatoes (*Ipomoea batatas* [L.] Poir.); on Colonel's Island, Ga., 6; on lower St. John's River, Fla., 77. *See also* Batata(s), Convolvulus batata.

Potato ("Potatoe") vines: sweet potato (*Ipomoea batatas* [L.] Poir.); Deer fond of, 194.

Potomac ("Patowmac") River: forming the boundary between Maryland and Virginia and entering Chesapeake Bay; Alexandria on, 479; crossed, 480.

Pottery (or earthen-ware); clay for, 456; made by Indian women, 513. *See also* Earthen-ware, Indian country, etc.

Poultry: on Georgia coastal islands, 67; prey of Gray Foxes, 283.

Powder horn, for each ranger at Fort James, Ga., 324.

Praying, to avert sickness at Otasse, Ala., 456.

Prenanthes ("Prenanthus"): gall-of-the-earth (*Prenanthes* sp.); near Suwannee River, Fla., 242.

Presents: for Indians, 440; for chiefs at Mucclasse, 499.

Priests (Indian), at Otasse, Ala., 454.

Priests, ancient, bird migration studied by, 285.

Priest, chief, at feast in Talahasochte, Fla., 236.

Priest, high, called by white people jugglers or conjurers: functions and attributes of, 497; producing new fire at the busk, 510.

Priests, junior: among Indians, 497; attributes of, 504.

Primula: a genus of Primulaceae, comprising the primroses; elegance, xviii.

Prince, Eastern, turban of, 155.

Prinos, curious species of: Bartram's holly (*Ilex amelanchier* M. A. Curtis); described, on Meherrin River, Va., 479.

This identification hinges on a flowering specimen in the Academy of Natural Sciences of Philadelphia, bearing the data "Bartram's Garden" and "Meherrin River." It was brought to attention by the late Arthur N. Leeds. The specimen was evidently grown from seed brought back by Bartram. However, the few known stations of this rare shrub are all in the Coastal Plain, with the exception of that on the Meherrin River. Thus there remains a suspicion of some confusion in seeds or localities.

Probably the following note pertains to the same species: *"Prinos nebulosa,* the same that you observed growing Near the Fishpond in our Garden" (Bartram to Muhlenberg, September 6, 1810; Muhlenberg Letters: 137). (Note the relation of this specific name to the "nebulae" of Bartram's description.)

Prinos glaber: gallberry (*Ilex glabra* [L.] Gray); near Alachua Savanna, Fla., 187.

Prinos varietas (or varieties): in Bartram's usage, *Prinos* was apparently equivalent to the current sections *Prinos* and *Prinoides* of the genus *Ilex* (gallberries, etc.); on Colonel's Island, Ga., 6; in Lime-Sink Region, 31; near Suwannee River, Fla., 242.

Privet (Ligustrum vulgare ["ruelgare"]): *L. vulgare* L.; food of Cedarbird, 298.

Property; among American aborigines, 511–513.

Provisions: replenished at Apalachicola, Ala., 395; old, burned at the busk, 509.

Prunus: a genus of Rosaceae, comprising the plums and cherries; in temperate zone, xv; soil adapted for, 337.

Prunus: in this case, probably wild black cherry (*P. serotina* Ehrh.); about Alachua Savanna, Fla., 198.

Prunus Caroliniana: laurel cherry (*P. caroliniana* [Mill.] Ait.) (cf. Merrill, 1945: 31); described, south side of Alachua Savanna, Alachua County, Fla., 187, 198. *See also* Prunus laurocerasus.

Pr[unus] cerasus: sour cherry (*P. cerasus* L.), native to Asia Minor; in temperate zone, xv.

Prunus *Chicasaw, Chicasaw "plumb": *nomen nudum* (Merrill, 1945: 34)—Chickasaw plum (*P. angustifolia* Marsh.); supposed to have been brought from beyond the Mississippi and cultivated by the ancients near Little River, Ga., 38; on Altamaha River, 50. *See also* Plum.

Prunus *Indica (or wild "plumb"): *nomen nudum* (Merrill, 1945: 34)—possibly Chickasaw plum (*P. angustifolia* Marsh.); along upper Savannah River, Ga., 320; in Montgomery or Lowndes Counties, Ala., 398; in Butler or adjacent county, 400.

Prunus laurocerasus ("laura cerapa," "Laura-cerasa," or "Lauro cerasa"): in these cases, not *P. laurocerasus* L., but laurel cherry (*P.*

caroliniana [Mill.] Ait.); on Colonel's Island, Ga., 6; about St. Mary's River, Ga.–Fla., 24; on Altamaha River, Ga., 50. *See also* Prunus Caroliniana.

Prunus *nemoralis: apparently laurel cherry (*P. caroliniana* [Mill.] Ait.) (cf. Fernald, 1944: 45; Merrill, 1945: 31); described, probably somewhere in vicinity of Boatyard Lake, about 4 miles west of Tensaw, Ala. (soil map of Baldwin County, 1912; Tensaw quadrangle), 408.

Prunus padus: in these cases, not the European *P. padus* L., but probably wild black cherry (*P. serotina* Ehrh.); along upper Savannah River, Ga., 320; in Warren County, 378.

Psidium: a genus of Myrtaceae, including the guavas; in the tropics, xiv.

Psittacus ("psitlicus" or "Psitticus") Caroliniensis (or "Carolinienses"), the parrot of Carolina, or parrakeet (cf. Catesby, 1730? *1*: 11, pl. 11): Carolina Paroquet (*Conuropsis carolinensis carolinensis* [L.]); listed, 290. *See also* Paroquets, Parrakeet.

Ptelea: wafer ash (*P. trifoliata* L.); on St. Simon's Island, Ga., 58; on St. John's River at Charlotia, Fla., 94; at Lake George, 157; near Salt Springs, 164; between Orange and Tuscawilla Lakes, 183; along upper Savannah River, Ga., 320; on Oconee (= Station) Mountain, Oconee County, S.C., 337; along Chattahoochee River, Ala., 394; in Butler or adjacent county, 400. *See also* "Telea."

Ptelea trifoliata: wafer ash (*P. trifoliata* L.); in Southern Red Hills, 32; along Cape Fear River, N.C., 476.

Pteris *scandens. *See* Fern, scandent.

Public house: tavern; on Little River, Ga., 321; at Little River, S.C.–N.C., 472.

Public square. *See* Square, public.

Puc Puggy or the Flower hunter: a name bestowed upon Bartram by the Seminoles, 185, 260–263.

"Puc Puggy taken literally means simply 'flower.' Faya means 'hunter' and would probably be appended if the name were given in full." (J.R.S.)

Pumpkins: perhaps Seminole pumpkins or crookneck squashes (*Cucurbita moschata* Duchesne) (cf. Small, 1922; 1930a: 14; 1933: 1287); at Palatka, Fla., 304; cultivation by Indians, 511. *See also* Pompions.

Punica: a genus of Punicaceae, comprising the pomegranates; in the tropics, xiv.

Punica granatum. *See* Pomegranate.

Purple berried bay. *See* Olea Americana.

Purveyor, at Beresford plantation, Fla., hunting Turkeys, 146.

Putorius. *See* Polecat.

Pyrites; at Silver Bluff, S.C., 314; along Cape Fear River, N.C., 475.

Pyrus: a genus of Rosaceae, comprising the pears, apples, chokeberries, and mountain ashes; in the temperate zone, xv; usefulness, xvii; soil adapted for, 337.

Pyrus coronaria: in these cases, not *P. coronaria* L., but perhaps narrow-leaved crab apple (*P. angustifolia* Ait.); in Lowndes or Butler Counties, Ala., 399; on White Plains, La., 432. *See also* Crab, wild.

Pyrus malus: apple (*P. malus* L.); in temperate zone, xv.

Quadrupeds: mammals; young preyed upon by Bald Eagle, 8. *See also* Horse(s).

Quail(s): Eastern Bob-white(s) (*Colinus virginianus virginianus* [L.]); south of Altamaha River, Ga., 20; in Suwannee River region, Fla., 235. *See also* Tetrao minor.

Quakers, settling Wrightsborough, Ga., 35.

Qualatchee ("Qualatche"): a former Cherokee town on the headwaters of Chattahoochee River in Georgia (Mooney, 1900: 529); listed, 374.

Quanuse: a former Cherokee town, perhaps the same as Clennuse, at the site of the present Murphy, Cherokee County, N.C. (Hunter's map of 1730; Romans' map of 1776; Mooney, 1900: 535; Fowler Bend quadrangle); listed, 373.

Quartzum ("Quartsum"): quartz; in middle region of Georgia, 45.

Quaw bird. *See* Ardea clamator.

Quercus, or Querci: oak(s) (*Quercus* spp.); in Lime-Sink Region, 30; on lower St. John's River, Fla., 90; at Lake George, 157; at Shell Bluff, Ga., 318; along upper Savannah River, Ga.–S.C., 327; along Chattahoochee River, Ala., 393; at White Cliffs, La., 436.

Querci, dwarf (Oaks): probably including scrub oak (*Quercus myrtifolia* Willd.), Chapman's oak (*Q. chapmani* Sarg.), and scrub live-oak (*Q. virginiana* var. *maritima* [Chapm.] Sarg.); west of Spalding's Lower Store, Fla., 171. *See also* Oaks, dwarf.

Quercus alba (cf. Catesby, 1730? *1*: 21, pl. 21): white oak (*Q. alba* L.); in lower Coastal Plain, 28; about Wrightsborough, Ga., 36; along upper Savannah River, 320; near Oconee Station, Oconee County, S.C., 335; near Wayah Gap, N.C., 362; in Warren County, Ga., 378; west of Chattahoochee River, Ala., 394; along Cape Fear River, N.C., 474. *See also* Oak, White-.

Quercus aquatica: water oak (*Q. nigra* L.; syn., *Q. aquatica* Walt.); on

Colonel's Island, Ga., 6; about St. Mary's River, Ga.–Fla., 24; west of
Chattahoochee River, Ala., 394; acorns eaten by Passenger Pigeons,
470; along Cape Fear River, N.C., 474. *See also* Oak, Water- .

Quercus aquatica, Delta ("Della") leaved Water Oak (cf. Catesby,
1730? *1:* 20, pl. 20): water oak (*Q. nigra* L.); in lower Coastal
Plain, 28.

Quercus aquatica, or Maryland Water Oak: water oak (*Q. nigra* L.);
along upper Savannah River, Ga., 320.

Quercus *castanea ("castania"): *nomen nudum* (Merrill, 1945: 34)—
perhaps rock chestnut oak (*Q. prinus* L.); about Wrightsborough,
Ga., 36.

Quercus *dentata: *nomen nudum* (Merrill, 1945: 34)—probably Dar-
lington oak (*Q. hemisphaerica* Bartr. ex Willd.); on Colonel's Island,
Ga., 6; in Liberty County, 10; about St. Mary's River, Ga.–Fla., 24; on
St. John's River below Palatka, Fla., 84, and above Lake Dexter, 131;
at Salt Springs, 161; at Alachua Sink, 204. *See also* Oak, Water;
Quercus hemispherica.

Q[uercus] *dentata, Narrow-leaved Wintergreen Oak: *nomen nudum*
(Merrill, 1945: 34)—probably Darlington oak (*Q. hemisphaerica*
Bartr. ex Willd.); in lower Coastal Plain, 28.

Quer[cus] *dentata, s[eu] *hemispherica: *nomina nuda* (Merrill,
1945: 34)—probably Darlington oak (*Q. hemisphaerica* Bartr. ex
Willd.); along upper Savannah River, Ga., 320. *See also* Quercus
hemispherica.

Quercus *flammula: *nomen nudum* (Merrill, 1945: 34)—probably
southern red oak (*Q. rubra* L.) or a closely related species; in
Escambia or adjacent county, Ala., 403; acorns eaten by Passenger
Pigeons, 470. *See also* Quercus sinuata.

Q[uercus] *glandifer: *nomen nudum* (Merrill, 1945: 34)—some undetermined species of oak; near Salt Springs, Fla., 164.

Quercus *hemispherica: *nomen nudum* (Merrill, 1945: 34)—Darlington oak (*Q. hemisphaerica* Bartr. ex Willd.) (cf. Elliott, 1824, *2:*
597–598; Fernald, 1946: 138–140, 143–144, pls. 1035, 1036); xv;
near Three Sisters Ferry, S.C., 309; west of Chattahoochee River,
Ala., 394; near The Rigolets, La., 421; on Amite River, 426; along
Cape Fear River, N.C., 474. *See also* Oak, Water; Quercus dentata.

Quercus Ilex: not the European *Q. ilex* L., but perhaps swamp chestnut oak (*Q. michauxii* Nutt.); near Salt Springs, Fla., 164.

Quercus *humila (misprint for pumila?) varietas: probably oak runner (*Q. pumila* Walt.); on Colonel's Island, Ga., 6.

Quercus *incana: upland willow oak (*Q. incana* Bartr.; syn., *Q. cinerea* Michx.) (cf. Harper, 1943; Fernald, 1944: 44–45; Merrill, 1945:

31); described, in Warren County (probably on or near the Fall-line Sand Hills), Ga., 378; in Escambia or adjacent county, Ala., 403.

Q[uercus] *laciniata ("lasciniata"): *nomen nudum* (Merrill, 1945: 34) —an undetermined oak, doubtless of the subgenus *Erythrobalanus;* about Wrightsborough, Ga., 36.

Q[uercus] *lobata, post White Oak: *nomen nudum* (Merrill, 1945: 34)—probably post oak (*Q. stellata* Wang., with its var. *margaretta* [Ashe] Sarg.); along upper Savannah River, Ga., 320; in Warren County, 378; west of Chattahoochee River, Ala., 394.

Q[uercus] *maritima: probably scrub oak (*Q. myrtifolia* Willd.) (cf. Fernald, 1944: 45; Merrill, 1945: 31); described, near Salt Springs, Marion County, Fla., 164.

The description applies much better to *Q. myrtifolia* than to the two other characteristic oaks of the "Florida scrub," *Q. chapmani* Sarg. and *Q. virginiana* var. *maritima* (Chapm.) Sarg.

Quercus nigra (cf. Linnaeus, 1753: 995–996 [reference to Catesby, 1730? *1:* 19, pl. 19]): in at least most of the following cases, doubtless black jack oak (*Q. marilandica* Muenchh.); west of Deep Creek, Putnam County, Fla., 173; near Alachua Savanna, 202, 209; in Warren County, Ga., 378; in Escambia or adjacent county, Ala., 403.

Quercus phellos (or "phillos") (cf. Catesby, 1730? *1:* 16, pl. 16): willow oak (*Q. phellos* L.); on Colonel's Island, Ga., 6; in Liberty County, 10; about St. Mary's River, Ga.–Fla., 24; in lower Coastal Plain, 28; on St. John's River above Lake Dexter, Fla., 131; near Three Sisters Ferry, S.C., 309; along upper Savannah River, Ga., 320; west of Chattahoochee River, Ala., 394; on Amite River, La., 425; acorns eaten by Passenger Pigeons, 470; along Cape Fear River, N.C., 474.

Q[uercus] prinos (or "prinus"), Swamp White Oak (cf. Catesby, 1730? *1:* 18, pl. 18): in the following cases, probably swamp chestnut oak (*Q. michauxii* Nutt.); in lower Coastal Plain, 28; about Wrightsborough, Ga., 36; near Three Sisters Ferry, S.C., 309.

Q[uercus] prinus: probably rock chestnut oak (*Q. prinus* L.); near Wayah Gap, N.C., 362.

Quercus pumila: oak runner (*Q. pumila* Walt.); near Salt Springs, Fla., 164; on Long Bay, S.C., 471. See also Quercus humila.

Quercus rubra, Red Oak (cf. Catesby, 1730?, *1:* 23, pl. 23): southern red oak (*Q. rubra* L.), though the record from near Wayah Gap may apply to the northern red oak (*Q. r.* var. *borealis* [Michx. f.] Farw.); in lower Coastal Plain, 28; in Southern Red Hills, 32; about

Wrightsborough, Ga., 36; east of Alachua Savanna, Fla., 209; near Three Sisters Ferry, S.C., 309; along upper Savannah River, Ga., 320; near Oconee Station, Oconee County, S.C., 335; near Wayah Gap, N.C., 362; in Warren County, Ga., 378; near Stockton, Ala., 403.

Quercus sempervirens, Live Oak (cf. Catesby, 1730? *1:* 17, pl. 17): live oak (*Q. virginiana* Mill.), probably including to some extent the scrub live-oak (*Q. v.* var. *maritima* [Chapm.] Sarg.); on the Mississippi and the Altamaha and in Florida, xv; on Colonel's Island, Ga., 6; in Liberty County, 10; about St. Mary's River, Ga.–Fla., 24; in lower Coastal Plain, 28; near Alachua Savanna, Fla., 187; in Levy County, 221; at Blue Springs, Screven County, Ga., 461; acorns eaten by Passenger Pigeons, 470. *See also* Oak(s), Live.

There may be some mistake about the record for Screven County, Ga., which seems too far inland for live oaks.

Quercus sinuata, Spanish Oak (or "scarlet Oak") (cf. Walter, 1788: 235): probably southern red oak (*Q. rubra* L.) or a closely related species; in lower Coastal Plain, 28; west of Deep Creek, Putnam County, Fla., 173; near Alachua Savanna, 202. *See also* Quercus flammula, Quercus rubra.

Q[uercus] sinuata, S[eu] *flamule: probably southern red oak (*Q. rubra* L.) or a closely related species; east of Alachua Savanna, Fla., 209. *See also* Quercus flammula.

Quercus *tinctoria, Great Black Oak: black oak (*Q. velutina* Lam.) (cf. Merrill, 1945: 31); in lower Coastal Plain, 28; about Wrightsborough, Ga., 36; along upper Savannah River, 320; near Oconee Station, Oconee County, S.C., 335; near Wayah Gap, N.C., 362; in Warren County, Ga., 378; along Chattahoochee River, Ala., 394; along Cape Fear River, N.C., 474. *See also* Oak, Black.

Querquedulae ("Querquidulae"): Teal; species listed, 295.

Probably Bartram did not intend to include in this grouping more than the first three or four species listed.

Quick-lime, 476.

Quinquina ("Quinqina"): quinine (*Cinchona officinalis* L.); usefulness, xvii.

Rabbits: Eastern Cottontails (*Sylvilagus floridanus mallurus* [Thomas]); young preyed on by snakes, 195; charmed by Rattlesnakes, 267; devoured by Pine Snake, 276.

Rabbit (lepus *minor): Eastern Cottontail (*Sylvilagus floridanus mallurus* [Thomas]); described, in Carolina and Florida, 284.

Lepus minor Bartram antedates *L. sylvaticus floridanus* Allen (1890) and, if valid, must replace it as a specific name.

Raccoons (or "racoons"): *Procyon lotor* (L.); on Colonel's Island, Ga., 7; on Drayton's Island, Fla., 103; depredations near Alachua Savanna, 194; in Florida and Carolina, 281.

The subspecies of Colonel's Island is the St. Simon's Island Raccoon (*P. lotor litoreus* Nelson and Goldman); that of Florida, the Florida Raccoon (*P. l. elucus* Bangs); that of "Carolina," the Hilton Head Island Raccoon (*P. l. solutus* Nelson and Goldman).

Raccoons ("racoons") (*Ursus cauda elongata*): St. Simon's Island Raccoons (*Procyon lotor litoreus* Nelson and Goldman); on St. Simon's Island, Ga., 63.

Raccoon bridge. *See* Bridge, raccoon.

Rackets (or "racquet") or hurl(s): netted rackets, used in the Cherokee ball play, which somewhat resembles lacrosse (cf. *Bur. Am. Ethnol. Bull., 30*, Pt. I: 127, 245, figs., 1907); at Cowee, N.C., 370; used in the ball play, 508–509.

Radishes ("raddishes") (raphanus): *Raphanus sativus* L.; time for planting, 288.

Raft, on a creek in Montgomery County, Ala., 444–445.

Rail, blue or slate coloured water, of Florida. *See* Rallus major subceruleus.

Rail, greater brown. *See* Rallus rufus Americanus.

Rail, little brown. *See* Rallus Virginianus.

Rail, little dark blue water. *See* Rallus aquaticus minor.

Raisins, *Vitis allobrogica* for, 460.

Rajana: perhaps eardrops (*Brunnichia cirrhosa* Gaertn.) (cf. Elliott, 1821, *1*: 521); on St. John's River above Lake Dexter, Fla., 136.

On a flyleaf of Bartram's copy of Linné's *Systema Vegetabilium* (13th ed., 1774) appears the following note, evidently in his script: "*Rajania* ovata—a Rambling Vine on the banks of the Large Rivers in Georgia the dry seeds have each a thin membrane or little wing resembling the Maple seeds. &c. common on the Banks of the Savana River."

"Rajana perhaps. R. ovata of Walter" (Bartram to Muhlenberg, September 6, 1810; Muhlenberg Letters: 137).

R[allus] aquaticus minor, the little dark blue water rail (cf. Edwards, 1750, *3*: 144, pl. 144, as "Little American Water Hen," and 1751, *4*: 246, as "Gallinula minor, *Canadensis*"): Sora (*Porzana carolina* [L.]), adult; listed, 296.

The symbol ‡ is erroneous here.

R[allus] major subceruleus, the blue or slate coloured water rail of Florida: Florida Gallinule (*Gallinula chloropus cachinnans* Bangs); listed, 296.

It is strange that Bartram should have apparently overlooked in this list the Purple Gallinule (*Porphyrula martinica* [L.]), unless possibly it is combined with the Florida Gallinule under the above designation.

R[allus] rufus Americanus, the greater brown rail: probably Virginia Rail (*Rallus limicola limicola* Vieillot); listed, 296.

A specimen of this species, sent from Pennsylvania by Bartram to Edwards, was figured by the latter (1760, 2: 144, 219, pl. 279) under the name of "American Water-Rail"—"Rallus aquaticus Americanus."

Rallus Virginianus, the soree bird or little brown rail, also called widgeon in Pennsyl.: Sora (*Porzana carolina* [L.]; syn., *R. virginianus* L.), immature; listed, 296.

This name is obviously based upon the "Gallinula Americana" or "Soree" of Catesby (1731, *1*: 70, pl. 70), who recorded it from Virginia. His plate represents an immature Sora. Bartram treats this as a species distinct from the adult Sora—his "Rallus aquaticus minor" (cf. Stone, 1930).

Rangers ("ranges"): mounted soldiers; at Fort James, Ga., 324.

Rapa: a synonym of *Brassica*, a genus of Cruciferae, comprising the mustards, cabbages, turnips, etc.; usefulness, xvii.

Raphanus. See Radishes.

Rat(s): in general, probably various native species of rats and mice (genera *Neotoma*, *Oryzomys*, *Sigmodon*, and *Peromyscus*), but in some cases perhaps including the introduced Old World species (genera *Rattus* and *Mus*); on Colonel's Island, Ga., 7; mentioned, 71; preyed on by snakes, 195; devoured by Four-lined Chicken Snake, 275.

Rat, common Norway: Brown Rat (*Rattus norvegicus* [Berkenhout]); compared in size with *Geomys*, 7.

Rat, domestic: in this case, probably Brown Rat (*Rattus norvegicus* [Berkenhout]); compared with Florida Wood Rat, 124.

Rat, house- , European: either Brown Rat (*Rattus norvegicus* [Berkenhout]) or Black Rat (*Rattus rattus rattus* [L.]); in Florida and Carolina, 281.

Rat, ground-, large: some form of Pocket Gopher (*Geomys*), no longer occurring on Colonel's Island and probably extinct; on Colonel's Island, Ga., 7.

In view of the plasticity of this genus, the isolated form on this island was probably distinct from any now known. It has not been present within the memory of the oldest inhabitant.

Rats, wild- , two species of: one doubtless the Eastern Cotton Rat

(*Sigmodon hispidus hispidus* Say and Ord), and the other perhaps Le Conte's Cotton Mouse (*Peromyscus gossypinus gossypinus* [Le Conte]); in Florida and Carolina, 281.

Bartram apparently confused the Cotton Rat and the Florida Wood Rat (*see* next entry).

Rat, wood- : animal and its nests described, at Lake Dexter, Fla., 124–125.

The "habitations" described here are unquestionably those of the Florida Wood Rat (*Neotoma floridana floridana* [Ord]). This was probably the animal that Bartram encountered at Lake Dexter and intended to describe. Actually, however, he describes another and smaller species, the Cotton Rat (*Sigmodon hispidus* Say and Ord), as Audubon and Bachman (1846, *1:* 36) have pointed out. The local name of "Wood Rat" is still applied to *Sigmodon* in southeastern Georgia. The subspecies in the vicinity of Lake Dexter is probably *S. h. floridanus* A. H. Howell.

Rattles, in sanctuary at Otasse, Ala., 454.

Rattle gourd: used by Seminoles, 245; used by Indians, 505.

Rattle-snakes: in this case, one or more of three species of the genera *Crotalus* and *Sistrurus;* on Colonel's Island, Ga., 7.

Rattle snake: in this case, probably the Diamondback (*Crotalus adamanteus* Beauvois); veneration of, by Seminoles, and adventure with, at Spalding's Lower Store, Fla., 260–263.

Rattle snake: in these cases, either the Diamondback (*Crotalus adamanteus* Beauvois) or the Timber or Seminole Rattler (*C. horridus* subspp.); general account of, and adventures with, 264–272; compared with Ground Rattler, 274, 275, and with Pine Snake, 276; skin used for tobacco pouch, 453.

Rattle snake, bastard, or ground rattle snake: Ground Rattler (*Sistrurus miliarius* subspp.); account of, 274–275.

The "nose . . . turned upwards" and the tendency to "swell and flatten themselves" suggest a partial confusion with the Hog-nosed Snake (*Heterodon contortrix* [L.]), the young of which bear a slight superficial resemblance to the Ground Rattler.

Rattle-snake, dreaded: Timber Rattlesnake (*Crotalus horridus horridus* L.); in middle region of Georgia, 46.

Raven(s): presumably Northern Raven(s) (*Corvus corax principalis* Ridgway); compared in plumage with Snake Birds, 133; at Cowpen Lake, Putnam County, Fla., 179; compared in color with a Coachwhip Snake, 219. *See also* Corvus carnivorus, Corvus maritimus.

There is no recent record of Ravens in Florida.

Razors, not formerly owned by the Creeks, 500.

Razor bill. *See* Rynchops niger.

"Rebicula." *See* Rubicula.

Red-belly: Red-breasted Bream (*Lepomis auritus* [L.]); described, in Liberty County, Ga., 12. *See also* Bream, red bellied.

Red bird. *See* Loxia cardinalis.

Redbird, sand-hill, of Carolina. *See* Merula flammula.

Red-bird, summer: Summer Tanager (*Piranga rubra rubra* [L.]) (cf. Harper, 1942*d:* 214–215); wrongly classed with *Muscicapa,* 302. *See also* Merula Marilandica.

Red Cedar. *See* Cedar, Red.

Red men. *See* Indian(s) (tribes not specified), Indians—Cherokees.

Red pole, yellow. *See* Parus aureus vertice rubro.

Red shank. *See* Numenius fluvialis.

Redstart. *See* Ruticilla Americana.

Reed(s): probably either small cane (*Arundinaria tecta* [Walt.] Muhl.) or giant cane (*A. gigantea* [Walt.] Chapm.); at Lake Dexter, Fla., 120, 125; on Alachua Savanna, 203; as a hair ornament among Indians, 501; Indian flute made of, 505.

Reeds or Canes (Arundo gigantea): giant canes (*Arundinaria gigantea* [Walt.] Chapm.); along Tensaw River, Ala., 406; on lower Tombigbee River, 410. *See also* Cane(s) (or Reed[s]).

Reed harpoon: probably small cane (*Arundinaria tecta* [Walt.] Muhl.); Salmon Trout struck with, 44.

Reedy bank: perhaps referring to *Phragmites communis* Trin.; at Lake Beresford, Fla., 142.

Regullets. *See* Rigolets, The.

Regulus atrofuscus minor, or marsh wren: Long-billed Marsh Wren (*Telmatodytes palustris palustris* [Wilson]); resident in Pennsylvania, 286.

R[egulus] cristatus, the golden crown wren (cf. Edwards, 1758, *1:* 95, pl. 254, lower fig., and 1760, *2:* 218, as "Regulus cristatus, s. Trochilus antiquorum"): Eastern Golden-crowned Kinglet (*Regulus satrapa satrapa* Lichtenstein); listed, 291.

Edwards' specimen was sent from Pennsylvania by Bartram. On the status of the generic name (*Regulus* Bartram), *see* Harper (1942*d:* 217).

R[egulus] cristatus alter vertice rubini coloris, the ruby crown wren. (G. Edwards.) (cf. Edwards, 1758, *1:* 95, pl. 254, upper fig., and 1760, *2:* 218, as "Regulus cristatus alter vertice rubini coloris"): Eastern Ruby-crowned Kinglet (*Regulus calendula calendula* [L.]); listed, 292.

Edwards' specimen was sent from Pennsylvania by Bartram, and his description became the basis for *Motacilla calendula* L.

Regulus *griseus ("griceus"), the little bluish grey wren (cf. Edwards, 1760, 2: 194, 220, pl. 302, as "Muscicapa parva subcoerulea"): *nomen nudum*—Blue-gray Gnatcatcher (*Polioptila caerulea caerulea* [L.]); listed, 291.

Edwards' specimens were sent by Bartram, presumably from Pennsylvania; his name became the basis for *Motacilla caerulea* L.

Reg[ulus] *magnus. *See* Motacilla *Caroliniana.

Reg[ulus] *minor. *See* Motacilla *palustris.

Reg[ulus] *peregrinus, gutture flavo, the olive coloured yellow throated wren (cf. Edwards, 1758, *1*: 54, pl. 237, lower fig., and 1760, 2: 218, as "Muscicapa Marilandica, gutture luteo"): Maryland Yellowthroat (*Geothlypis trichas* [L.]); listed, 292.

Edwards received a specimen and a drawing from Bartram.

Regulus *rufus. *See* Motacilla *domestica.

Reproduction, of plants and animals compared, xxii.

Reptile(s): in Bartram's usage, including amphibians as well as true reptiles; food of Wood Ibis, 150, of King Vulture, 151, and of toads, 280; driven on shore of Alachua Savanna, Fla., by Alligators, 193; prey of Rough Green Snake, 275.

Resin, of *Silphium,* chewed by Indians and traders, 399.

Rhamnus (or "Rhamus") frangula: buckthorn (not the European *R. frangula* L., but *R. caroliniana* Walt.); on Colonel's Island, Ga., 6; about St. Mary's River, Ga.–Fla., 24; on Altamaha River, Ga., 50; on St. Simon's Island, 58; at Lake George, Fla., 157; near Salt Springs, 164; west of Spalding's Lower Store, 171; between Orange and Tuscawilla Lakes, 183; near Suwannee River, 242; on upper Tensaw River, Ala., 408; at The Rigolets, La., 421; at Lake Pontchartrain, 424.

This shrub seems to have become decidedly less common since Bartram's time.

"Rhamnus frangula, R. caroliniana Walter" (Bartram to Muhlenberg, September 6, 1810; Muhlenberg Letters: 137).

Rhamnus volubilis (or "volubllis") (cf. Linné [filius], 1781: 152): rattan vine (*Berchemia scandens* [Hill] K. Koch) (F.W.P.); on St. Simon's Island, Ga., 59; on lower St. John's River, Fla., 87; about Alachua Savanna, 187, 198. *See also* Zizyphus scandens.

"Rhamnus volubilis, specimin imperfect for want of fructification. the flowers are hermophrodite fruit a little oval black berry, cantaining a single compress't striated seed or nut." (Bartram to Muhlenberg, November 29, 1792; Muhlenberg Letters: 25.)

Rheum rhabarbarum: rhubarb (*R. rhaponticum* L.; syn., *R. rhabar-barum* L.); usefulness, xvii.

Rhexia (or "Rhexea"): a genus of Melastomataceae, comprising the deer-grasses; beauty, xviii; near Lake Lochloosa, Fla., 180.

Rhexia ("Rhexea") *pulcherrima ("pulcherima"): *nomen nudum* (Merrill, 1945: 34)—deer-grass (*Rhexia* sp.); in Brunswick County, N.C., 472.

Rhizophora conjugata: in this case, not the Oriental *R. conjugata* L., but black mangrove (*Avicennia nitida* Jacq.) (Small, 1923: 28); on Mosquito River, Fla., xxviii.

"Rhizophora conjugata Wild. 843" (Bartram to Muhlenberg, September 6, 1810; Muhlenberg Letters: 137).

Rhododendron: a genus of Ericaceae, now comprising the azaleas as well as the rhododendrons, but in Bartram's time restricted to the latter; xvi; a shrub (*q.v.*) allied to, 171, 321.

Rhododendron: in these cases, probably white rhododendron (*R. maximum* L.); in Vale of Cowee, N.C., 346, 354.

Rhododendron ferrugineum ("ferruginium"): in these cases, not the European *R. ferrugineum* L., but presumably lesser rose-bay (*R. minus* Michx.); at cataracts of Augusta, Ga., 34; near Broad River, 44; at Shell Bluff, 318; between Little and Broad Rivers, 322; in Oconee County, S.C., 334; at Falling Creek, Rabun County, Ga., 342.

Rhododendron *spurium: *nomen nudum* (Merrill, 1945: 34)—tar-flower (*Befaria racemosa* Vent.); west of Spalding's Lower Store, Fla., v. *See also* Kalmia spuria; Shrub, beautiful, allied to Rhododendron.

A description in Bartram's manuscript copy for the *Travels* (p. 264; Hist. Soc. Pennsylvania) is sufficient to identify this shrub as *Befaria racemosa*.

Rhododendron, a new species of: presumably Carolina rose-bay (*R. carolinianum* Rehder); described, on Oconee (= Station) Mountain, Oconee County, S.C., 336.

Rhus vernix: poison sumac (*R. vernix* L.); in Lime-Sink Region, 31.

Ribband(s); Cherokee girls ornamented with, 370; worn by Indians, 503. *See also* Silk ribbands.

Rice: *Oryza sativa* L.; culture in Liberty County, Ga., 10, 11; plantations along Altamaha River, 16; on St. Mary's River, Ga.–Fla., 23; on Savannah, Ogeechee, Altamaha, and Satilla Rivers, 66; cooked with acorn oil by Indians, 85; cypresses on rice plantations, 91; land fit for, near Crescent Lake and Charlotia, Fla., 95, and at Lake Beresford, 144; among provisions, 124; Wood Ibis in rice plantations, 150; for supper, 158, 249; Suwannee River region suitable for, 234; shipped from Sunbury, Ga., to Liverpool, 306; near Three Sisters Ferry, S.C., 309; on Savannah River, S.C., 375; on Escambia River, Fla., 416; on the Mississippi, 430; swamps near Lake Waccamaw, N.C., fit for, 473.

Rice bird, (emberiza oryza vora): Bobolink (*Dolichonyx oryzivorus* [L.]); plumages, migration, and food of, 296–298. *See also* Emberiza oryzivora.

Rice bird, blue or slate coloured. *See* Emberiza livida.

Rice bird, pied. *See* Emberiza varia.

Rifle; of a Seminole, 20–22; used on an Alligator, 250; for each ranger at Fort James, Ga., 324.

Rifle gun; young Indian armed with, 361.

Rigolets ("Regullets"), The: a channel connecting Lake Borgne and Lake Pontchartrain in eastern Louisiana (Rigolets quadrangle); location, 421; passed through, 437.

River, a large, from the East: presumably the Hiwassee, which arises in northeastern Georgia, flows west-northwest, and joins the Tennessee about 40 miles above Chattanooga, Tenn.; 339.

Rivers, salt: tidal streams; in the Carolinas and Georgia, 29.

Rivulet, rapid, of cool, pleasant water: probably Wacasassa River, in Levy County, Fla., crossed, 222.

Road(s): excellent in Liberty County, Ga., 10; good and bad, between Midway and Darien, 12.

Roanoke (River): formed by the Dan and Staunton Rivers in south central Virginia and discharging into Albemarle Sound, N.C.; crossed, 479.

Roaring Creek: perhaps the present Falls Creek, a southern tributary of Burningtown Creek, Macon County, N.C. (Cowee quadrangle); leaving, 360.

Robe. *See* Mantle or robe.

Robins (turdus migratorius): Eastern Robins (*Turdus migratorius migratorius* L.); feeding on cedar berries, 298.

Robin redbreast, turdus migratorius: Eastern Robin (*Turdus migratorius migratorius* L.); resident in Pennsylvania, 286. *See also* Turdus migratorius.

Robinia hispida: rose acacia (*R. hispida* L.); on the Great Ridge, Ga., 41.

Robinia, incarnate: probably clammy locust (*R. viscosa* Vent.); on Oconee (= Station) Mountain, Oconee County, S.C., 336.

Robinia *montana: *nomen nudum* (Merrill, 1945: 34)—locust (*Robinia* sp.); at Falling Creek, Rabun County, Ga., 342.

Pursh (1813, 2: 488) lists "R. montana. Bartr. catal." as a synonym of *R. hispida.*

Robinia, a new(?) species of (cf. Catesby, 1748, 2, appendix: 20, pl. 20): probably clammy locust (*R. viscosa* Vent.); described, near Oconee Station, Oconee County, S.C., 335.

Robinia (or "Robinea") pseudoacacia ("pseudacacia"): black locust (*R. pseudo-acacia* L.); of the Northern States, xvi; near Oconee Station, Oconee County, S.C., 335; in Lowndes or Butler Counties, Ala., 399.

In the last case, Mohr (1901: 14) suggests a misidentification of *Gleditsia triacanthos* L.

Rock, friable white (cf. W. Bartram, 1943: 138, 177): apparently "a gray, arkosic sandstone" (Stephenson, in Veatch and Stephenson, 1911: 104); near Augusta, Ga., 45.

Rock[fish]: *Roccus saxatilis* (Walbaum); about Georgia coastal islands, 67.

Rock-fish (Creek): a westerly tributary of Cape Fear River in southern Cumberland County, N.C., crossed, 477.

Rocky Comfort Creek: an easterly tributary of Ogeechee River, in Warren, Glascock, and Jefferson Counties, Ga.; camp on, 379; rocks near, 384.

Since Bartram makes no mention of crossing the Ogeechee River on his westward journey, is it possible that he mistook it for, or confused it with, the Rocky Comfort?

Rocky Point: the present Rocky Point on Lake George, Fla., opposite Drayton's Island; visited and described, 168–169.

Roebuck (or "roe" or "American roe buck"): Virginia White-tailed Deer (*Odocoileus virginianus* [Boddaert]); on Altamaha River, Ga., 50; on Cumberland Island, 65; an Indian bounding like, 115; chased by a Seminole on Alachua Savanna, Fla., 188; Seminole horse compared with, 215; in Florida and Carolina, 282; in Vale of Cowee, N.C., 348; between Flint and Chattahoochee Rivers, Ga., 387; on coast of Florida, 488. *See also* Buck; Buckskin(s), Cervus sylvaticus, Deer, Venison.

Rolle, Den[ys]: founder of the settlement of Charlotia or Rollestown, on St. John's River between East Palatka and San Mateo, Putnam County, Fla.; origin and decline of his settlement, 93–95. *See also* Charlotia.

"Denys Rolle, one of East Florida's most energetic but unfortunate colonizing planters, was a Devonshire man of some wealth who at one time was a member of Parliament for Barnstaple. . . .

"He suffered many setbacks . . . and lost several of his indentured settlers whom the attractions of life in the disorderly capital enticed away from him. He therefore returned to England after a year, but . . . he came back to Rollestown with a new group of forty-nine settlers: vagrants, beggars, and debtors from London streets, they were called, while a later tradition included some fallen women in the population . . . The colony had a fitful existence . . . The commissioners for East Florida claims, when they came to his case, only gave him £6,597 out of the £19,886 which he demanded." (Mowat, 1943: 50–51, 71.) See also J. Bartram (1942: 46, 69–70, 100), W. Bartram (1943: 146, 219), Mrs. Corse (1928), and Wroth (1941: 43).

Romans, origin of war among, 392–393.

Rook. *See* Corvus maritimus.

Roots, collections of, 48, 252.

Rosa: a genus of Rosaceae, comprising the roses; xvi.

Rosa *paniculata: *nomen nudum* (Merrill, 1945: 35)—a wild rose (*Rosa* sp.); in Oconee County, S.C., 334; at Falling Creek, Rabun County, Ga., 342.

Probably identical with "mountain cluster rose" (*q.v.*).

"Rosa paniculata, Much taller than our wild upland rose, branches, divaricate, slender; Flowers larger and in panicles or bunches. undescribed." (Bartram to Muhlenberg, September 6, 1810; Muhlenberg Letters: 137.)

Rose: *Rosa* sp.; flower compared with that of magnolia, 86.

Rose, mountain cluster: a wild rose (*Rosa* sp.); near Cowee, N.C., 354.

Probably identical with "Rosa paniculata" (*q.v.*).

Rotunda; of Cherokees, described, 367–369; councils of the Muscogulges at, 496; of the modern Indians, 520. *See also* Council-house, Town house.

Rotunda or council-house ("counsel-house"); described, at Otasse, Ala., 450, 454–455; compared with that of Cherokees, 450; ceremony within, 450–453.

The "counsel-house" of pp. 454–455 is different from the "rotunda or counsel-house" of pages 450–453 (cf. W. Bartram, 1853: 53–57).

Royal Society; John Bartram a fellow of, xiii.

This statement is contrary to fact (Earnest, 1940: 78), insofar as the Royal Society of London is concerned, although eight papers by John Bartram were published in the *Philosophical Transactions* of that society (Barnhart, 1932: 53–55). He was, on the other hand, a member of the Royal Academy of Sciences of Stockholm. His certificate of membership, dated April 26, 1769, is among the Bartram Papers (*1:* 67).

Rubicula ("Rebicula") Americana, Cat[esby]. *See* Motacilla sialis.

Rudbeckia (or "Rudbeckea"): a genus of Compositae, comprising the cone-flowers, of which there are about 40 North American species; near Lake Lochloosa, Fla., 180; between Orange and Tuscawilla Lakes, 183; along upper Savannah River, Ga., 321; in Warren County, 379; in Brunswick County, N.C., 472.

Pursh records (1813, *2:* 574) the following Bartram specimens in the Banks Herbarium: *R. spathulata* Michx., Florida; *R. radula* Pursh [= *Helianthus radula* (Pursh) T. & G.], Georgia; and *R. aristata* Pursh [= *R. triloba* L.], South Carolina.

Ruellia: a genus of Acanthaceae, comprising the ruellias; west of Deep Creek, Putnam County, Fla., 173; near Lake Lochloosa, 180.

Ruellia *infundibuliformea: *nomen nudum* (Merrill, 1945: 35)—some undetermined species of *Ruellia;* in Levy County, Fla., 224.

Rumsey, Mr.: a plantation proprietor near The Rigolets, La.; hospitality of, 420–423; residence with, 431.

Rushes: perhaps *Juncus* spp.; on salt marshes in Georgia, 68; on Alachua Savanna, Fla., 203.

*Ruticilla Americana, the redstart (cf. Catesby, 1731, *1:* 67, pl. 67; Harper, 1942*d:* 217): *nomen nudum*—American Redstart (*Setophaga ruticilla* [L.]); listed, 292.

Rynchops niger, the shearwater or razor bill: Black Skimmer (*R. nigra nigra* L.); listed, 295.

Sabbath, observance at Otasse, Ala., 457.

Saddles, stuffed with long moss, 88.

Sage, tall blue: *Salvia azurea* Lam. (cf. Mohr, 1901: 15); described, in Baldwin or adjacent county, Ala., 412.

St. Anastatius Island: Anastatia Island, on the east coast of Florida opposite St. Augustine; coquina quarries on, 80.

St. Augustine: the first permanent settlement in the present limits of the United States, founded by the Spaniards in 1565 (on the east coast of Florida in the present St. John's County) and yielded by treaty to the British in 1763; Yamasees pursued by Creeks to gates of, 55; business of Mr. Egan in, 66; Mr. Egan departed for, 73; former acquaintance in, 78; council at, 78–79; proximity of St. John's River to, 95; treaty at, 96, 170, 191; old Spanish highway starting from, 208; Spaniards driven into, by Creeks, 208–209; a young man from, 215; Indian stores in, 228; Seminoles visiting, 255, 257, 258; garrison of, and vessel from, 270; Flamingo at, 296; Rice-birds at,

297; *Gilia rubra* near, 377; Spaniards at, 487; Spanish governor of, 488.

For descriptions of the old St. Augustine, *see* J. Bartram (1942: 51–53, 78, figs. 22, 23, 24, 26, 28, 37), Stork (1769: 7–9), Schoepf (1911, *2:* 226–251), Forbes (1821: 84–89), Fairbanks (1858), Reynolds (1885), Chatelain (1941: 30–32), and Mowat (1941).

St. Catherine ("Catharine"), island of: in this case, not actually St. Catherine's, but Colonel's Island, situated near the inner edge of the coastal marshes northwest of St. Catherine's, in Liberty County, Ga. (map of Liberty County, 1939); iii.

St. ("South") Catherine's ("Catharine's") Island: a coastal island of Liberty County, Ga.; defending Sunbury from the sea, 5.

Not visited by Bartram, as indicated in the Contents, page iii.

St. Helena Island: apparently a *lapsus* for Ossabaw Island, on the coast of Bryan County, Ga.; defending Sunbury from the sea, 5.

St. Ille. *See* Satilla.

St. John's Parish, Ga.: comprising parts of the present Liberty and adjoining counties; Midway Meeting in, 9; a rich district, 10.

St. John's (or "St. Juan's") River, Fla.: arising in Brevard and Osceola Counties, Fla., taking a general northerly course, and discharging into the Atlantic east of Jacksonville; Indian trading house on, 57; trading houses beyond, 64; determined to proceed up, 64; Cowford on, 66; set sail for, 70; ferry over, at the Cow-ford, 72; shores described, 78; magnolias on, 86; site of Denys Rolle's colony, 94–95; connection with Crescent Lake, 95; islands in, 96; store on, 97; voyage on, from Spalding's Lower Store to Lake Beresford and return, 98–169; Lake George a dilatation of, 102; width above Lake George, 110; communicating with Lake Beresford, 144; descending, 146; fish in, 168; shells in rocks on, 180; Orange Lake communicating with, 182; Lower Store and Fort Picolata on, 208; return to, 251; voyage up, from Spalding's Lower Store to Lake George and return, 252–254; orange groves on, 253; at Fort Picolata on, 270; crossed at Spalding's Lower Store, 304; voyage down, 306; Indian monuments on, 521.

St. Juan, Little. *See* Little St. Juan River.

St. Maria Galves Bay: Santa Maria De Galves Bay—in Bartram's usage, perhaps the entire Pensacola Bay, Fla., but in recent times restricted to the eastern portion, or East Bay; 415.

St. Mark's: an old settlement at the junction of St. Mark's and Wakulla Rivers, in Wakulla County, near the northernmost point on Apalachee Bay, Fla. (erroneously placed by Bartram near the mouth of Suwannee River); at the mouth of the Suwannee, 26; Rolle's plan to take up a grant near, 94–95; Spanish highway leading to, 208–209, 217; trading of Spaniards at, 227; mentioned, 235; listed, 464.

St. Mary's River: forming part of the boundary between Georgia and Florida, and discharging into the Atlantic between Cumberland and Amelia Islands; Indian trading-house on, 16; set out for, 20; arrived at, 22; fertility of land on, 23; its source in Okefinokee Swamp, 24, 26.

St. Pierre, Mons.: a French gentleman, owner of a plantation on the Carolina side of Savannah River, probably in vicinity of New Bordeaux; hospitality of, 375.

St. Rose Island: Santa Rosa Island, in Escambia County, Fla., bordering the Gulf of Mexico; 415.

St. Simon's Island: on the coast of Glynn County, Ga.; at mouth of Altamaha River, 53; Frederica on, 57, 306; exploration of, 58–62; former cultivation by English, 62.

An account of this island is given by Mrs. Cate (1930: 51–62).

St. Simon's Sound: between St. Simon's and Jekyl Islands on the east and Brunswick, Ga., on the west; a channel of Altamaha River passing through, 53.

Salix *fluvialis: *nomen nudum* (Merrill, 1945: 35)—probably black willow (*S. nigra* Marsh.); along Chattahoochee River, Ala., 393.

Salt: among provisions, 124; furnished to horses, 356.

Salt marsh(es); on Amelia Island, Fla., 65; those in the South formerly forests, 69; near Nassau Sound, Fla., 71; near The Rigolets, La., 421.

Salt plains: salt marshes; on St. Simon's Island, Ga., 59; along the Georgia coast, 68.

Salvia coccinea: scarlet sage (*S. coccinea* L.); on St. Simon's Island, Ga., 59.

Salvia *graveolens ("graviolens"): *nomen nudum* (Merrill, 1945: 35) —a sage (*Salvia* sp.); near Lake Lochloosa, Fla., 181; between Orange and Tuscawilla Lakes, 183.

"*Salvia graviolens,* a very beautiful plant in flower. Hamilton has it in perfection[.]" (Bartram to Muhlenberg, September 6, 1810; Muhlenberg Letters: 137.)

Sambucus (or "Sambricus"): in these cases, doubtless common elder (*S. canadensis* L.); in coastal swamps, 29; near Three Sisters Ferry, S.C., 309; along upper Savannah River, Ga., 321.

Sambucus (or "Sambuces"): in these cases, probably southern elder (*S. simpsonii* Rehder); on St. John's River at Charlotia, Fla., 94; between Orange and Tuscawilla Lakes, 183; on Amite River, La., 425.

Sanctuary (sanctorium or sacred temple); described, at Otasse, Ala., 454–455.

Sand birds (cf. Tringa parva, p. 294): probably some of the smaller sandpipers (genera *Ereunetes*, *Erolia*, and *Crocethia*); procured near Amelia Island, Fla., 70.

Sand-hills; south of Altamaha River, Ga., 18; in Lime-Sink Region, 30, 31; on St. Simon's Island, 58; on Cumberland Island, 65; west of Deep Creek, Putnam County, Fla., 173; at Cowpen Lake, 174; near Orange Lake, 182, 183; near Tuscawilla Lake, 184; near Alachua Savanna, 217; along Cape Fear River, N.C., 474, 477.

In general, in Bartram's usage, sand-hills in Georgia and Florida are probably the driest and most elevated parts of the pine barrens. On St. Simon's and Cumberland Islands they are probably sand dunes.

Sand ridges, in Levy County, Fla., 220.

Sandal. *See* Buskin(s), ancient, or sandal.

Sanguinaria: bloodroot (*S. canadensis* L.); at Falling Creek, Rabun County, Ga., 342.

Sanguisorba: burnet (*S. canadensis* L.); in Oconee County, S.C., 334.

Sanguisorba Canadensis: burnet (*S. canadensis* L.); near Clayton, Ga., 344.

"Have you Sanguisorba media, and canadensis? the former I saw abundantly growing in the natural Meadows & Strawberry fields in the Cheroke mountains; & the later grows in Wet lands in the Jersey's." (Bartram to Muhlenberg, November 29, 1792; Muhlenberg Letters: 25.)

"W. Bartram tells me that the Sanguisorba called in his Travels, S. canadensis is not canadensis, but S. media: very like, he says, to the European species. He saw thousands of acres of it to the southward in the valley & between the mountains. It was in flower in May, but he does not think that it flowers all the summer as the cattle are so fond of cropping it. As to S. canadensis he never saw it to the southward and never about Philadelphia, but he did see a specimen of it from a cedar-swamp in Jersey. Here Mr. John Bartram [Jr.] tells me he has seen a good deal of it in flower in September about 9 or X miles from Philadelphia[.]" (Benjamin Smith Barton, MS, 1805?)

Sapelo ("Sapello") bridge: on Sapelo River, McIntosh County, Ga., near the present Eulonia; came to, 14.

Sapelo ("Sapello") Island: the principal coastal island of McIntosh County, Ga.; near the mouth of Altamaha River, 53; adventure with rattlesnake on, 268–270.

Sapelo ("Sapello") River: a coastal stream of McIntosh County, Ga.; crossing waters of, 12, 13.

Sapindus: Florida soapberry (*S. marginatus* Willd.); on Colonel's Island, Ga., 6; on St. John's River below Palatka, Fla., 75, 84, and at Charlotia, 94; at Alachua Sink, 204. (Cf. Coker and Totten, 1937: 307.)

Sapling: in this case, probably a pine tree, and very likely one of considerable size; felled to make a "raccoon bridge," 445.

To this day, in the South, large pine trees are spoken of as "saplings."

Sarracenia, a new species of: *Sarracenia lacunosa* (*q.v.*); viii.

Sarracenia (or "Saracinia") flava (cf. Catesby, 1738, 2: 69, pl. 69): yellow trumpets (*S. flava* L.); beauty, xviii; compared with *S. lacunosa*, 417. *See also* Sarracenia, yellow.

Sarracenia *galeata: *nomen nudum* (Merrill, 1945: 35)—a pitcher-plant (*Sarracenia* sp.); beauty, xviii.

Sarracenia (or "Saracinia") *lacunosa: owing to a confusion of specimens or localities, Bartram describes under this name the hooded pitcher-plant (*S. minor* Walt.), although the species which he observed near Pensacola was doubtless Drummond's pitcher-plant (*S. drummondii* Croom) (cf. Small, 1933: 582; Wherry, 1935: 13, 17, figs. 5, 7; Merrill, 1945: 31–32); beauty, xviii; described, near Pensacola, Fla., 417.

Sarracenia purpurea (cf. Catesby, 1738, 2: 70, pl. 70): purple pitcher-plant (*S. purpurea* L.); beauty, xviii.

Sarracenia, yellow: yellow trumpets (*S. flava* L.); structure and function of parts, xviii–xx. *See also* Sarracenia flava.

Sash. *See* Belt(s) or sash.

Sassafras: sassafras (*S. albidum* [Nutt.] Nees); in Southern Red Hills, 32; on Oconee River, Ga., 379. *See also* Laurus sassafras.

Satilla ("St. Ille" or "St. Ille's") River: in southeastern Georgia, arising near Fitzgerald, and entering the Atlantic between Brunswick and St. Mary's; road to, and ferry on, 17; crossed, 20; said [erroneously] to rise in Okefinokee Swamp, 26; rice-growing on, 66.

The local pronunciation "Sintilla," still heard in southeastern Georgia, is reminiscent of the ancient form of this name.

Savanna(s): grassy areas, more or less level and moist, sometimes treeless, but in Bartram's usage evidently including the more open type of pine barrens; south of Altamaha River, Ga., 17, 18, 19; south of Satilla River, 20; about St. Mary's River, Ga.–Fla., 23–24; in Lime-Sink Region, 30–31; about Wrightsborough, Ga., 36; near

Little River, 38; on Altamaha River, 50; on St. Simon's Island, 58, 60; near Mount Royal, Fla., 99; on Drayton's Island, 103, 169; near Lake George, burnt by Indian hunters, 107; on St. John's River near St. Francis, 138, and at Hawkinsville, 140; at New Smyrna, 144; at Lake Dexter, 154, 155; near Salt Springs, 161, 163, 165; near Deep Creek, Putnam County, 172; about Cowpen Lake, Putnam County, 175, 179; near Orange Lake, 181; about Alachua Savanna, 187, 209, 251; in East and West Florida, 211; in Levy or adjacent county, 218, 220, 222, 223, 243, 248, 249; of Florida, 221; waters from the Alligator Hole emptying into a, 239–240; on Sapelo Island, Ga., 268, 269; Cricket Frogs and Little Tree-frogs in, 278; near Palatka, Fla., 303; near Three Sisters Ferry, S.C., 309; along lower Savannah River, Ga., 309, 310; along Tennessee River, Tenn. or Ala., 339; in Warren County, Ga., 379; about Cuscowilla, Fla., 380; west of Ocmulgee River, Ga., 382; between Flint and Chattahoochee Rivers, 384, 386, 387; between Chattahoochee and Tallapoosa Rivers, Ala., 394, 396; in Escambia or adjacent county, 402; near Stockton, 403; in northwestern Florida, 416; at Pensacola, 417; mentioned, 457; in Screven County, Ga., 461; in Brunswick County, N.C., 472–473.

Savanna, great: Alachua Savanna, Fla. (q.v.); departed for, 186; journey to, 215; road through, 217.

Savanna Crane. See Crane, savanna.

Savannas or Savan(n)ucas (Indians). See Indians—Savannas.

Savannah ("Savanna"), Ga.: capital of the Colony of Georgia, situated on Savannah River 15 miles above its mouth; arrived at, 4, 28, 46, 462; sojourn in, 5; set off from, 57; vessel leaving, 57; chest forwarded from, 64; trade produce shipped from St. John's River to, 97; return of schooner to, 170; timber rafted down river to, 313; road from, to Augusta, 313; vessels at, 317; seat of government removed from, 317; education of halfbreed children in, 449; depart for, 460; road between Augusta and, 461; left, 469; mentioned, 470.

Savannah ("Savanna") River: forming the boundary between Georgia and South Carolina; Augusta on, 28, 32; cataracts on, 33; divide between Savannah and Altamaha Basins, 35, 39, 42; Little River a branch of, 35; confluence with Broad River, 41, and Tugaloo River, 45; route through lowlands of, 46; Tugaloo River a branch of, 52; rice-growing on, 66; signs of Gopher Turtle near, 182; ferry on, 309; crossed, 309; timber rafts on, 313; Silver Bluff on, 314; shifting of channel at Fort Moore, 316; course of, 316–317; route up, 317; confluence with Broad River, 320, 323, 324, and Little River, 321; crossed, 326; crossed branches of, 328; waters of, 339; Fort Charlotte on, 375; water chinquapin in, 409; Jonathan Bryan's villa on, 469; crossed at Zubley's Ferry, 470; its basin as boundary between Cherokees and Muscogulges, 486; mentioned, 520.

Savannah or Keowee ("Savanna or Keowe") River: in this case, the Seneca and Keowee Rivers, tributary to the Savannah in northwestern South Carolina; Cherokee towns on, 374. See also Keowee River.

Savannuca: a former Shawnee town, incorporated with the Upper Creeks, apparently on both banks of the Tallapoosa River, in Elmore and Montgomery Counties, Ala., a mile or two east of Judkins Ferry, which is 8 miles northeast of Montgomery (cf. Taitt's map of 1772; Early's map of 1818; Bur. Am. Ethnol. Bull., 30, Pt. II: 481, 1910; soil map of Elmore County, 1911; Swanton, 1922: 319–320, pls. 7, 8, 9); camped opposite, 445; listed, 463.

Savannuca language (or tongue): erroneously considered by Bartram to be identical with the Yuchi language; spoken at Uche, Ala., 464; among tribes of Maryland and Virginia, 466; similar to Shawanese, 466.

Saw-mill(s), on Willis Creek and at Cross Creeks, Cumberland County, N.C., 477. See also Grist-mill, Mills.

Saxum: rock; in middle region of Georgia, 45.

Scarabei: probably lamellicorn beetles (family Scarabaeidae); prey of Six-lined Lizards, 172.

Scarlet Maple. See Maple, Scarlet.

Schambe River. See Escambia River.

Schooner(s) (or trading schooner): from St. John's River, Fla., 63; in Georgia coastal waters, 68; collections to be shipped on, 170; at Spalding's Lower Store, 209–210; due to return to Georgia, 252; set sail in, for Frederica, 306; ready to sail from Louisiana to Mobile, 437.

Schuylkill River: in eastern Pennsylvania, a tributary of the Delaware; John Bartram's house on, 480.

Sciurus: a genus of Sciuridae, comprising certain tree squirrels; several species described, 283.

Scolopax Americana rufa, the great red woodcock: American Woodcock (Philohela minor [Gmelin]); listed, 294. See also Woodcock.

S[colopax] minor arvensis, the meadow snipe (cf. Barton, 1799a: 2): Wilson's Snipe (Capella gallinago delicata [Ord]); listed, 294.

Scorpions. See Lizards, slender.

Scotch (people), in Mobile, Ala., 404.

Scotch gentleman, proprietor of a plantation on Amite River, La., 426.

Scotch grass (Panicum hirtellum): not *Panicum hirtellum* L., but some species of *Echinochloa* (Merrill, 1945: 30–31); described, introduced on the Mississippi between Manchac and Baton Rouge, La., from the West Indies, 430.

Scow; on St. John's River, Fla., 304–305.

Sculptures. *See* Paintings and sculptures.

Sea: Atlantic Ocean; not going out to, 306.

Sea coal: mineral coal (Webster); fossils compared with, 476.

Sea coast islands, at mouth of Altamaha River, Ga., 50.

Sea cow. *See* Manatee.

Sea shell(s): marine mollusks; mounds on Colonel's Island, Ga., 5; in rock near Augusta, 45; on St. Simon's Island, 58, 59; at Silver Bluff, S.C., 314; at Shell Bluff, Ga., 318; in limestone in Black Belt of Alabama, 399; near The Rigolets, La., 421, 422; on White Plains, 431; at Blue Springs, Screven County, Ga., 461; in rocks on Long Bay, S.C., 471; along Cape Fear River, N.C., 475, 476. *See also* Shells.

Sea-Trout. *See* Trout, Sea-.

Sedge: undetermined; on salt marshes in Georgia, 68.

Seeds: dissemination by animals and winds, xxiii; collections of, 48, 252.

Seminole(s) ("Siminole[s]"). *See* Indians—Seminoles.

Senates (Indian); composition of, 497; decisions on war, 497.

Seneca ("Senica" or "Sinica"): a former Cherokee town on both sides of Seneca River, in Oconee and Pickens Counties, S.C., about a mile below Clemson College (cf. Mouzon's map of 1775; Mooney, 1900: 522, pl. 3; Pickens quadrangle); a slave as pilot to, 328; arrived at, 329; described, 329–330; left, 330; mentioned, 332; *Magnolia auriculata* near, 339; congress at, 372; collections at, 372; listed, 374.

Senecio Jacobea: ragwort (not the European S. *jacobaea* L., but probably S. *glabellus* Poir.); on floating islets in St. John's River, Fla., 130. *See also* Jacobea, Corymbous.

"Senecio Jacobæa, perhaps S. aurea Wild." (Bartram to Muhlenberg, September 6, 1810; Muhlenberg Letters: 137).

Sepulchres. *See* Altars or sepulchres.

Serpents: imagined presence on floating islands in St. John's River, Fla., 89; as prey of the "Trout," 109; as food of Wood Ibis, 150, and of King Vulture, 152; brandishing tongue, 172; Little Tennessee River likened to a vast, 348; exposure to, 445; in sculptures at Otasse, Ala., 455.

Serratula: probably button snakeroot (*Liatris* sp.); in Brunswick County, N.C., 472.

Sette: a former Cherokee town, perhaps (if identical with "Setsi" of Mooney, 1900: 531) on Valley River, about 3 miles below Valley-town, in Cherokee County, N.C. (cf. "Tasetche" of Hunter's map, 1730; Nantahala quadrangle); listed, 373.

Settlements, on St. John's River, Fla., 73.

Settlements, back, of North Carolina, 478.

Settlements, Indian. *See* Indian country, etc.

Settlements, white: passed the frontier of, south of Satilla River, Ga., 20.

Shad: *Alosa sapidissima* (Wilson); season for, in Pennsylvania, 278.

Shallops: small vessels, usually with two masts carrying sails, 145; on Escambia River, Fla., 416.

Shambe River. *See* Escambia River.

Shark: any of various species of the subclass Selachii; about Georgia coastal islands, 67.

Sharks' teeth (dentes carchariae ["charchariae"]): teeth of fossil sharks of undetermined species; at Silver Bluff, S.C., 314.

Shawanese. *See* Indians—Shawanese.

Shearwater. *See* Rynchops niger.

Shed or pavilion: black drink brewed under, at Otasse, Ala., 451. *See also* Pavilion.

Sheep: *Ovis aries* L.; on St. Simon's Island, Ga., 58; range for, near Suwannee River, Fla., 235; prey of Bears, 282. *See also* Lambs.

Sheepshead (or "Sheeps head"): *Archosargus probatocephalus* (Walbaum); about Georgia costal islands, 67; at Salt Springs, Fla., 166.

Shells: the calcareous outer parts of mollusks (species undetermined in the following cases); marine, at Charlotia, Fla., 93; mound of, at Charlotia, 95; on St. John's River above Spalding's Upper Store, 114; in Salt Springs, 166; at Rocky Point, Lake George, 169; west of Cowpen Lake, Putnam County, 180; in Manatee Spring, 231; at Long Bay, S.C., 471. *See also* Sea shell(s).

[Shell Bluff,] Ga.: on west side of Savannah River, between the mouths of Boggy Gut and Newberry Creeks, in Burke County; described, 318.

Shell (or "shelly") bluff(s); on St. John's River above Lake Dexter, Fla., 131, 132, at St. Francis, 138–139, and at Huntoon Island, 140; at New Smyrna, 144; those on the St. John's possibly thrown up by wind and waves, 165.

Contrary to Bartram's view, it is now agreed that these shell bluffs were accumulated as kitchen middens of the aborigines, who discarded the shells after consuming the fleshy parts of the mollusks (cf. Wyman, 1875).

Shell-fish: mollusks—and (in Bartram's usage) other marine invertebrates as well; on St. Simon's Island, Ga., 60; about Georgia coastal islands, 68.

Shelly bank, on St. John's River above Lake Dexter, Fla., 134.

Shelly knolls, at Lake Dexter, Fla., 117.

Shelly promontory: apparently Zinder Point, on south side of Lake George, Fla.; 106.

Shelly rocks; at Kanapaha Sink, Fla., 217.

Shews. *See* Shows.

Shift. *See* Shirt or shift.

Shingles, Cherokee habitations roofed with, 367.

Ship Island, La.: between Mississippi Sound and Gulf of Mexico; pass by, 437.

Shirt(s): Seminoles in want of, 257, 260; worn by Indians, 502, 503, 504.

Shirt or shift, not worn by Indian women, 503.

Shot pouch, for each ranger at Fort James, Ga., 324.

Shows ("shews"), of Indians, 521.

Shrimp(s): various small, mostly marine, crustaceans; about Georgia coastal islands, 68; Mayfly larvae as food of, 83.

Shrub, beautiful, allied to Rhododendron: tar-flower (*Befaria racemosa* Vent.); west of Spalding's Lower Store, Fla., 171. *See also* Kalmia spuria, Rhododendron spurium.

A detailed description of the same plant, included in Bartram's manuscript copy for this portion of the *Travels* (MSS Div., Hist. Soc. Pennsylvania), establishes its identity as *Befaria*.

Shrub, a very curious, allied to Rhododendron or Kalmia: perhaps *Elliottia racemosa* Muhl. (cf. W. Bartram, 1943: 143, 220–221, fig. 10), although the description does not fit in all respects (E.T.W.); described, on Little River, Ga., 321.

Shrub of great singularity and beauty: tyty (*Cliftonia monophylla* [Lam.] Sarg.) (cf. Baldwin in Darlington, 1843: 333, under the name of *Mylocarium ligustrinum;* Nuttall, 1854, 2: 93; Michaux, 1889: 13, under the name of *Lapathum occidentale;* R. M. Harper, 1906: 122); described, in Lime-Sink Region, 31.

The particular place of occurrence, according to Michaux, was apparently in Screven County, Ga., somewhere northeast of Sylvania.

"*New shrub*. This is now called *Lyonia racemosa*. Lyon says that the 3 quetrous pericarpes has a seed in each angle of it." (Bartram to Muhlenberg, September 6, 1810; Muhlenberg Letters: 137.)

Shrubs, two new beautiful: the second one described is Georgia bark (*Pinckneya bracteata* [Bartr.] Raf.; syn., *P. pubens* Michx.) (cf.

Harper, 1942*b*: 6–7; Merrill, 1945: 23–24); near Fort Barrington, Ga., 16. *See also* Bignonia bracteata.

Sickness; at Otasse, Ala., 456.

Sideroxylon(s) (or "Sideroxilon[s]" or "Sideroxilum"): buckthorn(s) (*Bumelia* spp.); on St. Simon's Island, Ga., 58; at Lake George, Fla., 157; near Salt Springs, 164; near Alachua Savanna, 202; in southwestern Alachua County, 218; in Levy County, 221, 243; Painted Bunting among, 299; on upper Tensaw River, Ala., 408; at The Rigolets, La., 421; on White Plains, 432; on Long Bay, S.C., 471; along Cape Fear River, N.C., 476.

Sideroxylon sericeum ("Sideroxilon sericium") (cf. Walter, 1788: 100): buckthorn (*Bumelia* sp.); near Alachua Savanna, Fla., 187; near Suwannee River, 282.

This species of Walter's is currently rated a synonym of *S. tenax* (= *Bumelia tenax* [L.] Willd.), which Bartram records separately on p. 187.

Sid[eroxylon] ("Sideroxilon") tenax: buckthorn (presumably *Bumelia tenax* [L.] Willd., but see remark under preceding entry); near Alachua Savanna, Fla., 187.

Silex (cf. Lyell, 1849, 2: 24): probably silica; in middle region of Georgia, 45.

Silk: Suwannee River region, Fla., suitable for production of, 234.

Silk ribbands, in hair of Indian women, 503. *See also* Ribband(s).

Silk-worms (phalaena *bombyca [*nomen nudum*]): *Bombyx mori* (L.); mulberries cultivated for, 308; Morus for feeding, 460.

Silphium (or "Sylphium"): a genus of Compositae, comprising the rosin-weeds; near Lake Lochloosa, Fla., 180; between Orange and Tuscawilla Lakes, 183; near Suwannee River, 242; along upper Savannah River, Ga., 321; in Warren County, 379; in Brunswick County, N.C., 472.

Silphium, a tall species of: one of the rosin-weeds, perhaps *S. terebinthinaceum* Jacq. var. *pinnatifidum* (Ell.) Gray, which Elliott (1823? 2: 462) reported from the Alabama prairies, but which has not been recently found there (R.M.H.); described, from Montgomery or Lowndes Counties, Ala., 398–399.

The *Silphium* now commonly found in this prairie region is *S. laciniatum* L.

Silver: Seminole warriors ornamented with plates, chains, etc., 244; sought by Spaniards at Silver Bluff, S.C., 315; ornaments in hair and ears of Indians, 501; bells on boots and mantle of Indians, 502; crescents or gorgets, bands or bracelets, and chains, worn by Indians, 503; brooch ("broach") in hair of Indian women, 503.

Silver Bluff, S.C.: on Savannah River near mouth of Hollow Creek ("Holley" Creek of Augusta quadrangle), a dozen miles below Augusta, Ga.; visited and described, 313–315; mentioned, 318; journey to, 449; called at, 462.

"Sinica." *See* Seneca.

Sink(s): natural depressions or hollows in limestone regions, in many cases communicating with subterranean watercourses; near Alachua Sink, Fla., 204–205; in Levy County, 220, 222; west of Suwannee River, 233; waters from the Alligator Hole emptying into a, 240; description of two between Suwannee River and Alachua Savanna (one apparently fitting the "Alligator Hole," *q.v.*), 246–247.

Sink, Great: Alachua Sink, on northeastern border of Alachua Savanna, Fla., visited and described, 203–207.

Sink-hole: in this case, the so-called "Drummer's Pond," at south end of Cowpen Lake, Putnam County, Fla.; described, 174–175.

Sisymbrium: a genus of Brassicaceae, with wider limits in Bartram's time than at present; near Suwannee River, Fla., 242.

Sitta, or nuthatch (cf. Catesby, 1730? *1*: 22, pl. 22): Northeastern White-breasted Nuthatch (*Sitta carolinensis cookei* Oberholser); resident in Pennsylvania, 286.

Sitta Europea, grey black capped nuthatch: not S. *europaea* L., but Northeastern White-breasted Nuthatch (*S. carolinensis cookei* Oberholser); listed, 289 *bis.*

S[itta] *varia, ventre rubro, the black capped, red bellied nuthatch: Red-breasted Nuthatch (*Sitta canadensis* L.); listed, 289 *bis.*

Six mile Springs: Salt Springs, arising just east of Lake Kerr, Marion County, and flowing into Lake George, Fla.; visited and described, 160–168. *See also* Springs, Great.

Skate: one or more species of the genus *Raja;* about Georgia coastal islands, 67; at Salt Springs, Fla., 166.

    Skates seem out of place so far inland as Salt Springs.

Skins: probably, for the most part, those of Virginia White-tailed Deer (*Odocoileus virginianus* [Boddaert]); as bedding, 50, 75, 135, 158; goods covered with, 64, 387; Indians reclining on, 92; bartered to Spaniards in Cuba, 227.

Skipjack: perhaps *Pomolobus chrysochloris* Rafinesque, a species of herring; about Georgia coastal islands, 67.

Slaves (Indian) or servants; Yamasee captives as slaves at Cuscowilla, Fla., 185–186; at Talahasochte, 236; in ceremony in rotunda at Otasse, Ala., 452–453.

Slaves (Negro): on lower St. John's River, Fla., 77; Cottonmouth Moccasins a terror to, 273; at a cowpen on lower Savannah River,

Ga., 310–312; songs of their own composition, 312. *See also* Blacks, Negro(es), Negro slave(s).

Sloane ("Sloan"): Sir Hans Sloane (1660–1753), author of a notable two-volume work on the natural history of Jamaica (1707, 1725) and principal founder of the British Museum; reference to, 241, 430.

    He corresponded with John Bartram and presented him with a set of his work on Jamaica (Darlington, 1849: 302–306).

Sloop(s): in Georgia coastal waters, 68; mentioned, 145; Spaniards trading in Florida in small sloops, 227.

Smilax: a genus of Liliaceae, comprising the catbriers; various species in coastal swamps, 29, and on Long Bay, S.C., 471; berries as food of Cedar-bird, 298.

Smilax aspera. *See* China brier.

Smilax, pseudo China: bamboo or China brier (probably either S. *pseudo-china* L. or S. *bona-nox* L.) (cf. Fernald, 1944: 32–38); on St. Simon's Island, Ga., 58. *See also* China brier, Contee.

Smilax pumila: sarsaparilla vine (S. *pumila* Walt.); near Suwannee River, Fla., 243.

Smilax sarsaparilla: catbrier (*Smilax* sp., not S. *sarsaparilla* L.); near Suwannee River, Fla., 243.

Smiths; at Cross Creeks, N.C., 477.

Smith-shop; at Cross Creeks, N.C., 477.

Snake(s); compared in appearance with Snake Birds, 133; of Florida, Georgia, and Carolina, 264–276.

Snakes, ash-colored, with keeled scales and reddish belly: apparently a composite description, perhaps applying in part to the Florida Pine Snake (*Pituophis melanoleucus* [Daudin] or *P. mugitus* Barbour) (cf. Harper, 1940: 718–720; Barbour, 1940; W. Bartram, 1943: 150, 222); near Alachua Savanna, Fla., 195. *See also* Snake, pine or bull.

Snake, black: *Coluber constrictor constrictor* L.; in Florida and Carolina, 276.

Snake, chicken: Four-lined Chicken Snake (*Elaphe quadrivittata quadrivittata* [Holbrook]); account of, 275–276.

    In his original description of this snake as *Coluber quadrivittatus,* Holbrook (1836, 1st ed., *1*: 113) refers to this account by Bartram.

Snake, coach-whip: *Coluber flagellum flagellum* Shaw; on Colonel's Island, Ga., 7; encounter with a hawk in Alachua or Levy Counties, Fla., and description of, 218–220.

Snake, garter: perhaps Coral Snake (*Micrurus fulvius fulvius* [L.]) (cf. Halter, 1923: 105) rather than Eastern Garter Snake (*Thamnophis sirtalis sirtalis* [L.]); in Florida and Carolina, 276.

Snake, glass (or "glass-"): a limbless lizard of the genus *Ophisaurus* (cf. McConkey, 1954); on Colonel's Island, Ga., 7; in middle region of Georgia, 46; Six-lined Lizard compared with, in brittleness of tail, 280.

Snake, glass (anguis fragilis): not the European *A. fragilis* L., but another limbless lizard, of the genus *Ophisaurus* (cf. McConkey, 1954); described, near Alachua Savanna, Fla., 195–196.

Snake, green: Rough Green Snake (*Opheodrys aestivus* [L.]); account of, 275.

Snakes, horn. *See* Snake, pine or bull.

Snake, pine or bull (or "horn snakes"): Florida Pine Snake (*Pituophis melanoleucus* [Daudin] or *P. mugitus* Barbour) (cf. Harper, 1940: 718–720; Barbour, 1940); account of, 276. *See also* Snakes, ash-colored.

Snake, ribband: perhaps Scarlet King Snake (*Lampropeltis elapsoides elapsoides* [Holbrook]), though the color description is not accurate; account of, 275.

Snake, ring neck: Southeastern Ring-necked Snake (*Diadophis punctatus punctatus* [L.]); in Florida and Carolina, 276.

Snake, speckled: undetermined; skin adorning a pipe at Watauga, N.C., 351.

Snakes, switch: probably Coachwhips (*Coluber flagellum flagellum* Shaw); Glass Snakes compared with, 196.

Snake, wampum ("wampom"): probably Milk Snake (*Lampropeltis triangulum triangulum* [Lacepède]); compared with Moccasin, 273.

Snake, water: for the most part, probably Southern Water Snake (*Natrix sipedon fasciata* [L.]); in Florida and Carolina, 276.

Snake Birds, a species of cormorant or loon (Colymbus cauda elongata): Florida Water-turkeys (*Anhinga anhinga colubrina* [Bartram]; syn., *A. a. leucogaster* [Vieillot]); described, on St. John's River, Fla., 132–133. *See also* Colymbus colubrinus.

Snipes: various species of the family Scolopacidae; procured near Amelia Island, Fla., 70.

Snipe, little brown or ash coloured. *See* Tringa fusca.

Snipe, little pond. *See* Tringa griseus.

Snipe, meadow. *See* Scolopax minor arvensis.

Snipe, pool. *See* Numenius fluvialis.

Snow, in Virginia and Maryland, 480.

Snow bird. *See* Passer nivalis.

Soil(s): fertility of sand and clay soils compared, 23; in Lime-Sink Region, 31; favorable in Suwannee River region, Fla., 234.

Sokaspoge (properly Sukaispoga): a former Upper Creek town on the

west bank of Tallapoosa River, apparently on the point 1 mile north
of the present Sturdevant, Tallapoosa County, Ala. (Taitt, 1916:
529, 530 [indicated but not named on his map of 1772]; Swanton,
1922: 248, 251, pl. 2; Dadeville quadrangle); listed, 462.

Solanum tuberosum ("tuberosa"): white potato (*S. tuberosum* L.);
usefulness, xvii.

Solidago: goldenrod (*Solidago* spp.); near Suwannee River, Fla., 243;
along upper Savannah River, Ga., 321; in Warren County, 378; in
Brunswick County, N.C., 472.

Songs; of Seminoles, described, 245; by Seminoles at Spalding's Lower
Store, 255, 263; at Mucclasse, Ala., 507; among Indians, 505–508; at
the busk, 510.

Sophas. *See* Cabins or sophas.

Sophora: wild indigo (*Baptisia* spp.); near Lake Lochloosa, Fla., 181;
between Orange and Tuscawilla Lakes, 183; near Suwannee River,
242; near Long Pond, Levy County, 248.

Soree bird. *See* Rallus Virginianus.

Sounds, along the Georgia coast, 68.

Sound, betwixt Cat Island and the continent: Mississippi Sound, on
the coast of Mississippi; sailing through, 437.

Sour Gum (Nyssa sylvatica): *N. sylvatica* Marsh.; in Butler or adjacent county, Ala., 400. *See also* Nyssa sylvatica.

South America, Spaniards in, 88.

South Carolina: boundary, 472; British colonists of, 487. *See also* Carolina.

"South Catharine's Island." *See* St. Catherine's Island.

Southern States; travels in, 264 (see map which follows illustration
section); Cottonmouth Moccasins in, 272.

Spalding, James: a prominent planter of St. Simon's Island, Ga., and
proprietor of trading stores in Florida; hospitality and assistance to
Bartram, 57–58, 306; president of St. Simon's Island, 62; trade of
Seminoles with, 257.

   Spalding was born in Perthshire, Scotland, in 1734, and emigrated
to Charleston, S.C., in 1760. In 1763, when Spain ceded Florida to
Great Britain, he established trading posts there and was appointed
a member of the Colonial Council for that province. During the
Revolution he refused to bear arms against the mother country and
removed to Florida, but after the war he returned to St. Simon's. In
1787, by planting seed from the West Indies, he was instrumental
in establishing the sea-island cotton industry in Georgia. Spalding's
wife was Margery McIntosh (1754–1818), a daughter of Lachlan

McIntosh's brother William. His only son was Thomas Spalding (1774–1851). (Mrs. Cate, 1930: 123–124.) He died in Savannah on November 10, 1794.

Spalding and Co., M'Latche as agent for, 258.

Spalding's Upper Store: at the present Astor, Lake County, Fla.; establishment of, 97; trip to, 98–111; arrival at, and account of trader and Indians there, 111–113. *See also* Store, upper.

Spalding and Kelsall: partners in a trading firm; C. M'Latche as agent for, 96.

The senior partner was James Spalding (*q.v.*).

Spaniards: ancient fort on Altamaha River, Ga., supposedly their work, 53; sheltering Yamasees, and driven by Creeks into their fortifications, 55; Fort Picolata, Fla., built by, 80; in South America and West Indies, using long moss, 88; Alachuas as enemies of, 186; driven into St. Augustine by Creeks, 208–209; bringing Andalusian horses to Florida, 216; of Cuba, bartering with Florida Indians, 227; dealing with white trader at Talahasochte, 228; settlements of, near Suwannee River and at Apalachean Old Fields, 233; supposed ancient camps of, at Silver Bluff, S.C., 315; Indians in alliance with, 380; enemies of Muscogulges, 392; governor's palace in Pensacola built by, 416; fortress and garrison of, on the Mississippi just below Bayou Manchac (cf. "Spanish Post" on Romans' map of 1772), 428; capture of two youths by Creeks, 487–489; at war with Creeks, 488.

Spanish, at Mobile, Ala., 413.

Spanish fields, plantations, and settlement: on west side of Suwannee River, Fla., 232–233, 235.

Spanish highway, old, to St. Mark's: extending from St. Augustine westward, via Picolata, Lake Geneva, Alachua Savanna, Talahasochte on the Suwannee River, Clara, and Hampton Springs (approximately) (cf. Vignoles, 1823: 62; Pittman, 1934: 120–122); described, 208–209, 217.

For most of its extent west of the St. John's, this is a more southerly route than the one shown on the Purcell map of about 1779 (Boyd, 1938).

Spanish high road (or way) to Pensacola: in this section, evidently identical with the highway to St. Mark's (see preceding entry); on west side of Suwannee River, Fla., 232, 234.

Spanish Curlews. *See* Curlews, Spanish.

Spanish customs, influence on Seminole customs, 186.

Spanish settlements, broken up by Alachuas, 381.

Spanish shore of the Mississippi: the west shore; 430.

Sparrow, chirping: perhaps Pine-woods Sparrow (*Aimophila aestivalis aestivalis* [Lichtenstein]); at Cowpen Lake, Putnam County, Fla., 179.

Sparrow, large brown white throat. *See* Fringilla fusca.

Sparrow, little field. *See* Passer agrestis.

Sparrow, little house. *See* Passer domesticus.

Sparrow, red, or fox-coloured ground or hedge. *See* Fringilla rufa.

Sparrow, reed. *See* Passer palustris.

Specimens [of plants]; a book of, in a box, 142; dried after a hurricane, 143–144; roots and seeds collected, 168, 304; reviewing, 366; collected at Keowee, S.C., 372; left at Mobile for shipment to London, 438; shipped to England, 467. *See also* Plants.

Spiders: species of the order Araneida; Little Tree-frogs taken for, 278; as food of toads, 280.

Spider of the genus Araneus saliens. *See* Araneus saliens.

Spiraea ("Spirea") opulifolia: ninebark (*Physocarpus opulifolius* [L.] Maxim.); along upper Savannah River, Ga., 321.

Spirits: inhabitants of Apalachicola haunted by, 390; communion of high priests with invisible, 497; believed in by Indians, 498.

Spoon, at Watauga, N.C., 351.

Spoonbill. *See* Platalea ajaja.

Springs: great springs feeding Suwannee River, 225–226; vast fountains near St. John's River, 226. *See also* Fountain.

Springs, Great: in this case, Salt Springs, on west side of Lake George, Fla. (fig. 16); visited, 252. *See also* Six mile Springs.

Springs, Great: in this case, the present Blue Springs on Beaverdam Creek, 5 miles southeast of Hilltonia, Screven County, Ga. (fig. 29); visited and described, 461–462.

Square, public, or areopagus: a central feature of Creek towns, consisting "of four buildings of equal size, placed one upon each side of a quadrangular court" (for a further account, see W. Bartram, 1853: 53–57, figs. 3, 4); at ancient Apalachicola, Ala., 390; at Coolome, 397; at Alabama, 447; at Otasse, described, 450, 453–456 (in reference to "a large . . . square adjoining this town": p. 456, see Commentary); activities at, 491; councils at, 496; at Mucclasse, 499; cleaned at the busk, 509; feasting and dancing in, 509, 510; celebration of the busk in, 510; assembly at, 512.

Squash(es): *Cucurbita* spp.; at Palatka, Fla., 304; cultivation by Indians, 511.

These squashes, in part at least, were apparently cymlings (*C. pepo* var. *condensa* Bailey). *See* next entry, also Cucurbita verrucosa.

Squashes (Cucurbita verrucosa): cymlings, scalloped summer squashes (*C. pepo* var. *condensa* Bailey; syn., *C. verrucosa* L.); at Palatka, Fla., 93. *See also* Cucurbita verrucosa.

Squash, Wild (Cucurbita *peregrina): perhaps Okeechobee gourd (*C. okeechobeensis* [Small] Bailey) (cf. Small, 1922 and 1930a; Merrill, 1945: 25); described, on St. John's River above Lake Dexter, Fla., 137.

"*Cucurbita peregrina.* a new species undoubtedly. The hunters call it the Wild squash." (Bartram to Muhlenberg, September 6, 1810; Muhlenberg Letters: 137.)

Squilla. *See* Cancer, Squilla.

Squirrels: in the following cases, probably either Southern Gray Squirrels (*Sciurus carolinensis carolinensis* Gmelin) or Southern Fox Squirrels (*S. niger niger* L.), or both; on Colonel's Island, Ga., 7; on Drayton's Island, Fla., 103; near Alachua Savanna, 194; charmed by Rattlesnakes, 267; devoured by Pine Snake, 276.

Squirrel, black: Southern Gray Squirrel (*Sciurus carolinensis carolinensis* Gmelin), black phase; described, in Carolina and Florida, 283.

"Melanistic individuals of this form are very rare" (Bangs, 1898: 205).

Squirrel, common grey: Southern Gray Squirrel (*Sciurus carolinensis carolinensis* Gmelin); described, in Carolina and Florida, 283.

Squirrel, flying (sciurus volans): Florida Flying Squirrel (*Glaucomys volans querceti* [Bangs]), at least this subspecies for the most part; in Carolina and Florida, 284.

Squirrel, great black fox: Southern Fox Squirrel (*Sciurus niger niger* L.), black phase; described, in Carolina and Florida, 283.

The partially white tail, as described here, is a very exceptional feature.

Squirrel, grey fox: Southern Fox Squirrel (*Sciurus niger niger* L.), gray phase; described, in Carolina and Florida, 283.

Squirrel, red fox: presumably meant for the buff phase of the Southern Fox Squirrel (*Sciurus niger niger* L.), though not typical; described, in Carolina and Florida, 283.

Squirrel, little grey: perhaps based upon immature individuals of the Southern Gray Squirrel (*Sciurus carolinensis carolinensis* Gmelin), this subspecies, in any event, being smaller and somewhat browner than the Northern Gray Squirrel (*S. c. leucotis* Gapper); described, in Carolina and Florida, 283.

Squirrel, ground, or little striped squirrel: in southeastern Pennsylvania, Fisher's Chipmunk (*Tamias striatus fisheri* Howell); in mountains northwest of Carolina, Eastern Chipmunk (*T. s. striatus* [L.]); 284.

Stalactites ("Stalectites") (cf. Linnaeus, 1770, 3: 183–185); in middle region of Georgia, 45.

Standard, imperial. See Calumet, also next entry.

Standard, royal (or eagle's tail), of Creeks or Muscogulges, 151; displayed at Talahasochte, Fla., 236. See also Calumet.

    "This 'royal standard,' as appears from what Bartram says on page 454, was simply the calumet, and that was of late introduction among the Creeks" (J.R.S.).

Staphylaea: bladdernut (*S. trifolia* L.); near Oconee (= Station) Mountain, Oconee County, S.C., 337; near Wayah Gap, N.C., 362.

Staphylaea ("Staphylea") trifoliata (*lapsus* for trifolia): bladdernut (*S. trifolia* L.); along upper Savannah River, Ga., 321.

Stars; tattooed on Indians, 503.

Starling ("sterling") (sturnus): Eastern Redwing (*Agelaius phoeniceus phoeniceus* [L.]); bill structure compared with that of Summer Redbird, 302. See also Sturnus predatorius.

Steed. See Horse(s).

Steers: *Bos taurus* L.; slaughtered for a feast at Cuscowilla, Fla., 190. See also Beef, Cattle, Ox.

Sterling, red winged. See Starling, Sturnus predatorius.

Sterna stolida, the sea swallow, or noddy: Noddy Tern (*Anoüs stolidus stolidus* [L.]); listed, 295.

Stewart, John. See Stuart, John.

Stewartia: in the following cases, silky camellia (*S. malachodendron* L.); in Liberty County, Ga., 10; in lower Coastal Plain, 29; in Southern Red Hills, 32; in Monroe or adjacent county, Ala., 401, 402; along Cape Fear River, N.C., 476. See also Stewartia malachodendron.

Stewartia: in these cases, probably mountain camellia (*S. ovata* [Cav.] Weatherby); at Falling Creek, Rabun County, Ga., 342; near Wayah Gap, N.C., 362. See also Stewartia, mountain; Stewartia montana.

Stewartia, mountain: mountain camellia (*Stewartia ovata* [Cav.] Weatherby); on Oconee (= Station) Mountain, Oconee County, S.C., 337. See also Stewartia montana.

Stewartia malachodendron (cf. Catesby, 1748, 2, appendix: 13, pl. 13): silky camellia (*S. malachodendron* L.); near Three Sisters Ferry, S.C., 309; along upper Savannah River, Ga., 320.

Stewartia *montana: mountain camellia (*S. ovata* [Cav.] Weatherby) (cf. Merrill, 1945: 32); described, in vicinity of Tomassee Knob, Oconee County, S.C., 334. *See also* Stewartia, mountain.

Stibium. *See* Lead, black.

Sticoe, ancient famous town of: near the site of the present Clayton, Rabun County, Ga. (Mooney, 1900: 532, pl. 3; Walhalla quadrangle); ruins of, 345.

Stillepica or moccasin; worn by Indians, 502. *See also* Moccasins.

Stillingia: queen's delight (probably *S. sylvatica* L.); at The Rigolets, La., 421.

Stillingia *fructicosa: sebastian bush (*Sebastiana fructicosa* [Bartr.] Fernald) (cf. Fernald, 1944: 45; Merrill, 1945: 32); described, at Ashwood, on Northwest Cape Fear River, about 5 miles northeast of Council, Bladen County, N.C., 476.

Hitherto known as *Sebastiana ligustrina* (Michx.) Muell. Arg.

Stincard (properly Stinkard) tongue (or language): a language other than Muskogee; spoken at several towns in Alabama, 463–464, and by Seminoles, 464; spoken by remnants of nations from maritime parts of Carolina and Florida, 465.

Sting-ray: any of various species of such genera as *Dasyatis* and *Aëtobatus;* about Georgia coastal islands, 67; at Salt Springs, Fla. (probably *Dasyatis sabinus* [Le Sueur] in this case), 166.

Stingray, great Black: probably Spotted Stingray (*Aëtobatus narinari* [Euphrasen]); about Georgia coastal islands, 67.

Stockings, not worn by Indian women, 503.

Stone, seldom seen in Lime-Sink Region, 31.

Stones, as head ornaments among Indians, 502.

Stone consisting of sea-shells and sand: coquina; quarried on Anastasia Island, Fla., and used in buildings at St. Augustine, etc., 80.

Stony ("Stoney" in Contents, p. viii) Creek: the present Rocky Creek, a few miles west of Macon, Ga.; camp near, 381.

Stores, Indian: trading stores; in Georgia and St. Augustine, Fla., 228.

Stores on the St. Mary's: at the present King's Ferry, Nassau County, Fla.; arrived at, 22. *See also* Trading-house, Indian, in the river St. Mary.

Stores, or lower store: Spalding's Lower Store, at the present Stokes Landing, on the west side of St. John's River, 6 miles southwest of Palatka, Fla.; goods removed from, and hidden, 64; voyage down to, 156; Ocklawaha River above, 182; return to, 208; arrived at, 254, 304. *See also* Trading house on the St. John's.

Store, upper: Spalding's Upper Store, at the present Astor, on the west side of St. John's River, Lake County, Fla.; goods removed from, and hidden, 64; arrived at, 156; return from, 170. *See also* Spalding's Upper Store.

Stork, Dr. William: author of *A Description of East-Florida* (4 eds., 1766–1774, the last three including John Bartram's journal of his journey up St. John's River 1765–66); plantation of, on Lake George, Fla., 253.

"Dr. Stork, a botanist and member of the Royal Society, visited East Florida as agent for various land grantees " (Mowat, 1943: 50).

"It is said that Dr. Stork, who was near the spot when the insurrection [of Minorcans at New Smyrna] happened, died with the fright" (Romans, 1776: 272).

Stork(s): presumably Whooping Crane(s) (*Grus americana* [L.]), although there is a distinct possibility of confusion with the Wood Ibis (*Mycteria americana* L.) (cf. W. Bartram, 1943: 223); resting on cypresses, 91; at Alachua Savanna, Fla., 190.

The Whooping Crane is not known to perch on trees.

Storm, on lower St. John's River, Fla., 75. *See also* Gale, Hurricane, Tempest.

Strawberry (or strawberries): *Fragaria* spp.; at Keowee, S.C., 330–331; plains near Keowee River, 333; beds near Oconee (= Station) Mountain, Oconee County, 338; near Clayton, Ga., 344; in Vale of Cowee, Ga.–N.C., 346, 348, 349; near Cowee, N.C., 355, 356, 357–358; in Montgomery or Lowndes Counties, Ala., 398; on White Plains, La., 432. *See also* Fragaria.

Strix *acclamator, capite levi, corpore griseo ("grisco"), the whooting owl: Northern Barred Owl (*S. acclamator acclamator* Bartram; syn., *S. varia varia* Barton) (cf. Harper, 1942*d*: 211); listed, 289.

Strix *acclamatus: *nomen nudum*—Northern Barred Owl (*S. acclamator acclamator* Bartram; syn., *S. varia varia* Barton) (cf. Harper, 1942*d*: 211); resident in Pennsylvania, 286.

Strix *arcticus, capite levi[,] corpore toto niveo, the great white owl (cf. Edwards, 1747, 2: 61, pl. 61, and p. 127, as "Aluco albus, diurnus"): Snowy Owl (*Nyctea nyctea* [L.]); listed, 289.

Strix assio: Eastern Screech Owl (*Otus asio naevius* [Gmelin]); resident in Pennsylvania, 286.

Strix assio, capite aurito, corpore ferrugineo ("ferruginio"), the little screech owl (cf. Linnaeus, 1758: 92): Eastern Screech Owl (*Otus asio naevius* [Gmelin]); listed, 289.

Strix *maximus, capite aurito, corpore niveo, the great horned white owl: undetermined, unless possibly the Arctic Horned Owl (*Bubo virginianus wapacuthu* [Gmelin]), as suggested by Nuttall (1834: 561) and by Coues (1875: 344); listed, 289.

Strix *peregrinator, capite aurito, corpore versicolor, the sharp winged owl: probably Short-eared Owl (*Asio flammeus flammeus* [Pontoppidan]) rather than Eastern Long-eared Owl (*A. otus wilsonianus* [Lesson]); listed, 289.

Strix *pythaules, capite aurito, corpore rufo, the great horned owl (cf. Edwards, 1747, 2: 60, pl. 60): Great Horned Owl (*Bubo virginianus virginianus* [Gmelin]); listed, 289.

Strix *pythaulis (variant of preceding entry): Great Horned Owl (*Bubo virginianus virginianus* [Gmelin]); resident in Pennsylvania, 286.

Stuart ("Stewart"), John: Superintendent of Indian Affairs, with headquarters in Charleston; recommendation by, 9, 327; mentioned by the chief of Watauga, N.C., 351; discussed by Bartram and Atakullakulla, 365. *See also* Superintendent of Indian Affairs.

John Stuart (*ca.* 1700–1779) was one of the Scotch colonists who came to Georgia in 1733. He was an ensign during the Spanish invasion of 1742, and was left in command at Fort William, on Cumberland Island, where he repulsed a Spanish fleet of 28 vessels. The Cherokee and Creek Indians who were allied with the British became particularly attached to Stuart.

Later he kept a store in Charleston, and there he married a Miss Fenwick. In 1760 he was second in command at Fort Loudon, Tenn., when that fort capitulated to the Cherokees. In subsequent hostilities, when most or all of the British force were killed or captured, Stuart was claimed by his firm friend, the famous Cherokee chieftain, Ata-kullakulla. The latter soon afterward took him into the woods, ostensibly on a hunting excursion, but conducted him through the wilderness to Virginia and there delivered him into the hands of friends.

In 1762 or 1763 Stuart was appointed Superintendent of Indian Affairs for the southern colonies. He was a man of extraordinary influence among the Indians, and at the outbreak of the Revolution he incited them to join the Tories in warring upon the rebelling colonists. When the nature of his activities was exposed, he fled from Charleston just before June 1, 1775. He reached Florida and presently sailed for England, where he died in 1779. (Drayton, 1821, 1: 266, 293; J. Johnson, 1851: 106–108; Mooney, 1900: 44, 203.)

Stuart deserves to be remembered for his services in supervising some of the most valuable maps of the colonial period (e.g. Romans and Taitt, 1772; Purcell, about 1776 and about 1779; Faden, 1780), besides preparing at least one of his own—the Cherokee country (*Crown Coll.*, ser. 2, 3: 34–35, 1910). He was also unfailingly courteous and helpful to both John and William Bartram on their southern excursions, as testified by references to him in their journals.

The Stuart house (fig. 1), at the northwest corner of Tradd and Orange Streets, is a fine example of colonial architecture, and is one of the few residences remaining from that period in Charleston. It was erected before 1772, and it was confiscated by the Americans in 1779.

Sturnus ("Sturuus") *predatorius, the red winged sterling, or corn thief (cf. Catesby, 1730? 1: 13, pl. 13): nomen nudum—Eastern Redwing (Agelaius phoeniceus phoeniceus [L.]); listed, 291. See also Starling.

S[turnus] ("Sturuus") *stercorarius, the cowpen bird (cf. Catesby, 1730? 1: 34, pl. 34; Barton, 1799a: 16): nomen nudum—Eastern Cowbird (Molothrus ater ater [Boddaert]); listed, 291.

Styrax: a genus of Styracaceae, comprising the storaxes; xvi; on the Great Ridge, Ga., 41; along upper Savannah River, 320; in Oconee County, S.C., 334; on Oconee (= Station) Mountain, Oconee County, 337; at Falling Creek, Rabun County, Ga., 342; near Wayah Gap, N.C., 362; in Monroe or adjacent county, Ala., 402; along Cape Fear River, N.C., 476.

Styrax *latifolia: nomen nudum (Merrill, 1945: 35)—large-leaved storax (Styrax grandifolia Ait.); in Southern Red Hills, 32.

Sugar, brought by Indians from Cuba, 227.

Sugar-cane: Saccharum officinarum L.; ruined by hurricane at Lake Beresford, Fla., 143, 144; Suwannee River region suitable for, 234.

Sugar Town. See Kulsage.

Sulphurous ("sulphureous") nodules, along Cape Fear River, N.C., 475.

Summer yellow bird. See Parus luteus.

Sun: setting on Lake George, 158; the glorious sovereign of day, 190; shooting shadows on Alachua Savanna, 196; sunrise described, 245–246; rising, 344; smoke puffed toward, 351, 497; tattooed on Indians, 503.

Sunbury: now a "dead town," but formerly a thriving seaport near the mouth of Midway River, Liberty County, Ga. (Jones, 1878: 141–223; Harden, 1913, 1: 149–150; map of Liberty County, 1939); set off for, 5; left, 9; trade produce shipped from St. John's River to, 97; shipping collections from, 306–307; set sail from, 307.

Sunfish (or sun fish). See Bream, golden; Bream, yellow.

Suola-nocha: a former Seminole town, whose location is highly uncertain, though placed by Bartram on the Flint River; listed, 464.

Superintendent ("Superintendant") of Indian Affairs: John Stuart; on his way to Augusta, Ga., 28; recommending Bartram to Indian chiefs, 33. *See also* Stuart, John.

Surgeon, at Fort James, Ga.; excursion with, 324.

Survey, of lands ceded by Indians at treaty of Augusta, 39–40.

Surveyor: in this case, probably the distinguished but eccentric colonial surveyor and cartographer, John Gerar William De Brahm; surveying the site of New Smyrna, Fla., 144.

For information concerning De Brahm see Mowat (1942).

Surveyor(s): appointed to ascertain boundaries of lands purchased from Indians, 34; setting out from Augusta, Ga., 35; controversy with Indian chief, 39–40; taking observations on Broad River, 41; completing their observations, 46.

Susquehanna River: one of the principal rivers of New York, Pennsylvania, and Maryland, discharging into the head of Chesapeake Bay; frozen over, 480; crossed, 480.

Swaglaw (properly Sawokli), great: a former Hitchiti town on west side of Chattahoochee River, 6 miles below Oconee, probably near mouth of Little Barbour Creek in extreme northeastern Barbour County, Ala. (*Bur. Am. Ethnol. Bull.*, 30, Pt. II: 481, 1910; soil map of Barbour County, 1919; Swanton, 1922: 142, pls. 2, 9); listed, 464.

Swaglaw (properly Sawokli), little: a former Hitchiti town on east side of Chattahoochee River, 4 miles below Oconee, probably in vicinity of the present Florence, Stewart County, Ga. (Taitt's map of 1772; *Bur. Am. Ethnol. Bull.*, 30, Pt. II: 481, 1910; soil map of Stewart County, 1916; Swanton, 1922: 142, pls. 2, 9); listed, 464.

Swallows (hirundo): birds of the family Hirundinidae; supposedly hibernating in lakes, 285.

Swallow, chimney. *See* Hirundo cerdo.

Swallow, house (hirundo pelasgia): Barn Swallow (*Hirundo rustica erythrogaster* Boddaert); migrations of, 287. *See also* Hirundo pelasgia.

Swallow, sea. *See* Sterna stolida.

Swamps, coastal; in the Carolinas and Georgia, 29.

Swan, wild. *See* Cygnus ferus.

Swanson & Co., Indian traders and merchants; their warehouses at Manchac, La., 428; took leave of, 437.

This firm is evidently identical with Swanson and M'Gillivray (*q.v.*).

Swanson and M'Gillivray ("M'Gillavry" or "M'Gillivary"): traders at Mobile, Ala.; their buildings, 404; specimens left in their care, 438.

Swash, at Long Bay, S.C.: Lewis's Swash (the present Singleton's

Swash), about 8 miles northeast of Myrtle Beach (Faden map of 1780; soil map of Horry County, 1918); crossed, 472.

Sweet Gum (Liquidambar ["Liquid-amber"] styraciflua): *L. styraciflua* L.; in Butler or adjacent county, Ala., 400. See also Liquidambar; Liquidambar styraciflua.

Sweet Water Brook (cf. Darlington, 1843: 61; Swanton, 1922: pl. 7): probably Culpeper Creek, in the vicinity of Knoxville, Crawford County, Ga., and tributary to Flint River (map of Crawford County, 1939); encamped by, 382. See Commentary for this page.

Swine: *Sus scrofa* L. var.; on Georgia coastal islands, 67; snout resembling that of Soft-shelled Turtle, 178; voice compared with that of Southern Bullfrog, 277; prey of Bears, 282. See also Pigs.

"Sylphium." See Silphium.

Syngenesia Poly[gamia] Aequalis ("Oqul.") Linn.: a group of plants in the Linnaean classification (*Syst. Veget.:* 586, 1774); 164.

Syringa: a genus of Oleaceae, comprising the lilacs; xvi.

Taensa, a bluff and settlement on the eastern channel of the Mobile River: apparently at or near the mouth of Hall's Creek, 4 miles north of Stockton, Ala. (*Crown Coll.*, ser. 3, *1:* 48, 1915; soil map of Baldwin County, 1912; Tensaw quadrangle); arrived at, 403, 405; described, 405; mentioned, 406; returned to, 411; journey up the river from, 411–413; arrived at, 440; Indian mounds ("mountains") at, 521–522.

Taensapaoa. See Tangipahoa.

Tahasse: an unidentified Cherokee town on Tennessee River; listed, 373.

Talahasochte (or "White King's town"): a former Seminole town on Suwannee River, probably at either New Clay Landing or Ross Landing, Levy County, Fla.; establishment of a trading-house at, 97; on old Spanish highway, 208; journey to, 215–251; trading path to, 217; an Indian in, 223; arrived at, 224; description of, 226–227; a trader at, 228, 232; stay at, 229; return to, 235; feast at, 235–236; council and treaty at, 237; departed from, 238; final visit to, 241; Indians of, 241; a family of, on a hunt, 244; a prince of, described, 244–245; listed [not on Flint River, as indicated here], 464.

"There seems to have been an error in the way in which the name Talahasochte was recorded. Talahasochee or Talahasochie, the expected form, would mean 'Little Oldtown,' containing Tallahassee, identical with the name of the Florida State capital, and the diminutive ending. At the present time there is a town of the same name among the Oklahoma Seminole which may be directly descended from the one visited by Bartram. How the 't' got smuggled into the name is the problem." (J.R.S.)

Apparently the same spelling appears on Romans' map in the *American Military Pocket Atlas* (1776). Thus Bartram did not originate this form.

Talbot ("Talbert") Island: on the northeastern coast of Florida, just south of Amelia Island; [incorrectly stated by Bartram to be] at the mouth of St. Mary's River, 26.

Talasse (or great Tallase) (properly Talasse or Tulsa): a former Upper Creek town on the east bank of Tallapoosa River, just above the mouth of Uphapee Creek, Macon County, Ala. (Taitt, map of 1772 [as "Great Pallassies"—error for "Great Tallassies"] and 1916: 502; soil map of Macon County, 1905; Swanton, 1922: 244, pl. 2); journey to, 396; listed, 462. *See also* Tallase.

Tallapoosa ("Talapoose" or "Tallapoose") or Oakfuske River: arising in northwestern Georgia and joining the Coosa in central Alabama to form the Alabama River; Talasse on, 396; width and depth, 397; confluence of, 398, 408; arrived at, 445; junction with Coosa, 447; journey up, 449; list of Creek towns on, 462–463; no Indian mounds on, 521.

Tallase: a former Cherokee town on Little Tennessee River, about Tallassee Ford, in Blount County, Tenn. (Hunter's map of 1730; Mooney, 1900: 533, pl. 3; Swanton, 1922: pl. 7; Loudon quadrangle); listed, 373. *See also* Talasse.

Tallow-nut, or Wild Lime: *Ximenia americana* L.; on St. John's River at Charlotia, Fla., 94; described, on the St. John's below Lake Dexter, 114–115.

"*Tallow Nut.* I cant find this singular shrub mentioned by any Author. I believe to be a West India plant [cf. Aiton, 1789, 2: 7] as well as of the Bahamas and Florida. It is a tender plant, often injured by the frost, about the mouth of S^t. Juan, but up the river southward grows in perfection, and makes a fine appearance when full of ripe fruit[.]" (Bartram to Muhlenberg, September 6, 1810; Muhlenberg Letters: 137.)

Tamahle (properly Tamali): a former Cherokee town on Little Tennessee River, about Tomotley Ford, a few miles above Tellico River, in Monroe County, Tenn. (Mooney, 1900: 534; Swanton, 1922: pl. 7 [no. 32]; Loudon quadrangle); listed, 374. Cf. Tomothle.

Tambour: used by Indians, 505; made by Indian men, 513.

Tammany, King: a chief of the Delaware Indians in the seventeenth and eighteenth centuries; 13.

Tanagra [cyanea]. *See* Linaria cyanea.

Tanase. *See* Tennessee.

Tangipahoa ("Taensapaoa") (River): a river of southern Mississippi and southeastern Louisiana, emptying into Lake Pontchartrain; described, 424, 425.

Tanners: using red bay for dyeing, 162; at Cross Creeks, N.C., 477.

Tannier. *See* Arum, esculent.

Tantalus, or tantali: either Wood Ibises (*Mycteria americana* L.) or White Ibises (*Eudocimus albus* [L.]); nesting at Watermelon? Pond, Alachua County, Fla., and cooked for supper, 249.

Tantalus. The Wood Pelicane. *See* Tantalus loculator.

Probably Bartram did not intend to include under this heading on p. 293 more than the first five species listed.

T[antalus] alber, the white Spanish curlew: White Ibis (*Eudocimus albus* [L.]), adult; listed, 293. *See also* Curlews, Spanish; Tantalus fuscus.

Tantalus albus. *See* Curlews, Spanish.

T[antalus] fuscus, the dusky and white Spanish curlew (cf. Catesby, 1732, *1:* 83, pl. 83): White Ibis (*Eudocimus albus* [L.], immature; syn., Tantalus fuscus L.); listed, 293. *See also* Curlews, Spanish.

T[antalus] °Ichthyophagus, the gannet, perhaps little different from the Ibis: *nomen nudum*—Wood Ibis (*Mycteria americana* L.); listed, 293. *See also* Gannet.

Tantalus loculator, the wood pelican ("pelicane"): Wood Ibis (*Mycteria americana* L.; syn., *Tantalus loculator* L.); listed, 293. *See also* Pelican, solitary; Pelican, wood.

T[antalus] °pictus, (Ephouskyka Indian) the crying bird, beautifully speckled: Florida Limpkin (*Aramus guarauna pictus* [Bartram]) (cf. Harper, 1942d: 219) (fig. 15); listed, 293. *See also* Crying bird.

Tantalus °versicolor. *See* Curlews, Spanish.

Tap——y (or T——y), Mr.: John Adam Tapley (cf. Taitt, 1916: 509), a trader at Mucclasse, Ala.; caravan under direction of, 440; intercession for, 462. *See also* Trader, at Mucclasse, Ala.; Trader, principal.

Tar, iron pots for boiling, 419.

Tart[ar] Emet[ic], dose of, 411.

"Tatropha." *See* Jatropha.

[Tattooing], among Indians, 503.

Tavern; at Cross Creeks, N.C., 477.

Teal, blue winged. *See* Anas discors.

Teal, least green winged. *See* Anas migratoria.

Teal, painted summer: Wood Duck (*Aix sponsa* [L.]); at Lake Dexter, Fla., 118.

"Telea": either basswood (*Tilia* spp.) or wafer ash (*Ptelea trifoliata* L.); near Wayah Gap, N.C., 362; along Chattahoochee River, Ala., 394; in Lowndes or Butler Counties, 399; near The Rigolets, La., 421; along Iberville Canal, 427; along the Mississippi, 432; at White Cliffs, 436; along Cape Fear River, N.C., 474. *See also* Ptelea, Tilia.

Tellico: one of several former Cherokee towns of this name—perhaps in this case the one on Valley River, 5 miles above Murphy, in Cherokee County, N.C. (cf. "Little Telliquo" of Hunter's map of 1730; Mooney, 1900: 533; Nantahala quadrangle); listed, 373 (no. 11).

Tellico: one of several former Cherokee towns of this name—perhaps in this case the one on the site of Tellico Plains, Monroe County, Tenn. (cf. "Gt. Telliquo" of Hunter's map of 1730; Mooney, 1900: 533, pl. 3; "Gt. Tallico" of Swanton, 1922: pl. 7; Murphy quadrangle); listed, 373 (no. 17).

Tellowe: a former Cherokee town, located (if the spelling is a variant of "Talulu") on Tallulah or Tulula Creek, southeast of Robbinsville, Graham County, N.C. (Mooney, 1900: 533; Nantahala quadrangle); listed, 373.

Tempe, Vale of: a defile in Thessaly, Greece, between Mounts Olympus and Ossa; compared with Vale of Cowee, N.C., 354.

Temperate zone, plants of, xv, xvi.

Tempest, on Altamaha River, Ga., 51. *See also* Gale, Hurricane, Storm.

Temples, at Apalachean Old Fields, Fla., 233.

Tendrils of climbing plants, faculty of, xxi.

Tenements, at Cross Creeks, N.C., 477.

Tennessee ("Tanase") River: in the following cases, Little Tennessee River, which arises in northeastern Georgia, flows northwestward, and joins the Holston near Loudon, Tenn.; headwaters of, 345–349; in Vale of Cowee, 353, 355; the Jore a branch of, 360; Cowee near, 366.

Tennessee ("Tanase"), a large branch of: Nantahala River, N.C.; crossed, 364.

Tennessee ("Tanase") or Cherokee River: for the most part, Little Tennessee River; course of, 339; Cherokee towns on this river and its branches, 373–374.

[Tensaw] River: eastern channel of Mobile Delta, Ala.; voyage up, 405–411. *See also* Taensa.

Testudo naso cylindracea elongato, truncato. *See* Tortoise, great soft shelled.

Testudo *Polyphaemus. *See* Tortoise, great land.

Tetrao lagopus, the mountain cock, or grous (cf. Jefferson, 1782: 127; Wilson, 1811, *3:* 104; Coues, 1875: 349; Trumbull, 1888: 146): not *T. lagopus* L., but probably Heath Hen (*Tympanuchus cupido cupido* [L.]); listed, 290 *bis*. *See also* Tetrao urogallus.

Bartram uses three different technical names (*T. lagopus, T. tympanus,* and *T. urogallus*) for only two species. The first and third of these, being accompanied by identical common names, must be considered synonymous. Bartram supplies no characters in connection with any of these names. His contemporaries (John Bartram, Edwards, Jefferson, Barton, and Wilson) as well as subsequent authorities (Coues and Trumbull) are more or less at variance in the interpretation of these names, either technical or common. Under the circumstances it is perhaps better to follow John Bartram (in Edwards, 1758, *1:* 80) in applying the name "pheasant"—and therefore "Tetrao tympanus"—to the Ruffed Grouse; and to apply William Bartram's "T. lagopus" and "T. urogallus" to the Heath Hen. Our author himself was obviously lax in his nomenclature of the Tetraonidae.

The application of the names "mountain cock, or grous" may be gleaned from Doughtys' *Cabinet of Natural History and American Rural Sports* (*3:* 23, 1833): "Whenever you hear Sportsmen talk of Grouse shooting, they always allude to this bird" [the Heath Hen]. Its range includes "the Pocono and Broad Mountains, of Pennsylvania, and the whole range of high lands east of them to the river Delaware." The same paper states that the Ruffed Grouse "is usually called the Pheasant." On Long Island the Heath Hens "are known . . . emphatically by the name of Grouse" (Samuel L. Mitchill, in Wilson, 1811, *3:* 104).

Tetrao *minor sive coturnix, or partridge: not the Old World *Tetrao coturnix* L., but Eastern Bob-white (*Colinus virginianus virginianus* [L.]); resident in Pennsylvania, 286.

T[etrao] *minor, s[eu] coturnix, the quail or partridge: not the Old World *Tetrao coturnix* L., but Eastern Bob-white (*Colinus virginianus virginianus* [L.]); listed, 290 *bis*. *See also* Quail(s).

Tetrao *tympanus, or pheasant of Pennsylvania: *nomen nudum*— probably Eastern Ruffed Grouse (*Bonasa umbellus umbellus* [L.]); resident in Pennsylvania, 286; listed, 290 *bis*. *See also* Moor fowl, and discussion under Tetrao lagopus.

Tetrao urogallus, or mountain cock or grous: not the European *T. urogallus* L., but probably Heath Hen (*Tympanuchus cupido cupido* [L.]); resident in Pennsylvania, 286. *See also* Tetrao lagopus.

Thalame (properly thalamus): bridal chamber; of Creeks at Mucclasse, Ala., 446.

Thapsia (cf. Elliott, 1817, *1:* 359): meadow parsnip (*Thaspium* sp. or *Zizia* sp.); in Warren County, Ga., 379.

Theft, infamy as punishment for, 515.

Theobroma: a genus of Theobromaceae, comprising the cacao trees; in the tropics, xiv.

Thoulouse. *See* Fort Thoulouse.

Three Sisters, a public ferry on Savannah ("Savanna") River: doubtless identical with Two Sisters Ferry (now abandoned), 2 miles east of Clyo, Effingham County, Ga.; crossed river at, 309.

Thrush (turdus): in Bartram's usage, either a true thrush (some species of *Hylocichla*) or the Eastern Brown Thrasher (*Toxostoma rufum rufum* [L.]); affinity of Catbird with, 300; mentioned, 491.

Thrush, fox coloured: (t[urdus] rufus ["rufes"]): Eastern Brown Thrasher (*Toxostoma rufum rufum* [L.]); song of, 300.

Thrush, great or fox coloured: Eastern Brown Thrasher (*Toxostoma rufum rufum* [L.]); breeding range of, 301. *See also* Thrush, red; Turdus rufus.

Thrush, least golden crown. *See* Turdus minimus.

Thrush, less: perhaps Eastern Hermit Thrush (*Hylocichla guttata faxoni* Bangs and Penard); breeding range of, 301.

Thrush, little (t[urdus] minor) (cf. Edwards, 1760, 2: 183, 220, pl. 296; Gmelin, 1789: 809; Ridgway, 1907: 56, 65); in this case, probably Wood Thrush (*Hylocichla mustelina* [Gmelin]), although Bartram evidently did not clearly distinguish between it and the four other eastern thrushes of the genus *Hylocichla* (only one of these five appearing in the list on p. 290 *bis*); song, 300. *See also* Thrush, song; Thrush, wood; Turdus melodes.

Edwards received a Veery (*H. fuscescens fuscescens* [Stephens]) from Bartram, and described and figured it (1760, 2: 183, 220, pl. 296) as "Little Thrush"—"Turdus parvus."

Thrush, red (turdus rufus): Eastern Brown Thrasher (*Toxostoma rufum rufum* [L.]); song, xxxii. *See also* Thrush, fox coloured; Thrush, great or fox coloured; Turdus rufus.

Thrush, song or wood (turdus minor) (cf. Gmelin, 1789: 809): in this case, probably Wood Thrush (*Hylocichla mustelina* [Gmelin]); symphony, xxxii. *See also* Thrush, little; Thrush, wood; Turdus melodes.

Thrush, wood: *Hylocichla mustelina* (Gmelin); near Lake Lochloosa, Fla., 181. *See also* Thrush, little; Thrush, song; Turdus melodes.

Thunder; invoked by Long Warrior, 258–259.

Thymus: a genus of Labiatae, comprising the thymes; usefulness, xvii.

Tiber: an Italian river; 133.

Ticoloosa: a former Cherokee town at the site of the present Burning-town, Macon County, N.C. (Cowee quadrangle) (*Bur. Am. Ethnol. Bull., 30,* Pt. II: 750, 1910); listed, 373.

Tide; overflowing marshes, 69.

Tiger(s) (or "tyger[s]"): Cougar(s)—the Florida subspecies (*Felis concolor coryi* Bangs) in some or all of the following cases; on Colonel's Island, Ga., 7; hides traded by Seminoles, 211; in Baldwin or adjacent county, Ala., 412; skin of young one used for tobacco pouch at Otasse, Ala., 453.

This animal is still referred to as "Tiger" in southeastern Georgia.

Tigers ("tygers"), or Panther: in this case, probably Eastern Cougar (*Felis concolor couguar* Kerr); in middle region of Georgia, 46.

Tilia (or "Telia"): basswood (*Tilia* spp.); in lower Coastal Plain, 29; on St. John's River at Charlotia, Fla., 94; near Tuscawilla Lake, 183, 192–193; near Alachua Savanna, 187, 204; in Levy County, 221; near Three Sisters Ferry, S.C., 309; at Shell Bluff, Ga., 318; near Oconee Station, Oconee County, S.C., 335. *See also* "Telea."

Till[andsia] *lingulata, or Wild Pine: *T. utriculata* L. (cf. Merrill, 1945: 32); described, on St. Simon's Island, Ga., 61–62.

Renamed *T. bartrami* by Nuttall (1822: 292), who apparently overlooked the prior *T. bartramii* of Elliott (1817, *1:* 379).

Tillandsia *monostachya (cf. Elliott, 1817, *1:* 379): *nomen nudum* (Merrill, 1945: 35)—a wild pine, probably *T. tenuifolia* L.; on St. Simon's Island, Ga., 61.

Le Conte (1826: 130) is presumably in error in considering this the *T. utriculata* of Linnaeus.

Tillandsia (or "Tillandsea" or "Tillandsi" or "Tillansia") *usneascites (or "ulnea-adscites" or "ulneadscites"): Spanish moss (*T. usneoides* L.); described, on St. John's River, in vicinity of East Tocoi, St. John's County, Fla., iv, 87; at Lake Dexter, 154; in Montgomery County, Ala., 397. *See also* Moss, long.

Timber; production on lower Savannah River, Ga., 312–313.

Tinsel, on breech-clout, 502.

Titmouse, black cap. *See* Parus Europeus.

Titmouse, bluish grey crested. *See* Parus cristatus.

Titmouse, little chocolate breast. *See* Parus peregrinus.

Titmouse, yellow hooded. *See* Luscinia.

Toads. *See* Frogs, high land.

Tobacco: *Nicotiana tabacum* L.; brought by Indians from Cuba, 227;

in feast at Talahasochte, Fla., 236; at Palatka, 304; at Watauga, N.C., 351; presented to Indian, 362; near The Rigolets, La., 422; at Otasse, Ala., 450, 453; smoked by Indians, 491; Indians puffing smoke toward the sun, 497; presented to blind old chief, 499.

Tobacco (Nicotiana): *Nicotiana tabacum* L.; at Palatka, Fla., 93.

Tobesofkee ("Tabosachte" or "Tobosochte") Creeks, Great and Little (cf. Taitt's map of 1772; Early's map of 1818): the present Tobesofkee and Echeconnee Creeks, tributaries of the Ocmulgee west of Macon, Ga.; crossing, viii, 382.

Toco (misprinted "Joco"): a former Cherokee town on Little Tennessee River, about the mouth of Toco Creek, Monroe County, Tenn. (Hunter's map of 1751; Mooney, 1900: 514, pl. 3; Swanton, 1922: pl. 7, as "Toqua"; Loudon quadrangle); listed, 373.

Tolo-chlucco: the Creek name for *Magnolia grandiflora*, 232.

Tomahawk(s): Seminoles armed with, 261; for each ranger at Fort James, Ga., 324; kegs of spirits broken open with, 493; old Indians erroneously said to be dispatched with, 498; buried with the dead among Muscogulges, 516.

Tombigbee or Chickasaw ("Tombigbe or Chicasaw") River: a large river of northeastern Mississippi and southwestern Alabama, joining the Alabama River at the head of Mobile Delta; an arm of the Mobile, 408; voyage on, 408–411; confluence with the Alabama, 443.

Tomocos. *See* Indians—Tomocos.

Tomoko River: the present Tomoko Creek in Volusia County, Fla., entering Halifax River near its north end; 144.

Tomothle (properly Tamali): a former Cherokee town on the Valley River, about the present Tomotla, Cherokee County, N.C. (Hunter's map of 1730; Mooney, 1900: 534; Swanton, 1922: pl. 7 [no. 40]; Nantahala quadrangle); listed, 373. Cf. Tamahle.

Torch: Passenger Pigeons taken by torch light, 469.

Tortoise, fresh-water, large, with high shell: Florida Terrapin (*Pseudemys floridana floridana* [Le Conte]); in Florida and Carolina, 281.

Tortoise, fresh-water, small, with slightly elevated shell: probably Chicken Turtle (*Deirochelys reticularia* [Latreille]); in Florida and Carolina, 281.

Tortoise, great land, called Gopher, Testudo *Polyphaemus: Gopher Turtle (*Gopherus polyphaemus* [Bartram]) (cf. Harper, 1940: 694–695) (fig. 5); south of Altamaha River, Ga., 18; south of Savannah River, 182; described, in southeastern Alachua County, Fla., 182–183.

Tortoise, great soft shelled (Testudo naso cylindraceo ["cylindracea"] elongato, truncato): Southern Soft-shelled Turtle (*Amyda ferox* [Schneider]) (cf. Harper, 1940: 717); described, at Cowpen Lake, Putnam County, Fla., 177–178, 2 pls. following p. 176.

Tortoise, small land: doubtless including both Florida Box Turtle (*Terrapene bauri* Taylor) and Carolina Box Turtle (*T. carolina* [L.]); in Florida and Carolina, 281.

The reference to Edwards is not exact; the account occurs in his *Natural History of Birds* (4: 205, pl. 205, 1751).

Tournefort ("Tourn."): Joseph Pitton de Tournefort (1656–1708), a French botanist; reference to, on plate facing p. 155.

Among his important works are *Elémens de botanique* (3 vols. 1694), *Institutiones rei herbariae* (3 vols. 1700), and *Relation d'un voyage du Levant* (2 vols. 1717).

Towhee ("towee") bird (fringilla erythrophthalma): in this case, White-eyed Towhee (*Pipilo erythrophthalmus alleni* Coues); between Rodman and Deep Creek, Putnam County, Fla., 172. See also Fringilla erythrophthalma.

Town(s): list of, in Cherokee nation, 373–374, and in Creek Confederacy, 462–464; cleaned at the busk, 509. See also Indian country [etc.].

Town house or rotunda, at ancient Apalachicola, Ala., 390. See also Council-house, Rotunda.

Trader: in this case, perhaps Job Wiggens; as a companion on St. John's River, 109–110.

Trader, at Coolome, Ala.: James Germany; 396–397. See also Germany, James.

Trader, at Cowee, N.C.: unidentified; excursion with, 354–358; owner of horses, 356; bargaining for strawberries, 358.

Trader, at Keowee, S.C.: perhaps D. Ho[l?]mes; account of local antiquities, 372. See also Ho[l?]mes, D.

Trader, at Mucclasse, Ala.: John Adam Tapley; conducting Bartram across Tallapoosa River at Savannuca, 446; house and stores at Mucclasse, 446; amorous intrigue, 447–449; taking leave of, 449; intercession for, 462; conducting Bartram to public square, 499; a Mustee in service of, 507. See also Tap——y, Mr.; Trader, principal, of Swanson and M'Gillivray.

Trader, at Spalding's Upper Store, Fla.: in this case, unidentified; relations with Seminoles, 111–113.

Mowat (1943: 26) is evidently in error in identifying this trader as Job Wiggens.

Trader, at Spalding's Upper Store, Fla.: in this case, Job Wiggens; prospering, 156.

Trader, at Talahasochte, Fla.: unidentified; dealing with Spanish trading vessels, 228; as companion on Suwannee River, 229–232.

Trader, chief: in the following cases, perhaps Job Wiggens; conferring with Cowkeeper at Cuscowilla, Fla., 185; trading company for Talahasochte under direction of, 215; conference with chiefs at Talahasochte, 228, 235, 237; guiding Bartram to the Alligator Hole, and describing an eruption there, 238–240; showing Bartram some barren plains near Suwannee River, 242–243. *See also* Interpreter; Trader; Trader, at Spalding's Upper Store; Trader, old; Wiggens, Job.

Trader, chief, at Apalachicola, Ala.: unidentified; accompanying Bartram to ancient Apalachicola town, 389–391.

Traders, Creek and Cherokee, their name for *Angelica lucida*, 45.

Traders, English, interceding with Creeks in behalf of Spanish prisoners, 488–489.

Trader(s), Indian: Mr. Kean formerly one, 98; joining Bartram's party at Flat Rock, Ga., 377; method of breaking horses, 377–378; Swanson & Co. as, 428.

Trader, old: perhaps Job Wiggens; as delegate to Indians at Cuscowilla, Fla., 170; on tour of Alachua Savanna with Bartram, 196–207. *See also* Interpreter; Trader; Trader, at Spalding's Upper Store; Wiggens, Job.

Trader, principal, of Swanson and M'Gillivray: John Adam Tapley; set off from Mobile with, 440. *See also* Tap——y, Mr.; Trader, at Mucclasse, Ala.

Traders: using the name "physic-nut," 41; escaping with their lives at Spalding's Upper Store, Fla., 63; unjust dealing with Indians, and depredations of latter upon traders, 79; secreted on Murphy's Island in St. John's River, 96; sailing up St. John's River to Spalding's Upper Store, 98; their information concerning Orange Lake, 181–182; in quest of game and horses on Alachua Savanna, 196–207; their name for a disease of cattle and horses, 207; horses to be purchased of, 215; their account of Suwannee River, 224–225; barter with Spaniards at Bay of Calos, 227; securing and breaking young horses, 248–249; securing waterfowl at Watermelon? Pond, 249; torturing an Alligator, 250; joining a bacchanalian party of Seminoles, 255; in conference with Seminoles at Spalding's Lower Store, 257; letters from George Galphin to traders in Indian towns, 314; debts of Creeks to, 324; letters from Alexander Cameron to traders in Cherokee nation, 328; houses at Seneca, S.C., 330; their account of former Cherokee population in Vale of Keowee, 332; relations with Indians, 353–354; advising against a journey to Overhill towns, 359; attending a congress at Seneca, S.C., 372; rendezvous at Flat Rock, Ga., 376; separating at Apalachicola, 395; chewing resin of *Silphium,* 399; information on honey bees, 413; setting off for Creek Nation, 438; manner of traveling, 440–441; bound from Creek Nation to Mobile, 441–442; their friendship for Bartram, 442; never attacked on the road by Indians, 442; exchanging horses with Bartram, 442–443; setting off from Tuckabatche, 447; at Otasse, 450; ignorance concerning purpose of pine pillar at Otasse, 456; setting off from Otasse, 457; crossing Ocmulgee River, 458, 459; their names for various Creek towns, 463–464; their account of Indian languages, 465–466; crossing the Susquehanna in Pennsylvania, 480; report on American aborigines, 483; allowance of liquors, · 492; carrying Jamaica spirits to Creek Nation, 493; testimony on putting to death of aged Indians, 499; calling Choctaws flat-heads, 517.

Traders, Overhill: those in Overhill towns of the Cherokees; departure of, 359.

Traders, white: relations with Seminole girls, 194–195; their accounts of Indians, 212–213; attending a festival at Cowee, N.C., 369; massacred at Apalachicola, Ala., 390–391 (*see* Commentary for these pages); Indians supplied by, 513; area called by them the chunk yard, 520.

Tradescantia: spiderwort (*Tradescantia* spp.); near Long Pond, Levy County, Fla., 248; along upper Savannah River, Ga., 321.

Trading company, [Spalding's], resumption of relations with Indians, 251.

Trading company to Choctaws, 506.

Trading-house(s); three to be established in Florida, 97; at Talahasochte, 226, 235; Fort Prince George, S.C., serving as a, 332; in Vale of Cowee, N.C., 349.

Trading-house: in the following cases, Spalding's Lower Store, at Stokes Landing on St. John's River, Putnam County, Fla.; arrived at, 96; band of Seminoles at, 255–263; fruit brought to, 303; returned to, 305.

Trading houses, Indian: in this case, Spalding's Lower and Upper Stores on St. John's River, Fla.; journey to, 73–74.

Trading-house, Indian, in the river St. Mary: at the present King's Ferry, Nassau County, Fla.; set off for, 16; course to, 21. *See also* Stores on the St. Mary's.

Trading house on the St. John's: in this case, Spalding's Lower Store, at Stokes Landing, Putnam County, Fla.; arrived at, 209. *See also* Stores, or lower store; Trading-house; Trading house, lower.

Trading house, lower (or Spalding's lower): Spalding's Lower Store on St. John's River at Stokes Landing, Putnam County, Fla.; specimens transported to, 156; arrived at, 169; journey from, to Suwannee River, 215–251; set off on return to, 248; return to, 251. *See also* Stores, or lower store; Trading-house; Trading house on the St. John's.

Trading path; from Augusta, Ga., to the Creek Nation, 54, 376; west of Alachua Savanna, Fla., 251; through Vale of Cowee, N.C., 348, 349; through Alabama to West Florida, 397.

Trading path, from the Overhills to Cowee, N.C.: probably the present road through Wayah Gap, between Aquone and Franklin, N.C., 360–366.

Trading post, Indian; Fort Moore, S.C., as, 316.

Traveller(s); attention of, to works of nature, xiii; at Cambelton, N.C., 478; public granary of Indians for accommodation of, 513.

Traveller(s), fellow; on St. John's River, Fla., 73; on Lake George, 107, 108, 109.

Treaty of Augusta, Ga. [in June 1773]: forthcoming, 9; negotiations and terms, 33–34; incident at, 485–486.

Treaty with Cherokees, forthcoming, 372.

Treaty with Creek Nation at Picolata, Fla., present at, 270. (Cf. J. Bartram, 1942: 35, 51, 77.)

Treaty at St. Augustine, Fla.: concluded, 96; ratified at Cuscowilla, 191.

Treaty at Talahasochte, Fla., terms of, 237–238.

Tree, corner, marked at confluence of "Little" (= Tugaloo) and "Savanna" (= Seneca) Rivers, Ga., 45.

Trees, petrified: at Silver Bluff, S.C., 314; along and near Willis Creek, Cumberland County, N.C., 477.

Trees and shrubs, curious: specimens obtained, 26.

Tree frogs: species of the family Hylidae; near Lake Lochloosa, Fla., 181. *See also* Frogs.

Trichechus manatus. *See* Manatee.

Trichomanes. *See* Felix scandens.

Trillium cernuum ("canuum" or "cesnum") (cf. Catesby, 1730, *1:* 45, pl. 45): nodding wake-robin (*T. cernuum* L.); along upper Savannah River, Ga., 321; at Falling Creek, Rabun County, 342.

Trillium sessile (cf. Catesby, 1730, *1:* 50, pl. 50): sessile-flowered wake-robin (*T. sessile* L.); along upper Savannah River, Ga., 321; at Falling Creek, Rabun County, 342.

Trings, little, of the sea shore. *See* Tringa parva.

Tring, red cootfooted. *See* Tringa rufa.

Tringa, black cap cootfooted. *See* Tringa vertice nigro.

T[ringa] cinerea, gutture albo, the white throated cootfooted tringa (cf. Edwards, 1750, *3:* 143, pl. 143, and 1751, *4:* 246, as "Cock Coot-footed Tringa" or "Tringa fuscus, *Canadensis*," etc.; Latham, 1787: 292): Northern Phalarope (*Lobipes lobatus* [L.]), in female breeding plumage; listed, 294.

T[ringa] fusca, the little brown or ash coloured pool snipe: un-determined—not *T. fusca* L.; listed, 294.

T[ringa] griseus ("griceus"), the little pond snipe: possibly Spotted Sandpiper (*Actitis macularia* [L.]) in immature or winter plumage —not *T. grisea* Gmelin; listed, 294.

T[ringa] maculata, the spotted tringa (cf. Edwards, 1760, *2:* 139, pl. 277, lower fig., and 219, as "spotted Tringa" or "Tringa macu-lata"): Spotted Sandpiper (*Actitis macularia* [L.]) in adult summer plumage; listed, 294.

The specimen forming the basis of Edwards' account was secured by Bartram near Philadelphia. *Tringa macularia* L., in turn, was based mainly upon Edwards. The symbol ¶ is here employed erroneously.

T[ringa] *parva, the little trings of the sea shore, called sand birds: *nomen nudum*—doubtless composite, including such species as Semipalmated Sandpiper (*Ereunetes pusillus* [L.]), Least Sand-piper (*Erolia minutilla* [Vieillot]), and Sanderling (*Crocethia alba* [Pallas]); listed, 294.

Tringa *rufa, the red cootfooted tring (cf. Edwards, 1750, *3:* 142, pl. 142, and 1751, *4:* 245, as "Red Coot-footed *Tringa*" or "Tringa rufra, *Canadensis*," etc.): *nomen nudum*—Red Phalarope (*Phala-ropus fulicarius* [L.]); listed, 294.

The words "tring" and "trings," offered as common names of *T. parva* and *T. rufa,* represent perhaps an unauthorized Anglicizing of the generic name *Tringa.*

It is amazing that Coues (1875: 355) overlooked Edwards' work and so failed to recognize Bartram's "cootfooted tringas" as phala-ropes. He probably took too seriously the erroneous symbol *. Two Linnaean species of phalaropes were based upon "Coot-footed Tringas" of Edwards.

Tringa, spotted. *See* Tringa maculata.

T[ringa] vertice nigro, black cap cootfooted tringa (cf. Edwards, 1743, *1:* 46, pl. 46, and 1747, *2:* 126, as "Coot-footed Tringa" or "Tringa, pedibus Fulicae"): Northern Phalarope (*Lobipes lobatus* [L.]) in winter plumage; listed, 294.

Tringa, white throated cootfooted. *See* Tringa cinerea.

Tripe soup, in banquet at Cuscowilla, Fla., 191.

Tripsacum: gama grass (*T. dactyloides* L.); along upper Savannah River, Ga., 321.

Triticum: a genus of Gramineae, comprising the wheats; usefulness, xvii.

Triticum Cereale: wheat (the common species of which is *T. aestivum* L.); in temperate zone, xv. *See also* Wheat.

The specific name is possibly an original proposal by Bartram, unless perchance he was aware of its introduction by Schrank in 1789.

Trochilus colubris, the humming bird (cf. Catesby, 1731, *1:* 65, pl. 65): Ruby-throated Hummingbird (*Archilochus colubris* [L.]); listed, 289 *bis*. *See also* Hummingbird.

Tropics; plants of the, xiv, xv.

Tropic bird. *See* Phaëthon aethereus.

Trout: Large-mouthed Bass (*Micropterus salmoides* [Lacepède]); method of fishing for, and description of, at Lake George, Fla., 108–109; some secured for supper, and great numbers devoured by Alligators, at Lake Dexter, 117–124; as provisions, 134; at Lake Dexter, 153; carried off by Wolf at Lake George, 158–159; at Salt Springs, 166, and relations with Alligator and Bream there, 168; at Cowpen Lake, Putnam County, 176; in Alachua Sink, 205; in Suwannee River, 228; in Blue Springs, Screven County, Ga., 461.

This species is still commonly called "Trout" in the Southeastern States.

Trout, salmon: Large-mouthed Bass (*Micropterus salmoides* [Lacepède]); caught by an Indian in the Broad River region, Ga., 44.

Trout, Sea- [seems to be a species of Cod]: probably one or more species of Weakfish (*Cynoscion*); about Georgia coastal islands, 67.

Tube-rose (Polyanthus tuberosa): tuberose (*Polianthes tuberosa* L.); in a garden on the Mississippi, 429.

Tuckabatche (or "Tuccabache" or "Tuccabatche"—properly Tukabahchee): a former Upper Creek town in southeastern Elmore County, Ala., on the west bank of Tallapoosa River on a point opposite the mouth of Uphapee Creek (Taitt, map of 1772, and 1916: 501; *Bur. Am. Ethnol. Bull., 30*, Pt. II: 833–834, 1910; soil map of Elmore County, 1911; Swanton, 1922: 279–281, pls. 7, 8, 9, as "Tickabale," "Tookaubatchee," etc.; Swanton, 1946: 197); traders setting off from, 447; visit to, 447; recrossed river at, 450; listed, 463.

Tucpauska (properly Tukpafka): a former Upper Creek town on the Chattahoochee in western Georgia, perhaps in vicinity of Hillabahatchee Creek, Heard County (Swanton, 1922: 249, 258, pl. 2); listed, 463.

Tugaloo ("Tugilo") River: on boundary between Georgia and South Carolina, joining the Seneca to form the Savannah; mentioned, 52, 316; confluence with the "Keowe" (= Seneca), 328; Cherokee towns on, 374; Indian territory on, 485.

Tugaloo ("Tugilo"), the main branch of: Chattooga River, forming the northernmost part of the boundary between Georgia and South Carolina; crossed, 338.

Tugaloo ("Tugilo"): a former Cherokee town on Tugaloo River at junction of Toccoa Creek, in Habersham County, Ga. (Hunter's map of 1730; Mouzon's map of 1775; Mooney, 1900: 516; Walhalla quadrangle); listed, 374.

Tulip tree. *See* Liriodendron.

Tulipa: a genus of Liliaceae, comprising the tulips; elegance, xviii.

Tupelo ("Tupilo"): *Nyssa* sp.; formerly growing where salt marshes are, 69. *See also* Nyssa.

Turdus. *See* Thrush.

T[urdus] *melodes, the wood thrush: *nomen nudum*—Wood Thrush (*Hylocichla mustelina* [Gmelin]); listed, 290 *bis*. *See also* Thrush, little; Thrush, song; Thrush, wood.

Turdus migratorius, the fieldfare, or robin redbreast (cf. Catesby, 1730? *1*: 29, pl. 29): Eastern Robin (*Turdus migratorius migratorius* L.); listed, 290 *bis*. *See also* Field fare, Robins, Robin redbreast.

T[urdus] *minimus, vertice aurio, the least golden crown thrush (cf. Edwards, 1758, *1*: 91, pl. 252, lower fig., and 1760, *2*: 218): Eastern Oven-bird (*Seiurus aurocapillus aurocapillus* [L.]); listed, 290 *bis*.
      Edwards received a specimen from Bartram, and his description became the basis for *Motacilla aurocapilla* L.

Turdus minor. *See* Thrush, little; Thrush, song or wood.

T[urdus] polyglottos, the mocking bird: Eastern Mockingbird (*Mimus polyglottos polyglottos* [L.]); listed, 290 *bis*. *See also* Mock-bird.

T[urdus] rufus, the great, or fox coloured thrush (cf. Catesby, 1730? *1*: 28, pl. 28): Eastern Brown Thrasher (*Toxostoma rufum rufum* [L.]); listed, 290 *bis*. *See also* Thrush, fox coloured; Thrush, red.

Turkeys ("turkies"): Wild Turkeys (*Meleagris gallopavo* L. subspp.); prey of Wildcat, 282.

Turkey(s) (or "turkies"): in the following cases, Eastern Wild Turkey(s) (*Meleagris gallopavo americana* Bartram; syn., *M. g. silvestris* Vieillot) (cf. Harper, 1942d: 216); south of Altamaha River, Ga., 20; near mouth of Tugaloo River, 45; near Cowee, N.C., 356; in paintings at Otasse, Ala., 455.

Turkey(s) (or "turkies"): in the following cases, Florida Wild Turkey(s) (*Meleagris gallopavo osceola* Scott); on lower St. John's River, Fla., 75; on Drayton's Island, 103; at Lake George, 109–110; near Lake Beresford, 146; at Cowpen Lake, Putnam County, 179; at or near Alachua Savanna, 188, 196, 199, 201; in Suwannee River region, 235; in repast at Talahasochte, 241.

Turkey, wild: in this case, Eastern Wild Turkey (*Meleagris gallopavo americana* Bartram; syn., *M. g. silvestris* Vieillot); description of domesticated bird in McIntosh County, Ga., 14. *See also* Meleagris Americanus.

Turkey, wild (Meleagris *occidentalis): an invalid name applied to the Florida Wild Turkey (*Meleagris gallopavo osceola* Scott) (Harper, 1942d: 216); on lower St. John's River, Fla., 83–84.

Turnbull, [Dr. Andrew]; establishing a colony at New Smyrna, Fla., 144.

Turnbull "collected a colony from various parts of the Levant,— from Greece, from Southern Italy, and from the Minorcan Archipelago—and established his head quarters at New Smyrna. The heartless cruelty with which he treated these poor people, their birth-place and their fate, as well as the fact that from them most of the present inhabitants of St. Augustine receive their language, their character, and the general name of Minorcans, have from time to time attracted attention to their history." (Brinton, 1859: 58.) See also Romans (1776: 268–272), Vignoles (1823: 72), J. L. Williams (1837: 188–190), Fairbanks (1871: 216, 220–222), Schoepf (1911, 2: 233–236), Miss Doggett (1919), and Mowat (1943: 71–72).

Turnstone. *See* Morinella Americana.

Turpentine, resin of *Silphium* tasting like, 399.

Turtle, sea: undetermined; Soft-shelled Turtle resembling, 177.

Turtle dove. *See* Dove, turtle.

Tuskegee ("Tuskege"): a former Cherokee town on Little Tennessee River, just above the junction of Tellico River, in Monroe County, Tenn. (Mooney, 1900: 534, pl. 3; Loudon quadrangle); listed, 374.

Tyger(s). *See* Tiger(s).

Uchee ("Uche") town: a former town of the Uchee (or Yuchi) Indians on the west bank of Chattahoochee River just below the mouth of Uchee Creek, Russell County, Ala. (Early's map of 1818; Swanton, 1922: 309, pl. 2, as "Yuchi [3b]"; Columbus quadrangle); visited and described, 388–389; listed, 464.

Ufale (properly Eufaula), lower: a former Upper Creek town on the

west bank of Tallapoosa River, at or near Robinson Ferry, Tallapoosa County, Ala. (Taitt, map of 1772 [at the point erroneously
marked "Oakfuskee"], and 1916: 528; soil map of Tallapoosa County,
1912; Swanton, 1922: 261, pl. 2, as "Eufaula [3]"); listed, 462.

Ufale (properly Eufaula), upper: a former Upper Creek town on
Talladega Creek, a few miles south of the present Talladega, Ala.
(Swanton, 1922: 261, pl. 2, as "Eufaula [2]"; Talladega quad-
rangle); listed (as on Tallapoosa River), 462.
   Hawkins (in Swanton, 1922: 261) states that the site is 15 miles
up the creek (from Coosa River).

Ulmus (or "Ulmns"): elm (*Ulmus* spp.); of Virginia and Pennsylvania,
xvi; in lower Coastal Plain, 29; on St. John's River, Fla., below
Palatka, 84, and at Charlotia, 94; at Shell Bluff, Ga., 318; near
Oconee Station, Oconee County, S.C., 335; near Wayah Gap, N.C.,
362; along Chattahoochee River, Ala., 394; in Lowndes or Butler
Counties, 399; on Amite River, La., 425, 426; along Cape Fear
River, N.C., 474. *See also* Elm(s).

Ulmus campestris: not the European *U. campestris* L., but probably
white elm (*U. americana* L.); near Three Sisters Ferry, S.C., 309;
along Chattahoochee River, Ala., 393.

Ulmus *suberifera (or "suberifer" or "subifer"): *nomen nudum*
(Merrill, 1945: 35)—doubtless winged elm (*U. alata* Michx.); on
St. John's River above Lake Dexter, Fla., 130–131; near Three
Sisters Ferry, S.C., 309; along Chattahoochee River, Ala., 393.

Ulmus *sylvatica: *nomen nudum* (Merrill, 1945: 35)—perhaps white
elm (*U. americana* L.) or—in Florida—the closely related Florida
elm (*U. floridana* Chapm.); near Little River, Ga., 37; on St. John's
River above Lake Dexter, Fla., 130; near Alachua Savanna, 187;
along upper Savanna River, Ga., 320.

Umbrella, formed by leaves of *Magnolia auriculata*, 340.

Undertakers, among the Choctaws, 516.

Urtica: nettle (*Urtica* or a related genus); near Lake Lochloosa, Fla.,
181.

Usseta (properly Kasihta): a former Lower Creek town on the east
bank of Chattahoochee River in Chattahoochee County, Ga., below
the mouth of Upatoi Creek (Columbus quadrangle); crossed river
at, 457; listed, 463. *See also* Commentary for p. 389.
   According to Early's map of 1818 and to Hawkins (cf. Swanton,
1922: 222–223, pl. 2), the main Kasihta town seems to have been
only a couple of miles below Upatoi Creek. But the "Usseta" of
Bartram must have been approximately opposite Chehaw, and
therefore about 7 miles farther to the southeast. Perhaps it was one

of the branch villages of the main Kasihta town. On the other hand, Dr. Swanton suggests that Bartram may have actually meant Osochi ("Hooseche") instead of Kasihta ("Usseta").

Utensils, domestic (or household); purchased by Seminoles, 212; old exchanged for new at the busk, 509.

Utinas. *See* Indians—Utinas.

Uvularia: bellwort (*Uvularia* sp.); at Falling Creek, Rabun County, Ga., 342.

Vaccinium (or Vaccinium varietas): blueberry or related genus (*Vaccinium, Gaylussacia,* etc.); on Colonel's Island, Ga., 6; west of Spalding's Lower Store, Putnam County, Fla., 171; near Orange Lake, 181.

Vegetables, manner of receiving nourishment, xix–xx. *See also* Plants.

Vegetables, esculent: Suwannee River region suitable for, 234.

Vegetable productions, observations on those of southeastern Georgia, 26.

Vegetation, effect of sand and clay soils on, 23.

Venison: at home of Donald McIntosh, 13; brought in by hunters near mouth of Tugaloo River, Ga., 45; in repast on St. Simon's Island, 61, at Cuscowilla, Fla., 186, at Talahasochte, 241, and at Watauga, N.C., 351; sought on St. Simon's Island, 63; breakfasting on, 349. *See also* Buck, Deer, Roebuck.

Venus: sacrifices to, 255; young woman in Georgia as, 313.

Vera Cruz, Mexico, inland navigation to, 68.

Verbena: a genus of Verbenaceae, comprising the vervains; near Lake Lochloosa, Fla., 180.

Verbena °corymbosa: *nomen nudum* (Merrill, 1945: 35)—a vervain (*Verbena* sp.); at Lake Dexter, Fla., 155; west of Deep Creek, Putnam County, 173.

"Sept. 2nd 1805 W. Bartram informed me to-day that his Verbena corymbosa is a species distinct from any of our Pennsylvania kinds. It (he says) is called in South Carolina 'Mrs. Bee's Flower' see his Travels, p. 155, 173." (B. S. Barton, MS, Delafield Coll.)

Verbena, new species of, with blue flowers: perhaps V. *rigida* (L.) Spreng.; described, at Baton Rouge, La., 436.

"The verbena suggests *Verbena rigida,* a perennial species which is very common here and on the Plains" (Clair A. Brown, *in litt.,* July 24, 1941).

"This plant forms large, spreading patches of brilliant purple along roadsides and in waste-places in Louisiana and Texas" (Small, 1933: 1138).

Verbesina: a genus of Compositae, comprising the crown-beards; along upper Savannah River, Ga., 321.

Vermilion; Indians painted with, 503.

Vessel(s): boats of various descriptions, in Bartram's usage varying from canoe to schooner, etc.; embarked on at Charleston S.C., 4; set sail from St. Simon's Island, Ga., 63; anchoring by Cumberland Island, 63; chest forwarded in, 64; returning to Frederica, 64; Georgia coastal islands open to incursions of enemy vessels, 67; equipment of, on St. John's River, Fla., 74; damaged by wind, 74; on lower St. John's, 75–77; repaired by carpenters, 76; on St. John's below Lake George, 98; on Lake George, 101, 157; on upper St. John's, 114–115; repairs to, 155; embarked on, 156; creaking compared with that of Sandhill Cranes in flight, 221; Spanish trading vessels supplying goods at Talahasochte, 228; from St. Augustine, 270; at Spalding's Lower Store, 304, 305; sailed on, from Broughton Island to Sunbury, Ga., 306–307; size of vessels navigating Savannah River, 317; on Iberville Canal, La., 427; rivers navigable for, in Alabama, 447. *See also* Bark(s), Boat(s), Canoe(s).

Viaticum: provisions for a journey (Webster); 344.

Viburnum (or "Vibernum"): a genus of Caprifoliaceae, comprising the arrow-woods; in Lime-Sink Region, 31; along upper Savannah River, Ga.–S.C., 327; near Wayah Gap, N.C., 362.

Viburnum *Canadense: *nomen nudum* (Merrill, 1945: 35)—arrow-wood (*Viburnum* sp.); pleasing figure, xviii.

Viburnum dentatum: southern arrow-wood (*V. dentatum* L.); on Colonel's Island, Ga., 6; along upper Savannah River, 321.

Viburnum prunifolium: in this case, probably southern black haw (*V. rufidulum* Raf.) rather than *V. prunifolium* L.; on Colonel's Island, Ga., 6.

Vicia ("Vitia"): a genus of Leguminosae, comprising the vetches; near Lake Lochloosa, Fla., 181.

Vicia ("vitia") sativa. *See* Peas.

Village, Indian. *See* Indian country [etc.].

Vine, arborescent aromatic: undetermined; described, at Baton Rouge, La., 436.

    "*Anonimos volubilis* a vast oromatic vine mounts to the tops of Tall Trees, Near Manchac on Misisipi; leaves large oblong & placed oppositely" (Bartram to Muhlenberg, September 6, 1810; Muhlenberg Letters: 137).

    "I have not been able to find the aromatic vine that fits Bartram's statements" (Clair A. Brown, *in litt.*, July 24, 1941).

It was apparently the supple jack (*Berchemia scandens* [Hill] K. Koch), despite the discrepancy in the "opposite leaves" (Joseph Ewan, oral communication, 1952).

Vines (Vitis vinifera): the wine grape of Europe (*V. vinifera* L.); soil adapted for, 337. *See also* Vitis vinifera.

Vinegar, oranges as substitute for, 124.

Vineyard, on Savannah River, S.C., 375.

Viola: a genus of Violaceae, comprising the violets; at Lake Dexter, Fla., 155; west of Deep Creek, Putnam County, 173; near Lake Lochloosa, 181; in Levy County, 224; at Falling Creek, Rabun County, Ga., 342. *See also* Violets.

Violets: *Viola* spp.; about St. Mary's River, Ga.–Fla., 24.

Viper (or "bastard rattle snake"): Ground Rattler (*Sistrurus miliarius* [Linné] subspp.); account of, 274–275. *See also* Rattlesnake, bastard.

Vipers, two or three varieties of: in this case, probably Hog-nosed Snakes (*Heterodon* spp.); in Florida and Carolina, 276.

Viper tribe; Cottonmouth Moccasins of that tribe, 273.

Virginia; various trees of, xvi; name of a plant in, 45; inland navigation from, to Mississippi, 68; Blue Jay of, 172; size of animals in, 216; China brier in, 241; Wampum Snake in, 273; Bullfrog of, 277; bats in, 283; abundance of birds in, 286, 287; birds of, 288–302; plants common in, 362; tribes formerly inhabiting, 466; passage through, 479; citizens of, at Augusta, Ga., 486.

Virginians; Cherokees ill-treated by, 331; skirmishes with Overhill Indians, 359.

"Vitia." *See* Peas, Vicia.

Vitis: a genus of Vitaceae, comprising the grapes; faculty of tendrils, xxi.

Vitis *Allobrogica: *nomen nudum* (Merrill, 1945: 35)—a grape (*Vitis* sp.); proposed culture in Georgia, 460.

Vitis *campestris. *See* Grape vines (Vitis campestris).

Vitis *Corinthiaca: *nomen nudum* (Merrill, 1945: 35)—a grape (*Vitis* sp.); proposed culture in Georgia, 460.

Vitis labrusca: in these cases, not *V. labrusca* L., but perhaps redshank grape (*V. rufotomentosa* Small) (cf. Bailey, 1934: 185, 202); on St. John's River above Lake Dexter, Fla., 136; near Alachua Savanna, 187, 198.

Vitis vinifera: the wine grape of Europe (*V. vinifera* L.); in temperate zone, xv; usefulness, xvii; proposed culture in Georgia, 460. *See also* Vines (Vitis vinifera).

Vitis vulpina: in this case, not *V. vulpina* L., but perhaps bullace (*V.*

munsoniana Simpson); on St. John's River above Lake Dexter, Fla.,
136. Cf. *V. taurina* of Bartram (1803: 22)—apparently a composite
of *V. rotundifolia* Michx. and *V. munsoniana* Simpson.

Vultur *atratus, black vulture, or carrion crow: Black Vulture
(*Coragyps atratus* [Bartram]) (cf. Harper, 1942*d:* 212); listed, 289.
See also Vulture, coped.

Vultur aura, the turkey-buzzard (cf. Linnaeus, 1758, *1:* 86): Turkey
Vulture (*Cathartes aura septentrionalis* Wied); listed, 289. *See also*
Buzzard, turkey.

Vultur *sacra, the white tailed vulture: King Vulture (*Sarcoramphus
papa* [L.]) (cf. Harper, 1936); listed, 289. *See also* Eagle, white;
Vulture, painted.

Vultures: perhaps including both Turkey Vulture (*Cathartes aura
septentrionalis* Wied) and Black Vulture (*Coragyps atratus* [Bar-
tram]); at Cowpen Lake, Putnam County, Fla., 179; on Alachua
Savanna, 199, 201.

Vulture, black. *See* Vultur atratus.

Vulture, coped, or carrion crow: Black Vulture (*Coragyps atratus*
[Bartram]) (cf. Harper, 1942*d:* 212); described, from Florida, 152.
See also Vultur atratus.

    The type locality has been restricted to the St. John's River just
above Lake Dexter.

    The term "coped" (i.e. provided with a cope) may refer to the
"ruff . . . in which he can conceal his head and neck" (cf. the
"Coped Black Vulture" of Edwards, 1760, *2:* 171, pl. 290).

Vulture, painted, Vultur *sacra: King Vulture (*Sarcoramphus papa*
[L.]) (cf. Harper, 1936); described, from Florida, 150–152. *See also*
Eagle, white; Vultur sacra.

Vulture, white tailed. *See* Vultur sacra.

Waccamaw ("Wackamaw" or "Wakamaw") Lake. *See* Lake Waccamaw.

Waccamaw ("Wakamaw") River: arising in Lake Waccamaw, Columbus County, N.C., and discharging into Winyah Bay, S.C.; course,
473.

Waggons, commerce by, at Cambelton, N.C., 478.

Wagtail, water. *See* Motacilla fluviatilis.

Waistcoat, worn by Indian women, 503.

Wallet, provisions in, 361.

Walnut, Black: *Juglans nigra* L.; at Silver Bluff, S.C., 315; on Oconee
River, Ga., 379; in Butler or adjacent county, Ala., 400. *See also*
Juglans nigra.

Wampum: shell beads; wampum collar among Alachua Indians, 186; pipe adorned with, 351; Cherokee youths ornamented with, 370; as head ornament among Indians, 502.

War(s): causes of, among Indians, 391–392, and among various nations, 392–393; deliberations on, 496; a principal employment of Indian men, 513.

Warehouses: on Iberville Canal, La., 427; at Manchac, 428.

Warriors: at feast in Talahasochte, Fla., 236; a party of, at Long Pond, Levy County, 244; of the Lower Creeks, assembling at Coweta town, Ala., 389. See also Gun-men or warriors, Long Warrior.

Watauga ("Whatoga"): a former Cherokee town on Little Tennessee River, at mouth of Watauga Creek, Macon County, N.C. (Hunter's map of 1730; Romans' map of 1776; Mooney, 1900: 546, pl. 3; Swanton, 1922: pl. 7; Cowee quadrangle); visited and described, 350–352; hospitality of chief of, 350–352; listed, 373.

Various maps show the location on different sides of the river.

Waters; subterranean, in Florida, 225–226.

Water oak (or Water-Oak). See Oak, Water- .

Waterfall, unparalleled, in Vale of Cowee: Estatoah Falls, in extreme northern Rabun County, Ga. (Walhalla quadrangle); described, 347.

Water fowl, nesting at Watermelon? Pond, Alachua County, Fla., 249.

Water-grass: probably maiden-cane (*Panicum hemitomon* Schult.); on Alachua Savanna, Fla., 208.

Water-hen, squealing: perhaps Florida Gallinule (*Gallinula chloropus cachinnans* Bangs); at Salt Springs, Fla., 160.

Watermelons ("Water mellons"): *Citrullus vulgaris* Schrad.; feast of, at Palatka, Fla., 303. See also Citruel, Cucurbita citrullus, Melons.

Wax: traded by Seminoles, 212; *Myrica inodora* producing wax for candles, 406.

Wax tree: *Myrica inodora* Bartram so called by French in Alabama, 405.

Weasel: Alabama Weasel (*Mustela frenata olivacea* Howell), at least for the most part; in Florida and Carolina, 281.

Weddings, among Indians, 504. See also Marriage ceremonies, Nuptials.

Wells, Doctor: proprietor of plantations near Augusta, Ga.; visited, 460.

Humphrey Wells, surgeon, probably came from Maryland in 1773. His lands lay on Rae's Creek and on Kinnon's Creek, the latter rising in Quaker Spring, Columbia County, and flowing southeast into Rae's Creek, Richmond County. Quaker Spring is 8–9 miles from the center of Augusta. (Information supplied by Charles G. Cordle from *Historical Collections of the Georgia Chapters Daughters of the American Revolution*, 2, 1929.) Dr. Wells was probably one of the "citizens of Maryland" referred to by Bartram on p. 486.

West Florida. *See* Florida, West.

West Indies (or West India islands): Spaniards in, 88; Suwannee River region conveniently situated for West-India trade, 235; timber on Savannah River for, 312; navigation from Flint River to, 384; Scotch grass introduced from 430.

Whale: species undetermined; in the Atlantic, 3.

Whatoga. *See* Watauga.

Wheat: *Triticum* (the common species being *T. aestivum* L.); on Savannah River, S.C., 375; along Cape Fear River, N.C., 474. *See also* Triticum Cereale.

Wheelrights, at Cross Creeks, N.C., 477.

Whip(s), for horses, of cowskin, 440, 441.

Whip-poor-will(s): in Bartram's usage, apparently any one of the following three birds—Chuck-will's-widow (*Caprimulgus carolinensis* Gmelin), Eastern Whip-poor-will (*Caprimulgus vociferus vociferus* Wilson), and Nighthawk (*Chordeiles minor* [Forster] subspp.); on Altamaha River, Ga., 51; at Keowee, S.C., 331; near Clayton, Ga., 344. *See also* Caprimulgus, Night hawk.

By referring to "the night hawk or whip-poor-will" (pp. 154, 292), Bartram indicated that he did not distinguish between these two species; and in one place (p. 154) he applied the name "whip-poor-will" to the Chuck-will's-widow. Years later he was still confused, as shown by a quotation from one of his manuscripts (Barton, 1799*b*: 208).

Whip-poor-will, Caprimulgus rufus called chuck-will's-widow: not *C. rufus* Boddaert, but Chuck-will's-widow (*Caprimulgus carolinensis* Gmelin); at Lake Dexter, Fla., 154. *See also* Caprimulgus lucifugus.

Whites: trade with, and encroachments on, the Seminoles, 212, 214; esteem for the chief of Watauga, N.C., 352; Overhill Indians in ill humor with, 359. *See also* White inhabitants, White man, White people.

White Captain: a Seminole chief at Spalding's Upper Store, Fla.; relations with a white trader, 111–112.

White cliffs, now called Brown's cliffs (cf. Broutin's map of 1731, in Thomassy, 1860, map following p. 226, as "les Ecores blancs"; Lyell, 1849, 2: 137–142; *Crown Coll.*, ser. 3, *1:* 49, 1915; Bayou Sara quadrangle): on east bank of the Mississippi in the vicinity of the present Port Hudson, in East Baton Rouge Parish, La.; a plantation near, 430–431; visited and described, 435–436.

White hunters, visiting Okefinokee Swamp, Ga., 26.

White inhabitants: disturbances between those of East Florida and Lower Creeks, 78; *Angelica lucida* esteemed by, 327.

White King: an Indian chief at Talahasochte, Fla.; hunting, 226; audience and treaty with, 229; feast given by, 235–236; appearance and character of, 237; cordiality to Bartram, 237–238; final entertainment by, 241–242.

White King's town. *See* Talahasochte.

White man: a Seminole's threat to kill, 22; Turkeys called white man's dish, 241; union with a Creek woman, 440; bearing news of a Choctaw attack, 445–446. *See also* Whites, White inhabitants, White people.

White people: Cherokees on bad terms with, 55; no settlements about Mount Royal, Fla., in 1765, 99; relations with Creeks, 210; at feast in Talahasochte, 236; amity of Indians at Talahasochte with, 237, 241; settlements of, 281; Oconee town, Ga., in disagreeable proximity to, 380; murdered at Bay of Apalachee, Fla., 438; in ceremony in rotunda at Otasse, Ala., 451–453; example set to Indians, 490; conduct compared with that of Indians, 491–493; liquor prohibition in treaties with, 492; their names for high priests, 497; their goods introduced among the Creeks, 500; agriculture of Choctaws compared with that of, 517. *See also* Whites, White inhabitants, White man.

White Plains: in vicinity of Plains, half a dozen miles east of Port Hudson, East Baton Rouge Parish, La. (Bayou Sara quadrangle); visited and described, 431–432.

"The Plains is an isolated prairie, surrounded and intersected by timber, approximately 6–8 miles long, with an average width of two miles, perhaps three or four in the widest part. It is in the vicinity of Plains, La." (Clair A. Brown, *in litt.,* July 24, 1941.)

White Root. *See* Angelica lucida.

Whitfield, Mr.: chief of the caravan bound for West Florida; 375.

Whiting: one or more species of *Menticirrhus* or *Umbrula;* about Georgia coastal islands, 67.

Whittumke (properly Wetumpka or Witumpka): a former Upper Creek town on Tallapoosa River 1 mile east-southeast from the former Coosada, and about 3 miles south-southwest from the present Wetumpka, Elmore County, Ala. (Taitt, map of 1772, and 1916: 536–537; Wetumpka quadrangle); listed, 463.

Whoop: in ball-play dance of the Cherokees, 371; by trader driving horses, 440.

Wiccakaw (properly Wakokai): a former Upper Creek town on a branch (Jack's Creek?) of Hatchet Creek, Coosa County, Ala. (Taitt, map of 1772, and 1916: 534–535; *Bur. Am. Ethnol. Bull., 30,* Pt. II: 896, 1910; Swanton, 1922: 263–264, pls. 2, 7); listed, 463.

Widgeon. *See* Rallus Virginianus.

Wiggens, Job: a trader and interpreter, and companion to Bartram in his Florida travels; bid adieu to, 156. *See also* Interpreter; Trader; Trader, at Spalding's Upper Store; Trader, chief; Trader, old.

Perhaps the same individual is referred to in Michaux's journal for April 30 and May 14, 1788 (1889: 35, 38), as "M. Wigin or "Sʳ Wigins." He then had a dwelling on the St. John's, apparently at Rollestown or vicinity.

Wigwam, 90.

Wild-cat(s) (or "wild cat[s]"): Florida Wildcat(s) (*Lynx rufus floridanus* Rafinesque), at least for the most part; on Colonel's Island, Ga., 7; on Drayton's Island, Fla., 103; pulling to pieces a nest of Florida Wood Rat, 125; skin used for tobacco pouch at Otasse, Ala., 453.

Wild cats (Felis cauda truncata): in this case, probably Eastern Wildcats (*Lynx rufus rufus* [Schreber]); in middle region of Georgia, 46.

Wild-cats, felis cauda truncata, (lynx): in this case, Florida Wildcats (*Lynx rufus floridanus* Rafinesque); account of, 282.

Wild cat (lynx): in this case, Florida Wildcat (*Lynx rufus floridanus* Rafinesque); stalking Turkeys near Lake George, Fla., 110.

Wild fowl: various species of ducks, geese, ibises, cranes, etc.; at Lake Beresford, Fla., and vicinity, 144; at Tuscawilla Lake, 193; on the Mississippi near Anchor, La., 433.

Wild lime or Tallow nut. *See* Tallow-nut, or Wild Lime.

Will willet. *See* Hematopus ostrealegus.

Willets: either Eastern or Western Willets (*Catoptrophorus semipalmatus semipalmatus* [Gmelin] or *C. s. inornatus* [Brewster]); procured near Amelia Island, Fla., 70.

Wilmington, N.C.; commerce between Cambelton and, 478.

Winds, disseminating seeds of plants, xxiii.

Windows, isinglass suitable for, 364.

Wine, *Vitis vinifera* for, 460.

Winyah ("Winyaw") Bay: on coast of South Carolina, at Georgetown; crossed, 471; Waccamaw River discharging into, 473.

Wolf (or wolves): in the following cases, Florida Wolf (*Canis niger*

niger [Bartram]) (cf. Harper, 1942c); on Colonel's Island, Ga., 7; on Drayton's Island, Fla., 103; carrying off fish at Lake George, 158–159; hides traded by Seminoles, 212; wolf of Florida compared with black dog, 222; account of, 282; litter of young ones in Montgomery County, Ala., 398; in Baldwin or adjacent county, 412; in paintings at Otasse, 455. *See also* Wolves (lupus niger).

Wolves: in this case, perhaps Eastern Wolves (*Canis lupus lycaon* Schreber) (cf. Goldman, 1944: figs. 14, 15); in middle region of Georgia, 46.

Wolves (lupus *niger): Florida Wolves (*Canis niger niger* [Bartram]) (cf. Harper, 1942c); described, on Alachua Savanna, Fla., 199, 201; compared with dog, and with wolves of Canada and Pennsylvania, 199.

Wolf Island: a coastal island of Georgia, situated between Sapelo and St. Simon's Islands; at mouth of Altamaha River, 53.

Woodcock (scolopax): American Woodcock (*Philohela minor* [Gmelin]); nuptial flight at Macon, Ga., 459. *See also* Scolopax Americana rufa.

Woodcock, great red. *See* Scolopax Americana rufa.

Woodpeckers. *See* Picus.

Woodpecker, gold winged. *See* Picus auratus.

Woodpecker, greatest crested, having a white back. *See* Picus principalis.

Woodpecker, great red crested black. *See* Picus pileatus.

Woodpecker, hairy, speckled and crested. *See* Picus villosus.

Woodpecker, least spotted. *See* Picus pubescens.

Woodpecker, red bellied. *See* Picus Carolinus.

Woodpecker, red headed. *See* Picus erythrocephalus.

Woodpecker, yellow bellied. *See* Picus varius.

Wood-pelican. *See* Pelican, wood.

Wool, dyed with red bay, 162.

Worm(s): Glass Snake compared with, 195; Four-lined Chicken Snake innocent as, 276.

Wreck, at Perdido River, Ala.–Fla., 413, 414.

Wren, golden crown. *See* Regulus cristatus.

Wren, great, of Carolina. *See* Motacilla Caroliniana.

Wren, green. *See* Muscicapa cantatrix.

Wren, house. *See* Motacilla domestica.

Wren, little bluish grey. *See* Regulus griseus.

Wren, marsh. *See* Motacilla palustris, Regulus atrofuscus minor.

Wren, olive coloured yellow throated. *See* Regulus peregrinus.

Wren, ruby crown. *See* Regulus cristatus alter, etc.

Wright, Sir James: governor of Georgia; conference with, 4; a letter from, 15; surveyors appointed by, 34; Wrightsborough named in honor of, 35.

James Wright (1716–1785) was appointed lieutenant-governor in 1760, and governor in 1762. After opposing the efforts of the Revolutionists, he was arrested in 1776, but escaped. After the recapture of Savannah by the British in 1778, he returned from England and attempted to institute severe measures against the Revolutionary party. He abandoned the province in 1782.

Jones (1891: vii–viii) pays tribute to Governor Wright as an earnest and conscientious official, remarking that "he secured the respect and affection of his people. Although differing from many of the inhabitants upon the political questions which were then dividing the public mind, he never suffered himself to be betrayed into acts of violence or of revenge."

For further biographical information, see White (1854: 188–196), Stevens (1859, 2: 17 ff.), and Harden (1913, 1: 145–238).

Wright, [Sam.]: captain of Charleston Packet; 1.

Wrightsborough: a Quaker settlement on Wrightsborough Creek, in the present McDuffie County, Ga. (W. Bartram, 1943: fig. 6); arrived at, 35; history and environs of, 35–36; leave, 36; on a branch of Little River, 321.

Wright's ferry on the Susquehanna: at the present Wrightsville and Columbia, Pa.; arrived at, 480.

Yam, (ordinary): presumably Dioscorea sp.; Dioscorea bulbifera tasting like, 439; eddo tasting like, 469.

Yamases. See Indians—Yamasees.

Yaupon ("yapon"). See Cassine yapon.

Yawl: a ship's small boat; on Amite River, La., 437; lost on Lake Pontchartrain, 437.

Yellow bird, blue winged. See Parus aureus.

Yellow rump (parus *cedrus): Eastern Myrtle Warbler (Dendroica coronata coronata [L.]), in winter plumage; feeding on cedar berries, 298. See also Parus cedrus.

Yucca gloriosa: presumably Spanish bayonet (Y. gloriosa L.); at Lake George, Fla., 157. See also Palmetto royal.

Zamia: coontie (Z. integrifolia Ait.); v; near Long Pond, Levy County, Fla., 248.

I have found no basis for Small's indication (1921: 128, 129, 136) that this species was discovered by "John" Bartram. According to its describer, Aiton (1789, *3:* 478), it was introduced into England in 1768 by John Ellis. *Zamia* is mentioned in letters from Dr. Alexander Garden, of Charleston, to Ellis (February 2, 1767, and December 10, 1772) and to Linnaeus (June 20, 1771, and May 15, 1773) (J. E. Smith, 1821, *1:* 336–342, 552, 593).

Zamia pumila: coontie (in this case, not *Z. pumila* L., but *Z. integrifolia* Ait.); described, near Salt Springs, Fla., 162.

Zanthoxylum ("Zanthoxilon") (cf. Catesby, 1730? *1:* 26, pl. 26): Hercules' club, or toothache tree (probably *Xanthoxylum clava-herculis* L.); at Lake George, Fla., 107, 157; on St. John's River at Huntoon Island, 140; at Lake Dexter, 154; near Salt Springs, 164; between Orange and Tuscawilla Lakes, 183; near Alachua Savanna, 202, 204; in Levy County, 221, 223, 243; Painted Bunting among, 299; at Lake Pontchartrain, La., 423.

Zanthoxylum ("Zanthoxilon" or "Zanthoxilum") clava Herculis: Hercules' club, or toothache tree (*Xanthoxylum clava-herculis* L.) (cf. Nuttall, 1854, *3:* 10); on lower St. John's River, Fla., 88; near Alachua Savanna, 187; at The Rigolets, La., 421.

Zea: maize, or Indian corn (*Z. mays* L.); in temperate zone, xv; usefulness, xvii; near Alachua Savanna, Fla., 193; along Cape Fear River, N.C., 474. *See also* Corn.

Zizyphus *scandens: probably rattan vine (*Berchemia scandens* [Hill] K. Koch); on lower St. John's River, Fla., 87. *See also* Rhamnus volubilis.

Zoologist(s); information useful to, xiv; birds mentioned by, 284; their errors in classifying certain birds, 302.

Zubley's Ferry: on Savannah River, about 20 (not "fifty") miles above Savannah and 4 or 5 miles northwest of Hardeeville, S.C. (Campbell's map of 1780; Faden's map of 1780); crossed, 470.

REFERENCES

Literature (including manuscripts)

Adair, James
  1775. *The history of the American Indians.* London: [12] + 464, 1 map.
Aiton, William
  1789. *Hortus Kewensis; or a catalogue of the plants cultivated in the Royal Botanic Garden at Kew.* Vol. 2. London: 1–460, 4 pl.
Allen, Elsa G.
  1937. New light on Mark Catesby. *Auk 54*(3): 349–363, 1 pl.
  1951. The history of American ornithology before Audubon. *Trans. Am. Philos. Soc. 41*(3): 387–591, 55 fig.
Allen, J. A.
  1871. On the mammals and winter birds of East Florida. *Bull. Mus. Comp. Zoöl. 2*(3): 161–450, 5 pl.
  1876a. The availability of certain Bartramian names in ornithology. *Am. Naturalist 10*(1): 21–29.
  1876b. Bartramian names again: an explanation. *Am. Naturalist 10*(3): 176–177.
Amherst, Sir Jeffery
  MSS. Amherst Papers, 1758–1764. 8 vols. William L. Clements Library, Ann Arbor, Mich.
Arthur, John Preston
  1914. *Western North Carolina. A history (from 1730 to 1913).* Raleigh: 3–710, 13 pl.
Audubon, John James
  1827. Observations on the natural history of the Alligator. *Edinburgh New Philos. Jour. 2:* 270–280.
  1835. *Ornithological biography.* Vol. 3. Edinburgh: xvi + 638.
Audubon, John James, and John Bachman
  1846. *The viviparous quadrupeds of North America.* Vol. 1. New York: xv + 389.
Bailey, L. H.
  1934. The species of grapes peculiar to North America. *Gentes Herbarum 3*(4): 149–244, 35 fig.
  1935. The standard cyclopedia of horticulture. Vol. 1. New York: xxiv + 1200, 39 pl., 1470 fig.
Bangs, Outram
  1898. The land mammals of peninsular Florida and the coast region of

Georgia. *Proc. Boston Soc. Nat. Hist.* 28(7): 157–235, 8 fig., 1 map.

Barbour, Thomas

1940. Pine snakes, black and brown. *Copeia* 1940(3): 205.

Barnhart, John Hendley

1923. [John Ellis.] *Jour. New York Bot. Garden 24:* 147.

1932. Bartram bibliography. *Bartonia,* spl. issue: 51–67, "1931."

1933. Franklinia alatamaha. Addisonia *18*(1): 13–14, 1 pl.

Barton, Benjamin Smith

MSS. Benjamin Smith Barton Papers (15 letters, 2 MSS., 2 broadsides, and 1 printed paper). Am. Philos. Soc.

MSS. Letters, notes, and drawings. Delafield Coll., New York.

1799a. *Fragments of the natural history of Pennsylvania.* Part I. Philadelphia: xviii + 24.

1799b. Observations and conjectures concerning certain articles which were taken out of an ancient tumulus, or grave, at Cincinnati, in the county of Hamilton, and territory of the United-States, north-west of the River Ohio. *Trans. Am. Philos. Soc. 4:* 181–215.

Barton, William P. C.

1818. *Vegetable materia medica of the United States; or medical botany.* Vol. 2. Philadelphia: i–xvi, 9–243, 26 pl.

Bartram, John

1751. *Observations on the inhabitants, climate, soil, rivers, productions, animals, and other matters worthy of notice. Made by Mr. John Bartram, in his travels from Pensilvania to Onondago, Oswego and the lake Ontario, in Canada. To which is annex'd, a curious account of the cataracts at Niagara. By Mr. Peter Kalm, a Swedish gentleman who travelled there.* London: i–viii, 9–94, 1 pl.

1766. *A journal, kept by John Bartram of Philadelphia, Botanist to His Majesty for the Floridas; upon a journey from St. Augustine up the River St. John's.* In: William Stork, *An account of East-Florida,* 2nd ed. London: viii (introduction by Stork) + 67.

1767. An extract of Mr Wm. [sic] Bartram's observations in a journey up the River Savannah in Georgia, with his son, on discoveries. *Gentleman's Mag.* 37, April: 166–169.

1769. *A journal, kept by John Bartram of Philadelphia, Botanist to His Majesty for the Floridas; upon a journey from St. Augustine up the River St. John's, as far as the lakes.* In: William Stork, *A description of East-Florida,* 3rd ed. London: xii (introduction by Stork) + 36.

1942. Diary of a journey through the Carolinas, Georgia, and Florida from July 1, 1765, to April 10, 1766. (Annotated by Francis Harper.) *Trans. Am. Philos. Soc. 33,* pt. I: iv + 120, frontisp., 35 fig., 8 maps.

Bartram, John, and William Bartram

MSS. Bartram Papers. Vols. *1–4.* Hist. Soc. Pennsylvania. (About 415 items, mainly correspondence of John Bartram.)

Bartram, William

MSS. Bartram folder (several letters to and from William Bartram). New-York Hist. Soc.

MSS. Portions of original draft for the *Travels:* voyage on the St. John's; journey to Alachua Savanna; journey through the Vale of Cowee. Hist. Soc. Pennsylvania.

1791. *Travels through North & South Carolina, Georgia, East & West Florida, the Cherokee country, the extensive territories of the Muscogulges, or Creek Confederacy, and the country of the Chactaws; containing an account of the soil and natural productions of those regions, together with observations on the manners of the Indians,* 1st ed. Philadelphia: xxxiv + 522, 8 pl., 1 map. (Page numbers 265 and 266 are inadvertently omitted, and page numbers 289 and 290 are duplicated. The plates are not inserted uniformly in the same positions in all copies of the book.)

1792. *Travels* etc., first London ed. London: xxiv + 520, 8 pl., 1 map.

1793*a. Travels* etc. Dublin: xxiv + 520 + [12], 8 pl., 1 map.

1793*b. Reisen durch Nord- und Süd-Karolina, Georgien, Ost- und West-Florida, das Gebiet der Tscherokesen, Krihks und Tschaktahs, nebst umständlichen Nachrichten von den Einwohnern, dem Boden und den Naturproduckten dieser wenig bekannten grossen Länder.* Aus dem englischen. Mit erläuternden Anmerkungen von E. A. W. Zimmermann. In der Vossischen Buchhandlung, Berlin: xxvi + 501 [commonly cited as 469 by reason of a mistake in numbering the last five pages], 8 pl.

1793*c. Reisen* etc. (Magazin von merkwürdigen neuen Reisebeschreibungen, Vols. *19–20.*) Aus dem englischen. Mit erläuternden Anmerkungen von E. A. W. Zimmermann. 16 mo. F. U. Schrämbl, Vienna: *1:* xl + [8] + 404, 5 pl.; 2: ii + [12] + 427, 2 pl.

1794*a. Travels* etc., second London ed. London: xxiv + 520 + [7], 8 pl., 1 map.

1794*b. Reizen door Noord- en Zuid-Carolina, Georgia, Oost- en West-Florida; de Landen der Cherokees, der Muscogulges, of het Creek bondgenootschap en het Land der Chactaws.* Uit het Engelsch vertaald, door J. D. Pasteur. Haarlem: xxviii + 695, 1 fig., 1 map. (Citation from a 1-volume copy in Library of Congress; apparently different from a set at Am. Philos. Soc., cited in the following entry.)

1794, 1795, 1797? *Reizen* etc. Haarlem: [*1*]: xxvi + [2] + 226, 1 fig., 1 map, 1794; 2: [2], 227–550, 1795; 3 (missing).

1803. Account of the species, hybrids, and other varieties of the vine of North-America. *Med. Repository,* hexade 2, *1*(1): 19–24.

1804. Some account of the late Mr. John Bartram, of Pennsylvania. *Philadelphia Med. and Phys. Jour. 1,* pt. I: 115–124.

1853. Observations on the Creek and Cherokee Indians. 1789. (With prefatory and supplementary notes by E. G. Squier.) *Trans. Am. Ethnol. Soc. 3*, pt. I: 1–81, 7 fig.

1943. Travels in Georgia and Florida, 1773–74: a report to Dr. John Fothergill. (Annotated by Francis Harper.) *Trans. Am. Philos. Soc. 33*, pt. II: 121–242, frontisp., 47 fig., 5 maps.

Bartram, Williams [*sic*]

1799 (An VII). *Voyage dans les parties sud de l'Amérique septentrionale; savoir: les Carolines septentrionale et méridionale, la Georgie, les Florides orientale et occidentale, le pays des Cherokees, le vaste territoire des Muscogulges ou de la confédération Creek, et le pays des Chactaws; contenant des détails sur le sol et les productions naturelles de ces contrées, et des observations sur les moeurs des Sauvages qui les habitent.* Imprimé à Philadelphie, en 1791, et à Londres, en 1792, et trad. de l'angl. par P. V. Benoist. (Libraires Carteret et Brosson; Dugour et Durand.) Paris: *1*: 1–457 + [1], 3 pl.; *2*: 1–436 + [1], 1 pl., 1 map.

1801 (An IX). *Voyage* etc., second Paris ed. (Libraire Maradan.) Paris: *1*: 1–457 + [1], 3 pl., 1 map; *2*: 1–436 + [1], 1 pl. (Apparently identical with the 1799 edition, except for a different bookseller, and the transfer of the map from Vol. 2 to Vol. *1*.)

Bent, Arthur Cleveland

1922. Life histories of North American petrels and pelicans and their allies. *U. S. Nat. Mus. Bull.* 121: xii + 343, 69 pl.

Blatchley, W. S.

1902. *A nature wooing at Ormond by the sea.* Indianapolis: 1–245, 12 pl., 63 fig., 1 map.

Boyd, Mark F.

1938. A map of the road from Pensacola to St. Augustine, 1778. *Florida Hist. Quarterly 17*(1): 15–23, 9 pl.

1951. Florida aflame. *Florida Hist. Quarterly 30*(1): 1–115, 2 pl., 1 fig., 1 map.

Brannon, Peter A.

1939. The route of William Bartram. *Montgomery* [Ala.] *Advertiser*, June 25.

Brett-James, Norman G.

[1925.] *The Life of Peter Collinson.* London: 1–292, 18 pl.

Brinton, Daniel G.

1859. *Notes on the Floridian peninsula, its literary history, Indian tribes and antiquities.* Philadelphia: i–viii, 13–202.

Brown, John P.

1938. *Old frontiers.* Kingsport, Tenn.: xi + 570, 18 pl., 9 maps.

1957. Attakulla, Little Owl's father. *Flower and Feather 13*(1): 5–9.

Bryant, Henry

1859. [Birds of East Florida.] *Proc. Boston Soc. Nat. Hist. 7*: 5–21.

Buckley, S. B.
   1859. Mountains of North Carolina and Tennessee. *Am. Jour. Sci. and Arts*, ser. 2, 27: 286–294.
Carlyle, Thomas, and Ralph Waldo Emerson
   1883. *The correspondence of Thomas Carlyle and Ralph Waldo Emerson, 1834–1872*. Vol. 2. Boston: xiii + 383.
Carr, Archie Fairly, Jr.
   1940. A contribution to the herpetology of Florida. *Univ. Florida Publ., Biol. Sci. Ser.* 3(1): [1] + 118.
Carroll, B. R.
   1836. *Historical collections of South Carolina*. New-York: *1*: i–lxxx, 9–533, 1 map; *2*: i–v, 7–576.
Cassin, John
   1853–1855 ("1856"). *Illustrations of the birds of California, Texas, Oregon, British and Russian America. . . . And a general synopsis of North American ornithology*. Philadelphia: viii + 298, 50 pl. (Issued in 10 parts, 1853 to 1855; collected in one volume in 1856, with preface, contents, and index.)
Castiglioni, Luigi
   1790. *Viaggio negli Stati Uniti dell'America Settentrionale, fatto negli anni 1785, 1786, e 1787*. Milan: *1*: xii + 403, 4 pl., 4 maps; *2*: vi + 402, 5 pl., 1 map, 3 folding tables.
Cate, Margaret Davis
   1930. *Our to-days and yesterdays. A story of Brunswick and the coastal islands*. Revised ed. Brunswick, Ga.: xi + 302, illus.
   1943. Fort Frederica and the Battle of Bloody Marsh. *Georgia Hist. Quarterly* 27(2): 111–174.
Cate, Margaret Davis; Dolores B. Colquitt; and Mary Wylie McCarty
   [1940.] *Flags of five nations*. Sea Island, Ga.: 1–78, 4 fig., 1 map.
Catesby, Mark
   1730?–1748. *The natural history of Carolina, Florida and the Bahama Islands*. London: *1*: [i–iv] (title-p. and dedication), v–xii (preface), 1–100, 100 pl., 1 map, 1730?–1732; *2*: [i–vi] (title-p., dedication, and list of encouragers), 1–100, i–xliv, [6] (index to both vols.), 100 pl., 1734–1747; appendix: 1–21, 20 pl., 1748.
Chatelain, Verne E.
   1941. The defenses of Spanish Florida, 1565 to 1763. *Carnegie Inst. Washington Publ.* 511: vii + 192, 4 pl., 22 maps.
Cheston, Emily Read
   1953. *John Bartram, 1699–1777, his garden and his house. William Bartram, 1739–1823*. 2d ed. Philadelphia: 1–36, 7 fig.
Coker, W. C.
   1928. The distribution of Venus's fly trap (*Dionaea muscipula*). *Jour. Elisha Mitchell Sci. Soc.* 43(3/4): 221–228, 1 map.

Coker, William Chambers, and Henry Roland Totten
  1937. *Trees of the Southeastern States.* 2d ed. Chapel Hill: vii + 417, 4 pl., numerous fig.
Collins, Zaccheus
  MSS. Collins Correspondence (approximately 296 letters). Acad. Nat. Sci. Philadelphia.
Collinson, Peter
  MSS. Smaller volume. Linnean Soc. London.
Conrad, T. A.
  1834a. Observations on the Tertiary and more recent formations of a portion of the Southern States. *Jour. Acad. Nat. Sci. Philadelphia 7,* pt. I: 116–129.
  1834b. Descriptions of new Tertiary fossils from the Southern States. *Jour. Acad. Nat. Sci. Philadelphia 7,* pt. I: 130–157.
  1846. Observations on the geology of a part of East Florida, with a catalogue of Recent shells of the coast. *Am. Jour. Sci. and Arts,* ser. 2, 2: 36–48.
Cooke, C. Wythe
  1939. Scenery of Florida interpreted by a geologist. *Florida Dept. Conservation, Geol. Bull.* 17: 1–118, 48 fig., 10 maps.
Cooper, J. G.
  1861. On the forests and trees of Florida and the Mexican boundary. *Ann. Rept. Smithsonian Inst.* 1860: 439–442.
Cooper, Lane
  1905. Bartram redivivus? *Nation 80:* 152.
Corse, Carita Doggett
  1928. Denys Rolle and Rollestown. A pioneer for Utopia. *Florida Hist. Quarterly 7:* 115–134.
  1939. De Brahm's report on East Florida, 1773. *Florida Hist. Quarterly* 17(3): 219–226.
Coues, Elliott
  1875. Fasti ornithologiae redivivi.—No. 1, Bartram's 'Travels.' *Proc. Acad. Nat. Sci. Philadelphia 27:* 338–358.
  1876. Reply to Mr. J. A. Allen's "Availability of certain Bartramian names in ornithology." *Am. Naturalist 10*(2): 98–102.
  1878. Bibliographical appendix. List of faunal publications relating to North American ornithology. Pp. 567–784 in: *Birds of the Colorado Valley.* Washington.
  1884. *Key to North American birds.* 2d ed. Boston: xxx + 863, 1 pl., 561 fig.
Croom, H. B.
  1848. Observations on the genus *Sarracenia;* with an account of a new species. *Annals Lyceum Nat. Hist. New-York 4:* 95–104, 1 pl.

674   REFERENCES

Curtiss, A. H.
> 1879. A visit to the shell islands of Florida. *Bot. Gazette* 4(2): 117–119; (3): 132–137; (5): 154–158.

Cutler, William Parker, and Julia Perkins Cutler
> 1888. Life, journals and correspondence of Rev. Manasseh Cutler, LL.D. Vol. *1.* Cincinnati: xii + 524, 2 pl.

Darlington, William
> MSS. Papers, 19 vols. New-York Hist. Soc.
> 1843. *Reliquiae Baldwinianae: selections from the correspondence of the late William Baldwin, M.D.* Philadelphia: 1–347, 1 pl.
> 1849. *Memorials of John Bartram and Humphry Marshall. With notices of their botanical contemporaries.* Philadelphia: i–xv, 17–585, 3 pl., 2 fig.

Daudin, F. M.
> 1800. *Histoire naturelle des Quadrupèdes ovipares.* Livraisons 1 and 2. Paris: 24 unnumbered pp., 12 pl.
> 1802. *Histoire naturelle des Rainettes, des Grenouilles et des Crapauds.* Paris: 4to, 1–108, 38 pl.; folio, 1–71, 38 pl.
> 1803. *Histoire naturelle, générale et particulière des Reptiles.* Vol. *8.* Paris: 1–439, 8 pl.

De Brahm, John Gerar William
> 1849. *History of the Province of Georgia: with maps of original surveys.* Wormsloe, Ga.: 1–55, 6 pl.

Delafield Collection
> MSS. Consisting largely of papers of Benjamin Smith Barton and William Bartram and of drawings by the latter. New York.

De Renne Library
> 1931. *Catalogue of the Wymberley Jones De Renne Georgia Library at Wormsloe, Isle of Hope near Savannah, Georgia.* Vol. *3.* Wormsloe: v–xi, 897–1396, 1 pl.

Doggett, Carita
> 1919. *Dr. Turnbull and the New Smyrna Colony of Florida.* Jacksonville: viii, 11–212, illus.

Drayton, John
> 1821. *Memoirs of the American Revolution.* Charleston: *1:* xxvii + 430, 1 pl., 1 map; *2:* 1–399, 2 maps.

Dreer (Francis) Collection
> MSS., chiefly letters. Scientists, Vol. *1.* Hist. Soc. Pennsylvania. (About 124 items.)

Dunlap, William
> 1832. *A history of the American theatre.* New-York: viii + 420.

Durand, Elias
> 1860. Biographical notice of the late Thomas Nuttall. *Proc. Am. Philos. Soc.* 7: 297–315.

Earnest, Ernest

1940. *John and William Bartram.* Philadelphia: vii + 187, 2 pl.

Edwards, George

1743–1751. *A natural history of birds.* London: *1:* [4] + xxiv + 52, 53 pl., 1743; *2:* i–viii, 53–128, 53 pl., 1 map, 1747; *3:* [4], 106–157, 52 pl., 1750; *4:* [8], 158–248, 53 pl., 1751.

1758–1764. *Gleanings of natural history.* London: *1:* 1–108, 51 pl., 1758; *2:* [11], i–xxxv, 109–220, 50 pl., 1760; *3:* i–vii, 221–347, 52 pl., 1764.

Elliott, Stephen

1816–1824. *A sketch of the botany of South-Carolina and Georgia.* Charleston: *1:* 1–606, 1816–1821; *2:* viii + 743, 12 pl., 1821–1824.

Ettinger, Amos Aschbach

1936. *James Edward Oglethorpe, imperial idealist.* Oxford: xv + 348, 7 pl., 1 map.

Exell, A. W.

1927. William Bartram and the genus *Asimina* in North America. *Jour. Botany 65:* 65–70, 1 pl.

Fagin, N. Bryllion

1933. *William Bartram, interpreter of the American landscape.* Baltimore: ix + 229.

Fairbanks, George R.

1858. *The history and antiquities of the city of St. Augustine, Florida.* New York: 1–200, 7 pl.

1871. *History of Florida.* Philadelphia: i–xii, 13–350.

Fernald, Merritt Lyndon

1940. A century of additions to the flora of Virginia. First and second installments. *Rhodora 42*(502): 355–416, 1 pl., 26 maps; (503): 419–498, 23 pl., 4 fig.

1944. Overlooked species, transfers and novelties in the flora of eastern North America. *Rhodora 46*(541): 1–21, 5 pl.; (542): 32–57, 5 pl.

1946. Identifications and reidentifications of North American plants. [First installment.] *Rhodora 48:* 137–162, 16 pl.

1950. *Gray's manual of botany,* 8th ed. New York: lxiv + 1632, 1806 fig.

Fernald, Merritt Lyndon, and Alfred Charles Kinsey

1943. *Edible wild plants of eastern North America.* Cornwall-on-Hudson: xiv + 452, 25 pl., 128 fig.

Fitzpatrick, John C.

1925. *The diaries of George Washington, 1749–1799.* Vol. 3. Boston and New York: 1–458, 1 pl.

1939. *The writings of George Washington from the original manuscript sources, 1745–1799.* Vol. 31. Washington: xli + 571, 1 pl.

Flagg, Wilson

1872. *The woods and by-ways of New England.* Boston: xvi + 442, 22 pl.

Forbes, James Grant
    1821. *Sketches, historical and topographical, of the Floridas; more particularly of East Florida.* New-York: i–viii, 9–226, 1 map.

Fox, R. Hingston
    1919. *Dr. John Fothergill and his friends.* London: xxiv + 434, 13 pl.

Franklin, Benjamin
    MSS. Franklin Papers, Vol. *41* (204 letters, chiefly to Franklin). Am. Philos. Soc.

Gatschet, Albert S.
    1884. *A migration legend of the Creek Indians, with a linguistic, historic and ethnographic introduction.* Philadelphia: i–vii, 9–251.
    1888. Tchikilli's Kasi'hta legend in the Creek and Hitchiti languages, with a critical commentary and full glossaries to both texts. *Trans. Acad. Sci. St. Louis 5:* 33–239, 1 pl.

Gmelin, Jo. Frid.
    1788–1789. *Caroli a Linné, Systema naturae.* Leipzig: *1*, pt. I: [12], 1–500, 1788; *1*, pt. II: [2], 501–1032, 1789; *1*, pt. III: [2], 1033–1516, 1789.

Goff, John H.
    1954? Some major Indian trading paths across the Georgia Piedmont. *Georgia Mineral News Letter 6*(4): 122–131, 10 fig., 1 map.

Goggin, John M.
    1949. A Florida Indian trading post, circa 1763–1784. *Southern Indian Studies 1*(2): 35–38.

Goldman, Edward A.
    1944. *Classification of wolves.* Part II of: Stanley P. Young and Edward A. Goldman, *The wolves of North America:* 387–636, 44 pl., 1 map. Washington.

Goode, G. Brown
    1888. The beginnings of American science. The third century. *Proc. Biol. Soc. Washington 4:* 9–94.

Goodrich, Calvin
    1930. *Unio spinosa* Lea. *Nautilus 43*(4): 140.

Gowanloch, James N.
    1945. Economic importance of the water hyacinth, *Eichhornia crassipes,* in management of water areas. *Trans. Tenth N. Am. Wildlife Conf.:* 339–345.

Grant, Verne
    1949. Arthur Dobbs (1750) and the discovery of the pollination of flowers by insects. *Bull. Torrey Botanical Club 76*(3): 217–219.

Gratz, Simon
    MSS. Gratz Collections (several hundred thousand items, chiefly letters) Hist. Soc. Pennsylvania.

Gray, Asa
    1841. Notes of a botanical excursion to the mountains of North Carolina,

&c.; with some remarks on the botany of the higher Alleghany Mountains. *Am. Jour. Sci. and Arts* 42(1): 1–49.

Greene, Earl R.; William W. Griffin; Eugene P. Odum; Herbert L. Stoddard; and Ivan R. Tomkins

1945. *Birds of Georgia. A preliminary check-list and bibliography of Georgia ornithology. With a historical narrative by Eugene E. Murphey.* Athens: 1–111, 1 pl., 1 map.

Halter, C. R.

1923. The venemous Coral Snake. *Copeia* 123: 105–107.

Hamilton, Peter J.

1897. *Colonial Mobile.* Boston and New York: xiii + 446, 6 pl., 9 maps.

[Hammond, Harry]

1883. *South Carolina. Resources and population. Institutions and industries.* (Publ. by the State Board of Agriculture of South Carolina.) Charleston: viii + 726, 3 pl., 1 fig., 1 map, 3 folding tables.

Harden, William

1913. *A history of Savannah and South Georgia.* Vol. *1.* Chicago and New York: xxix + 529, 1 pl., 33 fig.

Harper, Francis

1926. Tales of the Okefinokee. *Am. Speech* 1(8): 407–420.

1927. The mammals of the Okefinokee Swamp region of Georgia. *Proc. Boston Soc. Nat. Hist.* 38(7): 191–396, 4 pl., 5 fig.

1930. Alligators of the Okefinokee. *Sci. Monthly* 31(1): 51–67, 8 fig.

1934. The Okefinokee wilderness. *Nat. Geog. Mag.* 65(5): 597–624, 35 fig., 1 map.

1936. The *Vultur sacra* of William Bartram. *Auk* 53(4): 381–392.

1939a. Arthur Newlin Leeds. *Jour. Mammalogy* 20(2): 282–283.

1939b. Distribution, taxonomy, nomenclature, and habits of the Little Tree-frog (*Hyla ocularis*). *Am. Midland Naturalist* 22(1): 134–149, 4 fig., 1 map.

1939c. The Bartram trail through the Southeastern States. *Bull. Garden Club America,* ser. 7, 5: 54–64, 4 fig.

1940. Some works of Bartram, Daudin, Latreille, and Sonnini, and their bearing upon North American herpetological nomenclature. *Am. Midland Naturalist* 23(3): 692–723, 1 fig.

1942a. The name of the warmouth. *Copeia* 1942(1): 50.

1942b. Two more available plant names of William Bartram. *Bartonia* 21: 6–8.

1942c. The name of the Florida wolf. *Jour. Mammalogy* 23(3): 339.

1942d. William Bartram's names of birds. *Proc. Rochester Acad. Sci.* 8(4): 208–221.

1943. *Quercus incana* Bartram. *Bartonia* 22: 3.

1946a. The name of the royal palm. *Proc. Biol. Soc. Washington* 59: 29–30.

Harper, Francis (*continued*)

1946*b*. Proposals for publishing Bartram's *Travels. Library Bull. Am. Philos. Soc.* 1945: 27–38, 2 fig.

1952. History and nomenclature of the Pocket Gophers (*Geomys*) in Georgia. *Proc. Biol. Soc. Washington 65:* 35–38.

1953. William Bartram and the American Revolution. *Proc. Am. Philos. Soc.* 97(5): 571–577.

Harper, Francis, and Arthur N. Leeds

1938. A supplementary chapter on *Franklinia alatamaha. Bartonia* 19: 1–13, 1 map.

Harper, Roland M.

1905. Phytogeographical explorations in the coastal plain of Georgia in 1903. *Bull. Torrey Bot. Club* 32(3): 141–171, 5 fig.

1906. A phytogeographical sketch of the Altamaha Grit Region of the coastal plain of Georgia. *Annals New York Acad. Sci. 17,* pt. I: 1–414, 28 pl., 23 fig., 1 map.

1913. Economic botany of Alabama. Part 1. Geographical report including descriptions of the natural divisions of the state, their forests and forest industries, with quantitative analyses and statistical tables. *Geol. Survey Alabama Monog.* 8: 1–222, 63 fig., 1 map.

1914. Geography and vegetation of northern Florida. *Florida State Geol. Survey Sixth Ann. Rept.:* 163–437, 51 fig.

1915. Vegetation types [of an area in central Florida]. *Florida State Geol. Survey Seventh Ann. Rept.:* 135–188, 14 fig.

1918. A new method of mapping complex geographical features, illustrated by some maps of Georgia. *School Sci. and Mathematics 18*(8): 699–708, 4 maps.

1921. Geography of central Florida. *Florida State Geol. Survey Thirteenth Ann. Rept.:* 71–307, 39 fig., 1 map.

1922. Development of agriculture in lower Georgia from 1850 to 1880. *Georgia Hist. Quarterly 6*(2): 97–121, 1 map.

1928*a*. Economic botany of Alabama. Part 2. Catalogue of the trees, shrubs and vines of Alabama, with their economic properties and local distribution. *Geol. Survey Alabama Monog.* 9: 1–357, 66 fig., 23 maps.

1928*b*. Notes on the distribution of *Dionaea. Torreya* 28(5): 92–94.

1930. The natural resources of Georgia. *Bull. Univ. Georgia 30*(3): xi + 105, 7 maps.

1943. Forests of Alabama. *Geol. Survey Alabama Monog.* 10: 1–230, 76 fig., 1 map.

Harris, John

1748. *Navigantium atque itinerantium bibliotheca. or, a complete collection of voyages and travels.* Vol. 2. London: [8] + 1056 + [22], 34 pl.

Hawes, Lilla M.

1954. The papers of Lachlan McIntosh, 1774–1799. Part 1. *Georgia Hist. Quarterly 38*(2): 148–169.

Hawkins, Benjamin

1848. A sketch of the Creek country, in the years 1798 and 1799. (With introduction by Wm. B. Hodgson.) *Colls. Georgia Hist. Soc. 3*, pt. I: 1–88.

1916. Letters of Benjamin Hawkins, 1796–1806. *Colls. Georgia Hist. Soc. 9:* 1–500, 1 map.

Hedrick, U. P., ed.

1919. Sturtevant's notes on edible plants. *New York Dept. Agric. 27th Ann. Rept.*, 2, pt. II. Albany: vii + 686, 1 pl.

Henderson, Archibald

1923. *Washington's southern tour, 1791.* Boston and New York: xxviii + 340, 66 pl.

Hitchcock, Charles Leo

1932. A monographic study of the genus *Lycium* in the Western Hemisphere. *Annals Missouri Bot. Garden 19* (2/3): 179–374, 13 pl., 2 fig.

Hodgson, Adam

1824. *Letters from North America.* Vol. *1.* London and Edinburgh: xv + 405, 1 pl.

Holbrook, John Edwards

1836. *North American Herpetology; or, a description of the reptiles inhabiting the United States,* 1st ed. Philadelphia: *1:* i–viii, 9–120, 23 pl.

Howell, Arthur H.

1921. A biological survey of Alabama. 1. Physiography and life zones. 2. The mammals. *U. S. Dept. Agric., N. Am. Fauna 45:* 1–88, 10 pl., 11 maps.

Hume, H. Harold

1926. *The cultivation of citrus fruits.* New York: xxi + 561, 236 fig., 1 map.

Jefferson, Thomas

1782. *Notes on the State of Virginia.* [Paris]: 1–391, 1 folding table.

1944. *Thomas Jefferson's garden book.* (Annotated by Edwin Morris Betts.) *Mem. Am. Philos. Soc. 22:* xv + 704, 37 pl.

Jenkins, Charles F.

1933. The historical background of Franklin's tree. *Pennsylvania Mag. Hist. and Biography 57*(3): 193–208, 4 pl.

1943. Franklin's tree. *Nat. Horticultural Mag. 22*(4): 119–127, 4 fig.

Johnson, Cecil

1943. *British West Florida 1763–1783.* New Haven: xi + 258, 2 maps.

Johnson, Joseph

1851. *Traditions and reminiscences, chiefly of the American Revolution in the South.* Charleston: viii + 592, 8 fig., 2 maps, 1 folding table.

Jones, Charles C., Jr.

1878. The dead towns of Georgia. *Colls. Georgia Hist. Soc. 4.* Savannah: 1–263, 5 pl.

1883. *The history of Georgia.* Vol. 2. Boston and New York: xv + 540, 10 pl.

Jones, Charles C., Jr. (continued)
1889. Address delivered at Midway Meeting House in Liberty County, Georgia . . . Augusta: 1–20.
1891. Biographical sketches of the delegates from Georgia to the Continental Congress. Boston and New York: x + 211.

Kellogg, Remington
1929. The habits and economic importance of alligators. U. S. Dept. Agric. Tech. Bull. 147: 1–36, 2 pl., 2 fig.
1939. Whales, giants of the sea. Nat. Geog. Mag. 72(1): 35–90, 24 pl., 27 fig., "1940."

Kelly, Howard A., and Walter L. Burrage
1920. American medical biographies. Baltimore: xix + 1320.

Kniffen, Fred B.
1935. Bayou Manchac: a physiographic interpretation. Geog. Rev. 25(3): 462–466, 1 map.

Latham, John
1787. Supplement to the general synopsis of birds. [Vol. 1.] London: iii + 298 + [15], 14 pl.

Le Conte, John [Eatton]
1826. On the North American plants of the genus Tillandsia, with descriptions of three new species. Annals Lyceum Nat. Hist. New-York 2: 129–132.
1830. Description of the species of North American tortoises. Annals Lyceum Nat. Hist. New-York 3: 91–131.
1830–1835. Observations on the United States species of the genus Pancratium. Annals Lyceum Nat. Hist. New-York 3: 142–147.
1854. Notice of American animals, formerly known, but now forgotten or lost. Proc. Acad. Nat. Sci. Philadelphia 7: 8–14.
1855. [Remarks on Magnolia pyramidata of Bartram.] Proc. Acad. Nat. Sci. Philadelphia 7: 174–175.

Le Conte, Joseph
1903. The autobiography of Joseph Le Conte. New York: xvii + 337, 8 pl.

Leeds, Morris E.
1939. Arthur Newlin Leeds. Westonian 45(3): 4–9. (Also issued as a separate, with the addition of two photographs.)

Lettsom, John Coakley
1784. The works of John Fothergill, M.D. London: [6] + xcv + 657, 11 pl.

Linnaeus, Carolus (see also Linné).
1753. Species plantarum. Stockholm: 1: [10] + 560; 2: 561–1200 + [31].
1758. Systema naturae. Editio decima, reformata, Vol. 1. Stockholm: [4] + 824.
1762, 1763. Species plantarum . . . 2d ed. Stockholm: 1: [14] + 784, 1 pl., 1762; 2: 785–1684, [64], 1763.

1770. *Systema naturae.* [Editio decima tertia], Vol. *3.* Vienna: 236 + [19].

Linné, Carolus a

1766–1768. *Systema naturae.* Editio duodecima, reformata. Stockholm: *1:* 1327 + [37], 1766–1767; *2:* 736 + [16], 1767; *3:* 236 + [20], 3 pl., 1768.

1774. *Systema vegetabilium secundum classes, ordines, genera, species, cum characteribus et differentiis,* 13th ed. Edited by J. A. Murray. Göttingen and Gotha: iv + 844.

Linné, Carolus a [filius]

1781. *Supplementum plantarum.* Brunswick: [14] + 467 + [1].

Little, Elbert L., Jr.

1945. Miscellaneous notes on nomenclature of United States trees. *Am. Midland Naturalist* 33(2): 495–513.

Little, John Buckner

1885. *The history of Butler County, Alabama, from 1815 to 1885.* Cincinnati: i–xi, 13–256, 13 pl.

Lowes, John Livingston

1927. *The road to Xanadu.* Boston and New York: xviii + 639, 8 pl., 6 fig., 2 maps.

Lyell, Charles

1845. *Travels in North America, in the years 1841–2.* Vol. *1.* New York: vii + 251, 3 pl., 6 fig., 1 map.

1849. *A second visit to the United States of North America.* New York and London: *1:* v–xii, 13–273, 6 fig.; *2:* iii–ix, 13–287, 8 fig.

Lyon, John

MS. Journal, 1799–1814. Am. Philos. Soc.

McCall, Hugh

1816. *The history of Georgia.* Vol. *2.* Savannah: vii + 424.

MacCauley, Clay

1887. The Seminole Indians of Florida. *Fifth Ann. Rept. Bur.* [*Am.*] *Ethnol.*: 469–531, 1 pl., 17 fig., 1 map.

McConkey, Edwin H.

1954. A systematic study of the North American lizards of the genus *Ophisaurus. Am. Midland Naturalist* 51(1): 133–169, 2 pl., 2 fig., 3 maps.

McIlhenny, E. A.

1935. *The alligator's life history.* Boston: 3–117, 18 pl.

McQueen, A. S., and Hamp Mizell

1926. *History of Okefenokee Swamp.* Clinton, S.C.: 1–191, 26 pl., 1 map.

McVaugh, Rogers

1943. The vegetation of the granitic flat-rocks of the southeastern United States. *Ecol. Monog.* 13(2): 119–166, 22 fig., 14 maps.

Marshall, Humphry

1785. *Arbustrum americanum.* Philadelphia: xx + 174.

Martin, Josephine Bacon
    1936. *Midway-Georgia in history and legend.* Savannah: 1–23, 3 fig.
Mereness, Newton D., ed.
    1916. *Travels in the American colonies.* New York: vi + 693.
Merrill, E. D.
    1945. In defense of the validity of William Bartram's binomials. *Bartonia* 23: 10–35.
[Meyer, Friedrich Albecht Anton]
    1794. Alphabetisches Verzeichniss aller jetzlebenden Zoologen. *Zool. Annalen 1:* 65–79.
Michaux, Andreas
    1803. *Flora boreali-americana.* Paris and Strasbourg: *1:* xii + 330, 29 pl.; *2:* 1–340, 22 pl.
Michaux, André
    1889. Portions of the journal of André Michaux, botanist, written during his travels in the United States and Canada, 1785 to 1796. (In French, with an introduction and explanatory notes by C. S. Sargent.) *Proc. Am. Philos. Soc. 26:* 1–145.
Michaux, F. A.
    1805. Travels to the west of the Alleghany Mountains, in the states of Ohio, Kentucky, and Tennessea, . . . in the year 1802, 2d ed. London: iii–xii, 1–294.
Miller, Gerrit S., Jr., and Remington Kellogg
    1955. List of North American Recent mammals. *U. S. Nat. Mus. Bull.* 205: xii + 954.
Miller, Philip
    1768. *The gardeners dictionary* . . . 8th ed. London: 7 p. 1. + 1332 unnumbered pp., 20 pl.
Miller, William Hubert
    1948. Mark Catesby, an eighteenth century naturalist. *Tyler's Quarterly Hist. and Geneal. Mag.* 29(3): 167–180.
Mohr, Charles
    1901. *Plant life of Alabama,* Alabama ed. (Reprint of *Contrib. U. S. Nat. Herbarium* 6, 1901.) Montgomery: xii + 921, 14 pl., 1 map.
Mooney, James
    1900. Myths of the Cherokees. *Nineteenth Ann. Rept. Bur. Am. Ethnol.,* pt. I: 1–576, 18 pl., 2 fig., 2 maps.
Moore, Clarence B.
    1894. Certain sand mounds of the St. John's River, Florida. *Jour. Acad. Nat. Sci. Philadelphia,* ser. 2, *10:* 5–103, 129–246, 36 pl., 195 fig., 4 maps.
Mowat, Charles L.
    1941. St. Augustine under the British flag, 1763–1775. *Florida Hist. Quarterly* 20(2): 131–150.
    1942. That "odd being," De Brahm. *Florida Hist. Quarterly* 20(4): 323–345.

1943. East Florida as a British province, 1763–1784. *Univ. California Publ. Hist. 32:* ix + 237, 1 pl., 1 map.

Muhlenberg, Henry

MS. Journal, 1790–1799. Am. Philos. Soc.

MSS. Letters, 1 vol. (approximately 210 items). Hist. Soc. Pennsylvania

Neill, Wilfred T.

1953. Dugouts of the Mikasuki Seminole. *Florida Anthropologist 6*(3): 77–84, 3 fig.

1954. Coracles or skin boats of the southeastern Indians. *Florida Anthropologist 7*(4): 119–126.

1955a. The identity of Florida's "Spanish Indians." *Florida Anthropologist 8*(2): 43–57.

1955b. The calumet ceremony of the Seminole Indians. *Florida Anthropologist 8*(3): 83–88.

1956. *Florida's Seminole Indians.* Silver Springs, Fla.: 1–91, 30 fig., 1 map.

Nuttall, Thomas

1822. A catalogue of a collection of plants made in East-Florida, during the months of October and November, 1821. By A. Ware, Esq. *Am. Jour. Sci. and Arts 5*(2): 286–304.

1832, 1834. *A manual of the ornithology of the United States and of Canada.* Cambridge: [1,] the land birds: viii + 683, 51 fig., 1832; [2,] the water birds: vii + 627, 62 fig., 1834.

1842–1849. *The North American sylva; or, a description of the forest trees of the United States, Canada, and Nova Scotia, not described in the work of F. Andrew Michaux* . . . Philadelphia: *1:* xii + 136, 39 pl., 1842; *2:* 1–123, 40 pl., 1846; *3:* 1–148, 41 pl., 1849.

1951. Nuttall's travels into the old Northwest. An unpublished 1810 diary. Ed. Jeannette E. Graustein. *Chronica Botanica 14*(1/2): 1–88, 12 pl., 4 fig., 1 map.

Ord, George

1815. Zoology of North America. In: William Guthrie, *A new geographical, historical, and commercial grammar,* Vol. 2 (2d Am. ed.), Philadelphia: 290–361.

1825. Supplement to the American Ornithology of Alexander Wilson. *Containing a sketch of the author's life, with a selection from his letters; some remarks upon his writings; and a history of those birds which were intended to compose part of his ninth volume.* Philadelphia: v–ccxxiv, 225–298 + [4], 4 pl., 2 fig.

?Ord, George

1832. *Biographical sketch of William Bartram.* In: J. and T. Doughty, *Cabinet of Natural History and American Rural Sports 2,* Philadelphia: i–vii, 1 portrait.

Park, Orville A.

1929. The Puritan in Georgia. *Georgia Hist. Quarterly 13*(4): 343–371.

684

Payne, John Howard
MS. Commonplace book. Hist. Soc. Pennsylvania.

Pennell, Francis W.
1935. The Scrophulariaceae of eastern temperate North America. *Acad. Nat. Sci. Philadelphia Monog.* 1: xiv + 650, 43 fig., 155 maps.
1940. Arthur N. Leeds. *Bartonia* 20: 30–32, 1 portrait.

Phillips, Ulrich Bonnell
1902. Georgia and state rights. *Ann. Rept. Am. Hist. Assoc.* 1901, 2: 3–224, 12 maps.

Pittman, Ph.
1934. Apalachee during the British occupation. *Florida Hist. Soc. Quarterly 12*(3): 114–122.

Porcher, Francis Peyre
1869. *Resources of the Southern fields and forests, medical, economical and agricultural,* new ed. Charleston: xv + 733.

Pound, Merritt B.
1951. *Benjamin Hawkins—Indian agent.* Athens, Ga.: ix + 270, 1 pl.

Pursh, Frederick
1813. *Flora Americae Septentrionalis.* London: *1:* xxxvi + 358, 16 pl.; *2:* 359–751, 8 pl.

Pyle, Francis C.
1939. William Bartram's voyage. *Subtropical Gardening,* December: 12–14, 2 maps.

Rehder, Alfred
1921. The azaleas of North America. *Publ. Arnold Arboretum* 9: 107–219.

Reynolds, Charles B.
1885. *Old Saint Augustine.* St. Augustine: i–x, 11–144, 12 pl.

Ridgway, Robert
1907. The birds of North and Middle America. *U. S. Nat. Mus. Bull.* 50, pt. IV: xxii + 973, 34 pl.

Roberts, William
1763. *Account of the first discovery & natural history of East-Florida, with a description of the country by T. Jefferys.* London: x + 102, 1 pl., 6 maps.

Romans, Bernard
1776. *A concise natural history of East and West-Florida.* New-York: 4 + 342, 6 pl., 1 folding table.

Rowland, Mrs. Dunbar (Eron Rowland)
1930. *Life, letters and papers of William Dunbar.* Jackson, Miss.: ii + 410, 4 pl.

Royce, Charles C.
1887. The Cherokee nation of Indians. *Fifth Ann. Rept. Bur. [Am.] Ethnol.:* 121–378, 3 pl.
1899. Indian land cessions in the United States. With an introduction by

Charles Thomas. *Eighteenth Ann. Rept. Bur. Am. Ethnol.*, pt. II: 521–997, 67 maps.

Rush, Benjamin

MSS. Rush Correspondence, 44 vols. Library Company of Philadelphia.

1793. An account of the sugar maple-tree of the United States. *Trans. Am. Philos. Soc. 3:* 64–81.

Sabin, Joseph

1868. *A dictionary of books relating to America, from its discovery to the present time.* Vol. *1.* New York: iii–xvi, 1–566.

Sargent, Charles Sprague

1886. Some remarks upon the journey of André Michaux to the high mountains of Carolina, in December, 1788, in a letter addressed to Professor Asa Gray. *Am. Jour. Sci.*, ser. 3, *22:* 466–473.

1902. The silva of North America. Vol. *14.* Boston and New York: [5] + 152, 36 pl.

Schenck, David

1889. *North Carolina. 1780–'81. Being a history of the invasion of the Carolinas by the British Army under Lord Cornwallis in 1780–'81.* Raleigh: 1–498, 4 pl., 7 maps.

Schmidt, Karl P.

1953. *A check list of North American amphibians and reptiles,* 6th ed. Chicago: vii + 280.

Schoepf, Johann David

1911. *Travels in the Confederation [1783–1784].* (Trans. Alfred J. Morrison.) Philadelphia: *1:* x + 426, 1 portrait; *2:* vi + 344.

Screven, Frank B.

1956. The Georgia Bryans and Screvens, 1685–1861. *Georgia Hist. Quarterly 40*(4): 325–348, 2 pl.

Sellards, E. H.

1914. Some Florida lakes and lake basins, 2d ed. *Florida State Geol. Survey Sixth Ann. Rept.:* 115–159, 4 pl., 1 fig., 5 maps.

Seton, Ernest Thompson

1929. *Lives of game animals.* Vol. *3,* pt. I, Garden City: xxi + 412, 61 pl., 14 fig., 5 maps.

Shelburne, (second) Earl of (Sir William Petty)

MSS. Shelburne Papers, 1663–1797, 179 vols. William L. Clements Library, Ann Arbor, Mich.

Shepard, Charles U.

1833. Geological observations upon Alabama, Georgia and Florida. *Am. Jour. Sci. and Arts 25*(1): 162–173.

Siebert, Wilbur H.

1928. East Florida as a refuge of southern Loyalists, 1774–1785. *Proc. Am. Antiquarian Soc.*, n.s., *37:* 226–246.

Sloane, Hans

1707, 1725. *A voyage to the islands Madera, Barbados, Nieves, S. Chris-*

Sloane, Hans (*continued*)

> *tophers and Jamaica, with the natural history of the herbs and trees, four-footed beasts, fishes, birds, insects, reptiles, &c. of the last of those islands.* London: *1:* [1] + [12] + cliv + 264, 155 pl., 1 map, 1707; *2:* [1] + xviii + 499, 118 pl., 1725.

Small, John K.

> 1921. Seminole bread—the conti. *Jour. New York Bot. Garden 22:* 121–137, 2 pl.

> 1922. Wild pumpkins. *Jour. New York Bot. Garden 23:* 19–23.

> 1923. Land of the question mark. *Jour. New York Bot. Garden 24* (277): 1–23, 2 fig.; (278): 25–43, 1 fig.; (279): 62–70, 1 fig.

> 1930*a.* The Okeechobee gourd. *Jour. New York Bot. Garden 31:* 10–14, 2 fig.

> 1930*b.* Chronicle of the palms of the continental United States. *Jour. New York Bot. Garden 31:* 57–66.

> 1931. Bartram's *Ixia coelestina* rediscovered. *Jour. New York Bot. Garden 32:* 155–161, 2 fig.

> 1933. *Manual of the Southeastern flora.* New York: xxii + 1554, numerous fig., 1 map.

Smith, James Edward

> 1821. *A selection of the correspondence of Linnaeus, and other naturalists, from the original manuscripts.* London: *1:* xiv + 605, 2 pl.; *2:* iv + 580 + [26], 8 pl.

Smith, Jared G.

> 1899. Cowpeas. *U. S. Dept. Agric. Farmers' Bull.* 89: 1–16, 1 fig.

Sonnini, C. S., and P. A. Latreille

> 1801 (An X). *Histoire naturelle des Reptiles.* Paris: *1:* xx + 280, 14 pl.; *2:* 1–332, 21 pl.; *3:* 1–335, 6 pl.; *4:* 1–410, 13 pl.

S[palding], T[homas]

> 1836. *Lachlin* [sic] *McIntosh.* In: *National Portrait Gallery of Distinguished Americans 3:* 1–10, 1 portrait. Philadelphia, New York, and London.

Spalding, Thomas

> 1840. A sketch of the life of General James Oglethorpe. *Colls. Georgia Hist. Soc. 1:* 239–295.

Speck, Frank G.

> 1909. Ethnology of the Yuchi Indians. *Univ. Pennsylvania, Anthrop. Publ. Univ. Mus. 1*(1): 1–154, 16 pl., 42 fig.

Stephenson, L. W.

> 1912. The Cretaceous formations. In: Clark, Miller, Stephenson, Johnson, and Parker, The Coastal Plain of North Carolina. *North Carolina Geol. and Econ. Survey 3:* 73–171, 5 pl., 9 fig., 6 maps.

Stevens, William Bacon

> 1847, 1859. *A history of Georgia.* New-York: *1:* xiii + 503, 3 pl., 2 maps, 1847; *2:* ix–xvi, 17–524, 1 pl., 1 map, 1859.

Stone, Witmer

1905*a*. Some early American ornithologists. I. Mark Catesby. *Bird-Lore* 7(2): 126–129.

1905*b*. Some early American ornithologists. II. William Bartram. *Bird-Lore* 7(3): 162–164.

1913. Bird migration records of William Bartram. 1802–1822. *Auk 30*(3): 325–358, 3 pl.

1930. Proper name of the Virginia Rail. *Auk 47*(4): 560.

1932. The work of William, son of John Bartram. *Bartonia,* spl. issue: 20–23, "1931."

Stork, William

[1766.] *An account of East-Florida, with a journal, kept by John Bartram of Philadelphia, Botanist to His Majesty for the Floridas; upon a journey from St. Augustine up the River St. John's,* 2d ed. London: [4], i–xxii, 23–90, i–viii, 1–70.

1769. *A description of East-Florida, with a journal, kept by John Bartram of Philadelphia, Botanist to His Majesty for the Floridas; upon a journey from St. Augustine up the River St. John's, as far as the lakes,* 3d ed. London: [2] + viii + 40 + xii + 36, 3 maps.

1774. *A description* etc., 4th ed. London: [2] + viii + 40 + xii + 36, 3 maps.

Swanton, John R.

1922. Early history of the Creek Indians and their neighbors. *Bur. Am. Ethnol. Bull.* 73: 1–492, 10 maps.

1946. The Indians of the Southeastern United States. *Bur. Am. Ethnol. Bull.* 137: xiii + 943, 107 pl., 5 fig., 13 maps.

Swanton, John R. (chairman); John R. Fordyce; Walter B. Jones; Carl D. Brorein; Caroline Dormon; Andrew O. Holmes; and V. Birney Imes.

1939. *Final report of the United States De Soto Expedition Commission.* 76th Congress, 1st Session, House Document 71: xvi + 400, 11 maps.

Taitt, David

1916. *Journal of David Taitt's travels from Pensacola, West Florida, to and through the country of the Upper and the Lower Creeks, 1772.* In: Newton D. Mereness, ed., *Travels in the American colonies,* New York: 491–565.

Thomas, Cyrus

1899. Indian land cessions in the United States. Introduction. *Eighteenth Ann. Rept. Bur. Am. Ethnol.,* pt. II: 527–644.

Thomassy, R.

1860. *Géologie pratique de la Louisiane.* New Orleans and Paris: lxviii + 264, 6 pl.

Tomkins, Ivan R.

1955. *Elliptio spinosus* in the Altamaha River. *Nautilus 68*(4): 132–133.

Torrey, Bradford

1894. *A Florida sketch-book*. Boston and New York: 1–242.

Torrey, John, and John H. Redfield

MSS. Torrey-Redfield Collection. *Acad. Nat. Sci. Philadelphia.* (Includes 283 autograph letters from 240 scientists.)

Trumbull, Gurdon

1888. *Names and portraits of birds which interest gunners.* New York: viii + 221, 91 fig.

Tucker, Philip C.

1929. Notes on the life of James Grant prior and subsequent to his governorship of East Florida. *Florida Hist. Soc. Quarterly* 8(2): 112–119.

Turner, B. L.

1951. Revision of the United States species of *Neptunia* (Leguminosae). *Am. Midland Naturalist* 46(1): 82–92, 5 fig., 4 maps

Van Doren, Carl

1943. The beginnings of the American Philosophical Society. *Proc. Am. Philos. Soc.* 87(3): 277–289, 5 pl.

Veatch, Otto, and Lloyd William Stephenson

1911. Preliminary report on the geology of the Coastal Plain of Georgia. *Geol. Survey Georgia Bull.* 26: 1–446, 30 pl., 10 fig., 5 maps.

Vignoles, Charles

1823. *Observations upon the Floridas.* New York: 1–197 + [1].

Walter, Thomas

1788. *Flora Caroliniana.* London: viii + 263, 1 pl.

Watt, George

1907. *The wild and cultivated cotton plants of the world.* London: xiv + 406, 53 pl.

Wayne, Arthur Trezevant

1910. Birds of South Carolina. *Contrib. Charleston Mus.* 1: xxi + 254 + [1], 1 map.

Wetmore, Alexander

1948. *Report of the Secretary of the Smithsonian Institution . . . for the year ended June 30, 1948.* Washington: ix + 158, 1 folding table.

Wherry, Edgar T.

1928. The history of the Franklin tree, *Franklinia alatamaha. Jour. Washington Acad. Sci.* 18(6): 172–176.

1935. *Distribution of the North American pitcherplants.* Reprint: 1–23, 10 maps, from: Mary Vaux Walcott, *Illustrations of North American pitcherplants.* Washington.

White, George

1849. *Statistics of the State of Georgia: including an account of its natural, civil, and ecclesiastical history.* Savannah: 624 + 77, 1 map.

1854. *Historical collections of Georgia.* New-York: xvi + 688, illus.

Willdenow, Carolus Ludovicus

1799. *Caroli a Linné, species plantarum . . .* Vol. 2, pt. I. Berlin: 1–823.

Williams, Belle
    1905. Fort Galphin. *The State* (Columbia, S.C.), January 1: 1 fig.
Williams, George G.
    1951. Rat Snake overpowers Red-shouldered Hawk, *Buteo lineatus.*
        Auk 68(3): 372.
Williams, John Lee
    1837. *The territory of Florida: or sketches of the topography, civil and
        natural history, of the country, the climate, and the Indian tribes, from
        the first discovery to the present time.* New York: i–vi, 7–304, 2 pl., 1
        map.
Wilson, Alexander
    1808–1812. *American ornithology; or, the natural history of the birds of
        the United States.* Philadelphia: *1:* vi + 158, 9 pl., 1808; *2:* iii–xii,
        13–167, 9 pl., 1810; *3:* iii–xvi, 17–120, 9 pl., 1811; *4:* iii–xii, 13–100,
        9 pl., 1811; *5:* iii–xii, 13–122, 9 pl., 1812.
Wright, John K.
    1956. From "Kubla Khan" to Florida. *Am. Quarterly* 8(1): 76–80.
Wright, Robert
    1867. *A memoir of General James Oglethorpe.* London: xvi + 414, 1 map.
Wroth, Lawrence C.
    1941. Source materials of Florida history in the John Carter Brown Li-
        brary of Brown University. *Florida Hist. Quarterly* 20(1): 3–46.
Wyman, Jeffries
    1868. On the fresh-water shell-heaps of the St. John's River, East Florida.
        Am. Naturalist 2(8): 393–403; (9): 449–463, 1 pl., 3 fig.
    1875. Fresh-water shell mounds of the St. John's River, Florida. *Peabody
        Acad. Sci. Mem.* 4: i–viii, 3–94, 9 pl., 1 fig., 1 map.
[Youmans, William Jay]
    1892. Sketch of John and William Bartram. *Pop. Sci. Monthly* 40: 827–
        839, 1 fig.
Youmans, William Jay
    1896. *Pioneers of science in America.* New York: vii + 508, 49 pl., 5 fig.

MAPS AND ATLASES

Alabama, geological map of. 1894. Geol. Survey Alabama. Scale 1:633,600.

Campbell, Archibald. 1780. Sketch of the northern frontiers of Georgia, extending from the mouth of the River Savannah to the town of Augusta. London (W. Faden).

Crown Collection of Photographs of American Maps. 1907–1920. (Selected and edited by Archer Butler Hulbert.) Cleveland: ser. 1, 1–5: 246 maps, 1907; ser. 2, 1–5: 250 maps, 1910; ser. 3, 1–4: 250 maps, 1915; ser. 4, 1: 13 maps, 1920.

Darby, Wm., and B. Tanner. 1821. Map of Florida. Philadelphia. Scale 1:2,400,000.

De Brahm, John Gerar William. 1771–1774? Map of East Florida (MS). Harvard College Library. Scale 1:180,000.

Early, Eleazer. 1818. Map of the State of Georgia, prepared from actual surveys and other documents for Eleazer Early [by] Daniel Sturges. Savannah. Scale 1:800,000.

Faden, William. 1776. The North American atlas. London.

————1780. A map of South Carolina and a part of Georgia. London. (Reprinted, 1937, by U.S. Geological Survey, and issued by U.S. Constitution Sesquicentennial Commission. Washington. Scale 1:840,000.)

Florida Mapping Project. Topographic map:
Hawthorn quadrangle (advance sheet). 1939. Scale 1:48,000.

Georgia, Secretary of State's Office. Atlanta.
Land-lot maps of Baldwin County. N.d.

Georgia, State Highway Board of. Atlanta.
Baldwin County. 1952. Scale 1:126,000.
Bibb County. 1953. Scale 1:63,000.
Camden County. 1953. Scale 1:126,000.
Chattahoochee County. 1939. Scale 1:63,000.
Crawford County. 1939. Scale 1:126,000.
Glynn County. 1938. Scale 1:126,000.
Hancock County. 1952. Scale 1:126,000.
Jones County. 1952. Scale 1:126,000.
Liberty County. 1939. Scale 1:126,000.
McDuffie County. 1953. Scale 1:63,000.
Marion County. 1950. Scale 1:126,000.
Oglethorpe County. 1950. Scale 1:126,000.

Taylor County. 1951. Scale 1:126,000.

Warren County. 1939. Scale 1:126,000.

Hall Brothers. 1895. Hall's original county map of Georgia, showing present and original counties and land districts. Atlanta. Scale 1:630,000.

Harper, Roland M. 1925. Generalized soil map of Florida. Florida State Geological Survey, Tallahassee. (Accompanies *Seventeenth Ann. Rept.* [1926] 1927.) Scale 1:1,000,000.

Hunter, George. 1730. Map of the Cherokee ("Chareeke") Nation, with the path to Charles Town (MS). Map Division, Library of Congress. Scale 1:1,240,000.

————1751. South Carolina. Crown Coll., ser. 3, *1:* 27–30, 1915.

Melish, John. 1816. Southern section of the United States including Florida &c. Scale 1:4,150,000.

Mouzon, Henry, and others. 1775. An accurate map of North and South Carolina, with their Indian frontiers. London. (Reprinted, 1938, by U.S. Geological Survey, and issued by U.S. Constitution Sesquicentennial Commission. Washington. Scale 1:930,000.)

Price, Jona., and John Strother. 1808. First actual survey of the State of North Carolina. Philadelphia. Scale 1:512,000.

Purcell, Joseph. *Circa* 1776. Map compiled in the interest of the British Indian trade by John Stuart, H. M. Sup't of Indian Affairs (MS). Newberry Library, Chicago. Scale approximately 1:1,110,000. (Reproduced in Swanton, 1922: pl. 7.)

————*Ca.* 1779. A map of the road from Pensacola in W. Florida to St. Augustine in East Florida. From a survey made by order of the late Hon. Col. John Stuart, Esq., His Majesty's Superintendent of Indian Affairs, Southern District, in 1778. (Colonial Office maps, Florida, no. 54, in Public Record Office, London; reproduced in *Crown Coll.*, ser. 3, *2* and *3:* 108–125, 1915, and by Boyd, 1938.) Scale approximately 1:230,000.

Romans, Bernard. *Ca.* 1772. A map of West Florida, part of E^t: Florida, Georgia, part of S^o Carolina including . . . Chactaw Chickasaw & Creek Nations. . . . Compiled under the direction of John Stuart Esqr: His Majesty's . . . Superintendent of Indian affairs . . . & by him . . . to His Ex[c]ellency ye Honble. Thomas Gage Esqr: General & Commander in Chief of all His Majesty's Forces in Nth America (MS; title not wholly legible). William L. Clements Library, Ann Arbor, Mich.

The accompanying "Remarks" by Romans show that the portion of this map covering the Choctaw, Chickasaw, and Creek Nations was prepared by David Taitt. Hence, in the present work, this portion is referred to as "Taitt's map of 1772."

————1776. A general map of the southern British Colonies in America, comprehending North and South Carolina, Georgia, East and West Florida, with the neighbouring Indian countries. London. (Reprinted, 1937, by U.S. Geological Survey, and issued by U.S. Constitution Sesquicentennial Commission. Washington. Scale 1:3,500,000.)

Taitt, David. *See* Romans, Bernard, *ca.* 1772.
Tanner, H. S. 1841. Georgia and Alabama. Philadelphia. Scale 1:1,750,000.
United States Coast and Geodetic Survey. Charts:
  St. John's River, Hibernia to Racy Point. No. 683. 1938. Scale 1:40,500.
  St. John's River, Lake George to Lake Harney. No. 509. 1938. Scale
    1:40,500.
  St. John's River, Palatka to Lake George. No. 508. 1938. Scale 1:40,500.
  St. John's River, Tocoi to San Mateo. No. 684. 1937. Scale 1:40,500.
United States Department of Agriculture, Bureau of Chemisty and Soils.
    Soil maps:
  Alachua County, Fla. (Series 1940, No. 10) 1954. Scale 1:48,000.
  Alamance County, N.C. (Field Operations 1901) 1902. Scale 1:63,360.
  Baldwin County, Ala. (Field Operations 1909) 1912. Scale 1:63,360.
  Barbour County, Ala. (Field Operations 1914) 1919. Scale 1:63,360.
  Bladen County, N.C. (Field Operations 1914) 1919. Scale 1:63,360.
  Brunswick County, N.C. (Field Operations 1932) 1937. Scale 1:63,360.
  Chatham County, Ga. (Field Operations 1911) 1914. Scale 1:63,360.
  Chattahoochee County, Ga. (Series 1924, No. 4) 1928. Scale 1:63,360.
  Clarke County, Ga. (Field Operations 1927) 1930. Scale 1:63,360.
  Columbus County, N.C. (Field Operations 1915) 1919. Scale 1:63,360.
  Cumberland County, N.C. (Field Operations 1922) 1928. Scale 1:63,360.
  East Baton Rouge Parish, La. (Field Operations 1905) 1907. Scale
    1:63,360.
  Elbert County, Ga. (Series 1928, No. 15) 1931. Scale 1:63,360.
  Elmore County, Ala. (Field Operations 1911) 1914. Scale 1:63,360.
  Hancock County, Ga. (Field Operations 1909) 1912. Scale 1:63,360.
  Hart County, Ga. (Series 1929, No. 12) 1933. Scale 1:63,360.
  Horry County, S.C. (Field Operations 1918) 1924. Scale 1:63,360.
  Lake County, Fla. (northern sheet). (Field Operations 1923) 1928.
    Scale 1:63,360.
  McIntosh County, Ga. (Series 1929, No. 6) 1932. Scale 1:63,360.
  Macon County, Ala. (Field Operations 1904) 1905. Scale 1:63,360.
  Madison County, Ga. (Field Operations 1918) 1924. Scale 1:63,360.
  Mobile County, Ala. (Field Operations 1911) 1914. Scale 1:63,360.
  Montgomery County, Ala. (Field Operations 1905) 1907. Scale 1:63,360.
  Oconee County, S.C. (Field Operations 1907) 1909. Scale 1:63,360.
  Putnam County, Fla. (Field Operations 1914) 1919. Scale 1:63,360.
  Russell County, Ala. (Field Operations 1913) 1916. Scale 1:63,360.
  St. John's County, Fla. (Field Operations 1917) 1923. Scale 1:63,360.
  Stewart County, Ga. (Field Operations 1913) 1916. Scale 1:63,360.
  Tallapoosa County, Ala. (Field Operations 1909) 1912. Scale 1:63,360.
  Washington County, Ala. (Field Operations 1915) 1919. Scale 1:63,360.
United States Department of Agriculture, Forest Service:
  Chattahoochee National Forest, Ga. 1937. Scale 1:126,720.
  Nantahala National Forest, N.C., S.C., and Ga. 1935. Scale 1:167,500.

Nantahala National Forest, N.C. 1938. Scale 1:126,720.
Ocala National Forest, Fla. 1938. Scale 1:126,720.
United States Geological Survey. Topographic maps:
  Abbeville quadrangle, S.C. 1892. Scale 1:125,000.
  Appling quadrangle, Ga. 1921. Scale 1:62,500.
  Arredondo quadrangle, Fla. (1891) 1934. Scale 1:62,500.
  Ashland quadrangle, Ala. (1891) 1898. Scale 1:125,000.
  Augusta quadrangle, S.C.-Ga. 1921. Scale 1:62,500.
  Baton Rouge quadrangle, La. 1908. Scale 1:62,500.
  Bayou Sara quadrangle, La. 1906. Scale 1:125,000.
  Boulogne quadrangle, Ga.-Fla. 1919. Scale 1:62,500.
  Carnesville quadrangle, Ga.-S.C. (1891) 1930. Scale 1:125,000.
  Cedar Point quadrangle, Ala. 1943. Scale 1:62,500.
  Charleston quadrangle, S.C. 1919. Scale 1:21,120.
  Citra quadrangle, Fla. (1895) 1929. Scale 1:62,500.
  Clark's Hill quadrangle, S.C.-Ga. 1921. Scale 1:62,500.
  Columbus quadrangle, Ga.-Ala. (1908) 1931. Scale 1:62,500.
  Cottageville quadrangle, S.C. 1918. Scale 1:62,500.
  Cowee quadrangle, N.C.-S.C. (1907) 1943. Scale 1:125,000.
  Crawfordville quadrangle, Ga.-S.C. (1906) 1935. Scale 1:125,000.
  Dadeville quadrangle, Ala. (1906) 1936. Scale 1:125,000.
  Dahlonega quadrangle, Ga.-N.C. (1903) 1922. Scale 1:125,000.
  Denham Springs quadrangle, La. 1934. Scale 1:62,500.
  Elberton quadrangle, Ga.-S.C. (1893) 1914. Scale 1:125,000.
  Everett City quadrangle, Ga. 1918. Scale 1:62,500.
  Fernandina, Fla.-Ga. (1919) 1932. Scale 1:62,500.
  Fowler Bend quadrangle, N.C.-Tenn. 1938. Scale 1:62,500.
  Green's Cut quadrangle, Ga.-S.C. 1920. Scale 1:62,500.
  Harlem quadrangle, Ga. 1922. Scale 1:62,500.
  Hephzibah quadrangle, Ga. 1922. Scale 1:62,500.
  Hilltonia quadrangle, Ga.-S.C. 1920. Scale 1:62,500.
  Hollinger's Island quadrangle, Ala. 1944. Scale 1:31,680.
  Hortense quadrangle, Ga. 1918. Scale 1:62,500.
  Interlachen quadrangle, Fla. (1916) 1937. Scale 1:62,500.
  Jacksonville quadrangle, Fla. (1918) 1932. Scale 1:62,500.
  Loudon quadrangle, Tenn. (1895) 1907. Scale 1:125,000.
  McCormick quadrangle, Ga.-S.C. (1892) 1913. Scale 1:125,000.
  Mayport quadrangle, Fla. (1918) 1932. Scale 1:62,500.
  Milledgeville quadrangle, Ga. 1912. Scale 1:62,500.
  Murphy quadrangle, Tenn.-N.C. 1914. Scale 1:125,000.
  Nahunta quadrangle, Ga. 1918. Scale 1:62,500.
  Nantahala quadrangle, N.C.-Tenn. 1906. Scale 1:125,000.
  New Roads quadrangle, La. 1939. Scale 1:62,500.
  Orange Park quadrangle, Fla. (1918) 1932. Scale 1:62,500.
  Palatka quadrangle, Fla. (1915) 1926. Scale 1:62,500.

Pickens quadrangle, S.C. (1894) 1928. Scale 1:125,000.
Pontchatoula quadrangle, La. 1939. Scale 1:62,500.
Ravenels quadrangle, S.C. 1920. Scale 1:62,500.
Rigolets quadrangle, La. 1936. Scale 1:62,500.
Seale quadrangle, Ala.-Ga. 1914. Scale 1:62,500.
Shirley quadrangle, S.C.-Ga. 1919. Scale 1:62,500.
Springfield quadrangle, La. 1939. Scale 1:62,500.
Talladega quadrangle, Ala. (1892) 1908. Scale 1:125,000.
Tensaw quadrangle, Ala. 1944. Scale 1:62,500.
Walhalla quadrangle, Ga.-S.C.-N.C. (1892) 1921. Scale 1:125,000.
Wayah Bald quadrangle, N.C. 1942. Scale 1:62,500.
Wetumpka quadrangle, Ala. 1903. Scale 1:125,000.
Williston quadrangle, Fla. (1895) 1935. Scale 1:62,500.
Yemassee quadrangle, S.C. 1918. Scale 1:62,500.

VARIANT OR INCORRECT ORTHOGRAPHY, PUNCTUATION, AND COMPOSITION

A close examination of the first edition of the *Travels* reveals ample evidence of Bartram's deficiencies and inconsistencies in orthography. There are also indications of something less than the most meticulous editing and proofreading. In the present edition the aim has been to take only a minimum of liberties with the original text; and this has been done in such a way that the interested reader will in virtually every case be able to ascertain the form of the original publication.

Technical and common names of plants, animals, and minerals, names of persons and Indian tribes, and geographical names have been left intact in the main text, but faulty spelling of such names is corrected in the Annotated Index.

There are certain words that, while having a more or less peculiar look to the modern reader, are nevertheless recognized in current dictionaries as merely archaic, obsolete, dialectal, or rare variants. These words also are printed here as originally published; but for the convenience and information of the reader the following alphabetical list is presented (the modern equivalents being added in parentheses):

alledging (alleging)
ancle (ankle)
antient (ancient)
avanced (advanced)
bason (basin)
baulk (balk)
benificent (beneficent)
birth (p. 414) (berth)
but (p. 398, l. 6) (butt)
cabbin (cabin)
cane-break (cane-brake)
carcase (carcass)
centinels (sentinels)
chace (chase)
chanel (channel)
characterises (characterizes)
chearful (cheerful)
chearfully (cheerfully)
chearfulness (cheerfulness)
chearing (cheering)
chesnut (chestnut)
choaked (choked)
choisest (choicest)

cloathed (clothed)
cloathing (clothing)
cloths (p. 460) (clothes)
compleat (complete)
compleatly (completely)
croud (crowd)
crouded (crowded)
cuniform (cuneiform)
desart (desert)
drougth (drought)
Eastermost (Easternmost)
encrease (increase)
enterance (entrance)
etherial (ethereal)
exoticks (exotics)
expence (expense)
ferrugineous (ferruginous)
frolick (frolic)
fulness (fullness)
gaity (gayety)
gate (gait)
gulph (gulf)
heroe (hero)

heterogenous (heterogeneous)
illucidating (elucidating)
impowers (empowers)
inchanting (enchanting)
incircling (encircling)
incompleat (incomplete)
incroaches (encroaches)
indulgencies (indulgences)
intangle (entangle)
inthral (enthral)
inticing (enticing)
intire (entire)
intirely (entirely)
intrap (entrap)
intreated (entreated)
irresistable (irresistible)
lay (lie)
lettice (lettuce)
lilly (lily)
linnen (linen)
loose (lose)
marle (marl)
marley (marly)
mater (matter)
mechanicks (mechanics)
ment (meant)
mimickry (mimicry)
morter (mortar)
musquet (musket)
musquitoes (mosquitoes)
negociations (negotiations)
[carried] of (off)
pannicle (panicle)
patrole (patrol)
peeks (peaks)
pennatifid (pinnatifid)

plaister (plaster)
plaistered (plastered)
plumb (plum)
poney (pony)
pulverised (pulverized)
re-imbarking (re-embarking)
ripling (rippling)
salade (sallet)
saliant (salient)
scolloped (scalloped)
set (p. 201, l. 21) (sit)
setling (settling)
shew (show)
smoak (smoke)
soal (sole)
spirted (spurted)
spungy (spongy)
squeeling (squealing)
steril (sterile)
stockado (stockade)
strait, streight (straight)
streights (straits)
stupified (stupefied)
subtil (subtle)
sulphurious (sulphureous)
surprized (surprised)
taught (taut)
tinct (tinge)
[came] too (to)
up (upon) [the Mediterranean]
venemous (venomous)
weeker (weaker)
wich (which)
withs (withes)
wreathes (wreaths)

In the case of words other than those dealt with above, outright misspellings are corrected in the text, in order to avoid confusion or misunderstanding. For the benefit, however, of those who may wish to know the form of these words in the original publication, and who may have occasion to make exact quotations from the work of 1791 merely through the use of the present volume, the following list is offered, with the pagination indicated for each occurrence. The misspelled words are followed by the corrections.

xv. exhilirating = exhilarating
xxii. aproximation = approximation
xxii. viviparious = viviparous
xxii. inveloped = enveloped
xxiii. pericarpes = pericarps
xxiv. mamoth = mammoth
xxvii. consumate = consummate
xxvii. beech = beach

xxix. papiles = papilios? Neither is a dictionary word; perhaps this is a clumsy attempt at an English plural of the generic name *Papilio*.
xxix. ocelle = ocellus
xxx. intripid = intrepid
xxxi. laguages = languages
xxxii. recal = recall

xxxiv. attonement = atonement
opp. 1. Malances = Matances (modern sp., Matanzas)
7. tenaceous = tenacious
7. cinerious = cinereous
9. Superintendant = Superintendent
10. causwayed = causewayed
10. Floriferus = floriferous
12. grean = green
12. branchiostega = branchiostege
14, l. 12. frome = from
16. brachtae = bracteae
17, 18. lanciolate = lanceolate
18. racemi = raceme
19, fn. folus = foliis
20. chimnies = chimneys
20. percieving = perceiving
23. arenacious = arenaceous
24. precumbent = procumbent
28. superintendant = superintendent
29. calcarious = calcareous
30. herbacious = herbaceous
31. lanciolate = lanceolate
31. pericarpi = pericarps
31. cinerious = cinereous
32, 36. redish = reddish
33. Superintendant = Superintendent
39. cinerious = cinereous
39. fossile = fossil
41, 42. lanciolate = lanceolate
42. verticilate = verticillate
42. pericarpi = pericarps
44. redish = reddish
49. controul = control
53. apposite =opposite
57. controul = control
64. istmus = isthmus
67. herbacious = herbaceous
76, l. 7 from bottom. where = were
76. pleasent = pleasant
79. promissed = promised
80. redish = reddish
88. mattrasses = mattresses
93. percieved = perceived
93. comman = common
94. petrefied = petrified
96, l. 2 from bottom. form = from
97. conferrences = conferences
103. umbeliferous = umbelliferous
104. pericarpii = pericarps
104. herbacious (2) = herbaceous
105. lanciolate = lanceolate
107. starol = standard. Although "starol" is not a recognized dictionary word, it has been copied exactly in British, Irish, and American reprints, and rendered as the equivalent of "stalk" in German, Dutch, and French editions. In Bartram's original manuscript draft of this portion of the *Travels* (Hist. Soc. Pennsylvania), the word is written clearly as "standard." After 166 years, "starol," as purely a printer's error, may be consigned to limbo.
109. branchiostega = branchiosteges
109. terible = terrible
110, l. 4. a = at
111. controul = control
113. ututored = untutored
115. lanciolate = lanceolate
116. uparalleled = unparalleled
124. listning = listening
126. padling = paddling
127, l. 6. where = were
128. squammae = squamae
130. swolen = swollen
133. ball = base
135. briliancy = brilliancy
135. geting = getting
135. surprisere cover = surprise recover
137, 138. midling = middling
139. stroling = strolling
141. tumultious = tumultuous
145. ebulition = ebullition
145. forbiding = forbidding
149. chrystal = crystal
149, l. 17. largst = largest
151. redish = reddish
153. branchiostega (2) = branchiostege
154, l. 8. whith = with
160. chrystal = crystal
160. pratling = prattling
160. reconoiter = reconnoiter
161. heighth = height
161. lanciolate = lanceolate
162. redish = reddish
163. ligenous = ligneous
163. aculea = aculei
163. pelucid = pellucid
163. polypetalus = polypetalous
164. heighth = height
164. obcunciformibus = obcuneiformibus
164. tribobis = trilobis
164. corymbes = corymbs
165. heighth = height
165. chrystal (2) = crystal
166. seperate = separate
167. chrystaline = crystalline
168. graves = groves
169. calcarious = calcareous

169. seperated = separated
170. chrystaline = crystalline
171. lanciolate = lanceolate
171. wholsome = wholesome
173. herbacious = herbaceous
174. eliptical = elliptical
176, 177. branchiostega = branchiostege
176, 177. redish = reddish
178. semicartilagenous = semicartilaginous
179. chrystaline = crystalline
182. squamea = squamae
183. overtoped = overtopped
183. herbacious = herbaceous
187. accumunatis = acuminatis
188. uncontrouled = uncontrolled
188. antled = antlered
192. transversly = transversely
199. seperated = separated
199. rout = route
204. herbacious = herbaceous
205. chuncks = chunks
206. intollerable = intolerable
210. accessable = accessible
210. dear = deer
210. vigilent = vigilant
216. seperated = separated
218. mishapen = misshapen
218. schreech = screech
218. fenns = fens
218. seperate = separate
218. seaking = seeking
221. webbs = webs
221. creek = creak
222. occurrance = occurrence
222. controul = control
223. journied = journeyed
223. pirennial = perennial
224. roaving = roving
225. uparalleled = unparalleled
225. occular = ocular
226. seperable = separable
228. houshold = household
229. amunition = ammunition
229, l. 21. through = though
229, 230. chrystal = crystal
230. seperately = separately
231. swolen = swollen
232. emminences = eminences
232. herbacious = herbaceous
235. turkies = turkeys
236. calamut = calumet
238. detatched = detached
240. stratas = strata
240. vallies = valleys
241. turkies = turkeys

242. pubesence = pubescence
243. seperated = separated
245. seperate = separate
248. progess = progress
252. amunition = ammunition
255. bachanalian = bacchanalian
257. controul = control
259, l. 7. but. The inversion of the "u" caused this letter to resemble an "n."
264. rivetted = riveted
270. seperately = separately
272. invaribly = invariably
272. caros = carious
273. distructive = destructive
274. administred = administered
275. cinerious = cinereous
276. perigrinations = peregrinations
278. preceeding = preceding
280. instrantly = instantly
282. turkies = turkeys
284. occular = ocular
288. exculent = esculent
289. journies = journeys
294. grisco = griseo-
294. violacrum = violaceum
298, last line. fonnd = found
299, l. 11. the = they
300. seperated = separated
300. hegdes = hedges
303. exhilerating = exhilarating
307. liesure = leisure
307. rout = route
308. meridan = meridian
308. Morus. The inversion of the "u" caused this letter to resemble an "n."
309. cinerious = cinereous
309. tennacious = tenacious
309. plantaions = plantations
310. partioned = partitioned
311. houshold = household
312. forgeting = forgetting
314. mucaeus = micaceous
317. meandring = meandering
318. petrefaction = petrifaction
318. antideluvian = antediluvian
320. tenaceous = tenacious
322. sedgments = segments
322. indiscrimintaely = indiscriminately
322. chrystaline = crystalline
324. ranges = rangers
325. apix = apex
326, l. 5 from bottom. and = an
327. superintendant = superintendent
327. splended = splendid
328. tenaceous = tenacious
329. thyrsis = thyrsus

335. squammae = squamae
340. radices = radius
340. lanciolate = lanceolate
340. laping = lapping
341. uparalleled = unparalleled
341. chrystal = crystal
341. elivation = elevation
342. chrystaline = crystalline
342. prettey = pretty
343. real = reel
344. pennatified = pinnatifid
346. acients = ancients
347. uparalleled = unparalleled
347. chrystal = crystal
347. swolen = swollen
348, fn. settlemenrs = settlements
349. boldy = boldly
350. colateral = collateral
351. unmodifyed = unmodified
356. chrystaline = crystalline
356. turkies = turkeys
357. cerulian = cerulean
357. tantalising = tantalizing
362. distace = distance
363. toublesome = troublesome
363. miceous = micaceous
363, 364. stratas = strata
364. releived = relieved
364. carravan = caravan
365. superintendant = superintendent
368. apropriated = appropriated
372. first word in l. 3. where = were
376. liniar = linear
382. cinerious = cinereous
385. probosces = proboscis
386. diveloping = developing
387. crystaline = crystalline
387, 388. detatched = detached
390. avacuated = evacuated
390. assylum = asylum
391. routs = routes
393. sheding = shedding
395. lanciolate = lanceolate
397. refited = refitted
401. blosoms = blossoms
402. perceptably = perceptibly
405. lanciolate = lanceolate
409. umbragious = umbrageous
412. lanciolate = lanceolate
412. herbacious = herbaceous
415. perigrinations = peregrinations
416. fortess = fortress
417. verticilate = verticillate
418. equiped = equipped
421. herbacious = herbaceous
422. admixtore = admixture

422. steril = sterile
422. stratas = strata
423. exhilerating = exhilarating
423. fubulated = subulated
426. purpleish = purplish
426. particulary = particularly
427. permited = permitted
428. consistance = consistence
428. tumbe = tumble
431. equipt = equipped
431. thiner = thinner
435. stratas = strata
438. rout = route
438. controul = control
439. boilen = boiled
441. forwad = forward
442. stillated = stellated
442. pericarpes = pericarp
442. oleagenous = oleaginous
445. tollerable = tolerable
446. thalame = thalamus
449. frienship = friendship
454. eves = eaves
454. wariors = warriors
454, fn. sanctorium. Not a recognized word, but obviously equivalent to sanctuary.
459. barke = bark
461. heterogenious = heterogeneous
461. testacious = testaceous
467. staminae = stamina
467, fn. seperate = separate
468. pericarpe = pericarp
475. miceous = micaceous
475. chrystallization = crystallization
475. alluminous = aluminous
475. petrefaction = petrifaction
475. calcarious = calcareous
475. fossile = fossil
476. desicated = desiccated
476. chrystallization = crystallization
476. alluminous = aluminous
476. miceous = micaceous
476. lanciolatis = lanceolatis
476. lanciolato = lanceolato-
476. baceis = baccis
478. immeiately = immediately
478, 479. lanciolate = lanceolate
480. furrs = furs
484. symetry = symmetry
484. difidence = diffidence
485. nights = rights
486. principle = principal
486. retun = return
486. complyed = complied
492. makind = mankind

492. repeling = repelling
495. elctive = elective
495, fn. excellentr = excellent
496. percieves = perceives
497. foretel = foretell
498. decrepid = decrepit
500. bareing = baring
501. frized = frizzed
501. tossil = tassel

501. cartilagenous = cartilaginous
503. hieroglyphick = hieroglyphic
503. scroles = scrolls
505. practifed = practised
509. neting = netting
509. seperately = separately
515. renegadoes = renegades
519. harrangues = harangues

The following list includes various cases of misplaced, superfluous, or omitted words, faulty punctuation, and disagreement in number between subject and verb, which it has seemed advisable to correct in the text. On too many pages to list here, Bartram has consistently but improperly written "sat" instead of "set" for the past tense of "set," in such expressions as "sat off" or "sat sail"; and this peculiarity of style also has been corrected as far as noted. On the other hand, numerous minor cases of substandard punctuation, offering no appreciable perplexity to the reader, have been retained as in the original.

xv. follows = follow (families)
xvii. (Palms and Magnolia) strikes = strike
xvii. Comma inserted after Linum.
xvii. remains = remain (tribes)
xxii. (larva and plant) rises = rise; increases = increase; arrives = arrive
xxii. (difference) are = is
xxv. (fruit) are = is
xxix. spider, on a leaf = spider on a leaf,
xxxi–xxxii. (harmony) animate = animates
xxxii. (red) thrush = thrushes
6. Commas inserted after Itea and Iva.
9–10. (congregation) consist = consists
10. Comma inserted after Itea.
15, l. 1, first word, "ped" deleted as inadvertent duplication of part of previous word.
24. proceed = proceeds (a peduncle)
24. Comma inserted after Itea.
29, l. 2. Comma inserted after Cercis.
81. Larva = Larvae (descend)
85. (Magnolia) are = is
86. like a an = like an
94. (ridges) produces = produce
105. (surface) are = is
133. (tail) represent = represents
133. (part) are = is
137. was = were (swamps)
149. (sides) is = are
149. is = are (eyes)
153. (angle) terminate = terminates

160. meanders = meandering
163. insect = insects (were)
164. (pubescence and vesiculae) feels = feel; emits = emit
169. (stone) serve = serves
172. (towee bird) are = is
172. are = is (a species)
174. (end) are = is
176. (skin) peel = peels
193. Comma inserted after Tobacco.
193. (plantations) lies = lie
209. genera = genus
221. Comma inserted after Morus.
225, l. 13. river = rivers
229. to fro = to and fro
234. (soil and climate) appears = appear
273. (snake) are = is
276. (snake) devour = devours
278. (frog) are = is (2)
279. (species) are = is (2)
280. naturalist = naturalists
281, l. 15. Semi-colon transposed from before to after (putorius).
281. (house-rat) are = is
281. muskrat = muskrats (are)
282. wild-cat = wild-cats (are)
282. (sides) is = are
284. (squirrel) are = is (2)
284. (rabbit) are = is
288, lines 3–4. Commas transposed from before to after: (vitia sativa), (raphanus), (lactuca), and (cepa). Comma inserted after (phaccolus).

292. and and reside = and reside
297. (oryz zizania) are = is
299. (nonpareil) are = is
302, last par. will will = will. The last seven words of the paragraph are missing in some copies of the book.
303. Citruel = Citruels (are)
314, 315. lamina = laminae
325. appears =appear (niches)
326. an inundation =inundations
328. (Azalea) abound = abounds; illuminate = illuminates
329. (There) are = is (abundance)
332. (grounds) was = were
342. Comma inserted after Viola.
342. (descent) were = was
347. (had) fell = fallen
381. lies = lie (fields)
384. (territory and space) presents = present
385. (this species) lie = lies
398. (fields) presents = present

408, lines 2–3. Question marks replaced by exclamation points.
410. appears = appear (vestiges)
412. drank = drunk
416. (rivers) fills = fill
423. (species) produce their = produces its
424. crocodile = crocodiles (are)
427. (expansion) strike = strikes
428, lines 4–5. inunda- about tions, are = inundations, are about
451. assembly taken = assembly have taken
452. (drink and light) continues = continue
459, l. 9. the the = the
469. (Tannier) are . . . plants = is a . . . plant
479, l. 1. to = from
496, l. 11. chief = chief's
504. (this) insignia = insigne
514. (each) contribute = contributes

GENERAL INDEX

THIS INDEX is essentially complementary to the Annotated Index (pp. 427–667). The latter pertains only to that part of the present volume which represents Bartram's own *Travels*. The present index covers most of the remaining parts (Preface, Introduction, Commentary, and definitions or remarks—but not first-position entries—in the Annotated Index). It may be expected to provide the readiest means for locating by their modern names the plants, animals, minerals, and geographical features discussed by Bartram. It also lists the names of persons mentioned in the new matter, including authors whose publications are cited. Locality names that appear in subordinate position in the Annotated Index in connection with the page references are not indexed here on the basis of such mention.

References in this General Index are to pages of the present volume.

Abbot, John, xxvi, 498
Abies balsamea, 595
Acacia, rose, 613
Academy of Natural Sciences of Philadelphia, ix, xi, 335, 405, 600
Acanthis linaria linaria, 465
Accipiter cooperii, 502
Acer pennsylvanicum, 429; *rubrum*, 429, 561; *saccharum*, 429; *spicatum*, 429
Aconitum uncinatum, 429
Acris gryllus dorsalis, 513; *gryllus gryllus*, 513
Actaea pachypoda, 429
Actinomeris alternifolia, 482
Actitis macularia, 652
Adair, James, cited, 345, 348, 424, 473
Adams, John, xxii
Adder's tongue, 500
Aëdes, 567
Aesculus glabra, 431; *neglecta*, 430; *oboriginea*, 431; *parviflora*, 400, 430; *pavia*, 431; *sylvatica*, 430, 431, 589
Aëtobatus narinari, 635
Agave neglecta, 431
Agelaius phoeniceus phoeniceus, 634, 638
Agkistrodon piscivorus, 566

Ahaya, 367
Aimophila aestivalis aestivalis, 632
Aiton, William, cited, xxii, 405, 641, 667
Aix sponsa, 436, 643
Ajaia ajaja, 597
Alabama River, Ala., 404, 405
Alachua, ancient, Fla., 368
Alachua country, Fla., 366
Alachua Savanna, Fla., 353, 363, 367, 368, 370, 371, 621, fig. 18
Alachua Sink, Fla., 369, 627, fig. 18
Allen, Elsa G., cited, 467
Allen, J. A., cited, 370, 468
Alligator(s), xxv, 348, 355, 356, 358, 369, 373, 433, 487, fig. 12
Alligator Hole, Fla., 374, 375
Alligator mississipiensis, 433, 487
Allium cepa, 582
Allspice, 572
Alnus rugosa, 433
Alosa sapidissima, 624
"Alph, the sacred river," 363
Altamaha Grit Region, Ga., 341
Altamaha River, Ga., 337, 338, 346, 348, 417, 571
Ameiurus natalis erebennus, 467
Amelia Island, Fla., 339, 349

703

American Philosophical Society, ix, xviii, 448, 510, 511, 555
American Quarterly Review, xxv
American Society Held in Philadelphia for Promoting Useful Knowledge, xviii
Americans, 445
Amherst Papers, 503
Amia calva, 570
Amianthum muscaetoxicum, 563
Amite River, La., 408
Ampelopsis arborea, 524
Amphibians, 611
Amyda ferox, 365, 648
Amygdalus persica var. *nucipersica*, 573
Ananas sativus, 456
Anas acuta, 435; *carolinensis*, 436; *platyrhynchos platyrhynchos*, 435
Anastasia Island, Fla., 616
Andrew, Benjamin, 336, 416
Andrews, Mr., 346
Anemone, rue, 438
Anemonella thalictroides, 438
Anhinga anhinga colubrina, 478, 629; *anhinga leucogaster*, 478, 629
Anise: purple, 532; yellow, 362, 532
Anolis carolinensis, 377, 469, 554
Anopheles, 567
Anoüs stolidus stolidus, 634
Anser albifrons, 441; *anser*, 519
Anthus rubescens rubescens, 433
Apalachicola, Ala., 399, 400, 401, 415
Aphelocoma coerulescens, 483, 543; *floridana*, 483, 543
Apios americana, 518
Apis mellifera, 452
Apple: 603; narrow-leaved crab, 486, 603
Aquila, 496; *chrysaëtos canadensis*, 359
Aramus guarauna pictus, 358, 488, 642, fig. 15
Arbutus, trailing, 499
Archilochus colubris, 530, 653
Archosargus probatocephalus, 624
Ardea herodias herodias, 442; *herodias wardi*, 443
Arenaria interpres morinella, 567
Arethusa bulbosa, 444
Arisaema triphyllum, 444
Aristolochia durior, 444
Arlington, Fla., 350
Arrow-wood, southern, 658
Arthur, John Preston, cited, 392, 446
Arundinaria gigantea, 405, 462, 463, 610; *tecta*, 462, 463, 610
Ascia monuste, 459

Asclepias humistrata, 444; *lanceolata*, 444; *pedicellata*, 445
Ash: water, 511; white, 511
Ashwood, N.C., 420, 438, 449
Asimina angustifolia, 439; *incana*, 440; *pigmea*, 439, 440; *secundiflora*, 440; *triloba*, 439, 440
Asio flammeus flammeus, 637; *otus wilsonianus*, 637
Aster, climbing, 445
Aster carolinianus, 445
Astor, Fla., 354, 631
Ata-kullakulla, 391, 392, 637
Audubon, John James, cited, 355, 359; and John Bachman, cited, 609
Augusta, Ga., 340–342, 345, 382, 414
Auricularia auricula-judae, 514
Avena sativa, 579
Avens, 466, 517
Avicennia nitida, 612
Avocado, 550
Aythya affinis, 436; *marila nearctica*, 436
Azalea: flame, 446, 447; pink, 447; showy, 446, 447; swamp, 447

Bailey, L. H., cited, 464, 659
Bailley, James, 417
Baldpate, 435
Baldwin, William, cited, xxiii, xxxii, 397, 540, 625
Balsam-apples, 566
Balsam fir, 595
Banana: common, 570; plantain, 570
Baneberry, white, 429
Bangs, Outram, cited, 633
Baobab tree, 429
Baptisia, 630
Barbour, Thomas, cited, 628, 629
Barclay, Robert, 559
Barnet, Colonel, 342, 344, 345, 393, 414, 477
Barnhart, John Hendley, cited, 498, 511, 615
Barrington Road, Ga., 337
Bartlett, Colonel, 448
Barton, Benjamin Smith, xxii, xxvi–xxviii, xxx, xxxi, xxxiii–xxxv, 405, 423, 430, 431, 466, 483, 619, 644, 657; cited, 376, 442, 464, 479, 512, 527, 548, 568, 622, 638, 662
Barton, William P. C., cited, xxxv
Bartram, John, xvii, xxi, 335, 336, 340, 360, 380, 381, 406, 415, 422, 431, 494, 503, 510, 511, 549, 568, 628,

638, 644, 666; cited, v–vii, xviii–xx, xxxii, 337–339, 351, 353–355, 358, 362, 373, 375, 376, 382, 414, 418–420, 449, 462, 466, 485, 509, 515, 521, 532, 569, 615, 616, 636, 651
Bartram, John, Jr., xxix, 619
Bartram, Mary, 420
Bartram, Moses, xix
Bartram, Sarah, 420
Bartram, Colonel William, xvii, xix, 420, 445
Bartram, William, 549, 568, 638; cited, v–vii, xi, xxi, xxvii, xxix, 336–338, 340, 342, 344–346, 350, 351, 353–358, 361, 363, 366, 368–371, 373–377, 379, 383, 400, 407, 414, 415, 423, 424, 441, 442, 449, 451, 454, 459, 469, 473, 481, 498, 499, 519, 520, 553, 560, 562, 569, 584, 614, 615, 625, 628, 636, 660, 666
Bartram, William, Jr., xix, 420
Bartram Association, John, viii
Bartram's Mound, Fla., 355
Basil, 476; red, 597
Bass: Calico, 449; Large-mouthed, 355, 653
Basswood, 643, 646
Baton Rouge, La., 409, 410
Battle Lagoon, Fla., 355, 360, fig. 10
Battle of Bloody Marsh, Ga., 512, 581
Bay: dune red, 572; loblolly, 519; red (*Gordonia*), 519; red (*Persea*), 450, 549; sweet, 549; white, 558, 559
Bayberry, northern, 572
Baygall, 364
Bayou Manchac, 408, 409, 531
Bean, wild, 592
Beans, 352
Bear(s): Eastern Black, 452; Florida, 451, 452; Louisiana, 410, 452
Bear-foot, 599
Beards Bluff, Ga., 346
Beaverdam Creek, Ga., 341
Beavers, Carolina, 452
Beck, Jeff, 386
Bee, honey, 406
Beech, American, 501
Beecher Point, Fla., 353, 569
Beetles, lamellicorn, 622
Befaria racemosa, 545, 612, 625
Beggar-ticks, 453, 482, 525
Belemnitella americana, 452
Bellwort, 657
Benham, Louisa Bryan Chaires, xi
Bent, Arthur Cleveland, cited, 479

Berchemia scandens, 611, 659, 667
Beresford, Lord, 358
Beresford plantation, Fla., 358
Bernard, Mr., 358
Betony, wood, 590
Betsy and Polly, 336
Betula lenta, 453; *nigra*, 453
Bidens, 482
Big Buffalo Creek, Ga., 395
Big Wacasassa River, Fla., 371
Bignonia capreolata, 453
Birch: black, 453; river, 453
Bird migration, 377
Birds, list of, 378
Birdtown, N.C., 580
Bishop, Sherman C., 428, 442
Bison, American, 377, 458
Bison bison bison, 458
Bittern: American, 443; Eastern Least, 443
Black Belt, Ala., 402, 596
Black's Brook, Ga., 388
Black's Creek, Ga., 388, 457
Blackbird, Rusty, 498
Bladdernut, 634
Blatchley, W. S., cited, 352, 355
Blazing star, 526
Bloodroot, 619
Bloody Marsh, Ga., 349
Blue beech, 465
Blue Creek, Fla., 354, 361
Blue flag, 541
Blue Island, Fla., 354
Blue Marl Region, Ala., 402
Blue Ridge, 442
Blue Sink, Fla., 374, 375, 434
Blue Springs, Fla., 358, 510
Blue Springs, Ga., 341, 414, 632, fig. 29
Blueberry, 657
Bluebird, Eastern, 455, 568
Boats, skin, 413
Boatswain or Bosten, 400
Bobolink, 498, 499, 613
Bob-white(s), Eastern, 603, 644
Bombus, 452, 459
Bombycilla cedrorum, 435
Bombyx mori, 626
Bonasa umbellus monticola, 566; *umbellus umbellus*, 644
Bos taurus, 458, 459, 461, 467, 485, 585, 634
Bosc, L. A. G., 376
Botanical Garden, Bartram's, xvii, xx, xxviii–xxxv, 448, 600
Botaurus lentiginosus, 443

Bowfin, 570
Boyd, Mark F., xi, 407; cited, 369, 373, 441, 631
Bramlitt, A. F., 343
Brannon, Peter A., x, 399; cited, 401
Branta canadensis canadensis, 441, 515
Brassica, 608
Bream: Copper-nosed, 455, 456; Red-breasted, 456, 610; Shell-cracker, 456; yellow, 360
Breech-clout, 506
Brett-James, Norman G., cited, 494, 510
Brevoort, J. C., 388
Brickell, John, xxvi
Brier Creek, Ga., 341, 342, 382
Brinton, Daniel G., cited, 349, 569, 655
British, 415–418, 445, 446, 458, 515, 564, 637, 666
British Museum (Natural History), ix, xx, 376, 439, 441, 486, 559, 628
Broad River, Ga., 344, 345, 393
Broughton Island, Ga., 348, 379, 380
Brown, Charles Brockden, xxx
Brown, Clair A., xi, 457, 475, 657, 658, 663
Brown, John P., cited, 392, 446
Brown, General Thomas, 420
Brown's Cliffs, La., 409
Browne, Governor Montfort, 409
Brunnichia cirrhosa, 607
Brunswick, Ga., 338
Brunswick, N.C., 419
Bryan, Jonathan, 418
Bryant, Henry, cited, 359
Bubo virginianus virginianus, 584, 637; *virginianus wapacuthu*, 636
Buccinum labyrinthus, 477
Bucephala albeola, 435, 436; *clangula americana*, 435
Buckeye: Carolina, 430, 431, 589; red, 430; white, 400, 430
Buckley, S. B., cited, 592
Buckthorn(s), 611, 626
Buffalo Bluff, Fla., 379
Buffalo Creek, Ga., 344
Buffalo Lick, Ga., vi, 343–345, fig. 7
Buffaloes, 382
Bufflehead, 435, 436
Bufo terrestris, 513
Bugbane, false, 530
Bullace, 659
Bullfrog, Southern, 377, 513
Bumblebees, 452
Bumelia tenax, 626
Bunting: Eastern Painted, 551, 575, 585; Indigo, 360, 531, 551, 552

Burke, R. P., xi, 402
Burnet, 619
Burningtown, N.C., 646
Burningtown Creek, N.C., 390, 391, 544
Burton, E. Milby, x
Busyon, 479
Buteo jamaicensis borealis, 502
Butorides virescens virescens, 443, 454
Butterflies, 587
Butterfly, Zebra, 459
Butterfly pea, 476
Button-bush, 468

Cacalia fruticosa, 460
Cacao trees, 645
Cadbury, John W., III, x, 428, 459, 476
Caesalpinia pulcherrima, 598
Calabash, 519
Calebee Creek, Ala., 412
Calhoun, Mrs. E. M., viii
Calhoun Ferry, Ga.-S.C., 383
Calico-bush, 545
Callicarpa americana, 461, 543
Callinectes sapidus, 362, 486
Calonyction aculeatum, 480
Calopogon, 551
Calumet, 373
Calvert, Philip P., x
Calycanthus floridus, 461
Camak, Ga., 393, 394
Cambarus, 486
Camellia: mountain, 634; silky, 634
Camellia japonica, 462
Cameron, Alexander, 383, 384, 392
Camp Branch, Fla., 363, 364
Campephilus principalis, 593
Camphor tree, 550
Campsis radicans, 453
Cane(s): giant, 405, 462, 463, 610; small, 462, 463, 610
Canis familiaris, 490, 494; *lupus lycaon*, 665; *niger niger*, 664
Canna: golden, 463; red, 463
Canna flaccida, 463
Cannabis sativa, 463, 525
Cape Fear River, N.C., xvii, xix, 420
Capella gallinago delicata, 622
Caper bush, 464
Capparis spinosa, 464
Capra hircus, 546
Caprimulgus carolinensis, 464, 662; *vociferus vociferus*, 464, 574, 662
Capsicum, 591; *frutescens*, 464
Carbo auritus, 479; *floridanus*, 479
Cardinal: Eastern, 555; red, 500
Cardinal flower, 554; spear, 499–500

Carlyle, Thomas, cited, xxvii
Carney's Cowpens, Ga., 339
Carpinus caroliniana, 465; *ostrya*, 465
Carpodacus purpureus purpureus, 512, 513
Carroll, B. R., cited, 450, 470, 521, 564
Carrot, 492
Cary, Mrs. C. Reed, viii
Carya, 526; *cordiformis*, 544; *glabra*, 544; *illinoensis*, 545; *ovata*, 544; *tomentosa*, 544
Casmerodius albus egretta, 442
Cassena, 531
Cassidix mexicanus major, 542; *mexicanus torreyi*, 520
Cassin, John, cited, 359
Castanea dentata, 472, 501; *pumila*, 501
Castiglioni, Luigi, cited, 393, 511
Castilleja coccinea, 449
Castillo de San Marcos, Fla., 466
Castor canadensis carolinensis, 452
Cat: Southeastern Yellow, 467; Southern Channel, 467
Catalpa bignonioides, 466
Catbrier(s), 628
Catchflys, 493
Cate, Margaret Davis, x; cited, 348, 508, 512, 574, 581, 618, 631
Cate, Margaret Davis, Dolores B. Colquitt, and Mary Wylie McCarty, cited, 348, 349, 564
Caterpillar, Tent, 467
Catesby, Mark, xx, xxi, 377, 378, 382, 427, 448; cited, 376, 429, 433, 435, 436, 440, 442–444, 447, 450, 453, 454, 461, 464, 466, 468, 470, 471, 476, 478, 479, 481, 483, 486, 488–490, 494, 495, 498, 499, 501–503, 512, 517, 519, 520, 522, 523, 527, 528, 543–545, 549, 551, 552, 555, 556, 559, 560, 563, 565–568, 570, 571, 576, 581, 583, 588–593, 598, 602–606, 608, 614, 616, 618, 620, 627, 634, 638, 642, 651, 653, 654, 667
Cathartes aura septentrionalis, 459, 660
Catoma Creek, Ala., 402, 411, 487
Catoptrophorus semipalmatus inornatus, 664; *semipalmatus semipalmatus*, 525, 664
Catskill Mountains, N.Y., xvii, 376
Cattle, 344, 367, 369, 382, 592
Caulophyllum thalictroides, 550
Cedar: red, 467, 545; southern red, 545
Cedar Bluff Landing, Ga., 381
Centropristis striatus, 449

Centurus carolinus carolinus, 593
Century-plant, wild, 431
Cephalanthus occidentalis, 468
Cephalopod mollusk, 452
Ceratiola ericoides, 499
Cercis canadensis, 468
Cereus, night-blooming, 460
Certhia familiaris americana, 468
Cervus canadensis canadensis, 498; *virginianus*, 469
Chacala Pond, Fla., 367–369, 547
Chaenobryttus coronarius, 360, 456, fig. 13; *gulosus*, 360, 456
Chaetura pelagica, 527
Chaires, McQueen, 372
Chalmers, Lionel, xix, 336
Chamaecyparis thyoides, 468, 491
Chamaedaphne, 437
Chamomile, 441
Chaptalia tomentosa, 591
Charadrius melodus, 470; *semipalmatus*, 469; *vociferus vociferus*, 470; *wilsonia wilsonia*, 470
Charleston, S.C., xx, 336, 346, 353, 380, 381, 415, 418
Charleston Packet, 336
Charlotia, Fla., 352
Chat, Yellow-breasted, 471
Chatelain, Verne E., cited, 466, 509, 617
Chattahoochee River, Ga.–Ala., 347, 366, 398, 399, 413, 441
Chattooga River, Ga.–S.C., 386, 654
Chelone glabra, 471
Chen caerulescens, 440, 441, 455; *hyperborea atlantica*, 441; *hyperborea hyperborea*, 441, 455
Cherokee Corner, Ga., 344, 345
Cherokee towns, 393; trail, Ga., 342–344
Cherry: laurel, 601, 602; sour, 601; wild black, 601, 602
Chesser, Allen, 355
Chester, Governor Peter C., 406
Chestnut, 403, 501
Cheston, Mrs. Edward M., viii; cited, 449
Chiaha, Ala., 413
Chickadee: Black-capped, 588; Northern Carolina, 588
Chiefland, Fla., 371
Chinquapin, Piedmont, 501
Chionanthus virginica, 474
Chipmunk: Eastern, 634; Fisher's, 634
Chironia dodecandra, 474
Choga Creek, N.C., 391

Chordeiles minor, 662; *minor chapmani,*
   574; *minor minor,* 464, 574
Chortophaga viridifasciata, 554
Christmas berry, 556
Chrysops, 445, 506
Chuck-will's-widow, 464, 662
Cicadas, 475
Cinchona officinalis, 606
Cinnamomum camphora, 550; *zeylani-
   cum,* 550
Cinnamon tree, 550
Circaea quadrisulcata var. *canadensis,*
   475
Circus cyaneus hudsonius, 502
Cirsium, 465
Citrullus vulgaris, 475, 489, 563, 661
Citrus aurantifolia, 551; *aurantium,* 475,
   582, 583; *limonia,* 475, 550; *medica,*
   475; *medica* var. *limon,* 475; *sinensis,*
   582
Clam: Hard, 475, 480; Soft, 475
Clarkson, Gerardus, xxix
Clayton, John, xx, 448
Clayton, Ga., 635
Cleistes divaricata, 444
Clements Library, William L., ix, 395,
   503
Cleome pentaphylla, 476
Cliftonia monophylla, 625
Clinopodium coccineum, 516, 597
Clitoria mariana, 476
Clove tree, 466, 572
Clover, bush, 525
Cnemidophorus sexlineatus, 554
Coachwhips, 629
Coast Strip, Ga., 341
Coastal Plain, 341
Coccus cacti, 476
Coccyzus americanus americanus, 488
Cochineal plant, 460
Coco palm, 477
Coffea, 477
Cohen, I. Bernard, 346
Cohosh, blue, 550
Coker, W. C., cited, 419
Coker, William Chambers, and Henry
   Roland Totten, cited, 430, 620
Colaptes auratus luteus, 593
Colden, Cadwallader, xx, 448
Coleridge, Samuel Taylor, xxiv, xxv,
   xxvii, 363, 371
Colinus virginianus virginianus, 603,
   644
Collins, Zaccheus, xxxii
Collinson, Peter, xvii–xxi, 360, 406, 419,
   448, 494

Colocasia antiquorum, 444, 497
Colonel's Island, Ga., 336, 542, 617
Coluber constrictor constrictor, 628;
   flagellum flagellum, 628, 629; *melano-
   leucus,* 376; *quadrivittatus,* 628
Columbigallina passerina passerina, 478,
   495
Comptonia peregrina, 552
Cone-flowers, 616
Conrad, T. A., cited, 365, 382, 475
Constitutional Convention, xxix
Contopus virens, 570
Conuropsis carolinensis carolinensis,
   587, 602
Convallaria montana, 480, 551
Cooke, C. Wythe, cited, 362
Coolome, Ala., 401, 402, 411, 412
Coontie, 666, 667
Cooper, J. G., cited, 354
Cooper, Lane, cited, v, xxvii
Cooper River, S.C., 418
Coosa River, Ala., 348
Coosawhatchie River, S.C., 348
Coot(s), American, 481, 514
Coquina, 419, 525, 635
Coragyps atratus, 359, 660
Cordle, Charles G., x, 662
Cormorant(s), 555; Double-crested,
   479; Florida, 479
Corn, Indian, 352, 667
Cornus alba, 482, 483; *amomum,* 482,
   483; *florida,* 483, 495; *foemina,* 483
Corse, Carita Doggett, cited, 615
Corvus brachyrhynchos brachyrhynchos,
   483; *brachyrhynchos pascuus,* 488;
   corax principalis, 483, 609; *floridanus,*
   364; *ossifragus,* 483, 488
Corylus, 504
Cotton: sea-island, 484, 485, 630; up-
   land, 484
Cottonmouth, 566
Cottontail(s), Eastern, 524, 606
Cottonwood, swamp, 599
Coues, Elliott, cited, xxx, 370, 378, 435,
   468, 497, 527, 568, 571, 593, 636,
   644, 652
Cougar(s): Eastern, 646; Florida, 377,
   646
Court House Gap, Ga., 386, 387, fig. 22
Cow-ford, Fla., 350
Cow parsnip, 525
Cowbird, Eastern, 498, 638
Cowee, N.C., 390, 392, fig. 23
Coweta, Ala., 399, 400
Cowkeeper, 351, 366, 367
Cowpea(s), 451, 495, 590

Cowpen Pond, Fla., 364, 365, 370, 375, 523, fig. 17
Crabs, Blue, 362, 486
Crane(s): Florida Sandhill, 358, 365, 367, 368, 371, 486, 522, fig. 14; Whooping, 522, 636
Creek Confederation, 346
Creek towns, 414
Creeper, Brown, 468
Crescent Lake, Fla., 496
Cresson, Ezra T., Jr., x, 428, 499, 518
Crickets, Black Field, 487
Crinum americanum, 487
Crocethia alba, 619, 652
Crocus, autumn, 477
Croom, H. B., cited, 335
Crossbill, Red, 556
Crotalus adamanteus, 609; horridus horridus, 609
Crow(s): Carrion, 359; Eastern, 483; Fish, 483, 488; Florida, 488
Crow poison, 525
Crown-beards, 658
Cuckoo, Yellow-billed, 488
Cucumber-root, Indian, 562
Cucumber tree, 558, 559
Cucumis sativus, 489
Cucurbita moschata, 599, 602; okeechobeensis, 633; pepo, 489; pepo var. condensa, 489, 632, 633
Culex, 567
Culpeper Creek, Ga., 397, 640
Cumberland Island, Ga., 339, 349
Cumberland River or Sound, Ga., 349
Cuming, Sir Alexander, 387, 392, 445
Curlew(s): Eskimo, 576; Hudsonian, 490, 576; Long-billed, 576; Spanish, 359
Curtiss, A. H., cited, 464, 586
Cuscowilla, Fla., 366, 367
Custard-apple, 465
Cutler, Manasseh, xxix
Cutler, William Parker, and Julia Perkins Cutler, cited, xxix
Cutoff (River), Ala., 405
Cyanocitta cristata bromia, 483, 543
Cydonia oblonga, 490
Cylindrosteus platostomus platyrhincus, 515
Cymling(s), 489, 632, 633
Cynoscion, 653
Cypress: pond, 489, 491; river, 489, 491
Cypress vine, 541
Cyprinus coronarius, 360
Cypripedium calceolus, 491
Cyrilla racemiflora, 437, 491

Dacre's Tavern, Ga., 341
Dahoon, 531
Daisy, pineland, 591
Daption capensis, 591
Darien, Ga., 337, 338, 346, 348
Darlington, E. P., 407
Darlington, William, xxxiii; cited, xviii, xxiii, xxix, xxxii, 336, 415, 437, 449, 467, 469, 487, 497, 510, 549, 628, 640
Dasyatis sabinus, 635
Daucus carota, 492
Daudin, F. M., cited, 377
Davenport, Jouett, x
Day-flower, 479
Deadman's Creek, Ala., 411
De Brahm, John Gerar William, xviii, 335, 639; cited, 508
Deep Creek, Fla., 364
Deer, White-tailed, 367, 368, 370, 458, 468, 492, 614, 627
Deer-flies, 445
Deer-grass(es), 612
Deer lick, 344
Deirochelys reticularia, 647
Delafield, Mrs. Violetta W., ix
Delafield Collection, ix
Delphinium, 548
Dendrocopos pubescens medianus, 593; villosus villosus, 593
Dendroica castanea, 588; coronata coronata, 588, 666; dominica dominica, 588; magnolia, 588; palmarum hypochrysea, 587; petechia aestiva, 588; pinus pinus, 468; virens virens, 588
Desmanthus illinoensis, 565
Desmodium, 525
De Soto, Hernando, 347, 368, 388, 424
Devil's shoestring, 514
Devil-wood, 581, 582
Diadophis punctatus punctatus, 629
Diamondback (Rattler), 609
Dianthus armeria, 465
Dickcissel, 460
Dickenson, Jonathan, 350
Didelphis marsupialis, 582; marsupialis pigra, 582
Dionaea muscipula, 419, 494, 498
Dioscorea, 666
Diospyros virginiana, 494, 591
Dirca palustris, 381
Dobbs, Governor Arthur, 419
Doctortown, Ga., 346
Doggett, Carita, 655
Dogwood: flowering, 483, 495; silky, 482, 483; stiff, 483

Dogwood forest, Ala., 403
Dolichonyx oryzivorus, 498, 499, 613
Dolichos, 451
Dolphin(s), Bottlenose, 600
Dove: Eastern Ground, 478, 495; Eastern Mourning, 478, 495
Drayton, John, cited, 380, 381, 384, 385, 387, 389, 393, 462, 500, 637
Drayton, W. H., 393
Drayton Hall, S.C., 381
Drayton's Island, Fla., 354, 363, 375, 497, 541, 542
Drum: Black, 495; Red, 495
Drummer's Pond, Fla., 364, 627, fig. 17
Dryocopus pileatus pileatus, 593
Duck, Wood, 643
Dugouts, 463
Dunbar, William, xxvi, 409, 450
Duncan, Wilbur H., x
Dunlap, William, cited, xxx
Du Pratz, Le Page, 415, 424
Durand, Elias, cited, xxxiv
Dutchman's pipe, 444

Eagle(s): Golden, 359; Northern Bald, 502, 503; Southern Bald, 359, 496
Eardrops, 607
Earnest, Ernest, cited, 449, 615
Ebenezer, Ga., 341
Echeconnee Creek, Ga., 397, 647
Echinochloa, 623
Echoe, Tenn., 389
Eclipse of moon, 346, 417
Ectopistes migratorius, 478, 593
Edinburgh Review, xxiv
Edisto River, S.C., 599
Edwards, George, xvii, 378, 427, 499; cited, xvii, xxi, xxix, 379, 433, 435, 436, 440, 441, 454, 468, 469, 478, 498, 502, 503, 513, 561, 563, 567, 575, 576, 582, 587, 588, 591, 607, 608, 610, 611, 636, 637, 644, 645, 648, 652, 654, 660
Egmont, John James Percival, Lord, 349
Egret: American, 442; Snowy, 442
Eichhornia crassipes, 352
Elanoïdes forficatus forficatus, 502, 524
Elanus glaucus glaucus, 502; *leucurus majusculus,* 502
Elaphe guttata, 566; *quadrivittata quadrivittata,* 628
Elder: common, 618; southern, 618
Elephantopus, 474
Elizabethtown, N.C., 420
Elk, Eastern, 382, 383, 498
Elliott, Stephen, 487; cited, 437, 444,

447, 482, 483, 577, 578, 591, 596, 607, 626, 645, 646
Elliottia racemosa, 625
Elliptio, 572; *spinosus,* 410, 571
Ellis, John, 473, 667
Elm: Florida, 656; white, 656; winged, 656
Emerson, Ralph Waldo, xxvii
Empidonax virescens, 571
Enchanter's nightshade, 475
English, 340, 347, 348
Epigaea repens, 499
Epinephilus, 522
Equus caballus, 478, 528, 599
Eremophila alpestris alpestris, 433
Erethizon dorsatum dorsatum, 600
Ereunetes, 619; *pusillus,* 652
Erolia, 619; *minutilla,* 652
Erythrina arborea, 500; *herbacea,* 500
Erythronium ?americanum, 500
Escambia River, Ala., 403
Estatoah Creek, Ga., 389, 486
Estatoah Falls, Ga., 661
Ettinger, Amos Aschbach, cited, 581
Euarctos americanus americanus, 451; *americanus floridanus,* 451, 452; *americanus luteolus,* 452
Eudocimus albus, 359, 490, 642
Eugenia aromatica, 466, 476, 572
Eumeces fasciatus, 554; *inexpectatus,* 554; *laticeps,* 554
Euonymus americanus, 500
Euphagus carolinus, 498
Euphorbia heterophylla, 500, 501
Evans, William Bacon, viii
Evening primrose, Bartram's, 580
Everlasting, 518
Ewan, Joseph, x
Exell, A. W., cited, 439, 440

Fagin, N. Bryllion, cited, 363, 371, 473
Fagus grandifolia, 501; *grandifolia* var. *caroliniana,* 452, 501
Fairbanks, George R., cited, 509, 521, 617, 655
Falco columbarius columbarius, 502; *peregrinus anatum,* 502; *sparverius sparverius,* 503
Falling Creek, Ga., 386, 387, fig. 21
Fall-Line Sand Hills, Ga., 341, 394, 395
Falls Creek, N.C., 391, 613
Farmar, Robert, 404, 405, 410, 516
Fatio, Francis Philip, 351
Fayetteville, N.C., 421, 462, 488
Felis catus, 466; *concolor coryi,* 646; *concolor couguar,* 646

Fen rose, 433
Fern: cinnamon, 504; climbing, 504, 505; royal, 504
Fernald, Merritt Lyndon, cited, 428, 430, 438, 473, 480, 521, 525, 602, 604, 605, 628, 635
Fernald, Merritt Lyndon, and Alfred Charles Kinsey, cited, 473
Fernandina, Fla., 349
Fetter-bush, 437
Fever, 346
Ficus carica, 504
Filix scandens, 504
Finch, Eastern Purple, 512, 513
Fishes, 355, 358, 362, 365, 373
Fitzpatrick, John C., cited, xxii, xxix
Flagg, Wilson, cited, xxviii
Flamingo, West Indian, 592
Flat Pine Lands, Ga., 341
Flat Rock, Ga., 393–395, 506, fig. 25
Flaxes, 552
Flicker, Northern, 593
Flies, 570
Flint River, Ga., 397, 398
Flintlock gun, 514
Florida, xxi, 370
Florida caerulea caerulea, 442, 443
Flower, Mrs. Bee's, 657
Fly poison, 563
Flycatcher: Acadian, 571; Northern Crested, 570
Forbes, James Grant, cited, 372, 520, 521, 617
Fort Barrington, Ga., 337, 338
Fort Charlotte, S.C., 393
Fort Frederica, Ga., 349
Fort Howe, Ga., 508
Fort James, Ga., 382, 383, 392, 393
Fort Moore, S.C., 341, 382
Fort Perry, Ga., 398
Fort Picolata, Fla., 351
Fort Prince George, S.C., 384, 385, fig. 24
Fort St. Simons, Ga., 348
Fort Thoulouse, Ala., 411
Fort William, Ga., 349, 508
Fothergill, John, xix, xx, 405, 448, 469
Fothergilla gardeni, 510
Fowler, Henry W., ix; cited, 428
Fowler, J. R., 374
Fox, R. Hingston, cited, 510
Foxes, Gray, 510
Foxglove, false, 516
Fragaria, 636
Franklin, Benjamin, xviii, xx, xxi, xxiii, 448

Franklin, N.C., 389, 575
Franklin tree, 511, 519, fig. 3
Franklinia alatamaha, 337, 416, 417, fig. 3
Fraxinus, 445; *americana,* 511; *caroliniana,* 511
Frederica, Ga., 346, 348, 349
Free Library of Philadelphia, ix
Fregata magnificens rothschildi, 590
French, 393, 410, 503
Frog(s): American, 376; Florida Cricket, 513; Northern Leopard, 514; Southern Cricket, 377, 513; Southern Leopard, 377, 514
Fruitland Cove, Fla., 353
Fulica americana americana, 481, 514

Gallahan, Mr., 391
Gallberry, 601
Gallinula chloropus cachinnans, 607, 661
Gallinule, Florida, 607, 608, 661; Purple, 481, 608
Gall-of-the-earth, 600
Gallus gallus, 473, 477, 510, 525
Galphin, George, xviii, 380, 382, 414
Galphin's store, S.C., 341
Gama grass, 653
Gar: Eastern Long-nosed, 515; Eastern Short-nosed, 515
Garberia fruticosa, 460; *heterophylla,* 460
Garden, Alexander, xviii, xx, 448, 473, 498, 667
Gardenia jasminoides, 515
Gatschet, Albert S., cited, 414, 466
Gauterais, M. de la, 407
Gavia, 555; *arctica pacifica,* 478; *immer,* 479; *stellata,* 478
Gaylussacia, 657
Gelsemium sempervirens, 453, 543
General's Pond, Fla., 371
Gentian, soapwort, 516
Gentiana saponaria, 516
Geomys, 608; *pinetis pinetis,* 338, fig. 4
Georgia bark, 417, 449, 453, 625
Geothlypis trichas, 611
Gerardia, 516
Germany, James, 402, 411, 473, 648
Gervais, John Lewis, 380
Geum, 466
Gilia rubra, 394, 541
Ginseng, 586
Glaucomys volans querceti, 633
Gleditsia aquatica, 517; *triacanthos,* 517, 614

Gmelin, Jo. Frid., 497; cited, xxii, 645
Gnatcatcher, Blue-gray, 611
Godwit: Hudsonian, 576; Marbled, 575
Goff, John H., cited, 345, 394
Goggin, John M., 372; cited, 353
Goldeneye, American, 435
Goldenrod, 630
Goldfinch, Eastern, 465
Gold-fish, 344
Goldman, Edward A., cited, 665
Goodby's Creek, Fla., 351
Goode, G. Brown, cited, 469
Goodrich, Calvin, cited, 410, 571
Goose (or Geese): Blue, 440, 441, 455;
    Canada, 441, 515; Graylag, 519;
    Greater Snow, 441; Lesser Snow, 441,
    455; White-fronted, 441
Gopher, Georgia Pocket, 338, fig. 4;
    Pocket, 608
Gopherus polyphaemus, 366, 647
Gordon, Lord Adam, cited, 473, 494
Gordonia lasianthus, 417, 519
Gossypium barbadense, 484; hirsutum,
    484
Gourd, 489; Okeechobee, 633
Gowanloch, James N., cited, 352
Grackle(s): Boat-tailed, 520, 542;
    Florida, 454, 542; Stone's, 520
Grant, Governor James, xviii, 367, 509,
    564
Grant, Verne, cited, 494
Grant's Pass, Ala., 407, 581
Grape: Cherokee, 521; fox, 521; red-
    shank, 659; wine, 659
Graphite, 550
Grasshoppers, 554
Gray, Asa, cited, 438, 446, 447, 480, 530
Great Ridge, Ga., 344
Great Spirit, 424
Grebe: American Horned, 478; Pied-
    billed, 479
Greene, Earl R., et al., cited, 418
Greenwood's plantation, Fla., 351
Gromwell, false, 497
Gronovius, Joh. Fred., xvii, xx, 448
Grosbeak, Blue, 498, 555
Groundnut, 518
Grouse: Appalachian Ruffed, 566; East-
    ern Ruffed, 644
Grus americana, 486, 522, 636; canaden-
    sis pratensis, 486, 522, fig. 14
Gryllotalpa, 487
Gryllus assimilis, 487
Guavas, 602
Guggenheim Memorial Foundation,
    John Simon, viii, ix
Guiraca caerulea caerulea, 555

Gulf Hammock Region, Fla., 371
Gulf of Mexico, 406
Gull: Herring, 548; Ring-billed, 548
Gum: black, 576, 577; tupelo (Nyssa
    aquatica), 576; tupelo (Nyssa
    ogeche), 577
Gwinnett, Button, 557
Gymnocladus dioica, 522

Hackberry, 468
Haematopus palliatus palliatus, 525
Halesia carolina, 523; diptera, 523; te-
    traptera, 523
Half-way Pond, Fla., 363–365, 370, 375,
    fig. 17
Haliaeetus leucocephalus alascanus, 502,
    503; leucocephalus leucocephalus,
    359, 496
Hall's Creek, Ala., 404, 405
Halter, C. R., cited, 628
Hamamelis virginiana, 523
Hamilton, Alexander, xxix
Hamilton, Peter J., cited, 404, 405, 503,
    508, 517, 555
Hamilton, William, xxix, xxxiii, 618
Hammocks, 373
Hammond, Harry, cited, 341, 381, 500
Hanna, A. J., xi
Harden, William, cited, 458, 638, 666
Hargrett, Felix, viii
Harlequin Duck, 436
Harper, Francis, cited, vii, xi, xxi, 336,
    338, 354–360, 365, 366, 368, 376–
    378, 390, 413, 417, 441, 443, 449, 453,
    456, 460, 467, 468, 479, 483, 484,
    486, 488, 496, 502, 503, 511, 513,
    520, 522, 543, 548, 551, 554, 556–
    558, 560, 563, 564, 570, 571, 575,
    581, 584–588, 591, 604, 610, 616,
    626, 628, 629, 636, 642, 647, 648,
    654, 655, 660, 665
Harper, Francis, and Arthur N. Leeds,
    cited, 337, 417, 511
Harper, Roland M., vii, x, 372, 626;
    cited, 341, 362, 363, 371, 373, 381,
    402, 403, 405, 419, 430, 451, 493,
    516, 524, 560, 597, 625
Harris, John, cited, 337, 349
Harrold, Charles C., x, 395–397
Haw, southern black, 658
Hawk: Cooper's, 502; Duck, 502; East-
    ern Pigeon, 502; Eastern Red-tailed,
    502; Eastern Sparrow, 503; Marsh,
    502
Hawkins, Benjamin, 339, 398; cited,
    336, 387, 388, 401, 481, 505, 656
Hawkinsville, Fla., 358, 359

Hawthorn, Fla., 365
Hazelnut, 484
Head of Island, La., 408, 410
Heath Hen, 644
Hedrick, U. P., cited, 473
Helianthemum, 475
Helianthus radula, 616
Heliconius charithonius, 459
Helix, 477
Hemans, Felicia Dorothea, 340, 473
Hemlock: Canada, 525, 595; Carolina, 525
Hemp, 463
Hemp-vine, climbing, 500
Henderson, Archibald, cited, 421
Henry, Mrs. Bayard, viii
Henry, Mrs. J. Norman, viii
Hepatica, 438
Hepatica americana, 438
Heracleum lanatum, 525
Hercules' club, 667
Herlong, Z. C., xi, 366, 367
Heron(s), 375; Black-crowned Night, 442, 454; Eastern Green, 443, 454; Great Blue, 442; Little Blue, 442, 443; Louisiana, 443; Ward's, 443; Yellow-crowned Night, 443, 454
Heterodon, 659; *contortrix*, 609
Hewson, Thomas T., 335
Hexagenia limbata, 499; *orlando*, 499
Hibiscus aculeatus, 526; *coccineus*, 526; *moscheutos*, 526
Hickory, 545; bitternut, 544; pignut, 544; white-heart, 544
Hirundo pelagica, 527; *rustica erythrogaster*, 527, 639
Historical Society of Pennsylvania, ix, xxxii, 423, 510, 569
Histrionicus histrionicus, 436
Hitchcock, Charles Leo, cited, 557
Hiwassee River, Ga.–N.C.–Tenn., 613
Hobbs, Horton H., Jr., xi, 374, 428, 499
Hodgson, Adam, cited, 411
Hogarth, William, 392
Hog-choker, Southern, 507
Hog Island, Fla., 354, 542
Holbrook, John Edwards, cited, 628
Holly: American, 531; Bartram's, 600; myrtle-leaved, 531; narrow-leaved dahoon, 531
Ho[l?]mes, D., 648
Holt's Shop, Ga., 398
Homo sapiens, 561
Honeysuckle, coral, 555
Hoorah bush, 438
Hornbeam, hop, 465, 466
Horse(s), 348, 369, 370, 398, 410

Horse sugar, 528
Horseflies, 506, 527
Hosack, David, xxxiii
Howe, General William, 415
Howell, Arthur H., cited, 402
Howells, John Mead, xi
Hubbell, Theodore H., xi, 363
Hudson River, Ga., 345
Hume, H. Harold, cited, 582–583
Hummingbird, Ruby-throated, 530, 653
Hunt, Mrs. Roy Arthur, viii
Hunter, George, 387
Huntoon Island, Fla., 358
Hurricanes, 358
Hyacinths, 530
Hydranassa tricolor ruficollis, 443
Hydrangea, oak-leaved, 530
Hydrangea quercifolia, 397, 530
Hydrastis canadensis, 530
Hydrocotyle umbellata, 530
Hyla cinerea cinerea, 513; *gratiosa*, 513; *ocularis*, 513; *squirella*, 513
Hylocichla fuscescens fuscescens, 645; *guttata faxoni*, 645; *mustelina*, 645, 654
Hymenocallis coronaria, 587
Hypericum aureum, 398; *frondosum*, 398, 531
Hyssop, 531
Hyssopus officinalis, 531

Ibis(es): White, 359, 490, 642; Wood, 359, 515, 590, 636, 642
Ictalurus lacustris punctatus, 467
Icteria virens virens, 471, 515
Icterus, golden, 360
Icterus galbula, 360, 448, 531, 583; *spurius*, 448, 583
Ictinia misisippiensis, 503; *subcerulia*, 503
Ilex amelanchier, 600; *cassine*, 466, 531; *cassine* var. *angustifolia*, 531; *glabra*, 601; *myrtifolia*, 531; *opaca*, 531; *vomitoria*, 414, 466
Illicium floridanum, 532; *parviflorum*, 362, 532
Indian(s), v, x, xxv, 342, 345, 351, 354, 372, 382, 520, 583; Alachua, 368, 447; Atasi, 412; Atcik-hata, 347, 399, 400, 415; Calusa, 373, 396; Catawba, 347, 348; Cherokee, xxx, 380, 384, 385, 390–392, 400, 423, 445, 447, 462, 509, 520, 637; Chickasaw, 400, 414; Choctaw, 339; Coosa, 348, 536; Creek, xxx, 336, 339, 340, 347, 348, 351, 366, 399, 400, 415, 423, 424, 458, 637; Cusabo, 347, 348; Guale,

Indian(s) (*continued*)
  350; Hitchiti, 339, 340, 347, 399,
  415; Icosan, 348; Lower Creek, 400,
  414; Muscogulge, 359; Muskogee,
  347; Natchez, 410, 414, 415; Oconee,
  366, 396; Ogeechee, 347, 350; Osochi
  (or "Hooseche"), 415; Patica, 348;
  Potano, 368; Santee, 347; Savannah,
  347; Savannuca, 414; Seminole, xviii,
  339, 340, 348, 363, 366, 367, 372,
  396, 416; Shawnee, 347, 399, 414;
  Spanish, 366; Timucua, 348, 415;
  Tukabahchee, 347; Tuskegee (or
  Taskigi), 432; Upper Creek, 340,
  347, 348, 414; Utina, 348, 368; Wapoo, 347; Westo, 347; Yamacraw,
  340; Yamasee, 339, 340, 347, 348,
  357, 366, 396; Yuchi, 347, 350, 399,
  414
Indian: monuments, 383; mound(s),
  343, 349, 358, 366, 385, 388, 389;
  reed, 542; settlement, 352; town, 379;
  trading-path, 394
Indigo, 353; wild, 540, 630
Indigofera anil, 540; *caroliniana,* 540;
  suffruticosa, 540; *tinctoria,* 540
International Rules of Zoological No-
  menclature, 378, 428
Iotla Creek, N.C., 390
Ipomoea batatas, 450, 481, 600
Iridoprocne bicolor, 527
Iris, 506
Iron, 504
Isle Edelano, Fla., 354
Isle of Palms, Fla., 354, 361
Itea virginica, 542
Iva frutescens, 542
Ixea caelestina, 360
Ixia, purple-flowered, 361
Ixobrychus exilis exilis, 443

Jack-in-the-pulpit, 444
Jackson, Andrew, 408
Jacksonboro, S.C., 381, 418
Jacksonville, Fla., 350, 485
James and Johnson, xxii, 368
Jarrett Creek, N.C., 391
Jasmine, Cape, 515
Jasminum, 576
Jatropha stimulosa, 543
Jay: Florida, 364, 483, 543; Northern
  Blue, 483, 543
Jefferson, Thomas, xxvi, xxvii, xxix, 409;
  cited, xxii, 443, 489, 644
Jellyfish, 563
Jenkins, Charles F., viii; cited, 511

Jenkins, Mrs. Charles F., viii
Jessamine, yellow, 453
Johnson, Albert, 374
Johnson, Cecil, cited, 409, 457, 472,
  503, 553, 555
Johnson, Joseph, cited, 380, 462, 508,
  515, 637
Johnson, Fla., 364
Johnson's Spring, Fla., 361
Johnstone, Governor George, 503
Jones, Charles C., Jr., cited, 336, 348,
  383, 389, 398, 415, 437, 448, 450,
  512, 515, 562, 564, 638, 666
Jones, Frank Morton, 428, 459
Jones, John Paul, 515
Jones, Walter B., 404
Jore Mountain, N.C., 390
Jore (River), N.C., 390
Jore village, N.C., 390
Juglans nigra, 660
Junaluska Creek, N.C., 391, 392
Junco, Slate-colored, 589
Junco hyemalis hyemalis, 589
Juncus, 616
Juniper Creek, Fla., 361
Juniperus silicicola, 545; *virginiana,*
  467, 468, 545

Kalmia hirsuta, 338, 545; *latifolia,* 545
Kanapaha Sink, Fla., 371, 375, 547
Kaolin, 564
Kasihta (or "Usseta"), Ga., 399, 400,
  413
Keilman, Doctor, 335
Kellogg, Remington, cited, 356, 600
Kelly, Howard A., and Walter L. Bur-
  rage, cited, 469
Kelly, Hy., 380
Kentucky coffee-tree, 522
Kenwood, Fla., 364
Keowee, S.C., 392
Keowee River, S.C., 384, 385
Killdeer, 470
King of England, 392, 449
Kingbird, Eastern, 548
Kingfisher, Eastern Belted, 433
Kinglet: Eastern Golden-crowned, 610;
  Eastern Ruby-crowned, 610
King's Ferry, Fla., 339, 416, 650
Kingsley Creek, Fla., 350, 434
Kitchen middens, 624
Kite: Mississippi, 503; Swallow-tailed,
  502, 524; White-tailed, 502
Kniffen, Fred B., cited, 408
Kosteletzkya virginica, 433
Kubla Khan, 363

Lacerta, 554
Lactuca sativa, 550, 551
Ladies'-tresses, 582
Lady's slipper, 491
Lagenaria vulgaris, 519
Lake: Beresford, Fla., 353, 357, 358, 547, 554; Dexter, Fla., 354–357, 360, 361, 496, 547; George, Fla., 354, 361, 363, 521; Kerr, Fla., 362; Maurepas, La., 408, 410; Pontchartrain, La., 408; Waccamaw, N.C., 420
Lamarck, J. B. P. A. de Monet de, cited, xxii, 440
Lamboll, Thomas, 346
Lampropeltis elapsoides elapsoides, 629; *triangulum triangulum,* 629
Lanius ludovicianus ludovicianus, 459, 548; *ludovicianus migrans,* 548
Lantana camara, 548
Lapathum occidentale, 625
Larix laricina, 595
Lark, Northern Horned, 433
Larkspur, 493
Larus argentatus smithsonianus, 548, 549; *delawarensis,* 548, 549
La Salle, Sieur de, 538
Latham, John, cited, 652
Latherbush, 476
Laudonnière, René Goulaine de, 368
Laurel, mountain, 545
Laurens, Henry, xviii, 348, 557
Lawson, John, 424
Lazenby, C. P., 394
Lead plant, 435
Leatherwood, 494
Le Conte, John Eatton, 377; cited, xxxiv, 336, 587, 646
Le Conte, Joseph, cited, 337
Leeds, Arthur N., vi, xi, xii, 343, 346, 428, 505, 601
Leeds, Esther, viii
Leeds, Morris E., cited, xi
Lehmann, Rudolf, 344
Lepisosteus osseus osseus, 515
Lepomis auritus, 456, 610; *macrochirus purpurescens,* 455, 456; *microlophus,* 456
Lepus minor, 377; *sylvaticus floridanus,* 606
Lespedeza, 525
Lettsom, John Coakley, cited, 510
Leucophoyx thula thula, 442
Leucothoë acuminata, 437; *axillaris,* 437
Lewis Swash, S.C., 419, 639
L'Héritier de Brutelle, Charles Louis, cited, xxii

Liatris, 623
Library Company of Philadelphia, ix
Library of Congress, ix
Lichen(s), 482, 568
Ligusticum canadense, 438
Lilacs, 640
Lilium catesbaei, 551; *superbum,* 551
Lily: atamasco, 434; Bartram's celestial, 542; climbing, 517; leopard, 551; spider, 587; swamp, 487; Turk's cap, 551
Lily-of-the-valley, Alleghanian, 480
Lime Hills, Ala., 402
Lime-Sink Region, Ga., 341
Limosa fedoa, 575; *haemastica,* 576
Limpkin, Florida, 358, 488, 642, fig. 15
Linaria ciris ciris, 551, 575, 585; *cyanea,* 360, 552
Lindera bnezoin var. *pubescens,* 549
Linnaeus, Carolus, xviii, xx, 377, 427, 448, 497, 498, 667; cited, 335, 435, 436, 438, 447, 460, 464, 466, 478, 479, 482, 563, 575, 605, 634, 636, 660
Linné, Carolus a, cited, 435, 436, 446, 447, 462, 476, 479, 482, 484, 522, 563, 640
Linné, Carolus a (filius), cited, 611
Linnet, blue, 360
Linum, 506
Liquidambar styraciflua, 640
Liriodendron tulipifera, 552, 599
Listera smallii, 582
Little, Elbert L., Jr., cited, 417, 511, 519, 577
Little, J. B., cited, 403
Little Buffalo Creek, Ga., 395
Little Lake George, Fla., 353, 547, 552
Little Ogeechee Creek, Ga., 413
Little Orange Lake, Fla., 365, 548
Little River, Ga., 342, 343, 345
Little River, S.C., 419
Little St. Simon's Island, Ga., 349
Little Tennessee River, Ga.–N.C.–Tenn., 388–390, 472, 485, 643
Livingston, Philip, Jr., 472
Lizard(s): Green, 377; Pine, 377, 554; Six-lined, 554
Lobipes lobatus, 652
Lochloosa Creek, Fla., 365, 366, 370, 486
Locust: black (tree), 614; clammy, 613, 614; honey, 517; water, 517
Locust, Green-striped (Orthoptera), 554

Long, Bayard, ix, 394, 428, 541
Long Creek, Ga., 395
Long Pond, Fla., 371, 374, 375, 547
Long Warrior, 351; Pl. I
Longwood Foundation, viii
Loon: Common, 479; Pacific, 478; Red-throated, 478
Lophodytes cucullatus, 563
Loughabber, S.C., 383, 384, 392
Lowes, John Livingston, cited, 363
Loxia cerulea, 498; *curvirostra*, 556
Lucar carolinensis, 467, 556
Lupine, 339; lady, 556, fig. 6; sand-hills, 556
Lupinus nuttallii, 556; *villosus*, 339, 556, fig. 6
Lupus niger, 377
Luscinia megarhynchos, 592
Lutra canadensis lataxina, 584; *canadensis vaga*, 584
Lycium carolinianum, 556; *halimifolium*, 557
Lyell, Charles, cited, 341, 349, 350, 356, 382, 405, 409, 410, 511, 597, 626, 662
Lygodium palmatum, 504, 505
Lynx rufus, 466; *rufus floridanus*, 664; *rufus rufus*, 664
Lyon, John, 398, 417, 460, 517, 531, 592, 625
Lyonia ferruginea, 437; *fruticosa*, 437; *lucida*, 438; *racemosa*, 625

McCall, Hugh, cited, 417, 448, 562
MacCauley, Clay, cited, 473
McConkey, Edwin H., cited, 629
Macfie, T. G., x, 343
McIlhenny, E. A., cited, 356
McIntosh, Donald, 337
McIntosh, John, 381, 414
McIntosh, Lachlan, xxvii, 337, 348, 358, 370, 416, 417
McIntosh, Margery, 630
McIntosh, William, 557, 631
McIntosh family, 376, 447
McLatchie, Charles, 346
McLean, Richard A., x, 428, 446, 477, 479, 480, 523, 572
McQueen, A. S., and Hamp Mizell, cited, 356, 581
McVaugh, Rogers, cited, 394
Macon, Ga., 347
Macranthera flammea, 516
Maddox, (Jos.?), 562
Madison, James, xxix
Magnolia(s): Bartram's, 558, 560;

large-leaved, 559; mountain, 558, 559; southern, 549, 558–560
Magnolia acuminata, 558, 559; *auriculata*, 387; *fraseri*, 387, 558, 559; *glauca*, 560; *grandiflora*, 549, 558–560; *macrophylla*, 559; *pyramidata*, 337, 405, 558; *tripetala*, 560; *virginiana*, 558–560; *virginiana* var. *australis*, 558
Maiden-cane, 661
Maize, 482, 667
Malacosoma americana, 467
Mallard, Common, 435
Mallory, R. B., xi, 381
Mallow, 526
Malva paniculata, 561; *volubilis*, 560
Mammals, 377, 603
Manatee(s), Florida, 373, 561
Manatee Spring, Fla., 371, 373, fig. 19
Mangosteen, 515
Mangrove, black, 612
Manhatten, Fla., 354
Man-o'-war-bird, West Indian, 590
Maple: ash-leaved, 429; mountain, 429; red, 429, 561; sugar, 429
Mareca americana, 435
Marsh elder, 542
Marshall, Humphry, cited, 417, 422, 429
Marshall, Moses, 417
Marshall plantation, Fla., 351, 379
Martin, Alexander, xxix
Martin, Josephine Bacon, cited, 564
Martin, Purple, 527
Martin Creek, Ga., 503, fig. 21
Mason, George, xxix
Mason, Thomas, 336
Massachusetts Magazine, xxiv
Mayfield, Ga., 413
Mayflies, 499
May-pop, 520
Meadowlark, Eastern, 433
Medeola virginiana, 562
Meek, Alexander B., 388
Megaceryle alcyon alcyon, 433
Meherrin River, Va., 422
Melanerpes erythrocephalus erythrocephalus, 593
Melanitta perspicillata, 436
Meleagris gallopavo americana, 563, 654, 655; *gallopavo osceola*, 655; *gallopavo silvestris*, 563, 654, 655; *satyra*, 563
Melospiza georgiana, 589
Melsheimer, F. V., xxvi
Menticirrhus, 663

Mephitis mephitis elongata, 598, 599
Merganser: Hooded, 563; Red-breasted, 563
Mergus serrator serrator, 563
Merrill, E. D., cited, 407, 417, 430, 431, 437–440, 444, 445, 447, 449, 453, 460, 476, 481, 484, 500, 501, 504, 505, 511, 516, 517, 519, 521, 524, 525, 530, 531, 541, 542, 544, 545, 556, 558–561, 565, 577, 580, 582, 586, 587, 596, 601, 602, 604–606, 612, 613, 615, 616, 620, 623, 626, 633, 635, 638, 646, 656, 657, 659
Meyer, F. A. A., cited, xxvi, 379
Micanopy, Fla., 366
Mice: Cotton, 564; House, 564
Michaux, André, 460, 517, 551, 561, 565; cited, xxix, 362, 381, 387, 388, 437, 559, 625, 664
Michaux, François André, cited, xxix
Micheliella anisata, 477
Mico, 424
Micropterus salmoides, 653
Micrurus fulvius fulvius, 628
Middle Florida Flatwoods, 371
Midway, Ga., 336, 337, fig. 2
Midway River, Ga., 336
Mifflin, Thomas, xxii, xxiii, xxvii
Mikania scandens, 500
Milfort, Le Clerc, 415
Milkweed, 444
Miller, Gerrit S., Jr., and Remington Kellogg, cited, 428
Miller, Philip, cited, 463, 510
Miller, William Hubert, cited, 467
Mills, William H., v, 384
Mimosa procumbens, 565
Mimus polyglottos polyglottos, 566, 654
Mink, Salt-marsh, 565
Minnow, Bartram's, 519, fig. 8
Minorcans, 636, 655
Mississippi River, 346, 409
Mississippi Sound, Miss., 407, 630
Mitchell, John, xx
Mitchill, Samuel L., cited, 644
Mniotilta varia, 468
Mobile, Ala., 340, 404, 406, 407, 410
Mobile Delta, Ala., 404, 410
Mockingbird, Eastern, 566, 654
Mohr, Charles, cited, 559, 598, 614, 616
Mole(s): Florida, 566; Howell's, 566
Mole-crickets, 487
Mollusks, 349, 623–625; gastropod, 446, 476, 477, 479, 523; pelecypod, 475, 479, 572
Molothrus ater ater, 498, 638

Monkshood, clambering, 429
Montgomery, Charles B., 419, 494
Monthly Review, xxv
Moon flower, 480
Mooney, James, cited, 389, 392, 393, 445, 450, 471, 472, 474, 475, 497, 500, 527, 546, 572, 575, 580, 603, 623, 635, 637, 641, 643, 647, 654, 655, 661
Moore, Clarence B., cited, 360, 361, 569
Morning-glories, 480, 481, 541
Morus alba, 567, 570; *rubra*, 567, 570
Mosquito Grove, Fla., 357
Mosquito River (Lagoon), Fla., 335, 358
Motacilla aurocapilla, 654; *caerulea*, 611; *calendula*, 611; *chrysoptera*, 587; *virens*, 588
Moths, 591
Mount Hope, Fla., 353
Mount Magnolia, Ga., 386, 387
Mount Pleasant, Ga., 341, 381
Mount Royal, Fla., 353, 363, 568, fig. 9
Mouse, Le Conte's Cotton, 609
Mowat, Charles L., cited, 351, 353, 367, 373, 458, 497, 499, 508, 509, 520, 521, 542, 562, 615, 617, 636, 639, 648, 655
Mucclasse, Ala., 411
Mud Lake, Fla., 356, 360, 450, fig. 10
Mugil cephalus, 570; *curema*, 570
Muhlenberg, Henry, xxiii, xxvi, xxxi, xxxii, xxxv
Mulberry: French, 461, 543; red, 567, 570; white, 567, 570
Mullet: Common, 570; Silver, 570
Murphey, Eugene Edmund, x
Murphy's Island, Fla., 353, 496, 542
Mus musculus, 564
Musa paradisiaca ssp. *sapientum*, 570
Muscadine, 521
Muscicapa phoebe, 570
Muscovite, 541
Museum of Comparative Zoology, ix
Muskrat, Common, 571
Mustela frenata olivacea, 661; *vison lutensis*, 565
Mya arenaria, 475
Mycteria americana, 359, 515, 590, 636, 642
Mylocarium ligustrinum, 625
Myrica inodora, 404, 572, 661; *pensylvanica*, 572; *pusilla*, 572
Myristica, 558
Myrtle(s): the classic, 572; dwarf wax, 572; odorless wax, 572; wax, 571, 572

Myrtle Beach, S.C., 419
Myrtus communis, 572
Mytilus, 479

Nantahala Mountains, N.C., 390, 543
Nantahala River, N.C., 391, 643
Narváez, Pánfilo de, 368
Nassau Sound, Fla., 350
Natrix erythrogaster erythrogaster, 481;
    sipedon fasciata, 566, 629
Negroes, 381, 419
Neill, Wilfred T., cited, 374, 413, 533,
    537
Nelumbo lutea, 576
Neocleome, 476
Neotoma floridana floridana, 355, 609
Neptunea lutea, 565
Nettle, 656
New Bordeaux, S.C., 393
New Clay Landing, Fla., 372
New Hope, Ga., 379
New Smyrna, Fla., 358
New Switzerland Point, Fla., 351
New-York Historical Society, ix, 557
Nicotiana tabacum, 646, 647
Nighthawk, 662; Eastern, 464, 574;
    Florida, 574
Nightingale, 592
Ninebark, 632
Nonpareil, 585
Nopalea cochenillifera, 460
Notropis lutipinnis, 344, 519, fig. 8
Nucasse, N.C., 389
Numenius americanus americanus, 576;
    borealis, 576; *phaeopus hudsonicus,*
    490, 576
Nuthatch: Northeastern White-breasted,
    627; Red-breasted, 627
Nutmeg, 558, 576
Nuttall, Thomas, xxxiv; cited, 406, 560,
    625, 636, 646
Nyctanassa violacea violacea, 443, 454
Nyctea nyctea, 636
Nycticorax nycticorax hoactli, 442, 443,
    454
Nyssa, 654; *ogeche,* 577, 580; *sylvatica,*
    576, 577

Oak(s): black, 577, 606; black jack,
    605; Chapman's, 578, 603; Darling-
    ton, 578, 604; live, 352, 353, 365,
    371, 577, 606; northern red, 605; post,
    605; rock chestnut, 604, 605; scrub,
    578, 603, 605; scrub live-, 578, 603,
    606; southern red, 604–606; swamp
    chestnut, 604, 605; upland willow,

604; water, 603, 604; white, 603;
    willow, 605
Oak runner, 604, 605
Ocelot, 377
Ochillee, Ga., 398
Ocmulgee Fields, Ga., 347
Ocmulgee National Monument, Ga., 347
Ocmulgee mounds, Ga., 397, fig. 26
Ocmulgee River, Ga., 347, 396, 397,
    413
Oconee king, 351
Oconee River, Ga., 344, 366, 396, 413
Oconee Station, S.C., 385
Odocoileus virginianus, 458, 469, 492,
    614, 627
Oenothera grandiflora, 404
Ogeechee mounts, Fla., 349, 350
Ogeechee River, Ga., 342, 343, 350,
    395, 413, 614
Oglethorpe, General James Edward,
    349, 512
O'Hagan, Tom, 349
Oil-nut, 592
Okefinokee Swamp, Ga., vi, 339, 340,
    355, 372
Oklawaha River, Fla., 340
Old Augusta Road, Ga., 341, fig. 20
Old College in Philadelphia, xvii, xxi
Old Federal Road, Ala., vi, 401–403,
    411, fig. 27
Old Fernandina, Fla., 349
Old Fort Jackson, Ala., 432, 509
Old Georgetown Road, N.C., 419
Old man's beard, 474
Old National Highway, Ga., 338, 339
Old Spanish Highway, Fla., 369, 370,
    372
Old Stage-coach Road, Ga., 341
Old Town, N.C., 419
Oldtown, Fla., 373
Oldtown Hammock, Fla., 373
Olea europaea, 581, 582
Olive, 581; wild, 582
Ondatra zibethicus zibethicus, 571
Onosmodium virginianum, 497
Operculina dissecta, 480, 481
Opheodrys aestivus, 629
Ophioglossum scandens, 504
Ophisaurus, 629
Ophrys insectifera, 582
Opintlocco Creek, Ala., 401
Opuntia, 460; *ammophila,* 460, 504
Orange(s), 352, 358; bitter-sweet, 475,
    582, 583; sweet, 582, 583
Orange Bluff, Fla., 361
Orange Lake, Fla., 365, 547

Ord, George, xxxii, xxxiii; cited, xxxi, xxxv, 381, 409, 416, 483, 557
Oriole: Baltimore, 360, 448, 531, 583; Orchard, 448, 583
Ortega, Fla., 350
Oryza sativa, 583, 612
Osmanthus americana, 581, 582
Osmunda cinnamomea, 504; *regalis*, 504
Osochi, Ala., 413
Osprey, 502
Ossabaw Island, Ga., 336, 617
Ostrea georgiana, 382, 585; *virginica*, 479, 585
Ostrya virginiana, 465, 466
Otasse (Atasi, Attasse, or Ottasse), Ala., 401, 411, 412
Otus asio naevius, 636
Ovenbird, Eastern, 654
Ovis aries, 548, 624
Owen's Ferry, Ga., 339
Owl(s): Arctic Horned, 636; Eastern Long-eared, 637; Eastern Screech, 636; Florida Barred, 357, 584; Great Horned, 637; Northern Barred, 636; Short-eared, 637; Snowy, 636
Oxydendrum arboreum, 437
Oyster(s), 479; fossil, 382, 584
Oyster-catcher, American, 525

Paint-brush, Indian, 449
Painted leaf, 500
Palatka, Fla., 352, 379
Palawana Island, S.C., 347, 348
Palisot de Beauvois, A. M. F. J., 387
Palma elata, 354
Palmetto(es): cabbage, 352, 459, 484, 585, 586; dwarf or blue-stem, 484; saw, 469, 484, 586
Palms, royal, 354, 585, 586
Panax quinquefolius, 517, 586, 587
Pandion haliaetus carolinensis, 502
Panicum hemitomon, 661
Papaver somniferum, 599
Papaya, 465
Papilio marcellus, 459
Paralichthys, 507
Park, Orville A., cited, 564
Paroquet(s), Carolina, 587, 602
Parrish, Robert, xxii
Parrott, Mrs. Raymond, viii
Parsnip, 589; meadow, 645
Parthenocissus quinquefolia, 524, 525
Partridge berry, 565
Parula americana, 588
Parus atricapillus atricapillus, 588; *bicolor*, 588; *carolinensis extimus*, 588

Pass Manchac, La., 408
Passerella iliaca iliaca, 513
Passerina ciris ciris, 551, 575, 585; *cyanea*, 551, 552
Pastinaca sativa, 589
Patsiliga Creek, Ga., 398, 487
Pavo cristatus, 589
Pavonia spinifex, 526
Pawpaw: dwarf, 439, 440; northern, 439, 440; showy, 440
Payne, John Howard, 423, 569
Payne's Prairie, Fla., 367, 432
Peale, Charles Willson, xxvi, xxx
Pearis, Richard, 393
Peas, English, 590, 596
Pecan, 545
Pecten, 480
Pedicularis canadensis, 590
Pelecanus occidentalis carolinensis, 582, 590
Pelican: Eastern Brown, 582, 590; Wood, 359
Peninsular Lime-Sink Region, Fla., 371
Pennell, Francis W., viii–x, 394, 428, 449, 514, 517, 541, 611; cited, xi, 516
Pensacola, Fla., 406
Pepper, bird, 464
Pepper vine, 524
Percey, Mr., 584
Peromyscus gossypinus gossypinus, 564, 609
Persea borbonia, 450, 500, 550; *borbonia* f. *pubescens*, 450, 550; *gratissima*, 550; *humilis*, 451; *indica*, 550; *littoralis*, 572
Persimmon, 494
Petalostemum, 517
Petersburg, Ga., 383, 492
Petrel, Pintado, 591
Pewee, Wood, 570
Phaëthon aethereus, 591
Phalacrocorax floridanus, 555; *floridanus floridanus*, 479; *floridanus migratorius*, 479
Phalarope: Northern, 652; Red, 652
Phalaropus fulicarius, 652
Phaseolus, 451; *polystachios*, 592
Philadelphia, Pa., xvii–xxii, xxvii–xxxv, 336, 415, 422
Phillips, Ulrich Bonnell, cited, 574
Philohela minor, 622, 665
Philomath, Ga., 343, 344
Phoebe, Eastern, 570, 591
Phoenicopterus ruber, 506
Phoenix City, Ala., 399
Phoenix dactylifera, 492

Phragmites communis, 610
Physocarpus opulifolius, 632
Pickens, Andrew L., x, 384, 428, 450
Pickering, Charles, 406
Picolata, Fla., 351
Piedmont Region, Ga., 341
Pieris, 437
Pigeon(s), Passenger, 418, 478, 593
Pike, Zebulon M., 409
Pilsbry, H. A., x
Pimenta officinalis, 572
Pimpinella anisum, 439
Pinchony Creek, Ala., 402
Pinckneya, 337; *bracteata,* 417, 449, 453, 625; *pubens,* 449, 453, 625
Pine(s): black, 595; loblolly, 596; longleaf, 594–596; shortleaf, 595, 596; slash, 595; white, 596
Pine barrens, 619, 620
Pineapple, 456
Pink: marsh, 474; swamp, 444
Pinnacle Knob, Ga., 386, 387, 569, fig. 22
Pintail, 435
Pintlalla Creek, Ala., 402
Pinus australis, 594–596; *echinata,* 595, 596; *elliottii,* 595; *serotina,* 595; *taeda,* 595
Pinweed, 550
Pipewood, 437
Pipilo erythrophthalmus alleni, 648; *erythrophthalmus erythrophthalmus,* 512
Pipit, American, 433
Piranga olivacea, 563; *rubra rubra,* 563, 610
Pirogues, 591
Pistachio tree, 596
Pistacia vera, 596
Pistia stratiotes, 352, 596
Pisum sativum, 590
Pitcher-plant(s), 335, 573; Drummond's, 620; hooded, 407, 620; purple, 620
Pittman, Ph., cited, 631
Pituophis melanoleucus, 628, 629; *mugitus,* 628, 629
Plantain, hoary, 597
Platanus occidentalis, 597
Plover, American Golden, 469; Piping, 470; Semipalmated, 469; Wilson's, 469
Plum, Chickasaw, 598, 601
Pluvialis dominica dominica, 469
Pocotaligo, S.C., 381
Podiceps auritus cornutus, 478

Podilymbus podiceps podiceps, 479
Podostigma pedicellata, 444
Pogonia, spreading, 444
Pogonias cromias, 495
Poinciana, dwarf, 598
Pointe Coupee, La., 409
Polianthes tuberosa, 653
Polioptila caerulea caerulea, 611
Polygonum, 591
Polymnia uvedalia, 599
Pomacea paludosa, 352, 477
Pomegranates, 602
Pomolobus chrysochloris, 627
Pomoxis nigro-maculatus, 449
Ponce de Leon, 396
Poplar, Carolina, 599
Poppy, opium, 587
Populus deltoides, 599
Porcher, Francis Peyre, cited, 473
Porcupine, Canada, 600
Porphyrula martinica, 481, 608
Port Hudson, La., 409, 410
Portland, Duchess of, xix, 498
Porzana carolina, 607, 608
Post Road, Ga., 338, 339
Potato(es), 352; sweet, 450, 481, 600; white, 630
Potsherds, 372
Pottburg (plantation), Fla., 350
Pound, Merritt B., cited, 398
Powel, Samuel, xxii
Prevost Island, La., 408
Prickly pear, 460, 504; scrub, 460
Primroses, 600
Prince of Wales (brigantine), 336
Prinos nebulosa, 601
Procyon lotor elucus, 607; *lotor litoreus,* 607; *lotor solutus,* 607
Progne subis subis, 527
Prunus angustifolia, 598, 601; *armeniaca,* 442; *caroliniana,* 602; *communis,* 434, 435; *domestica,* 598; *hortulana,* 598; *nemoralis,* 405; *pensylvanica,* 472; *persica,* 589; *serotina,* 601, 602
Pseudemys floridana floridana, 647
Ptelea trifoliata, 602, 643
Pumpkin(s), 352; bush, 489; field, 489; Seminole, 599, 602
Punica granatum, 599
Pursh, Frederick, cited, xxxiii, 616
Purysburgh, S.C., 418
Pyle, Francis C., x, 350
Pyrularia pubera, 592
Pyrus angustifolia, 486, 603; *communis,* 589; *coronaria,* 486; *malus,* 442

Queen's delight, 635
Quercus alba, 578, 603; aquatica, 603; chapmani, 578, 603, 605; cinerea, 604; hemisphaerica, 578, 604; marilandica, 605; michauxii, 604, 605; myrtifolia, 578, 603, 605; nigra, 603, 604; phellos, 605; prinus, 604; rubra, 604–606; rubra var. borealis, 605; stellata, with var. margaretta, 605; velutina, 577, 606; virginiana, 577, 578, 606; virginiana var. maritima, 578, 603, 605, 606
Quince, 490
Quinine, 606
Quiscalus quiscula quiscula, 454, 542; quiscula stonei, 520

Rabbit, Carolina Marsh, 524
Rabun Gap, Ga., 388
Raccoon: Florida, 607; Hilton Head Island, 607; St. Simon's Island, 607
Ragwort, 543, 623
Rail, Virginia, 608
Raja, 627
Rajana ovata, 607
Rallus limicola limicola, 608
Rana catesbeiana, 458; grunniens, 377, 513; grylio, 513; pipiens pipiens, 514; pipiens sphenocephala, 514
Rangia cyrenoides, 475
Rankin, H. A., x, 420, 421, 428, 462, 488
Raphanus sativus, 607
Rat: Black, 608; Brown, 608; Eastern Cotton, 608; Florida Wood, 355, 609; ground, 338
Rattan vine, 611, 667
Rattler: Diamondback, 376, 609; Ground, 609, 659; Seminole or Timber, 609
Rattlesnake, xviii, 376
Rattlesnake-master, 431
Rattus norvegicus, 608; rattus rattus, 608
Raven(s), Northern, 483, 609
Redbud, 468
Redpoll, Common, 465
Redstart, American, 616
Redwing, Eastern, 634, 638
Reese, M. L., x
Regulus calendula calendula, 610; satrapa satrapa, 610
Rehder, Alfred, cited, 447
Rehn, James A. G., x, 428, 487
Rembert's Bottom, Ga., 383
Revolution, American, xx, 380, 393, 413, 415–417, 445, 446, 458, 514, 520, 557, 630, 637
Revolutionists, American, 392, 462, 492, 666
Reynolds, Charles B., cited, 617
Rhamnus caroliniana, 611
Rheum rhaponticum, 612
Rhododendron, white, 612
Rhododendron calendulaceum, 446, 447; carolinianum, 612; maximum, 386, 612; minus, 612; nudiflorum, 447; speciosum, 446, 447; viscosum, 447
Rhubarb, 612
Rice, 583; wild, 583
Richards, Horace G., x
Richmondena cardinalis cardinalis, 555
Ridgway, Robert, cited, 645
Riparia riparia riparia, 527, 562
Rittenhouse, David, xxx
River of Styx, Fla., 365, 366, 375, 562
Roanoke River, Va., 421
Roaring Creek, N.C., 391
Roberts, H. Radclyffe, x, 428, 554
Roberts, William, cited, 406, 472, 509
Robeson, David Gillespie, x, 420, 449
Robeson, John A., x
Robeson, Thomas, 420
Robin(s), 504; Eastern, 613, 654
Robinia hispida, 614; viscosa, 613, 614
Roccus saxatilis, 614
Rochelle, Fla., 369, 370
Rock, 622
Rock Landing, Ga., 396, 413, 580
Rockfish Creek, N.C., 421
Rock-rose, 475
Rocky Comfort Creek, Ga., 395
Rocky Creek, Ga., 397, 635
Rocky Gap, S.C., 385
Rocky Point, Fla., 363
Rodman, Fla., 364
Rolle, Denys, 470
Rollestown, Fla., 351, 352, 470
Rolling Wire-Grass Country, Ga., 341
Romans, Bernard, cited, 403, 407, 470, 521, 555, 636, 655
Rope's Island, Fla., 354
Rose(s), 615
Rose Creek, N.C., 390
Rose-bay: Carolina, 612; lesser, 612
Rose-mallow, swamp, 526
Rosemary, 499
Rosin-weeds, 626
Ross Landing, Fla., 372
Rowland, Mrs. Dunbar, cited, 409

Royal Academy of Sciences of Stockholm, 448, 616
Royal Society of London, 448, 615
Royce, Charles C., cited, 574
Roystonea elata, 354, 585, 586; *regia*, 586
Rudbeckia spathulata, 616; *triloba*, 616
Rumsey, Mr., 407
Rush, Benjamin, 361; cited, 429
Rutledge, John, xxix
Rynchops nigra nigra, 616

Sabal minor, 484; *palmetto*, 459, 484, 585, 586
Sabatia, 474
Sabin, Joseph, cited, xxvii
Saccharum officinarum, 638
Sage, scarlet, 618
St. Augustine, Fla., 351, 367
St. Catherine's Island, Ga., 336
St. Francis, Fla., 357–360
St. Francis Dead River, Fla., 357
St. John's Parish, Ga., 337
St. John's River, Fla., 335, 348, 350, 352, 353, 356, 357, 359, 361, 370, 375
St. John's-wort, golden, 531
St. Mary's River, Ga.–Fla., 338, 339, 415, 416
St. Pierre, M., 393
St. Simon's Island, Ga., 348, 349
Salix nigra, 618
Salpingostylis caelestina, 360, 542
Salsola kali, 448
Salt Springs, Fla., 361–363, 375, 627, 632, fig. 16
Salt Springs Run, Fla., 362, 363
Saltwort, 448
Salvia azurea, 616
Sambucus canadensis, 618; *simpsonii*, 618
San Carlos Bay, Fla., 461
Sand, 517; dunes, 619
Sand Fort, Ala., 401
Sand Prairie, Fla., 374, 596
Sandbar Ferry, Ga.–S.C., 414
Sanderling, 652
Sandpiper: Least, 652; Semipalmated, 652; Spotted, 652
Sandstone, 484, 614
Sanguinaria canadensis, 619
Sanguisorba media, 619
Santa Rosa Island, Fla., 618
Santee River, S.C., 347, 418
Sapelo Island, Ga., 376
Sapelo River, Ga., 337
Sapindus marginatus, 369, 620

Sapsucker, Yellow-bellied, 593
Sarcoramphus papa, 359, 496, 660
Sargent, Charles Sprague, cited, 387, 465
Sarracenia, 335; *drummondii*, 620; *minor*, 407, 620
Sarsaparilla vine, 628
Sassafras, 550
Sassafras albidum, 550, 620
Satilla River, Ga., 339
Savannah, Ga., 336, 338, 340, 341, 345, 346, 414, 415, 418
Savannah River, Ga.–S.C., 341, 345, 347, 414
Savannah-Packet, 336
Savannuca, Ala., 411
Sawpit Creek, Fla., 350
Sayornis phoebe, 570, 591
Scallop, 480
Scalopus aquaticus australis, 566; *aquaticus howelli*, 566
Scaup Duck: Greater, 436; Lesser, 436
Sceloporus undulatus undulatus, 377, 554
Schenck, David, cited, 421
Schmidt, Karl P., cited, 428
Schoepf, Johann David, cited, xxi, xxix, 380, 418, 470, 617, 655
Schoolcraft, Henry R., 388
Schrankia microphylla, 565
Schuylkill River, Pa., xx, xxix
Sciaenops ocellata, 495
Scipio, John, xi
Sciurus carolinensis carolinensis, 633; *carolinensis leucotis*, 633; *niger niger*, 633
Scorpion (lizard), 554
Scotch gentleman, 408
Scoter, Surf, 436
Screven, Frank B., cited, 458
Scrub, Florida, 362–364, 493
Sea-bass, Black, 449
Sebastian bush, 635
Sebastiana fructicosa, 635; *ligustrina*, 635
Seiurus aurocapillus aurocapillus, 654; *motacilla*, 568
Selenicereus grandiflorus, 460
Sellards, E. H., cited, 367, 369
Selma Chalk, Ala., 402
Seminole pottery, 353
Seneca, S.C., 384, 392
Senecio glabellus, 543, 623
Sensitive briar, 565
Serenoa repens, 469, 484, 586
Seton, Ernest Thompson, cited, 383

Setophaga ruticilla, 616
Seven Sister Islands, Fla., 379
Shad, Florida Lesser, 355
Shadine, 355
Sharks, fossil, 454
Sharp, Howard, 367
Shelba, Ga., 396
Shelburne Papers, 470, 473, 517
Shell: bluff, 357, 358; mound, 353, 354.
    See also Shells
Shell Bluff, Ga. (a hill), 382
Shell Bluff, Ga. (a settlement), 341
Shell-fish, 349
Shells, 352, 353, 355
Shepard, Charles U., cited, 372
Sherman, H. B., xi, 363
Shooting-star, 494
Shrike: Loggerhead, 459, 548; Migrant,
    548
Sialia sialis sialis, 455, 568
Siebert, Wilbur H., cited, 508
Sigmodon hispidus floridanus, 609; *his-
    pidus hispidus,* 608
Signalosa petensis vanhyningi, 355
Silene baldwinii, 493
Silica, 626
Silphium laciniatum, 626; *terebinthina-
    ceum* var. *pinnatifidum,* 626
Silver Bluff, S.C., 341, 382, 414
Silver Glen Spring, Fla., 361, 362
Silverbell: four-winged, 523; two-
    winged, 523
Simpson, J. Clarence, xi
Singleton Swash, S.C., 419, 639
Siskin, Northern Pine, 465
Sister Creek, Fla., 350
Sistrurus miliarius, 609, 659
Sitta canadensis, 627; *carolinensis
    cookei,* 627
Skimmer, Black, 616
Skink, Broad-headed, 554
Skunk(s), Florida, 598, 599
Sloane, Hans, cited, 556, 592
Small, John K., cited, 358, 360, 428,
    431, 460, 473, 482, 484, 500, 526,
    569, 572, 580, 602, 612, 620, 633,
    657, 666
Smartweed, 591
Smilacina racemosa, 480
Smilax bona-nox, 473, 480, 628; *pseudo-
    china,* 473, 480
Smiley, A. Keith, Jr., viii
Smith, James Edward, cited, 473, 498,
    667
Smith, Jared G., cited, 451
Smith, John, 424

Snake(s): Coral, 628; Corn, 566; East-
    ern Garter, 628; Florida Pine, 628,
    629; Four-lined Chicken, 376, 628;
    Hog-nosed, 609, 659; Milk, 629; Pine,
    376; Red-bellied Water, 481; Rough
    Green, 629; Scarlet King, 629; South-
    eastern Ring-necked, 629; Southern
    Water, 566, 629
Snakeroot, button, 499, 623
Sneezeweed, 525
Snipe, Wilson's, 622
Snowdoun, Ala., 402
Soapberry, 369, 620
Society Hill, Ala., 401
Solander, Daniel C., 405
Solomon's seal, false, 480
Sonnini, C. S., and P. A. Latreille, cited,
    377
Sora, 607, 608
Sour-wood, 437
South-Carolina Gazette, 336
South Newport, Ga., 337
Southern Red Hills, Ala., 402
Southern Red Hills, Ga., 341
Southwestern Pine Hills, Ala., 403
Spalding, James, 346, 348, 416, 558
Spalding, Thomas, 631; cited, 557, 581
Spalding's: Lower Store, Fla., 350, 353,
    363, 370, 375, 379, 635, 650, 651;
    Upper Store, Fla., 354, 361, 635, 650
Spaniards, 349, 366, 368, 512, 580, 581
Spanish: bayonet, 666; dagger, 586;
    moss, 568, 646
Sparrow: Eastern Chipping, 589; East-
    ern Field, 568, 589; Eastern Fox, 513;
    Pine-woods, 632; Swamp, 589; White-
    throated, 512
Spawn, Willman, xxiii
Speck, Frank G., cited, 399
Sphyrapicus varius varius, 593
Spice-bush, 549
Spider, jumping, 442
Spider-flower, 476
Spiderwort, 650
Spinus pinus pinus, 465; *tristis tristis,*
    465
Spiranthes, 582
Spirit Creek, Ga., 342
Spiza americana, 460
Spizella passerina passerina, 589; *pusilla
    pusilla,* 568, 589
Spoonbill, Roseate, 597
Spring Garden Creek, Fla., 360
Springs, Six-mile, Fla., 361, 362
Spurge, 500; nettle, 543
Squashes, 352; crookneck, 599, 602

Squier, E. G., 423
Squirrel(s): Florida Flying, 633; Northern Gray, 633; Southern Fox, 633; Southern Gray, 633; tree, 622
Stage-coach Road, N.C., 421
Stagger-bush, 437
Standing cypress, 394, 541
Staphylaea trifolia, 634
Star-grass, 433, 531
Station Mountain, S.C., 579
Steele, J. E. M., 384
Stephenson, L. W., cited, 452, 454
Sterna hirundo hirundo, 549
Stevens, William Bacon, cited, 448, 497, 562, 666
Stewartia ovata, 634
Stiggins, George, cited, 410
Stillingia sylvatica, 635
Stingray, Spotted, 635
Stirling, M. W., cited, 383
Stokes Island, Fla., 379
Stokes Landing, Fla., 353, 363
Stokley, James, 346
Stomatopod crustacean, 462
Stone, Witmer, cited, 378, 460, 467, 512, 527, 608
Stone-root, 477
Storax, large-leaved, 638
Stork, William, cited, 375, 617
Story, Enoch, Jr., xxi–xxiii
Strawberry, 511
Strawberry bush, 500
Strix acclamator acclamator, 357, 636; *acclamator georgica*, 357, 584; *varia varia*, 636
Strong, Caleb, xxix
Stuart, John, xviii, 349, 351, 367, 392, 445, 473, 509, 517
Sturnella magna magna, 433
Styrax grandifolia, 638
Sula, 590
Sumac, poison, 612
Sumstine, David R., 428, 514
Sunbury, Ga., 336, 380
Sundew, round-leaved, 495
Sunflower, 525
Supple jack, 659
Sus scrofa, 593, 640
Sutton, Clement E., xi, 383
Suwannee River, Fla., 370, 372, 553
Swallow: Bank, 527, 562; Barn, 527, 639; Cliff, 527; Rough-winged, 527; Tree, 527
Swan, Whistling, 491
Swanton, John R., x, 340, 344, 347, 348, 357, 367, 368, 373, 399, 410–413, 423, 428, 473, 602, 634, 657; cited, 385, 388, 389, 391–393, 396, 397, 409, 412, 414, 415, 424, 429, 432, 442, 446, 471, 474, 476, 481, 496, 509, 514, 526–528, 533–539, 546, 573, 579, 580, 584, 598, 622, 630, 639–641, 643, 647, 653–656, 661, 664
Sweet fern, 552
Sweet gum, 552
Sweet shrub, 461
Sweetwater Branch, Fla., 369, 456
Sweetwater Creek, Ga., 342
Swem, E. G., x
Swertia carolinensis, 551
Swift, Chimney, 527
Sycamore, 597, 598
Sylvilagus floridanus mallurus, 524, 606; *palustris palustris*, 524
Symplocos tinctoria, 528
Syringa, 592

Tabanus, 506, 527
Taitt, David, 395, 397, 398, 401, 412; cited, 413, 424, 429, 432, 471, 473, 481, 517, 526, 546, 573, 584, 598, 630, 641, 642, 653, 656, 664
Talahasochte, Fla., 370, 372
Talasse, Ala., 401
Talbot Island, Fla., 339, 350
Talc, 564
Tallapoosa River, Ala., 347, 401, 411
Tamarack, 595
Tamias striatus fisheri, 634; *striatus striatus*, 634
Tanager, Scarlet, 563; Summer, 563, 610
Tangier, Louise F. A., 428, 436
Tantalus pictus, 358
Tapley, John Adam, 642, 648, 649
Tar-flower, 545, 612, 625
Taro, 444, 497
Taxodium ascendens, 489, 491; *distichum*, 489, 491
Teal, 606
Telmatodytes palustris palustris, 568, 610
Tennessee River, 527
Tensaw River, Ala., 404, fig. 28
Tephrosia, 514
Tern: Common, 549; Noddy, 634
Terrapene bauri, 648; *carolina*, 648
Terrapin, Florida, 377, 647
Testudo Polyphaemus, 366, 377
Thamnophis sirtalis sirtalis, 628
Thaspium, 645
Thistle, 465
Thomas, A. M., 353

Thomas, Cyrus, cited, 342
Thomas, Isaiah, xxiv
Thomassy, R., cited, 410, 509, 598, 662
Thomson, Charles, xvii
Thoreau, Henry David, xxviii
Thrasher, Eastern Brown, 645, 654
Threadcraft, Sarah, 558
Three Sisters Ferry, Ga.–S.C., 381
Threskiornis aethiopicus aethiopicus, 531
Thrush, Eastern Hermit, 645
Thryothorus ludovicianus ludovicianus, 568
Tick Island, Fla., 360
Tilia, 643, 646
Tillandsia bartrami, 646; *bartramii*, 646; *tenuifolia*, 646; *usneoides*, 568, 646; *utriculata*, 646
Titmouse, Tufted, 588
Toad(s), 513; American, 376; Southern, 377, 513
Tobacco, 352
Tobesofkee Creek, Ga., 397
Tombigbee River, Ala., 405
Tomkins, Ivan R., cited, 571
Tonyn, Governor Patrick, 351, 458, 519, 520
Toothache tree, 667
Torrey, Bradford, cited, 451
Torrey, John, 406
Tortoise: great land, 365; great soft-shelled, 365
Totanus flavipes, 576; *melanoleucus*, 576
Towhee: Red-eyed, 512; White-eyed, 648
Townes, Henry K., x, 428, 506
Toxostoma rufum rufum, 645, 654
Trader, old, 363, 368, 376
Trader(s), 365, 372, 389, 390, 400, 414, 446
Tragopan, Himalayan, 563
Trautvetteria carolinensis, 530
Treaty of Augusta, Ga., 342
Tree, Line, Ga., 345
Tree-frog: Georgia, 377, 513; Green, 513; Little, 377, 513; Southern, 377, 513
Trees, petrified, 420
Trichechus manatus latirostris, 561
Trinectes maculatus fasciatus, 507
Tringa macularia, 652
Tripsacum dactyloides, 653
Triticum aestivum, 653, 662
Troglodytes aëdon aëdon, 568
Tropic-bird, Red-billed, 591
Trout, 345, 355, 359

Troutman, Mrs. A. C., viii
Trumbull, Gurdon, cited, 436, 525, 644
Trumpet: creeper, 453; flower, 453
Trumpets, yellow, 620
Tsuga canadensis, 525, 595; *caroliniana*, 525
Tuckabatche (or Tukabahchee), Ala., 411, 412
Tucker, John, 353, 499
Tucker, Philip C., cited, 521
Tugaloo River, Ga.–S.C., 342, 344, 345, 553
Tulip tree, 552, 599
Tulips, 654
Turdus migratorius, 504; *migratorius migratorius*, 613, 654; *pilaris*, 504
Turkey(s): Eastern Wild, 563, 654, 655; Florida Wild, 655
Turk's head, 460
Turner, B. L., cited, 565
Turnstone, Ruddy, 567
Tursiops truncatus, 600
Turtle(s): Carolina Box, 648; Chicken, 647; Florida Box, 648; Gopher, 338, 365, 366, 377, 404, 647, fig. 5; Southern Soft-shelled, 365, 648
Turtle-head, 471
Turtle Mound, Fla., 358, 569
Turtle River, Ga., 338
Tuscawilla Lake, Fla., 366, 367, 490, 547
Tuskegee, Ala., 432
Twayblade, Small's, 582
Two Sisters Ferry, Ga.–S.C., 645
Tympanuchus cupido cupido, 644
Tyrannus tyrannus, 548
Tyty, 491, 625

Uchee (a former Indian town), Ala., 398, 399
Uchee (a modern town), Ala., 401
Uchee Creek, Ala., 401
Ulmus, 498; *alata*, 656; *americana*, 656; *floridana*, 656
Umbrella tree, 560
Umbrula, 663
Underwood, J. E., 344
Universal Asylum and Columbian Magazine, xxiii, xxviii
University of Pennsylvania, 511
Upatoi Creek, Ga., 398, 595
Uphapee Creek, Ala., 401
Urocyon cinereoargenteus, 510

Vale of Cowee, N.C., 389, 390
Van Doren, Carl, cited, 448
Vaughan, John, xxix

Veatch, Otto, and Lloyd William Ste-
    phenson, cited, 382, 614
Veery, 379, 645
Venus, 480; *mercenaria*, 475
Venus' fly-trap, 419, 493, 494
Verbena, shrub, 548
Verbena rigida, 657
Vermivora chrysoptera, 587; *pinus*, 587
Vernonia, 474
Vervain, 657
Vetches, 658
Viburnum rufidulum, 658
Vigna sinensis, 451, 495, 590
Vignoles, Charles, cited, 509, 631, 655
Villa Real, Fla., 351
Viper, Common, 445
Vipera berus, 445
Vireo: Northern White-eyed, 570; Red-
    eyed, 571
Vireo griseus noveboracensis, 570; *oli-
    vaceus*, 571
Virginia creeper, 524, 525
Vitis labrusca, 521; *munsoniana*, 659,
    660; *rotundifolia*, 521, 660; *rufoto-
    mentosa*, 659; *taurina*, 660; *vinifera*,
    521
Viviparus georgianus, 352, 477
Voluta, 477
Vultur atratus, 360; *sacra*, 359
Vulture: Black, 359, 660; King, 359,
    496, 660; Turkey, 459, 660

Wacasassa River, Fla., 613
Wafer ash, 602, 643
Wake-robin: nodding, 651; sessile-
    flowered, 651
Walker, E. Perot, vii, x, 362
Walnut, black, 544
Walter, Thomas, 400, 565; cited, xxii,
    387, 483, 596, 606, 626
Wapiti, 498
War Woman Creek, Ga., 386
Warbler: Bay-breasted, 588; Black and
    White, 468; Black-throated Blue,
    379; Black-throated Green, 588;
    Blue-winged, 468, 587; Chestnut-
    sided, 379; Eastern Myrtle, 588, 666;
    Eastern Yellow, 588; Golden-winged,
    587; Hooded, 556; Magnolia, 379,
    588; Northern Pine, 468; Parula,
    588; Worm-eating, 379; Yellow Palm,
    587; Yellow-throated, 588
Warblers, wood, 454
Warmouth, 360, 456, fig. 13
Warrenton, Ga., 413
Warriors, (Seminole), 375

Washington, George, xxii, xxiii, xxix, 415
Water: chinquapin, 368, 576; hyacinth,
    352, 369; lettuce, 352, 596; penny-
    wort, 530
Watermelon(s), 352, 475, 489, 563
Watermelon Pond, Fla., 371, 375, 454,
    599
Water-rot, 494
Water-thrush, Louisiana, 568
Water-turkey(s), Florida, 478, 629
Watkins, E. W., xi, 363, 364, 366
Watt, George, cited, 485
Waxwing, Cedar, 435
Wayah Creek, N.C., 391
Wayah Gap, N.C., 391
Wayne, Arthur T., cited, 498
Weakfish, 653
Weasel, Alabama, 661
Wells, Randall, xi, 363
West, Francis D., viii
West Indies, 347
West's Mill, N.C., 390, 485
Whatoga, N.C., 389
Wheat(s), 653
Wherry, Edgar T., ix, 344, 428, 446,
    493, 541, 625; cited, 407, 511, 620
Whetstone Creek, S.C., 386
Whip-poor-will, Eastern, 464, 574, 662
White, George, cited, 381, 383, 396–
    398, 418, 446, 458, 492, 564, 581,
    583, 666
White Cliffs, La., 409
White Point Creek, S.C., 419
White's Creek, Ga., 343
Wiggens, Job, 363, 368, 376, 541, 648,
    649
Wildcat(s), 466; Eastern, 664; Florida,
    664
Will, chief of Whatoga, N.C., 389
Willdenow, Carolus Ludovicus, cited,
    438
Willet: Eastern, 525, 664; Western,
    664
Williams, Belle, cited, 515
Williams, George G., cited, 371
Williams, John Lee, cited, 359, 470, 655
Williams Creek, Ga., 342, 343, 553
Williamson, Andrew, 380, 385–387
Williamson, Hu (or Hugh), xxix, 555
Willis' Creek, N.C., 420, 421, 487
Willow, black, 618
Wilson, Alexander, ix, xxxi–xxxiii, xxxv,
    378, 381, 409, 483, 512; cited, 460,
    464, 498, 527, 568, 570, 571, 574,
    587–589, 644
Wilson, Chas. N., 392

Wilsonia citrina, 556
Wine Spring Bald, N.C., 391
Winyah Bay, S.C., 418
Wire Road, Ga., 397
Wistar, Caspar, xxvi
Wister, John C., viii
Wisteria, American, 518
Wisteria frutescens, 518
Witch-alder, dwarf, 510
Witch hazel, 523
Wolf (Wolves), 361, 402; Eastern, 665;
    Florida, 367, 368, 664, 665
Wolf King, 473, 517
Wolff, George E., 349
Wood Duck, 436
Woodcock, American, 622, 665
Woodpecker: Eastern Hairy, 593; East-
    ern Red-bellied, 593; Eastern Red-
    headed, 593; Ivory-billed, 593; North-
    ern Downy, 593; Southern Pileated,
    593
Wordsworth, William, xxv
Wren: Carolina, 568; Eastern House,
    568; Long-billed Marsh, 568, 610
Wright, Carl, 344
Wright, Governor James Wright, xviii,
    336, 351, 473, 517
Wright, John K., cited, 363
Wright, Robert, cited, 581

Wright, Sam., 336
Wrightsborough, Ga., 342
Wroth, Lawrence C., cited, 615
Wyman, Jeffries, cited, 353–355, 357,
    358, 479, 569, 624

Xanthoxylum clava-herculis, 667
Ximenia americana, 641

Yam-root, wild, 493
Yaupon, 390, 414, 466
Yellowlegs: Greater, 576; Lesser 576
Yellowthroat, Maryland, 611
Young, William, 498
Yucca aloifolia, 586

Zamia integrifolia, 473, 666, 667
Zea mays, 482, 667
Zenaidura macroura carolinensis, 478,
    495
Zenobia pulverulenta, 438
Zephyranthes atamasco, 434
Zigadenus densus, 525
Zimmermann, E. A. W., cited, xxvi
Zinder Point, Fla., 468
Zizania aquatica, 583
Zizia, 645
Zonotrichia albicollis, 512
Zubley's Ferry, Ga.–S.C., 418

On the following three pages the "Taitt" map of 1772 is reproduced.

Section 1: Alabama and West Florida.
Section 2: Central Georgia and Eastern Alabama.
Section 3: Southern South Carolina and Eastern Georgia.

Redrawn from the original in the William L. Clements Library.

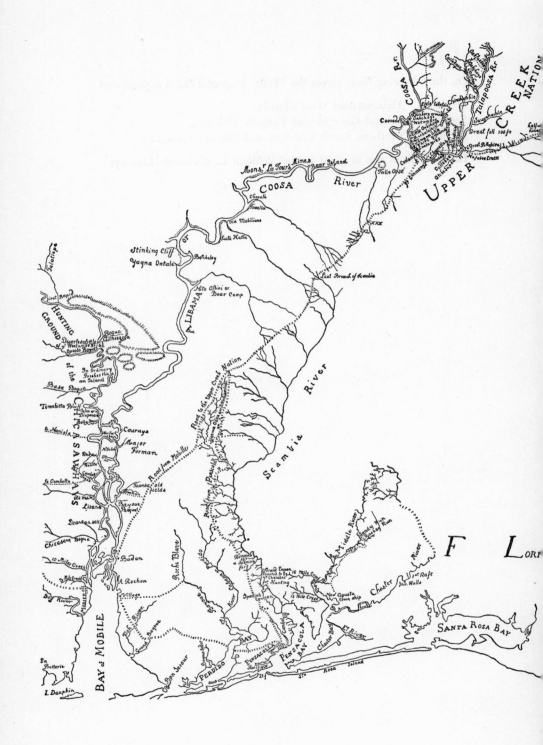

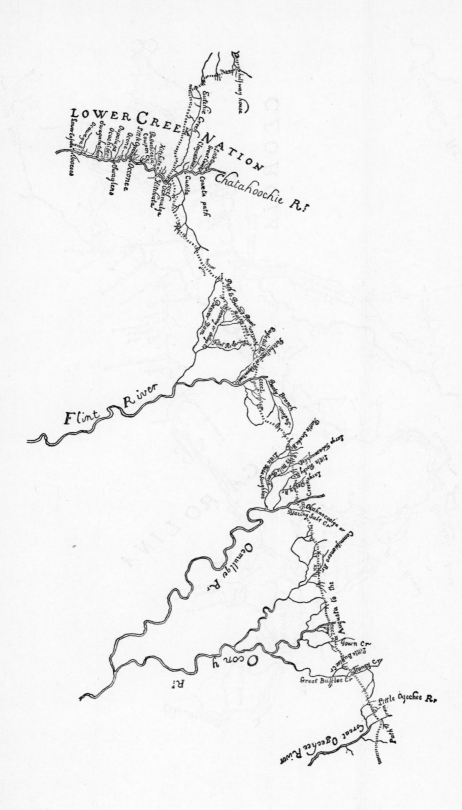

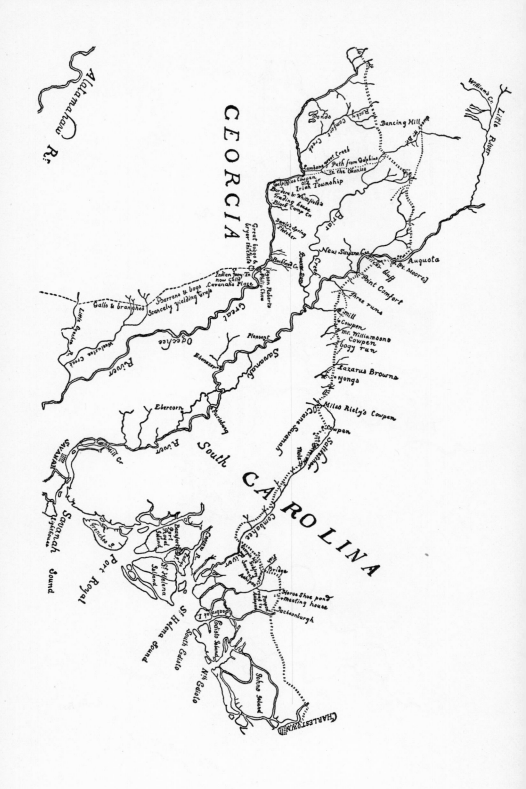

1. The John Stuart House on Tradd Street, Charleston, S.C. May 29, 1939. Built before 1772, and visited by Bartram

2. Midway Cemetery and Church, Liberty County, Ga. April 7, 1933. Live oak, pine, Spanish moss

3. Bartram's drawing of the Franklin tree; original in British Museum (Natural History). "Franklinia alatamaha. A beautiful flowering Tree. discoverd growing near the banks of the R. Alatamaha in Georgia. Will.ᵐ Bartram. Delin. 1788"

4. Georgia Pocket Gopher (*Geomys pinetis pinetis*), captured alive at Scotchville School, Camden County, Ga., and photographed August 14, 1922

5. Gopher Turtle (*Gopherus polyphaemus*) and burrow. Camp Cornelia, Charlton County, Ga. May 29, 1929

6. Lady lupine (*Lupinus villosus*). Dry pine barrens along Post Road southeast of Waynesville, on the Brantley-Glynn county boundary, Ga. April 16, 1936

7. Bartram's Buffalo Lick, near Philomath, Oglethorpe County, Ga.; looking southeast. May 28, 1934. Willow oak, persimmon, hawthorn

8. Bartram's Minnow (*Notropis lutipinnis*), from Little Brier Creek, 9 miles south of Thomson, McDuffie County, Ga. May 2, 1933

either in a vast savannah or natural plain, or an artificial pond or lake. A remarkable example occurs at Mount Royal, from whence opens a glorious view of Lake George and its environs.

Fig. 24.

"Fig. 24 exhibits a view of the great mound last referred to. Fig. 25 is a plan of the same structure with its accompanying avenue, which leads off to an artificial lake or pond, on the verge of an expansive savannah or natural meadow. A, the mound, about forty feet in perpendicular height; B, the highway leading from the mound in a straight line to the pond C, about half a mile distant. What may have been the motive for making this pond I cannot conjecture, since the mound and other vestiges of the ancient town are situated close on the banks of the river St.

Juan.* It could not therefore be for the conveniency of water. Perhaps they raised the mound with the earth taken out of the pond. The sketch of this mound also

Fig. 25

illustrates the character of the mounds in the Cherokee country; but the last have not the highway or avenue, and are always accompanied by vast square terraces

9. Bartram's sketches of Mount Royal and adjacent features, Putnam County, Fla. (From *Smithsonian Contributions to Knowledge 1:* 122, 1848)

10. Mud Lake, adjoining the St. John's River near the southwestern corner of Lake Dexter in Lake County, Fla.; looking southwest. The "Battle Lagoon" of Bartram, whose chief adventures with Alligators took place here. July 3, 1939. Water hyacinth behind a wire barricade; cabbage palmetto

11. The Lake County side of the St. John's River opposite Lamb's Bluff (near Lake Beresford), Fla. April 3, 1940. Cabbage palmetto, cypress, hickory, ash, Spanish moss, water hyacinth, yellow water-lily

12. Bartram's drawing of Alligators; original in British Museum (Natural History).

"Fig 1. Represents the action of this terrable monster when they bellow in the Spring Season they force the water out of their throat which falls from their mouth like a Cataract. & a steam or vapour from their Nostrals like smoke

"Fig 2. Represents them rising up out of the water when they devour the fish. &c."

13. Bartram's drawing of "Great Yellow Bream. calld Old Wife of St John's E^t Florida. 1774. W B.": Warmouth (*Chaenobryttus coronarius*). Original in British Museum (Natural History)

14. Bartram's drawing of "Wattoola Great Savanah Crane": Florida Sandhill Crane (*Grus canadensis pratensis*). Original in British Museum (Natural History)

15. Bartram's drawing of the "Crying Bird": Florida Limpkin (*Aramus guarauna pictus*). (From Barton, 1818: pl. 1)

Tantalus Ephouskyca.

16. Salt Springs, west of Lake George, Marion County, Fla.; looking northwest. June 29, 1939. Live oak, hickory, cabbage palmetto, Spanish moss

17. Cowpen Pond, Putnam County, Fla., including a sink-hole ("Drummer's Pond") in the foreground; looking northwest. The "Halfway Pond" of Bartram. June 28, 1939. Live oak, longleaf pine, wax myrtle, St. John's-wort, switch-grass

18. Alachua Savanna, Alachua County, Fla.; looking southwest from a knoll above Alachua Sink. June 26, 1939. Live oak, persimmon, hackberry, Spanish moss, water hyacinth

19. Manatee Spring, near Suwannee River, Levy County, Fla.; looking northeast. June 24, 1939. Live oak, cypress, buttonbush, Spanish moss

20. Old Augusta Road, north of Clyo, Effingham County, Ga. April 26, 1940. Water oak, maple, sweet gum, blackberry, Spanish moss

21. The "unparalleled cascade of Falling Creek" (Martin Creek of the map of Chattahoochee National Forest, 1937), 3.5 miles east-northeast of Clayton, Rabun County, Ga. July 11, 1939. Shrubs chiefly *Rhododendron maximum*

22. Court House Gap and Pinnacle Knob (at right); looking east-northeast from highway north of Clayton, Rabun County, Ga. July 12, 1939

23. The Cowee Mountains; looking north over West's Mill (Bartram's "Cowe"), Macon County, N.C. July 12, 1939. ("The vale is closed at Cowe by a ridge of mighty hills"—p. 353)

24. Site of Fort Prince George (just beyond and to right of large mulberry tree in the field); looking southwest. Keowee River just within the border of the woods. Pickens and Oconee Counties, northwest of Six Mile, S.C. July 10, 1939

25. Lazenby's Flat Rock (perhaps the "Flat-rock" of Bartram); looking east. On a headwater of Middle Creek, 1 mile northwest of Camak, Warren County, Ga. April 28, 1940. Loblolly pine, Georgia hackberry, red cedar, winged elm, *Rhododendron canescens*

26. One of the Ocmulgee mounds—a truncated pyramid; looking south-southeast. East of Macon, Bibb County, Ga. June 11, 1939

27. A section of the Old Federal Road, along the Monroe-Conecuh county boundary, 5 miles east of Midway, Ala.; looking northeast. June 17, 1939. Beech, great-leaf magnolia, white oak, hickory, loblolly pine, black gum

28. Tensaw River, looking downstream (west-northwest) from Melton's Landing, 4 miles north of Stockton, Baldwin County, Ala. June 18, 1939

29. Blue Springs (Bartram's "Great Springs") on Beaverdam Creek, Screven County, Ga.; looking south-southwest. April 22, 1936. Cypress, maple, Spanish moss

Date Due

MAY 2 5 1962		
OCT 9		

Demco 293-5